G000116145

The Media Guide
2000

Edited by Paul Fisher
& Steve Peak

Researched by Jo Wallace
& Emma Johnson

Fourth Estate • London

Published in Great Britain by:
Fourth Estate Ltd, 6 Salem Road, London W2 4BU
The eighth annual edition

Copyright 1999 Guardian News Service Ltd and Steve Peak
119 Farringdon Road, London EC1R 3ER

A catalogue record for this book is available from the British Library: ISBN 1 84115 232-3

The right of Paul Fisher and Steve Peak to be identified as joint authors of this work has been asserted by them in accordance with the Copyright, Designs and Patents Act 1988.

Publisher: Gerald Knight

Picture research: Judith Caul

Picture credits

14 Dominic Lawson, Garry Weaser	161 Carol Vorderman, Frank Baron	275 Jim Pines
16 Jonathan Aitken, Sean Smith	162 Bob Geldof, Graham Turner	293 Harold Evans, Kenneth Saunders
16 David Montgomery, Guardian	171 Macdonald & Blair, Martin Argles	338 Vanessa Feltz, Frank Martin
31 Janet Street-Porter, UPPA	173 Greg Dyke, Martin Argles	339 Piers Morgan, Garry Weaser
37 Frank Branston, LSNG	192 Pobyl y Cwm, s4C	340 Des Lynam, S&P In Focus
86 Felix Dennis, Dennis Publishing	201 Bill Gates, Frank Martin	347 Eastenders, BBC
151 China, Gunnar Knechtel	206 Elisabeth Murdoch, M Argles	351 Robert Maxwell, Sean Smith
153 Marmaduke Hussey, Sean Smith	231 Jenny Abramsky, Martin Argles	353 Ted Heath, E Hamilton West
154 Jill Dando's death, Martin Argles	234 Chris Smith, Guardian	361 Lennon & Ono, Jane Bown

Advertisement manager: Kassandra Farrington
Acknowledgements: Mathew Clayton, Roger Harrison, Ben Hayes, Ros Holmes, Elaine Lynch, Amanda Kelly, Jodie Owen, Gary Phillips, Donna Skuse

Advertisement index

INSIDE FRONT IRN	158 Channel Guide	307 Henderson
3 IBM	160 Edinburgh Television Festival	314 Media Junction
10/11 Traxdata	217 News Direct	317 Pricewaterhouse Coopers
12 Camera Press	291 Digital Pictures	319 One World
22 Press Gazette	295 Olswang	321 PMA
25 Media Week	296 Crockers, Oswald, Hickson	324 Press Fund
137 Media Lawyer	299 Biddle	365 Chadwyck Healey
155 BBME	302/303 Hiscox	386 Chadwyck Healey
157 GMTV	304 Robert Fleming	INSIDE BACK LBC Radio

Designed by Gary Phillips and produced on Apple computers using Quark Express by Paul Fisher and Emma Johnson. Based on an idea of Steve Peak. Set in Scala and Helvetica

Printed in Great Britain by Bath Press

To order the 2001 MEDIA GUIDE, phone Jem Marketing on 01483 204455

Southern Comfort!

*41% of Sussex tunes in every week and,
with a *21% share in the county,
Southern FM is market leader for the
seventh year in succession!

So...If you want to talk to Sussex
...talk to Southern FM.

Telephone: 01273 430111
Fax: 01273 430098
e-mail: info@southernradio.co.uk

UK PRESS

UK BROADCASTING

CROSS MEDIA

OUTSIDE CONTACTS: THE STATE

OUTSIDE CONTACTS: DISASTERS AND EMERGENCIES

OUTSIDE CONTACTS: SOCIETY

A SOLUTION FOR

Traxdata have a range of products designed to suit all office applications, whether you simply need to make copies of that presentation, price list or multimedia files, or you are required by law to store documentation for years to come on secure media, Traxdata have a solution for your requirement.

The TRAXRCHIVER Range

If you need to store up to 20,000 pages of text on a single CD-R for immediate document or word by word retrieval, the TRAXRCHIVER range offers the simplest and most effective solution.

The TRAXTOWER Range

From a single copy up to 16 immediate copies, the TRAXTOWER range offers it all. Simple disc in disc out operations, perfect for any company needing immediate and reliable copies of data.

The TRAXCOPIER Range

The office CD photocopier, from 50 to 150 copies, the TRAXCOPIER range offers consistent and reliable overnight CD duplication.

TRAXDATA

ALL REQUIREMENTS

Our range of CD Recordable media has been carefully researched and developed to offer the highest quality, durability and security for your music, data, photos and videos.

**TX Audio
74 minute
CD-Recordable**

**TX Audio
80 minute
CD-Recordable**

**TX Audio
74 minute
CD-ReWritable**

The TX AUDIO media range allows you to record 74 or 80 minutes of perfect digital quality sound onto one CD. This is a great way of preserving your favourite vinyl and making your own compilations collections.

Each Traxdata CD-R undergoes testing in extremes of heat, humidity, and light exposure and have long term storage stability in excess of 100 years. A protective lacquer coating resists scratches, dirt, rough handling and other hazards of normal office conditions. The final result is a CD-R disc that is extremely reliable and can be written on in multi-speed by CD-R writers which conform to the Orange Book, Part II Standard. They are also perfect for use with our Professional Products range of archiving and duplication systems.

**CD Recordable Silver
74 Minute 8x Speed**

**CD Recordable Gold
74 Minute 8x Speed**

**CD Recordable Silver
80 Minute 8x Speed**

**CD ReWritable Gold
74 Minute 4x & 2x Speed**

Rankin

Camera
Press

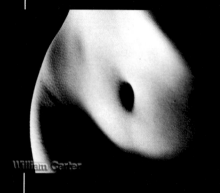

William Carter

21 Queen Elizabeth St
London SE1 2PD

www.camerapress.cc

Tel. +44 (0)20 7378 130
Fax. +44 (0)20 7278 512

Snowdon

a whole body of images...

National newspapers

FEARLESS REPORTING

1 AUGUST 1998 "No journalist ... has anything to fear from a screen or keyboard,"declared a triumphant Financial Times executive after the High Court rejected damages claims lodged by four sub-editors who asserted keyboard work had inflicted injuries to their upper limbs. The case dated back to 1988 and the NUJ spent upwards of £1 million attempting to secure recompense for "bio-mechanical injuries". "No," commented the FT. "The problems are psycho social." Yes, the judge agreed. "I remain unconvinced the plaintiffs have on the balance of probability suffered from the physical problems they variously set out to establish."

BRIEF ENCOUNTER

12 AUGUST The marketing brief for a "more rounded" Sun resulted in a remodelled Page 3 format with brief CVs of the models replacing punning captions, and pairs of briefs replacing strategic drapes. "It's not so brash and has a more modern feel," the Sun's picture editor, Geoff Webster, revealed in an exclusive briefing.

LORD ROTHERMERE DIES

10 SEPTEMBER Blair and Murdoch joined mourners at Lord Rothermere's funeral. The proprietor of the Daily Mail, MoS and Evening Standard died, aged 73, three months after his star editor Sir David English. "He intuitively understood what people wanted," said Jonathan Harmsworth, his 30 year old son and heir. "He saw the increasing significance of women in society and gave them a resounding voice."

SURFING TO SUCCESS

11 SEPTEMBER The time couldn't have been worse at 7pm on Friday evening when the 42,000 word Starr Report on President Clinton's sex life went out on the internet. First editions, normally due out at 8pm, were held so the 42,000 word report could be dragged off the web, typeset and commented on to go to the presses just before midnight. By breakfast extra copy sales proved news still sells newspapers.

SUNDAY MIRROR EDITOR

11 SEPTEMBER Colin Myler, 46, was confirmed as Sunday Mirror editor. He'd replaced Brendon Parsons, who'd left for six months compassionate leave in March having been in post two months. Myler, who was Sunday Mirror editor between 1992 and 1994, said: "The Sunday Mirror has had a pretty awful time. It needs consistency and stability."

MAIL ON SUNDAY EDITOR

18 SEPTEMBER Jonathan Holborow, 54, departed from the Mail on Sunday despite six years of circulation success. Holborow, who was immediately replaced by the Daily Mail deputy editor Peter Wright, moved to a part time job helping Conservative Central Office sell its New Tory message.

MAIL OVERTAKES MIRROR

27 SEPTEMBER ABC figures revealed that the Daily Mail had 2.4 million copy sales a day to the Mirror's 2.38 million. In September the mid-market Mail finally achieved what had been predicted for several years and outsold its red-top rival.

APOLOGY FEST

10 OCTOBER A Daily Telegraph apology - having erroneously reported Natasha Richardson and Liam Neeson's marital disharmony - extended to a £100,000 cheque and this bit of grovelling: "The plaintiffs were astounded to read these untrue allegations, particularly in a paper of such repute as the Daily Telegraph." The fourth estate's tendency to the luvvie grovel had accelerated in May when the Mail on Sunday splashed an apology to Brooke Shields for alleging she'd been searched for drugs at Nice airport. And later in the month the Express paid Tom Cruise and Nicole Kidman approaching £250,000 having alleged their marriage was a business arrangement. More mundane (and less expensive) mea culpas are part of the daily diet in daily corrections columns carried by the Times and Guardian.

FISHY TALE

7 OCTOBER 1998 Mr Hay - aka the former Express journalist James Hughes Onslow - visited the Express editor Rosie Boycott's house with an estate agent. The prospective buyer - possibly out of funds due to Boycott having recently sacked him - stuffed some fish fingers behind the bath. A week later a nasty smell emerged and Boycott paid a plumber £57 to discover the source.

DAILY STAR CULL

13 OCTOBER Phil Walker quit as Daily Star editor when Express Newspapers announced a further 46 redundancies bringing staff numbers to 80, half the complement of a year earlier. In that time the Star had a marketing inspired relaunch and lost 90,000 sales. Ian Hill, Walker's deputy, took over as editor.

OK TO WOODWARD £40K

1 DECEMBER A £40,000 Daily Mail payment to Louise Woodward, the British nanny cleared by US courts of murdering a child in her care, didn't breach the PCC Code of Practice. In such cases the Press Complaints Commission applies four tests:
Is there a public interest?
Is payment necessary?
Is new information obtained?
Is there any profit?
The answers in the Woodward case were all yes.

NO MONEY, NO EUROPEAN

14 DECEMBER One Money for Europe was the headline to launch Robert Maxwell's European in May 1990. The European - which revamped itself as a weekly mag under Andrew Neil's editorship - closed weeks before the introduction of a single European currency. The Barclay Brothers, who bought it for £1 million in 1992, pulled out when circulation dropped to 35,000.

SPY STORY

20 DECEMBER Dominic Lawson, the Sunday Telegraph editor, faced allegations he was an MI6 spy. First hints that a national editor might be on the MI6 payroll emerged in October in the Sunday Business. The Times repeated the tittle-tattle on 12 December and two days later, under the cloak of parliamentary privilege, Lawson was named and the Press Association put his name on the wire. Evidence for Lawson's Bondish tendencies was that whilst editor of the Spectator he'd published two articles by an MI6 officer posing as a freelance called Kenneth Roberts. Lawson was left to prove a negative. "I am not and never have been an agent either paid or unpaid," he said, though he was positive the Times had also published articles by Roberts. The silliness ended when the Sunday Business had no proof of MI6 payments to Lawson.

Dominic Lawson, the Sunday Telegraph editor

CHRISTMAS 1998: Guardian headlines which forced Peter Mandelson and Geoffrey Robinson to resign

MANDELSON & ROBINSON RESIGN

22 DECEMBER The Guardian broke the story of Peter Mandelson's undeclared £373,000 home loan from Geoffrey Robinson. It was the biggest scandal this government had had to face and both the trade secretary and the paymaster general had to go. The What the Papers Say Awards made this scoop of the year. David Hencke, Ewen Macaskill, Seamus Milne and Nick Hopkins "scooped the Mandelson story right out from under the nose of the opposition and brought one of New Labour's brightest stars to earth with a bump," said the judges.

COLUMN INCHES

30 DECEMBER A Times trawl of national newspaper databases revealed the number of stories that politicians (and their helpers) appeared in during 1998.

Tony Blair	28,653
Gordon Brown	11,753
Robin Cook	6,861
John Prescott	6,402
Jack Straw	6,385
Peter Mandelson	6,323
William Hague	5,991

MIRROR TAKEOVER

JANUARY 1999: Two regional newspaper owners circled the Mirror Group. Regional Independent Media, owners of the Yorkshire Post, offered £900 million; and before that Trinity put in for a £1.3 billion share deal. At the end of March the Monopolies and Mergers Commission (now renamed the Competition Commission) announced an 11 June deadline for "evidence of the proposed acquisition of Mirror Group plc by Trinity plc and Regional Independent Media Holdings". See 30 July.

MOANING TONE vs HONEST JOHN

12 JANUARY: The prime minister Tony Blair attacked the press for a news agenda "dominated by scandal gossip and trivia". John Witherow - the Sunday Times editor who had just serialised a book by the foreign secretary's ex-wife - took the public interest defence. "Politicians use their families to get elected and Mrs Cook was part of the ... wider team which enabled Robin Cook to become a senior cabinet minister."

On 24 January Blair complained to the PCC over a Mail on Sunday story about his 10 year old daughter's winning a place at a Catholic comprehensive school. See 17 July.

BYE FOR NOW: Jonathan Aitken (left) outside the Old Bailey and David Montgomery outside the Mirror

AITKEN PLEADS GUILTY

19 JAN 1999 Jonathan Aitken, the former Tory cabinet minister who summoned imagery of the "sword of truth and the trusty shield of British fair play" in his libel action against the Guardian and Granada, pleaded guilty to perjury and intending to pervert the cause of justice. "I've learned my lessons," Aitken said. "Sometimes you become a prisoner of your own lie, I have no excuses. I know I am going to prison. As far as the physical miseries go, I am sure I will cope." In May he declared himself bankrupt and thus unable to meet legal costs and on 8 June he began an 18 month prison sentence.

M&S UNLAWFUL COPYING

19 JANUARY The High Court ruled that Marks and Spencer had infringed copyright law by photocopying newspaper articles without paying a licence fee. The Newspaper Licensing Authority hailed it as a "landmark judgment". M&S was granted leave to appeal.

MONTY GOES

26 JANUARY After months of hostility from the City, his board and his staff, David Montgomery resigned as Mirror Group chief executive. He took a £1 million pay-off in a departure interpreted by some as the removal of an impediment to the Mirror Group's sale.

MONTGOMERY TRIBUTES

Andrew Marr, ex-Indie editor, said: "He will do much less harm to the business counting his money than doing anything else."

Ian Hargreaves, another ex-Indie editor, said: "The least mourned departure in British journalism."

Roy Greenslade, ex-Mirror editor, said: "Once he was the City's solution. Now he is the City's problem."

Richard Stott, another ex-Mirror editor, said: "He shouldn't go anywhere near newspapers again." John Pilger, ex-Mirror journalist, said: "He brought the virus of Murdochism to the Mirror and amassed a personal fortune in the process."

ANOTHER EXPRESS EDITOR

19 JANUARY Amanda Platell, the Express on Sunday editor, lost her job. Rosie Boycott, Platell's editor-in-chief, made Michael Pilgrim the fifth Sunday Express editor in six years. Platell lasted 38 issues, her predecessor Richard Addis 84 issues and Sue Douglas 33 issues. Pilgrim's career progress included a recent stint as head of David Montgomery's Mirror Group Academy of Excellence. Within two months Platell was back in work as chief Tory PR.

CROSS CORPORATE PUFFERY

24 JANUARY "Millions of FREE books for schools" a Sunday Times ad trumpeted. The majority of books on offer were from HarperCollins - a News International subsidiary, just like the Sunday Times.

LOSING THE MAXWELL PLOT

2 FEBRUARY Robert Maxwell's accountants were fined £3.5 million for "accepting representations ... without adequate investigation". Coopers & Lybrand, now part of Price Waterhouse Coopers, "lost the plot", according to the accountancy trade's Joint Disciplinary Tribunal. The firm worked for Maxwell from the early Seventies - when a government report described their client as "a person who cannot be relied upon to exercise proper stewardship of a publicly-quoted company" - to his death in November 1991 when, having raided Mirror and associated pension funds to the tune of £425 million, the Mirror owner toppled off his yacht. In May the auditors agreed to pay Maxwell creditors £68 million, an out-of-court deal believed to be the largest ever such settlement by a British accountancy firm. Meanwhile Maxwell's twin daughters Isabel and Christine, popped up on the Sunday Times rich list having made £100 million from internet stocks in California. This feat, the Sunday Times said, was "everything to do with their entrepreneurial savvy rather than any help from their father". In March Kevin Maxwell was cleared of contempt of court for his refusal to answer Department of Trade questions about the collapse of his father's business.

MAIL REACHES FTSE 100

3 FEBRUARY The Daily Mail and General Trust entered the Financial Times' list of top 100 publicly quoted companies. The new status means it will be subject to greater scrutiny from investment fund managers. City talk favoured a restructuring whereby the Harmsworth family, which owns 80 per cent of the £3.4 billion company's voting shares, would have to dismantle a corporate constitution allowing them to make use of new shareholders' cash without ceding any voting rights.

SUNDAY BUSINESS

15 FEBRUARY The Sunday Business, launched in 1996 and now solidly established with a 50,000+ circulation, celebrated its first year of ownership by the Barclay Brothers. Its most recent scoop had been revealing Candover's bid for Mirror Group. Its silliest scoop was identifying Dominic Lawson as an MI6 agent. See 20 December.

MONSANTO vs THE MEDIA

28 FEBRUARY Monsanto, the main developer of genetically modified crop strains, produced ads which were "confusing, misleading, unproven and wrong", according to an Advertising Standards Authority report. Criticism attached to ad lines such as: "Food biotechnology is a matter of opinion and GM crops are grown in a more environmentally sustainable way". It was the second time in two months that Monsanto ended up with genetically unmodified egg on its face, for the press Complaints Commission had rejected the company's complaints that the Guardian had made misleading statements about it.

STAR BID

6 MARCH: Chris Evans, the star DJ and Virgin Radio owner, proposed to United News and Media that he swapped a stake in his company Ginger Productions for the ailing Daily Star. The announcement was made in the Sunday Express, another UNM paper. "It makes sense why Ginger would be interested in the Star," said Ricardo Tejada of Express Newspapers. "But no deal is to be expected in the near future."

SNAP DECISION

10 MARCH 1999 Elton John's complaint that pictures taken of David Beckham and Victoria Adams and published in the Daily Star and Sport was an invasion of privacy was upheld by the Press Complaints Commission. The PCC code says: "The use of long-lens photography to take pictures of people in private places without their consent is unacceptable."

GOOD NEWS AT THE INDIE

12 MARCH "A turnaround story" is how the Independent's owners heralded Simon Kelner's What the Papers Say award as editor of the year and a 1.5 per cent rise in February sales to 219, 549. The investment bank Merrill Lynch commented: "Under single ownership by a group with proven management ability, the Independent's performance can be improved."

THE BEST OF BRITISH JOURNALISM

15 MARCH Journalists at the British Press Awards ceremony turned from the written word to the shouted when hecklers yelled that only two of the 18 gongs had gone to red-top tabloids. "You only sing when you're winning," chanted victorious Guardian journalists to a table of Mirror journalists. Shouting turned to jostling and a couple of fights broke out.

TWICE THROWN OVER

16 MARCH Benjamin Wegg-Prosser, Peter Mandelson's former aide at the Department of Trade, threw a leaving party also intended to celebrate his new £50,000 a year appointment as assistant editor of the Sun. He was thrown out of that job before he ever started amidst rumours that News International feared his appointment might queer the pitch for Department of Trade approval of its Man U bid.

EX-JOURNALISTS

24 MARCH Amanda Platell, former editor of the Sunday Mirror and then sacked from editing the Sunday Express in February, started a new job as Tory director of communications. She joined former MoS editor Jonathan Holborow and the former Times correspondent Nick Wood as ex-journalists to take a New Tory coin.

NATS ON THE NET

30 MARCH The Sun splashed an online announcement promising free net access and email plus an electronic copy of the paper on currantbun.com. The Mirror countered with the late April launch of ic24.co.uk and southern editions of the Express came with CDs with software to connect readers to Express Online.

SPORTING LIFE DIES

3 APRIL Mirror Group's plans to relaunch Sporting Life as a daily were finally scuppered a year after the appointment of John Mulholland (formerly editor of Guardian Media and now Observer deputy editor) as editor.

FT IN RUSSIA

8 APRIL The Financial Times joined up with the Wall Street Journal to prepare for the August launch of a Russian language business paper. It will recycle Western copy and have a staff of 20 for Russian news. Another FT joint venture with Izvestia newspaper collapsed late in 1998.

FOLKIES DEAD

20 APRIL A Telegraph obituary said Fairport Convention's Dave Swarbrick was "charismatic and dynamic". Well, maybe - but he wasn't dead, just on his way to recovery from emphysema.

MAIL STAYS PUT

29 APRIL Mail journalists celebrated Associated Newspapers' decision to sign a lease on their smart West London offices until 2017. Canary Wharf had been so anxious to attract Associated's 1,800 staff that it offered to rechristen the building as Northcliffe Tower.

ROYAL PRESS DEAL

29 APRIL The Press Complaints Commission cleared the Mirror and Star of intruding on princes William and Harry and announced a new code of agreement between the press and Buckingham Palace. The PCC recommended royal PRs put forward enough stories to satiate tabloid appetite for prince copy and that editors should "seek a view" on the impact of stories they intend to run.

SOARAWAY EDUCATION

10 MAY The Sun announced a graduate training scheme to award a pair of two-year City University scholarships with work placements to include a flight to News International in Australia plus "subbing a political lead [and] attending a Page Three glamour shoot". Linda Christmas, director of City U's journalism school said: "For once, people have actually sat down and thought what to do with trainees when they come back from their course at City." The Sun editor David Yelland recalled the days when he was trying to break into journalism and wrote "40-odd applications".

CRINGEAWAY EDUCATION

23-26 MAY While the Sun and News of the World owner Rupert Murdoch had asked for privacy in his own disintegrated personal life, his papers were busy invading the lives of others. In four consecutive days News International papers ran intrusive splashes about the England rugby captain Lawrence Dallaglio, the comedian Lenny Henry, the cricketer Ian Botham and the royal bride-to-be Sophie Rhys-Jones. On the fifth day the Sun editor had to learn how to apologise, though his grovelling to Buckingham Place for publishing an old and much touted topless snap of Rhys-Jones increased the likelihood of David Yelland writing his 41st odd job application.

EXPRESS BIDS

23 MAY The Barclay Brothers - owners of Scotland on Sunday, Sunday Business and the recently closed European - joined a line of prospective purchasers for Express Newspaper titles. Andrew Neil, now the Barclay's editor in chief, prepared a £300 million bid with bankers Morgan Grenfell in 1996. More recently Chris Evans bid for the Star and David Montgmery also expressed a purchasing interest. United News and Media - current owners of the Express, Sunday Express and Star - confirmed a £200 million Barclay bid was in the offing and said it was rejected.

SOB-U-LIKE SPOOF

30 MAY Richard Geefe began a new Observer column called Time to Go. "Last week I decided to end it all," he wrote in announcement of his imminent suicide. "No one understood me. No one liked me ..." Geefe, who is better known as Chris Morris, was following a line of spoof columns such as the Independent's Bridget Jones (Helen Fielding) and Wallace Arnold (Craig Brown) and the Guardian's Bel Littlejohn (also Craig Brown). Time to Go was different because, along with satirising newspapers, it also sent up real "I'm dying" journalism by Martyn Harris, John Diamond and the Observer's Ruth Picardie. Some of Picardie's friends and relatives complained to the Observer, but the column still ran. "These people cannot have it both ways," Decca Aitkenhead wrote in the Guardian. "They cannot argue that private lives are fit subjects for the public, then cry foul and demand the delicate respect that only private friends accord."

FEMAIL WEB SITE

10 JUNE The Daily Mail announced the September launch of CharlotteStreet.com, an internet site for women. The Daily Mail said it wasn't intended as competition for similar red top offerings from the Sun and Mirror.

MIRROR SNEAKS PAST MAIL

10 JUNE ABC figures for May revealed the Mirror had regained its lead over the Daily Mail and was 2.5 per cent up on May 1998.

STEVENS LEAVES UNM

15 JUNE Lord Stevens retired from an 18 year tenure as chairman of United News and Media's Express newspapers. Stevens' departure ended an uneasy working relationship between the Conservative peer and his Labour peer chief executive Lord Hollick. He was replaced by Sir Ronnie Hampel.

PLAIN MR BLACK

18 JUNE Conrad Black's elevation to the peerage was blocked by the Canadian prime minister Jean Chrétien. Despite the Telegraph proprietor getting a nomination for the peerage from William Hague and despite his taking on dual Canadian/British nationality, Black's north American prime minister wouldn't sanction the ennoblement. In August Black sued Chrétien for "abuse of public office".

ELDERLY YOOF FOR IOS

30 JUNE Janet Street-Porter, 52, was appointed editor of the Independent on Sunday. She began working life as a columnist on the Daily Mail and Evening Standard, found fame in the seventies as an LWT presenter and executive status followed in the eighties when she took charge of the BBC's youth programming. Simon Kelner, the Indie editor who made the appointment, said: "It irritates me that people are seeing this as a publicity stunt. We could have employed a good, solid, old-school journalist. But we realised that if we are going to put the paper back on the agenda, to make it buzz, we needed someone with dynamism, flair and individuality."

POLICE CAN'T SEE DEMO FOOTAGE

2 JULY Police demands for photographs and film of those taking part in "the carnival against capitalism" - held in the City of London on 18 June - were rejected by an Old Bailey judge. Manula Barca, a TV lawyer, said: "If court orders become routine, journalists, cameramen and photographers will only be able to attend demonstrations under police protection or behind police cordons." Judge Henry Pownall agreed that police demands should not be seen as "routine requests for judicial rubber stamp".

BLAIR WINS PRESS BATTLE

16 JULY The prime minister Tony Blair won a crucial ruling against the press when the Press Complaints Commission backed his complaint that the Mail on Sunday had intruded into the privacy of his 11 year old daughter. The case was important for two reasons: one, it was the first complaint lodged with the PCC by a prime minister; two, it was the first to be made under clause six of the newspaper code practice which protects the children of public figures at school. "Make no mistake: the most media-savvy prime minister in British history has landed a mighty blow against newspapers on behalf of individual privacy," Roy Greenslade commented.
* Meanwhile, the PCC censured the Daily Telegraph for publishing an article by Jonathan Aitken's daughter which ignored the PCC ban on payments to "family, friends and colleagues of convicted criminals".

FREEDOM OF INFORMATION?

The home secretary's Freedom of Information bill came under increased fire when MPs on the Commons all-party public administration committee pointed out that Jack Straw's bill is more concerned with the discretionary release of documents than a public right to know. The MPs said: "A statutory freedom of information regime should be based, as much as possible, on enforceable rights of access to information; not on an undertaking to consider the discretionary release of information." See page 293.

MIRROR/TRINITY MERGER

30 JULY Trinity succeeded in forming Britain's biggest newspaper group with its £1.5 billion merger with the Mirror Group. The new company -to be known as Trinity Mirror - includes the Mirror and Sunday Mirror, the Sunday People and Sunday Record and Sunday Mail in Scotland plus 155 regional papers. The merger's terms leave 51.6 per cent of the share capital with Mirror shareholders with Trinity investors holding the remainder. The Trinity Mirror chairman is Victor Blank (former Mirror Group boss) and the chief executive is Philip Graf (former Trinity boss). They hope to save £15 million by 2002.

Local and regional newspapers

AD SALES I

18 AUGUST 1998 Media analysts at Salomon Smith Barney stoked recessionary fears with a prediction of fractional growth in local paper advertising revenues. Meanwhile Newsquest, the UK's largest local paper publisher which derives 80 per cent of turnover from ads, reported a 10 per cent increase in advertisement sales.

VIVE LA LOCALS

SEPTEMBER Independent Newspapers, the Dublin based owner of The Independent and IoS, started looking at local paper acquisitions to find a home for the £52 million gathered from the sale of its French outdoor advertising business.

"HEADCOUNT REDUCTION"

30 OCTOBER A leaked letter from Chris Oakley, chief executive of Regional Independent Media, confirmed his intention for a "rapid 10 per cent headcount reduction" and urged management to go for "a well-planned, big bang approach". Some 350 jobs in Yorkshire and Lancashire were thus threatened in a cost cutting drive widely interpreted to have been initiated by financial people at Candover, Regional Independent Media's main backer.

DEMOGRAPHICS

1 NOVEMBER David Gledhill, editor of the Bath Chronicle, told the Guild of Editors conference that local newspapers are wasted on the young. "In chasing after the youth market, we divert precious resources into an ungrateful black hole and we do further damage by alienating our existing readers." By 2020, about 25 per cent of the population will be over 65. Meanwhile the number of teenagers will fall from 9 million in 1990 to 6 million in 2010.

AD SALES II

10 NOVEMBER Newsquest, publisher of nearly 200 local papers, said revenue growth fuelled by recruitment ads was tailing off.

REPORTING RESTRICTIONS

JANUARY 1999 Clause 43 in the Youth Justice and Criminal Evidence Bill suggested a ban on the identification of under 18s involved in a criminal allegation. The Guild of Editors'said: "As drafted, the Bill would have made it impossible to report the Dunblane massacre, nursery nurse Lisa Potts' heroism or the murder of the head teacher Philip Lawrence ... [it] would have prevented full reporting of the case against Jonathan Aitken for putting lies into his statement by his teenage daughter." The clause was amended so that the ban started the beginning of a criminal investigation but the Guild's barrister Santha Rasaiah rejected this: "Newspapers could still face prosecution if they report matters of legitimate interest involving young people."

MIRROR TAKEOVER

JANUARY Two regional newspaper owners circled the Mirror Group in the hope of moving in for a takeover. Regional Independent Media, owners of the Yorkshire Post, offered £900 million; and before that Trinity put in for a £1.3 billion share deal. Disarray on the Mirror board spurred the departure of chief executive David Montgomery, viewed by many as an impediment to the sale plans of his chairman Sir Victor Blank. In March the Competition Commission(the former Monopolies and Mergers Commission) announced an 11 June deadline for "evidence of the acquisition of Mirror Group by Trinity and RIM".

... ANTI MONOPOLISTS

APRIL Eight new members were appointed to Competition Commission's newspaper panel:

Sawar Ahmed: Southnews Ethnic Media Group;
Linda Christmas: journalism director at City University;
William Gibson: ex-chairman of Westminster Press;
Gerry Holbrook: ex-MD of the Yorkshire Post;
Joyce Hopkirk: ex-editor of She magazine;
Eve Pollard: ex-editor of the Sunday Express;
Donald Trelford: ex Observer editor and head of journalism at Sheffield University;
Charles Wilson: ex-editor of the Times.

Get your own personal copy of Press Gazette delivered straight to your door every week

You can rely on **press gazette** to bring you weekly coverage of all the issues that affect you on a daily basis. And with the new improved look designed to help you access the latest news and developments in the industry, can you afford to do without it?

Simply call **01858 438872** or fax **01858 434958** for further details.

LOCAL PAY

5 FEBRUARY 1999 Tony Harcup, a Leeds university journalism lecturer, called regional journalists' pay a national scandal. "Over the past three years I have said farewell to some excellent trainees who have got jobs on local papers at salaries that make we want to weep rather than celebrate," he said. "I'm talking of wage rates of around £6,000 to £11,000 a year, most frequently around £8,000 to £9,500. Having emerged from university with a degree and a hefty overdraft - the average is £3,883 before tuition fees - they have then been compelled to go on to pay for their own training and upkeep for a further year."

NEW SCOTTISH SUNDAY

7 FEBRUARY Scottish Media Group, the publisher of the Herald newspaper and the owner of STV and Grampian TV companies, launched the Sunday Herald. The new paper, which started with a £10 million investment, must compete in a market already served by a dozen Sundays. The editor, former Observer editor Andrew Jaspan, pointed out that around three-quarters of Scots read a Sunday paper, compared with less than two thirds south of the border.

NEW GREENWICH DAILY

12 FEBRUARY Associated Newspapers beat off competition from the Express and Mirror groups to win the contract to produce a free daily newspaper for visitors to the Millennium Dome. The Daily Dome will combine exclusive reporting of Dome events with copy lifted from the Evening Standard, Daily Mail and Mail on Sunday.

NEW LONDON DAILY

16 MARCH: London Metro, a morning freesheet distributed at London Underground stations, was launched by Associated Newspapers, publisher of the Evening Standard. In a turbulent run in to the first Associated Newspaper launch in 17 years, Kim Chapman the original editor was sacked and News International promised (but failed to deliver) a revived version of Today as a spoiler.

"HISTORY'S FIRST DRAFT"

22 MARCH A national microfilm programme to preserve 3,500 local newspapers went ahead with a £5 million lottery grant backed by £2.3 million from libraries and publishers. Newsplan will be installed in libraries and record newsprint from 1800 onwards. The culture and media secretary Chris Smith said: "Newspaper have been called history's first draft. The conservation of our stock of local newspapers is incredibly important because it forms a considerable part of our nation's archives."

LOCAL NET

23 MARCH "Almost national coverage of local news" was the slightly odd billing for a new website announced by Newsquest, Trinity and Associated Newspapers. This is Britain, an unusual collaboration between rivals, will draw on regional news from the major publishers' newspapers.

WORLD'S BIGGEST NEWSPAPER

1 APRIL The Grimsby Evening Telegraph earned a place in the Guinness Book of Records (plus £5,000 for Comic Relief) by producing a 700 square centimetre newspaper.

UK'S FASTEST GROWING LOCAL

1 APRIL ABC figures revealed the Reading Evening Post as the fastest growing local evening paper with a 2.3 per cent circulation rise since its purchase by Guardian Media Group in 1994. Much credit for the success went to the editor Kim Chapman - who had recently left the paper to launch the London Metro (see 16 March opposite).

ABLE TABLES

APRIL Regional Independent Media reversed a centralised subbing desk installed on the north west titles it bought from United Provincial Newspapers. "It was an accountant's invention to try and save money," said Chris Oakley, the RIM chief exec. "You don't save money and you deter quality on individual papers. Sub-editors don't get the buzz they would from working for a single newspaper rather than subbing 30 different titles."

ADS FOR ADS

19 APRIL 1999 The Newspaper Society launched £3 million worth of advertising to win a greater share of a £1.35 billion overall national advertising pot. The advertisements pointed out that more than 10 million people who read one of Britain's 1,400 local papers don't take a national title.

SOCIETY OF EDITORS

26 APRIL The Guild of Editors and the Association of British Editors merged to form a new 400 strong Society of Editors representing both the national and local press. Geoff Elliott, its president and editor of the News in Portsmouth, said the SoE would campaign against reporting restriction within the Freedom of Information Bill, the Youth Justice Bill, the Data Protection Act, the Human Rights Act and changes to the prevention of Terrorism Act. Peter Preston, the former Guardian editor and a Society of Editors vice-president, said: "The time is absolutely right to make the united voice of Britain's editors - in national and regional newspapers, in broadcasting, in magazines and in the media - to be heard loud and clear."

TV BEATS LOCALS

14 MAY: Figures produced by the Independent Television Commission were interpreted as proof that "1998 was the first year that television has become the leading source for local news". Some 40 per cent of respondents to an ITC survey said they preferred television as a source of local news, with 38 per cent citing newspapers.

JOHNSTON BUYS P&SN

18 MAY Johnston Press paid £254 million to take over Portsmouth and Sunderland Newspapers to take the group out of Storey family ownership dating back to 1873. Johnston defeated competition from Newsquest and Newscom and its chairman, Fred Johnston, said the purchase - which includes The News, Portsmouth, the Sunderland Echo, Hartlepool Mail and Shields Gazette - was the beginning of the consolidation of local paper ownership into four or five companies.

NEWSQUEST TRAINING

24 MAY Newsquest and the Darlington College of Journalism announced a training scheme to provide a 20 week course to include NCTJ pre-entry exams. Sue Campbell, Darlington's main media lecturer, said: "The days of take-it-or-leave-it training are over. Training providers have to respond to employers' needs."

NEIL PROMOTED

18 JUNE Andrew Neil was promoted from Press Holding's editor-in-chief to publisher in charge of the Scotsman, Scotland on Sunday, Edinburgh Evening News and Sunday Business. The man with the American style job title said Press Holdings - which is owned by the Barclay Brothers - was "in the mood to expand if the right properties came along".

US MOVE FOR NEWSQUEST

24 JUNE Newsquest, the UK's largest local newspaper group with 63 paid for titles and 120 frees, accepted a £904 million offer from a US media group. Gannett owns 74 papers including USA Today. Newsquest's management led a buyout from Reed three years ago and three top men stand to pocket £17.5 million. Gannett, mindful of public distrust of the media, recently introduced five rules for good journalism which forbid:
1) Lying to obtain a story
2) Deliberately concealing the identity of an informant
3) Fabricating or plagiarising
4) Making misleading alterations to photographs
5) Slanting the news

ANTI TRADE UNIONISM

27 JULY A leaked Newspaper Society memo briefed local newspaper proprietors on ways of getting around the government's proposed employment relations legislation. The NS advised Chris Oakley, chief executive of Regional Independent Media, that the legal right to union representation where more than half the workforce wants it can be countered by the introduction of staff councils to "develop infertile ground for union recruitment" and recognition of "non-independent unions".

TRINITY/MIRROR

See page 20, 30 July

Speed is nothing without control

Transferring digital files quickly is only half the problem. Ensuring they've arrived successfully makes point-to-point ISDN and courier transfers an uphill process. But now, you can transfer files electronically on the Vio network. It's easy to get started and it makes the whole transfer process quicker and much more controllable.

Senders and receivers will know immediately that files have arrived, and when they have been viewed and downloaded; whilst recipients can prioritise and automate file downloads to make their workflow much more efficient. So everyone stays in complete control - even at speeds of up to 15MB per minute.

For a comprehensive information pack, contact Vio now. You'll save yourself a mountain of problems.

VIO DIGITAL FILE TRANSFER – FASTER AND MORE CONTROLLABLE!

The Digital Graphics Network
from BT and Sciex

Freephone: 0800 068 2009 **Fax:** 01923 251356 **E-mail:** marketing@vio-dgn.com **Web:** www.vio-dgn.com

44/S

Magazines

MASTHEAD FIRST

17 SEPTEMBER 1998 Dazed and Confused magazine became a Channel 4 TV programme, a first on British terrestrial TV and timed to come immediately after the ITC lifted a ban on masthead programming. Rankin Waddell, one the people behind the one-off TV show, told Edinburgh TV Festival delegates: "Irony and irreverence are what programme-makers use to disguise lack of content."

GREEN PULP

28 SEPTEMBER Penwell Printers took a unilateral decision to pulp the 14,000 print run of the Ecologist magazine, scared that an issue attacking the genetic engineering company Monsanto might attract a libel action. Monsanto played no part in the pulping and the publisher (Teddy Goldsmith, brother of James) found a bolder printer and published in late October.

DEMISE OF THE INKIES

NOVEMBER NME and Melody Maker both reported annual sales drops of over 10 per cent in the face of competition from lad mags, newspapers, TV and radio also targetting 16 to 24 year olds. NME said it would branch out into TV and radio.

NEW STATESMEN

10 DECEMBER Robert Harris (the journalist turned millionaire novelist and friend of Tony Blair) was in talks with Geoffrey Robinson (the millionaire turned paymaster general and friend of trade secretary Peter Mandelson) to buy the New Statesman. Harris said there was no reason why the rightwing Spectator should more than double the New Statesman 25,000 weekly sale. "Why should the devil have all the good tunes?" he asked. Robinson, who acquired the New Statesman for £125,000 in 1997, gave no indication that he wanted to sell. Harris next made a splash when criticising the press coverage which led to Mandelson's resignation - for accepting an interest free loan from Robinson.

MAG GLOOM

13 DECEMBER Reed Elsevier announced a 6 per cent drop in 1998 profit to £770 million. Meanwhile IPC, whose managers arranged a £860 million buyout from Reed Elsevier in 1997, braced staff for a winter of cost-cutting. Orlando Murrin, a former editor of IPC's Woman and Home, said: "Editors at IPC are constantly having their minds taken off their titles because ... a penny-pinching mentality has taken over and it shows in the product."

EMAP EYES AMERICA

15 DECEMBER Emap, the magazine, radio and exhibitions company, had 8 per cent wiped off share values when news leaked of a renewed attempt to spend £720 million on the Petersen magazine group in the US. "Emap has chosen the right company but was probably paying the wrong price at the wrong time," said Lorna Tilbian, media analyst for West LB Panmure.

IPC: WOMEN'S MAGS

17 DECEMBER IPC - bought a year before by its management (with about £860 million help from Cinven venture capitalists) - announced a £9 million marketing drive for its women's weeklies. This sector accounts for 8 million sales per week but, with the exception of Northern and Shell's OK!, most circulations were falling. It's still a large market: L'Oreal, the biggest spender in women's mag, placed £4.8 million worth of ads in 1998 whereas Rover Group, the men's splashiest advertiser, spent £584,000.

IPC: STAFF CUTS

15 JANUARY 1999 IPC announced the closure of Options and 200 job cuts for savings of £6 million. The management team, which took over from Reed Elsevier, made IPC's five publishing groups - TV, Women, Country & Leisure and Music & Sport - into subsidiaries. "We are giving power to the people who actually run the magazines," said Mike Matthew, the chairman. "It will free up the organisation to act like a group of young growth companies."

GO WEST YOUNG LAD

28 JANUARY: Maxim, whose 800,000 readers and £700,000 annual ad turnover had it billed as Britain's fastest growing mag, brought out an American edition. The rise of jockism - the American counterpart to laddism - had other mags like FHM looking West at the US.

LAD GOES FOR A BURTON

18 FEBRUARY GQ editor James Brown got his marching orders having included Rommel and the Nazis on a list of the century's most stylish men. Brown, who founded Loaded and found a new market for men's mags, was already under fire from the publisher Condé Nast for disappointing sales figures.

REED ON THE WEB ...

20 MARCH Reed Business Information offered internet access to free "portal sites" containing New Scientist, Farmer's Weekly, Estates Gazette and Computer Weekly. Jim Muttram, RBI's director of electronic publishing, revealed plans to sign up e-commerce titles from across its 30 different business areas. "We send out 1.5 million magazines a week and they are read by around 5 million people, Muttram said. "Half are online already."

... REED ON THE ROCKS

9 APRIL Reed Elsevier management continued a long tradition of boardroom bickering when two directors resigned in protest at the failure to appoint a new chief executive. This fed rumours of plans for a £4 billion sale of Reed business titles which in 1998 made a profit of £260 million on a £1.3 billion turnover. Both Emap and UNM were said to be interested.

NEWSPRINT CARTEL

1 APRIL A four year European Commission investigation found evidence that paper producers had operated a price fixing cartel. Newsprint account for around a quarter of magazine costs and British publishers had made loud complaints when prices rose by 30 per cent in 1995. The investigation could open newsprint companies to law suits from publications forced out of business by high prices.

EURO MAG

2 MAY EuroBusiness, the first magazine to be sold in euros, was relaunched by the Sunday Business founder Tom Rubython and the Formula One magnate Bernie Ecclestone. Could this be a new European? "No one could ever say who the European was aimed at," said Rubython. "We are doing what the European should have done if it had wanted to be a business magazine. Britain has always been limited for business magazines because of the size of the market compared to the US. The single market in Europe has opened everything up."

IPC REVENUE UP, PROFIT DOWN

2 JUNE Half year results to the end of March showed that IPC while revenues were 2.8 per cent up at £175.2 million, profits were down 10 per cent to £29.3 million. Marketing investment in its women's and TV mags were held to blame.

FAG ADS STUBBED OUT

17 JUNE Cigarette adverts in magazines will be outlawed from 10 December, in compliance with European legislation. Frank Dobson, the British health secretary, said the aim was to protect children from a drug which kills 120,000 Britons every year. "It doesn't make sense," fumed Felix Dennis, the chairman of Dennis Publishing, whose titles take in about £150,000 a year from cigarette ads. "It is OK to send 18 to 34 year olds to Kosovo to be shot dead by maniacs but it is not OK to be allowed to read an advert about smoking."

EMAP BUYS THE FACE

1 JULY Emap bought the eightie's style bible with the purchase of the Face for an undisclosed sum believed to be at least £10 million. Nick Logan, the founding editor, left the company.

JOHNSON EDITS SPECTATOR

28 JULY The Spectator took on a brand new Johnson when Frank J was moved from the editor's chair in favour of Boris J. "Boris is hugely controversial and great at producing scoops," said Daniel Colson, the chief executive of the Telegraph Group.

The nationals

There are ten national dailies and ten national Sundays. In the year since summer 1998 there have been no closures, unless you count The European which had staggered into a magazine format before its owners finally shut it just before Christmas 1998.

Though the roll call of trusty old mastheads remains intact, the sales of national newspapers continues to fall. In 1990 the circulation of all dailies exceeded 15 million, now it is 13 million. Over the same period the Sundays' circulations have fallen from over 17 million to between 14 and 15 million. This decline is likely to continue with the rise of the internet plus the rise of local radio and the proliferation of TV channels. The response has been more colour, more pages, more sections, more lifestyle, more sport, more columns - more and more of everything except

hard news. The largest continuing success and bucker of overall trends is the Sunday Times which dominates a Sunday scene of otherwise unequivocal decline and accounts for over half the national broadsheet sale.

In terms of relative decline, the tabloid red tops are doing worst of all and this isn't really surprising in an era of increasing educational standards and the redefinition of class stereotypes. Tony Blair's Britain isn't the place for the Sun to pass itself off as the Daily Zeitgeist and we now have News International marketeers pushing a "more rounded product". Meanwhile the Sun reverted to political stereotype with a headline pointing at a scowling prime minister asking "Is THIS the most dangerous man in Britain?". Elsewhere consensus ruled. Blair attended the funeral of

National newspaper circulations

DAILIES	JAN-JUN 99	JAN-JUN 98	CHANGE
1 Sun	3,715,079	3,713,476	0.16%
2 Mirror	2,340,588	2,298,991	0.03%
3 Daily Mail	2,295,791	2,152,874	2.92%
4 Express	1,091,852	1,168,598	-6.53%
5 Daily Telegraph	1,044,709	1,073,822	-2.95%
6 Times	742,595	787,788	-5.99%
7 Daily Star	525,949	579,516	-7.99%
8 Guardian	398,938	402,842	-0.48%
9 Financial Times	382,879	353,928	9.22%
10 Independent	222,064	220,534	0.53%
11 Daily Record	671,564	672.718	-0.17%
12 Scotsman	79,915		
SUNDAYS			
1 News of the World	4,214,897	4,334,115	-3.25%
2 Mail on Sunday	2,272,274	2,211,804	3.04%
3 Sunday Mirror	1,974,342	2,070,804	-5.60%
4 Sunday People	1,655,977	1,761,528	-5.99%
5 Sunday Times	1,372,979	1,354,285	1.58%
6 Express on Sunday	996,990	1,085,804	-8.35%
7 Sunday Telegraph	814,521	841,062	-3.81%
8 Observer	405,168	412,632	-1.87%
9 Independent on Sunday	251,627	257,601	-3.00%
10 Sunday Business	55,691		
11 Scotland on Sunday	120,982	n/a	

Source: ABC

the Daily Mail proprietor Lord Rothermere and, although their politics barely intersected, they spoke the same market-speak. "People who used to be working class now think of themselves as middle class," Rothermere said shortly before his death. "This is one of the things Tony Blair realised and which enabled him to create New Labour. The party appeals to the lower middle class, which is fast becoming the majority in this country. And the Daily Mail is right in there with them, which is why we're growing."

Neither Lord Rothermere or his star Daily Mail editor David English were alive to catch the late September 1998 ABC figures showing that the Mirror - whose editor Piers Morgan is in more stories than royalty these days - sold fewer copies than the Daily Mail. A significant first in modern

times, and in February 1999 the Daily Mail and General Trust entered the list of top 100 publicly quoted companies. A month later the upmarket/downmarket clash got physical at the British Press Awards, the Oscars of British journalism and the only set of gongs where journalists are judged by their peers. When a mere two of the 20 awards went to tabloids Neil Wallis, editor of the Sunday People, grabbed the microphone to condemn the judging as an "absolute disgrace".

The received wisdom is that papers can only retain readers by chasing after scandal. Scandal is evidently what the public wants - the same public which, in opinion polls, also says it wants privacy laws. What the public gets is a series of pointless slaps in the face to minor celebrity. In

Historic national newspaper circulations

DAILIES	1958	1968	1978	1988
Express	4,062,587	3,819,674	2,458,792	1,658,252
Financial Times	84,858	159,536	181,678	282,675
Guardian	177,962	274,638	283,494	454,038
Herald	1,513,217			
Independent				381,210
Daily Mail	2,104,932	2,067,468	1,973,580	1,775,695
Mirror	4,527,208	4,991,616	3,806,003	3,119,365
News Chronicle	1,255,233			
Record	523,748	721,796	770,589	
Sketch/Graphic 1	,213,184	900,336		
Daily Star				990,110
Sun		1,037,577	3,960,076	4,182,848
Daily Telegraph		1,393,094	1,358,875	1,133,173
Times	248,338	408,300	295,863	443,462
Today				478,220
SUNDAYS	1958	1968	1978	1988
Empire News	2,155,132			
Mail on Sunday				1,926,047
NoW	6,716,258	6,161,138	4,919,905	5,287,190
Observer	642,588	878,266	712,712	735,826
The People	4,906,019	5,479,878	3,901,314	2,746,348
Reynolds News	356,676			
Sunday Dispatch	1,752,101			
Sunday Express	3,412,333	4,221,914	3,260,600	2,088,086
Sunday Graphic	933,214			
Sunday Mirror			3,865,926	2,866,007
Sunday Pictorial	5,378,189	5,076,344		
Sunday Sport				551,377
Sunday Telegraph		729,942	855,803	704,737
Sunday Times	813,924	1,450,694	1,399,073	1,338,623

Source: ABC

four consecutive days in May, Murdoch papers splashed stories about the England rugby captain Lawrence Dallaglio, the comedian Lenny Henry, the cricketer Ian Botham and a royal bride-to-be. All grist to the mill of those who support a privacy law but difficult to legislate against if more noteworthy scandals - Peter Mandelson's secret property deal springs to mind - are to get aired. The Press Complaints Commission sits between the scandalised and the scandal-seeking and still adheres to the ideal of a self-regulated press which - for journalists who hold to the rule that real news is what someone somewhere doesn't want published - is Good News. The bad news came in a British Social Attitudes survey revealing that only 15 per cent of readers trust journalists on national newspapers to pursue the truth above getting a good story.

One sure symptom of a business uncertain of its future are a rapid turnaround of top staff and, by this benchmark, things are improving with only four new national editors since the last Media Guide went to press in August 1998. In the first half of 1998 there were eight change of national editors. Janet Street-Porter's appointment as the Independent on Sunday editor is loaded with symbolic significance. While her CV contains nothing about newspaper news reporting, she began working life as a columnist on the Daily Mail and the Evening Standard. She found fame in the seventies as an LWT presenter, and executive status followed in the eighties when she took charge of the BBC's youth programming. Def II and Rough Guides were among her successes. Failure - and a mauling by Kelvin MacKenzie - followed at Live TV. Though aged 52, she has a reputation for grabbing the attention of youth, and newspaper marketeers have always deemed that the most precious of commodities.

Street-Porter is a TV features woman blessed with TV notoriety and her appointment must be more about marketing than anything else. It isn't, as she swiftly conceded, about newspaper production skills. "I'll have people around me," she said. "Look, [editing a paper] isn't some kind of mystical science that can't be learned. Papers are a team thing similar to making TV programmes." Maybe. Simon Kelner, her editor in chief and the most important of the people around her, said: "It irritates me that people are seeing this as a publicity stunt. We could have employed a good, solid, old-school journalist. But we realised that if we are going to put the paper back on the agenda, to make it buzz, we needed someone with dynamism, flair and individuality." Her appointment could just be a smart move and another vindication of the undoubted marketing talents of the Independent's new(ish) proprietor Tony O'Reilly.

The good news - or perhaps merely an encouraging feature - about national newspapers is that over half the population still reads a daily. Newspapers remain embedded in our culture and - being portable, easy to read, easy to store and accessible - will continue playing a central role in our lives. They help people define an identity and, at their best, still set the news agenda, shape debate and allow the space for news to be interpreted.

Newspapers get some further encouragement from a recent crisis-what-crisis? report preparedby the Henley Centre for Forecasting. It says: "Rather than merely mediating reality, for many the newspaper seems to be an anchor of it, despite all the other media sources currently available." Like the best such reports, it takes what was often thought and expresses it in market-speak with a smattering of statistics. Did you know, for example, that 55 per cent of the population say they often debate what they read in the paper and that 34 per cent agree very strongly that they would miss their daily newspaper? To summarise the prose:

New editors

TITLE	DATE	OUT	IN
1 Mail on Sunday	September 1998	Jonathan Holborrow	Peter Wright
2 Daily Star	October 1998	Phil Walker	Ian Hill
3 Express on Sunday	January 1999	Amanda Platell	Michael Pilgrim
4 Independent on Sunday	June 1999	Kim Fletcher	Janet Street-Porter

newspapers are embedded in our culture and are a cohesive force in society; newspapers - being portable, easy to read, easy to store and accessible - will continue playing a central role in our lives; they allow people to turn dead time on a train, say, into fruitful time; they help people define an identity; they still set the news agenda, shape debate and allow the "discursive space" where the news gets its interpretation.

Jargon, maybe, but carrying an optimism to counter the standard issue gloom that concentrates on falling circulations in the face of rising competition. Try this from young Lachlan Murdoch, who says: "Many of my friends who should read a morning paper don't bother. These are young, intelligent ambitious people who understand the power of information. They should be natural newspaper readers and yet they aren't." While it is surprising the rapidly promoted son of Rupe has any friends of his own age, it is not at all remarkable he should be preoccupied with a global decline in newspaper circulations. Newsprint is the most profitable part of News Corp's operation. However, Lachlan - along with nearly every other newspaper executive - may well grow to temper

their fashionable preoccupation with youth and all its predilections. The most recent set of census predictions for the next decade estimates that the number of retired people in the United Kingdom will grow, and that life expectancy will continue to increase and that the number of under 16s will fall. Assuming pensions don't fail entirely, there are many readers with an engrained newspaper habit and a need for "discursive space" who are going to be here for a while yet.

ON THE JOB TRAINING Janet Street-Porter, the most recent of the Independent on Sunday editors. "I'll have people around me," says the woman whose career has centred on TV. "Look, editing a paper isn't some kind of mystical science that can't be learned."

NATIONAL DAILIES

Some entries will have changed since this book went to press at the beginning of September 1999.

Daily Mail
2 Derry Street, Kensington, London W8 5TT
Fax 020-7937 3251   Tel 020-7938 6000
News fax 020-7937 4463   Tel 020-7938 6372
Web site: www.dailymail.com
Editor-in-chief: Paul Dacre since 1998, editor since 1992.
Deputy editor: Alistair Sinclair
News editor: Tony Gallagher
Features editor: Veronica Wadley
Deputy foreign editor: Gerry Hunt
Picture editor: Paul Silva
City editor: Andrew Alexander
Diary editor: Nigel Dempster
Advertising director: John Teal
Managing director: Guy Zitter
Financial director: Guy Morgan
Founded: 1896.
Owner: Daily Mail & General Trust

Daily Star
245 Blackfriars Road, London SE1 9UX
Fax 020-7620 1644   Tel 020-7928 8000
News fax 020-7620 1654   Tel 020-7922 7070
Editor: Peter Hill
Deputy editor: Hugh Whittow
Associate editor: Jim Mansell
Executive editor: Henry McRory
Assistant editor, features: Dawn Neefom
Picture editor: Mark Moylan
Sports editor: Jim Mansell
Managing director: Andy Jonesco
Marketing director: Paul Woolfenden
Sales director, (circulation): Richard Miller
Advertisement director: Richard Bogie
Founded: 1978.
Owner: United News and Media

Daily Telegraph
1 Canada Square, Canary Wharf, London E14 5DT
Fax 020-7538 6242   Tel 020-7538 5000
News fax 020-7513 2506   Tel 020-7538 6355
E-mail: corprels@telegraph.co.uk
Web site: www.telegraph.co.uk
Editor: Charles Moore, since 1995
Deputy editor: Sarah Sands
Home editor: Neil Darbyshire
Arts editor: Sarah Crompton
Foreign editor: Stephen Robinson
Business editor: Roland Gribben
City editor: Neil Collins
Education editor: John Clare
Picture editor: Bob Bodman
Advertising director: Len Sanderson
Editorial director: Brenda Haywood
Managing director: Jeremy Deedes
Financial director: Niamh O'Donnell-Keenan
Marketing director: Hugo Drayton
Founded: 1855.
Owner: The Telegraph

The Express
245 Blackfriars Road, London SE1 9UX
Fax 020-76201654   Tel 020-7928 8000
News   Tel 020-7922 7070
E-mail newsdesk@dailyexpress.co.uk
Editor: Rosie Boycott since April 1998
Deputy editor: Chris Blackhurst
Executive editors: Michael Pilgrim, Chris Williams
Assistant editor, news: Michael Streeter
Assistant editor, comment: John Price
Head of features : Albert Read
Head of City: Robert Miller
Diary: John McEntee
Head of pictures: Chris Djukanovic
Foreign editor: Jacqui Goddard
Group managing editor: Lindsay Cook
Managing director: Andy Jonesco
Marketing director: Paul Woolfenden
Circulation director: Richard Miller
Advertising director: Richard Bogie
Founded: 1900.
Owner: United News and Media

Financial Times
1 Southwark Bridge, London SE1 9HL
Fax 020-7873 3076   Tel 020-7873 3000
News fax 020-7407 5700   Tel 020-7873 3616
Website: www.ft.com
Editor: Richard Lambert, since 1991
Managing editor: John Ridding
News editor: Lionel Barber
Foreign editor: William Dawkins
Finance director: Richard Leishman
Founded: 1888.
Owner: Pearson

The Guardian
119 Farringdon Road, London EC1R 3ER
Fax 020-7837 2114   Tel 020-7278 2332
Website: www.guardian.co.uk
Editor: Alan Rusbridger, since 1995
Deputy editor: Georgina Henry
Managing editor: Brian Whitaker
Deputy editor (news): Paul Johnson
Home editor: Harriet Sherwood
News editor: Clare Margetson
Features editor: Ian Katz
Deputy features editor: Ben Clissitt
Political editor: Michael White
Economics editor: Larry Elliot
Arts editor: Dan Glaister
Media editor: Kamal Ahmed
Weekend magazine editor: Katharine Viner
Picture editor: Eamonn McCabe
Sports editor: Michael Averis
Internet editor: Simon Waldman
Managing director: Caroline Marland
Marketing director: Stephen Palmer
Finance director: Paul Naismith
Deputy managing director: Carolyn McCall
Founded: 1821
Owner: Guardian Media Group

Independent
1 Canada Square, Canary Wharf, London E14 5DL
Fax 020-7293 2435   Tel 020-7293 2000
E-mail letters@independent.co.uk
Website: www.independent.co.uk
Editor: Simon Kelner since April 1998
Deputy editor: Ian Birrell
Executive editors: Tristan Davies (features), Michael Williams (news)
News editor: Jason Burt
Arts editor: Ian Irvine
Foreign editor: Leonard Doyle
Picture editor: Andy Blackmore
Sports editor: Paul Newman
Commercial director: Stephen Miron
Head of marketing; Duncan Eaton
Managing director: Brendan Hopkins
Founded: 1986.
Owner: Independent Newspapers

The Mirror
1 Canada Square, Canary Wharf, London E14 5AP
Fax 020-7293 3843   Tel 020-7510 3000
News fax 020-7510 3409   Tel 020-7293 3831
Editor: Piers Morgan, since 1995
Deputy editor: Tina Weaver
News editor: Eugene Duffy
Foreign editor: Mark Dowdney
Features editor: Mark Thomas
Picture editor: Ron Morgans
Advertisement director: Mark Pritchett
Managing director: Roger Eastoe
Marketing director: Jill Playle
Founded: 1903.
Owner: Trinity Mirror

The Sun
1 Virginia Street, Wapping, London E1 9BD
Fax 020-7488 3253   Tel 020-7782 4000
Editor: David Yelland, since June 1998
Deputy editor: Rebekah Wade
City editor: Isabelle Murray
Political editor: Trevor Kavanagh
Picture editor: Jeff Webster
Features editor: Sam Carlisle
Sports editor: Ted Chadwick
Women's page: Vicki Grimshaw
Advertising director: Richard Webb
Founded: 1912 Daily Herald; in present form since '69.
Owner: News International

The Times
1 Pennington Street, Wapping, London E1 9XN
Fax 020-7488 3242   Tel 020-7782 5000
Website: www.the-times.co.uk
Editor: Peter Stothard, since 1992
News editor: Ben Preston
Deputy editor: John Bryant
Business/city/financial editor: Patience Wheatcroft
Diary editor: Jasper Gerard
Environment: Nick Nuttall
Saturday editor: Nick Wapshott
Political editor: Philip Webster
Sports editor: David Chappell
Features editor: Sandra Parsons
Founded: 1785.
Owner: News International

NATIONAL SUNDAYS

Express on Sunday
245 Blackfriars Road, London SE1 9UX
Fax 020-7620 1654   Tel 020-7928 8000
Tel 020-7922 7070
Editor: Rosie Boycott since April 1998
Deputy editor: Chris Blackhurst
Executive editors: Michael Pilgrim, Chris Williams
Executive editor (Sunday): Michael Pilgrim
Sunday news editor: Simon Young
Assistant editor, comment: John Price
Head of features : Albert Read
Head of City: Robert Miller
Diary: John McEntee
Head of pictures: Chris Djukanovic
Foreign editor: Jacqui Goddard
Group managing editor: Lindsay Cook
Managing director: Andy Jonesco
Marketing director: Paul Woolfenden
Circulation director: Richard Miller
Advertising director: Richard Bogie
Founded: 1900.
Owner: United News and Media

Independent on Sunday
1 Canada Square, Canary Wharf, London E14 5DL
Fax 020-7293 2043   Tel 020-7293 2000
Newsfax 020-7293 2943   Tel 020-7293 2480
E-mail: sunday letters@independent.co.uk
Website: www.independent.co.uk
Editor: Janet Street-Porter since July 1999
Executive editor: Paul Valleley
News editor: Barry Hugil
Arts editor: Jenny Turner
Foreign editor: Ray Whitaker
Picture editor: Sophie Batterbury
Sports editor: Neil Morton
Commercial editor: Stephen Miron
Head of marketing:: Duncan Eaton
Managing director: Brendan Hopkins
Founded: 1990.
Owner: Independent Newspapers

Mail on Sunday
2 Derry Street, London W8 5TT
Fax 020-7937 3745   Tel 020-7938 6000
Tape Room Fax 020-7937 7896/3829
Editor: Peter Wright, since 1998
Deputy editor: Rod Gilchrist
Executive editor: Peter Dobbie
News editor: Ray Clancy
Features editor: Sian James
City editor: William Kay
Assistant editor (news & pictures): Jon Ryan
Picture editor: Andy Kyle
Sports editor: Don Evans
Advertising director: Sally de la Bedoyese
Founded: 1982.
Owner: Daily Mail & General Trust

News of the World
1 Virginia Street, Wapping, London E1 9XR
Fax 020-7782 4463   Tel 020-7782 4000
Editor: Phil Hall
Assistant editor: Bob Bird
Assistant editor (news): Greg Miskiw
Features editor: Ray Levine
Art director: Danny Fox
Picture editor: Lynn Cullen
Production editor: John Mellowdrew
Associate editor: Robert Waren
Sports editor: Mike Dunn
Colour supplement editor: Judy McGuire
Advertising director: Richard Webb
Managing editor: Stuart Kuttner
Chairman: Rupert Murdoch
Founded: 1843.
Owner: News International

Observer
119 Farringdon Road, London EC1R 3ER
Fax 020-7713 4250   Tel 020-7278 2332
Editor: Roger Alton, since 1998
Editor-in-chief: Will Hutton
Deputy editors: Paul Webster and John Mulholland
Home news editor: Andy Malone
Political editor: Patrick Wintour
Arts editor: Jane Ferguson
Foreign editor: Peter Beaumont
Economics editor: William Keegan
Science editor: Robin McKie
Review editor: Lisa O'Kelly
Business editor: Emily Bell
Picture editor: Greg Whitmore
Executive editor: Alan Rusbridger
Managing director: Caroline Marland
Marketing director: Stephen Palmer
Finance director: Paul Naismith
Deputy managing director: Carolyn McCall
Founded: 1791.
Owner: Guardian Media Group

The People
1 Canada Square, Canary Wharf, London E14 5AP.
News fax 020-7293 3810   Tel 020-7293 3201
Editor: Neil Wallis since January 1998
News editor: David Wooding
Features editor: Kay Goddard
Sports editor: Ed Barry
Business editor: Cathy Gunn
Art director: Bruce Preston
Picture editor: Steve Hodgson
Advertising manager: Phil O'Hara
Founded: 1881.
Owner: Trinity Mirror

Sunday Business

The Isis Building, 193 Marsh Wall, London E14 9SU
Fax 020-7418 9605   Tel 020-7418 9600
E-mail: sundaybusiness@the-european.com
Editor-in-chief: Andrew Neil
Editor: Jeff Randall, since 1998
Deputy editor: Richard Northedge
Associate editor: Martin Baker
News editor: Frank Kane
Political correspondent: Sebastian Hamilton
Internet correspondent: Carl Franklin
Features editor: Vivien Goldsmith
Leisure industries reporter: Matthew Goodman
Transport & construction correspondent: Dominic O'Connell
City editor: Nils Prately
Re-launched: February 1998
Owner: Barclay Brothers

Sunday Mirror

1 Canada Square, Canary Wharf, London E14 5AP
Fax 020-7293 3405   Tel 020-7293 3000
News fax 020-7293 3939   Tel 020-7293 3601
Website: www.sundaymirror.co.uk
Editor: Brendon Parsons
Executive editors: Paul Bennett & Mike Ryder
Assistant editor (news): John Meshan
Assistant editor (features): Fiona Wyten
Associate editor: Michael Ryder
Magazine editor: Fiona Wingett
Picture editor: Paul Bennett
Sports editor: Steve McEnlay
Group sales director: Mark Pritchett
Managing director: Steve Barber
Financial director: John Allwood
Founded: 1915 as Sunday Pictorial
Owner: Trinity Mirror

Sunday Sport

19 Great Ancoats Street, Manchester M60 4BT
Fax 0161-236 4535   Tel 0161-236 4466
E-mail: features@sport.demon.co.uk
Website: www.sundaysport.co.uk
Editor: Mark Harris
Deputy editor: Jon Wise
News editor: Paul Carter
Features editor: Sarah Stevens
Picture editor: Paul Currie
Advertising manager: Alan Pollock
Managing director: Tony Livesey
Founded: 1986
Owner: Sport Newspapers (David Sullivan).

Sunday Telegraph

1 Canada Square, Canary Wharf, London E14 5DT
Fax 020-7538 6242   Tel 020-7538 5000
News fax 020-7513 2504   Tel 020-7538 7350
Editor: Dominic Lawson, since 1995
Deputy editor: Matthew d'Ancona
News editor: Chris Anderson
Features editor: Rebecca Nicolson
Reviews editor: Sandy Mitchell
Arts editor: John Preston
Literary editor: Miriam Gross
City editor: Neil Bennett
Foreign editor: Con Coughlin
Political editor: David Wastell
Picture editor: Nigel Skelsey
Advertising director: Len Sanderson
Chairman: Conrad Black   **MD:** Jeremy Deedes
Finance director: Niamh O'Donnell-Keenan
Founded: 1961
Owner: The Telegraph

Sunday Times

1 Pennington Street, London E1 9XW
Fax 020-7782 5658   Tel 020-7782 5000
Website: www.sunday-times.co.uk
Editor: John Witherow since 1994
Deputy editor: Martin Ivens
News review editor: Sarah Baxter
News editor: Mark Skipworth
Associate editor (politics): Michael Jones
Political editor: Michael Prescott
Managing editor, business news: John Jay
Picture editor: Ray Wells
Insight editor: David Leppard
Arts editor: Helen Hawkins
Music critic: Hugh Canning
Design editor: Gordon Beckett
Travel editor: Christine Walker
Economics editor: David Smith
Education: Judith O'Reilly
Environment/transport correspondent: Jonathan Leake
Literary editor: Caroline Gasgoigne
Style editor: Jeremy Langmead
Colour supplement, editor: Robin Morgan
Chairman: Rupert Murdoch
Founded: 1822
Owner: News International

Local and regional papers

"Once regarded as the Cinderella of the media world, Britain's regional and local press has undergone a renaissance over the past three years." So says a publicity handout issued by an upbeat Newspaper Society which sees itself a beauty amongst other media beasts. They've even found a real life Prince Charming with the Prince of Wales telling the Yorkshire Post: "Regional and local newspapers form a vital ingredient in a cement that holds communities together. They help give people a sense of pride in the place in which they live and they campaign on the issues and challenges that confront them. Above all, they play a thoroughly responsible role in their communities. They make a difference and I applaud that." The applause of Chas extended to the Prince's Trust offices taking a direct role in the most recent Local Newspaper Week.

Another mark of establishment cred came from a £5 million lottery grant to fund Newsplan, a national microfilm programme to preserve 3,500 local newspapers. "Newspapers have been called history's first draft," enthused Chris Smith, the culture and media secretary. "The conservation of our local newspapers is incredibly important because it forms a considerable part of our nation's archives."

Though the claim that local papers have "undergone a renaissance" is standard issue trade body hyperlative, local papers have undeniably done well. The Newspaper Society dates the reversal of bad fortune back to late 1995, the beginning of a series of buyouts, mergers and acquisitions which put "regional press ownership ... back in the hands of regional specialists". New owners have pressed ahead to "improve overall circulation performance year-on-year". Well, nearly, because the 1998 ABC circulation figures the Newspaper Society was celebrating showed the rate of decline has practically halted from 2.2 per cent in 1995 to 0.5 per cent.

Such stability is a large achievement when set against a broader backdrop of media fragmentation where, for the most pertinent example, national newspaper sales have fallen 3.7 per cent year on year. Such is the confidence of the new local proprietors that both Trinity and Regional Independent Newspapers put in rival £1 billion bids to buy the Mirror Group and all the national and local titles that sail with it.

National ownership of local newspapers is an old tradition, well established within the Guardian and Mail hierarchies. Another revived tradition means that, once again, locals are seen

Local papers at a glance

1   Nine out of ten people read a local paper every week
2   The local press is considered the most trustworthy of all media
3   Some 4,000 local papers are sold in the UK every minute
4   There are nearly 1,400 local newspapers in the UK today
5   The local press is the UK's second biggest advertising medium
6   Two-thirds of all paid-for regional titles increased their circulation in the 1998-99
7   Most of the UK's national newspapers are printed on regional newspaper presses
8   British people spend more than £663 million each year on buying local papers
9   The average regional newspaper cover price is 34p
10 There are 126 regional press publishing groups, 65 of whom own just one title
11 More than three-quarters of the local press operates a web site
12 The local newspaper industry employs around 40,000 people
13 77 per cent of the regional press has changed ownership in the past three years
14 More than 2,000 million paid-for regional newspapers are bought each year
15 Three-quarters of the adult population (32 million people) read local paper small ads
Source: The Newspaper Society

as a good place to begin a career in journalism. While some newcomers follow the old apprenticeship route via direct entry straight after school, a majority start after completing a postgraduate course accredited by the NCTJ.

An unchanging feature of local newspaper tradition is bad pay. Tony Harcup, a journalism lecturer, called it a national scandal. "I'm talking of wage rates circa £6,000 to £11,000 a year, most frequently around £8,000 to £9,500," he said. "Having emerged from university with a degree and a hefty overdraft - the average is £3,883 before tuition fees - students have gone on to pay for their own training and upkeep for a further year." According to a recent Guardian report about the Dimbleby Newspaper group in SW London: "A 31-year-old sports editor is expected to work evening and weekends on top of his basic 75 hour fortnight for a standard reporter's salary of £7,800 a year. On a contractual basis, that is just above the government's minimum wage of £3.60. In terms of hours worked, it falls below it."

What was that about Cinderella?

Frank Branston, chairman of the Local Sunday Newspaper Group in Bedford, says: "Independently-owned free newspapers are a shrinking band. "Before long, they will need their own preservation society. In the 1980s, the Association of Free Newspapers had dozens of members accounting for hundreds of titles. Its annual conferences were jamborees of conspicuous consumption with personalised number-plated Rollers, Bentleys and Jags lining up outside the hotels. Now the AFN is no more, and nor are most of the entrepreneurs. Many of their papers still exist, but they are owned by big groups, usually with paid-for interests to defend, groups like Johnston and Newsquest."

Top 20 regional press publishers - listing of main owners pages 41-47

GROUP NAME	TITLES	WEEKLY CIRCULATION
1 Trinity Plc	117	8,240,574
2 Northcliffe Newspapers Group	55	8,017,465
3 Newsquest Media Group	130	7,550,547
4 Johnston Press	166	6,050,187
5 Mirror Group Newspapers	45	4,028,970
6 Regional Independent Media	34	3,319,084
7 Guardian Media Group	37	2,794,362
8 Eastern Counties Newspapers	54	2,739,633
9 Newscom Plc	59	2,693,051
10 Southnews	49	2,545,006
11 Midland News Association	20	2,256,687
12 Bristol United Press	14	1,396,162
13 Scotsman Publications	6	1,369,303
14 Scottish Media	3	1,305,390
15 Adscene Group	44	1,235,827
16 Yattendon Investment Trust	21	862,170
17 Kent Messenger Group	19	764,083
18 DC Thomson & Co	2	763,398
19 Independent Newspapers	25	718,974
20 CN Group	9	502,885

Source: The Newspaper Society

Top 50 regional dailies - listings page 48-53

DAILIES	CIRCULATION	OWNER
1 Daily Record - Glasgow	676,411	Trinity Mirror
2 London Evening Standard	450,089	London Evening Standard
3 Birmingham Evening Mail	187,598	Trinity Mirror
4 Express and Star	186,969	The Midland News Association
5 Manchester Evening News	173,446	Guardian Media Group
6 Liverpool Echo	157,999	Trinity Mirror
7 Belfast Telegraph	124,530	Trinity Mirror
8 Glasgow Evening Times	116,486	Scottish Media
9 Newcastle Evening Chronicle	109,685	Trinity Mirror
10 Leicester Mercury	108,478	Northcliffe Newspapers Group
11 Aberdeen Press and Journal	104,548	Northcliffe Newspapers Group
12 The Herald - Scotland	101,079	Scottish Media
13 Yorkshire Evening Post	100,596	Regional Independent Media
14 Dundee Courier and Advertiser	95,508	DC Thomson & Co
15 Sheffield Star	94,664	Regional Independent Media
16 Nottingham Evening Post	92,903	Northcliffe Newspapers Group
17 Stoke the Sentinel	90,368	Northcliffe Newspapers Group
18 Shropshire Star	89,619	The Midland News Association
19 Hull Daily Mail	84,605	Northcliffe Newspapers Group
20 Coventry Evening Telegraph	82,417	Trinity Mirror
21 Edinburgh Evening News	80,754	Scotsman Publications
22 The Scotsman	79,686	Scotsman Publications
23 Bristol Evening Post	79,346	Bristol United Press
24 Norfolk Eastern Daily Press	78,647	Eastern Counties Newspapers Group
25 Leeds Yorkshire Post	75,836	Regional Independent Media
26 South Wales Echo	74,630	Trinity Mirror
27 Liverpool Daily Post	72,240	Trinity Mirror
28 Portsmouth News	71,843	Portsmouth & Sunderland Newspapers
29 Darlington Northern Echo	70,358	Newsquest
30 Aberdeen Evening Express	66,244	Northcliffe Newspapers Group
31 Teesside Evening Gazette	65,028	Trinity Mirror
32 South Wales Evening Post	63,856	Northcliffe Newspapers Group
33 Derby Evening Telegraph	60,691	Northcliffe Newspapers Group
34 Southern Daily Echo	60,343	Newscom
35 Preston Lancs Evening Post	60,339	Regional Independent Media
36 Bristol Western Daily Press	60,139	Bristol United Press
37 Western Mail - Cardiff	57,673	Trinity Mirror
38 Sunderland Echo	57,327	Portsmouth & Sunderland Newspapers
39 Plymouth Evening Herald	53,626	Northcliffe Newspapers Group
40 Newcastle Journal	51,936	Trinity Mirror
41 Bradford Telegraph & Argus	51,838	Newsquest
42 Western Morning News	51,677	Northcliffe Newspapers Group
43 Evening Argus - Brighton	51,405	Newsquest
44 Irish News - Belfast	50,344	Irish News
45 East Anglian Daily Times	46,008	Eastern Counties Newspaper Group
46 Basildon Evening Echo	45,784	Newsquest
47 Bournemouth Daily Echo	45,090	Newscom
48 Grimsby Evening Telegraph	44,656	Northcliffe Newspapers Group
49 Lancashire Evening Telegraph	43,753	Newsquest
50 Yorkshire Evening Press	42,074	Newsquest

Source: The Newspaper Society

Top 50 paid weeklies - listings page 55-57

TITLE	CIRCULATION	OWNER
1 West Briton	50,603	Northcliffe Newspapers Group
2 Essex Chronicle	49,683	Northcliffe Newspapers Group
3 Surrey Advertiser	45,492	Guardian Media Group
4 Kent Messenger	45,383	Kent Messenger Group
5 Chester Chronicle	44,322	Trinity Mirror
6 Western Gazette	44,077	Bristol United Press
7 Derbyshire Times	41,950	Johnston Press
8 Kent & Sussex Courier	40,751	Northcliffe Newspapers Group
9 Hereford Times	40,433	Newsquest
10 South London Press (Fri ed)	40,258	Trinity Mirror
11 Croydon Advertiser series	40,075	Southnews
12 Barnsley Chronicle	39,639	The Barnsley Chronicle
13 Isle of Wight County Press	38,374	Isle of Wight County Press
14 Cornish Guardian	37,788	Northcliffe Newspapers Group
15 Cumberland News	37,088	CN Group
16 North Devon Journal	35,419	Northcliffe Newspapers Group
17 Warrington Guardian	35,159	Newsquest
18 Chichester Observer series	35,114	Portsmouth Sunderland Newspapers
19 Harrogate Advertiser series	34,460	Regional Independent Media
20 Surrey Mirror series	34,167	Trinity Mirror
21 Aldershot News series	33,624	Guardian Media Group
22 Herts Mercury series	33,426	Yattendon Investment Trust
23 Westmorland Gazette	33,108	Newsquest
24 Mansfield CHAD	32,712	Johnston Press
25 Falkirk Herald	32,676	Johnston Press
26 Darlington & Stockton Times	32,521	Newsquest
27 Somerset County Gazette	30,584	Newscom
28 Doncaster Free Press	30,343	Johnston Press
29 Farnham Herald series	30,268	Tindle Newspapers
30 Wakefield Express	29,985	Johnston Press
31 Reading Chronicle	29,840	Trinity Mirror
32 Oxford Times	29,435	Newsquest
33 Bury Free Press	29,119	Johnston Press
34 Tamworth Herald series	28,694	Adscene Group
35 Maidenhead Advertiser	28,608	Baylis & Co
36 Rotherham & S Yorkshire Adv	28,169	Garnett Dickinson
37 South London Press (Tue ed)	28,103	Trinity Mirror
38 Ayrshire Post	27,685	Trinity Mirror
39 Salisbury Journal	27,606	Newscom
40 Rochdale Observer (Sat)	27,564	Guardian Media Group
41 Bucks Free Press	27,398	Newsquest
42 Hamilton Advertiser	27,316	Trinity Mirror
43 Dyfed Western Telegraph	27,304	Newscom
44 Eastbourne Herald	26,891	Johnston Press
45 Lynn News (Fri)	26,442	Johnston Press
46 Derry Journal (Fri)	26,419	Mirror Regional Newspapers
47 Newbury Weekly News	26,332	Newbury Weekly News
48 Dewsbury Reporter Group	26,009	Regional Independent Media
49 Wiltshire Gazette & Herald	25,885	Newsquest
50 Derry Journal (Tues)	25,810	Mirror Regional Newspapers

Source: The Newspaper Society

Top paid for Sundays - listings page 54

TITLE	CIRCULATION	OWNER
1 Sunday Mail - Glasgow	810,353	Mirror Regional Newspapers
2 Sunday Post - Dundee	738,848	DC Thomson & Co
3 Sunday Mercury - Birmingham	149,639	Mirror Regional Newspapers
4 Scotland on Sunday	125,124	Scotsman Publications
5 Newcastle upon Tyne Sunday	112,918	Trinity Mirror
6 Sunday Life - Belfast	101,210	Trinity Mirror
7 Wales on Sunday	62,286	Trinity Mirror
8 Plymouth Sunday Independent	38,958	Newscom Plc
9 Sunday Herald - Scotland		Scottish Media

Source: The Newspaper Society

Top free weeklies - listings page 57-58

TITLE	CIRCULATION	OWNER
1 Manchester Metro News	300,130	Guardian Media Group
2 The Glaswegian	201,575	Mirror Regional Newspapers
3 Nottingham Topper	196,200	Topper Newspapers
4 Liverpool Weekly Nwprs Group	190,761	Trinity Mirror
5 Bristol Observer series	180,881	Bristol United Press
6 Edinburgh Herald & Post	175,478	Scotsman Publications
7 Nottingham Recorder	175,239	Northcliffe Newspapers Group
8 Leeds Weekly News	167,820	Regional Independent Media
9 Kingston Guardian series	167,082	Newsquest
10 Dorset Advertiser series	166,994	Newscom
11 Advertiser series - Hull	164,656	Northcliffe Newspapers Group
12 Portsmouth Journal series	164,421	Portsmouth & Sunderland Newspapers
13 Birmingham Metronews	160,422	Mirror Regional Newspapers
14 Bex'heath/Dart/Sid News Shopper	143,026	Newsquest
15 Wirral News group	141,597	Trinity Mirror
16 Wirral Globe	141,061	Newsquest
17 Leicester Mail series	140,368	Northcliffe Newspapers Group
18 Southampton Advertiser	138,725	Newscom
19 Hendon Times series	127,145	Newsquest
20 North Staffs Advertiser	125,598	Northcliffe Newspapers Group
21 Aberdeen Independent	125,336	Aberdeen & District Independent
22 Sheffield Weekly Gazette	122,856	Regional Independent Media
23 Aberdeen Herald & Post	122,220	Northcliffe Newspapers Group - listings
24 Coventry Citizen series	122,120	Mirror Regional Newspapers
25 Derby Express series	121,722	Northcliffe Newspapers Group

Source: The Newspaper Society

Top free Sundays

1 Luton on Sunday	96,596	Local Sunday Newspaper Group
3 Bedfordshire on Sunday Borough	60,890	Local Sunday Newspaper Group
4 Bedfordshire on Sunday Mid	47,824	Local Sunday Newspaper Group
2 Bedfordshire on Sunday L Buzz	14,941	Local Sunday Newspaper Group
5 Hertfordshire on Sunday		Local Sunday Newspaper Group

Source: The Newspaper Society

LOCAL PAPER OWNERS

KEY CONTACT

Newspaper Society
Bloomsbury House, 74-77 Great Russell Street,
London WC1B 3DA
Fax 020-7631 5119   Tel 020-7636 7014
E-mail: ns@newspapersoc.org.uk
Website: www/newspapersoc.org.uk
Association for the publishers of UK regional and local
newspapers. More details page 146

Adnews
Albert Chambers, Canal Street, Congleton CW12 4AA
Fax 01260-299324   Tel 01260-281012
E-mail: adnews.midlands@virgin.net
Adscene Group
Newspaper House, Canterbury, Kent CT1 3YR
Fax 01227-470308   Tel 01227-767321
74 titles.
The group publishes titles in Kent, Greater London,
Lincs, Notts, Leics, South Yorks and Hereford.
Advertiser & Times (Hants)
62 Old Milton Road, New Milton, Hants BH25 6EH
Fax 01425 638635   Tel 01425-613384
E-mail: nma@globalnet.co.uk
Publishes New Milton Advertiser & Lymington Times.
Alpha Newspaper Group
56 Scotch Street, Armagh, N Ireland BT61 7DQ
Fax 028-37 527029   Tel 028-37 522639
Website: www.ulsternet-ni.co.uk
Anglia Advertiser
The Precinct, High Street, Great Yarmouth NR31 6RL
Fax 01493-652082   Tel 01493-601206
5 titles.
Angus County Press
Craig O'Loch Road, Forfar DD8 1BT
Fax 01307-466923   Tel 01307-464899
Publishes 9 papers.
The Arbroath Herald
Burnside Drive, Arbroath DD11 1NS
Fax 01241-878789   Tel 01241-872274
Arran Banner Printing & Publishing
Brodick, Isle of Arran KA27 8AJ
                 Tel 01770-302142
Associated Newspapers
Northcliffe House, 2 Derry Street, London W8 5TT
Fax 020-7937 3745   Tel 020-7938 6000
Evening Standard.
See also Northcliffe Newspapers
Banbridge Chronicle Press
14 Bridge Street, Banbridge, County Down BT32 3JS
Fax 018206-24397   Tel 018206-62322
Barnsley Chronicle
47 Church Street, Barnsley, South Yorkshire S70 2AS
Fax 028-406 734444   Tel 028-406 734734
E-mail: editorial@barnsley-chronicle.co.uk
3 titles.

Baylis & Co
48 Bell Street, Maidenhead, Berkshire SL6 1HX
Fax 01628-419523   Tel 01628-798048
E-mail: maidads@maidenhead-advertiser.co.uk
Website: www.maidenhead-advertiser.co.uk
Bristol Evening Post & Press
Temple Way, Bristol BS99 7HD
Fax 0117-934 3570   Tel 0117-934 3000
Web: www.epost.co.uk
E-mail: mail@epost.co.uk
10 titles.
Bute Newspapers
10 Castle Street, Rothsay, Bute PA20 9HB
Fax 01700-505159   Tel 01700-502931
CN Group
PO Box 7, Newspaper House, Dalston Road, Carlisle,
Cumbria CA2 5UA
Fax 01228-612601   Tel 01228-612600
Website: www.cngroup.co.uk
Caledonian Newspaper Publishing
195 Albion Street, Glasgow G1 1QP
Fax 0141-552 1344   Tel 0141-552 6255
2 titles.
A company formed in 1992 by the management buyout
of The Herald and The Evening Times from Lonrho
and George Outram and Co. Now owned by Scottish
Newspapers. Two titles, The Herald and The Evening
Times, part of the Scottish Media Group. Acquired in
October 1996 from Caledonian Publishing.
Candover
See Regional Independent Media
Cambrian News
Publishing Centre, Unit 7, Cefn Llan Science Park,
Aberystwyth, Dyfed SY23 3AH
Fax 01970-624699   Tel 01970-615000
E-mail: edit@cambrian-news.co.uk
5 titles.
Champion Newspapers
Clare House, 166 Lord Street, Southport, Merseyside
PR9 0QA
Fax 01704-531327   Tel 01704-531302
                 ISDN 01704-514309
E-mail: sales@chanpion.u-net.com
Cheadle & Tean Times
18 Tape Street, Cheadle, Staffordshire ST10 1BD
Fax 01538-754465   Tel 01538-753162
3 titles.
Chester Standard Newspapers
Linen Hall House, Stanley Street, Chester CH1
2LR
Fax 01244-351536   Tel 01244-351234
3 titles.
Chew Valley Gazette
Wellington Place, Tunbridge Road, Chew Magna,
Bristol BS40 8SP
Fax 01275-333067   Tel 01275-332266

Chronicle Publications
102 Boothferry Road, Goole, Yorkshire DN14 6AE
Fax 01405-720003   Tel 01405-720110
E-mail: gooletimes@btinternet.com
Website: www.gooletimes.co.uk
Publishers of The Goole Times.
City of London & Docklands Times
13 Coopers Row, London EC3M 2BQ
Fax 020-7488 3889   Tel 020-7488 3888
Clyde & Forth Press
Pitreavie Business Park, Dunfermline, KY11 8QS
Fax 01383-737040   Tel 01383-728201
Coates & Parker
36 Market Place, Warminster, Wiltshire BA12 9AN
Fax 01985-217680   Tel 01985-213030
Publishes the Warminster Journal.
The County Press
North Wales series, County Press Buildings, Bala,
Gwynedd LL23 7PG
Fax 01678-521262   Tel 01678-520262
Courier Newspapers (Oxford)
2-4 Ock Street, Abingdon, Oxon OX14 5AH
Fax 01235-554465   Tel 01235-553444
E-mail: 106314.653@compuserve.com
6 titles. The 3 best sellers are: The Oxford Journal;
Oxford Courier series; Reading's Thames Valley Weekly.
SR & VI Crane
30 Queen Street, Redcar, Cleveland TS10 1BD
Fax 01642-477143   Tel 01642-480397
E-mail: mail@clarion1.freeserve.co.uk
Publishes The Clarion.
W Y Crichton & Co
2-4 Church St, Downpatrick, Co Down BT30 6EJ
Fax 028-44 614624   Tel 028-44 613711
E-mail: downr@sol.co.uk
D & J Croal
18 Market Street, Haddington, East Lothian EH41 3JL
Fax 01620-826143   Tel 01620-822451
E-mail: courier@croal.demon.co.uk
Cumberland & Westmorland Herald
14 King Street, Penrith, Cumbria CA11 7AH
Fax 01768-890363   Tel 01768-862313
E-mail: cwherald@globalnet.co.uk
Derry Journal Co
Buncrana Road, Londonderry BT48 8AA
Fax 028-71 272218/272260 Tel 028-712 72200
E-mail: derry@sol.co.uk
5 titles. The 3 best sellers are: Derry Journal (Friday);
Derry Journal (Tuesday); Donegal Democrat.
Dimbleby Newspaper Group
14 King Street, Richmond, Surrey TW9 1NF
Fax 020-8332 1899   Tel 020-8940 6030
E-mail: ad@dimbleby.oc.uk
Website: www.dimbleby.co.uk
11 editions.
Dumfriesshire Newspapers Group
96 High St, Annan Dumfriesshire DG12 6DW
Fax 01461-205659   Tel 01461-202078
The group publishes the Dumfries Courier, Annandale
Observer, Annandale Herald and Moffat News.

Dunfermline Press
A Romanes & Son, Pitreavie Business Park,
Dunfermline, Fife KY11 8QS
Fax 01383 737040   Tel 01383-728201
Dungannon Development Association
1 Savings Bank Street, Dungannon, County Tyrone
BT70 1DT
Fax 028-772 4666   Tel 028-772 5445
Eastern Counties Newspapers Group
Prospect House, Rouen Road, Norwich, Norfolk NR1
1RE
Fax 01603-612930   Tel 01603-628311
E-mail: ecnmail@ecn.co.uk
Website: www.ecn.co.uk
Echo Press
Echo House, Jubilee Drive, Belton Park,
Loughborough, Leicestershire LE11 5TQ
Fax 01509-238363   Tel 01509-232632
E-mail: postmaster@echoweb.demon.co.uk
Website: www.loughborough-echo.co.uk
12 titles, the best seller is: Loughborough Echo.
Ellerman Investment (aka Barclay Bros)
20 St James's Street, London SW1A 1ES
Fax 020-7930 9131   Tel 020-7915 0915
6 titles. Ellerman Investment bought The Scotsman
Publications off Thomson Regional Newspapers for
£90 million in November 1995.
Ellesmere Press
The British School, Otley Street, Skipton BD23 1EW
Fax 01756-799766   Tel 01756-799765
E-mail: rufus@epltd.demon.co.uk
Eskdale & Liddesdale Newspapers
Commercial House, High Street, Langholm,
Dumfriesshire DG13 0JH
Fax 013873-80345   Tel 013873-80012
E-mail: langham.paper@iname.com
Forest of Dean Newspapers
Woodside Street, Cinderford, Gloucestershire GL14
2NN
Fax 01594-826213   Tel 01594-822126
The Forester, incorporating Dean Forest Guardian,
Dean Forest Mercury and the Lydney Observer.
Friday Ad Group
Eastbourne Road, Uckfield, E Sussex TN22 5ST
Fax 01825-766318   Tel 01825-766000
E-mail: sales@friday-ad.co.uk
Galloway Gazette
71 Victoria Lane, Newton Stewart, Wigtownshire DG8
6PS
Fax 01671-403391   Tel 01671-402503
Garnett Dickinson Publishing
Eastwood Works, Fitzwilliam Road, Rotherham S65
1JU
Fax 01709-820588   Tel 01709-364721
E-mail: info@gdpublishing.co.uk
Website: www.gdprint.co.uk

Guardian Media Group
164 Deansgate, Manchester M60 2RD
Fax 0161-832 5351   Tel 0161-832 7200
Around 100 titles.
The Guardian Media Group's national titles are The
Guardian and The Observer. Its local papers are
published by the Greater Manchester Division, and by
the Surrey and Berkshire Division. Autotrader
publishes regional editions in conjunction with Hurst
Publishing All ordinary shares of the Guardian Media
Group are owned by the Scott Trust and any dividends
"shall be devoted towards building up the reserves of
the company and expanding, improving and increasing
the circulation of its newspapers."

The Guernsey Press Co
Braye Road, Guernsey, Channel Islands GY1 3BW
Fax 01481-40235   Tel 01481-45866
E-mail: gp@guernsey-press.com
Website: guernsey-press.com
2 titles.

Hawick News
24 High Street, Hawick TD9 9EH
Fax 01450-370706   Tel 01450-372204
E-mail: jasonm@northeast-press.co.uk

Heads (Congleton)
11 High Street, Congleton, Cheshire CW12 1BW
Fax 01260-280687   Tel 01260-273737
E-mail: 100554.1443@compuserve.com
Website:
ourworld.compuserve.com/homepages/Jeremy_Con
dliffe
3 titles. Last independent paid-for weekly in Cheshire.

Heathrow Villager
260 Kingston Road, Staines, Middlesex TW18 1PG
Fax 01784-453196   Tel 01784-453196
Heathrow's only independent newspaper.

Herald Observer Newspapers
Webb House, 20 Church Green East, Redditch B98
8BP
Fax 01527-584371   Tel 01527-67714
E-mail: editorial@obsgraphics.demon.co.uk

Higgs Group (Henley Standard)
Caxton House, 1 Station Road, Henley-on-Thames,
Oxon RG9 1AD
Fax 01491-419401   Tel 01491-419444
E-mail: webmaster@higgsgroup.co.uk
Website: www.henley-on-thames.com

Hill Bros (Leek)
Newspaper House, Brook Street, Leek, Staffordshire
ST13 5JL
Fax 01538-386975   Tel 01538-399599
6 titles including the Post Times series in North
Staffordshire.

John H Hirst & Co
1 Market Street, Cleckheaton, W Yorks BD19 3RT
Fax 01274-851304   Tel 01274-874635
Part of Dewsbury Reporter series which is owned by
RIM.

Hirst, Kidd & Rennie
172 Union Street, Oldham, Lancashire OL1 1EQ
Fax 0161-627 0905   Tel 0161-633 2121
E-mail: hjhirst@oldham-chronicle.co.uk
Publishes 1 daily and 1 free weekly: Oldham Evening
Chronicle; Chronicle Weekend.

Edward Hodgett
4 Margaret Street, Newry, Co Down BT34 1DF
Fax 028-302 63157   Tel 028-302 67633

Holderness Newspapers
1 Seaside Road, Withernsea, E Yorkshire HU19 2DL
Fax 01964-615303   Tel 01964-612777

Home Counties Newspapers
63 Campfield Road, St Albans, Hertfordshire AL1 5HX
Fax 01727-837993   Tel 01727-866166
5 titles.In Jan 98 bought by the ECN group for £58
million, part of the CML division. Publishing The
Comet, The Herts Advertiser and Welwyn and Hatfield
Times, Welwyn Herald and Stevenage Herald.

Horley Publishing
76a Victoria Road, Horley, Surrey RH6 7PZ
Fax 01293-409653   Tel 01293-409649

Independent Newspapers (UK)
Newspaper House, 2 Whalebone Lane South,
Dagenham, Essex RM8 1HB
Fax 020-8592 7407   Tel 020-8517 5577
43 titles. The 3 best sellers are: East London Advertiser;
Barking & Dagenham Post; Islington Gazette.

E & R Inglis
219 Argyll Street Dunoon, Argyll PA23 7QT
Fax 01369-703458   Tel 01369-703218
E-mail: info@dunoon-observer.co.uk
Website: www.dunoon-observer.co.uk

Irish News
113-117, Donegall Street, Belfast BT1 2GE
Fax 028-9033 7505   Tel 028-9032 2226
E-mail: newsdesk@irishnews.com
Website: www.irishnews.com

Isle of Wight County Press
Brannon House, 123 Pyle Street, Newport, Isle of
Wight PO30 1ST
Fax 01983-527204   Tel 01983-521333
E-mail: adman@iwcpress.demon.co.uk
Website: www.iwcp.co.uk
1 paid for weekly.

J & M Publishing
13-15 West Church Street, Buckie, Banff AB56 1BN
Fax 01542-834316   Tel 01542-832265
E-mail: ba@moray.com
Website: www.moray.com
3 titles.

Jacob & Johnson
57 High Street, Winchester, Hampshire SO23 9BY
Fax 01962-842313   Tel 01962-841772
E-mail: news@hampshirechronical.co.uk
Website: www.hampshirechronical.co.uk

Jersey Evening Post
W E Guiton & Co, PO Box 582, Five Oaks, St Saviour, Jersey CI, JE4 8XQ
Fax 01534-611620   Tel 01534-611611
E-mail: jepdaily@itl.net
Website: www.jerseyeveningpost.com

Johnston Press
53 Manor Place, Edinburgh EH3 7EG
Fax 0131-225 4580   Tel 0131-225 3361
E-mail: tbowdler@johnstonpress.co.uk
Website: www.johnstonpress.co.uk
156 titles with over four million weekly circulation. The three best sellers are: Derbyshire Times; Falkirk Herald; Kettering Evening Telegraph. Johnston is the fourth largest regional newspaper publisher. Has expanded over recent years with several acquisitions, the major one being Emap Newspapers in 1996 costing £211 million.

Kent Messenger
Messenger House, New Hythe Lane, Larkfield Aylesford ME20 6SG
Fax 01622-719637   Tel 01622-717880
E-mail: kmgroup@kent-online.co.uk
Website: www.kent-online.co.uk
20 titles. The 3 best sellers are: the Kent Messenger; Kentish Gazette; Kentish Express.

Kentish Times Newspapers
38-46 Harmer Street, Gravesend, Kent DA12 2AY
Fax 01474-353758   Tel 01474-363363
Now owned by Independent Newspapers(UK). 17 titles, the three best sellers are: Gravesend Reporter, Dartford Times, Bromley & Beckenham Times.

La
301 Bothar an Ghleanna, Beal Feirste BT11 8BU
Fax 028-9058 1112   Tel 028-9058 1111
Website: www.nuacht.com

Leigh Times Co
34a The Broadway, Leigh-on-Sea SS9 1AJ
Fax 01702-478710   Tel 01702-477666

Lichfield Mercury
Graphic House, 17 Bird Street, Lichfield, Staffordshire WS13 6PX
Fax 01543-415814   Tel 01543-414414
E-mail: mercnews@aol.com
4 titles including the Lichfield Mercury, Rugeley Mercury and Cannock Mercury.

Local Publications (Bourne)
Newspaper House, 17 Abbey Road, Bourne, Lincolnshire PE10 9EF
Fax 01778-394087   Tel 01778-425876

Local Publications (Saffron Walden)
10 Emson Close, Saffron Walden, Essex CB10 1HL
Fax 01799-520561   Tel 01799 516161

Local Sunday Newspapers Group
22 Mill Street, Bedford MK40 3HD
Fax 01234-304404   Tel 01234-304403

Loot
Loot House, 24-32 Kilburn High Road, Kilburn, London NW6 5TF
Fax 020-7625 7921   Tel 020-7625 0266
Website: www.loot.com
E-mail: freeads@lootlon.loot.co.uk

The Manchester Reporter Group
24 School Lane, Didsbury, Manchester M20 6RG
Fax 0161-434 9921   Tel 0161-446 2212
2 titles. South Manchester Reporter; Heatons & Reddish Reporter.

G W McKane & Son
Reliance Works, 32-34 Station Street, Keswick, Cumbria CA12 2HF
Fax 017687-71203   Tel 017687-72140
1 title, the Keswick Reminder.

Midland Independent Newspapers
28 Colmore Circus,Queensway, Birmingham B4 6AX
Fax 0121-233 3958   Tel 0121-236 3366
Website: www.go2birmingham.co.uk
30 titles.
Midland Independent was formed in 1991 and concentrates activites on local papers in the West and East Midlands. Now part of the Mirror Group.

Midland News Association
51-53 Queen Street, Wolverhampton, West Midlands WV1 1ES
Fax 01902-710106   Tel 01902-313131
E-mail: feedback@expressandstar.co.uk
Website: www.westmidlands.com
Holding company to two of the countries largest independent regional publishing houses - Express & Star and Shropshire Newspapers. As a group the MNA publishes 2 evening titles, 7 paid weeklies and 15 free weekly titles, covering the West Midlands and Shropshire. The two top sellers are the two evenings: Express & Star and Shropshire Star.

Montrose Review Press
59 John Street, Montrose DD10 8QU
Fax 028-38 676232   Tel 028-38 672605
Top 3 titles: Montrose Review, The Leader, The Kincardineshire Observer.

Morton Newspapers Group
2 Esky Drive, Portadown, Craigavan BT63 5YY
Fax 01762-393940   Tel 01762-393939
25 titles. The 3 best sellers are: East Antrim series; Ulster Star, Portadown Times. Bought by Scottish Radio Holdings for £11.2 million in 1995.

Mortons of Horncastle
Newspaper House, Morton Way, Horncastle, Lincolnshire LN9 6JR
Fax 01507-527840   Tel 01507-523456
E-mail: admin@mortons.co.uk
Website: www.mortons.co.uk
6 titles.

Mourne Observer
The Roundabout, Castlewellan Road, Newcastle, Co Down BT33 0JX
Fax 028-437 24566   Tel 028-437 22666

NW Ireland Printing & Publishing Co
10 John St, Omagh, Co Tyrone, Ireland BT78 1DT
Fax 028- 82 242206   Tel 028- 82 243444
E-mail: editor@ulsterherald.com
Website: www.ulsterherald.com
4 titles: Ulster Herald, Derrypeople/Donegal News,
Fermanagh Herald, Strabane Chronicle.

Nairnshire Telegraph Co
10 Leopold Street, Nairn IV12 4BG
Fax 01667-455277   Tel 01667-453258
E-mail: 113103.474@compuserve.com

New Journal Enterprises
40 Camden Road, London NW1 9DR
Fax 020-7209 1322   Tel 020-7419 9000
E-mail: letters.cnj@cablenet.co.uk

New Rutland Times
Times House, 16b Mill Street, Oakham, Rutland LE15
6EA
Fax 01572-755599   Tel 01572-757722

Newark Advertiser Co
Appletongate, Newark, Notts NG24 1JX
Fax 01636-681122   Tel 01636-681234
Website: www.newarkadvertiser.co.uk

Newbury Weekly News (Printers)
Newspaper House, Faraday Road, Newbury,
Berkshire RG14 2DW
Fax 01635-522922   Tel 01635-564525
E-mail: editor@newburynews.co.uk
Website: www.newburynews.co.uk

Newscom
Newspaper House, Test Lane, Redbridge,
Southampton, Hampshire SO16 9JX
Fax 023-8042 4969   Tel 023-8042 4777
Website: www.southern-newspapers.co.uk
News Communications and Media, formerly Southern
Newspapers.

Newsquest Media Group
Newspaper House, 34-44 London Road, Morden,
Surrey SM4 5BR
Fax 020-8646 3997   Tel 020-8640 8989
Website: www.newsquest.co.uk
182 titles.
Newsquest Media was formed by a management
buyout of Reed Regional Newspapers for £205 million
in November 1995. Much of the funding was supplied
by the American financier Kohlberg Kravis Roberts.
Newsquest bought the Bury Times from Johnston in
April 1996 at the same time selling it Doncaster
Newspapers. In August 1996 it bought Westminster
Press. in October 1997 the company floated on the
Stock Exchange and in 1998 it bought Property Weekly
and Review Free Newspapers.

Newtownards Chronicle
25 Frances Street, Newtownards, Co Down BT23
3DT
Fax 028-91 820087   Tel 028-91 813333

Normanton Advertiser
4 West Street, Normanton, W Yorks WF6 2AP
Fax 01924-215327   Tel 01924-892117
E-mail: norad@demon.co.uk

North Devon Gazette & Advertiser
16 Tuly Street, Barnstaple, Devon EX31 1DH
Fax 01271-324608   Tel 01271-344303

North Edinburgh News
6 West Pilton Crescent, Edinburgh EH4 4HP
Fax 0131-343 3911   Tel 0131-332 1236
E-mail: maryburnside@btconnect.com

North Wales Newspapers
Mold Business Park, Wrexham Road, Mold, Flintshire
CH7 1XY
Fax 01352-752180   Tel 01352-707707
E-mail: nwnfd@netwales.co.uk
Website: www.nwn.co.uk

Northcliffe Newspapers Group
31 John Street, London WC1N 2QB
Fax 020-7400 1207   Tel 020-7400 1100
Website: www.nng.co.uk
57 titles. including Evening Standard.
Northcliffe Newspapers is part of the Daily Mail and
General Trust of which Associated Newspapers is the
overall management company. The group publishes the
Daily Mail and Mail on Sunday. Northcliffe is the
second largest regional newspaper publisher and
operates from 23 centres. It bought Aberdeen Journals
form Thomson Regional Newspapers in 1995.

Northern Newspaper Group
20 Railway Road, Coleraine, Northern Ireland BT52
1PD
Fax 028-70 43606   Tel 028-70 43344
3 titles and 1 free. Coleraine Chronicle; Ballymena
Guardian; Northern Constitution.

Nuachtain
301 Glen Road, Anderstown, Belfast, County Antrim
BT11 8ER
Fax 028-9062 0602   Tel 028-9061 9000
E-mail: editor@belfast-news.ie
Website: www.belfast-news.ie
Publishes Anderstown News and North Belfast News

Nuneaton & District Newspapers
Newspaper House, 11-15 Newtown Road, Nuneaton,
Warwickshire CV11 4HR
Fax 024-7635 3481   Tel 024-7635 3534

Oban Times Group
John Street, Oban, Argyll PA34 5PY
Fax 01631-565470   Tel 01631-563058
E-mail: editor@obantimes.co.uk

Observer Newspapers (NI)
Ann Street, Dungannon, Co Tyrone BT70 1ET
Fax 028-87 727334   Tel 028-87 722557

The Orcadian
Hatston Industrial Estate, Kirkwall, Orkney KW15 1DW
Fax 01856-879001   Tel 01856-879000
E-mail: orcadian-the.co.uk

Outlook Press
Castle Street, Rathfriland, Co Down BT34 5QR
Fax 028-406 31022   Tel 028-406 30202

PM Publications
The Messenger, 2 Kings Road, Haslemere, Surrey
GU27 2QA
Fax 01428-661658   Tel 01428-653999

John Penri Press
11 St Helens Road, Swansea SA1 4AL
Fax 01792-650647   Tel 01792-652092
W Peters & Son
16 High Street, Turriff, Aberdeenshire AB53 4DT
Fax 01888-563936   Tel 01888-563589
3 titles.
Portsmouth & Sunderland Newspapers
37 Abingdon Road, London W8 6AH
Fax 020-7590 6611   Tel 020-7590 0640
19 titles.
Founded in 1873. The groups main activities are in
central, southern and north east England. Taken over by
Johnston Press for £254 million in May 1999.
Recorder (Wales)
Cambria House, Wyndham Street, Bridgend, Mid
Glamorgan CF31 1ED
Fax 01656-656894   Tel 01656-669330
E-mail: recorder@globalnet.co.uk
Regional Independent Media Group
PO Box 168, Wellington Street, Leeds, West Yorks
LS1 1RF
Fax 0113-242 1814   Tel 0113-243 2701
Website: www.rim.co.uk
74 titles. Formerly United Provincial Newspapers until
taken over by the Candover venture capital group. It
operates from centres in Yorkshire and the North West.
Review & Advertiser Newspaper Group
Kinetic Business Centre, Theobald Street,
Borehamwood, Hertfordshire WD6 4PJ
                      Tel 020-8953 9119
Review Free Newspapers
The William Henry Building, Porters Wood, St Albans,
Hertfordshire AL3 6PQ
Fax 01727-852770   Tel 01727-834411
Ross Gazette
35 High St, Ross-on-Wye, Herefordshire HR9 5HE
Fax 01989-768023   Tel 01989-562007
SC Publishing Co
14b-14c Birmingham Road, Sutton Coldfield, West
Midlands B72 1QG
Fax 0121-355 0600   Tel 0121-355 6901
6 titles. The 3 best sellers are: Sutton Coldfield
Observer; Geat Barr Observer; Walsall Advertiser.
The Scotsman Publications
20 North Bridge, Edinburgh EH1 1YT
                      Tel 0131-225 2468
Website: www.scotsman.com
Scottish and Universal Newspapers
40 Craigs, Stirling FK8 2DW
Fax 01786-459486   Tel 01786 459426
Website: www.inside-scotland.co.uk
Scottish County Press
Sherwood Industrial Estate, Bonnyrigg, Midlothian
EH19 3LW
Fax 0131-663 6863   Tel 0131-663 4606
5 titles, the top three are: The Advertiser, East Lothian
News and Musselburgh News.

Scottish Daily Record & Sunday Mail
40 Anderston Quay, Glasgow G3 8DA
Fax 0141-242 3545   Tel 0141-248 2727
E-mail: editor@features.dailyrecord.co.uk
Website: www.record-mail.co.uk
Scottish Media Group
195 Albion Street, Galsgow G1 1QP
Fax 0141-552 3050   Tel 0141-552 6255
E-mail: herald@scottishmedia.com
Website: www.the herald.co.uk
Owns Caledonian Magazines and Caledonian
Newspapers.
Scottish Provincial Press
13 Henderson Road, Inverness, Scotland IV1 1SP
Fax 01463-221251   Tel 01463-713700
Sheffield Mercury Newspaper (Baycro)
PO Box 70, Sheffield, South Yorkshire S8 0QA
Fax 0114-274 6444   Tel 0114-274 6555
E-mail: sheffmerc@aol.com
The Shetland Times
Prince Alfred Street, Lerwick, Shetland ZE1 0EP
Fax 01595-694637   Tel 01595-693622
E-mail: editorial@shetland-times.co.uk
Website: www.shetland-times.co.uk
Slough Observer Group
Upton Court, Datchet Road, Slough, Berkshire SL3
7NR
Fax 01753-693895   Tel 01753-523355
G H Smith & Son
Market Place, Easingwold, York YO61 3AB
Fax 01347-822576   Tel 01347 821329
E-mail: ghsmith@globalnet.co.uk
Southern Newspapers
See Newscom
Southnews
326 Station Road, Harrow, Middlesex HA1 2DR
Fax 020-8863 0932   Tel 020-8424 0033
32 titles.
A company formed in 1986 by a management team
which had previosuly worked for Westminster Press or
Reed Regional Newspapers. Bought the Croydon
Advertiser for £12.95 million from Portsmouth and
Sunderland Newspapers in November 95. Its most
recent purchase was the southern part of United
Provincial.
Southwark News
Unit J104, Tower Bridge Business Complex,
Clement's Road, London SE16 4DG
Fax 020-7237 1578   Tel 020-7231 5258
E-mail: news@southwark87.freeserve.co.uk
Spalding & South Lincs Herald
3 St Thomas Road, Spalding, Lincs PE11 2XY
Fax 01775-713714   Tel 01775-713723
Spectator Newspapers
109 Main Street, Bangor, Co Down BT20 4AF
Fax 028- 91 271544   Tel 028- 91 270270
E-mail: spectator@dial.pipex.com
The St Ives Printing & Publishing Co
High Street, St Ives, Cornwall TR26 1RS
Fax 01736-795020   Tel 01736-795813
E-mail: times@echo.clara.net

Star Publishing
6-8 Mill Street, Maidstone, Kent ME15 6XH
Fax 01622-675071   Tel 01622-678556
Website: www.starpublishing.co.uk

Star Newspapers (Camberley)
192 Victoria Road, Aldershot, Hants GU11 1JZ
Fax 01252-343042   Tel 01252-316311
                              Tele-ads: 01252-317171
E-mail: advertising@starnewspaper.co.uk

Starbuys
3 Kings Arcade, Lancaster LA1 1LE
Fax 01524-843649   Tel 01524-66902

The Tamworth Herald Co
Ventura Park Road, Bitterscote, Tamworth,
Staffordshire B78 3LZ
Fax 01827-848511   Tel 01827-848610
E-mail: therald@aol.com
3 titles, the best seller is the Tamworth Herald.

Teesdale Mercury
24 Market Place, Barnard Castle, County Durham
DL12 8NB
Fax 01833-638633   Tel 01833-637140
E-mail: sales@teesdalemercury.co.uk

DC Thomson & Co
2 Albert Square, Dundee, Tayside DD1 9QJ
Fax 01382-322214   Tel 01382-223131
E-mail: dct@dcthomson.co.uk
2 titles.
A family owned company which also publishes the
Beano and the Dandy.

Tindle Newspapers
114 West Street, Farnham, Surrey GU9 7HL
Fax 01252-723950   Tel 01252-723938
Website: www.tindlenews.co.uk
80 titles. A family-owned company which publishes in
the South West, Surrey, Hampshire, Kent, Lancashire
and Wales.

Topper Newspapers
Maychalk House, 8 Musters Road, Notts NG2 7PL
Fax 0115-982 6565   Tel 0115-982 6974

Trident Midland Newspapers
Bridge Road, Coalville, Leicester LE67 3QP
Fax 01530-811361   Tel 01530-813101
E-mail: info@impartialreporter.com
4 titles. Top three sellers are the Ashby, Coalville and
Swadlincote Times.

William Trimble
8-10 East Bridge Street, Enniskillen, N Ireland BT74
7BT
Fax 028-66 325047   Tel 028-66 324422

Trinity
Kingsfield Court, Chester Business Park, Chester,
Cheshire CH4 9RE
Fax 01244-687100   Tel 01244-687000
E-mail: trinity@trinity.plc.uk
Website: www.trinity.plc.uk
120 titles. The Liverpool Daily Post and Echo until 1985,
Trinity expanded by buying Argus Newspapers in
London and the home counties plus titles in Wales and
Scotland. It became the largest regional paper publisher
in Britain with the £327.5 million purchase, in
November 1995, of the Thomson Regional Newspaper
titles: Belfast Telegraph, Chester Chronicle and Assoc.
Newspapers, Newcastle Chronicle and Journal, North
Eastern Evening Gazette and Western Mail and Echo.
In July 1999 Trinity merged with the Mirror Group in a
£1.5 billion deal that formed Trinity Mirror.

The Tweeddale Press Group
PO Box 10, 90 Marygate, Berwick Upon Tweed,
Northumberland TD15 1BW
Fax 01289-307377   Tel 01289-306677
E-mail: Tweeddale@aol.com
Website: www.tweeddalepress.co.uk
The 3 best sellers are: Southern Reporter; Berwick
Advertiser; Berwickshire News.

Tyrone Constitution Group
25-27 High Street, Omagh, Co Tyrone BT78 1BD
Fax 028-82 243549   Tel 028-82 242721
E-mail: editor@tyroneconstitution.com

United Advertising Publications
Alexander House, 94-96 Talbot Road, Old Trafford,
Manchester M16 0PG
Fax 0161-877 9134   Tel 0161-872 6996

United Provincial Newspapers
Sold by UNM to Candover and Southnews. See entries
for Regional Indpenedent Media and Southnews

West Highland Publishing Co
Broadford, Isle of Skye IV49 9AP
Fax 01471-822694   Tel 01471-822464
E-mail: newsdesk@whsp.co.uk

Westminster Press
Now owned by Newsquest

Wigtown Free Press
St Andrew Street, Stranraer, Wigtownshire DG9 7EB
Fax 01776-706695   Tel 01776-702551

Yattendon Investment Trust
Barn Close, Yattendon, Berkshire RG18 0UX
Fax 01635 202564   Tel 01635-202909

TOP REGIONAL DAILIES

Aberdeen Evening Express
PO Box 43, Lang Stracht, Mastrick Aberdeen AB9 8AF
Fax 01224-699575   Tel 01224-690222
E-mail: editor@ee.ajl.co.uk
Editor: Donald Martin
Picture editor: Kenny Allan
Sports editor: Alan Brown
Advertising director: Janice Gallon-Smith
Managing director: Alan Scott
Owner: Northcliffe

Basildon Evening Echo
Newspaper House, Chester Hall Lane, Basildon SS14 3BL
    Tel 01268-522792
Editor: Martin McNeill
Features editor: Pamela Horne
Picture editor: Nick Ansell
Sports editor: Paul Alton
Advertising director: Richard Byham
Managing director: Eric Robinson
Founded: 1969   **Owner:** Newsquest (Essex)

Belfast Telegraph
124-144 Royal Avenue, Belfast BT1 1EB
Fax 028-9055 4506   Tel 028-9026 4000
E-mail: editor@belfasttelegraph.co.uk
Websote: www.belfasttelegraph.co.uk
Editor: Edmund Curran
Deputy editor: Jim Flanagan
News editor: Paul Connolly
Features editor: John Caruth
Arts editor: Neil Johnston
Picture editor: Gerry Fitzgerald
Sports editor: John Laverty
Advertising director: John Leslie
Managing director: Derek Carvell
Financial director: Ken Simpson
Founded: 1870   **Owner:** Trinity Mirror

Birmingham Evening Mail
28 Colmore Circus, Birmingham B4 6AX
Fax 0121-233 0271   Tel 0121-236 3366
E-mail: eveningmail@mrn.co.uk
Website: www.go2birmingham.co.uk
Editor: Ian Dowell
Deputy editor: Tony Dickens
News editor: Norman Stinchcombe
Features editor: Paul Cole
Picture editor: Roland Rowley
Sports editor: Leon Hickman
Advertising director: Paul Carter
Managing director: Geraldine Aitken
Financial director: Caroline Payne
Founded: 1857
Owner: Mirror Regional Newspapers

Bolton Evening News
Newspaper House, Churchgate, Bolton BL1 1DE
Fax 01204-365068   Tel 01204-522345
E-mail: ben_editorial@newsquest.co.uk
Web: www.thisislancashire.co.uk
Editor: Mark Rossiter
Features editor: Angela Kelly
Picture editor: Derek Ralphs
Sports editor: Peter Mensforth
Advertising director: Sue Staff
Managing director: John Waters
Founded: 1867   **Owner:** Newsquest

Bournemouth Daily Echo
Richmond Hill, Bournemouth BH2 6HH
    Tel 01202-554601
Editor: Neal Butterworth
Features editor: Sally Amess
Sports editor: Andy Goodall
Pictures editor: Duncan Lee
Advertising manager: Shelley Gorham
General manager: Mike Denny
Founded: 1900   **Owner:** Newscom

Bradford Telegraph and Argus
PO Box 234, Hall Ings, Bradford BD1 1DR
Fax 01274-723634   Tel 01274-729511
E-mail: contact.bradford.newsquest.co.uk
Web: www.thisisbradford.co.uk
Editor: Perry Austin-Clarke
Features editor: Jan Brierley
Sports editor: Alan Birkenshaw
Advertising director: John Lee
Managing director: Tim Blott
Founded: 1947   **Owner:** Newsquest

Bristol Evening Post
Temple Way, Bristol BS99 7HD
Fax 0117-934 3575   Tel 0117-934 3000
Editor: Mike Lowe
News editor: Kevan Blackadder
Features editor: Matthew Shelley
Sports editor: Chris Bartlett
Advertising director: John Pajak
Managing director: Paul Kearney
Owner: Bristol United Press

Coventry Evening Telegraph
Corporation Street, Coventry, CV1 1FP
Fax 024-7663 1736   Tel 024-7663 3633
E-mail: editorial@go2coventry.co.uk
Website: www.go2coventry.co.uk
Editor: Alan Kirby
Deputy editor: Charles Barker
News editor: John West
Business editor: Alison Williams
Features editor: Steve Chilton
Sports editor: Roger Draper
Advertising manager: Hazel Pilling
Managing director: Dan Mason
Founded: 1857   **Owner:** Trinity Mirror

Courier & Advertiser
80 Kingsway East, Dundee DD4 8SL
Fax 01382-454590   Tel 01382-223131
E-mail: courier@dcthomson.co.uk
Website: www.dcthomson.co.uk/courier
Editor: Adrian Arthur
Deputy editor: Alastair Fyfe
News editor: Arliss Rhind
Features editor: Shona Lorimer
Arts editor: Joy Watters
Sports editor: Graeme Dey
Advertisement manager: C McGeoghie
Owner: DC Thomson & Co

Daily Record
40 Anderston Quay, Glasgow, Strathclyde G3 8DA
Fax 0141-242 3340   Tel 0141-248 7000
E-mail editor@dailyrecord.co.uk
Editor-in-chief: Martin Clarke
Deputy editor: Peter Cox
Assistant editor (news): Gordon Hay
Assistant editor (features): Jane Johnson
Assistant editor: Allan Rennie
Features editor: Lorna Frame
Group art director: Lucy Allsopp
Picture editor: Stuart Nicol
Assistant editor (sport): James Traynor
Sales and circulation director: Steve McLaughlin
Managing director: Mark Hollinshead
Financial controller: John Foley
Advertising director: Pat Moore
Commercial director: Jim Chisholm
Founded: 1847.
Owner: Trinity Mirror

Derby Evening Telegraph
Northcliffe House, Meadow Road, Derby DE1 2DW
Fax 01332-253027   Tel 01332-291111
E-mail: admin@derbytelegraph.co.uk
Web: www.thisisderbyshire.co.uk
Editor: Keith Perch
Features editor: Nigel Poulson
Picture editor: Stuart Wild
Sports editor: Steve Nicholson
Advertising director: Carol Adlard
Managing director: Tim Kitchen
Founded: 1879
Owner: Northcliffe News Group

East Anglian Daily Times
Press House, 30 Lower Brook Street, Ipswich IP4 1AN
                  Tel 01473-230023
Editor: Terry Hunt
Picture editor: Paul Nixon
Sports editor: Nick Garnham
Advertising director: Peter Swallow
Owner: Eastern Counties Newspapers

Eastern Daily Press
Prospect House, Rouen Road, Norwich, Norfolk NR1 1RE
Fax 01603-612930   Tel 01603-628311
E-mail: edp@ecn.co.uk
Website: www.ecn.co.uk
Editor: Peter Franzen
Assistant editor: James Ruddy
News editor: Paul Durrant
Business editor: Ken Hurst
Picture editor: Dennis Whitehead
Sports editor: David Thorpe
Publishing director: Jonathan Hostler
Advertising director: Stephen Phillips
Founded: 1870
Owner: Eastern Counties

Edinburgh Evening News
20 North Bridge, Edinburgh, EH1 1YT
Fax 0131-225 7302   Tel 0131-225 2468
Editor: John McLellan
Deputy editor: Simon Reynolds
Associate news editor: David Lee
Associate editor (features): Sandra Dick
Picture editor: Tony Marsh
Business editor: Ian Burrell
Managing director: Michael Jones
Advertising director: Stephen Tait
Finance director: Gordon Affleck
Founded: 1873
Owner: Scotsman Publications

Evening Argus (Brighton)
Argus House, Crowhurst Road, Hollingbury BN1 8AR
Fax 01273-555046   Tel 01273-544544
Web: www.thisisbrighton.co.uk
Editor: Simon Bradshaw
Picture editor: Richard Taylor
Managing director: Ian Ferguson
Owner: Newsquest

Evening Chronicle
Thomson House, Groat Market, Newcastle-upon-Tyne NE1 1ED
Fax 0191-230 4144   Tel 0191-232 7500
E-mail: ec.news@ncjmedia.co.uk
Website: www.evening-chronicle.co.uk
Editor: Alison Hastings
Deputy editor: David Bourn
News editor: Mick Smith
Features editor: Richard Ord
Production editor: Adrian Mogg
Picture editor: Rod Wilson
Sports editor: Paul New
Sales director: Shaun Bowron
Managing director: Stephen Parker
Marketing director: Jane Nugent
Financial director: John Williams
Training director: John Williams
Founded: 1885
Owner: Trinity Mirror PLC

Evening Gazette (Teeside)
105-111 Borough Road, Middlesbrough, Cleveland TS1 3AZ
Fax 01642-210565   Tel 01642-245401
Web: www.eveninggazette.co.uk
Editor: Ranald Allan
Features editor: Katherine Armstrong
Picture editor: Dave Jamieson
Sports editor: Allan Boughey
Advertising director: Val Ward
Consumer marketing: Russell Borthwick
Managing director: Steven Brown
Founded: 1869   **Owner:** Trinity Mirror

Evening Standard
2 Derry Street, London W8 5EE
Fax 020-7937 3193   Tel 020-7938 6000
Website: www.thisis london.com
Editor: Max Hastings
Deputy editor: Andrew Bordiss
News editor: Stephen Clackson
Features editor: Bernice Davison
Picture editor: David Ofield
Sports editor: Simon Greenberg
Advertising director (classified): Sally Smith
Advertising director (display): Sue Minnikin
Managing director: Kevin Beatty
Financial: Pamela French
Founded: 1827
Owner: Associated Newspapers

Evening Times
195 Albion Street, Glasgow G1 1QP
Fax 0141-553 1355   Tel 0141-552 6255
Editor: John Scott
Deputy editor: Alistair Nicol
News editor: Ally McLaws
Features editor: Russell Kyle
Picture editor: Alistair Stairs
Sports editor: David Stirling
Acting commercial director: Howard Warren
Managing director: Des Hudson
Financial director: Gary Hughes
Founded: 18th century
Owner: Scottish Media Group

Express and Star
51-53 Queen Street, Wolverhampton, West Midlands WV1 1ES
Fax 01902-319721   Tel 01902-313131
E-mail: express and star.co.uk
Editor: Warren Wilson
Deputy editor: Richard Ewels
News editor: John Bray
Features editor: Gary Copeland
Picture editor: Geoff Wright
Sports editor: Steve Gordos
Advertising manager: Trevor Lee
Managing director: Anthony Witts
Financial director: David Hughes
Founded: 1874   **Owner:** Midland News Association

Grimsby Evening Telegraph
80 Cleethorpe Road, Grimsby DN31 3EH
Fax 01472-372235   Tel 01472-359232
E-mail: grimsbytelegraph@dial.pipex.com
Editor: Peter Moore
Features editor: Barrie Farnsworth
Picture editor: Dave Moss
Sports editor: Geoff Ford
Commercial director: Mark Webb
Managing director: Mike Wood
Founded: 1898
Owner: Northcliffe Newspapers Group

The Herald
195 Albion Street, Glasgow G1 1QP
Fax 0141-552 2288   Tel 0141-552 6255
E-mail: lettersheraldmail@cims.co.uk
Website: www.theherald.co.uk
Editor: Harry Reid
Deputy editor: Alf Young
News editor: Bill McDowall
Features editor: Drew Allan
Arts editor: Keith Bruce
Picture editor: Jim Connor
Sports editor: Iain Scott
Acting commercial director: Howard Warren
Managing director: Des Hudson
Financial director: Gary Hughes
Founded: 1783
Owner: Scottish Media Group

Hull Daily Mail
Blundells Corner, Beverley Road, Hull HU3 1XS
Fax 01482-584353   Tel 01482-327111
E-mail: hdm@dial.pipex.com
Website: www.hulldailymail.co.uk
Editor: John Meehan
Deputy editor: Mel Cook
Community & campaigns editor: Stan Szecowka
Head of news: Marc Astley
Women's page: Jo Davison
Arts editor: Tracy Fletcher
Picture editor: Dave Barker
Sports editor: Mark Woodward
Advertising director: Steve Hollingsworth
Managing director: Ken Thompson
Financial director: Jonathon Wells
Founded: 1885   **Owner:** Northcliffe

Irish News (Belfast)
113-117 Donegall Street, Belfast BT1 2GE
Fax 028-9033 7505   Tel 028-9032 2226
E-mail: newsdesk@irishnews.com
Web: www.irishnews.com
Editor: Noel Doran
Features editor: Anna Marie McFaul
Picture editor: Brendan Murphy
Sports editor: John Haughey
Advertising director: Patrick Meehan
Managing director: Dominic Fitzpatrick
Founded: 1891   **Owner:** Fitzpatrick family

Lancashire Evening Telegraph

New Telegraph House, High Street, Blackburn BB1 1HT
Fax 01254-680429   Tel 01254-678678
E-mail: nnunn@newsquest.co.uk
Web: www.thisislancashire.co.uk
Editor: Peter Butterfield
Features editor: Nick Nunn
Picture editor: John Napier
Sports editor: Neil Bramwell
Advertising director: Christine Lambe
Managing director: Brenda Rudge
Founded: 1860   **Owner:** Newsquest

Leicester Mercury

St George Street, Leicester LE1 9FQ
Fax 0116-262 4687   Tel 0116-251 2512
Website: www.thisisleicester.co.uk
Editor: Nick Carter
Deputy editor: Jeremy Clifford
News editor: Simon Orrell
Acting features editor: Alex Dawson
Picture editor: Richard Elliott
Sports editor: Alan Parr
Advertising director: Phil Brewin
Managing director: Tony Hill
Financial director: Christine Dooley
Founded: 1874
Owner: Northcliffe Newspapers Group

Liverpool Daily Post

PO Box 48, Old Hall Street, Liverpool L69 3EB
Fax 0151-236 4682   Tel 0151-227 2000
E-mail: liverpool.com
Web: www.liverpool.com
Editor: John Griffith
Features editor: Mark Davies
Picture editor: Stephen Shakeshaft
Sports editor: Ken Rogers
Advertising director: Heather Vasco
Managing director: Lee Coligan
Founded: 1879   **Owner:** Trinity Mirror

Liverpool Echo

Old Hall Street, Liverpool L69 3EB
Fax 0151-236 4682   Tel 0151-227 2000
E-mail: letters@liverpoolecho.co.uk
Website: www.liverpool.com
Editor: John Griffith
Deputy editor: Tony Storey
News editor: Andrew Edwards
Picture editor: Stephen Shakeshaft
Arts editor: Joe Riley
Sports editor: Ken Rogers
Newspaper sales & marketing director: Lorraine O'Brien
Advertising director: Heather Vasco
Managing director: Leo Coligan
Financial director: Les Ball
Founded: 1879
Owner: Trinity Mirror

Manchester Evening News

164 Deansgate, Manchester M60 2RD
Fax 0161-832 5351   Tel 0161-832 7200
E-mail:
Website: www.manchesteronline.co.uk
Editor: Paul Horrocks
Managing editor: Brian Rhodes
Assistant editor: Maria McGeoghan
News editor: Lisa Roland
Features editor: Maggie Henfield
Arts editor: Rachel Pugh
Picture editor: Dave Thomas
Sports editor: Peter Spencer
Deputy managing director: Mark Dodson
Managing director: Ian Ashcroft
Financial director: Nick Castrio
Owner: Guardian Media Group

Newcastle Journal

Thomson House, Groat Market, Newcastle upon Tyne NE1 1ED
    Tel 0191-232 7500
Editor: Mark Dickinson

The Northern Echo

PO Box 14, Priestgate, Darlington DL1 1NF
Fax 01325-380539   Tel 01325-381313
E-mail: echo@nen.co.uk
Web: www.thisisthenortheast.co.uk
Editor: Peter Barron
Features editor: Chris Lloyd
Picture editor: Mike Gibb
Sports editor: Nick Loughlin
Advertising director: Linda Burnside
Managing director: David Kelly
Founded: 1870
Owner: Newsquest Media Group

Nottingham Evening Post

Castle Wharf House, Nottingham NG1 7EU
Fax 0115-964 4032   Tel 0115-948 2000
E-mail: nep.editorial@dial.pipex.com
Website: www.thisisnottingham.co.uk
Editor: Graham Glen
Deputy editor: Jon Grubb
Assistant editor: Duncan Hamilton
Features editor: Jeremy Lewis
Picture editor: Scott Riley
Sports editor: Kevin Pick
Advertising director: Niki Hall
Managing director: Steve Anderson-Dixon
Financial director: Jonathan Persent
Founded: 1878
Owner: Northcliffe Newspapers Group

Plymouth Evening Herald
17 Brest Road, Derriford Business Park, Plymouth
PL6 5AA
Fax 01752-765530   Tel 01752-765500
E-mail: editor@thisisplymouth.co.uk
Web:www.thisisplymouth.co.uk
Editor: Rachel Campey
Features editor: Mike Branhall
Picture editor: Pete Holdgate
Sports editor: Andy Phelan
Advertising director: Tim Randell
Managing director: Andy Gough
Founded: 1895
Owner: Northcliffe Newspapers Group

Portsmouth News
The News Centre, Hilsea, Portsmouth PO2 9SX
Fax 023-9266 4488   Tel 023-9266 4488
E-mail: newsdesk@thenews.co.uk
Web: www.thenews.co.uk
Editor: Geoff Elliott
Features editor: John Millard
Picture editor: Kevin Clifford
Sports editor: Dave King
Advertising director: Gary Fearon
Managing director: Ben Stoneham
Founded: 1877
Owner: Portsmouth & Sunderland Newspapers

Press and Journal
Lang Stracht, Mastrick, Aberdeen AB15 6DF
Fax 01224-663575   Tel 01224-690222
E-mail: editor@pj.ajl.co.uk
Website: www.pressandjournal.co.uk
Editor: Derek Tucker
Assistant editors: Ron Knox, Kay Drummond
News editor: David Knight
Features editor: Kay Drummond
Sports editor: Jim Dolan
Advertising director: Janis Gallon Smith
Managing director: Alan Scott
Founded: 1747
Owner: Northcliffe Newspaper Group

Preston Lancs Evening Post
Oliver's Place, Fulwood, Preston PR2 4ZA
Fax 01772-880173   Tel 01772-254841
Editor: Roger Borrell
Features editor: Peter Richardson
Picture editor: Bernard Howe
Sports editor: Brian Ellis
Advertising director: Mike Liddiard
Managing director: Mike Hutchby
News editor: David Barnett

The Scotsman
20 North Bridge, Edinburgh H1 1YT
Fax 0131-226 7420   Tel 0131-225 2468
Website: www.scotsman.com
Publisher: Andrew Neil
Editor: Alan Ruddock
Deputy editor: Tim Luckhurst
Business news editor: David King
Sports editor: Donald Walker
Features editor: Ailean Easton
Literary editor: Catherine Lockerbie
Scottish government editor: David Scott
News editor: Magnus Llewellin
Assistant editor (politics): Peter MacMahon
Supplements editor: Ken Houston
Owner: Scotsman Publications
Founded: 1817

The Sentinel
Sentinel House, Stoke-on-Trent, Staffs ST1 5SS
Fax 01782-280781   Tel 01782-289800
Editor: Sean Dooley
Deputy editor: Roger Clift
News editor: Michael Woods
Features editor: Roy Coates
Arts editor: Roy Coates
Picture editor: Trevor Slater
Sports editor: Nigel Wiskar
Advertising directors: Graham White, Rudd Apsey
Managing director: Peter Keller
Financial director: John Adams
Founded: 1873
Owner: Northcliffe Newspapers Group

Shropshire Star
Ketley, Telford, Shropshire TF1 4HU
Fax 01952-254605   Tel 01952-242424
Editor: Andy Wright
Deputy editor & news editor: Sarah Jane Smith
Features and arts editor: Alun Owen
Picture editor: Ken Done
Sports editor: Pete Byram
Advertising director: Alan Harris
Managing director: Keith Parker
Financial director: Roger Glews
Founded: 1964
Owner: Claverley Co

South Wales Echo
Thomson House, Havelock Street, Cardiff CF1 1XR
Fax 029-2058 3624   Tel 029-2022 3333
E-mail: letters@wme.co.uk
Web: www.totalwales.com
Editor: Robin Fletcher
Features editor: Tom Edwards
Picture editor: Chris Gordon
Sports editor: Richard Williams
Managing director: Mark Haysom
Founded: 1884
Owner: Trinity Mirror

South Wales Evening Post
Cambrian House, Swansea SA1 1RQ
Fax 01792-469665   Tel 01792-510000
Web: www.swep.co.uk
Editor: George Edwards
Features editor: Andy Pearson
Picture editor: Alan Trethewy
Sports editor: David Evans
Advertising director: Chris Rees
Managing director: Duncan Caroll
Founded: 1930   **Owner:** Northcliffe Newspapers Group

Southern Daily Echo
Newspaper House, Test Lane, Redbridge SO16 9JX
Fax 023-8042 4770   Tel 023-8042 4777
E-mail: mike.wright@solon-echo.co.uk
Editor: Ian Murray
Picture editor: Paul Collins
Sports editor: David Briers
MD newspaper division: Alan Jones
Regional managing director: Stewart Dunn
Founded: 1988   **Owner:** NewsCom

The Star
York Street, Sheffield, South Yorks S1 1PU
Fax 0114-272 5978   Tel 0114-276 7676
Website: www.sheffweb.co.uk
Editor: Peter Charlton
Business editor: Bob Rae
News editor: Bob Westerdale
Picture editor: Dennis Lound
Sports editor: Martin Smith
Advertising director: Paul Bentham
Managing director: David Edmonson
Founded: 1889
Owner: Regional Independent Media

Sunderland Echo
Echo House, Pennywell Sunderland SR4 9ER
Fax 0191-534 5975   Tel 0191-534 3011
E-mail: echo@npress.demon.co.uk
Web: www.sunderland-echo.co.uk
Editor: Andrew Smith
News editor: Patrick Lovelle
Picture editor: Gilbert Johnston
Sports editor: Neil Watson
Advertising director: Mike Kerney
Managing director: Stuart Bell
Founded: 1849
Owner: Johnson Press

Western Daily Press
Temple Way, Bristol Avon BS99 7HD
Fax 0117-934 3574   Tel 0117-9343000
Editor: Ian Beales
Sports editor: Bill Beckett
Advertising director: John Pajak
Managing director: Paul Kearney
Founded: 1858
Owner: Bristol United Press

The Western Mail
Thomson House, Havelock Street, Cardiff CF1 1XR
Fax 029-2058 3652   Tel 029-2022 3333
E-mail: readers@wme.co.uk
Web: www.totalwales.com
Editor: Neil Fowler
Features editor: D Fletcher
Picture editor: Tim Dichesan
Sports editor: Mark Tattersall
Advertising director: Gavin Steacy
Managing director: Mark Naysom
Founded: 1869
Owner: Trinity Mirror

Western Morning News
17 Brest Road, Derriford Business Park, Plymouth PL6 5AA
Fax 01752-765535   Tel 01752-765500
Editor: Barrie Williams
News editor: Jason Clark
Picture editor: Michael Cranmer
Sports editor: Rick Cowdery
Advertising director: Tim Randell
Managing director: Andy Gough
Founded: 1860
Owner: Northcliffe Newspapers Group

Yorkshire Evening Post
Wellington Street, Leeds, West Yorks LS1 1RF
Fax 0113-238 8536   Tel 0113-243 2701
E-mail: eped@tpn.co.uk
Editor: Neil Hodgkinson
Features editor: Anne Pickles
Womens editor: Carmen Bruegmann
Picture editor: Mike Fisher
News editor: David Helliwell
Advertising director: Mike Pennington
Managing director: Steve Auckland
Financial director: Katherine Armitage
Founded: 1890
Owner: Regional Independent Media

Yorkshire Post
Wellington Street, Leeds, West Yorks LS1 1RF
Fax 0113-244 3430   Tel 0113-243 2701
E-mail: yp.newsdesk@ypn.co.uk
Editor: Tony Watson
Deputy editor: Nick Jenkins
Womens editor: Jill Armstrong
Features editor: Michael Hickling
Business editor: Peter Curtain
Sports editor: Bill Bridge
Managing director: Steve Auckland
Advertising director: Mike Pennington
Finance director: Kathryn Armitage
Founded: 1754
Owner: Regional Independent Media

TOP SUNDAYS

Scotland on Sunday
20 North Bridge, Edinburgh EH1 1YT
Fax 0131-220 2443   Tel 0131-225 2468
Website: www.scotsman.com
Editor: John McGurk
Deputy editor: Kevin McKenna
News editor: Ian Stewart
Features editor: Margot Wilson
Picture editor: Clive Howes
Sports editor: Ginny Clark
Owner: European Press Holdings

Sunday Herald
195 Albion Street, Glasgow G1 1QP
Fax 0141-302 7809   Tel 0141-552 6255
Website: www.sundayherald.com
Editor: Andrew Jispan
Deputy editors: Rob Brown, George Rosie
News editor: David Milne
Features editor: Charlotte Ross
Arts editor: Barry Didcock
Foreign editor: Trevor Royle
Sports editor: Donald Cowey
Advertising editor: Howard Warren
Founded: 1999
Owner: Scottish Media Newspapers

Sunday Independent
Burrington Way, Plymouth, Devon PL5 3LN
Fax 01752 206164   Tel 01752 206600
Editor: tba
Deputy editors: Nikki Rowlands
News editor: Anthony Abbott
Features editor: Kirsty Turner
Picture editor: Steve Porter
Sports editor: Kevin Marriott
Owner: Southern Newspapers

Sunday Life (Belfast)
124-144 Royal Avenue, Belfast BT1 1EB
Fax 028-9055 4507   Tel 028-9026 4300
E-mail: barnold@belfasttelegraph.co.uk
Editor: Martin Lindsay
Deputy editor: Dave Culbert
News editor: Martin Hill
Features editor: Sue Corbett
Picture editor: Fred Hoare
Sports editor: Jim Gracey
Advertising manager: John Leslie
Managing director: Derek Carvell
Owner: Trinity Mirror

Sunday Mail
Anderston Quay, Glasgow G3 8DA
Fax 0141-242 3587   Tel 0141-248 7000
Website: www.record-mail.co.uk
Editor: Jim Cassidy
Assistant editor: Andy Sannholm
Assistant editor (news): Brian Steel
Features editor: Rob Bruce
Women's editor: Melanie Reid
News editor: Brian Steel
Sports editor: George Cheyne

Magazine editor: Liz Wilson
Advertising director: Pat Moore
Managing director: Mark Hollinshead
Owner: Mirror Group

Sunday Mercury
28 Colmore Circus, Birmingham B4 6AZ
Fax 0121-234 5877   Tel 0121-236 3366
Website: www.go2birmingham.com
Editor: Fiona Alexander
Deputy editor: Alf Bennett
Head of content: Bernard Cole
News editor: Bob Haywood
Assistant editor (sport): Lee Gibson
Advertising sales manager: Denize McNeish
Managing director: Geraldine Aitken
Owner: Midland

Sunday Post
2 Albert Square, Dundee DD1 9QJ
Fax 01382-201064   Tel 01382-223131
E-mail: post@dcthomson.co.uk
Website: www.dcthomson.co.uk
Editor: Russell Reid
Deputy editor: David Pollington
News editor: Tom McKay
Features editor: Brian Wilson
Sports editor: David Walker
Magazine editor: Maggie Dun
Advertising manager: Ian Foggie
Managing director: Brian Thomson
Owner: DC Thomson & Co

Sunday Sun
Thomson House, Groat Market, Newcastle NE1 1ED
Fax 0191-230 0238   Tel 0191-201 6330
E-mail: office@sundaysun.demon.co.uk
Website: www.sundaysun.co.uk
Editor: Peter Montellier
Assistant editor: Mike McGiffen
News editor: Jim Oldfield
Feature writer: Coreena Ford
Sports editor: Dylan Younger
Chief photographer: Paul Forrest
Advertising manager: Vanessa Moore
Managing director: Stephen Parker
Owner: Trinity Mirror

Wales on Sunday
Havelock Street, Cardiff CF1 1XR
Fax 029-2058 3725   Tel 029-2058 3733
E-mail: wosmail@wme.co.uk
Website: www.totalwales.co.uk
Editor: Alan Edmunds
Senior assistant editor: Mike Smith
News editor: Ceri Gould
Sports editor: Paul Abbandonato
Advertising director: Gavin Staecey
Managing director: Mark Haysom
Owner: Trinity Mirror International

TOP 20 PAID-FOR WEEKLIES

Aldershot News series
Albert Road, Aldershot, Hampshire GU11 1NU
Fax 01252-341033   Tel 01252-328221
Editor: Marnie Wilson
Senior assistant editor: vacant
Assistant editor (production): June Sparey
Sports editor: Jon Couch
Ad director: John Connor
MD: Chris Roberts
Founded: 1895
Owner: Surrey Advertiser Holdings

Barnsley Chronicle
47 Church Street, Barnsley, Yorkshire S70 2AS
Fax 01226-734455   Tel 01226-734734
E-mail: ac@barnsley-chronicle.co.uk
Web: www.barnsley-chronicle.co.uk
Editor: Robert Cockroft
Senior assistant editor: Ian Thompson
Assistant editor (production): Judith Halkerston
News editor: John Threlkeld
Sports editor: Keith Lodge
Ad director: Mike Shenton
MD: Nicholas Hewitt
Founded: 1858   **Owner:** Barnsley Chronicle Holdings

Chester Chronicle
Commonhall Street, Chester CH1 2BJ
Fax 01244-322262   Tel 01244-340151
E-mail: newsroom@cheshirenews.co.uk
Web: www.cheshirenews.co.uk
Editor: Paul Chamberlain
Senior assistant editor: Mike Green
Assistant editor (production): Rex Thelwall
News editor: Jim Brakell
Sports editor: Ian Bedford
Adv director: Paul Taylor
MD: David Faulkner
Founded: 1715   **Owner:** Trinity Mirror

Cornish Guardian
30 Fore Street, Bodmin, Cornwall PL31 2HQ
Fax 01208-72109   Tel 01208-78133
E-mail: cwncg@eurobell.co.uk
Web: www.thisiscornwall.co.uk
Editor: Alan Cooper
Senior assistant editor: Nick Knight
Chief reporter: Simon Fernley
Sports editor: David Henderson
Advertising director: Trevor Lee
Managing director: Alan Cooper
Founded: 1901   **Owner:** Northcliffe Newspapers Group

Croydon Advertiser series
19 Bartlett Street, South Croydon CR2 6TB
Fax 020-8763 6633 (ed) Tel 020-8763 6666
E-mail: CroydonAd@compuserve.com
Editor: Malcolm Starbrook
Deputy editor: Chris Harding
News editor: Ian Austen
Sports editor: Martin Bryce
Ad manager: Katharine Glass   **Publisher:** Patrick Crean
Founded: 1869   **Owner:** South News

The Cumberland News
Newspaper House, Dalston Road, Carlisle CA2 5UA
Fax 01288-612640   Tel 01288-612600
Editor: Keith Sutton
Senior assistant editor: Steve Johnston
Assistant editor (production): Richard Eccles
Assistant editor: Nick Turner
News editor: Steve Orrell
Sports editor: John Reynolds
Advertising director: Terry Hall
Managing director: Kevin McNulty
Founded: 1815
Owner: CN Group

Derbyshire Times
Station Road, Chesterfield, Derbyshire S41 7XD
Fax 01246-504580   Tel 01246-504500
Editor: Mike Wilson
Deputy editor: Dave Welford
News editor: Tracy Mitchell
Sports editor: Andrew Jarvis
Advertising director: Nick Mills
Managing director: Danny Cammiade
Founded: 1854
Owner: Johnston Press

Essex Chronicle
Westway, Chelmsford, Essex CM1 3BE
Fax 01245-603353   Tel 01245-600700
E-mail: name@essexchronicle.demon.co.uk
Editor: Stuart Rawlins
Assistant editor (production): John Hill
Assistant editor: Roger Thurlow
News editor: Roger Thurlow
Sports editor: Gary Stubbings
Advertising director: Malcolm White
Managing director: Michael Coates
Founded: 1764
Owner: Northcliffe

Harrogate Advertiser series
1 Cardale Park, Beckwith Head Road, Harrogate,
North Yorkshire HG3 1RZ
Fax 01423-501228   Tel 01423-564321
E-mail: ackmunews@upn.co.uk
Web: www.harrogate-advertiserseries.co.uk
Editor-in-chief: Jean MacQuarrie
Head of news: Rita Sobot
Sub-editor: Steve Bramley
Sports editor: Mark Flanagan
Ad manager: Lisa Brown   **MD:** Stephen Plews
Founded: 1850
Owner: RIM

Hereford Times
Holmer Road, Hereford HR4 9UKJ
Fax 01432-343235   Tel 01432-274413
E-mail: stewartg@newsquestmidlands.co.uk
Editor: Stewart Gilbert
Deputy editor: David Hetterley
Assistant editor (production): Terry Homer
News editor: Nigel Heins
Sports editor: Jeremy Finney
Advertising manager: Tina Hurley   **MD:** Mike Pagett
Founded: 1832   **Owner:** Newsquest Media Group

Herts Mercury series
1 Fore Street, Bishop's Stortford FG14 1OB
Fax 01992-589470   Tel 01992-554611
E-mail: mercury@hertsessex-news.co.uk
Web: www.mercury@herts-essex-news.co.uk
Editor: Paul Winspear
Senior sub-editor: Sarosh Daruvala
News editor: Lois Prior
Sports editor: Andrew Franczak
Advertising director: Barbara Eatenton
Managing director: John Holland
Founded: 1772
Owner: Yattendon Investment Trust

Isle of Wight County Press
Brannon House, 123 Pyle Street, Newport PO30 1ST
Fax 01983-527204   Tel 01983-521333
E-mail: adman@iowpress.demon.co.uk
Web: www.iwcp.co.uk
Editor: B Dennis
Senior assistant editor: M Sutcliffe
Assistant editor (production): A Marriott
News editor: P Wolsey
Sports editor: J Hanom
Advertising director: A Porteous
Managing director: R Freeman
Founded: 1884

Kent Messenger
6 & 7 Middle Row, Maidstone, Kent ME14 1TG
Fax 01622-695666   Tel 01622-757227
E-mail: kmgroupcommercial@kentonline.co.uk
Web: www.kent-online.co.uk
Editor: Simon Irwin
Community editor: Cathy Tyce
Assistant editor (production): Ian West
News editor: Robert Barman
Sports editor: Steve Constable
Advertising director: Simon Clubley
Chairman: Edwin Boorman
Founded: 1815
Owner: Boorman family

Kent and Sussex Courier
Longfield Road, Tunbridge Wells TN2 3HL
Fax 01892-510400   Tel 01892-681000
E-mail: editor@ourier.co.uk
Web: www.thisiskentandeastsussex.co.uk
Editor: Martin Oxley
Senior assistant editor: Faith Lee
Assistant editor (production): Barry Kingdom
Assistant editor: Lindsey Jones
News editor: Melanie Whittaker
Sports editor: Brian Harris
Advertising director: Amanda Hallworth
Managing director: Tim Bishop
Founded: 1825
Owner: Northcliffe Newspapers Group

North Devon Journal
96 High Street, Barnstaple, Devon EX31 1HT
Fax 01271-323165   Tel 01271-343064
E-mail: editorial@northdevonjournal.co.uk
Web: www.northdevonjournal.co.uk
Managing editor: Andy Cooper
Senior assistant editor: Mary-Ann Bloomfield
Assistant editor (production): Chris Machin
News editor: Simon Williams
Sports editor: Dave Pedler
Advertising director: Norma Stevens
Managing director: Tony Hazell
Founded: 1824
Owner: Northcliffe Newspapers Group

South London Press (Friday edition)
2-4 Leigham Court Road, Streatham, London SW16 2PD
Fax 020-8769 1742   Tel 020-8769 4444
E-mail: robbowden@slp.co.uk
Web: www.slp.co.uk
Editor: Rob Bowden
Chief sub- editor: Clare Nannery
News editor: Janet Carberry
Sports editor: Kevin Brennan
Advertising director: Sharon Montgomery
Managing director: Simon Edgley
Founded: 1865
Owner: Trinity Mirror International Holdings

Surrey Advertiser
Stoke Mill, Woking Road, Guildford GU1 1QA
Fax 01483-532843   Tel 01483-508900
E-mail: editorial@surreyad.co.uk
Web: www.surreyad.co.uk
Editor: Graham Collyer
Deputy editor: Janet Russell
News editor: Jane Garrett
Sports editor: Richard Spiller
Advertising director: Trevor Reevell
Managing director: Ian McEwan
Founded: 1864
Owner: Guardian Media Group

Warrington Guardian
The Academy, 138 Bridge Street, Warrington,
Cheshire WA1 2RU
Fax 01925-434115   Tel 01925-434000
E-mail: webmaster@info-quest.com
Web: www.thisischeshire.co.uk
Editor: Jan Lever
Deputy editor: Nicola Priest
News editor: Chris Wood
Sports editor: Mike Parsons
Advertising director: Steve Sawyer
Managing director: Andy Tipler
Founded: 1853
Owner: Newsquest Media Group

West Briton
Harmsworth House, Lemon Quay, Truro, TR1 2LP
Fax 01872-265016   Tel 01872-271451
Web: www.thisiscornwall.co.uk
Editor: John Pearn
Deputy editor: Jeremy Ridge
Chief sub- editor: Gary Kay
Sports editor: Rhod Mitchell
Advertising director: Trevor Lee
Managing director: Tony Hazell
Founded: 1810
Owner: Northcliffe Newspapers Group

Western Gazette
Sherborne Road, Yeovil, Somerset BA21 4YA
Fax 01935-426963   Tel 01935-700500
E-mail: editor@westgaz.co.uk
Web: www.westgaz.co.uk
Editor: Martin Heal
Assistant editor (production): Peter Brooke
News editor: Peter O'Reilly
Sports editor: Richard Briggs
Advertising director: Nikki Donnelly
Managing director: Ken Hayward
Founded: 1737
Owner: Bristol United Press

TOP FREE WEEKLIES

Bexley Dartford Sidcup News Shopper
Mega House, Crest View, Orpington, Kent BR5 1BT
Fax 01689-875367   Tel 01689-836211
E-mail: aparkes@london.newsquest.co.uk
Web: www.thisislondon.co.uk
Editor: Andrew Parkes
Deputy editor: Jean May
News editors: Victoria Watkins, Roger Wright
Sports editor: John Thynne
Advertising director: Martyn Willis
Managing director: John Banks
Founded: 1965
Owner: Newsquest Media Group

Birmingham Metronews
28 Colmore Circus, Birmingham B4 6AX
                     Tel 0121-234 5962
Editor: Ross Crawford
Senior assistant editor: Mike Critchley
News editor: Zoë Chamberlain
Sports editor: Mike Critchley
Advertising director: Bill Vieisey
Managing director: Mike Donovan
Founded: 1991
Owner: Trinity Mirror

Bournemouth Advertiser series
Yelverton Road. Bournemouth BH1 1DD
Fax 01202-292115   Tel 01202-554601
Web: www.newscom.co.uk
Editor: Neal Butterworth

Deputy editor: Nick Rowe
Assistant editor: Ed Perkins
News editor: Andy Martin
Sports editor: Andy Goodall
Advertising director: Shelley Gorham
Managing director: Mike Denny
Founded: 1900
Owner: Newscom

Coventry Citizen
Corporation Street, Coventry CV1 1FP
Fax 024-7655 3820   Tel 024-7663 3633
Editor: Beverly Marun
Owner: Mirror Group

Croydon Guardian
Guardian House, Sandiford Road, Sutton SM3 9RN
Fax 020-8770 2277   Tel 020-8644 4300
E-mail: cwarren@london.newsquest.co.uk
Web: www.thisislondon.co.uk
Editor: Claire Warren
Production editor: Tamsin Coates
News editor: Samantha Tillyer
Sports editors: Dave Watters, Robin Marriott
Advertising director: John Banks
Managing director: John Banks
Founded: 1988
Owner: Newsquest Media Group

Edinburgh Herald and Post
7 Newhaven Road, Edinburgh EH6 5QA
Fax 0131-556 5177   Tel 0131-243 3242
E-mail: edinhp@scotsman.com
Editor: Millind Kathatkar
Chief reporter: Andrea Mullarey
Advertising director: Stephen Tait
Managing director: Michael Jones
Founded: 1978
Owner: Press Holdings

The Glaswegian
40 Anderston Quay, Glasgow G3 8DA
Fax 0141-242 3596   Tel 0141-242 3502
Editor: Liz Steele
News editor: Ray McHugh
Managing director: Mark Hollinshead
Owner: Trinity Mirror

Kingston Guardian
Guardian House, Sandiford Road, Sutton SM3 9RN
Fax 020-8770 2277   Tel 020-8644 4300
E-mail: cwarren@london.newsquest.co.uk
Web: www.londonnews.co.uk
Editor: Claire Warren
Production editor: Tamsin Coates
News editor: Samantha Tillyer
Sports editors: Dave Watters, Robin Marriott
Advertising director: John Banks
Managing director: John Banks
Founded: 1975
Owner: Newsquest Media Group

Leeds Weekly News
PO Box 49, Wellington Street, Leeds LS1 1LW
Fax 0113-238 8484   Tel 0113-238 8769
Web: www.pn.co.uk
Editor: Neil Hodgkinson
News editor: Sheila Holmes
Sports editor: John Baron
Commercial director: Helen Oldham
Sales manager: Nicola Atkinson
Managing director: Steve Auckland
Founded: 1980
Owner: Regional Independent Newspapers

Metro
164 Deansgate, Manchester M60 2RD
Fax 0161-834 0556   Tel 0161-834 9677
E-mail: metro@mcr-eveing-news.co.uk
Editor: John Jeffay
Senior assistant editor: Richard Butt
Owner: Guardian Media Group

North Staffs Advertiser
Sentinel House, Etruria, Stoke-on-Trent ST1 5SS
Fax 01782-21477   Tel 01782-271100
Chief executive: Stuart Birkinshaw
Advertising manager: Nicola Clarkson
Founded: 1975

Nottingham Recorder
PO Box 99, Forman Street, Nottingham NG1 4AB
Fax 0115-964 4000   Tel 0115-948 2000
Editor: G Glen
Managing director: S Anderson-Dixon
Founded: 1979
Owner: Nottingham Post Group

Portsmouth Journal
The News Centre, Hilsea, Portsmouth PO2 9SX
Fax 01705-221229   Tel 023-9266 4488
E-mail: journal.editor@ppp.co.uk
Web: www.journal.co.uk
Editor: Andrew Griffin
Senior reporter: Caryl Lawrence
Reporter: Graeme Moir
Advertising director: Gary Fearon
Managing director: Ben Stoneham
Founded: 1982
Owner: Johnston Press

Sefton, West Lancashire & Southport Visiter series
26-32 Tulketh Street, Southport, Merseyside PR8 1BT
Fax 01704-398297   Tel 01704-536655
Web: www.southportvisiter.co.uk
Editor: John Dempsey
Assistant editor (production): Alan Heaton
News editor: Deborah Ramsay
Sports editor: Dave Chalmers
Advertising director: Gary Taylor
Managing director: Leo Colligan
Founded: 1844   **Owner:** Trinity Mirror

Sheffield Weekly Gazette
York Street, Sheffield, South Yorkshire S1 1PU
Fax 0114-272 5978   Tel 0114-276 7676
Editor: Peter Charlton

Southampton Advertiser
Newspaper House, Test Lane, Redbridge, Hampshire SO16 9JX
Fax 023-8042 4545   Tel 023-8042 4444
E-mail: info@satton-echo.co.uk
Editor: Ian Murray
Deputy editor: Andy Bissell
Assistant editor: Keith Hamilton
News editor: Gordon Sutter
Sports editor: David Briers
Advertising director: Sue Mayhew
Managing director: John Dux
Owner: Newscom

Southend Standard
Newspaper House, Chester Hall Lane, Basildon, Essex SS14 3BL
Fax 01268-282884   Tel 01268-522792
E-mail: evening.echo@notes.newsquest.co.uk
Editor: Martin McNeill
Deputy editors: Peter Bailey, Keith Bartels
News editors: Sandra Hembury, David Hyman, Claire Ogley
Sports editor: Paul Alton
Advertising director: Richard Byham
Managing director: Eric Robinson
Founded: 1873
Owner: Newsquest Media Group

Sutton and Epsom Guardian
Guardian House, Sandiford Road, Sutton SM3 9RN
Fax 020-8770 2277   Tel 020-8644 4300
E-mail: cwarren@london.newsquest.co.uk
Web: www.thisislocallondon.co.uk
Editor: Claire Warren
New editor: Samantha Tillyer
Production editor: Tamsin Coates
Sports editor: Dave Watters, Robin Marriott
Advertising director: John Banks
Managing director: John Banks
Founded: 1988
Owner: Newsquest Media Group

Wirral Globe
Globe House, Catherine Street, Birkenhead CH41 6HW
                        Tel 0151-906 3000
E-mail: smorris@guardiangrp.co.uk
Web: www.wirralglobe.co.uk
Editor: Robin Bird
Associate editor: David Williams
Sports editor: David Williams
Advertising manager: Siobhan Morris
Managing director: Jane Longden
Founded: 1973
Owner: Newsquest Media Group

LOCAL PAPER LISTINGS BY REGION

By and large, for the sake of easier access, this local paper list uses the old county boundaries. For the correct, post-1998 two-tier and unitary divisions, turn to Local Government on page 380-384.

BEDFORDSHIRE
Ampthill & Flitwick Herald wf
Eastern Counties Newspapers
01234-364221
Bedford Citizen series wf
Johnston Press
01234-363101
Bedford & Kempston Herald wf
Herald Newspapers
01234-364221
Bedfordshire On Sunday s
Local Sunday Newspapers
01234-345191
Biggleswade & Sandy Herald wf
Eastern Counties Newspapers
01234-364221
Biggleswade Chronicle w
Johnston Press
01767-313479
Dunstable Gazette w
Eastern Counties Newspapers
01582-21222
Leighton Buzzard Citizen wf
Johnston Press
01908-371133
Leighton Buzzard Herald wf
Eastern Counties Newspapers
01727-846866
Leighton Buzzard Observer w
Eastern Counties Newspapers
01525-370251
Luton Leader wf
Eastern Counties Newspapers
01582-870200
Luton News w
Eastern Counties Newspapers
01582-870200
Luton/Dunstable Herald & Post wf
Trinity Mirror
01582-700600

BERKSHIRE
The Advertiser wf
Newbury Weekly News
01635-524111
Ascot & Sunningdale Observer wf
Slough Observer
01753-523355
Berks & Bucks Observer wf
Frank Lawrence
01753-523355
Bracknell & Ascot Times w
Berkshire Press
0118-957 5833
Bracknell & Wokingham News wf
Trinity Mirror
01344-56611
Bracknell & Wokingham Std wf
Guardian Media Group
0118-957 5833
Bracknell News w
Trinity Mirror
01344-56611
Crowthorne, Sandhurst Newsweek w
Reading Newspaper Co
01344-56611
Crowthorne & Sandhurst Times w
Berkshire Press
0118-957 5833
Maidenhead Advertiser w
Baylis & Co
01628-771100
Newbury/Thatcham Chronicle wf
Trinity Mirror
01625-32771
Newbury Local Mart wf
Local Mart Publications
01635-31855
Newbury Weekly News w
Newbury Weekly News
01635-524111
Reading Chronicle w
Trinity Mirror
0118-950 3030
Reading Chronicle Midweek wf
Trinity Mirror
0118-950 3030
(Reading) Evening Post d
Guardian Media Group
0118 9575833
Reading Standard wf
Berkshire Press
0118 9575833
Sandhurst/Crowthorne News wf
Guardian Media Group
01252-328221

Slough & Langley Observer w
Frank Lawrence
01753-523355
Slough,Windsor & Eton Express w
Southnews
01753-825111
Windsor/Maidenhead Leader wf
Southnews
01753-825111
Windsor & Maidenhead Obs wf
Frank Lawrence
01753-523355
Wokingham & Bracknell Times w
Guardian Media Group
0118- 957 5833
Wokingham News w
Reading Newspaper Co
01344-56611
Woodley Chronicle w
Reading Newspaper Co
0118-950 3030

CITY OF BRISTOL
Bristol Evening Post d
Bristol Evening Post
0117-934 3000
Bristol Observer wf
Bristol Evening Post
0117-934 3000
(Bristol) Western Daily Press d
Bristol Evening Post
0117-934 3000
Clevedon Mercury wf
Bristol Evening Post
01275-874248
Glos & Avon Gazette w
Bailey Newspapers
01453-320111
Keynsham & District Adv wf
Southern Newspapers
01225-446800
Northavon Gazette w
Southern Newspapers
01453-544000
Portishead Admag wf
Southern Newspapers
01934-417921
Thornbury Gazette w
Southern Newspapers
01453-544000

d=daily, w=weekly, s=sunday, f=free

BUCKINGHAMSHIRE

Bletchley Citizen wf
Johnston Press
01908-371133
Buckingham Advertiser w
Johnston Press
01280-813434
Buckinghamshire Advertiser w
Southnews
020-8367 2345
Bucks Advertiser
Johnston Press
01296-318300
Bucks Examiner w
Southnews
01494-792626
Bucks Free Press w
Newsquest Media Group
01494-521212
Bucks Herald
Johnston Press
01296-318300
(High Wycombe) Midweek w
Newsquest Media Group
01494-521212
High Wycombe Leader wf
Southnews
020-8424 0044
Milton Keynes Citizen wf
Johnston Press
01908-371133
Milton Keynes Herald wf
Eastern Counties Newspapers Group
01727-866166
Milton Keynes & District Observer w
Eastern Counties Newspapers
01727-866166
South Bucks Star wf
Newsquest Media Group
01494-521212

CAMBRIDGESHIRE

Cambridge Evening News d
Yattendon Investment Trust
01223-434434
Cambridge Weekly News wf
Yattendon Investment Trust
01223-434434
Cambs Times/March Adv w
Eastern Counties Newspaper Group
01603-628311
Cambs Town Crier East wf
Johnston Press
01223-369966

Cambs Town Crier West wf
Johnston Press
01223-369966
Ely Standard w
Eastern Counties Newspaper Group
01353-667831
Ely Weekly News wf
Yattendon Investment Trust
01223-434434
Fenland Citizen wf
Johnston Press
01733-555111
Huntingdon Weekly News wf
Yattendon Investment Trust
01223-434434
Huntingdon Town Crier w
Peterborough Evening Telegraph
01733-555111
The Hunts Post wf
Eastern Counties Newspaper Group
01603-628311
Peterborough Citizen wf
Johnston Press
01733-555111
Peterborough Evening Telegraph d
East Midlands Newspapers
01733-555111
Peterborough Herald & Post wf
Midland Independent Newspapers
01733-318600
St Neots Weekly News wf
Yattendon Investment Trust
01223-434434
Wisbech Standard w
Eastern Counties Newspaper Group
01603-628311

CHANNEL ISLANDS

Guernsey Evening Press & Star d
The Guernsey Press Co
01481-45866
Guernsey Weekly Press w
Guernsey Press Co
01481-45866
Jersey Evening Post d
Jersey Evening Post
01534-611611
Jersey Weekly Post w
Jersey Evening Post
01534-611611

CHESHIRE

Bramhall & District Courier wf
Courier Group
01625-586140
Chester & District Standard wf
Chester Standard Newspapers
01244-351234

Chester Chronicle w
Trinity Mirror
01244-340151
Chester Herald & Post wf
Trinity Mirror
01244-340151
Congleton Adnews wf
Adnews (Midlands)
01260-281012
Congleton Chronicle series w
Heads (Congleton)
01260-273737
Congleton Guardian wf
Newsquest Media Group
01925-633033
Crewe & District Herald Post wf
Trinity Mirror
01244-340151
Crewe & Nantwich Guardian wf
Newsquest Media Group
01925-633033
Crewe Chronicle w
Trinity Mirror
01244-340151
Didsbury & District Courier wf
Courier Group
01625-586140
Ellesmere Port Pioneer w
Trinity Mirror
01244-340151
Ellesmere Port Standard wf
Chester Standard Newspapers
01244-351234
High Peak Courier wf
United Provinicial Newspapers
01246-504500
Knutsford Express Advertiser wf
Guardian Media Group
0161-480 4491
Knutsford Guardian w
Newsquest Media Group
01925-633033
Macclesfield Express Adv. w
Guardian Media Group
0161-480 4491
Macclesfield Messenger wf
Newsquest Media Group
0161-477 4600
Macclesfield Times wf
Guardian Media Group
0161-480 4491
Middlewich Chronicle w
Chronicle Newspapers
01244-340151
Northwich Chronicle w
Trinity Mirror
01244-340151
North Cheshire Herald w
Ashton Weekly Newspapers
0161-303 1910

Northwich Guardian w
Newsquest Media Group
01925-633033
Northwich Herald & Post wf
Trinity Mirror
01244-340151
Poynton Times wf
Guardian Media Group
0161-480 4491
Runcorn Herald & Post wf
Trinity Mirror
01244-340151
Runcorn Weekly News w
Trinity Mirror
01244-340151
Runcorn World wf
Newsquest Media Group
0151-424 7711
Sandbach Chronicle w
Heads (Congleton)
01260-273737
South Cheshire Mail wf
Chronicle Newspapers
01244-340151
South Wirral Herald wf
Trinity Mirror
01244-340151
Warrington Guardian w
Newsquest Media Group
01925-633033
Warrington Mercury wf
Kinsman Reeds
01925-51131
Widnes Weekly News w
Trinity Mirror
01244-340151
Widnes World wf
Newsquest Media Group
0151-424 7711
Wilmslow Express Advertiser wf
Guardian Media Group
0161-480 4491
Wilmslow Messenger wf
Newsquest Media Group
0161-477 4600

CORNWALL & SCILLY ISLES
Bude & Stratton Post w
Cornish & Devon Post
01566-772424
Camelford & Delabole Post w
Cornish & Devon Post
01566-772424
Camborne & Redruth Packet wf
Tindle Newspapers
01326-370500
Cornish and Devon Post w
Tindle Newspapers
01566-772424

Cornish Guardian w
Northcliffe Newspapers Group
01208-78133
Cornish Times w
Tindle Newspapers
01579-342174
The Cornishman w
Northcliffe Newspapers Group
01736-362247
Falmouth Packet w
Packet Newspapers
01326-370500
Hayle Times w
St Ives Printing & Publishing Co
01736-795813
Helston & District Gazette wf
Packet Newspapers
01326-370500
Launceston Gazette wf
Tindle Newspapers
01566-772766
Liskeard Gazette wf
Tindle Newspapers
01579-47444
Mid Cornwall Advertiser wf
North Cornwall Advertiser
01208-815096
North Cornwall Advertiser wf
North Cornwall Advertiser
01208-815096
Packet Series w
Southern Newspapers
01326-373791
Penwith Pirate wf
Packet Newspapers
01326-370500
Redruth & Camborne Tinner
Packet Newspapers
01326-370500
St Austell, Newquay Packet wf
Southern Newspapers
01326-373791
St Ives Times & Echo w
St Ives Printing & Publishing
01736-795813
Truro Packet wf
Southern Newspapers
01326-370500
West Briton w
Northcliffe Newspapers Group
01872-271451

CUMBRIA
The Advertiser wf
CN Group
01229-821835
(Barrow) N West Evening Mail d
CN Group
01229-821835

(Carlisle) News & Star d
CN Group
01228-612600
Cumberland Herald w
Cumberland & Westmorland Herald
Newspapers
01768-862313
Cumberland News w
CN Group
01228-612600
East Cumbrian Gazette wf
CN Group
01228-616100
Keswick Reminder w
G W McKane & Son
01768-772140
Lakeland Echo wf
United Provinicial Newspapers
01539-730630
Lakes Leader wf
Newsquest Media Group
01539-720555
W Cumberland Times & Star w
CN Group
01900-601234
West Cumbrian Gazette wf
CN Group
01228-616100
Westmorland Gazette w
Newsquest Media Group
01539-720555
Whitehaven News w
CN Group
01946-595100

DERBYSHIRE
Alfreton & Ripley Echo wf
Johnston Press
01246-504500
Alfreton Chad wf
Johnston Press
01623-456789
Ashboourne News Telegraph w
Yattendon Investment Trust
01283-512345
Belper Express wf
Northcliffe Newspapers Group
01332-291111
Belper News w
Johnston Press
01773-820971
Bolsover Advertiser wf
Derbyshire Times
01246-200144
Buxton Advertiser w
Johnston Press
01246-200144

d=daily, w=weekly, s=sunday, f=free

DERBYSHIRE CONTD.

Buxton Times wf
Derbyshire Times
01246-200144
Chesterfield Advertiser wf
Johnston Press
01246-202291
Chesterfield Express wf
North Derbyshire Newspapers
01246-234920
Chesterfield Gazette wf
Johnston Press
01246-200144
Derby Evening Telegraph d
Northcliffe Newspapers Group
01332-291111
Derby Express wf
Northcliffe Newspapers Group
01332-291111
Derby Journal wf
Journal Publishing
01332-202393
Derby Trader wf
Midland Independent Newspapers
01332-253999
Derbyshire Times w
Johnston Press
01246-200144
Dronfield Advertiser wf
Johnston Press
01246-202291
Eckington Leader wf
Johnston Press
01246-434343
Glossop Chronicle w
United Provinicial Newspapers
0161-303 1910
High Peak Courier wf
Johnston Press
01246-504500
Ilkeston Advertiser w
Johnston Press
0115-932 4285
Ilkeston Express wf
Northcliffe Newspapers Group
01332-291111
Matlock Mercury w
Johnston Press
01629-582432
Ripley & Heanor News w
Johnston Press
01773-742133
Swadlincote Times w
Trident Midland Newspapers
01530-813101

DEVON

Axminster News wf
Eastern Counties Newspapers Group
01392-447766
Dartmouth Chron/S Hams Gazette w
Tindle Newspapers
01548-853101
Dawlish Gazette w
Tindle Newspapers
01626-864161
Dawlish Post wf
Devon & Cornwall Newspapers
01626-353555
East Devon News series wf
Eastern Counties Newspapers Group
01225 460556
(Exeter) Express & Echo d
Northcliffe Newspapers Group
01392-442211
Exeter Leader wf
Northcliffe Newspapers Group
01392-442211
(Exeter) Midweek Herald wf
Eastern Counties Newspapers Group
0117-923 1153
Exmouth Herald wf
Eastern Counties Newspapers Group
01225 460556
Exmouth Journal w
Eastern Counties Newspapers Group
01225 460556
Holsworthy Post w
Cornish & Devon Post
01566-772424
Honiton & Cullompton News wf
Eastern Counties Newspapers Group
01392-447766
Ivybridge Gazette w
Tindle Newspapers
01548-853101
Kingsbridge Gazette w
Tindle Newspapers
01548-853101
Mid-Devon Advertiser series w
Tindle Newspapers
01626-355566
Mid-Devon Express & Star wf
Southern Newspapers
01884-255977
Mid Devon Gazette w
Northcliffe Newspapers Group
01884-242500
Newton Abbot Weekender wf
Northcliffe Newspapers Group
01803-676000
North Devon Gazette & Adv wf
Eastern Counties Newspapers Group
01225 460556
North Devon Journal w
Northcliffe Newspapers Group
01271-343064

Okehampton Times w
Tavistock Newsapers
01822-613666
(Plymouth) Evening Herald d
Northcliffe Newspapers Group
01752-765500
Plymouth Extra wf
Northcliffe Newspapers Group
01752-765500
Plympton News wf
Tindle Newspapers
01548-853101
Pulmans Weekly News w
Bristol Evening Post
01297-35417
Sidmouth Herald w
Eastern Counties Newspapers Group
01225 460556
South Devon & Plymouth Times w
Devon & Cornwall Newspapers
01803-862585
Sunday Independent w
West of England Newspapers
01752-206600
Tavistock Times Gazette w
Tindle Newspapers
01822-613666
Teignmouth News wf
Tindle Newspapers
01626-779494
Teignmouth Post w
Devon & Cornwall Newspapers
01626-353555
Torbay Weekender wf
Northcliffe Newspapers Group
01803-676000
(Torquay) Herald Express d
Northcliffe Newspapers Group
01803-676000
Totnes Times Series w
Tindle Newspapers
01803-862585
Western Morning News d
Northcliffe Newspapers Group
01752-765500

DORSET

Avon Adv (Hants & Dorset) wf
Southern Newspapers
01722-337466
Bournemouth/Christchurch/
Poole Advertiser wf
Southern Newspapers
01202-411411
(Bournemouth) The Daily Echo d
Southern Newspapers
01202-554601
Bridport News w
Southern Newspapers
01823-725000

Christchurch Advertiser wf
Advertiser Series
01202-411411
Dorset Evening Echo d
Southern Newspapers
01305-784804
Poole Advertiser wf
Advertiser Series
01202-411411
Stour Valley News wf
Southern Newspapers
01258-456067
Swanage & Wareham Adv wf
Southern Newspapers
01202-411411
West Dorset Express & Star wf
Southern Newspapers
01823-725000
Weymouth Advertiser wf
Southern Newspapers
01305-776101

DURHAM
Chester le Street Advertiser wf
Newsquest Media Group
01325-381313
The Clarion wf
SR & VI Crane
01642-480397
Consett & Stanley Advertiser wf
Newsquest Media Group
01325-381313
Darlington Advertiser wf
Newsquest Media Group
01325-381313
Darlington & N Yorks Herald wf
Trinity Mirror
01642-245401
Darlington & Stockton Times w
Newsquest Media Group
01325-381313
Durham Advertiser wf
Newsquest Media Group
01325-381313
Darlington, Aycliffe & Sedgfield
Advertiser wf
Newsquest Media Group
01325-381313
(Darlington) Northern Echo d
Newsquest Media Group
01325-381313
Hartlepool Mail d
Portsmouth & Sunderland Newspapers
01429-274441
Hartlepool Star wf
Portsmouth & Sunderland Newspapers
0191-417 0050
Peterlee Star wf
Portsmouth & Sunderland Newspapers
0191-417 0050

South Durham Herald wf
Trinity Mirror
01642-245401
Teesdale Mercury w
Teesdale Mercury
01833-637140
Wear Valley Advertiser wf
Newsquest Media Group
01325-381313

ESSEX
(Basildon) Evening Echo d
Newsquest Media Group
01268-522792
Basildon Standard Recorder wf
Newsquest Media Group
01268-522792
Basildon Yellow Advertiser wf
United Provincial Newspapers
01268-522722
Braintree & Witham Times w
Newsquest Media Group
01206-761212
Braintree & Witham Yellow Ad wf
United Provincial Newspapers
01268-522722
Brentwood Gazette w
Northcliffe Newspapers Group
01277-219222
Brentwood Weekly News wf
Newsquest Media Group
01206-761212
Castlepoint Yellow Advertiser wf
United Provincial Newspapers
01268-522722
Castlepoint Recorder wf
Newsquest Media Group
01268-522792
Chelmsford Weekly News wf
Newsquest Media Group
01206-761212
Chelmsford Yellow Advertiser wf
United Provincial Newspapers
01268-522722
Clacton Coastal Express wf
Newsquest Media Group
01206-761212
Clacton & Frinton Gazette w
Newsquest Media Group
01206-761212
Colchester Evening Gazette d
Newsquest Media Group
01206-761212
Colchester Express wf
Newsquest Media Group
01206-761212
Colchester Yellow Adv wf
United Provincial Newspapers
01268-522722

Dunmow Broadcast wf
Eastern Counties Newspapers
01371-874537
Epping Forest Herald wf
Eastern Counties Newspapers
020-8478 4444
Epping Forest Independent wf
Newsquest Media Group
020-8531 4141
Epping Forest Recorder wf
Eastern Counties Newspapers
020-8478 4444
Epping, Ongar & District Gazette w
Newsquest
020-8531 4141
Epping Yellow Advertiser wf
United Provincial Newspapers
01268-522722
Essex Chronicle w
Northcliffe Newspapers Group
01245-60700
Essex County Standard w
Newsquest Media Group
01206-761212
Essex Weekly News wf
Newsquest Media Group
01206-761212
Frinton & Walton Gazette w
Newsquest
01206-761212
Grays Herald wf
Eastern Counties Newspapers
01708-766044
Halstead Gazette&Advertiser w
Newsquest Media Group
01206-761212
Harlow & Epping Herald wf
Eastern Counties Newspapers
01727-846866
Harlow Citizen wf
Newsquest Media Group
020-8531 4141
Harlow/Epping Star wf
Yattendon Investment Trust
01992-586401
Harwich Standard w
Newsquest Media Group
01206-761212
Loughton, Chigwell Gazette w
Newsquest
020-8531 4141
Maldon Standard w
Newsquest Media Group
01206-761212
Rayleigh Recorder wf
Newsquest Media Group
01268-522792
Rayleigh Times Group wf
Leigh Times Co
01702-77666

d=daily, w=weekly, s=sunday, f=free

ESSEX CONTD.

Redbridge Guardian w
Newsquest Media Group
020-8531 4141
Saffron Walden Observer wf
Yattendon Investment Trust
01992-586401
Saffron Walden Reporter wf
Eastern Counties Newspapers
01799-525100
Saffron Walden Weekly News wf
Yattendon Investment Trust
01223-434434
Southend on Sunday w
Leigh Times
01702-77666
Southend Standard Recorder wf
Newsquest Media Group
01268-522792
Southend Yellow Advertiser wf
United Provincial Newspapers
01268-522722
Thurrock Gazette wf
Newsquest Media Group
01268-522792
Thurrock & Lakeside Recorder wf
Eastern Counties Newspapers
01708-766044
Thurrock, Lakeside, Grays Post w
Independent Newspapers
020-8517 5577
Thurrock Yellow Advertiser wf
United Provincial Newspapers
01268-522722
Walden Local wf
Local Publications
01799-516161
Waltham Abbey Gazette w
Newsquest Media Group
020-8531 4141

GLOUCESTERSHIRE

Berkeley & Sharpness Gazette w
Southern Newspapers
01453-544000
Cheltenham News wf
Northcliffe Newspapers
01242-271900
Dursley County Independent wf
Southern Newspapers
01453-544000
Forest of Dean Review wf
Tindle Newspapers
01594-841113
The Forester w
Forest of Dean Newspapers
01594-822126

Gloucester News wf
Northcliffe Newspapers Group
01452-419791
Gloucestershire Citizen d
Northcliffe Newspapers Group
01452-424442
Gloucestershire County Gazette w
Southern Newspapers
01453-544000
Gloucestershire Echo d
Northcliffe Newspapers Group
01242-271900
Stroud News & Journal w
Southern Newspapers
01453-544000
Tewkesbury Admag wf
Newsquest Media Group
01386-446544
Wilts & Gloucester Standard w
Southern Newspapers
01285-642642

HAMPSHIRE

Aldershot Courier series wf
Guardian Media Group
01252-328221
Aldershot Mail w
Guardian Media Group
01252-328221
Aldershot News series w
Guardian Media Group
01252-328221
Alton Gazette w
Tindle Newspapers
01420-84446
Alton Herald w
Farnham Castle Newspapers
01252-725224
Alton Times & Mail wf
Tindle Newspapers
01252-716444
Andover Advertiser w
Southern Newspapers
01264-323456
Andover Advertiser Midweek w
Southern Newspapers
01264-323456
Arlesford & District Times wf
Gazette Newspapers
01256-461131
Avon Advertiser (Hants/Dorset) w
Southern Newspapers
01722-337466
Basingstoke & N Hants Gaz. w
Southern Newspapers
01256-461131

Bordon Herald w
Farnham Castle Newspapers
01252-725224
Bordon Times & Mail wf
Tindle Newspapers
01252-716444
Eastleigh & S Hants News w
Hampshire Chronicle Group
01962-841772
Eastleigh Gazette Extra wf
Southern Newspapers
01256-461131
Fareham & Gosport Journal wf
Portsmouth & Sunderland Newspapers
023-9266 4488
Farnborough Courier wf
Aldershot News
01252-328221
Farnborough Mail w
Aldershot News
01252-328221
Farnborough News w
Aldershot News
01252-328221
Fleet & District Courier wf
Aldershot News
01252-328221
Fleet Mail w
Aldershot News
01252-328221
Fleet News w
Aldershot News
01252-328221
The Forest Journal w
Salisbury Journal Newspapers
01722-412525
Hampshire Chronicle w
Jacob & Johnston
01962-841772
Hart Courier Series wf
Guardian Media Group
01252-328221
Havant Journal wf
Portsmouth &Sunderland Newspapers
023-9266 4488
Liphook Times & Mail wf
Tindle Newspapers
01252-716444
Lymington Times w
Advertiser & Times
01425-613384
New Forest Post wf
Southern Newspapers
01590-671122
New Milton Advertiser w
Advertiser & Times
01425-613384

Petersfield Herald w
Farnham Castle Newspapers
01252-725224
Petersfield Mail wf
Tindle Newspapers
01252-716444
Petersfield & Bordon Post w
Portsmouth & Sunderland Newspapers
01730-268021
(Portsmouth) The News d
Portsmouth & Sunderland Newspapers
023-9266 4488
Portsmouth/Southsea Journal wf
Portsmouth & Sunderland Newspapers
023-9266 4488
Romsey Advertiser w
Portsmouth & Sunderland Newspapers
01962-841772
Solent Advertiser wf
Southern Newspapers
01329-280752
Southampton Advertiser wf
Southern Newspapers
023-8042 4920
Southern Daily Echo d
Southern Newspapers
023-8042 4920
Surrey & Hants Star wf
Star Newspapers (Camberley)
01252-316311
Winchester Gazette Extra wf
Southern Newspapers
01256-461131
Yately & District Courier wf
Aldershot News
01252-328221
Yately Mail
01252-322121

HEREFORDSHIRE

Hereford & Leominster Jouranl wf
Midland News Association
01432-355353
Hereford Admag wf
Adscene Group
01432-351544
Hereford Times w
Newsquest Media Group
01432-274413
Ross Gazette w
Ross Gazette
01989-768023

HERTFORDSHIRE

Bishops Stortford Citizen wf
Newsquest Media Group
020-8531 4141
Borehamwood Times wf
Newsquest Media Group
01923-242211
Cheshunt & Waltham Telegraph w
North London & Herts Newspapers
020-8367 2345
Dacorum Independent w
01442-264464
Harpenden Advertiser wf
Eastern Counties Newspapers
01727-811555
Hemel Hempstead Express wf
Johnston Press
01442-213211
Hemel Hempstead Gazette w
Johnston Press
01442-213211
Herts & Essex Observer w
Yattendon Investment Trust
01992-586401
Herts Mercury w
Yattendon Investment Trust
01992-586401
Herts Star wf
Yattendon Investment Trust
01992-586401
Herts Advertiser wf
Eastern Counties Newspapers
01727-811555
Lea Valley Star wf
Yattendon Investment Trust
01992-586401
North London Review w
Review & Advertiser Newspaper Group
020-8953 9119
Potters Bar & Cuffley Press wf
Southnews
020-8367 2345
Potters Bar Times wf
Newsquest Media Group
01923-242211
Royston & Buntingford Crow w
Eastern Counties Newspapers
01763-245241
Royston Weekly News wf
Yattendon Investment Trust
01223-434433
Saffron Walden Reporter wf
01763-245241

St Albans & Harpenden Observer wf
Newsquest Media Group
01923-242211
St Albans /Harpenden Review wf
Review Free Group Newspapers
01727-834411
Star Classified
01992-586401
Stevenage Comet wf
Eastern Counties Newspapers
01462-422280
Stevenage/Letchworth Herald wf
Eastern Counties Newspapers
01462-42280
Watford Free Observer wf
Newsquest Media Group
01923-242211
Welwyn & Hatfield Herald wf
Eastern Counties Newspapers
01707-327551
Welwyn & Hatfield Times w
Eastern Counties Newspapers
01707-327551
Welwyn Garden Review wf
Review Free Group Newspapers
01727-834411
West Herts & Watford Observer w
Newsquest Media Group
01923-242211

ISLE OF MAN

Isle of Man Courier wf
Johnston Press
01624-623451
Isle of Man Examiner w
Johnston Press
01624-623451
Manx Independent w
Johnston Press
01624-623451

ISLE OF WIGHT

Isle of Wight County Press w
Isle of Wight County Press
01983-521333

KENT

Ashford & Tenterden Adscene wf
Adscene Group
01227-767321
Ashford Extra wf
Kent Messenger
01622-717880
Canterbury Adscene wf
Adscene Group
01227-767321
Canterbury Extra wf
Kent Messenger
01622-717880
County Border News wf
Tindle Newspapers
01959-564766
Dartford/Swanley Informer wf
Local Publications
01322-220791
Dartford Leaderwf
Fletcher Newspapers
01474-363363
Dartford Times w
Fletcher Newspapers
01474-363363
Dartford News Shopper wf
01689 836211
Dover/Deal/Sandwich Adscene wf
Adscene Group
01227-767321
Dover Express w
Adscene Group
01304-240660
Dover Mercury w
01622-717880
East Kent Gazette w
Adscene Group
01795-475411
East Kent Mercury w
Kent Messenger
01622-717880
Edenbridge Chronicle wf
Chronicle Newspapers
01732-865455
Faversham News w
Kent Messenger
01622-717880
Faversham Times w
Adscene Group
01795-536555
Folkestone & Hythe Adscene wf
Adscene Group
01227-767321

Folkestone Extra wf
Kent Messenger
01622-717880
Folkestone Herald w
Adscene Group
01303-850999
Gravesend & Dartford Extra wf
Kent Messenger
01622-717880
Gravesend Leader wf
Fletcher Newspapers
01474-363363
Gravesend Messenger
01622-717880
Gravesend Reporter w
Fletcher Newspapers
01474-363363
Herne Bay Gazette w
Kent Messenger
01622-717880
Herne Bay Times w
Adscene Group
01227-771515
Hythe Herald w
Adscene Kent Newspapers
01303-850999
Isle of Thanet Gazette w
Adscene Group
01843-221313
Kent & Sussex Courier w
Northcliffe Newspapers Group
01892-526262
Kent Messenger w
Kent Messenger
01622-717880
Kent Today d
Kent Messenger
01622-717880
Kentish Express w
Kent Messenger
01622-717880
Kentish Gazette w
Kent Messenger
01622-717880
Maidstone Adscene wf
Adscene Group
01227-76321
Maidstone Extra wf
Kent Messenger
01622-717880
Maidstone Star wf
Southern Newspapers
01622-678556
Medway & Disrict Adscene wf
Adscene Group
01227-767321
Medway Extra wf
Kent Messenger
01622-717880

Medway News w
Adscene Group
01634-841741
Medway Standard w
Adscene Group
01634-841741
Romney Marsh Herald w
Adscene Kent Newspapers
01303-850999
Sevenoaks Chronicle w
Northcliffe Newspapers Group
01892-526262
Sevenoaks Focus wf
Northcliffe Newspapers Group
01892-526262
Sevenoaks & Tonbridge Leader wf
Fletcher Newspapers
01474-363363
Sheerness Times Guardian w
Kent Messenger
01622-717880
Sheppey Gazette w
Adscene Group
01795-475411
Sittingbourne Extra wf
Kent Messenger
01622-717880
Swanley Times w
011474 363363
Thanet Adscene wf
Adscene Group
01227-767321
Thanet Extra wf
Kent Messenger
01622-717880
Thanet Times w
Adscene Group
01843-221313
Tonbridge & District Friday-Ad wf
Friday Ad Group
01825-766000
Tunbridge Wells Adscene wf
Adscene Group
01227-767321
Tunbridge Wells Extra wf
Kent Messenger
01622-717880
(Tunbridge Wells) News in Focus wf
Northcliffe Newspapers Group
01892-526262
Tunbridge Wells Friday-Ad wf
Friday Ad Group
01825-766000
Tunbridge Wells Leader wf
Fletcher Newspapers
01474-363363
Wealden Advertiser wf
01580-753235
Whitstable Gazette w
Kent Messenger Group
01622-717880

LANCASHIRE

Accrington Observer w
Guardian Media Group
01706-354321
Blackburn Citizen wf
Newsquest Media Group
01254-678678
Blackpool Citizen wf
Newsquest Media Group
01253-729081
(Blackpool) The Gazette d
United Provincial Newspapers
01253-400888
Burnley Citizen wf
Newsquest Media Group
01282-452138
Burnley Express & News w
United Provincial Newspapers
01282-426161
Chorley Citizen
Newsquest Media Group
01257-269011
Chorley Guardian w
United Provincial Newspapers
01257-264911
Clitheroe Advertiser & Times w
United Provincial Newspapers
01282-426161
Fleetwood Weekly News w
Tindle Newspapers
01253-772950
Fylde Extra wf
United Provincial Newspapers
01253-400888
Garstang Courier w
United Provincial Newspapers
01995-602494
The Garstang Guardian w
Lancaster & Morcambe Newspapers
01524-833111
Hyndburn Express wf
Guardian Media Group
01706-354321
Lancashire Evening Telegraph d
Newsquest Media Group
01254-678678
Lancashire Evening Post d
United Provincial Newspapers
01772-254841
Lancaster/Morecambe Citizen wf
Newsquest Media Group
01524-382121
Lancaster Guardian w
United Provincial Newspapers
01524-833111
Leyland Guardian
The Chorley Guardian
01257-264911
Longridge News w
United Provincial Newspapers
01772-783265

Lytham St Annes Express w
United Provincial Newspapers
01253-400888
The Morecambe Guardian w
Lancaster & Morcambe Newspapers
01524-833111
(Morecambe) The Visitor w
United Provincial Newspapers
01524-833111
Nelson Leader Series w
United Provincial Newspapers
01282-426161
Ormskirk Advertiser w
United Provincial Newspapers
01695-572501
Ormskirk Visiter wf
Trinity Mirror
01704-536655
Preston Weekly Mail wf
United Provincial Newspapers
01257-254841
Preston Citizen wf
Newsquest Media Group
01772-824631
Rossendale Express wf
Guardian Media Group
01706-354321
Rossendale Free Press w
Guardian Media Group
01706-354321
Skelmersdale Advertiser w
Ormskirk Advertiser
01695-572501
Thornton Cleveleys News w
Tindle Newspapers
01253-772950
Todmorden News & Advertiser w
01422 260200

LEICESTERSHIRE

Ashby & Coalville Mail wf
Northcliffe Newspapers Group
0116-222 4600
Ashby Times w
Trident Midland Newspapers
01530-813101
Coalville/Ashby Echo wf
Echo Press
01509-232632
Coalville Leader wf
01530-813101
Coalville Times w
Trident Midland Newspapers
01530-813101
Grantham &Melton Trader News wf
01476 574433
Harborough Mail w
Adscene Group
01858-462626

Hinckley Herald & Journal wf
Midland Independent Newspapers
01455-891981
Hinckley Times w
Hinckley Times
01455-238383
Leicester Journal w
Journal Publishing Co
0116-233 3633
Leicester Mail wf
Northcliffe Newspapers Group
0116-222 4600
Leicester Mercury d
Northcliffe Newspapers Group
0116-251 2512
Long Eaton Advertiser w
Echo Press
01509-232632
Long Eaton Trader wf
Midland Independent Newspapers
0115-948 1200
Loughborough Echo w
Echo Press
01509-232632
Loughborough Echo Extra wf
Echo Press
01509-232632
Loughborough Herald & Post wf
Midland Independent Newspapers
0116-247 1000
Loughborough Mail wf
Northcliffe Newspapers Group
0116-222 4600
Market Harborough Herald wf
Midland Independent Newspapers
01604-614600
Melton Citizen wf
Johnston Press
01664-66666
Melton Times w
Adscene Group
01664-66666
NW Leicestershire Leader wf
Trident Midland Newspapers
01530-813101
Nu News w
Echo Press
01509-232632
Oadby & Wigston Mail wf
Northcliffe Newspapers Group
0116-222 4600
Rutland Times w
New Rutland Times
01572-757722
Shepshed Echo w
Echo Press
01509-232632

d=daily, w=weekly, s=sunday, f=free

LINCOLNSHIRE

Alford Standard w
Lincolnshire Standard Group
01205-311433
Boston Standard w
Adscene Group
01205-311433
Boston Target wf
Northcliffe Newspapers Group
01205-356262
Bourne Local w
Local Publications (Bourne)
01778-425876
Gainsborough Standard w
Adscene Group
01205-311433
Gainsborough Target wf
Northcliffe Newspapers Group
01427-810148
Gainsborough Trader News w
Adscene Group
01205-311433
Grantham & Melton Trader wf
Adscene Group
01909-483333
Grantham Citizen wf
Adscene Group
01476-562291
Grantham Journal w
Adscene Group
01476-562291
Grimsby Evening Telegraph d
01472 360360
Grimsby Target wf
01472 360360
Horncastle News w
Mortons of Horncastle
01507-526868
Horncastle Standard Series w
Adscene Group
01205 311433
Horncastle Target wf
Lincolnshire Publishing Co
01205-356262
Lincoln Chronicle w
Lincolnshire Standard Group
01205-311433
Lincolnshire Standard w
Lincolnshire Standard Group
01205-311433
Lincoln Target wf
Northcliffe Newspapers Group
01522-525252
Lincolnshire Evening Echo d
Northcliffe Newspapers Group
01522-525252
Lincolnshire Free Press w
Adscene Group
01775-725021
Louth Leader w
Mortons of Horncastle
01507-523456

Louth Standard w
Adscene Group
01205-311433
Louth Target wf
Northcliffe Newspapers Group
01205-356262
Mablethorpe & Sutton Leader w
Mortons of Horncastle
01507-523456
Mablethorpe & Sutton Standard s
Lincolnshire Standard Group
01205-311433
Market Rasen Mail w
Mortons of Horncastle
01673-844644
Rutland & Stamford Mercury w
Adscene Group
01780-762255
Scunthorpe Evening Telegraph d
Northcliffe Newspapers Group
01724-273273
Scunthorpe Target wf
Northcliffe Newspapers Group
01724-272273
Scunthorpe Trader News wf
Adscene Group
01205-311433
Skegness News w
Mortons of Horncastle
01507-523456
Skegness Standard w
Adscene Group
01205-311433
Skegness Target wf
Lincolnshire Standard Group
01205 356202
Sleaford Herald & Express wf
Newark Advertiser
01636-643456
Sleaford Standard w
Adscene Group
01205-311433
Scunthorpe Trader News wf
Lincolnshire Standard Group
01205-311433
Spalding Guardian w
Adscene Group
01775-725021
Spilsby Standard w
Lincolnshire Standard Group
01205-311433
Spilsby Target wf
Lincolnshire Publishing Co
01205-356262
Stamford Herald wf
Midland Independent Newspapers
01775-713723
Stamford Citizen wf
Adscene Group
01780-762255
Woodhall Spa Target wf
Lincolnshire Publishing Co
01205-356262

LIVERPOOL AREA

Anfield & Walton Star wf
Trinity Mirror
0151-236 4422
Bebington News wf
Trinity Mirror
0151-647 7111
Birkenhead News wf
Trinity Mirror
0151-647 7111
Bootle Times wf
Trinity Mirror
0151-236 4422
Crosby Herald w
Trinity Mirror
0151-236 4422
Formby Times w
Trinity Mirror
0151-236 4422
Heswall News wf
Trinity Mirror
0151-647 7111
Hoylake/West Kirkby News wf
Trinity Mirror
0151-647 7111
Huyton & Raby Star wf
Trinity Mirror
0151-236 4422
(Liverpool) Daily Post d
Trinity Mirror
0151-227 2000
Liverpool Echo d
Trinity Mirror
0151-227 2000
Maghull Star wf
Trinity Mirror
0151-236 4422
Neston News wf
Trinity Mirror
0151-647 7111
Newton & Golborne Guardian w
Newsquest Media Group
01925-633033
Prescot Reporter wf
Regional Independent Media
01942-228000
Skelmersdale Champion wf
Champion Newspapers
01704-531302
South Liverpool Merseymart wf
Trinity Mirror
0151-236 4422
Southport Champion wf
Champion Newspapers
01704-531302
(Southport) Midweek Visiter wf
Trinity Mirror
0151-236 4422
Southport Visiter wf
Trinity Mirror
0151-236 4422

St Helens Reporter wf
Regional Independent Media
01942-228000
St Helens Star wf
Newsquest Media Group
01744-611861
Wallasey News wf
Trinity Mirror
0151-236 7320
West Derby Merseymart wf
Trinity Mirror
0151-236 4422
Wirral Globe wf
Newsquest Media Group
0151-666 2222

LONDON - NORTH

Barking & Dagenham Advertiser wf
United Provincial Newspapers
01268-522722
Barking & Dagenham Express wf
Independent Newspapers
020-8517 5577
Barking & Dagenham Post w
Independent Newspapers
020-8517 5577
Barking & Dagenham Recorder wf
South Essex Recorders
020-8478 4444
Barnet & Finchley Press wf
Southnews
020-8367 2345
Barnet Advertiser wf
United Provincial Newspapers
020-8449 5577
Barnet Borough Times wf
Newsquest Media Group
020-8441 7400
Brent & London Recorder wf
Tindle Newspapers
020-8450 5272
Brent Leader wf
Tindle Newspapers
020-8364 4040
Brentwood Recorder w
South Essex Recorders
01708-766044
Camden New Journal wf
New Journal Enterprises
020-7482 1960
Camden/St Pancras Chronicle w
Independent Newpapers
020-8340 6868
Central London Review & Adv
Review & Advertiser Group
020-8953 9119
Chelsea News w
Adscene Group
020-8741 1622
Chingford Guardian w
Newsquest Media Group
020-8531 4141

City of London Times w
City of London & Dockland Times
020-7628 2841
City Post w
Adscene Group
020-8741 1622
City of London Recorder w
Eastern Counties Newspapers
(Holdings)
020-8478 4444
City of Westminster Post wf
Adscene Group
020-8741 1622
Docklands Express wf
Independent Newspapers
020-7790 8822
Docklands Recorder w
South Essex Recorders
020-8472 1421
Ealing & Acton Gazette w
Southnews
020-8424 0044
Ealing & London Recorder wf
Tindle Newspapers
020-8568 1313
Ealing & Southall Informer wf
United Provincial Newspapers
01784-433773
Ealing Leader wf
Southnews
020-8367 2345
East London Advertiser w
Independent Newspapers
020-7790 8822
Edgware & Mill Hill Times wf
Newsquest Media Group
020-8952 5217
Enfield Advertiser wf
United Provincial Newspapers
020-8367 2345
Enfield Express wf
Southnews
020-8367 2345
Enfield Gazette series w
Southnews
020-8367 2345
Enfield Independent wf
Newsquest Media Group
020-8531 4141
Evening Standard d
Associated Newspapers
020-7938 6000
Finchley & Hendon Advertisers
United Provincial Newspapers
020-8449 5577
Fulham Chronicle w
Adscene Group
020-8741 1622
Greenford & Northolt Gazette w
Middlesex County Press
020-8579 3131

Hackney Echo wf
Newsquest Media Group
020-7790 8822
Hackney Gazette w
Independent Newspapers (UK)
020-7254 6311
Hammersmith Chronicle w
Adscene Group
020-8741 1622
Hammersmith/Fulham Post wf
Adscene Group
020-8741 1622
Hammersmith Guardian wf
Tindle Newspapers
020-8568 1313
Hammersmith/Fulham Times wf
Southnews
020-7381 6262
Hampstead & Highgate Express
Home Counties Newspaper Holdings
020-7433 0000
Harefield Gazette w
Middlesex County Press
020-7381 6262
Haringey Advertiser wf
United Provincial Newspapers
020-8367 2345
Haringey Independent wf
Newsquest Media Group
020-8531 4141
Haringey Weekly Herald wf
Independent Newspapers (UK)
020-8340 6868
Harrow Independent wf
Southnews
020-8424 0044
Harrow Informer wf
United Provincial Newspapers
01784-433773
Harrow Leader wf
Southnews
020-8427 4404
Harrow Observer w
Southnews
020-8427 4404
Harrow Recorder wf
Tindle Newspapers
020-8568 1313
Hayes & Harlington Gazette w
Middlesex County Press
020-7381 6262
Hendon & Finchley Times wf
Newsquest Media Group
020-8203 0411
Highbury and Islington Express w
020-7433 0000
Hornsey Journal w
Independent Newspapers (UK)
020-8340 6868

d=daily, w=weekly, s=sunday, f=free

LONDON - NORTH CONTD.

Hounslow Borough Chronicle w
Southnews
020-8424 0044
Hounslow/Chiswick Informer wf
United Provincial Newspapers
020-8943 5171
Hounslow Feltham Times w
Dimbleby & Sons
020-8940 6030
Hounslow & Isleworth Leader wf
Southnews
020-8424 0044
Hounslow Recorder wf
Tindle Newspapers
020-8568 0022
Ilford Herald wf
Eastern Counties Newspapers
01708-766044
Ilford Recorder w
Eastern Counties Newspapers
020-8478 4444
Ilford & Redbridge Post wf
Independent Newspapers
020-8517 5577
Ilford Yellow Advertiser
United Provincial Newspapers
01268-522722
Islington Chronicle wf
Independent Newspapers
020-8340 6868
Islington Gazette w
Independent Newspapers
020-8340 6868
Kensington & Chelsea Mail w
Middlesex County Press
020-7381 6262
Kensington & Chelsea Post wf
Adscene Group
020-8741 1622
Kensington & Chelsea Independent
wf
020-8752 0052
Kensington News w
Adscene Group
020-8741 1622
Kilburn & Brent Advertiser w
Independent Newspapers
020-8450 5272
Kilburn Times w
Independent Newspapers
020-8450 5272
Leyton Guardian w
Newsquest Media Group
020-8531 4141
London Weekly Times wf
Southnews
020-8381 6886
London West End Extra w
New Journal Enterprises
020-7482 1960

Marylebone Mercury w
Adscene Group
020-8741 1622
Notting Hill & Bayswater Independent
w
020-8752 0052
Paddington Mercury w
Adscene Group
020-8741 1622
Paddington Times w
Independent Newspapers
020-8450 5272
Putney Chronicle w
Adscene Group
020-8741 1622
Redbridge Guardian & West
  Essex Gazette w
Newsquest Media Group
020-8531 4141
Romford & Havering Post wf
Independent Newspapers
020-8517 5577
Romford Advertiser wf
United Provinicial Newspapers
01268-522722
Romford Recorder w
Home Counties Newspaper Holdings
01708-766044
Ruislip Informer wf
United Southern Publications
01784-433773
Ruislip Recorder wf
Tindle Newspapers
020-8568 1313
Southall Gazette w
Middlesex County Press
020-7381 6262
Stanmore Observer w
Middlesex County Press
020-7381 6262
Stratford & Newham Express wf
Independent Newspapers (UK)
020-7790 8822
Tottenham & Wood Green Journal w
Independent Newspapers
020-8340 6868
Uxbridge & Hillingdon Leader wf
Southnews
020-8367 2345
Uxbridge Gazette w
Southnews
01859-233133
Uxbridge Informer wf
United Provinicial Newspapers
01784-433773
Uxbridge & London Recorder wf
Independent Newspapers (UK)
020-8568 1313
Victoria & Pimlico Times wf
Southnews
020-8381 6886

Waltham Forest Guardian w
Newsquest Media Group
020-8531 4141
Waltham Forest Independent wf
Newsquest Media Group
020-8531 4141
Walthamstow Guardian w
Newsquest
0120-8531 4141
Wembley & Brent Times w
Independent Newspapers (UK)
020-8450 5272
Wembley & Kenton Recorder wf
Tindle Newspapers
020-8568 0022
Wembley & Kingsbury Leader wf
Middlesex County Press
020-7381 6262
Westminster Mail w
Middlesex County Press
020-7381 6262
Westminster & Pimlico News
Southnews
020-8741 1622
Willesden & Brent Chronicle w
Independent Newspapers (UK)
020-8450 5272
Wood Green Herald w
Independent Newspapers
020-8340 6868

LONDON - SOUTH

Barnes, Mortlake Times w
Dimbleby & Sons
020-8940 6030
Battersea News w
Dimbleby & Sons
020-88744226
Bexley Borough Mercury wf
Trinity Mirror
020-8769 4444
Bexley Leader wf
Fletcher Newspapers
020-8301 6663
Bexley News Shopper series wf
Newsquest Media Group
01689-836211
Bexleyheath Mercury wf
Newsquest Media Group
020-8692 1122
Bexleyheath/Welling Times w
Fletcher Newspapers
01474-363363
Biggin Hill News wf
Tindle Newspapers
01959-564766
Brentford, Chiswick Times
Dimbleby & Sons
020-8940 6030
Bromley, Beckenham Times w
Fletcher Newspapers
01474-363363

Bromley News wf
Tindle Newspapers
01959-564766
Bromley Leader wf
Fletcher Newspapers
01474 363363
Bromley News Shopper wf
Newsquest Media Group
01689-836211
Chislehurst Times w
Kentish Times Newspapers
01474-363363
Croydon Advertiser series w
Southnews
020-8668 4111
Croydon Guardian wf
Newsquest Media Group
020-8646 4300
Croydon Post wf
Southnews
020-8668 4111
Eltham & Greenwich Times w
Kentish Times Newspapers
01474-363363
Erith & Crayford Times
Kentish Times Newspapers
01474-363363
Greenwich Borough Mercury wf
Trinity Mirror
020-8769 4444
Kingston Guardian series wf
Newsquest Media Group
020-8646 6336
Kingston Informer wf
United Provincial Newspapers
020-8943 5171
Kingston, Surbiton Malden Times w
Dimbleby & Sons
020-8874 4226
Lewisham & Catford News wf
Trinity Mirror
020-8769 4444
Lewisham Mercury wf
Newsquest Media Group
020-8769 4444
Lewisham News Shopper wf
Newsquest Media Group
01689-836211
Newham Recorder w
Eastern Counties Newspapers
020-8472 1421
Newham Yellow Advertiser wf
United Provincial Newspapers
01268-522722
Orpington & Petts Wood Times
Kentish Times Newspapers
01474-363363
Putney & Wimbledon Times w
Dimbleby & Sons
020-8940 6030

Richmond Informer wf
United Provinicial Newspapers
020-8943 5171
Richmond/Twickenham Guardian wf
South London Guardian
020-8646 6336
Richmond/Twickenham Times w
Dimbleby & Sons
020-8940 6030
Sidcup & Bexley Mercury wf
Newsquest Media Group
020-8692 1122
Sidcup & Blackfen Times w
Kentish Times Newspapers
01474-363363
South London Press w
Trinity Mirror
020-8769 4444
Southwark News w
Southwark News
020-7232 1639
Streatham Mercury wf
Trinity Mirror
020-8769 4444
Streatham Guardian wf
Newsquest Media Group
020-8646 4300
Surrey Comet w
Newsquest Media Group
020-8646 6336
Sutton & Cheam Herald w
Trinity Mirror
01737-732000
Sutton & Epsom Guardian wf
Newsquest Media Group
020-8646 6336
Teddington & Hampton Times
Dimbleby & Sons
020-8940 6030
Wandsworth/Putney Guardian wf
Newsquest Media Group
020-8646 6336
Wandsworth Borough News w
Dimbleby & Sons
020-8940 6030
Wimbledon Guardian wf
Newsquest Media Group
020-8646 6336
Woolwich/Charlton Mercury wf
Newsquest Media Group
020-8692 1122

MANCHESTER AREA
(Ashton) The Advertiser wf
Guardian Media Group
0161-339 7611
Blythe & Forsbrook Time w
01538-753162
Bolton Evening News d
Newsquest Media Group
01204-522345

Bolton Journal wf
Newsquest Media Group
01204-522345
Bury Journal/Messenger wf
Newsquest Media Group
0161-764 9421
Bury Times w
Newsquest Media Group
0161-764 9421
(Cheadle) District Advertiser wf
Guardian Media Group
0161-480 4491
Denton Reporter w
Regional Independent Media
0161-303 1910
Droylsden Reporter w
Regional Independent Media
0161-303 1910
East Manchester Reporter w
Regional Independent Media
0161-303 1910
Hale, Altrincham Courier w
Courier Group
01625-586140
Heywood Advertiser w
Guardian Media Group
01706-354321
High Peak Echo wf
Guardian Media Group
0161-339 8200
Leigh & Tyldesley Journal wf
Newsquest Media Group
01942-672241
Leigh Reporter/Golborne Star wf
Regional Independent Media
01942-228000
Manchester Evening News d
Guardian Media Group
0161-832 7200
Manchester Metro News wf
Guardian Media Group
0161-834 9677
Middleton Guardian w
Guardian Media Group
01706-354321
Middleton/Moston Express wf
Guardian Media Group
01706-354321
Mossley Reporter w
Regional Independent Media
0161-303 1910
North Cheshire Herald w
Ashton Weekly Newspapers
0161-303 1910
(Oldham) The Advertiser wf
Guardian Media Group
0161-626 3663
(Oldham) Evening Chronicle d
Hirst, Kidd & Rennie
0161-633 2121

d=daily, w=weekly, s=sunday, f=free

MANCHESTER CONTD.

(Oldham) Chronicle Weekend wf
Hirst, Kidd & Rennie
0161-633 2121
(Prestwich) The Advertiser wf
Guardian Media Group
0161-789 5015
Prestwich Guide w
Newsquest Media Group
0161-764 9421
Radcliffe Times w
Newsquest Media Group
0161-764 9421
Reddish Reporter wf
South Manchester Reporter
0161-442 2584
Rochdale/Heywood Express wf
Guardian Media Group
01706-354321
Rochdale Observer w
Guardian Media Group
01706-354321
Sale & Altrincham Messenger wf
Newsquest Media Group
0161-477 4600
Sale & District Courier w
Courier Group
01625-586140
Salford City Reporter wf
Guardian Media Group
0161-789 5015
South Manchester Express wf
Guardian Media Group
0161-480 4491
South Manchester Reporter wf
Mortons of Horncastle
0161-446 2212
Stalybridge Reporter w
United Provinicial Newspapers
0161-303 1910
(Stockport) Express Advertiser w
Guardian Media Group
0161-480 4491
Stockport Messenger wf
Newsquest Media Group
0161-477 4600
Stockport Times wf
Guardian Media Group
0161-480 4491
Stretford Messenger wf
Newsquest Media Group
0161-477 4600
Tameside Reporter w
United Provinicial Newspapers
0161-303 1910
Wigan Evening Post d
Regional Independent Media
01772 254841

Wigan Observer w
Regional Independent Media
01942-228000
Wigan Reporter wf
Regional Independent Media
01942-228000

NORFOLK

Dereham & Fakenham Times w
Eastern Counties Newspapers
01603-628311
Diss Express w
Johnston Press
01379 642264
Diss Mercury wf
Eastern Counties Newspapers
01603-628311
Great Yarmouth Advertiser wf
Anglia Advertiser
01493-601206
Great Yarmouth Mercury w
Eastern Counties Newspapers
01603-628311
Hunstanton,Citizen wf
Adscene Group
01533-761188
Lynn News w
Johnston Press
01553-761188
Norfolk Citizen wf
Johnston Press
01553-761188
North Norfolk News w
Eastern Counties Newspapers
01603-628311
Norwich Advertiser wf
Eastern Counties Newspapers
01603-740222
(Norwich) Eastern Daily Press d
Eastern Counties Newspapers
01603-628311
(Norwich) Evening News d
Eastern Counties Newspapers
01603-628311
Thetford & Watton Times wf
Eastern Counties Newspapers
01603-628311
Wymondham Mercury wf
Eastern Counties Newspapers
01603-628311

NORTHAMPTONSHIRE

Brackley & Towcester Advertiser w
Central Counties Newspapers
01280-813434
Corby & District Citizen wf
Johnston Press
01536-506100
Corby Advertiser
Johnston Press
01536 416777
Daventry Weekly Express w
Johnston Press
01327-703383
Kettering & Disrict Citizen wf
Johnston Press
01536-506100
Northamptonshire EveningTelegraph d
Johnston Press
01536-506100
Kettering Herald & Post wf
Midland Independent Newspapers
01604-614600
(Northampton) Chronicle & Echo d
Johnston Press
01604-231122
Northampton Mercury wf
01604-231122
Northants Herald & Post wf
Midland Independent Newspapers
01604-614600
Wellingborough Herald & Post wf
Midland Independent Newspapers
01604-614600
Wellingborough Citizen wf
Johnston Press
01536-506100

NORTHUMBERLAND

Berwick Advertiser w
Tweeddale Press Group
01289-306677
Berwick Gazette wf
Northeast Press
01289-308995
Hexham Courant w
CN Group
01434-602351
Morpeth Herald/Leader wf
Portsmouth & Sunderland Newspapers
01665-602234
News Post Leader w
Northeast Press
01670-517171
Northumberland Gazette w
Portsmouth & Sunderland Newspapers
01670-602234
Northumberland Herald wf
Trinity Mirror
01670-517362

NOTTINGHAMSHIRE

Ashfield Chad wf
Johnston Press
01623-26262
Eastwood Advertiser w
Johnston Press
01773-760444
Hucknell & Bulwell Dispatch w
Johnston Press
01623-456789
Mansfield Chad w
Johnston Press
01623-456789
Mansfield Recorder wf
Northcliffe Newspapers Group
0115-948 2000
Mansfield & Sutton Observer wf
North Notts Newspapers
01623-465555
Mansfield Weekly Post wf
Northcliffe Newspapers Group
0115-948 2000
Newark Advertiser ~Series w
Newark Advertiser Co
01636-681234
Newark Trader News wf
Adscene Group
01606-640650
Nottingham Evening Post d
Northcliffe Newspapers Group
0115-948 2000
Nottingham/Trent Valley Journal wf
Journal Publishing Co
0115-958 8387
(Nottingam) Recorder wf
Nottingham Post Group
0115-948 2000
Nottingham Weekly Post wf
Northcliffe Newspapers Group
0115-948 2000
Retford & Worksop Times w
Northcliffe Newspapers Group
01777-702275
Retford & Bawtry Guardian wf
Johnston Press
01777-704242
Retford & Bawtry Trader wf
01777-704099
Sandiacre and Stapleford News w
Adscene Group
0115-946 9909
(Worksop) Midweek Guardian wf
Johnston Press
01909-500500
Worksop Trader News wf
Adscene Group
01909-483333

OXFORDSHIRE

Abingdon Herald w
Oxford & County Newspapers
01865-244988
Banbury Cake wf
Bailey Group
01295-256111
Banbury Citizen wf
Johnston Press
01295-264321
Banbury Guardian w
Johnston Press
01295-264321
Bicester Advertiser w
Newsquest Media Group
01865-244988
Bicester Review wf
Johnston Press
01280-813434
Didcot Herald w
Oxford & County Newspapers
01865-244988
Henley Standard wf
Higgs and Co
01491-419400
Oxford Courier wf
Courier Newspapers (Oxford)
01235-553444
Oxford Guardian wf
Journal Pubishing Co
01926-888755
Oxford Journal wf
Courier Newspapers (Oxford)
01235-553444
Oxford Mail d
Newsquest Media Group
01865-244988
Oxford Star wf
Newsquest Media Group
01865-244988
Oxford Times w
Newsquest Media Group
01865-244988
South Oxfordshire Courier wf
Courier Newspapers (Oxford)
01235-553444
Wantage & Grove Herald w
Oxford & County Newspapers
01865-244988
Witney & W Oxon Gazette w
Newsquest Media Group
01865-244988

SHROPSHIRE

Bridgnorth Journal w
Midland News Association
01743-248248
Ludlow Advertiser w
Newsquest Media Group
01432-274413
Ludlow Journal wf
Midland News Association
01743-248248
Newport & Market Drayton Ad w
Midland News Association
01743-248248
Oswestry Advertiser w
North Wales Newspapers
01691-655321
Shrewsbury Admag wf
Adscene Group
01743-241414
Shrewsbury Chronicle w
Midland News Association
01743-248248
Shropshire Star d
Midland News Association
01743-248248
Telford Journal wf
Midland News Association
01743-248248
Whitchurch Herald w
Trinity Mirror
01244-340151

BATH & NE SOMERSET

Bath Chronicle d
Newsquest Media Group
01225-322322
Bath & District Advertiser wf
Southern Newspapers
01225 446800
Bath Oberserver wf
Newsquest Media Group
01225-322322

SOMERSET

Bridgwater Mercury w
Southern Newspapers
01823-725000
Bridgwater/Burnham Times wf
Bristol United Press
01749-672430
Burnham & Highbridge News w
Southern Newspapers
01823-725000
Chard & Ilminster News w
Southern Newspapers
01823-725000
Clevedon Mercury wf
01275-874248
Mid-Somerset Gazette w
Bristol United Press
01749-672430
Norton Radstock Advertiser wf
Southern Newspapers
01225-446800
Portishead Advertiser
01934 417921

d=daily, w=weekly, s=sunday, f=free

SOMERSET CONTD.

Sedgemoor Express & Star
Southern Newspapers
01823-725000
Somerset & Avon Guardian w
Newsquest Media Group
01225-322322
Somerset & Dorset News wf
Bristol Evening Post
01935-700500
Somerset County Gazette w
Southern Newspapers
01823-725000
Somerset Standard w
Bristol United Press
01225-322322
Taunton Express & Star
Southern Newspapers
01823-725000
(Taunton) Midweek Gazette wf
Southern Newspapers
01823-335361
Wellington Weekly News w
Northcliffe Newspapers Group
01823-664633
West Somerset Free Press w
Tindle Newspapers
01984-632731
West Somerset Trader wf
Tindle Newspapers
01984-632731
Western Gazette w
Bristol Evening Post
01935-700500
Weston & Somerset Mercury w
Southern Newspapers
01934-414010
Weston & Worle News wf
Bristol Evening Post
01275-874248
Weston-Super-Mare Admag wf
Southern Newspapers
01934-417921
Yeovil Express & Star wf
Southern Newspapers
01823-725000

STAFFORDSHIRE

Biddulph Chroicle w
Heads (Congleton)
01260-273737
Blythe & Forsbrook Times w
Cheadle & Tean Times
01538-753162
Brownhills Advertiser w
SC Publishing
01992-721234
Burntwood Mercury wf
Adscene Group
01543-414414
Burton Advertiser wf
Yattendon Investment Trust
01283-512345

Burton Daily Mail d
Yattendon Investment Trust
01283-512345
Burton Trader wf
Midland Independent Newspapers
024-7651 2000
Cannock Chase Chronicle wf
Midland News Association
01543-506311
Cannock Mercury wf
Adscene Group
01543-414414
Chase Post wf
Newsquest Media Group
01902-456776
Cheadle & Tean Times w
Cheadle & Tean Times
01538-399599
Cheadle & Post Times w
Hill Bros (Leek)
01538-750011
East Staffordshire Journal wf
Journal Publishing Co
01332-202532
Leek Post & Times w
Hill Bros (Leek)
01538-399599
Lichfield Chronicle wf
Midland News Association
01543-258604
Lichfield Mercury wf
Adscene Group
01543-414414
Lichfield Trader wf
Midland Independent Newspapers
01827-308000
North Staffs Advertiser wf
Northcliffe Newspapers Group
01782-271100
Rugeley Mercury w
Adscene Group
01543-414414
Stafford Chronicle wf
Midland News Association
01902-313131
Stafford Post wf
Newsquest Media Group
01902-875800
Staffordshire Newsletter w
Yattendon Investment Trust
01785-257700
(Stoke) Evening Sentinel d
Northcliffe Newspaper Group
01782-289800
Tamworth Herald wf
Adscene Group Co
01827-848586
Tamworth Post wf
Tamworth Herald
01827-848520
Uttoxeter Advertiser w
Yattendon Investment Trust
024-7651 2345

Uttoxeter Echo w
Cheadle & Tean Times
01889-562479
Uttoxeter Post & Times w
Hill Bros (Leek)
01538-399599

SUFFOLK

Beccles & Bungay Journal w
Eastern Counties Newspaper Group
01603-628311
Bury Citizen wf
Johnston Press
01284-768911
Bury Free Press w
Johnston Press
01284-768911
Bury St Edmunds Mercury wf
Eastern Counties Newspapers Group
01284-755661
East Suffolk Mercury
Eastern Counties Newspapers
01473-230023
(Ipswich) E Anglian Daily Times d
Eastern Counties Newspapers
01473-230023
(Ipswich) Evening Star d
Eastern Counties Newspapers
01473-230023
Haverhill Echo w
Adscene Group
01440-703456
Haverhill Weekly News wf
Yattendon Investment Trust
01223-434434
Ipswich Advertiser wf
Anglia Advertiser
01473-611363
Lowestoft Journal w
Eastern Counties Newspapers
01603-628311
Mid Suffolk Advertiser wf
Anglia Advertiser
01473-611363
Newmarket Journal w
Johnston Press
01638-668441
Newmarket Weekly News wf
Yattendon Investment Trust
01223-434434
Suffolk Advertiser wf
Anglia Advertiser
01473-611363
Suffolk Free Press w
Johnston Press
01787-375271
Waveney Advertiser wf
Anglia Advertiser
01493-601206
West Suffolk Mercury wf
Eastern Counties Newspapers Group
01284-702588

SURREY

Addlestone & Byfleet Review wf
Guardian Media Group
01483-769991
Ash Mail
Aldershot News
01252-328221
Banstead Herald
Surrey & South London Newspapers
01737-732000
Camberley & District Courier wf
Guardian Media Group
01252-328221
Camberley Mail w
Guardian Media Group
01252-328221
Camberley News w
Guardian Media Group
01252-328221
Caterham Mirror wf
Trinity Mirror
01737-732000
Chobham & Windlesham News w
Surrey Advertiser
01483-755755
Cobham News & Mail w
Surrey Advertiser
01372-463553
County Border Times & Mail wf
Tindle Newspapers
01252-716444
County Border News wf
01959 564766
Cranleigh Times wf
Guardian Media Group
01483-579244
Dorking Advertiser w
Trinity Mirror
01737-732000
Epsom/Banstead Informer w
Southnews
020-8943 5171
Epsom & Ewell Herald wf
Trinity Mirror
01737-732000
Farnham Herald w
Tindle Newspapers
01252-725224
Farnham Mail w
Aldershot News
01252-328221

Godalming Times wf
Guardian Media Group
01483-579244
Guildford Times wf
Guardian Media Group
01483-579244
Haslemere Herald w
01252 725224
(Haslemere) Messenger wf
PM Publications
01428-653999
Leatherhead Advertiser w
Trinity Mirror
01737-732000
Liphook Times wf
Tindle Newspapers
01252-716444
Molesey News w
Surrey Advertiser
01372-463553
Reigate & Banstead Ind. wf
Portsmouth & Sunderland Newspapers
01737-249372
Staines Informer wf
Southnews
01784-433773
Surrey & Hants News wf
Tindle Newspapers
01252-716444
Surrey Advertiser w
Guardian Media Group
01483-571234
Surrey Mirror w
Trinity Mirror
01737-732000
Walton & Hersham News & Mail w
Surrey Advertiser
01372-463553
Walton & Weybridge Informer wf
Southnews
020-8943 5171
Walton & Weybridge Leader wf
Southnews
01932-561111
Woking Informer wf
Southnews
01784-433773
Woking News & Mail w
Guardian Media Group
01483-755755
Woking Review wf
Guardian Media Group
01483-769991

EAST SUSSEX

Bexhill Adnews wf
Johnston Press
01424-854242
Bexhill Observer w
Johnston Press
01424-854242
(Brighton) Evening Argus d
Newsquest Media Group
01273-544544
Brighton & Hove Leader wf
Newsquest Media Group
01273-544544
Brighton Friday-Ad wf
Friday-Ad Group
01825-766000
Byfleet News and Mail w
Guardian Media Group
01483-755755
Eastbourne Advertiser wf
Johnston Press
01323-722091
Eastbourne Gazette w
Johnston Press
01323-722091
Eastbourne Herald w
Johnston Press
01323-722091
Hailsham Gazette w
Johnston Press
01323-722091
Hastings Observer w
Johnston Press
01424-854242
Hastings Friday-Ad wf
Friday-Ad Group
01825-766000
Hastings Ad News wf
Johnston Press
01424-854242
Horley and Gatwock Mirror w
Trinity Holdings
01737-732000
Rye & Battle Observer w
Johnston Press
01424-854242
Seaford Friday-Ad wf
Friday-Ad Group
01825-766000
Seaford Gazette w
Johnston Press
01323-722091
South Coast Leader wf
Newsquest Media Group
01273-544544
Sussex Express & Herald w
Johnston Press
01273-480601
Uckfield Friday-Ad wf
Friday Ad Group
01825-766000

d=daily, w=weekly, s=sunday, f=free

WEST SUSSEX

Bognor Chichester Journal wf
Portsmouth & Sunderland Newspapers
01243-534143
Bognor Regis Observer wf
Portsmouth &Sunderland Newspapers
01243-534143
Burgess Hill Leader wf
Newsquest Media Group
01273-54454
Crawley News
Trinity Mirror
01737-732000
Crawley News Extra
Trinity Mirror
01293-732000
Crawley Observer w
Johnston Press
01403-253371
Crawley Weekend Herald wf
Johnston Press
01293-562848
East Grinstead Courier w
Northcliffe Newspapers Group
01892-526262
East Grinstead Observer wf
Trinity Mirror
01737-732000
Haywards Heath Friday-Ad wf
Friday-Ad Group
01825-766000
Haywards Heath Leader wf
Newsquest Media Group
01273-544544
Horley Life wf
Horley Publishing
01293-409649
Horsham Advertiser wf
Johnston Press
01403-253371
Lancing Herald w
TR Beckett
01903-230051
Littlehampton Guardian wf
Johnston Press
01903-209025
Littlehampton Gazette w
Johnston Press
01903-714135
Mid-Sussex Citizen/Times
Johnston Press
01444-452201
Mid-Sussex Leader wf
Newsquest
01273-544544

Shoreham Herald w
Johnston Press
01903-230051
Steyning Herald w
TR Beckett
01903-230051
West Sussex County Times w
Johnston Press
01403-253371
West Sussex Gazette w
Portsmouth & Sunderland Newspapers
01243 533660
Worthing Advertiser wf
Johnston Press
01903-230051
Worthing Guardian wf
Johnston Press
01903-209025
Worthing Herald w
Johnston Press
01903-230051

TYNE & WEAR

Gateshead Post f
Trinity
0191-477 3245
Houghton Star wf
Portsmouth & Sunderland Newspapers
0191-417 0050
(Newcastle) Evening Chronicle d
Trinity PLC
0191-232 7500
(Newcastle) The Journal d
Trinity PLC
0191-232 7500
Newcastle Herald & Post wf
Trinity PLC
0191-477 3245
(Newcastle) Sunday Sun w
Trinity PLC
0191-232 7500
News Guardian w
Northeast Press
0191-251 8484
North Tyneside Herald & Post wf
Trinity
0191-477 3245
Seaham Star wf
Portsmouth & Sunderland Newspapers
0191-417 0050
(S Shields) The Gazette d
Portsmouth & Sunderland Newspapers
0191-455 4661
South Tyne Star wf
Portsmouth & Sunderland Newspapers
0191-417 0050

S Tyneside Herald & Post wf
Trinity PLC
0191-477 3245
Sunderland Echo d
Portsmouth & Sunderland Newspapers
0191-534 3011
Sunderland Star wf
Portsmouth & Sunderland Newspapers
0191-417 0050
Washington Star wf
Portsmouth & Sunderland Newspapers
0191-417 0050

WARWICKSHIRE

Atherstone Herald w
Tamworth Herald Co
01827-848586
Bedworth Echo w
Midland Independent Newspapers
024-7631 2785
Coleshill Herald w
Tamworth Herald Co
01827-848586
Kenilworth Weekly News w
Johnston Press
01926-888222
Leamington Review wf
Johnston Press
01926-888222
Leamington Spa Courier w
Johnston Press
01926-888222
Leamington Spa Observer wf
Herald Observer Newspapers
01926-451771
(Nuneaton) Heartland Evening News d
Nuneaton & Disrict Newspapers
024-7635 3534
Nuneaton Tribune wf
Midland Independent Newspapers
024-7635 1111
Rugby Advertiser w
Adscene Group
01788-535363
Rugby Observer wf
Herald Observer Newspapers
01926-451771
Rugby Review wf
Adscene Group
01788-535363
Stratford Gazette wf
Journal Publishing
01926-831338
Stratford Standard wf
Herald Observer Newspapers
01789-415717
Warwick Courier w
Central Counties Newspapers
01926-888222

WEST MIDLANDS

Aldridge Advertiser Weekly
01922-721234
(Birmingham) Evening Mail d
Midland Independent Newspapers
0121-236 3366
Birmingham Metronews wf
Midland Independent Newspapers
0121-234 5073
Birmingham News wf
Midland Independent Newspapers
0121-626 6600
The Birmingham Post d
Midland Independent Newspapers
0121-236 3366
(Birmingham) Sunday Mercury w
Midland Independent Newspapers
0121-236 3366
Bloxwich Advertiser w
SC Pubishing
01922-721234
Chase Post wf
Midland Independent Newspapers
01902-875800
County Chronicle wf
Midland News Association
01902-313131
Coventry & Warks. Journal wf
Journal Publishing Co
01926-450405
Coventry Citizen wf
Midland Independent Newspapers
024-7663 3633
Coventry Evening Telegraph d
Midland Independent Newspapers
024-7663 3633
Dudley Chronicle wf
Midland News Association
01384-355355
Dudley News wf
Newsquest Media Group
01384-239461
The Express & Star d
Midland News Association
01902-313131
Falcon Lodge Observer w
SC Publishing
0121-355 6901
Great Barr Chronicle wf
Midland News Association
0121-553 7171
Great Barr Observer wf
Adscene Group
0121-355 6901

Halesowen Chronicle wf
Midland News Association
01384-355355
Halesowen News wf
Newsquest Media Group
01384-442466
Little Aston Observer w
SC Publishing
0121-355 6901
Sandwell Chronicle wf
Midland News Association
0121-553 7171
Solihull Journal wf
Journal Publishing Co
0121-693 5750
Solihull News wf
Midland Independent Newspapers
0121-626 6600
Solihull Times wf
Midland Independent Newspapers
0121-711 4777
Stourbridge Chronicle wf
Midland News Association
01384-355355
Stourbridge News wf
Newsquest Media Group
01384-442466
Sutton Coldfield News wf
Midland Independent Newspapers
0121-626 6600
Sutton Coldfield Observer wf
Adscene Group
0121-355 6901
Vesey Observer w
SC Publishing
0121-355 6901
Walmley Observer
SC Publishing
0121-355 6901
Walsall Advertiser wf
SC Publishing
0121-355 6901
Walsall Chronicle wf
Midland News Association
01922-444444
Walsall Observer wf
Midland Independent Newspapers
0121-236 3366
News of Willenhall, Wednesbury wf
Midland Independent Newspapers
01902-875800
Wolverhampton Chronicle wf
Midland News Association
01902-313131

WILTSHIRE

Amesbury Journal w
Salisbury Journal Newspapers
01722-412525
Calne Gazette & Herald w
Newsquest Media Group
01793-528144
Chippenham Gazette & Herald w
Newsquest Media Group
01793-528144
Chippenham News w
Newsquest Media Group
01793-528144
Devizes Gazette & Herald w
Newsquest Media Group
01793-528144
Devizes News wf
Southern Newspapers
01380-729001
Devizes Star wf
Newsquest Media Group
01793-528144
Kennet Star wf
Newsquest Media Group
01793-528144
Malmesbury Gazette w
Newsquest Media Group
01793-528144
Marlborough Pewsey Gazette w
Newsquest Media Group
01793-528144
North & West Wilts Star wf
Newsquest Media Group
01793 528144
Salisbury Journal w
Southern Newspapers
01722-412525
Salisbury Times w
Southern Newspapers
01722-412525
Salisbury Advertiser wf
Southern Newspapers
01722-337466
(Swindon) Evening Advertiser d
Newsquest Media Group
01793-528144
Swindon Star wf
Newsquest Media Group
01793-528144
Trowbridge/Melksham Adv wf
Eastern Counties Newspapers Group
01225-760945

d=daily, w=weekly, s=sunday, f=free

WILTSHIRE CONTD.

Warminster Journal w
Coates & Parker
01225-760945
West Wiltshire Advertiser wf
Eastern Counties Newspapers
01225-760945
Westbury/Warminster Adv wf
Eastern Counties Newspapers Group
01225-760945
Wiltshire Gazette & Herald w
Newsquest Media Group
01793-528144
Wiltshire Star wf
Newsquest Media Group
01793-528144
Wiltshire Times w
Newsquest Media Group
01225-777292

WORCESTERSHIRE

Berrow's Worcester Journal wf
Newsquest Media Group
01905-748200
Bromsgrove/Droitwich Ad wf
Newsquest Media Group
01384-442466
B'grove/Droitwich Standard wf
Herald Observer Newspapers
01527-585588
Evesham Journal wf
Newsquest Media Group
01386-442555
Kidderminster Chronicle wf
Midland News Association
01902-313131
Kidderminster Shuttle wf
Newsquest Media Group
01905-748200
Kidderminster Why wf
Goodhead Publishing
01527-853625
Malvern Gazette w
Newsquest Media Group
01905-748200
Redditch & Bromsgrove Jnl wf
Journal Publishing
0121-693 3740
Redditch Advertiser wf
Newsquest Media Group
01384-442466
Redditch/Alcester Standard wf
Herald Observer Newspapers
01527 585588
(Worcester) Evening News d
Newsquest Media Group
01905-748200
Worcester Why wf
Goodhead Publishing
01527-853625

EAST YORKSHIRE

Beverley Advertiser wf
Northcliffe Newspapers Group
01482-327111
Beverley Guardian wf
Johnston Press
01377-253213
Bridlington Free Press w
Johnston Press
01262-606606
Driffield Times w
Johnston Press
01377-253213
Goole HowdenThorne Courier wf
Johnston Press
01302-814399
Grimsby Evening Telegraph d
Northcliffe Newspapers Group
01472-360360
Grimsby Target wf
Northcliffe Newspapers Group
01472-360360
Haltemprice Advertiser wf
Northcliffe Newspapers Group
01482-327111
Holderness Advertiser wf
Northcliffe Newspapers Group
01482-327111
Holderness Gazette w
Holderness Newspapers
01964-614325
Hornsea Gazette w
Holderness Newspapers
01964-614325
Hull Advertiser series wf
Northcliffe Newspapers Group
01482-327111
Hull Daily Mail d
Northcliffe Newspapers Group
01428-327111

NORTH YORKSHIRE

Cleveland Clarion wf
SR & VI Crane
01642-480397
Craven Herald & Pioneer w
Newsquest Media Group
01756-792577
Easingwold Weekly News w
GH Smith
01347-821329
East Cleveland Herald & Post wf
Trinity International
01642-245401

The Gazette & Herald
York & County Press
01904-653051
Harrogate Advertiser w
Regional Independent Media
01423-564321
Harrogate Herald wf
Regional Independent Media
01423-564321
Knaresborough Post
Regional Independent Media
01423-564321
(Middlesbrough) Evening Gazette d
Trinity Mirror
01642-245401
Middlesbrough Herald & Post wf
Trinity Mirror
01642-245401
North Yorkshire Advertiser wf
Newquest Media Group
01325-381313
North Yorkshire News wf
Regional Independent Media
01423-564321
North Yorkshire Star wf
Newsquest Media Group
01325-381313
Northallerton Times w
Regional Independent Media
01423-564321
Pateley Bridge Herald w
Regional Independent Media
01423-564321
Ripon Gazette w
Regional Independent Media
01423-564321
Ryedale Star wf
Newsquest Media Group
01904-611488
Scarborough Evening News d
Johnston Press
01723-363636
(Scarborough) The Mercury w
Johnston Press
01723-363636
Selby Chronicle wf
Johnston Press
01924-375111
Selby Star wf
Newsquest Media Group
01904-611488
Selby Times w
Johnston Press
01924-375111
Stockton Herald & Post wf
Trinity Mirror
01642-245401
Whitby Gazette w
Adscene Group
01947-602836

SOUTH YORKSHIRE

Axholme Herald w
Northcliffe Newspapers Group
01427-874417
Barnsley Chronicle w
Barnsley Chronicle
01226-734734
Barnsley Independent wf
Barnsley Chronicle
01226-734734
Barnsley Star d
Sheffield Newspapers
0114-276 7676
Dearne Valley Weekender wf
Garnett Dickinson Publishing
01709-571111
Dinnington Guardian wf
Johnston Press
01909-550500
Dinnington Trader News wf
Adscene Group
01909-565200
Doncaster Advertiser wf
Johnston Press
01302-819111
Doncaster Courier wf
Johnston Press
01302-819111
Doncaster Free Press w
Johnston Press
01302-819111
Doncaster Star d
Sheffield Newspapers
0114-276 7676
Epworth Bells Advertiser w
Adscene Group
01205-311433
Goole, Thorne & Howden Courier wf
Johnston Press
01405-720888
Rotherham Advertiser w
Garnett Dickinson Publishing
01709-364721
Rotherham Star d
United News & Media
0114-276 7676
Sheffield Mercury w
Sheffield Mercury Newspapers
0114-274 6555
Sheffield Telegraph w
Regional Independent Media
0114-275 4896
(Sheffield) The Star d
Regional Independent Media
0114-276 7676
Sheffield Weekly Gazette wf
Regional Independent Media
0114-276 7676
South Yorkshire Times w
Johnston Press
01302-819111

WEST YORKSHIRE

Aire Valley Target w
Newsquest Media Group
01274-729511
Batley News w
Regional Independent Media
01924-468282
Birstall News w
The Reporter
01924-468282
Bradford Star wf
Newsquest Media Group
01274-729511
(Bradford) Telegraph & Argus d
Newsquest Media Group
01274-729511
Brighouse Echo w
Johnston Press
01484-721911
Calderdale News wf
Johnston Press
01422-260300
Colne Valley Chronicle w
Express & Chronicle
01484-684011
Dewsbury Reporter w
Regional Independent Media
01924-468282
(Dewsbury) The Weekly Adv wf
Regional Independent Media
01924-468282
(Halifax) Evening Courier d
Johnston Press
01422-365711
Hebden Bridge Times w
Johnston Press
01422-842106
Hemsworth Express wf
Johnston Press
01924-375111
Holme Valley Express w
Express & Chronicle
01484-684011
Huddersfield Daily Examiner d
Trinity Mirror
01484-430000
Huddersfield District Chronicle w
Express & Chronicle
01484-684011
Huddersfield Weekly News wf
Trinity Mirror
01484-430000
Ilkley Gazette w
Newsquest Media Group
01943-465555
Keighley News w
Newsquest Media Group
01535-606611
Leeds Skyrack Express wf
Johnston Press
01924-375111
Leeds Weekly News wf

Regional Independent Media
0113-243 2701
Mirfield Reporter w
The Reporter
01924-468282
Morley Advertiser w
Johnston Press
01924-375111
Morley Observer w
Regional Independent Media
01924-468282
Normanton Advertiser wf
Normanton Advertiser
01924-892117
Ossett & Horury Observer wf
Johnston Press
01924-375111
Pontefract Express w
Johnston Press
01924-375111
Pontefract Weekend Times wf
Johnston Press
01924-375111
Pudsey Times wf
Regional Independent Media
01423-564321
Spenborough Guardian w
Regional Independent Media
01274-874635
Todmorden News w
Johnston Press
01706-815231
Wakefield Express w
Johnston Press
01924-357111
(Wakefield) Midweek Extra wf
Johnston Press
01924-357111
Weekend Times wf
Yorkshire Weekly Newspapers
01924-375111
Wetherby Advertiser wf
Four Counties Newspapers
01904-639136
Wetherby News w
Regional Independent Media
01423-564321
Wharfe Valley Times wf
Regional Independent Media
01423-564321
Wharfedale Observer w
Newsquest Media Group
01943-465555

d=daily, w=weekly, s=sunday, f=free

YORK
York Advertiser wf
Adscene Group
01904-639136
York Star wf
Newsquest Media Group
01904-653051
Yorkshire Coast Leader wf
Adscene Group
01723-363636
Yorkshire Evening Post d
Regional Independent Media
0113-243 2701
Yorkshire Evening Press d
Newsquest Media Group
01904-611488
Yorkshire Gazette & Herald w
Newsquest Media Group
01904-611488
Yorkshire Post d
Regional Independent Media
0113-243 2701

WALES

BLAENAU GWENT
Gwent Gazette w
Trinity Mirror
029-2058 3583
North Gwent Campaign wf
Regional Independent Media
029-2085 1100

COUNTY OF BRIDGEND
Bridgend Recorder wf
Recorder (Wales)
01656-669330
Bridgend & Ogwr Post wf
Trinity Mirror
029-2058 3583
Glamorgan Gazette w
Trinity Mirror
029-2058 3583

COUNTY OF CAERPHILLY
Blackwood & Risca News wf
01633-810000
Blackwood Campaign wf
029-2085 1100
Caerphilly Campaign wf
All three are Southern Newspapers
029-2085 1100

CARDIFF
Cardiff Post wf
Trinity Mirror
029-2058 3583
(Cardiff) South Wales Echo d
Trinity Mirror
029-2058 3583
(Cardiff) Western Mail d
Trinity Mirror
029-2058 3583
Wales on Sunday
Trinity Mirror
029-2022 3333

CARMARTHENSHIRE
Burry Port Star
Northcliffe Newspapers Group
01792-510000
Carmarthen Citizen wf
Northcliffe Newspapers Group
01267-221234
Carmarthen Journal w
Northcliffe Newspapers Group
01792-510000
Llanelli Star w
Northcliffe Newspapers Group
01792-510000
South Wales Guardian w
Regional Independent Media
01269-592074

CEREDIGION
Cambrian News w
Cambrian News
01970-615000
Cardigan Advertiser w
Southern Newspapers
01239-612513

COUNTY OF CONWY
Abergele Visitor w
Trinity Mirror
01745-344444
Caernarfon Herald w
Trinity Mirror
01286-584321
Lladudno Advertiser wf
Trinity Mirror
01492-584321
(North Wales) The Pioneer wf
North Wales Newspapers
01352-707707
North Wales Weekly News w
Trinity Mirror
01492-584321

DENBIGHSHIRE
Corwen Times w
County Press
01678-520262
Denbighshire Free Press w
North Wales Newspapers
01352-700022
Rhyl/Prestatyn Journal wf
North Wales Newspapers
01352-707707
Rhyl & Prestatyn Visitor wf
Trinity Mirror
01745-344444

FLINTSHIRE
The Chroncile
Trinity Mirror
01244-340151
Flintshire Herald & Post wf
01244-340151
Flintshire Leader wf
North Wales Newspapers
01352-707707

VALE OF GLAMORGAN
Barry& District News w
Southern Newspapers
01495-751133
Barry Gem wf
Tindle Newspapers
01446-774484
Cowbridge Gem wf
Tindle Newspapers
01446-774484
Glamorgan Gem wf
Tindle Newspapers
01446-774484

Llantwit Major Gem wf
Tindle Newspapers
01446-774484
Penarth Times w
Southern Newspapers
029-2070 7234
Vale Post wf
Trinity Mirror
029-2058 3583

GWENT
Blackwood & Risca News wf
Southern Newspapers
01633-810000

GWYNEDD
Anglesey Chronicle wf
North Wales Newspapers
01248-352051
Bangor Mail wf
Trinity Mirror
01248-362747
Y Cyfnod w
The County Press
01678-520262
Y Cymro w
North Wales Newspapers
01352-700022
Y Dydd
The County Press
01341-422547
Yr Herald w
Trinity Mirror
01286-671111
Merioneth Express w
The County Press
01678-520262
North Wales Chronicle wf
North Wales Newspapers
01352-700022

ISLE OF ANGLESEY
Bangor & Caernarfon Chronicle wf
Trinity Mirror
01248-352051
Holyhead Mail w
01286-671111

COUNTY OF MERTHYR
Merthyr Express w
029-2058 3583
Merthyr Campaign wf
Southern Newspapers
029-2085 1100
Merthyr Tydfil wf
Campaign Free Newspapers
029-2085 1100

MONMOUTHSHIRE
Abergavenny Chronicle w
Tindle Newspapers
01873-852187

Chepstow News wf
Southnews
01633-810000
Mon & Abergavenny News wf
Southnews
01633-810000
Monmouthshire Beacon w
Tindle Newspapers
01600-712142

NEATH/PORT TALOT
Neath & Port Talbot Guardian wf
Trinity Mirror
029-2058 3583

COUNTY OF NEWPORT
South Wales Argus d
Southern Newspapers
01633-810000
Newport Free Press wf
Southern Newspapers
01453-751133
Newport News wf
Southnews
01633-810000

PEMBROKESHIRE
County Echo &St Davids Chronicle w
County Echo Newspapers
01348-874445
Fishguard County Echo w
Tindle Newspapers
01348-874445
Narberth & Whitland Obs w
Tindle Newspapers
01834-843262
Western Telegraph w
Southnews
01437-763133
Tenby Observer w
Tindle Newspapers
01834-843262

POWYS
Heart of Wales Chronicle wf
01597-824151
Mid Wales Journal w
Midland News Association
01584-876311
(Welshpool) County Times w
North Wales Newspapers
01352-700022

RHONDDA CYNON TAFF
Cynon Valley Leader w
Trinity Mirror
01685-873136
Pontypridd Campaign wf
Southern Newspapers
029-2085 1100

Pontypridd Observer w
Trinity Mirror
029-2058 3583
Rhondda Campaign wf
Southnews
029-2085 1100
Rhondda Leader w
Trinity Mirror
029-2058 3583

COUNTY OF SWANSEA
South Wales Evening Post d
Northcliffe Newspapers Group
01792-510000
Swansea Herald of Wales wf
Northcliffe Newspapers Group
01792-510000
Y Tyst w
John Penry Press
01792-652092

TORFAEN
Cwmbran & Pontypool News wf
Southnews
01633-810000
Cwmbran Free Press wf
Southern Newspapers
01495-751133
Pontypool & District Press w
Southern Newspapers
01495-751133

COUNTY OF WREXHAM
(Wrexham) Evening Leader d
North Wales Newspapers
01978-355151
Wrexham Leader wf
North Wales Newspapers
01978-355151

d=daily, w=weekly, s=sunday, f=free

SCOTLAND

CITY OF ABERDEEN
Aberdeen & District Independent wf
Aberdeen & District Independent
01224-618300
(Aberdeen) Evening Express d
Northcliffe Newspaper Group
01224-690222
Aberdeen Herald & Post wf
Northcliffe Newspaper Group
01224-690222
(Aberdeen) Press & Journal d
Northcliffe Newspaper Group
01224-690222
Deeside Piper w
Angus County Press
01307-464899
Donside Piper & Herlad w
Angus County Press
01307-464899
Ellon & District Advertiser w
W Peters & Son
01888-56389
Ellon Times w
Eastern Counties Newspapers Group
01779-472017
Inverurie Advertiser w
W Peters & Son
01888-563589
Inverurie Herald w
Angus County Press
01307-464899

ABERDEENSHIRE
Banffshire Advertiser w
J & M Publishing
01542-832265
Banffshire Journal w
Scottish Provincial Press
01261-812551
Buchan Observer w
Eastern Counties Newspapers Group
01358-724488
Ellon Times w
Eastern Counties Newspaper Group
01358-724488
Fraserburgh Herald w
Eastern Counties Newspapers Group
01346-513900
Huntly Express w
J & M Publishing
01542-832265
Kincardineshire Observer w
Montrose Review Press
01674-672605
Mearns Leader w
Montrose Review Press
01569-762139
Turriff & District Advertiser w
W Peters & Son
01888-563589

ANGUS
Arbroath Herald w
The Herald Press
01241-872274
Brechin Advertiser w
Angus County Press
01356-622767
Forfar Dispatch w
Angus County Press
01307-464899
Kirriemuir Herald w
Angus County Press
01307-464899
Montrose/Brechin Review w
Montrose Review Press
01674-672605

ARGYLL & BUTE
The Buteman w
Bute Newspapers
01700-502931
Campbeltown Courier w
Oban Times
01586-554646
Dunoon Observer w
E & R Inglis
01369-703218
Helensburgh Advertiser w
Clyde & Forth Press
01436-673434
Oban Times w
Oban Times
0131-551 2942

AYRSHIRE EAST
Cumnock Chronicle w
Clyde & Forth Press
01290-421633
Kilmarnock Leader wf
Eastern Counties Newspapers
01292-611666
Kilmarnock Standard w
Trinity Mirror
01563-525113

AYRSHIRE NORTH
Ardrossan/Saltcoats Herald w
Clyde & Forth Press
01294-464321
Arran Banner w
Arran Banner Printing & Publishing
01770-302142
Clyde Weely News wf
Trinity Mirror
01389-742299
Garnock Valley Herald w
Clyde & Forth Press
01383-728201
Irvine Herald w
01294-278312

Irvine Times
Clyde & Forth Press
01294-73421
Largs Weekly News w
Clyde & Forth Press
01475-689009
North Ayrshire Leader wf
Eastern Counties Newspapers Group
01292-611666
North Ayrshire World wf
Trinity Mirror
0141-353 3366

AYRSHIRE SOUTH
Ayr Advertiser w
Clyde & Forth Press
01292-267631
Ayr Leader wf
Community Leader
01292-611666
Ayrshire Post w
Trinity Mirror
01292-262200
Ayrshire World wf
Trinity Mirror
01292-261111
Carrick Gazette w
01465-712688
Carrick Herald w
Clyde & Forth Press
01383-728201
Troon & Prestwick Times
Clyde & Forth Press
01383-728201

BORDERS
Berwickshire News w
Tweeddale Press Group
01289-306677
Berwick & Borders Gazette wf
Portsmouth & Sunderland Newspapers
01670-516066
Border Telegraph w
D & J Croal
01896-758399
Hawick News w
Hawick News
01450-372204
Peebles Times wf
Scottish County Press
0131-663 2404
Peeblesshire News w
D & J Croal
01896-758399
Selkirk Weekend Advertiser w
Portsmouth & Sunderland Newspapers
01750-21969
Southern Reporter w
The Tweeddale Press Group
01750-21581

DUMBARTON/C'BANK
Clydebank Post w
Clyde & Forth Press
0141-952 1345
Clydebank Weekly News wf
01294- 222288
Dumbarton Lennox Herald w
Scottish & Universal
0141-353 3366
Dumbarton Reporter w
Clyde & Forth Press
01383-728201

DUMFRIES & GALLOWAY
Annandale Herald w
Dumfriesshire Newspapers Group
01461-202417
Annandale Observer w
Dumfriesshire Newspapers Group
01461-202417
Carrick Gazette w
The Galloway Gazette
01465-712688
Dumfries Courier wf
Dumfriesshire Newspapers Group
01461-202417
Dumfries & Galloway Standard w
Trinity Mirror
01387-255252
Eskdale & Liddesdale Ad. w
Eskdale & Liddesdale Newspapers
01387-380066
Galloway Gazette w
Galloway Gazette
01671-402503
Galloway News w
Trinity Mirror
0141-353 3366
Moffat News w
Dumfriesshire Newspapers Group
01461-202417
Stornoway Gazette w
Stornoway Gazette
01851-702687
Wigtown Free Press w
01776-702551

CITY OF DUNDEE
Broughty& Carnoustie Gazette w
The Herald Press
01241-872274
(Dundee) Courier & Advertiser d
DC Thomson
01382-223131
(Dundee) Evening Telegraph d
DC Thomson
01382-223131
(Dundee) The Sunday Post w
DC Thomson
01382-223131
(Dundee) Sporting Post w
DC Thomson
01382-223131

CITY OF EDINBURGH
Edinburgh Herald & Post wf
Barclay Bros/Ellerman
0131-225 2468
(Edinburgh) Evening News d
Barclay Bros/Ellerman
0131-225 2468
(E'burgh) Scotland on Sunday w
The Scotsman Publications
0131-225 2468
(Edinburgh) The Scotsman d
Barclay Bros/Ellerman
0131-225 2468
Lothian Times w
Scottish County Press
0131-663 2404

FALKIRK
Falkirk Advertiser wf
Johnston Press
01324 624959
Falkirk Herald w
Johnston Press
01324-624959

FIFE
Central Fife Times w
Dunfermline Press
01383-728201
Clyde Post wf
Clyde & Forth Press
01475-726511
Dunfermline Herald & Post wf
Barclay Bros/Ellerman
01383-621818
Dunfermline Press w
Dunfermline Press
01383-728201
East Fife Mail w
Johnston Press
01592-261451
Fife Advertiser wf
Johnston Press
01592-261451
Fife Free Press w
Johnston Press
01592-261451
Fife Herald w
Strachan & Livingston
01592-261451
Fife & Kinross Extra wf
Dunfermline Press
01383-728201
Fife Leader wf
01592-261451
Glenrothes Gazette w
01592-261451
Greenock Telegraph d
Clyde & Forth Press
01475-726511
St Andrews Citizen w
Johnston Press
01592-261451

CITY OF GLASGOW
Barrhead News w
Clyde & Forth Press
0141-889 8873
Bearsden Milngavie Courier w
Community Media
0141-427 7878
Cumbernauld Advertiser wf
Johnston Press
01324-624959
Cumbernauld News w
Johnston Press
01324-624959
East End Independent wf
East End Independent
0141-550 2220
East Kilbride News w
Trinity Mirror
01355-266000
East Kilbride World wf
Trinity Mirror
01698-283200
(Glasgow) Daily Record d
Scottish Daily Record and Sunday Mail
0141-248 7000
(Glasgow) The Herald d
Caledonian Publishing
0141-552 6255
Glasgow South Extra wf
Eastern Counties Newspapers
0141-427 7878
(Glasgow) Sunday Mail w
Trinity Mirror
0141-248 7000
The Glaswegian wf
Trinity Mirror
0141-248 7000
Kirkintilloch Herald w
Johnston Press
0141-775 0040
Milngavie & Bearsden Herald w
Johnston Press
0141-775 0040
Rutherglen Reformer w
Trinity Mirror
0141-647 2271
Sunday Post
DC Thomspm w
01382-223131
Weekly News w
DC Thomspm w
01382-223131

d=daily, w=weekly, s=sunday, f=free

HIGHLANDS

Caithness Courier w
Scottish Provincial Press
01955-602424
Fort William Extra wf
Oban Times
01397-703003
Highland News w
Scottish Provincial Press
01463-710999
Inverness Courier w
01463-233059
Inverness Herald wf
01463-710999
John O'Groats Journal w
01955-602424
Lochaber News w
Preceding four Scottish Provincial Press
01463-710999
North Star w
01349-863248
Northern Times w
01408-633993
Ross-shire Herald wf
01463-710999
Ross-shire Journal w
01349-863436
Strathspey/Badenoch Herald w
Preceding five Scottish Provincial Press
01463-710999
West Highland Free Press w
West Highland Publishing
01471-822464

LANARKSHIRE NORTH

Airdrie & Coatbridge Advertiser w
Trinity Mirror
01236-748048
Airdrie & Coatbridge World wf
Trinity Mirror
01698-283200
Bellshill speaker w
D MacLeod
0141-775 0040
Carluke Gazette w
Johnston Press
01324-624959
Hamilton Advertiser w
Trinity Mirror
01698-283200
Hamilton People wf
Eastern Counties Newspapers
01698-261321
Hamilton World wf
Trinity Mirror
01698-283200
Lanarkshire People wf
Community Media
01698-261321
Lanarkshire World wf
Scottish & Universal
01698-283200

Motherwell People wf
Eastern Counties Newspapers
01698-261321
Motherwell Times w
Johnston Press
01698-264611
Wishaw Press w
Trinity Mirror
01698-283200
Wishaw World wf
Trinity Mirror
01698-283200

LANARKSHIRE SOUTH

Lanark Gazette w
Johnston Press
01324-624959

EAST LOTHIAN

East Lothian Courier w
D & J Croal
01620 822451
East Lothian News w
Scottish County Press
0131-663 2404
Musselburgh News w
Scottish County Press
0131-663 2404

WEST LOTHIAN

Linlithgow Gazette w
Johnston Press
01324-624959
Lothian Courier w
Trinity Mirror
01506-633544
Lothian World wf
Trinity Mirror
01506-633544
West Lothian Herald wf
Scotsman Publications
01506-634400

MIDLOTHIAN

Midlothian Advertiser w
Scottish County Press
0131-663 2404

MORAY

Banffshire Herald w
J & M Publishing
01542-886262
Forres Gazette w
Scottish Provincial Press
01309-672615
Northern Scot w
Scottish Provincial Press
01463-710999

ORKNEY ISLANDS

The Orcadian w
The Orcadian
01856-879000

PERTHSHIRE & KINROSS

Blairgowrie Advertiser w
Trinity Mirror
0141-353 3366
Perth Shopper wf
Trinity Mirror
01738-626211
Perthshire Advertiser w
Trinity Mirror
01738-626211
Strathearn Herald w
Trinity Mirror
0141-353 3366

RENFREWSHIRE

Johnstone & Linwood Gazette w
Clyde & Forth Press
01383-728201
Paisley Daily Express d
Trinity Mirror
0141-353 3366
Paisley People wf
Clyde & Forth Press
0141-889 8873
Paisley & Renfrewshire News wf
Eastern Counties Newspapers
0141-427 7878
Renfrew Gazette w
Clyde & Forth Press
0141-889 8873
Renfrewshire World wf
Trinity Mirror
0141-353 3366

SHETLAND ISLANDS

Shetland Times w
Shetland Times
01595-693622

STIRLING

Stirling & Alloa Shopper wf
Trinity Mirror
01786-451110
Stirling News wf
Dunfermline Press
01259-214416
Stirling Observer w
Trinity Mirror
01786-451110

WESTERN ISLES

Stornoway Gazette w
The Galloway Gazette
01851-702687

N IRELAND

ANTRIM

Antrim Guardian w
Northern Newspapers
028-703 43344
Ballyclare Gazette w
028-37 522639
Ballymena Chronicle w
Observer Newspapers (NI)
028-87 722557
Ballymena Guardian w
Northern Newspapers
028-703 43344
Ballymena Times w
Morton Newspapers
028-25 653300
Ballymoney Times w
Morton Newspapers
028-38 326161
(Belfast) News Letter d
Trinity Mirror
028-9068 0000
Belfast Sunday Life w
Trinity Holdings
028-9033 0000
Belfast Telegraph d
Trinity Holdings
028-9026 4000
Castlereagh Star w
Morton Newspapers
01846-679111
East Antrim Guardian w
Northern Newspapers
028-703 43344
East Belfast Herald & Post wf
Trinity Mirror
028-9043 9993
East Belfast News wf
Trinity Mirror
028-90 680010
Larne Gazette w
Alpha Newspapers
028-37 522639
Larne Times w
Morton Newspapers
028-28 272303
Lisburn Echo wf
Morton Newspapers
028-92 601114
North Newtownabbey Post wf
Trinity Mirror
028-9043 9993
Portadown Times w
Morton Newspapers
028-38 339421
South Belfast Herald and Post wf
Trinity
028-9043 9993
Ulster Star w
Morton Newspapers
028-92 679111

ARMAGH

Armagh Down Observer w
Observer Newspapers (NI)
028-87 722557
Craigavon Echo wf
Morton Newspapers
028-38 350041
Lurgan Examiner w
Observer Newspapers (NI)
028-87 722557
Lurgan Mail w
Morton Newspapers
028-38 327777
Ulster Gazette w
Alpha Newspaper Group
028-37 522639

DERRY

Coleraine Chronicle w
Northern Newspaper Group
028-703 43344
Coleraine Leader w
Northern Newspaper Group
028-703 43344
Coleraine Times w
Morton Newspapers
028-703 55260
Derry Journal w
Trinity Mirror
028-777 272200
Derry People & Donegal News w
NW Ireland Printing & Publishing Co
028-82 243444
(Londonderry) NW Echo wf
Morton Newspapers
028-777 268459
Londonderry Sentinel w
Morton Newspapers
028-777 48889
Mid-Ulster & S Derry Mail w
Morton Newspapers
028-79 762288
Mid-Ulster Echo wf
Morton Newspapers
028-79 761364
Mid-Ulster Observer w
Observer Newspapers (NI)
028-87 722557
Northern Constitution w
Northern Newspaper Group
028-703 43344

COUNTY DOWN

Armagh Down Observer w
Observer Newspapers (NI)
028-87 722557
Banbridge Chronicle w
Banbridge Chronicle w
028-406 662322
Banbridge Leader w
Morton Newspapers
028-406 662745

County Down Spectator w
Spectator Newspapers
028-91 270270
Down Recorder w
W Y Crichton & Co
028-44 613711
Dromore Leader w
Morton Newspapers
028-92 692217
Mourne Observer w
Mourne Observer
028-44 722666
Newtownards Chronicle w
028-91 813333
Newtownards Spectator w
Spectator Newspapers
028-91 270270
North Down Herald & Post wf
Trinity Mirror
028-9043 9993
The Outlook w
028-406 630202

FERMANAGH

Fermanagh Herald w
North West of Ireland Printing County
028-82 243444
Fermanagh News w
Observer Newspapers (NI)
028-87 722557
Impartial Reporter w
William Trimble
028-66 324422

TYRONE

(Dungannon) About Town wf
Dungannon Development Association
028-87 725445
Dungannon Observer w
Observer Newspapers (NI)
028-87 722557
Strabane Chronicle w
North West of Ireland Printing County
028-82 243444
Strabane Weekly News w
Tyrone Constitution Group
028-82 242721
Tyrone Constitution w
Tyrone Constitution Group
028-82 242721
Tyrone Courier w
Alpha Newspaper Group
028-87 722271
(Tyrone) The Democrat w
Observer Newspapers (NI)
028-87 722557
Tyrone Times w
Morton Newspapers
028-87 752801
Ulster Herald w
North West of Ireland Printing County
028-82 243444

d=daily, w=weekly, s=sunday, f=free

Magazines

As Felix Dennis grapples with his middle age he follows a familiar route from youthful rebel to business success to Cassandra. The man who found fame as a defendant in the Oz obscenity trial and fortune at Dennis Publishing scared the Periodical Publishers' Association annual conference in May with his gloomy visions of the future, a future so gloomy that he said he had considered selling off his magazine company.

He spoke of a four-pronged threat to magazines. One, that large wholesale and retail groupings committed only to large circulation titles were restricting sales of smaller titles. Two, that the growing illiteracy he sees all around him might advance to the level where there aren't enough people able to read magazines. Three, that environmental pressures might make his "business of killing trees" unviable. And four - the thing which is rendering the experience of middle age an anachronism - the internet .

"Here is a killer of tree killers," Dennis said. "I do not predict the death of magazines, but I fear a slow decline as our readers become viewers and magazine publishers become content providers." The same PPA conference heard a similar story from Jo Cappo, who was billed as a senior vice president international of Crain Communications. "I can tell you that a new media is in our midst and that can cause the same traumatic changes in business publishing that television caused in radio and newspapers 50 years ago," he intoned. Meanwhile, publishers are treating the net as

Felix Dennis of Dennis Publishing lists four threats to magazine publishers:
1) Greedy wholesalers
2) Growing illiteracy
3) Environmental pressures
4) The internet

just another publishing opportunity with some 16 internet titles launched since 1994 and less than half remaining. Top of the pile are Future's .Net, Emap's internet Magazine and, launched in June 1999, Haymarket's the net. A deal with Dixons means the latter starts with a 200,000 print run, though the others must survive on 50,000 circulations.

The mega-tree killers are customer magazines, some 300 giveaways - such as the AA Magazine and periodicals for M&S and Asda - whose individual circulations far outstrip any paid for title. Though they look like real magazines, they are purely promotional vehicles and financed through corporate marketing budgets. A leading publisher in an arena claiming a £300 million annual turnover is Redwood which, by more than coincidence, is owned by the advertising agency Abbott Mead Vickers. "Our editors understand that these magazines are not their own and even Redwood's," says Redwood's Sue Thomas. "We don't pretend to journalists that we are talking objectivity, but if articles come over as loaded and unfairly biased, no consumer is going to be fooled."

The competition is fuming. Joanne O'Hara, the Condé Naste advertising director, told the PPA conference that consumer mags are "junk food" which threaten conventional newsstand sales. "It is difficult to assess the true readership," she said. "But many read them because they are stuffed inside a shopping bag and because they have free coupons inside." Redwood's Jules Rastelli said his titles "create their own distinctive style".

Nicholas Coleridge, the managing director of Condé Naste, stuck the boot in when he asked: "Don't you feel embarrassed working for a company whose readers say 'I take the coupons out and bin it'?"

Meanwhile the bulk of writing about magazines was pegged against a battle-of-the-sexes men's vs women's magazines. All good knockabout stuff and easily written copy which usually forgets to point out that the men's market (excluding pornography) is still relatively small. True men's mags like FHM, Loaded and Maxim had a combined circulation growth of 6 per cent in 1998 as against a 4 per cent increase in titles like Cosmopolitan, Marie Claire and Sugar. However, annual sales of women's mags at 9 million compared with lad mag sales of 5 million.

Estimates of the number of magazines vary according to definition. Taking all the tiddlers into account there are probably 10,000 titles, though a slightly more conservative estimate comes from British Rate and Data (Brad) which lists 7,945 titles that take advertising. Of these 5,511 are business and professional magazines and the remaining 2,794 are consumer mags, which the Periodical Publishers Association defines as "providing people with leisure time information and entertainment". While most consumer titles are paid for by their readers, many of the business magazines are financed by advertising to so-called "controlled circulation readerships" - magazine managements' euphemism for uncontrolled circulation via mailing lists.

Over the past ten years the number of magazines published has increased by over a third. Total turnover in the sector is now approaching £2 billion and profit margins have increased from an average 6 per cent in 1991 to nearly 12 per cent for the last three years. The growth has been fuelled by a healthy economy plus increasing advertising expenditure and the fact that, generally, cover prices have been running ahead of inflation.

MAGAZINE OWNERS

KEY CONTACT

Periodical Publishers Association
Queens House, 28 Kingsway, London WC2B 6JR
Fax 020-7404 4167   Tel 020-7404 4166
E-mail: info1@ppa.co.uk
Website: www.ppa.co.uk
The trade association for magazine publishers, representing nearly 200 companies generating 80 per cent of the industry's revenue.

Aceville Publications
97 High Street, Colchester, Essex CO1 1TH
Fax 01206-564214   Tel 01206-540621
E-mail: mail@maze.u-net.com
Trading/collectors magazines.

Addax Media
150-152 High Street, Tonbridge, Kent TN9 1BB
                        Tel 01732-368368
Buisiness, leisure, transport magazines.

Addison Wesley Longman Group
Edinburgh Gate, Harlow, Essex CM20 2JE
Fax 01279-431059   Tel 01279-623623
A subsidiary of Pearson publishing journals and directories.

Advanstar Communications
Advanstar House, Park West, Sealand Road, Chester CH1 4RN
                        Tel 01244-378888
Science and medical.

Affinity Publishing
2nd Floor, 1-5 Clerkenwell Road, London EC1M 5PA
Fax 020-7251 5490   Tel 020-7251 5489

Aim Publications
Silver House, 31-35 Beak Street, London W1R 3LD
Fax 020-7734 5383   Tel 020-7437 3493
Weddings.

Angel Business Communications
361-373 City Road, London EC1V 1PQ
Fax 020-7417 7500   Tel 020-7417 7400
E-mail: london@angelbcl.co.uk
Website: http://www.angelbc.co.uk
Electronics and packaging.

Asian Trade Publications
1 Silex Street, London SE1 0DW
Fax-020-7261 0055   Tel 020-7928 1234
Trade and catering.

Aspen Publishing
Avon House, Avonmore Road, London W14 8TS
Fax 020-7906 2043   Tel 020-7906 2000
Customer magazines.
Attic Futura
17-18 Berners Street, London W1P 3DD
Fax 020-7323 1854   Tel 020-7636 5095
Youth and entertainment publisher.
Auto Trader
1 Francis Grove, London SW19 4DT
Fax 020-8879 0110   Tel 020-8946 1155
E-mail: ak80@dial.pipex.com
Website: http://www.autotrader.co.uk
Publishes the 13 regional editions of Auto Trader.
Owned 50 per cent by the Guardian Media Group.
Avia Press Associates
75 Elm Tree Road, Weston-super-Mare, BS24 8EL
Fax 01934-822400   Tel 01934-822524
E-mail: helicopter.international@compuserve.com
Website: www.helidata.rotor.com
Specialist publishers of rotary-wing/helicopter
magazines with defence and civil content.
Axon Publishing
5th floor, 77-79 Farringdon Road, London EC1M 3JT
Fax 020-7242 1900   Tel 020-7242 0600
E-mail: axonpublish@compuserve.com
Ballantyne Ross
16 Hamden Gurney Street, London W1H 5AL
                              Tel 020-7724 5444
Website: www.balross.com
Business to business, recruitment and security.
H Bauer Publishing
Shirley House, 25 Camden Road, London NW1 9LL
Fax 020-7241 8030   Tel 020-7241 8000
Women, TV and puzzles.
BBC Worldwide UK
Woodlands, 80 Wood Lane, London W12 0TT
Fax 020-8749 0538   Tel 020-8743 5588
A division of BBC Worldwide Publishing.
Bennett Publishing
2&3 The Centre, Weston-super-Mare BS23 1US
                              Tel 0934-622000
Property news.
Big Issue
Fleet House,57 Clerkenwell Road, London EC1M 5NP
                              Tel 020-020-7418 0418
Web: www.cocoon.co.uk/users/bigissue
BLA Group
Vinery Court, 50 Banner Street, London EC1Y 8QE
Fax 020-7577 9344   Tel 020-7577 9300
E-mail: bla@blagroup.co.uk
Blackwell Publishers
108 Cowley Road, Oxford, Oxfordshire OX4 1JF
Fax 01865-791347   Tel 01865-791100
Website: http://www.blackwellpublishers.co.uk
Humanities and social science journals .
Blackwell Science
Osney Mead, Oxford, Oxfordshire OX2 0EL
Fax 01865-721205   Tel 01865-206206
Website: http://www.blackwell-science.com
Technical, medical, scientific and academic journals.

Blenheim Business Publications
See Miller Freeman
Bloomsbury House
1 Cecil Court, 49-55 London Road, Middlesex EN2
6DN
                              Tel 020-8342 2222
Weightwatchers.
BMJ Publishing Group
BMA Ho, Tavistock Square, London WC1H 9JR
Fax 020-7383 6668   Tel 020-7383 6438
E-mail: 100336.3120@compuserve.com
Web: www.bmgpg.com
Publisher of the British Medical Journal and 28 other
journals.
Bowker Saur
Maypole House, Maypole Road, East Grinstead, W
Sussex RH19 1HU
                              Tel 01342-330100
Web: www.bowker.saur.com/service/
International journals.
BPL Business Publications
Broklyn House, 22 |the Green, West Drayton UB7
7PQ
                              Tel 01895-421111
Brass Tacks Publishing
143 Charing Cross Road, London WC2H 0EE
Fax 020-7478 4701   Tel 020-7478 4700
E-mail: enquiries@brasstacks.co.uk
Customer magazines.
British European Associated Publishers
2nd Floor, Glenthorne House, Hammersmith Grove,
London W6 0LG
Fax 020-8741 1956   Tel 020-8846 9922
Website: www.beap.bogo.co.uk
A VNU subsidiary which publishes puzzle magazines.
Builder Group
Exchange Tower, 2 Harbour Exchange Square,
London E14 9GE
Fax 020-7560-4008   Tel 020-7560 4000
French-owned publisher of construction and security
magazines.
Business Magazine Group
Briarwood House, St John Street, Mansfield,
Nottinghamshire NG18 1QH
                              Tel 01623-450500
Website: www.bmgroup.co.uk
Regional business.
Caledonian Magazines
6th Floor, 195 Albion Street, Glasgow G1 1QQ
Fax 0141-302 7799   Tel 0141-302 7700
E-mail: info@calmags.co.uk
6 titles including The Scottish Farmer and The Great
Outdoors.
Cambridge University Press
The Edinburgh Building, Shaftesbury Road,
Cambridge, Cambs CB2 2RU
Fax 01223-315052   Tel 01223-312393
E-mail: rsymons@cup.com.ac.uk
Website: www.cup.cam.ac.uk
Publisher of over 120 academic journals.

Carfax Publishing
PO Box 25, Abingdon, Oxfordshire OX14 3UE
Fax 01235-401550   Tel 01235-401000
E-mail: enquiries@carfax.co.uk
Website: www.catchword.co.uk
Publishes around 180 academic titles. One of the
largest social science publishers.

Carnyx Group
9 Park Street, Glasgow G3 8BG
                              Tel 0141-332 3255
Contract publishing, supplements.

Catholic Herald
Lambs Passage Bunhill Row, London EC1Y 8TQ
Fax 020-7256 9728   Tel 020-7588 3101
E-mail: catholic@atlas.co.uk
Intellectual Catholic broadsheet.

Centennial Publishing
2nd Floor, 1-5 Clerkenwell Road, London EC1M 5PA
Fax 020-7251 5490   Tel 020-7251 0777
E-mail: info@fengshui-magazine.co.uk

Centaur Communications
50 Poland Street, London W1V 4AX
Fax 020-7970 4521   Tel 020-7970 4000
Around 20 business titles.

Chapman and Hall
North Way, Andover, Hampshire
Fax 01264-342787   Tel 01264-332424
Website: www.chapmanhall.com
The subsidiary of the Thomson which publishes a
range of specialist technical and scientific journals.

Charterhouse Communications
4 Tabernacle Street, London EC2A 4IU
                              Tel 020-7638 1916
Consumer finance.

Choice Publications
Apex House, Oundle Road, Peterborough PE2 9NP
                              Tel 01733-555123

Combined Service Publications
PO Box 4, 273 Farnborough Road, Farnborough,
Hampshire GU14 7LR
Fax 01252-517918   Tel 01252-515891
E-mail: csp@btconnect.com
Many British Army regimental journals.

Computer Wire
4th floor, 12 Sutton Row, London W1V 5FH
Fax 020-7439 1105   Tel 020-7208 4200
E-mail: marketing@computerwire.co.uk
Website: www.computerwire.com
IT business intelligence and publishes Busines Review.

Conde Nast Publications
Vogue House, Hanover Square, London W1R 0AD
Fax 020-7493 1345   Tel 020-7499 9080
The US-owned publisher of lifestyle magazines.

Consumers Association
2 Marylebone Road, London NW1 4DF
Fax 020-7830 6220   Tel 020-7830 6000
E-mail: which@which.net
Website:www.which.net
The campaigning body for consumers and a good place
to start any consumer feature. The Association
produces five magazines, including Which?

Croner Publications
Croner House, London Road, Kingston-upon-
Thames, Surrey KT2 6SR
Fax 020-8547 2637   Tel 020-8547 3333
E-mail: info@croner.co.uk
Website: www.croner.co.uk
Publishes reference guides on technical and business
topics. Owned by the Dutch company Wolters Kluwer.

Cross-Border Publishing
111-113 Great Titchfield Street, London W1P 7FQ
Fax 020-7637 3594   Tel 020-7637 3579
Website: www.xborder.com

Dalesman Publishing
Stable Courtyard, Broughton Hall, Skipton BD23 3AE
                              Tel 01756-701381
Dalesman, Peak and Pennine Magazine.

Dennis Publishing
19 Bolsover Street, London W1P 7HJ
Fax 020-7636 5668   Tel 020-7631 1433
Consumer and business to business magazines, also
heavy metal, men's and one to one titles.

Director Publications
116 Pall Mall, London SW1Y 5ED
                              Tel 020-7839 1233
E-mail: director-ed@iod.co.uk
Website: www.iod.co.uk
Publishes Director magazine for members of the
Institute of Directors.

Distinctive Publishing
146 Cromwell Road, London SW7 4EF
                              Tel 020-7591 5809

DMG Busness Media
Queensway House, 2 Queensway, Redhill, Surrey
RH1 1QS
                              Tel 01737-768611
Website: www.dmg.co.uk/dmgbm/
Business and technical.

DMG Home Interest Magazines
Equitable House, Lyon Road, Harrow, Middlesex HA1
2EW
Fax 020-8515 2080   Tel 020-8515 2000
Website: www.dmg.co.uk

Dog World
Somerfield House, Wotton Road, Ashford, Kent TN23
6LW
Fax 01233-645669   Tel 01233-621877
E-mail: editorial@dogworld.co.uk

Economist Group
15 Regent Street, London SW1Y 4LR
Fax 020-7499 9767   Tel 020-7830 1000
Website: www.economist.com

Economist Newspaper
25 St James's Street, London SW1A 1HG
Fax 020-7930 3092   Tel 020-7830 7000
E-mail: letters@economist.com
Website: www.economist.com
Part of the Pearson Group.

Egmont Fleetway
25-31 Tavistock Place, London WC1H 9SU
Fax 020-7388 4154   Tel 020-7344 6400
A Danish-owned comic publisher with about 19 titles.

Elsevier Science Publishers
The Boulevard, Langford Lane, Kidlington, Oxon OX5 1GB
Fax 01865-843010   Tel 01865-843000
Website: www.elsevier.nl
Part of Reed Elsevier, Elsevier Science publishes over 400 scientific and technical journals for industry, science and academia.

European Magazines
IPC Kings Reach Tower, Stamford Street, London SE1 9LS
Fax 020-7261 5277   Tel 020-7261 5240
E-mail: marieclaire@ipc.co.uk
A subsidiary of IPC Magazines.

Emap
1 Lincoln Court, Lincoln Road, Peterborough, Cambs PE1 2RF
Fax 01733-358081   Tel 01733-568900
E-mail: janetj@plc.emap.co.uk
Website: www.emap.co.uk
Emap has three publishing divisions, two in the UK and one in France. It also has a radio division and a publications distribution arm.

Emap Business Communications
Meed House, 21 John Street, London WC1N 2BP
Fax 020-7831 3540   Tel 020-7470 6200
Website: www.emap.co.uk
Over 100 titles are published in the UK and Europe by eleven subsidiaries.

Architecture	020-7505 6600
Fashion	020-7520 1500
Freight	020-7505 6600
Cars	01733-467000
Local Govt/Finance	020-7505 8000
Media/Marketing	020-7505 8000
Business/Commercial fishing/	
Middle East	020-7470 6200
Trade/Retail	020-8277 5000

Emap Consumer Magazines
Mappin House, 4 Winsley Street, London W1N 7AR
Fax 020-7312 8950   Tel 020-7436 1515
Nearly 100 consumer titles are published from seven centres:

Bikes/Cars	01733-237111
Computers/Games	020-7972 6700
Photography/Gardens/Pets/Rail	
	01733-898100
Retirement	01733-555123
Health/Parenting/Lifestyle/Women	
	020-7437 9011
Music/Entertainment/Men's lifestyle	
	020-7436 1515
Country pursuits/Sport	
	01733-264666

Faversham House Group
Faversham House, 232a Addington Road, Croydon, Surrey CR2 8LE
Fax 020-8651 7117   Tel 020-8651 7100
E-mail: fhg@dial.pipex.com

Financial Times Business
Maple House, 149 Tottenham Court Road, London W1P 9LL
Fax 020-7896 2099   Tel 020-7896 2000
It publishes numerous business newsletters, plus financial magazines. Its publishing centres are:

FTB Magazines	020-7463 3000
FTB Newsletters	020-7896 2222

Findlay Publications
Franks Hall, Franks Lane, Horton Kirby, Kent DA4 9LL
Fax 01322-289577   Tel 01322-222222

Fox Publishing
135 Greenford Road, Harrow HA1 3YD
Tel 020-8869 8410

Frank Cass and Co
Newbury House, 890-900 Eastern Ave, Newbury Park, Ilford, Essex IG2 7HH
Fax 020-8599 0984   Tel 020-8599 8866
E-mail: info@frankcass.co,
Over 50 academic journals on a range of topics, including: international affairs, politics, history, culture and military science.

Freedom House Publications
44 North Street, chichester, W Sussex PO19 1NF
Tel 01243-533394

Freestyle Publications
Alexander House, Ling Road, Tower Park, Poole BH12 4NZ
Tel 01202-735090
Specialist interest titles.

FT Media & Telecoms
Maple House, 149 Tottenham Court Road, London W1P 9LL
Tel 020-7896 2700
Website: www.ftmedia.com

Future Publishing
Beauford Court, 30 Monmouth Street, Bath, BA1 2BW
Fax 01225-446019   Tel 01225-442244
Website: www.futurenet.co.uk
A pioneer of the cover mount freebie computer disc and (with Classic CD) the sampler compact disc. Once owned by Pearson but in 1998 bought back by a consortium including the original owner.

G & J of the UK
197 March Wall, London E14 9SG
Fax 020-7519 5518   Tel 020-7519 5500
Publishes the two women's magazines Best and Prima, and the popular science title Focus.

GJ Palmer & Sons
St Mary's Works, Norwich, Norfolk NR3 3BH
Fax 01603-624483   Tel 01603-612914
Publishes Church Times, The Sign and Home Words.

Gramophone Publications
135 Greenford Road, Harrow, Middx HA1 3YD
Fax 020-8869 8400   Tel 020-8422 4562
E-mail: info@gramophone.co.uk
Publishes Gramophone and a series of specialist quarterly classical music titles.

Granta Publications
2-3 Hanover Yard, Noel Road, London N1 8BE
Fax 020-7704 0474   Tel 020-7704 9776
E-mail: editorial@grantamag.co.uk
Website: www.granta.com
Publishes Granta the magazine of new writing and Granta books.
GTI
6 Hithercroft Court, Wallingford, Oxon OX10 9TB
                       Tel 01491-826262
Harcourt Brace
24-28 Oval Road, London NW1 7DX
Fax 020-7482 2293   Tel 020-7424 4200
Website: www.hbuk.co.uk
Haymarket Group
174 Hammersmith Road, London W6 7JP
Fax 020-7413 4504   Tel 020-8943 5000
Website: www.marketing.haynet.com
Publishes 40 of the leading business, medical and consumer magazines, from offices at Lancaster Gate and Teddington (both on the same phone number).
Hello!
Wellington House, 69-71 Upper Ground, London SE1 9PQ
Fax 020-7667 8742   Tel 020-7667 8740
E-mail: advertising@hello-magazine.co.uk
Hemming Group
32 Vauxhall Bridge Road, London SW1V 2SS
Fax 020-7233 5056   Tel 020-7973 6400
Website: www.hemming-group.co.uk
Henry Hemming Publishing
49a Goldhawk Road, London W12 8QP
Fax 020-8743 0888   Tel 020-8743 8111
E-mail: info@hhpublishing.demon.co.uk
Contract publisher specialising in travel and technology.
Highbury House Communications
1-3 Highbury Station Road, London N1 1SE
Fax 020-7704 0758   Tel 020-7226 2222
International publisher specialising in sport, leisure, finance, travel and business magazines.
HMSO
see The Stationery Office
Ian Allan Publishing
Riverdene Business Park, Molesey Road, Hersham, Surrey KT12 4RG
Fax 01932-266600   Tel 01932-266601
E-mail: zsiap@aol.com
Website: www.ianallanpub.co.uk
Publishes popular transport magazines, books and videos.
IBC Business Publishing
57-61 Mortimer Street, Gilmore House, London W1N 8JX
Fax 020-7631 3214   Tel 020-7637 4383
Website: www.intbuscom.com
Specialises in financial technology and telecomms.
Icom Publications
Chancery House, St Nicholas Way, Sutton, Surrey SM1 1JB
                       Tel 020-8642 1117
International communications.

IDG Communications
99 Grays Inn Road, London WC1X 8UT
Fax 020-7405 0262   Tel 020-7831 9252
Website: www.digitmag.co.uk
Publisher of newspapers, magazines and books on IT, including Macworld and Digit magazines.
Illustrated London News Group
20 Upper Ground, London SE1 9PF
Fax 020-7805 5911   Tel 020-7805 5555
IML Group
184 High Street, Tonbridge, Kent TN9 1BQ
Fax 01732-770049   Tel 01732-359990
E-mail: imlgroup@dial.pipex.com
Business to business, trade and technical publications.
Inside Communications
8th floor, Tubs Hill House, London Road, Sevenoaks, Kent TN13 1BL
Fax 01732-464454   Tel 01732-464154
Insider Group
43 Queensbury Street Lane, Edinburgh EH2 4PF
                       Tel 0131-535 5555
Corporate magazines and news letters.
Insight
15 Little Portland Street, London W1N 5DE
                       Tel 020-7580 6222
Retail.
IPC Magazines
King's Reach Tower, Stamford Street, London SE1 9LS
                       Tel.020-7261 5000
Website: www.ipc.co.uk
Britain's largest publisher of consumer and leisure magazines.
Jobson Publishing Corporation
Jobson House, Holbrooke Place, Hill Rise, Richmond, Surrey TW10 6UD
Fax 020-8332 6918   Tel 020-8332 6882
E-mail: sfarrer@jobson.co.uk
Publisher of optical magazines and special reports.
John Brown Publishing
The New Boathouse, 136-142Braley Road, London W10 6SR
                       Tel 020-7565 3000
Website: www.johnbrowncontract.com
Viz, Fortean Times, customer magazines.
John Wiley & Sons
Baffins Lane, Chichester, Sussex PO19 1UD
Fax 01243-775878   Tel 01243-779777
E-mail: publicity@wiley.co.uk
Website: www.wiley.co.uk
Publishes 411 journals of all kinds.
Keesing (UK)
Keesing House, Stonecroft, 69 Station Road, Redhill, Surrey RH1 1DL
Fax 01737-767248   Tel 01737-769799
Publisher of quality puzzle magazines.
Killen International Partnership
34 Rose Street, London WC2E 9BS
                       Tel 020-7240 8295
Customer magazines.

The Lady
39-40 Bedford Street, London WC2E 9ER
Fax 020-7836 4620   Tel 020-7379 4717
The Lancet
42 Bedford Square, London WC1B 3SL
Fax 020-7436 7570   Tel 020-7436 4981
E-mail: Clas.Advertising@ellsevier.co.uk
Website: www.thelancet.com
Law Society of England & Wales
113 Chancery Lane, London WC2A 1PL
Fax 020-7242 1309   Tel 020-7242 1222
Website: www.lawsociety.org.uk
Liberty Publishing
100 Brompton Road, London SW3 1ER
Fax: 020-7225 6725   Tel: 0171 225 6716
E-mail: adsales@punch.co.uk
Link House Magazines
Link House, Dingwall Avenue, Croydon, Surrey CR9
2TA
Fax 020-8760 0973   Tel 020-8686 2599
Website: www.linkhouse.co.uk
LLP
Sheepen Place, Colchester, CO3 3LP
Fax 01206-772771   Tel 01206-772277
E-mail: subscriptions@llplimited.com
Website: www.llplimited.com
Publisher specialising in the provision of commercial,
legal and financial information and data relating t o
shipping, maritime services, insurance, freighting and
transport, commodities and energy.
Macmillan Magazines
Porters South, 4 Crinan Street, London N1 9XW
Fax 020-7843 4640   Tel 020-7833 4000
Website: www.macmillanmags.com
Publishes 13 titles, mainly health service and scientific.
Manor Publishing
Manor Ho, Edison Road, Eastbourne BN23 6PT
Fax 01323-509306   Tel 01323-507474
E-mail: manorgroup@mistral.co.uk
Trade mags and annual factbooks for the sports market.
Mark Allen Publishing
286a-288 Croxted Road, London SE24 9BY
Fax 020-8671 1722   Tel 020-8671 7521
E-mail: 100676.56@compuserve.com
Website: www.markallengroup.com
Mainly medical titles.
Marvel Comics
Panini House, Coach and Horses Passage, The
Pantiles, Tunbridge Wells, Kent TN2 5UJ
Fax 01892-545666   Tel 01892-500100
E-mail: paniniuk@aol.com
13 titles. Part of the Panini sticker group.
Mature Times
The Wharf, 121 Schooner Way, Cardiff CF1 5EQ
                    Tel 029-2046 8504
Maze Media
97 High Street, Colchester, Essex CO1 1TH
Fax 01206-564214   Tel 01206-540621
E-mail: mail@maze.u/net.com
Hobby and leisure magazines.

Mediamark Publishing
5th & 6th floors, 11 Kingsway, London WC2B 6PH
                    Tel 020-7580 3105
Customer magazines.
Metal Bulletin
Park Terrace, Worcester Park, Surrey KT4 7HY
Fax 020-8337 8943   Tel 020-7827 9977
E-mail: subscriptions@metalbulletin.plc.uk
Website: www.metalbulletin.co.uk
Miller Freeman
City Reach, 5 Greenwich View Place, Mill Harbour,
London E14 9NN
Fax 020-8309 7000   Tel 020-8885 7777
Website: www.mfplc.co.uk
A subsidiary of United News and Media, Miller
Freeman specialises in business, trade and professional
magazines. Divisions include: Miller Freeman Business
Information Services (annual directories), and Miller
Freeman Entertainment.
Mining Journal
60 Worship Street, London EC2A 2HD
Fax 020-7216 6050   Tel 020-7216 6060
E-mail: editorial@mining-journal.com
Website: www.mining-journal.com
AE Morgan
Stanley House, 9 West Street, Epsom KT18 7RL
Fax 01372-744493   Tel 01372-741411
E-mail: t.morgan@easynet.co.uk
Myatt McFarlane
4 Ambassador Place, Stockport Road, Altrincham,
WA15 8DB
Fax 0161-941 6897   Tel 0161-928 3480
National Geographic Society
16 The Pines, Broad Street, Guildford, Surrey GU3
3NX
Fax 01483-506331   Tel 01483-537111
Website: www.nationalgeographic.com
National Magazine Company
National Magazine House, 72 Broadwick Street,
London W1V 2BP
Fax 020-7437 6886   Tel 020-7439 5000
Owned by the Hearst Corporation.
Needmarsh Publishing
71 Newcomen Street, London SE1 1YT
Fax 020-7378 6883   Tel 020-7403 0840
Website: www.rightstartmagazine.co.uk
New Crane Publishing
20 Upper Ground, London SE1 9PD
                    Tel 020-7633 0266
Publishes Sainsbury's magazine.
New Internationalist
55 Rectory Road, Oxford OX4 1BW
Fax 01865-793152   Tel 01865-728181
E-mail: newint@gn.apc.org
Website: www.newint.org
New Statesman
7th Floor, Victoria Station House, 191 Victoria Street,
London SW1E 5NE
Fax 020-7828 1881   Tel 020-7828 1232
E-mail: info@newstatesman.co.uk
Website: www.newstatsman.co.uk

Newhall Publications
Newhall Lane, Hoylake, Wirral, Merseyside CH47 4BQ
Fax 0151-632 5716   Tel 0151-632 3232
Website: www.candis.co.uk

Newsweek
18 Park Street London W1Y 4HH
Fax 020-7629 0050   Tel 020-7318 1600
E-mail: promotions@newsweek.co.uk
Website: www.newsweek-int.com

Nexus Media/Nexus Special Interests
Nexus House, Azalea Drive, Swanley, Kent BR8 8HU
Fax 01322 667633   Tel 01322 660070
                      Tel 01442-66551
Website: www.nexusonline.com
The Nexus group of companies publish magazines and
books, and organize events on a variety of subjects.
These include: industry, architecture, lifestyle, business,
education, horticulture, health, IT, hobbies, crafts and
puzzles.

Nursery World
Admiral House, 66-68 East Smithfield, London E1 9XY
Fax 020-7782 3398   Tel 020-7782 3396
Website: www.nurseryworld.com

Oxford University Press
Great Clarendon Street, Oxford OX2 6DP
Fax 01865-556646   Tel 01865-556767
E-mail: jnl.info@oup.co.uk
Website: www.oup.co.uk
Publishes 170 academic journals.

G J Palmer
St Mary's Works, St Mary's Plain, Norwich NR3 3BH
                      Tel 01603-612914

Parliamentry Communications
10 Little College Street, London SW1P 3SH
Fax 020-7878 1585   Tel 020-7233 1388
E-mail: parliament.magazine@skynet.be
Publishers of The House Magazine, covering
government policies and parliament.

Paul Raymond Publications
2 Archer Street, London W1V 8JJ
Fax 020-7734 5030   Tel 020-7292 8000
Website: www.sexclub.co.uk
Britain's largest porn magazine publisher.

Personnel Publications
17 Britton Street, London EC1M 5TP
Fax 020-7336 7637   Tel 020-7880 6200
Website: www.peoplemanagement.co.uk

Philip Allan Publishers
Market Place, Deddington, Oxon OX15 0SE
Fax: 01869 337590   Tel: 01869 338652
E-mail: sales@philipallan.co.uk
14 student-educational mags plus exam guides and
resource packs for teachers.

Phillips Business Information
Forum Chambers, Stevenage SG1 1EL
Fax 01438-740154   Tel 01438-742424
E-mail: kbrody@phillipslid.co.uk
Website: www.the-phillips-group.com
Publisher of business newsletters in telecoms, IT, cable,
satellite, broadcast and new media markets.

Police Review Publishing
Celcon House, 289-293 High Holborn, London WC1V
7HZ
Fax 020-7405 7167   Tel 020-7440 4700
E-mail: fabiana.angelini@policereview.co.uk
Website: www.policereview.com
Publishes three magazines, training books and course
material.

Practical Publications
Suite C, 21 Heathmans Road, London SW6 4TJ
                      Tel 020-7384 3261

Premier Publishing
1 Oxendon Street, London SW1Y 4EE
Fax 020-7839 4491   Tel 020-7925 2544
Website: www.premiermags.co.uk
A client publishing agency.

The Publishing Team
Exmouth House, 3-11 Pine St, London EC1R 0JH
Fax 020-7923-5401   Tel 020-7923 5400
E-mail: info@publishing-team.co.uk
Webste: www.publishing-team.co.uk
Customer magazines and corporate communications,
clients include: Barclays, Abbey National and Virgin.

Quantum Publishing
Quantum House, 19 Scarbrook Rd, Croydon CR9 1LX
Fax 020-8565 4444   Tel 020-8565 4200
Formed in 1989. In 1997 Quantum bought 13 Emap
titles including Press Gazette and Media Week.

Raven-Fox
Nestor House, Playhouse Yard, London EC4V 5EX
Fax 020-7779 8249   Tel 020-7779 8228
E-mail: ravenfox@compuserve.com

RCN Publishing
Nursing Standard House, 17-19 Peterborough Road,
Harrow HA1 2AX
Fax 020-8423 4302   Tel 020-8423 1066
E-mail: nursing.standard@rcn.org.uk
Website: www.nursing-standard.co.uk
Publishes the weekly Nursing Standard and a wide
range of journals for nurses in different specialties.

Reader's Digest Association
11 Westferry Circus, Canary Wharf, London E14 4HE
Fax 020-7715 8181   Tel 020-7629 8144
Website: www.readersdigest.co.uk

The Redan Company
1st Floor, Ramillies Building, 1-9 Hills Place, London
W1R 1AG
Fax 020-8563 1478   Tel 020-8563 1563
E-mail: sam@redan.co.uk

Redwood Publishing
12-26 Lexington Street, London W1R 4HQ
Fax 020-7312 2601   Tel 020-7312 2600
Website: www.redwood-publishing.com
Redwood is a contract publisher, with clients including:
AA, BSkyB, Boots, BT, Dulux, Harvey Nichols,
Homebase, Marks & Spencer, PSION, Safeway, Volvo,
Yellow Pages.

Reed Business Information
Quadrant House, The Quadrant, Sutton, Surrey SM2 5AS
Fax 020-8652 3960   Tel 020-8652 3500
E-mail: andrea@macpherson.rbi.co.uk
Website: www.reedbusiness.com
One of Britain's largest business publishers.
Reed Elsevier
25 Victoria Street, London SW1H 0EX
Fax 020-7227 5799   Tel 020-7222 8420
Website: www.reed-elsevier.com
In January 1993 Reed and the Dutch group Elsevier set up Reed Elsevier plc to create one of the world's biggest publishing companies employing over 25,000 people. The main UK magazine divisions (listed elsewhere in this section) are:
Butterworth-Heinemann
Elsevier Science Publishers
IPC Magazines
Reed Business Publishing
River Publishing
Victory House, Leicester Square, London WC2 7QH
Tel 020-7306 0304
Customer magazines.
Rodale Press
7-10 Chandos Street, London W1M 0AD
Fax 020-7291 6080   Tel 020-7291 6000
Romsey Publishing Company
4 The Courtyard, Denmark Street, Wokingham, Berkshire RG11 2AZ
Tel 01189-771677
UK travel and gardens.
Routledge
11 New Fetter Lane, London EC4P 4EE
Fax 020-7842 2298   Tel 020-7583 9855
Web: www.routledge.com/routledge.html
Saga Publishing
The Saga Building, Middleburg Square, Folkestone, Kent CT20 1AZ
Fax 01303-776699   Tel 01303-771523
E-mail: editor@saga.co.uk
Website: www.saga.co.uk/publishing/
Magazines for the over 50s.
Sage Publications
6 Bonhill Street, London EC2A 4PU
Fax 020-7374 8741   Tel 020-7374 0645
E-mail: market@sagepub.co.uk
Website: www.sagepub.co.uk/
An academic and professional publisher of social science books, journals and software.
Scholastic
Villiers House, Clarendon Avenue, Leamington Spa, Warwickshire CV32 5PR
Fax 01926-883331   Tel 01926-887799
Website: www.scholastic.co.uk
TG Scott
10 Savoy Street, London WC2E 7HR
Fax 020-7379 7118   Tel 020-7240 2032
E-mail: ian@tgscott.co.uk
Website: www.mcmscott.com
Specialist advertising sales company.

Shepherd Press
111 High Street, Burnham. Buckinghamshire SL1 7JZ
Fax 01628-664334   Tel 01628-604311
E-mail: publishing@shepherd.co.uk
Website: www shepherd.co.uk
Publishers of international specialist aerospace and defence magazines.
The Spectator
56 Doughty Street, London WC1N 2LL
Fax 020-7242 0603   Tel 020-7405 1706
Website: www.spectator.co.uk
SPL
Berwick House, 8-10 Knoll Rise, Orpington, Kent BR6 0PS
Tel 01689-874025
Security and cars.
The Stage Newspaper
Stage House, 47 Bermondsey Street, London SE1 3XT
Fax 020-7403 1418   Tel 020-7403 1818
E-mail: info@thestage.co.uk
Websites: www.thestage.co.uk
www.showcall.co.uk
The Stationery Office
St Crispin's, Duke Street, Norwich NR3 1PD
Fax 01603-695607   Tel 01603-622211
Website: www.national-publishing.co.uk
To order material on credit card via phone, tel: 020-7873 9090.
HMSO was privatised in September 1996. A residual part of HMSO remains within the Cabinet Office putting legal material on the internet.
Website: www.hmso.gov.uk
Sterling Publishing Group
86 Edgware Road, London W2 2YW
Fax 020-7915 9643   Tel 020-7915 9600
Website: www.sterlingpublications.co.uk
120 technical and business journals and directories.
Style Publishing
126 Great Portland Street, London W1N 5PH
Fax 020-7436 9957   Tel 020-7436 9766
E-mail: Style.Publishing@btinternet.com
Publishers of hair and beauty consumer and trade titles.
Summerhouse Publishing
St James' Yarn Mill, Whitefriars, Norwich NR3 1XU
Fax 01603-664410   Tel 01603-664242
E-mail: ghd@summerho.demon.co.uk
Website: www.summerhouse-publishing.com
Part of the ECN Group, Summerhouse Publishing produce customer publications.
Sweet and Maxwell
100 Avenue Road, London NW3 3PF
Fax 020-7393 7010   Tel 020-7393 7000
E:mail: webmaster@smlawpub.co.uk
Website: www.smlawpub.co.uk
Legal publishing.
The Tablet Publishing Company
1 King St Cloisters, Clifton Walk. London W6 0QZ
Fax 020-8748 1550   Tel 020-8748 8484
Website: www.thetablet.co.uk

Taylor and Francis
11 New Fetter Lane, London EC4P 4EE
Fax 020-7842 2298   Tel 020-7583 0490
Website: www.taylorandfrancis.com
Over 100 scientific and technical newsletters and journals.

DC Thomson and Co
2 Albert Square, Dundee, Tayside DD1 9QJ
Fax 01382-322214   Tel 01382-223131
Website: www.dcthomson.co.uk
A Scottish based, family owned company which produces more than 2 million magazines, comics and newspapers every year. Titles include, The Beano, The Dandy, The Scot's Magazine and The Sunday Post.

Thomson Corporation
180 Wardour Street, London W1A 4YG
Fax 020-7734 0561   Tel 020-7437 9787
Website: www.thomcorp.com.uk
The magazine publishing subsidiary of the Thomson Corporation of Canada. Its main UK subsidiaries are:
  Derwent Information
  Janes Information Group
  Primary Source Media
  Routledge
  Sweet and Maxwell
  Thomson Financial Services
  Westlaw

Time Life International
Brettenham House, Lancaster Place, London WC2E 7TL
Fax 020-7322 1005   Tel 020-7499 4080
Publishes Time magazine

Time Out
Universal House, 251 Tottenham Court Road, London W1P 0AB
Fax 020-7813 6001   Tel 020-7813 3000
E-mail net@timeout.co.uk.
Website: www.timeout.co.uk

Times Supplements
Admiral House, 66-68 East Smithfield, London E1 9XY
Fax 020-7782 3200   Tel 020-7782 3000
Website: www.tes.co.uk
A subsidiary of News International and publisher of the Times Educational Supplement ,Times Higher Educational Supplement, Times Literary Supplement and Nursery World.

Timothy Benn Publishing
39 Earlham Street, Covent Garden, London WC2H 9LD
Fax 020-7306 7101   Tel 020-7306 7000
E-mail: postmag@benn.co.uk
Website: www.tbp.co.uk
Trade titles and directories for insurance and photography.

Butterworths Tolley
2 Addiscombe Road, Croydon, Surrey CR9 5AF
Fax 020-8686 3155   Tel 020-8686 9141
E:mail: customer-services@tolley.co.uk
Website: www.tolley.co.uk
A business publishing subsidiary of Reed Elsveir.

TPD Publishing
Long Island Ho, 1-4 Warple Way, London W3 0RG
Fax 020-8600 9101   Tel 020-8600 9100
Website: www.tpd.co.uk
Producer of contract publications for technology companies. Can publish in any country, in any language, in print and online.

Trinity Publications
Edward House, Tindal Bridge, Edward Street, birmingham B1 2RA
                          Tel 0121-233 8712
Buying and selling.

United Advertising Publications
Link House, West Street, Poole, Dorset BH15 1LL
                          Tel 01202-445000

United News and Media
245 Blackfriars Road, London SE1 9UY
Fax 020-7921 5002   Tel 020-7921 5000
Website: www.unm.com
United News and Media (formerly United Newspapers) has a total of about 120 magazines in Britain, and roughly 150 abroad. Its main magazine subsidiaries are:
  Benn Business Publishing
  Miller Freeman

Unity Media Communications
Quebec Square, Westerham, Kent TN16 1TD
Fax 01959-564390   Tel 01959-565690
Publishers of ten business and professional titles from Unity Business Press and three consumer motoring titles from Unity Consumer division.

VNU Business Publications
32-34 Broadwick Street, London W1A 2HG
Fax 020-7316 9003   Tel 020-7316 9000
Website: www.vnu.co.uk

Voice Communications Group
370 Coldharbour Lane, London SW9 8PL
Fax 020-7274 8994   Tel 020-7737 7377
E-mail: veeteeay@gn apc.org

Warners Group
The Maltings, West Street, Bourne, Lincolnshire PE10 9PH
                          Tel 01778-391000
Caravans, motoring and roofing.

Which?
See Consumer Association

William Reed Publishing
Broadfield Park, Brighton Road, Crawley, W Sussex RH11 9RT
Fax 01293-610322   Tel 01293-613400
Website:www.foodanddrink.co.uk

Yachting Press
196 Eastern Esplanade, Southend SS1 3AB
Fax 01702-588434   Tel 01702-582245
E-mail: YandY@compuserve.com

Ziff-Davis UK
International House, 1 St Katherine's Way, London E19 UN
Fax 020-7403 0668   Tel 020-7378 6800
Website: www.zdnet.co.uk

ALTERNATIVE MAGS: LEFT

The majority of magazines are about TV, sex or shopping. This section lists the other mags which, for want of a better title, are the alternative ones and whose ideology extends beyond boosting circulations in order to sell more advertising. "Why," Searchlight asked, "are you publicising fascist groups?. Some of their articles are clearly in breach of the Public Order Act (1986)." One reason for inclusion of mags like the Flag is balance. Another, and much better reason, is that journalists sometimes need to talk to these people.

Big Issue, The
236-240 Pentonville Road, London N1 9JY
Fax 020-7526 3201   Tel 020-7526 3200
E-mail: london@bigissue.com
Website: www.bigissue.com
Top-selling magazine, campaigning for the homeless, sold by the homeless. Weekly. Editor: Matthew Colly.

Black Flag
BM Hurricane, London WC1N 3XX.
Analysis of the revolutionary anarchist movement. 4pa.

CARF
BM Box 8784, London WC1N 3XX
                      Tel 020-7837 1450
E-mail: info@carf.demon.co.uk
Website: www.carf.demon.co.uk
Voice of Campaign Against Racism and Fascism. 6pa.

Contemporary Review
14 Upper Mulgrave Rd, Cheam, Surrey SM2 7AZ
Fax 020-8241 7507   Tel 020-8643 4846
A liberal look at life. Founded 1866. Monthly.

Counter Culture
see Third Way

Earth First! Action Update
c/o Norfolk EF, the Greenhouse, 42-46 Bethel Street, Norwich NR2 1NR
E-mail: actionupdate@gn.apc.org
News and diary of the environmental direct action movement. Monthly.

Earth Matters
FoE, 26-28 Underwood St, London N1 7JQ
Fax 020-7490 0881   Tel 020-7490 1555
E-mail: andyn@foe.co.uk
Website: www.foe.co.uk
Friends of the Earth news, background and updates. 4pa. Editor: Andy Neather; Deputy: Jean McNeil

Ecologist, The
Unit 18, Chelsea Wharf, 15 Lots Road, London SW10 0QJ
Fax 020-7351 3578   Tel 0120-7351 3617
E-mail: ecologist@gn.apc.org
Website: www.gn.apc.org/ecologist
Journal with a wide academic perspective. 6pa. Editor: Edward Goldsmith, Zac Goldsmith.

Environmental Politics
Frank Cass, 900 Eastern Ave, Ilford IG2 7HH
Fax 020-8599 0984   Tel 020-8599 8866
E-mail: info@frankcass.com
Website: www.frankcass.com/jnls/ep.htm
For an academic slant. 4pa.

Ethical Consumer
Unit 21, 41 Old Birley Street, Manchester M15 5RF
Fax 0161-226 6277   Tel 0161-226 2929
E-mail: ethicon@mcr1.poptel.org.uk
Website: www.ethicalconsumer.org
An alternative Which? 6pa.

Feminist Review
Routledge Journals, 11 New Fetter Lane, London EC4P 4EE
Fax 020-7842 2298   Tel 020-7583 9855
E-mail: sophie.harrap@routledge.co.uk
Website: www.routledge.com
Academic journal "contesting feminist orthodoxies". Published 3pa.

Festival Eye
BCM Box 2002, London WC1N 3XX.
                      Tel 020-7794 1708
E-mail: festivaleye@stones.com
Website: www.festivaleye.com
Annual. News and forum for alternative festivals.

Fortnight
7 Lower Crescent, Belfast BT7 1NR
Fax 028-9023 2650   Tel 028-9023 2353
E-mail: mairtin@fortnite.dnet.co.uk
Northern Ireland news. Monthly.

Fuascailt (Liberation)
PO Box 6191, London NW5 !RA
Fax 020-8442 8778   Tel 020-8442 8778
Campaigning bi-monthly on Irish reunification.

Free Press
Campaign for Press and Broadcasting Freedom, 8 Cynthia St, London N1 9JF
Fax 020-7837 8868   Tel 020-7278 4430
E-mail: freepress@cpbf.demon.co.uk
Campaigning for a diverse and accountable media. 6pa.

Freedom
84b Whitechapel High St, London E1 7QX
Fax 020-7377 9526   Tel 020-7247 9249
Website: www.tao.ca/~freedom
Anarchist commentary on current affairs. Founded 1886 (longest-running anarchist paper in UK). 24pa.

Gay Scotland
17-23 Carlton Road, Edinburgh EH8 8DL
Fax 0131-557 2625   Tel 0131-556 3331
E-mail: Paul@gayscotland.co.uk
Monthly.

Gay Times
116-134 Bayham St, London NW1 0BA
Fax 020-7284 0329   Tel 020-7482 2576
E-mail: info@gaytimes.co.uk
Website: www.gaytimes.co.uk
Europe's biggest selling gay news and information magazine. Monthly. Editor: David Smith.

Green Anarchist
BCM 1715, London WC1N 3XX
Action-packed paper. 4pa.

Green Line
Catalyst Collective, PO Box 5, Lostwithiel, Cornwall,
PL22 0YT
Tel 0870-7334970
E-mail: greenline@clara.net
Eco news: environment, roads, animal rights . Monthly.

Green World
49 York Road, Aldershot, Hants GU11 3JQ
Fax 01252-330506   Tel 01252-330506
E-mail: greenworld@btinternet.com
Website: greenparty.org.uk/greenworld
News, action and networks of the Green Party.
Editor: Peter Barnett. 4pa.

HHH Video Mag
PO Box 888, 10 Martello St, London E8 3PE
Visuals from the anarcho video co-operative.

In Balance
50 Parkway, Welwyn Garden City, Herts AL8 6HH
Fax 01707 395550   Tel 01707-339007
E-mail: vbrown@pintail.u-net.com
Quarterly. Holistic health magazine with a source
directory of courses, clinics and therapists.

International Journal of Human Rights
Frank Cass, 900 Eastern Ave, Ilford IG2 7HH
Fax 020-8599 0984   Tel 020-8599 8866
E-mail: info@frankcass.com

International Peacekeeping
Frank Cass, 900 Eastern Ave, Ilford IG2 7HH
Fax 020-8599 0984   Tel 020-8599 8866
E-mail: info@frankcass.com

International Socialism
See: Socialist Worker

Irish Democrat
244 Grays Inn Rd, London WC1X 8JR
Tel 020-7833 3022
Views of Irish politics. Founded 1939. 6pa.

Jewish Socialist
BM 3725, London WC1N 3XX
E-mail: js@bardrose.dircon.co.uk
Debate, news and reviews. 4pa.

Labour Left Briefing
PO Box 2378, London E5 9QU
Fax 020-8985 6785   Tel 020-8985 6597
E-mail: llb@labournet.org.uk
Website: www.llb.labournet.org.uk/
Independent voice for socialist ideas in the labour
movement. 10pa.

Labour Research
78 Blackfriars Rd, London SE1 8HF
Fax 020-7928 0621   Tel 020-7928 3649
E-mail: lrd@geo2.poptel.org.uk
Website: www.lrd.org.uk
Data and research from the independent Labour
Research Department. Formed 1917. Monthly.

LM
Informinc (LM) Ltd, Signet House, 49/51 Farringdon
Road, London EC1M 3JB
Fax 020-7269 9395   Tel 020-7269 9220
E-mail: lm@informinc.co.uk
Website: www.informnc.co.uk
Outspoken monthly: culture and curent affairs.
Formerly Living Marxism. Editor: Mick Hume.

Lobster
214 Westbourne Ave, Hull HU5 3JB
Tel 01482-447558
E-mail: robin@lobster.karoo.co.uk
Digs into the clandestine activities of the state. 2pa.

Militant
see The Socialist.

Morning Star
1-3 Ardleigh Rd, London N1 4HS
Fax 020-7254 5950   Tel 020-7254 0033
E-mail: morsta@geo2.poptel.org.uk
The former Communist Party newspaper, founded
1930. Daily. Owned and published by People's Press
Printing Society, a co-operative. Editor: John Haylett.

Mother Earth
see Third Way

New Ground
SERA, 11 Goodwin St, London N4 3HQ
Fax 020-7263 7424   Tel 020-7263 7389
E-mail: SERAoffice@aol.com
Website: www.netlink.co.uk/users2/sera
Magazine of SERA, the environment group affiliated to
the Labour Party. News, campaigns and features. 2pa.

New Humanist
Rationalist Press Association, 47 Theobalds Rd,
London WC1X 8SP
Fax 020-7430 1071   Tel 020-7430 1371
E-mail: jm.rpa@humanism.org.uk
Quarterly.news on life from a humanist point of view.

New Internationalist
55 Rectory Rd, Oxford OX4 1BW
Fax 01865-793152   Tel 01865-728181
E-mail: veroniques@newint.org
Reports on world poverty and inequalities. Monthly.

New Left Review
6 Meard St, London W1V 3HR
Fax 020-7734 0059   Tel 020-7734 8830
E-mail: newleftreview@compuserve.com
Academic thoughts and theories on politics. 6pa.

New Statesman
191 Victoria Street, London SW1E 5NE
Fax 020-7828 1881   Tel 020-7828 1232
E-mail: info@newstatesman.co.uk
Website: www.newstatesman.co.uk
Britain's leading left of centre political magazine.
Founded 1913. Editor: Peter Wilby. Weekly.

News Line
BCM Box 747, London WC1N 3XX
Fax 020-7620 1221   Tel 020-7928 3218
Daily newspaper of the Trotskyite Workers
Revolutionary Party (with TV and sport).

New Times
6 Cynthia St, London N1 9JF
Fax 020-7278 4425   Tel 020-7278 4451
E-mail: newtimes@pop3.poptel.org.uk
Magazine of the modernising left, published by
Democratic Left. Monthly. Editor: Rosemary Bechler

Organise!
84b Whitechapel High St, London E1 7QX.
Journal of the Anarchist Communist Federation. 2pa.

Pagan Dawn
Pagan Fed. BM Box 5896, London WC1N 3XX.
E-mail: kate@pagmedia.demon.co.uk
Pre-Christian beliefs as practised today.

Peace News
5 Caledonian Road, London N1 9DX
Fax 020-7278 0444   Tel 020-7278 3344
E-mail: Peacenews@gn.apc.org
Website: www.gn.apc.org/peacenews
For non-violent revolution. 11 x pa.

Pink Paper, The
72 Holloway Rd, London N7 8NZ
Fax 020-7957 0046   Tel 020-7296 6210
E-mail: editorial@pinkpaper.co.uk
Lesbian and gay news. Weekly.
Editor: Cary James

Political Quarterly/Political Studies
Blackwell, 108 Cowley Road, Oxford OX4 1JF
Fax 01865-791347   Tel 01865-791100
Politics from many perspectives. 4pa. Also Politics(3pa).

Radical History Review
Cambridge University Press, Edinburgh Bldg,
Shaftesbury Rd, Cambridge CB2 2RU
Fax 01223-315052   Tel 01223-325757
Website: www.journals.cup.ac.uk
Academic study of the past from a non-sectarian
perspective. 3pa. CUP also publishes British Journal of
Political Science (4pa). Editor: Prof. Van Gosse.

Radical Philosophy
75 Balfour Road, London N5 2HD
                          Tel 020-7226 2724
Website:
www.speke.ukc.ac.uk/secl/philosophy/rp/index.html
Journal of a socialist and feminist philosophy. 6pa.

Raven, The
84 b Whitechapel High Street, London E1 7QX
                          Tel 020-7247 9249
Website: www.tao.ca/~freedom
In-depth anarchist discussion and analysis. 4pa.

Red Kite
Brynmadog, Gwernogle, Carmarthen SA32 7RN
Fax 01267-202471   Tel 01267-202375
E-mail: redkite@democraticleft.org.uk
Independent radical magazine of Wales.

Red Pepper
1b Waterlow Road, London N19 5NJ
Fax 020-7263 9345   Tel 020-7281 7024
E-mail: redpepper@online.rednet.co.uk
Website: www.redpepper.org.uk
Non-partisan news mag of the British left. Monthly.

Resistance
84b Whitechapel High St, London E1 7QX.
Agitational newsheet of the Anarchist Communist
Federation. 5pa.

Resurgence
Ford House, Hartland, Bideford, Devon EX39 6EE
Fax 01237-441203   Tel 01237-441293
E-mail: ed@resurge.demon.co.uk
Website: www.gn.apc.org/resurgence
Aesthetic environmental and ecological magazine with
a spiritual approach. 6pa. Editor: Satish Kumar.

Rural Socialism
25 Townholm Crescent, London W7 2LY
Campaigning for a Labour Party "rural revival".
Occasional.

SchNews
Justice?, PO Box 2600, Brighton, East Sussex BN2
2DX.
Fax 01273-685913   Tel 01273-685913
E-mail: schnews@brighton.co.uk
Website: www.schnews.org.uk/
The inside news story from the direct action alternative
frontline. Weekly.

Scottish Workers Republic
135 London Road, Glasgow G1 5BS
Fax 0141-552 7304   Tel 0141-357 3690
E-mail: alba-pubn@glaschu.freeserve.co.uk
Website: www.glaschu.freeserve.co.uk
Campaigning for an independent socialist Scotland.

Searchlight
37b New Cavendish Street, London W1M 8JR
Fax 020-7284 4410   Tel 020-7284 4040
E-mail: editor@s-light.demon.co.uk
Website: www.s-light.demon.co.uk
International in-depth news and research on the
extreme right. Monthly.

Socialism Today
See below (The Socialist)

Socialist, The
3-13 Hepscott Rd, London E9 5HB
Fax 020-8985 9445   Tel 020-8533 3311
E-mail: socialistparty.org.uk
Website: www.socialistparty.org.uk
The newspaper voice of the Socialist Party (known as
Militant Labour until early 1997; the paper was called
Militant). Weekly. The party also publishes the monthly
Socialism Today. Editor: Ken Smith.

Socialist Affairs
Socialist International, Maritime House, Old Town,
Clapham, London SW4 0JW
Fax 020-7720 4448   Tel 020-7627 4449
E-mail: secretariat@socialistinternational.org
Website: www.socialistinternational.org
Debates of the international movement. 4pa.

Socialist Appeal
PO Box 226, London N1 7SQ
Fax 020-7251 1095   Tel 020-7251 1094
E-mail: socappeal@easynet.co.uk
Website:
http://easyweb.easynet,co.uk/-socappeal/IDOM.html
Marxist view of the labour movement. 12pa.Editor: Alan
Woods.

Socialist Standard
Socialist Party of Great Britain (aka Socialist Party), 52
Clapham High St, London SW4 7UN
Fax 020-7720 3665   Tel 020-7622 3811
E-mail: spgb@worldsocialism.org
Website: www.worldsocialism.org/spgb
A venerable Marxist monthly founded in 1904.

Socialist Worker
PO Box 82, London E3 3LH
Fax 020-7538 0140   Tel 020-7538 0828
E-mai: editorial@socialstworker.co.uk
Website: www.swp.org.uk
Socialist Workers Party's newspaper. Weekly. SWP also publishes Socialist Review (monthly) and the more theoretical International Socialism journal(4pa).

Sorted?
7 Rock Place, Brighton, East Sussex BN2 1PF
Fax 01273-620203   Tel 01273-683318
E-mail: sorted@nacro.org
Website: www.nacro.org/sorted/welcome.htm
A free speech platform for wannabe journalists, photographers and illustrators. Written by young people for young people on a variety of issues.

Soundings
Lawrence & Wishart, 99a Wallis Rd, London E9
Fax 020-8533 7369   Tel 020-8533 2506
E-mail: soundings@l-w-bks.demon.co.uk
Website: www.l-w-bks.co.uk
"A journal of culture and politics". 3pa. Editors: Stuart Hall, Doreen Massey, Michael Rustin.

The Spark Magazine
86-88 Colston Street, Bristol BS1 5BB
Fax 0117-914 3444   Tel 0117-914 3434
E-mail: john@spark.u-net.com.

Statewatch
PO Box 1516, London N16 0EW.
Fax 020-8880 1727   Tel 020-8802 1882
E-mail: office@statewatch.org
Website: www.statewatch.org
Monitor of the state and civil liberties in the UK and Europe. £15pa.

Taking Liberties
PO Box 446, Sheffield S1 1NY
Prison issues, from the Anarchist Black Cross.

Tribune
308 Grays Inn Rd, London WC1X 8DY
Fax 020-7833 0385   Tel 020-7278 0911
Website: www.abel.co.uk/~rost2000/tribune
The "voice of the left". Launched 1937. Weekly.

Trouble and Strife
PO Box 8, Diss, Norfolk IP322 3XG
Feminist magazine. 2pa.

Undercurrents
16b Cherwell Street, Oxford OX4 1BG
Fax 01865-243562   Tel 01865-203663
E-mail: underc@gn.apc.org
Website: www.undercurrents.org
An alternative video news magazine. Quarterly.

Voice, The
370 Coldharbour Lane, London SW9 8PL
Fax 020-7274 8994   Tel 020-7737 7377
General newspaper for Britain's black community, especially the young. Weekly.

ALTERNATIVE MAGS: RIGHT

Candour
Forest House, Liss Forest, Liss, Hants GU33 7DD
                    Tel 01730-892109
Defending national sovereignty from international monetary power. Founded 1953. Monthly.

The Flag
PO Box 2269, London E6 3RF
Website: www.natdems.org.uk
News of the rightwing National Democrats. Monthly. Editor: Ian Anderson. Also publish Vanguard magazine (4pa).

Freedom Today
Freedom Association, 35 Westminster Bridge Rd, London SE1 7JB
Fax 020-7928 9524   Tel 020-7928 9925
E-mail: 100703.2174@compuserve.com
Website: www.tfa.net/ft/
Exposure of official actions and attitudes which reduce choices and freedoms. Editor: Alec Paris. 6pa.

Freemasonry Today
87 Guildhall Street, Bury St Edmunds, Suffolk IP33 1PU
E-mail: freemasonry.today@btinternet.com
Quarterly launched in July 1997. Ed: Tobias Churton.

Masonic Square
Coomblands House, Coomblands Lane, Addlestone, Surrey KT15 1HY
Fax 01932-821258   Tel 01932-820552
Forum for the freemasons.

Right Now
PO Box 2085, London W!A 5SX
Fax 020-8692 7099   Tel 020-8692 7099
E-mail: rightnow@compuserve.com
Website: www.right-now.org
Right-of-centre conservative comment. 4pa.

Salisbury Review
33 Canonbury Park South, London N1 2JW
Fax 020-7354 0383   Tel 020-7226 7791
E-mail: salisbury-review@easynet.co.uk
Website: www.easyweb.easynet.co.uk/~salisburyreview
Dry conservative thought, comment and analysis. Editor: Roger Scruton. 4pa.

The Spectator
56 Doughty Street, London WC1N 2LL
Fax 020-7242 0603   Tel 020-7405 1706
E-mail: editor@spectator.demon.co.uk
Website: www.spectator.co.uk
Best-known and most popular vehicle of centre-right news and reviews. Founded 1828. Weekly. Editor: Boris Johnson.

Third Way
PO Box 1243, London SW7 3PB
Fax 020-7681 1191   Tel 020-7373 3432
E-mail: thirdway@dircon.co.uk
Website: www.users.dircon.co.uk/~thirdway
"Voice of the Radical Centre", seeking alternatives to capitalism and communism. 6pa. Also publishes: ecological newsletter Mother Earth (4pa) and Counter Culture (4pa).

Top selling magazines by circulation

1 AA Magazine	4,084,622
2 Sky TV Guide	3,408,912
3 Safeway Magazine	1,997,083
4 Cable Guide1	1,880,622
5 What's on TV	1,785,389
6 Radio Times	1,400,391
7 Reader's Digest	1,302,059
8 Take a Break	1,273,820
9 Somerfield Magazine	1,177,307
10 Debenhams	1,109,902
11 Saga Magazine	923,872
12 TV Times	850,282
13 FHM	751,490
14 TV Quick	740,800
15 Woman	711,199
16 Woman's Own	664,473
17 Bella	610,843
18 Homebase	598,500
19 Woman's Weekly	594,680
20 Birds	586,830
21 That's Life	540,009
22 You & Yours	510,675
23 Hello	510,552
24 Prima	510,142
25 Best	501,205
26 Chat	497,791
27 Cosmopolitan	478,288
28 Candis	458,779
29 Loaded	457,918
30 Sugar	451,696
31 Marie Claire	445,288
32 People's Friend	438,980
33 Top of the Pops	437,090
34 Sainsbury's	410,787
35 National Geographic	402,215
36 OK!	400,701
37 Good Housekeeping	400,063
38 Official Playstation mag	380,186
39 The Economist	372,796
40 My Weekly	358,381
41 Now	350,999
42 It's Bliss	337,188
43 Woman & Home	330,001
44 Maxim	321,947
45 BBC Gardeners' World	321,366
46 BBC Good Food	303,457
47 Viz	301,019

Source: ABC, June 1998

MAG LISTINGS

19	020-7261 5000
100 Arrows/Crosswords/Word search	01737-769799
20/20	020-8332 6882

A

AA Magazine	020-7747 0700
ABC Freight Guide	020-7439 4222
Accolade	020-7487 5155
Accountancy	020-7833 3291
Accountancy Age	020-7316 9000
Acorn User	01625-878888
Active Life	020-7906 2000
Aeroplane Monthly	020-7261 5000
Aerosol Review	020-8309 7000
African Affairs	01865-556767
African Review of Business	020-7834 7676
Air Forces Monthly	01780-755131
Air International	01780-755131
Air Mail	020-8994 8504
Air Navigation International	020-8652 3096
Air Pictorial	01424-720477
Aircraft Illustrated	01932-266600
Aircraft Technology	020-7828 4376
Airline Business	020-8652 3500
Airliners	01780-755131
Airports International	01892-839200
Airport Review	020-8700 3700
Airtrade	020-7505 3560
AJ Focus	020-7505 6600
Al Aalam Magazine	020-7608 3454
Al Hawadeth	020-8740 4500
Al Majalla	020-7831 8181
Al Wasat	020-7602 9988
Amar Deep	020-8840 3534
Amateur Gardening	01202 440840
Amateur Photographer	020-7261 5000
Amiga Format	01225-442244
Amenity Management	020-8943 5000
Amusement Business Europe	020-7439 4222
An Phoblacht (Sinn Fein/IRA)	028-9060 0279
Angler's Mail	020-7261 5000
Angling Plus	01733-264666
Angling Times	01733-264666
Animal Life/Action	01403-264181
Antique Interiors	020-7359 6011
Antiques & Art Ind	07000-765263
Antiques Diary	0118-940 2165
Antiques Trade Gazette	020-7930 7192

Apollo	020-7233 8906
Appropriate Technology	
	020-7436 9761
Arable Farming	020-8309 7000
Architectural Design	020-7262 5097
Architecture Today	020-7837 0143
Arena	020-7278 1578
Art Business Today	020-7381 6616
Art & Craft	01926-887799
Art Monthly	020-7240 0389
Art Quarterly	020-7225 4800
Art Review	020-7236 4880
ArtWork	01651-842429
Asda Magazine	0113-242 2228
Asian Electricity	01737-768611
Asian Review of Business &Tech.	
	020-7834 7676
Astronomy Now	01732-367542
Athletics Weekly	01733-264666
Attitude	020-7308 5090
Audio Visual	020-8565 4200
The Author	020-7373 6642
Auto Express	020-7928 8000
Automotive Digest	01733-467000
Automotive Marketing Review	
	01733-467000
Auto Trader	020-8543 8000
Autocar	020-8943 5000
The Automobile	01932-864212
Autosport	020-8943 5000
AutoTrade	01733-467000
AV Magazine	020-8565 4200
Axiom Magazine	020-7833 3399

B

B	020-7664 6500
Baby	020-7331 1000
Back Hill Reporter	020-7514 6500
The Band	01225-442244
The Banker	020-7896 2525
Baptist Times	01235-517670
Barbie	020-7344 6400
Bassist	01225-442244
BBC Gardener's World	
	020-8576 2000
BBC Good Food	020-8576 2000
BBC Good Homes	020-8576 2000
BBC Learning is Fun	
	020-8576 2000
BBC Match of the Day	
	020-8576 2000
BBC Music Magazine	
	020-8576 2000
BBC Toybox	020-8576 2000
BBC Wildlife	0117-9738402
Beano	01382-223131
Beautiful Homes	020-7261 5000
Bee World	029-2037 2409

Beekeeping & Development	
	01600-713648
Bella	020-7241 8000
Best	020-7519 5500
Best of Postman Pat	
	020-8653 1563
Best of Rosie & Jim	020-8653 1563
Best of Thomas The Tank Engine	
	020-8653 1563
Best of Tots TV	020-8653 1563
Better Satellite	020-7331 1000
Big!	020-7436 1515
The Big Issue	020-7526 3200
Bike	01733-237111
Billboard	020-7323 6686
Birmingham What's On	
	0121-626 6600
The Biochemist	020-7580 5530
Biologist	020-7581 8333
Bird Keeper	020-7261 5000
Bird Life	01767-680551
Bird Watching	01733-898100
Birds	01767-680551
Birdwatch	020-7704 9495
Bizarre	020-7565 3000
Bliss	020-7437 9011
Blue Pages	020-7878 1500
Blueprint	020-7906 2000
Blues & Soul	020-7402 6869
Boat Angler	01733-237111
The Bomb	01305-266360
Bonhams Auction Guide	
	020-7393 3900
Book & Magazine Collector	
	020-8579 1082
Books & Company	01386-593352
Books in the Media	01494-792269
Books in Wales	01970-624151
The Bookseller	020-7420 6000
Bowls International	01780-755131
Boxing News	020-7734 4784
Boys Toys	01202-735090
Boyz	020-7296 6000
Brand Strategy	020-7439 4222
Breakthru	01753-856433
Bride & Groom Magazine	
	020-7437 0796
Brides & Setting Up Home	
	020-7499 9080
British Archaeology	01904-671417
British Baker	020-8565 4200
British Birds	01767-640025
British Dental Journal	
	020-7935 0875
British Jeweller	020-7520 1500
British Journal of Community	
Nursing/Health Care	
Management/Hospital Medicine/	
Midwifery/Nursing/Practice	
Nursing	020-8671 7521

British Journal of Photography	
	020-7306 7000
British Medical Journal	
	020-7387 4499
British Printer	01732-364422
British Rate & Data (BRAD)	
	020-7505 8000
Broadcast	020-7505 8000
Budgerigar World	01604-624549
Building	020-7560 4000
Building Design	020-8309 7000
Bunty	01382-223131
Burlington Magazine	
	020-7388 8157
Bus Fayre	01274-881640
Business Equipment Digest	
	01732-359990
Business and Technology	
	020-8652 3500
BusinessAfrica/Asia/China/Europe/	
Latin America/Middle East/Russia	
	020-7830 1000
Business Franchise	020-8742 2828
Business Travel World	
	020-7470 6200
Butterfly Conservation	
	01206-322342
Buy a Boat	01243-533394
Buying Cameras	01733-898100
The Buzz	01232 331694

C

Cab Driver	020-7493 5267
Cabinet Maker	01732-364422
Cable Guide	020-7419 7300
Cable & Satellite Europe	
	020-7896 2700
Cable Television Engineering	
	0191-281 7094
CadCam	020-8277 5000
Cage & Aviary Birds	020-7261 5000
Cake Decorating	01225-442244
Cakes & Sugarcraft	01252-727572
Camcorder User	020-7331 1000
Campaign	020-8943 5000
The Campaigner	020-8846 9777
Camping & Caravanning	
	024-7669 4995
Canal & Riverboat	01372-741411
Candis	0151-632 3232
Canoeist	01235-847270
Car & Accessory Trader	
	020-8943 5000
Car Boot Calendar	0118-940 2165
Car Mechanics	01959 541444
Caravan Club Magazine	
	01342-326944
Caravan Life	01778-391000
Caravan Magazine	020-8686 2599
Caribbean Times	020-7702 8012

Caribbean World   020-7581 9009
Cars & Car Conversions
                           020-8686 2599
CarSport   01232 783200
The Cartoonist   020-7353 2828
Car World   01733-237111
Cash & Carry Management
                           020-8688 2696
Cat   020-8943 5000
The Cat   01403-221900
Catalyst   01869-338652
Caterer & Hotelkeeper
                           020-8652 3500
Catering Update   020-8652 3500
Catholic Herald   020-7588 3101
Cats   0161-236 0577
Caves & Caving   01524-262770
C B Radio Active   023-9261 3800
Celebrations in Cross Stitch
                           01225-442244
Centrepoint   020-8539 3876
Chat   020-7261 5000
Checkout   020-8652 3500
Checkout Fresh   020-8652 3243
Chemical Engineer   01788-578214
Chemist & Druggist   020-8309 7000
Chemistry in Britain   01223-420066
Chemistry Review   01869-338652
Chess   020-7388 2404
China Economic Review
                           020-7834 7676
China In Focus   01253-894582
Choice   01733-555123
Christian Family   01903-821082
Christian Socialist   020-7833 0666
Church Times   020-7359 4570
City Life   0161-839 1416
Civil Engineer International
                           020-7505 6600
Class   020-7247 1455
Classic & Sportscar   020-8943 5000
Classic Bike   01733-237111
Classic Boat   020-8686 2599
Classic Car Weekly   01733-237111
Classic CD   01225-442244
Classic Stitches   01382-223131
Club Mirror   020-8565 4200
Club On   020-7247 1100
Coach & Bus Week   01733-467000
Coarse Angling   020-7261 5000
Coat of Arms   0118-932 0210
Comagazine   01895-444055
Combat   0121-344 3737
Combat & Survival   01484-435011
Commercial Motor   020-8652 3500
Commercial Vehicle Manager
                           01733-467000
Common Cause   020-7281 4101
Communications Africa
                           020-7834 7676

Communications International
                           020-7505 8000
Communications Law
                           020-8686 9141
Community Care   020-8652 3500
Community Nurse   020-7843 3600
Community Pharmacy
                           020-7334 7333
Community Transport Magazine
                           0161-351 1475
Company   020-7439 5000
Computer Active   020-7316 9000
Computer Arts   01225-442244
Computer & Video Games
                           020-7972 6700
Computer Buyer/Shopper
                           020-7631 1433
Computer Music   01225-442244
Computer Success   020-8600 2000
Computer Video   020-7331 1000
Computer Weekly   020-8652 3500
Computing   020-7316 9000
Conde Nast Traveller
                           020-7499 9080
Conference and Incentive Travel
                           020-8943 5000
Construction News   020-7505 6600
Containerisation International
                           020-7505 3550
Contemporary Visual Arts
                           020-7740 1704
Contract Journal   020-8652 3500
Control & Instrumentation
                           020-8309 7000
Control Systems   01732-359990
Convenience Store   01293-613400
Cornish Banner   01726-843501
Corporate Money   020-7439 4222
Cosmopolitan   020-7439 5000
Counter Culture   020-7373 3432
Country Homes & Interiors
                           020-7261 5000
Country Life   020-7261 5000
Country Living   020-7439 5000
Country Music International
                           020-8261 2897
Country Music People
                           020-8692 1106
Country Sports   01206-263234
Country Walking   01733-264666
The Countryman   020-7261 2897
Countryside   01242-521381
Couples   020-8688 5670
CPRE Voice   020-7976 6433
Crafts   020-7278 7700
Craftsman Magazine
                           01377-255213
Creative Review   020-7439 4222
Creative Technology   020-7357 6161

Cricketer International
                           020-8699 1796
Crops   020-8652 3500
Cross Stitch   01225-442244
Cross Stitch Collection
                           01225-442244
Cross Stitcher   01225-442244
CTN   020-8565 4200
Cult Times   020-8875 1520
Current Archaeology
                           020-7435 7517
Cuts   020-7437 0801
Cycle Sport   020-7261 5000
Cycle Touring & Campaigning
                           01483-417217
Cycling Plus   01225-442244
Cycling Weekly   020-7261 5000

D

Dairy Farmer   01473-241122
Dalton's Weekly   020-8949 6199
Dance & Dancers   020-7813 1049
Dance Express   01372-741411
Dance News   01483-428679
Dancing Times   020-7250 3006
Dandy   01382-223131
Darts World   020-8650 6580
Day by Day   020-8856 6249
Dazed & Confused   020-7336 0766
Deadpan   020-8579 5414
Dealer Principal   01733-467000
Debenhams   020-7565 3000
Decanter   020-7610 3929
Decor   020-8877 0077
Defence Helicopter   01628-604311
Defence Industry Digest
                           020-7242 2548
Defence Upgrades   020-8700 3700
Defence Weekly   020-8700 3700
Demon Dispatches   020-7251 6688
The Dentist   01483-304944
Design Engineering   020-8309 7000
Design Products & Applications
                           01732-359990
Design Week   020-7439 4222
The Devil   020-8994 7767
Diesel Car   01225-442244
Digital Photo FX   01733-898100
Diplomat   020-7837 5600
Disability Now   020-7619 7100
Disability Times   020-7233 7970
Disco International (DI)
                           01322-660070
Disney & Me   020-7344 6400
Diva   020-7482 2576
Diver Magazine   020-8943 4288
DIY Week   01732-364422
DJ   01322-660070
Docklands Recorder
                           020-8472 1421

Going Wild In London
020-7261-0447
Golf Industry News 020-7477 7399
Golf Monthly 020-7261 5000
Golf Weekly 01733-264666
Golf World 01733-264666
Good Food (BBC) 020-8576 2000
Good Housekeeping
020-7439 5000
Good Times 020-7526 2400
Good Vibrations 01733-370777
Good Woodworking
01225-442244
The Gospel Magazine
01462-811204
GQ 020-7499 9080
GQ Active 020-7499 9080
Gramophone 020-8422 4562
Grand Prix Review 020-8943 5000
Granta 020-7704 9776
Grassroots Campaigner
01422-843785
The Great Outdoors 0141-302 7700
Greek Review 020-7272 2722
Green Futures 01223-568017
The Grocer 01293-613400
Ground Engineering 020-7505 6600
The Guardian Weekly
020-7713 4400
The Guide 020-8297 0809
Guiding 020-7834 6242
Guitarist 01225-442244
Guitar Techniques 01225-442244

H
Hair 020-7261 5000
Hairdressers' Journal
020-8652 3500
Ham Radio Today 01707-853300
Hansard 020-7873 0011
Harpers & Queen 020-7439 5000
Hazards Magazine 0114-276 5695
Headlight 020-8660 2811
Headlines 01442-233656
Health & Beauty Salon
020-8652 3500
Health & Fitness 01322-660070
Health Insurance 020-7505 8000
Health & Safety at Work
020-8686 9141
Health Club Management
01462-431385
Health Service Journal
020-7843 3600
Heat 020-7312 8902
Heavy Horse World 01243-811364
Helicopter International
01934-822524
Hello! 020-7667 8700
Here's Health 020-7437 9011

Heritage Scotland 0131-226 5922
Heritage Today 020-7973 3000
Hi-Fi Choice 020-7631 1433
High Life 020-7925 2544
Hindsight 01869-338652
Hip Hop Connection
01225-442244
History Today 020-7534 8000
History Workshop Journal
01865-556767
HN 020-7747 0700
Home & Country 020-7371 9300
Home Entertainment
020-7631 1433
Home & Family 020-7222 5533
Home Magic 020-7581 1371
Homebase Living 020-7747 0700
Homes & Antiques (BBC)
020-8576 2000
Home Furnishings 01732-364422
Homes & Gardens 020-7261 5000
Homes & Ideas 020-7261 5000
Homestyle 020-7928 5869
Horoscope 01202-881749
Horse 020-7261 5000
Horse Exchange 020-7261 5000
Horse & Hound 020-7261 5000
Horse Magazine 020-7261 5000
Horse & Pony 01733-264666
Horticulture Week 020-8943 5000
Hospital Doctor 020-8652 3500
Hospital Equipment & Supplies
01322-277788
Hot Shoe International
01622-687031
Hotel 01323-507474
Hotel & Restaurant Magazine
020-8681 2099
The House 020-7827 9929
House & Garden 020-7499 9080
House Beautiful 020-7439 5000
Housewares 01732-364422
Housing 020-7837 8727
Housing Today 020-7843 2275

I
I-D Magazine 020-7813 6170
IBM Computer Today
020-8652 3500
Ideal Home 020-7261 5000
The Idler 020-7239 9575
Illustrated London News
020-7805 5555
Image 01603-664242
Improve Your Coarse Fishing
01733-264666
Improve Your Sea Angling
01733-264666
In Balance 01707-339007
In-Store Marketing 020-7439 4222

Independent Retail News
020-8652 8754
Index on Censorship
020-7278 2313
India Weekly 020-7251 3290
Individual Homes 020-7439 4222
Industrial Exchange & Mart
01202-445000
Inside Cosmetics 020-8855 7777
Inside Eye 020-7439 4222
Inside Soap 020-7636 5095
Inspirations 020-7836 0519
Insurance Age 020-7505 8000
Intelligence & National Security
020-8599 8866
Intelligence Review 020-8700 3700
InterMedia 020-7388 0671
International 020-7896 2525
International Defense Review
020-8700 3700
International Express
020-7928 8000
International Food Ingredients
020-8309 7000
International Food Manufacture
020-8309 7000
International Freighting Weekly
020-7470 6200
International Money Marketing
020-7439 4222
International Police Review
020-7440 4700
International Risk Management
020-7505 8000
International Socialism
020-7538 5821
Internet 020-7477 7399
Internet Magazine 020-7477 7399
Internet Works 01225-442244
Interzone Science Fiction
01273-504710
Investment Fund Index (CD Rom)
020-7439 4222
Investors Chronicle 020-7896 2525
Irish Post 020-8741-0649
Irish World 020-8453 7800
IT-Mag 020-7355 4489

J
Jam 01865-268400
Jane's Defence Weekly
020-8700 3700
Jane's Intelligence Review
020-8700 3700
Janomot Bengali Newsweekly
020-7377 6032
Japan Forum 01264-343062
Jazz Journal International
020-7608 1348
Jewish Chronicle 020-7415 1500

Jewish Quarterly 020-7629 5004
Jewish Telegraph 0161-740 9321
Jewish Tribune 020-8800 6688
The Job (The Met) 020-7230 1212
The Journalist 020-7278 7916
Journal of Wound Care
020-7874 0200
Junior 020-7630 5500
Just 17 020-7437 9011

K
Kerrang! 020-7436 1515
Kindred Spirit 01803-866 686
Kitchens, Bedrooms & Bathrooms
020-8515 2000
Knave 01376-534534
Kriss Kross 020-8846 9922

L
Labour Left Briefing 020-8985 6597
Labour Market Trends
020-7873 9090
Labour Research 020-7928 3649
The Lady 020-7379 4717
The Lancet 020-7436 4981
Land Rover Owner International
01733-237111
The Landworker 020-7828 7788
Law Society's Gazette
020-7242 1222
The Lawyer 020-7439 4222
Leather 01732-364422
Legal Action 020-7833 2931
Legal Business 020-7396 9292
Leisure Manager 01491-874800
Leisure Painter 01580-763315
Leisure Week 020-7439 4222
Level 01305-251263
Library Association Record
020-7636 7543
Lifeguard 01789-773994
Lifewatch 020-7722 3333
Linedancer 01704-501235
Line Up 01323-491739
The List 0131-558 1191
Literary Review 020-7437 9392
The Little Ship 020-7236 7729
Live & Kicking 020-8576 2000
Living 020-7261 5000
Lloyd's List International
01206-772277
Loaded 020-7261 5000
Lobster 01482-447558
Local Government Chronicle
020-7505 8000
Local Government News
020-8680 4200
Local Government Tenders
020-7505 8000

Local History Magazine
0115-9706473
Logisitic Europe 020-8943 5000
London Cyclist 020-7928 7220
London Gazette 020-7394 4580
London Hotel Mag 020-7373 7282
London Magazine 020-7925 2544
London Review of Books
020-7209 1141
London Theatre Guide
020-8545 8300
Looks 020-7437 9011
Loot 020-7625 0266

M
M magazine 020-7439 5000
M & S Magazine 020-7747 0700
Mac Format 01225-442244
MacUser 020-7631 1433
MacWorld 020-7831 9252
Mad About Dogs 020-7240 2032
Madam 0131-662 4445
Magazine News 020-7404 4166
Mailout 01484-469009
Majesty 020-7436 4006
Making Music 01322-660070
Management Today 020-8943 5000
Manchester United Magazine
0161-872 1661
Manufacturing Chemist
020-8309 7000
Marga Max 020-7620 0200
Marie Claire 020-7261 5000
Marie Claire Health & Beauty
020-7261 5000
Marine Conservation
01989-566017
Marketing 020-8943 5000
Marketing Direct 020-8943 5000
Marketing Events 020-8943 5000
Marketing Week 020-7439 4222
Master Builder 020-7242 7583
Match 01733-264666
Materials Recycling Week
020-8277 5540
Maxim 020-7631 1433
Max Power 01733-237111
Mayfair 020-7734 9191
MBUK 01225-442244
M & E Design 020-8652 3115
Meat Trades Journal
020-8565 4200
Medeconomics 020-8943 5000
Media & Marketing Europe
020-7505 8000
Media, Culture & Society
020-7374 0645
Media International 020-8652 3500
Media Week 020-7565 4200

Medical Imprint 020-8943 5000
Melody Maker 020-7261 5000
Men Only 020-7734 9191
Men's Health 020-7291 6000
Men's Wear 020-7520 1500
Metal Bulletin 020-7827 9977
Metal Hammer 020-7631 1433
Metalworking Production
020-8309 7000
Methodist Recorder 020-7251 8414
Micro Computer Mart
0121-233 8712
Microwave Engineering Europe
0181 309 7000
Middle East Economic Digest
020-7470 6200
Middle East Electricity
01737-768611
Middle East International
020-7373 5228
Midweek Magazine 020-7636 3666
Milap Weekly 020-7385 8966
Mims UK 020-8943 5000
Mind Your Own Business
020-8771 3614
Mining Journal/Magazine
020-7216 6060
Ministry 020-7378 6528
MiniWorld 020-8686 2599
Minx 020-7437 9011
Missles And Rockets
020-8700 3700
The Mix 01225-442244
Mixmag 020-7436 1515
Mizz 020-7261 5000
Model Rail 01733-898100
Modern History Review
01869-338652
Mojo 020-7436 1515
Money Management
020-7896 2525
Money Marketing 020-7439 4222
Money Marketing Focus Surveys
020-7439 4222
Money Observer 020-7713 4188
Moneywise 020-7715 8000
More! 020-7437 9011
Mother & Baby 020-7437 9011
Motor Cycle News 01536-411111
Motor Industry Management
01992-511521
Motor Ship 020-8652 3500
Motor Sport 020-8943 5000
Motor Trader 020-8652 3500
Motor Transport 020-8652 3500
Motorboat & Yachting
020-7261 5333
Motorcaravan Monthly
01778-393313
Motoring News 020-8943 5000

Mountain Bike Rider	020-7261 5000
Mountain Biker International	
	020-8686 2599
Mountain Bike UK	01225-442244
Movie Idols	020-8875 1520
Movie International	020-8574 2222
Moving Pictures International	
	020-7520 5200
Mslexia	0191-281 9772
MS London Magazine	
	020-7636 3322
Municipal Journal	020-7973 6400
Musclemag International	
	0121-327 7525
Museums Journal	020-7250 1834
Music Magazine	01733 370777
Music Week	020-7620 3636
Muzik	020-7261 5000

N

N64	01225-442244
National Trust Magazine	
	020-7222 9251
National Geographic	
	020-7365 0916
Natural World	020-7306 0304
Nature	020-7833 4000
Navy International	020-8700 3700
Navy News	023-9282 6040
Needlecraft	01225-442244
.net	01225 442244
the net	020-8943 5000
Network Week	020-7453 1300
Netwrok World	020-7453 1300
New Christian Herald	
	01903-821082
New Civil Engineer	020-7505 6600
New Eden	020-7261 5000
New Ground	020-7263 7424
New Humanist	020-7430 1371
New Internationalist	01865-728181
New Law Journal	020-7400 2500
New Left Review	020-7734 8830
New MediaAge	020-7439 4222
New MediaFinance	020-7439 4222
New Musical Express	
	020-7261 5000
New Scientist	020-7331 2701
New Statesman	020-7828 1232
New Stitches	01227-750215
New Times	020-7278 4451
New Woman	020-7437 9011
Newsweek International	
	020-7629 8361
Nine to Five	020-7436 3331
Nineteen	020-7261 6390
Nintendo Magazine	020-7972 6700
Ninento Official Mag	020-7880 7415
NME	020-7261 5000
Noddy	020-8576 2000

Northamptonshire Image	
	01604-231122
Now	020-7261 7366
Nursery Choice	020-7713 7000
Nursery World	020-7782-3120
Nursing Standard	020-8423 1066
Nursing Times	020-7843 3600

O

O Magazine	020-8600 9100
Observer Life (free)	020-7278 2332
Occupational Health	
	020-8652 3500
Off-Licence News	01293-613400
Office Equipment News	
	01322-277788
The Official Playstation Magazine	
	01225-442244
Offshore Engineer	020-8277 5000
Offshore Financial Review	
	020-7896 2525
OK!	020-7308 5090
Old Glory	01780-763063
The Oldie	020-7734 2225
Omnia	020-7925 2544
On Digital	020-8600 9100
On Target	01787-376374
One Shots	020-7631 1433
Opera	020-7359 1037
Opera Now	020-7333 1740
Optician	020-8652 3198
Oral History	01206-873055
Orbit	020-8780 2266
Our Baby	020-7261 5000
Our Dogs	0161-236 2660
Outsourcing	01732-359990

P

Pacemaker Update	020-8943 5000
Packaging News	020-8565 4200
Packaging Magazine	
	01732-364422
Panel Building	01732-359990
Parent Talk	01460-30500
Parents	020-7437 9011
Parikiaki	020-7272 6777
Parkers Car Price Guide	
	020-7477 7306
Parliament Magazine	
	020-7878 1500
Parliamentary Monitor	
	020-7878 1500
PASS	020-8652 3500
PC Advisor	020-7831 3191
PC Answers/Format/Plus	
	01225-442244
PC Dealer/Week	020-7316 9000
PC Direct/Magazine	020-7378 6800
PC Gamer	01225-442244
PC Gaming World	020-7903 6800

PC Guide	01225-442244
PC Know How	020-7581 1371
PC Pro	020-7917 3870
PC Review	01225 442244
PCS Magazine	020-7924 2727
PC Zone	020-7631 1433
Peace News	020-7278 3344
Pensions Week	020-7463 3000
Pensions Management	
	020-7896 2525
Pensions World	020-7896 2525
Penthouse	020-7308 5090
People's Friend	01382-223131
Perfect Home	020-8515 2000
Performance Bike	01733-237111
Performance Chemicals	
International	020-8652 8126
Period Living	020-7437 9011
Personal Computer World	
	020-7316 9000
Personnel Today	020-8652 3500
Pet Magic	01903-816600
Pet Product Marketing	
	01733-898100
Pet Reptile	01202-735090
Petroleum Economist	
	020-7831 5588
The PFI Report	020-7439 4222
Pharmacy Today	020-7334 7333
Pharmaceutical Journal	
	020-7735 9141
Photo Technique	020-7261 5000
The Photographer	01920-464011
Physics Review	01869-338652
Physics World	0117-929 7481
The Picture Business	
	020-8855 9201
Pig Farming	020-8309 7000
Pingu	020-8576 2000
Pink Paper	020-7296 6210
Plain Truth	020-8953 1633
Planet	01970-611255
Planet Playstation	01625-878888
Planned Savings	020-7505 8000
Planning	020-7413 4454
Plant Managers Journal	
	020-8652 3500
Plastics & Rubber Weekly	
	020-8277 5000
Play	01202-299900
Playdays	020-8576 2000
Playstation Plus	020-7972 6000
Playstation Power	01225-442244
Playststion Pro	01625-878888
Pocket Arrows/Crosswords/	
Wordsearch	01737-769799
Pocket Kidz!	01737-769799
Police	020-8399 2224
Police Review	020-7393 7600
Policing Today	020-8700 3700

Politics Review	01869-338652	
Popular Crafts	01322-660070	
Popular Patchwork	01322-660070	
Postgraduate Doctor		
	01243-576444	
Pot Black	020-8959 3611	
Poultry World	020-8652 3500	
Powerstation	01202-299900	
PR Week	020-7943 5000	
Practical Boat Owner		
	020-7261 5000	
Practical Caravan	020-8943 5000	
Practical Classics	01733-237111	
Everyday Practical Electronics		
	01202-881749	
Practical Fishkeeping		
	01733-898100	
Practical Householder		
	01322 660070	
Practical Internet	01202-299900	
Practical Parenting	020-7261 5000	
Practical Photography		
	01733-898100	
Practical Wireless	01202-659910	
Practical Woodworking		
	01322-660070	
Practice Nurse	020-8652 3123	
The Practitioner	020-8309 7000	
Precision Marketing	020-7439 4222	
Prediction	020-8686 2599	
Pregenancy & Birth	020-7437 9011	
Premiere	020-7208 3563	
Premises & Facilities Management		
	01732-359990	
Pre Press World	01732-364422	
Press Gazette	020-8565 4448	
Pride	020-7228 3110	
Prima	020-7519 5500	
Prima - Baby	020-7519 5500	
Prima- Christmas Traditions		
	020-7519 5500	
Prima - Your Home	020-7519 5500	
Prime Time Puzzles	01737-769799	
Print Week	020-8943 5000	
Printing World	01732-364422	
Private Eye	020-7437 4017	
Process Engineering		
	020-8309 7000	
Processing	01732-359990	
Production Journal	01442-233656	
Production Solutions		
	020-7505 8000	
Professional Engineering		
	01284-763277	
Professional Nurse	020-7843 3600	
Professional Printer	01892-538118	
Promotions and Incentives		
	020-8943 5000	
Property Week	020-7560 4000	
Prospect	020-7255 1281	

Psychic News	01279-817050	
The Psychologist	0116-254 9568	
Psychology Review	01869-338652	
Public Administration		
	01865-791100	
Public Finance	020-7543 5728	
Public Service & Local Govt		
	01959-565690	
Public Treasurer	020-7505 8000	
Publican	020-8565 4200	
Publishing News	020-7692 2900	
Pulse	020-8309 7000	
Punch	020-7225 6716	
Punjab Times	01332-372851	
Puzzle Compendium		
	020-8846 9922	
Puzzle Corner	01737-769799	
Puzzle Corner Special		
	01737-769799	
Puzzle Kids	01737-769799	
Puzzle Monthly	01322-660070	
Puzzle Mix Special	01737-769799	
Puzzle World	01322-660070	
Puzzler Collection/Puzzler		
	020-8846 9922	

Q

Q	020-7436 1515	
Quick and Easy Cross Stitch		
	01225-442244	
Quizkids	01737-769799	
Quizkids Special	01737-769799	

R

Race and Class	020-7837 0041	
Racing & Football Outlook		
	01635-578080	
Radio Communication		
	01707-659015	
Radio Control Models		
	01322-660070	
Radio Magazine	01536-418558	
Radio Modeller	01322-660070	
Radio Times	020-8576 2000	
Rail	01733-898100	
Railway Gazette International		
	020-8652 3500	
Railway Magazine	020-7261 5000	
Rambling Today	01480-496130	
The Raven	020-7247 9249	
Readers Digest	020-7715 8000	
Ready Steady Cook	020-7836 0519	
Record Collector	020-8579 1082	
Red	020-7437 9011	
Redline	01225-442244	
Red Pepper	020-7281 7024	
Regiment	01322-660070	
Resident Abroad	020-7896 2525	
Resurgence	01237-441293	
Retail Jeweller	020-7520 1500	

Retail Newsagent	020-7689 0600	
Retail Week	020-8277 5000	
Review of Social Economy		
	01264-343062	
The Review - Worldwide Insurance		
	020-7505 8000	
Revolution	020-8943 5000	
Revs	01733-237111	
Rhythm	01225-442244	
RIBA Journal	020-7560 4000	
Ride	01733-237111	
Right Start	020-7403 0840	
The Round Organ	01202-889669	
Rugby News	020-7323 1944	
Rugby World	020-7261 5000	
Runners World	020-7291 6000	
RUSI Journal	020-7930 5854	

S

Safeway Magazine	020-7747 0700	
Saga Magazine	01303-771527	
Sailing Today	01225-442244	
Sainsbury's: The Magazine		
	020-7633 0266	
Salisbury Review	020-7226 7791	
Satellite Times	0113-258 5008	
Satellite Trader	020-7896 2700	
Sayidaty	020-7831 8181	
Scene	01702-435328	
SchNews Magazine	01273-685913	
Scots Law Times	0131-225 4879	
Scots Magazine	01382-223131	
Scottish Farmer	0141-302 7700	
Scottish Field	0131-551 2942	
Scottish Memories	0141-204 3104	
Scouting	020-7584 7030	
Screen Digest	020-7482 5842	
Screen International	020-7505 8000	
Sea Angler	01733-264666	
Sea of Faith	015396-25321	
Searchlight	020-7284 4040	
Seatrade Review	01206-545121	
Security Management Today		
	01689-874025	
Select	020-7436 1515	
Sen- Shop Equipment & Shop		
Fitting News	020-8277 5000	
Sewing World	01684-594505	
SFX	01225 442244	
She	020-7439 5000	
Shivers	020-8875 1520	
Shoot!	020-7261 5000	
Shooting & Conservation		
	01244-573000	
Shooting Times	020-7261 5000	
Shopping Centre	01293-613400	
Short Wave Magazine		
	01202-659910	
Shropshire Magazine		
	01743-362175	

Sibyl	020-7226 2160
Sight & Sound	020-7255 1444
The Sign	01603-615995
The Singer	020-7333 1733
Skin Deep	01565-652424
Sky	020-7436 1515
Sky Digital TV Guide	020-7747 0700
Slimming	020-7437 9011
Smallholder	01453-544000
Smash Hits	020-7436 1515
Soccer Stars	020-7261 5000
Social Housing	020-7700 4199
Socialism Today	020-8533 3311
Socialist Affairs	020-7627 4449
Socialist Standard	020-7622 3811
Socialist Worker	020-7538 0828
Sociology Review	01869-338652
Solicitors Journal	020-7242 2548
Somerfield Mag	020-7478 4700
Sorted?	01273-683318
Special Schools in Britain	
	020-7439 4222
The Spectator	020-7405 1706
Spectrum	020-7478 4700
Spirit	020-8533 6667
Sport First	020-7878 1507
Sporting Gun	020-7261 5000
Sports Management	
	01462-431385
Sports Marketing	020-7439 4222
Spot	0181 576 2000
Spotlight	020-7437 7631
Stage, Screen & Radio	
	020-7437 8506
The Stage & Television Today	
	020-7403 1818
Star Trek	020-7620 0200
Starburst	020-8875 1520
Stargirl	01892-523767
Stars & Cars	020-8943 5000
Statewatch	020-8802 1882
Steam Railway	01733-898100
Steam World	01753-898100
Stillwater Trout Angler	
	020-7261 5000
Storyland	020-8653 1563
Straight No Chaser	020-7613 1594
The Strad	020-8863 2020
Streetwise	01737-769799
Structural Engineer	020-7235 4535
Subcon	020-8309 7000
Sunday Express Magazine (free)	
	020-7922 7297
Sunday Mirror Magazine (free)	
	020-7293 3000
Sunday Times Magazine (free)	
	020-7782 4000
SuperMarketing	020-8652 3500
Surrey County Magazine	
	01622-687031

The Surveyor	020-7973 6400
Sussex Life	01903-218719
Swarovski Magazine	
	020-7747 0700
Sweet FA	020-7284 0417

T

T3	01225-442244
The Tablet	020-8748 8484
Take a Break/Crossword/	
Look/Puzzle	020-7241 8000
The Taste	01780-763063
Tatler	020-7499 9080
Taxation	020-8686 9141
Technical Review Middle East	
	020-7834 7676
Teeny Weeny Families	
	01737-769799
Telegraph Magazine (free)	
	020-7538 5000
Teletubbies	020-8576 2000
Television (Reed)	020-8652 3500
Television (Royal TV Soc)	
	020-7430 1000
Television Business Internat	
	020-7896 2700
Televisual	020-7439 4222
That's Life!	020-7462 4700
Third Text	020-7372 0826
Third Way	020-7373 3432
The Thomas Cook Magazine	
	020-7747 0700
Timber For Architects	
	01732-364422
Timber Trades Journal	
	01732-364422
Time Life International	
	020-7499 4080
Time Out	020-7813 3000
Times Education Supplements	
	020-7782 3000
Times Literary Supplement	
	020-7782 3000
Titbits	020-7351 4995
Today's Golfer	01733-264666
Today's Runner	01733-264666
Top Of The Pops	020-8576 2000
Top Gear	020-8576 2000
Top Sante	020-7437 9011
Top Sante Health & Beauty	
	020-7938 3033
Total 64	01392-495155
Total Bike	01225-442244
Total Film	01225-442244
Total Football	01225-442244
Total Guitar	01225-442244
Total Production	01702-291292
Total Sport	020-7436 1515
Touch	020-7739 5727
Townswoman	01603-616005

Toybox	020-8576 2000
Toy Soldier & Model Figures	
	01403-711511
Toy Trader	01993-775545
Trade It	01202-445000
Trade Marks Journal	
	01633-811448
Traditional Homes	020-7437 9011
Trail	01733-264666
Training	020-8652 3500
Transit	01733-467000
Transport Retort	020-7388 8386
Travel Trade Gazette	
	020-8309 7000
Treasure Hunting	01376-521900
Trees	01342-712536
Trees are News	01342-712536
Tribune	020-7278 0911
Trout Fisherman	01733-264666
Trout & Salmon	01733-264666
Truck	020-8652 3500
Truck & Driver	020-8652 3500
TV & Satellite Week	020-7261 5000
TV Hits	020-7636 5095
TV Quick	020-7241 8000
TV Times	020-7261 5000
TV World	020-7505 8000
Tunnels and Tunnelling	
	020-8309 7000
Twinkle	01382 223131

U

UFO Times	01924-444049
UK press gazette	020-8565 4448
Ulster Nation	020-7373 3432
Ultimate PC	01392-495155
Uncut	020-7261 5000
Under Five Contact	020-7833 0991
Union Review	020-8462 7755
The Universe	0161-236 8856
Unmanned Vehicles	01628-664334
Untold	020-7729 8384
Update	020-8652 3500
Used Car Dealer	01733-467000
Utility Europe	020-8652 3500

V

Vanguard (Nat Dems)	
	07071-226074
Vanity Fair	020-7499 9080
The Vegetarian	0161-928 0793
Vegetarian Good Food (BBC)	
	020-7576 2000
Veterinary Times	01733-325522
Vintage Motor Cycle	
	01283-540557
Viz	020-7565 3000
Vogue	020-7499 9080
The Voice	020-7737 7377
Volvo Magazine	020-7747 0700

W

Wanderlust	01753-620426
The War Cry	020-7332 0022
Water	020-7240 2032
Water Gardener	01233-621877
Waterways	01283-790447
Wax	0141-353 1118
Wedding Cakes	01252-727572
Wedding & Home	020-7261 5000
The Week	020-7229 0006
Weekly Law Digest	020-8686 9141
Weekly News	01382-223131
Weight Watchers	020-8342 2222
What Bike?	01733-237111
What Camcorder?	020-7331 1000
What Car?	020-8943 5000
What Digital Camera?	
	020-7261
5000What Hi-Fi?	020-8943 5000
What Investment?	020-7827 5454
What Mobile & Cellphone	
	020-7251 6688
What Mortgage?	020-7827 5454
What PC & Software?	
	020-7316 9000
What Plant?	020-7505 6600
What Satellite?	020-7331 1000
What to Buy for Business	
	020-8652 3500
What Video?	020-7331 1000
What's New in Building/Design	
/Electronics/Farming/Industry/	
Interiors/Process & Control	
	020-8309 7000
What's On TV	020-7261 5000

When Saturday Comes	
	020-7729 1110
Which Motorcaravan	
	01778-391000
Which?	020-7830 6000
Whisky Magazine	020-8563 2975
Wide World	01869-338652
Wild London	020-7261 0447
Wildfowl and Wetlands	
	01453 890333
Windows Expert	01625-878888
Wine	020-7549 2575
The Wire	020-7439 6422
Wisden Cricket Monthly	
	01483-570358
WM	029-2058 3583
Woman	020-7261 5000
Woman & Home	020-7261 5000
Woman Alive	01903-821082
Woman's Journal	020-7261 5000
Woman's Own	020-7261 5000
Woman's Realm	020-7261 5000
Woman's Weekly	020-7261 5000
Women & Golf	020-7261 5000
Women in General Practice	
	020-7843 3600
Wood Based Panels International	
	01732-364422
Woodworker	01322-660070
Woodworking News	
	01474-536535
Word Search	020-8846 9922
Workers' Health	0114-276 5695
Working Women	020-8947 3131

Works Management	
	01689-850156
World of Interiors	020-7499 9080
World Soccer	020-7261 5000
The World Today	020-7957 5700
World's Fair	0161-624 3687
Working Together	01522-544400
Writers News	01667-454441
Writers Newsletter	020-7723 8074
Writing Magazine	01667-454441

X

X Files Monthly	020-7620 0200
XL for Men	020-7436 1515
Xpose	020-8875 1520

Y

Yachting Monthly	020-7261 5000
Yachting World	020-7261 5000
You Magazine (free)	020-7938 6000
You & Your Wedding	
	020-7437 3493
The Young Dancer	01769-574929
Your Cat/Dog	01733-898100
Your Garden	01202 440840
Your Greatest Guide to Calories	
	020-7437 9011
Your Horse	01733-264666
Your Mortgage?	020-7833 5566
Yours	01733-555123

Z

Zest	020-7439 5000
Zipper	020-7482 2576
Zit	01273-773224
ZM	020-7439 5000

TO ALL MAGAZINE PUBLISHERS

UPDATE FOR THE 2001 MEDIA GUIDE

Use this space below to list new magazines or changes of phone number

PHOTOCOPY AND SEND TO: Paul Fisher, Media Guide, The Guardian, 119 Farringdon Road, London EC1R 3ER

E-mail: paulfisher@online.rednet.co.uk

Book publishing

Rich authors getting richer and the rise of multi-media have replaced corporate mergers as the main book publishing news lines.

A flurry of transfer activity saw the likes of Sue Townsend and John Lanchester making small headlines. Bigger headlines went to Martin Amis when he signed with Miramax in a $1 million American deal which involves an autobiography, a novel, a collection of essays and a film script. Then there was the £2 million transfer which had Nick Hornby move from Gollancz to Penguin. Then again there was HarperCollins swooping for Michael Owen, a sublime footballer who probably couldn't even draft a bus ticket. His £2 million three book deal puts him £1 million ahead of that other publishing sensation, Alex Ferguson.

Meanwhile technology advanced and the net was brought to book. Increasing numbers of conventional books were sold on the web via amazon.com. Advance internet orders established JK Rowling's third Harry Potter book as number one seller before it had actually reached the book shops. Meanwhile reference works migrated to CD ROM and Digital Video Discs and Macmillan's announced it is putting its Dictionary of Art and New Grove Dictionary of Music and Musicians on line.

Top 50 publishers by sales (£m)

	'97/98 sales	%increase		'97/98 sales	%increase
1 **Reed Professional**	£1,076.0m	3.8%	26 **Parragon**	£25.7m	-50.8%
2 **Reed Scientific**	£571.0m	3.3%	27 **Cassell**	£23.3m	-4.8%
3 **Pearson Education**	£563.6m	1.7%	28 **Stanley Thomas**	£22.7m	10.3%
4 **Harper Collins**	£436.0m	1.1%	29 **Reed Children's**	£20.7m	-1.5%
5 **Macmillan**	£295.0m	8.9%	30 **Simon & Schuster UK**	£20.3m	3%
6 **OUP**	£282.0m	1.4%	31 **Tolley Publishing**	£19.6m	10.7%
7 **Dorling Kindersley**	£184.0m	2.2%	32 **Thames & Hudson**	£18.8m	-3%
8 **Random House**	£100.0m	7.5%	33 **Thomas Nelson**	£18.5m	-14.9%
9 **Penguin UK**	£99.1m	4.5%	34 **David & Charles**	£17.9m	6.5%
10 **Hodder Headline**	£93.2m	0.4%	35 **IOP Publishing**	£17.8m	9.5%
11 **Blackwell Science**	£92.7m	4.1%	36 **BPP Publishing**	£16.8m	7.7%
12 **Quarto**	£81.8m	1.5%	37 **Bloomsbury**	£13.7m	0.4%
13 **Transworld**	£69.3m	4.4%	38 **Usborne**	£13.3m	0.3%
14 **Wiley Europe**	£56.2m	9.3%	39 **Kingfisher Publications**	£13.1m	-9.7%
15 **Croner Publications**	£48.5m	18.1%	40 **Collins & Brown**	£12.3m	47.2%
16 **Routledge**	£47.1m	32.7%	41 **Element**	£12.0m	23.7%
17 **Octopus**	£44.8m	-	42 **Phaidon Press**	£11.0m	24.7%
18 **Orion**	£37.2m	17.4%	43 **Faber**	£10.6m	6.3%
19 **Little, Brown**	£36.8m	6.4%	44 **Wayland Publishers**	£9.6m	3.8%
20 **Scholastic**	£36.4m	32.9%	45 **Chivers**	£9.0m	2.7%
21 **Walker Books**	£31.7m	8.2%	46 **Chadwyck-Healey**	£8.2m	-15.7%
22 **Grolier (Watts Publ)**	£31.6m	8.5%	47 **Kogan Page**	£7.5m	1.1%
23 **Taylor & Francis**	£30.1m	4.9%	48 **A & C Black**	£7.1m	0.8%
24 **Haynes**	£28.7m	4.7%	49 **Lion Publishing**	£6.8m	5.8%
25 **Blackwell Publishers**	£27.7m	16.6%	50 **Andre Deutsch**	£5.3m	61.9%

Source: The Bookseller.

TOP BOOK PUBLISHERS

Andre Deutsch
76 Dean Street, London W1V 5HA
Fax 020-7316 4499   Tel 020-7316 4450
Website: www.vci.co.uk

A & C Black
35 Bedford Row, London WC1R 4JH
Fax 020-7831 8478   Tel 020-7242 0946
E-mail: enquiries @acblack.co.uk

Blackwell Publishers
108 Cowley Road, Oxford OX4 1JF
Fax 01865-791347   Tel 01865-791100
Part of the independently held book and journal
company, the Blackwell Group.The list spans the
humanities, social sciences and business and publishes
textbooks, professional periodicals and software.

Blackwell Science
Osney Mead, Oxford OX2 0EL
Fax 01865-721205   Tel 01865-206206
Website: www.blackwell-science.com

Bloomsbury
38 Soho Square, London W1V 5DF
Fax 020-7434 0151   Tel 020-7494 2111
Website: www.bloomsbury.com

BPP (Publishing)
142-144 Uxbridge Road, London W12 8AW
Fax 020-8740 1184   Tel 020-8740 2211
E-mail: publishing@bpp.co.uk
Website: www.bpp.co.uk

Cassell
125 Strand, London WC2R 0BB
Fax 020-7240 7261   Tel 020-7420 5555
E-mail: jyc@orionbooks.co.uk
Website: www.cassell.co.uk
A memberof the Orion Group. Best sellers include: The
Plant Hunters, Musgrave et al; Cassell Dictionary of
Slang, Jonathon Green; Risotto! Risotto!, Valentina
Harris.

Chadwyck-Healey
The Quorum, Barnwell Road, Cambridge CB5 8SW
Fax 01223-215513   Tel 01223-215512
E-mail: mail@chadwyck.co.uk
Website: www.chadwyck.co.uk
Leading electronic publisher of the arts, humanities and
social sciences. Their top three titles are: Literature
Online, KnowUK, Periodicals Contents Index.

Collins & Brown
London House, Parkgate Road, London SW11 4NQ
Fax 020-7924 7725   Tel 020-7924 2575

Croner Publications
London Road, Kingston upon Thames, KT2 6SR
Fax 020-8547 2637   Tel 020-8547 3333
E-mail: info@croner.co.uk
Website: www.croner.co.uk

David & Charles
Brunel House, Forde Close, Newton Abbot, Devon
TQ12 4PU
Fax 01626-364463   Tel 01626-323200
Website: www.davidandcharles.co.uk

Dorling Kindersley
9 Henrietta Street, London WC2E 8PS
Fax 020-7836 7570   Tel 020-7836 5411
E-mail: comments@dkonline.com
Website: www.dk.com

Egmont Children's Books
See Reed Children's

Element Books
The Old School House, The Courtyard, Bell Street,
Shaftesbury, Dorest SP7 8BP
Fax 01747 855721   Tel 01747 851448
Health, colour illustrated books, children.

Faber and Faber
3 Queen Square, London WC1N 3AU
Fax 020-7465 0034   Tel 020-7465 0045
E-mail: faber.co.uk
Top sellers include: Birthday Letters, Ted Hughes; A
Certain Justice, P D James; Intimacy, Hanif Kureishi.

Financial Times Business
149 Tottenham Court Road, London W1P 9LL
Fax 020-7896 2099   Tel 020-7896 2000

Fourth Estate
6 Salem Road, London W2 4BU
Fax 020-7792 3176   Tel 020-7727 8993
E-mail: general@4thestate.co.uk

Grolier
29 Morgan Way, Bowthorpe, Norwich NR5 9PP
Fax 01603-740401   Tel 01603-740740

Guinness Publishing
33 London Road, Middlesex EN2 6DJ
Fax 020-8367 5912   Tel 020-7891 4567

Harlequin Mills & Boon
18-24 Paradise Road, Richmond, Surrey TW9 1SR
Fax 020-8288 2899   Tel 020-8288 2800

HarperCollins Publishers
77-85 Fulham Palace Road, London W6 8JB
Fax 020-8307 4440   Tel 020-8741 7070
E-mail: name.surname@harpercollins.co.uk
Website: www.fireandwater.com

Haynes
Sparkford, Yeovil, Somerset BA22 7JJ
Fax 01963-440001   Tel 01963-440635
E-mail: sales@haynes-manuals.co.uk
Website: www.haynes.com
Haynes publish a range of motoring, motorcycling, motorsport, camping, cycling and DIY publications.

Hodder Headline
338 Euston Road, London NW1 3BH
Fax 020-7873 6024   Tel 020-7873 6000
Website: www.headline.co.uk

IOP Publishing
Dirac House, Temple Back, Bristol BS1 6BE
Fax 0117-929 4318   Tel 0117-929 7481
E-mail: margaret.ogorman@ioppublishing.co.uk
Website: www.iop.org

John Murray
50 Albemarle Street, London W1X 4BD
Fax 020-7499 1792   Tel 020-7493 4361
E-mail: s.allen@jmpub.freeserve.co.uk
General and education publisher. Best sellers include: No Voice from the Hall, John Harris; Mama Tina, Christina Noble; Cunningham: The Greatest Admiral Since Nelson, John Winton.

John Wiley & Sons
Baffins Lane, Chichester, West Sussex PO19 1UD
Fax 01243-775878   Tel 01243-779777
E-mail: europe@wiley.co.uk

Kingfisher Publications
283-288 High Holborn, London WC1V 7HZ
Fax 020-7242 4979   Tel 020-7903 9999
E-mail: initialsurname@kingfisherpub.co.uk
Top seller: The Kingfisher Book of Space, Martin Redfern

Kogan Page
120 Pentonville Road, London N1 9JN
Fax 020-7837 6348   Tel 020-7278 0433
E-mail: kpinfo@kogan-page.co.uk
Website: www.kogan-page.co.uk

Lion Publishing
Peter's Way, Sandy Lane West, Oxford OX4 5HG
Fax 01865-747568   Tel 01865-747550
Website: www.lion/publishing.co.uk

Little Brown
Brettenham Ho, Lancaster Place, London WC2E 7EN
Fax 020-7911 8100   Tel 020-7911 8000
Hardback and large format paperbacks, its imprints are Abacus, Orbit, Virago and Warner.

Macmillan Publishers
25 Eccleston Place, London SW1W 9NF
Fax 020-7881 8001   Tel 020-7881 8000

Michael O'Mara Books
9 Lion Yard, Tremadoc Road, London SW4 7NQ
Fax 020-7627 8953   Tel 020-7720 8643
E-mail: firstname.surname@michaelmarabooks.com
General non-fiction - royalty, history and humour. Top sellers include: Diana: The Secret Years, Simone Simmons; Diana: Her True Story, Andrew Morton; The History of Farting, Dr Benjamin Bart.

Mills and Boon
See Harlequin Mills and Boon

Octopus
2-4 Heron Quay, London E14 4JP
Fax 020-7531 86503   Tel 020-7531 8400

Orion
5 Upper St Martin's Lane, London WC2H 9EA
Fax 020-7240 4822   Tel 020-7240 3444

OUP (Oxford University Press)
Great Clarendon Street, Oxford OX2 6DP
Fax 01865-556646   Tel 01865 556767
Website: www.oup.co.uk

Parragon
Queen Street House, 4 Queen Street, Bath BA1 1HE
Fax 01225 443681   Tel 01225 478888
E-mail: firstname@parragon.com

Pearson Education
Edinburgh Gate, Harlow, Essex CM20 2JE
Fax 01279-431059   Tel 01279-623623
E-mail: pearsoned-ema.com
Website: www.pearsoned-ema.com
Major educatioal publisher for ELT, higher education and schools.

Pearson Professional
see Financial Times Business

Penguin Books
Bath Road, Harmondsworth, Middx UB7 0DA
Fax 020-8899 4099   Tel 020-8899 4000
27 Wrights Lane, London W8 5TZ
Fax 020-7416 3099   Tel 020-7416 3000
Website: www.penguin.co.uk

Phaidon Press
Regent's Wharf, All Saints Street, London N1 9PA
Fax 020-7843 1010   Tel 020-7843 1000
E-mail: sales@phaidon.com
Leading publishers of books on art, architecture, design, photography, decorative arts and music.

Piatkus
5 Windmill Street, London W1P 1HF
Fax 020-7436 7137   Tel 020-7631 0710
E-mail: info@piatkus.co.uk

Quarto
The Old Brewery, 6 Blundell Street, London N7 9BH
Fax 020-7700 4191   Tel 020-7700 6700

Random House
20 Vauxhall Bridge Road, London SW1V 2SA
Fax 020-7932 0761   Tel 020-7840 8400
Website: www.randomhouse.co.uk

Reed Children's
239 Kensington High Street, London W8 6SA
Fax 020-7761 3510   Tel 020-7761 3500

Reed Elsevier
25 Victoria Street, London SW1H 0EX
Fax 020-7227 5799   Tel 020-7222 8420
Website: www.reed-elsevier.com

Reed Educational & Professional Publishing
Halley Court, Jordan Hill, Oxford OX2 8EJ
Fax 01865-314641   Tel 01865-314097
E-mail: reeed.educational@repp.co.uk
Website: www.repp.com
Publishes educational and scientific books.

Routledge
11 New Fetter Lane, London EC4P 3EE
Fax 020-7842 2298   Tel 020-7842 2299
Website: www.tandf.co.uk
Part of the Taylor Francis Group.

Scholastic
Commonwealth House, 1-19 New Oxford Street, London WC1A 1NU
Fax 020-7421 9001   Tel 020-7421 9000
Website: www.scholastic.co.uk
Publishes fiction and non-fiction for children. Top sellers include the Goosebumps and Horrible Histories series.

Simon & Schuster UK
Africa House, 64-78 Kingsway, London WC2B 6AH
Fax 020-7316 0331   Tel 020-7316 1900

Stanley Thornes
Ellenburgh House, Wellington Street, Cheltenham GL50 1YW
Fax 01242-221914   Tel 01242-228888
Website: www.thornes.co.uk

Taylor & Francis
11 New Fetter Lane, London EC4P 3EE
Fax 020-7842 2298   Tel 020-7842 2299
E-mail: first name.surname@tandf.co.uk
Website: www.tandf.co.uk
International academic publisher of books and over 450 journals a year.

Thames & Hudson
181a High Holborn, London WC1V 7QX
Fax 020-7845 5050   Tel 020-7845 5000
E-mail: mail@thbooks.demon.co.uk
Website: www.thameshudson.co.uk

Thomas Nelson & Sons
Nelson House, Mayfield Road, Walton-on-Thames, Surrey KT12 5PL
Fax 01932-246109   Tel 01932-252211
E-mail: nelinfo@nelson.co.uk
Website: www.nelson.co.uk
Educational publishing company.

Tolley Publishing
Tolley House, 2 Addiscombe Road, Croydon, Surrey CR9 5AF
Fax 020-78681 7986   Tel 020-8686 9141
E-mail: sales@tolley.co.uk

Transworld Publishers
61-63 Uxbridge Road, London W5 5SA
Fax 020-8579 5479   Tel 020-8579 2652
E-mail: info@transworld-publishers.co.uk
Publishes general trade fiction and non-fiction, plus children's books, and the Expert list of gardening books.

Usborne
83-85 Saffron Hill, London EC1N 8RT
Fax 020-7430 1562   Tel 020-7430 2800
Website: www.usborne.com

Walker Books
87 Vauxhall Walk, London SE11 5HJ
Fax 020-7587 1123   Tel 020-7793 0909
Books for children.

Wayland Publishers
61 Western Road, Hove, East Sussex BN3 1JD
Fax 01273-329314   Tel 01273-722561
Children's information books.

Whitaker
12 Dyott Street, London WC1A 1DF
Fax 020-7836 2909   Tel 020-7420 6000
Website: www.thebookseller.com

PUBLISHERS

A

AA Publishing	01256-20123
Addison Wesley Longman	01279-623623
Allen Lane	020-7416 3121
Allison & Busby	020-7636 2942
Andre Deutsch	020-7580 2746
Anness Publishing	020-7401 2077
Arrow Books	020-7840 8400
Athlone Press	020-8458 0888
Aurum Press	020-7637 3225

B

Bantam	020-8579 2652
Batsford	020-7471 1100
Baylin Publications	0118-941 4468
BBC Books	020-8576 3017
Bedford Square Press	020-7713 6161
Billboard	020-7323 6686
A&C Black	020-7242 0946
Blackwell	01865-791100
Blandford Press	020-7420 5555
Bloodaxe Books	01434-684855
Bloomsbury	020-7494 2111
Bodley Head	020-7840 8400
Bowker-Saur	01342-326972
Boxtree	020-7881 8000
British Film Institute	020-7255 1444
Broadcast Books	020-8769 3483
Butterworth	020-7400 2500
Butterworth-Heinemann	01865-310366

C

Cambridge University Press	01223-312393
Carcanet Press	020-7734 7338
Cassell	020-7420 5555
Cavendish Publishing	020-7278 8000
CBD Research	020-8650 7745
Chambers	020-7903 9889
Chapman & Hall	020-7865 0066
Chatto & Windus	020-7840 8400
Collins & Brown	020-7924 2575
Conran Octopus	020-7240 6961
Constable	020-8741 3663
Corgi	020-8579 2652
Coronet	020-7873 6000

D

Darton, Longman & Todd	020-8875 0155
David & Charles	01626-61121
Demos	020-7353 4479
JM Dent & Sons	020-7240 3444
Dorling Kindersley	020-7836 5411
Doubleday	020-8579 2652
Dragonflair Publishing	01694-722504

E

Ebury Press	020-7840 8400
Egmont Fleetway	020-7344 6400
Element Books	01747-851339
Emap Media	020-7837 1212
Euromonitor	020-7251 8024

F

Faber & Faber	020-7465 0045
Flicks Books	01225 760756
Focal Press	01865-311366
Fontana	020-8741 7070
Fourth Estate	020-7727 8993
Frank Cass	020-8599 8866
Frederick Warne	020-7416 3000
FT Management	020-7379 7383

G

Gaia Books	020-7323 4010
George Philip	020-7581 9393
GMP Publishers	01366-328101
Guinness Publishing	020-8891 4567

H

Hamish Hamilton	020-7416 3000
Hamlyn	020-7581 9393
Harcourt Brace	020-7267 4466
HarperCollins	020-8741 7070
Harrap	0131-557 4571
Heinemann	020-7840 8400
HMSO Books	020-7873 0011
Hodder Headline	020-7873 6000
Hollis Directories	020-8977 7711
How To Books	01865-793806
Hutchinson Books	020-7840 8400

I

Interactive Media Publications	020-7837 3345

J

Jarrold	01603-763300
John Libbey & Co	020-8947 2777
John Wiley & Sons	01243-779777
Jonathan Cape	020-7840 8400
Journeyman Press	020-8348 2724

K

Kingfisher	020-7903 9999
Kogan Page	020-7278 0433

L

Ladybird Books	01509-268021
Larousse	020-7903 9999
Lawrence & Wishart	020-8533 2506
Longman Group	01279-623623
Lutterworth Press	01223-350865

M

Macdonald Young Books	01273-722561
McGraw-Hill	01628-623432
Macmillan Publisher	020-7881 8000
Mandarin	020-7840 8400
Mansell Publishing	020-7420 5555
Marion Boyars	020-8788 9522
Marshall Cavendish	020-7734 6710
Methuen	020-7840 8400
Michael Joseph	020-7416 3000
Miller Freeman	01732-362666
Mills & Boon	020-8948 0444
Mitchell Beazley	020-7840 8400

N

Network Books	020-8576 3017
New English Library	020-7876 6000
Nicholas Brealey	020-7713 7455
NTC Publications	01491-574671

O

Octopus Publishing	020-7531 8400
Osprey	020-7225 9365
OUP	01280-823388
OUP	01865-556767

P

Paladin Books	020-8741 7070
Pan Books	020-7373 4997
Pandora Press	020-8741 7070
Parragon Books	01225 478888
PDQ Publishing	01865-820387
Penguin Books	020-7416 3000
Pergamon Press	01865-310111
Piatkus Books	020-7631 0710
Picador	020-7373 6070
Philips	020-7225 9826
Pitkin Guides	01264 334303
Pluto Press	020-8348 2724
Polity Press	01223-324315
Puffin	020-7416 3000

Q

Quartet Books	020-7636 3992

R

Random House	020-7840 8400
Readers Digest	020-7629 8144
Reed Information Services	01342-335832
Reed Books	020-7581 9393
Routledge	020-7583 9855
Rushmere	01502-574515

S

Salamander Books	020-7700 7799
Secker & Warburg	020-7840 8400
Shire Publications	01844-344301
Sidgwick & Jackson	020-7373 6070
Simon & Schuster	020-7316 9100
Sweet & Maxwell	020-7538 8686

T

Thames & Hudson	020-7636 5488
Thames Publishing	020-8969 3579
Thomas Nelson & Sons	01264-342832
Tolley Publishing	020-8686 9141
Transworld Publishers	020-8579 2652

U

Usborne Publishing	020-7430 2800

V

Verso	020-7437 3546
Victor Gollancz	020-7420 5555
Viking	020-7416 3000
Virago Press	020-7383 5150
Virgin Publishing	020-7386 3300

W

Ward Lock	020-7420 5555
Weidenfeld & Nicolson	020-7240 3444
J Whitaker & Sons	020-7420 6000
William Heinemann	020-7840 8400
Windrush Press	01608-652012
Womens Press	020-7251 3007

Z

Zed Books	020-7837 4014

LITERARY AGENTS

KEY CONTACT

Association of Authors' Agents
62 Grafton Way, London W1P 5LD
Fax 020-7387 2042   Tel 020-7387 2076
The Association of Authors' Agents maintains a code of professional practice to which all members of the Association commit themselves; holds regular meetings to discuss matters of common professional interest; and provides a vehicle for representing the view of authors' agents in discussion of matters of common interest with other professional bodies.

AM Heath & Co
79 St Martins Lane, London WC2N 4AA
Fax 020-7497 2561   Tel 020-7836 4271
Main authors: Anita Brookner, Graham Hancock, George Orwell
Areas covered: Fiction, non-fiction, reference etc.
AP Watt
20 John Street, London WC1N 2DR
Fax 020-7831 2154   Tel 020-7405 6774
E-mail: apw@apwatt.co.uk
Abner Stein Agency
10 Roland Gardens, London SW7 3PH
Fax 020-7370 6316   Tel 020-7373 0456
The Agency (London)
24 Pottery Lane, London W11 4LZ
Fax 020-7727 9037   Tel 020-7727 1346
Main authors: Jimmy McGovern, Ian McEwa, Kay Mellor
Areas covered: Film and TV.
Aitken & Stone
29 Fernshaw Road, London SW10 0TG
Fax 020-7376 3594   Tel 020-7351 7561
E-mail: 100303.1765@compuserve.com
Main authors: Pat Barker, Agatha Christie, Susan Howatch, Paul Theroux
Andrew Lownie
17 Sutherland Street, London SW1V 4JV
Fax 020-7828 7608   Tel 020-7828 1274
E-mail: lownie@globalnet.co.uk
Website: www.andrewlownie.co.uk
Main authors: Norma Major, Alan Whicker
Areas covered: Hisotry, biography, current affairs, UFOs, food & wine, special forces.
Andrew Mann
1 Old Compton Street, London W1V 5PH
Fax 020-7287 9264   Tel 020-7734 4751
E-mail: manscript@compuserve.com
Areas covered: Fiction, non-fiction, TV, radio, film.
Andrew Nurnberg Associates
Clerkenwell House, 45-47 Clerkenwell Green, London EC1R 0HT
Fax 020-7417 8812   Tel 020-7417 8800
E-mail: anurnberg@nurnberg.co.uk
Areas covered: Fiction and non-fiction.

Barbara Levy
64 Greenhill, Hampstead High Street, London NW3 5TZ
Fax 020-7431 2063   Tel 020-7435 9046
Areas covered: General non-fiction and fiction, TV presenters.
Blake Friedmann
122 Arlington Road, London NW1 7HP
Fax 020-7284 0442   Tel 020-7284 0408
E-mail: firstname@blakefriedmann.co.uk
Main authors: Gilbert Adair, Jane Asher, John Harvey, Ken Hom, Glenn Meade, Joseph O'Connor, Michael Ridpath
Areas covered: Commercial and literary fiction, wide range of non-fiction. No juvenile, poetry, science ficiton or fantasy.
Campbell Thomson & McLaughlin
1 King's Mews, London WC1N 2JA
Fax 020-7242 2408   Tel 020-7242 0958
Areas covered: Most areas except academic and childrens.
Caroline Sheldon Literary Agency
71 Hillgrove Place, London
                           Tel 020-7727 9102
Areas covered: Fiction, particularly women's and children'c books.
Cat Ledger Literary Agency
33 Percy Street, London W1P 9FG
Fax 020-7 631 4273   Tel 020-7436 5030
Charles Pick Consultancy
Flat 3, 3 Bryanston Place, London W1H 7FN
Fax 020-7724 5990   Tel 020-7402 8043
E-mail: 100551.3554@compuserve.com
Main authors: Wilbur Smith, Deidre Purcell, Julie Parsons
Areas covered: Fiction, non-fiction especially human rights and international relations.
Christine Green
40 Doughty Street, London WC1N 2LF
Fax 020-7405 3935   Tel 020-7831 4956
Areas covered: Fiction and general non-fiction, no sci-fi, childrens or poetry.
Christopher Little
10, Eel Brook Studios, 125 Moore Park Road, London SW6 4PS
Fax 020-7736 4490   Tel 0171 736 4455
E-mail: christopher@clittle.co.uk
Main authors: J K Rowling, Simon Singh, Michael Cordy, Robert Mawson, Rebbecca Ray
Areas covered: Literary and commercial fiction and non-fiction, first novelists and scientists.
Curtis Brown
Haymarket House, 28/29 Haymarket, London SW1Y 4SP
Fax 020-7396 0110   Tel 020-7396 6600
E-mail: cb@curtisbrown.co.uk

Darley Anderson
Estelle House, 11 Eustace Road, London SW6 1JB
Fax 020-7386 5571   Tel 020-7385 6652
E-mail: DAnderson6652@aol.com
Main authors: Paul Carson, Lee Child, Martina Cole,
John Connolly, Lesley Pearse, Peter Sheridan, Beryl
Kingston, Joan Jonker, Jane English, Adrian Plass
Areas covered: Popular commercial fiction and non-
fiction including crime and C20 romantic sagas.
Investigative books, popular psychology and self-
improvement.

David Higham Associates
5/8 Lower John Street, Golden Square, London W!R
4HA
Fax 020-7437 1072   Tel 020-7437 7888

Deborah Owen
78 Narrow Street, London E14 8BP
Fax 020-7538 4004   Tel 020-7987 5119
Main authors: Delia Smith, Amos Oz, Ellis Peters
No new authors at present.

Dinah Wiener
12 Cornwall Grove, Chiswick, London W4 2LB
Fax 020-8994 6044   Tel 020-8994 6011
E-mail: dinahwiener@enterprise.net

Ed Victor
6 Bayley Street, Bedford Square, London WC1B 3HB
Fax 020-7304 4111   Tel 020-7304 4100
E-mail: edvicltd@dircon.co.uk
Main authors: Douglas Adams, Frederick Forsyth,
Josephine Hart, Jack Higgins, Erica Jong, Kathy Lette,
Erich Segal, Lisa St Aubin de Tera'n
Areas covered: Fiction and non-fiction.

Edwards Fuglewicz
49 Great Ormond Street, London WC1N 3HZ
Fax 020-7405 6726   Tel 020-7405 6725
Areas covered: Fiction (literary and quality commercial),
non-fiction.

Faith Evans Associates
27 Park Avenue North, London N8 7RU
Fax 020-8340 9410   Tel 020-8340 9920

Felicity Bryan
2A North Parade, Banbury Road, Oxford OX2 6LX
Fax 01865-310055   Tel 01865 513816
Main authors: Karen Armstrong, Liza Cody, Angela
Huth, John Julius Norwich, Iain Pears, Rosamunde
Pilcher, Matt Ridley, Roy Strong
Areas covered: History, science, literary fiction.

Frances Kelly
111 Clifton Road, Kingston-upon-Thames Surrey KT2
6PL
Fax 020-8547 0051   Tel 020-8549 7830
Areas covered: Non-fiction

Futerman Associates
17 Deanhill Road, London SW14 7DQ
Fax 020-8286 4861   Tel 020-8286 4860
Main authors: Judy Upton, Joseph Miller, Peter King,
Angela Meredith, Sally Becker, Brian Milton
Areas covered: Fiction with film potential, stage plays,
screen plays, biography, show business.

Greene & Heaton
37 Goldhawk Road, London W12 8QQ
Fax 020-8749 0318   Tel 020-8749 0315

Gregory & Radice
3 Barb Mews, London W6 7PA
Fax 020-7610 4686   Tel 020-7610 4676
E-mail: info@gregoryradice.co.uk
Main authors:Minette Walter, Val McDermid, Mo
Hayder, Sophie Hannah
Areas covered: Literary and commercial fiction, crime,
thrillers, politics, non-fiction.

Intercontinental Literary Agency (Translation
rights only)
5th Floor, the chambers, Chelsea Harbour, London
SW10 0XF
Fax 020-8351 4809   Tel 020-8351 4763

Jane Conway Gordon
1 Old Compton Street, London W1V 5PH
Fax 020-7287 9264   Tel 020-7494 0148
Areas covered: Fiction and non-fiction, no poetry
or science fiction.

Jane Judd Literary Agency
18 Belitha Villas, London N1 1PD
Fax 020-7607 0623   Tel 020-7607 0273
Areas covered: General fiction and non-fiction.

Jane Turnbull
13 Wendell Road, London W12 9RS
Fax 020-8749 6079   Tel 020-8743 9580

John Farquharson
4th Floor, Haymarket House, 28/29 Haymarket,
London SW1Y 4SP
Fax 020-7396 0110   Tel 020-7396 6600
E-mail: cb@curtisbrown.co.uk

John Johnson
Clerkenwell House, 45-47 Clerkenwell Green, London
EC1R 0HT
Fax 020-7251 2172   Tel 020-7 251 0125
E-mail: johnjohnson@btinternet.com

Jonathan Clowes
10 Iron Bridge House, Bridge Approach, London NW1
8BD
Fax 020-7722 7677   Tel 020-7722 7674

Judith Chilcote
8 Wentworth Mansions, Keats Grove, London NW3
2RL
Fax 020-7794 7431   Tel 020-7794 3717
Main authors: Jane Alecxander, Fiona Harold
Areas covered: Commecial fiction, sport, cinema, self-
help, health, TV tie-ins.

Limelight Management
33 Newman Street, London W1P 3PD
Fax 020-7637 2529   Tel 020-7637 2538
E-mail: limelight.management@virgin.net
Areas covered: Non-fiction only.

Lisa Eveleigh
26a Rochester Square, London NW1 9SA
Fax 020-7485 6960   Tel 020-7267 5245
E-mail: eveleigh@dial.pipex.com
Areas covered: Literary and commercial fiction.

Lucas Alexander Whitley
14 Vernon Street, London W14 0RJ
Fax 020-7471 7910   Tel 020-7471 7900
E-mail: law@lawagency.co.uk
Areas covered: fiction, non-fiction, not poetry, short
stories or children's books.

Lutyens & Rubinstein
231 Westbourne Park Road, London W11 1EB
Fax 020-7792 4833   Tel 020-7792 4855
E-mail: name@luru.demon.co.uk
Areas covered: Literary and commercial fiction, non-fiction. No sci-fi, fantasy, poetry or children's books.

MBA Literary Agency
62 Grafton Way, London W1P 5LD
Fax 020-7387 2042   Tel 020-7387 2076
E-mail: agent@mbalit.co.uk
Main authors: Anne McCaffery, Anne Parry
Areas covered: Everything.

Maggie Noach Literary Agency
21 Redan Street, London W14 0AB
Fax 020-7603 4712   Tel 020-7602 2451
Areas covered: Literary fiction, travel writing, history, biography, children's books (7 upwards).

Maggie Pearlstine
31 Ashley Gardens, London SW1P 1QE
Fax 020-7834 5546   Tel 020-7828 4212
E-mail: mp@authsagt.demon.co.uk
Main authors: John Biffen, Menzies Campbell, Uri Geller, Roy Hattersley, Lisa Jardine, Charles Kennedy, Mark Leonard, Raj Persaud, Lesley Reagan, Jack Straw, Robert Winston, Shaun Woodward.
Areas covered: No unsolicited mss.

Margaret Hanbury
27 Walcot Square, London SE11 4UB
Fax 020-7793 0316   Tel 020-7735 7680
E-mail: mhanbury@mhanbury.demon.co.uk

Mark Paterson & Associates
10 Brook St., Wivenhoe, Colchester, Esex CO7 9DS
Fax 01206-822990   Tel 01206-225433
E-mail: markpatterson@compuserve.com
Main authors: DW Winnicott, E Balint, W Bion
Areas covered: Psycho analysis for professional market.

The Marsh Agency
11-12 Dover Street, London W1X 3PH
Fax 020-7399 2801   Tel 020-7399 2800
E-mail: enquiries@march-agency.co.uk
Areas covered: Translation rights.

Mary Clemmey
6 Dunollie Road, London NW5 2XP
Fax 020-7267 1290   Tel 020-7267 1290
Main authors: Paul Gilroy, Sheila Kitzinger
Areas covered: High quality fiction/non-fiction with an international market.

Michelle Kass Associates
36-38 Glasshouse Street, London W!r 5RH
Fax 020-7734 3394   Tel 020-7439 1624

The Peters, Fraser & Dunlop Group
5th Floor, The Chambers, Chelsea Harbour, London SW10 0XF
Fax 020-7352 7356   Tel 020-7344 1000
E-mail: rschoular@pfd.co.uk
Areas covered: Most, no sci-fi or poetry.

Rogers, Coleridge & White
20 Powis Mews, London W11 1JN
Fax 020-7229 9084   Tel 020-7221 3717
E-mail: tomb@rcwlitagency.demon.co.uk
Areas covered: Literary fiction and non-fiction but no unsolicited mss.

Rupert Crew
!a King's Mews, Grays Inn Road, London WC1N 2JA
Fax 020-7831 7914   Tel 020-7242 8586
E-mail: rupertcrew@compuserve.com
Areas covered: General fiction and non-fiction. No plays, poetry, film or TV scripts.

Serafina Clarke
98 Tunis Road, London W12 7EY
Fax 020-8740 6862   Tel 020-8749 6979

Sheil Land Associates
43 Doughty Street, London WC1N 2LF
Fax 020-7831 2127   Tel 020-7405 9351
E-mail: info@sheilland.co.uk
Main authors: Peter Ackroyd, Melvyn Bragg, Catherine Cookson, John Keegan, Richard Mabey, Van Morrison, Tom Sharpe, Alan Titchmarch, Rose Tremain
Areas covered: General commercial and literary fiction and non-fiction. Also theatre, film, radio and TV scripts.

Shelley Power Literary Agency
Le Montaud, 24220 Berbiquires, France
Fax 00 33 55329 6254   Tel 0033 55329 6252
E-mail: puissant@easynet.fr
Areas covered: Adult trade fiction and non-fiction.

Shirely Stewart Literary Agent
36 Brand Street, Greenwich, London SW10 8SR
Fax 020-7305 2175   Tel 020-8305 2175
Areas covered: Literary fiction and non-fiction. No drama, screenplays, poetry or childrens.

Simpson Fox Associates
52 Shaftesbury Avenue, London W1V 7DE
Fax 020-7494 2887   Tel 020-7434 9167
Main authors: Julie Burchill, Andrew Greig, Andrew Roberts, Henry Porter

Tanja Howarth
19 New Row, London WC2N 4LA
Fax 020-7379 0969   Tel 020-7240 5553
E-mail: tanja.howarth@vrgin.net
Main authors: Patricia Highsmith, Patrick Süskind, Peter Ustinov

Tessa Sayle Agency
11 Jubilee Place, London SW3 3TE
Fax 020-7823 3363   Tel 020-7823 3883
E-mail: rcalder@tessasayle.demon.co.uk
Areas covered: Literary fiction, history, biography, travel, curent affairs.

Trevor, Lavinia
49a Goldhawk Road, London W12 8QP
Fax 020-8749 7377   Tel 020-8749 8481
E-mail:
Main authors:
Areas covered: Fiction, general non-fiction including popular science.

Vanessa Holt
59 Crescent Road, Leigh-on-Sea, Essex SS9 2PF
Fax 01702-471890   Tel 01702-473787
Areas covered: Commercial fiction.

Watson, Little
Capo di Monte, Windmill Hill, London NW3 6RJ
Fax 020-7431 7225   Tel 020-7431 0770

William Morris Agency (UK)
Stratton House, 1 Stratton Street, London W1V 6HB
Fax 020-7355 8600   Tel 020-7355 8500

News agencies

KEY CONTACT

National Association of Press Agencies
41 Lansdowne Crescent, Leamington Spa,
Warwickshire CV32 4PR
Fax 01926-424760   Tel 01926-424181
Trade association for news and photographic agenies.

24/7 Media
Bradford Court, Bradford Street, Birmingham, B12
0NS
Fax 0121-608 1171   Tel 0121-608 1166
News, pictures and features from West Midlands,
Warwickshire, Staffordshire, Worcestershire.

Advance Features
Stubbs Wood Cottage, Hammerwood, East
Grinstead, West Sussex RH19 3QE
Fax 01342-850480   Tel 01342-850480
Provides text, cartoons, crosswords and puzzles for
newspapers, magazines and TV.

AFI Research
Media House, 76 Queen Street, Newton Abbot,
Devon TQ12 2ER
Fax 01626-208014   Tel 01626-208011
E-mail: swift@eurobell.co.uk
International research and consultancy in areas of
politics, defence, INS, history and biography.
Specializes in discreet info gathering for media and
corporate markets.

AFX News
13-17 Epworth Street, London EC2A 4DL
Fax 020-7490 3007   Tel 020-7253 2532
Website: www.afxnews.com
A joint venture of the AFP and the FT Group, AFX is
the fourth largest global financial news agency.

Agence France Presse
78 Fleet Street, London EC4Y 1HY
Fax 020-7353 8359   Tel 020-7353 7461
E-mail: london.bureau@afp.com
Website: www.afp.com
London office of the global news agency. Supplies
international news and pictures. The reporting network
covers 167 countries and uses the latest technologies.

AllScot News & Features Agency
PO Box 6, Haddington, East Lothian EH41 3NQ
Fax 01620-825079   Tel 01620-822578
E-mail 101324.2142@compuserve.com
Provides social, religious, political, economic, industrial.
business, environmental, news and sports services
across Scotland for UK and overseas media outlets.

Andes Press Agency
26 Padbury Court, London E2 7EH
Fax 020-7739 3159   Tel 020-7613 5417
                         Tel.020-7739 3159
E-mail: photos@andespress.demon.co.uk
Covers global social, religious, political, economic and
environmental, especially in Latin America.

Anglia Press Agency
91 Hythe Hill, Colchester, Essex CO1 2NU
Fax 01206-797962   Tel 01206-797961
Covers: Essex, Suffolk and Norfolk, news and pictures.

Anglo-Danish Press Agency
Grosvenor Works, Mount Pleasant Hill, London E5
9NE
Fax 020-8806 3236   Tel 020-8806 3232

ANSA
12-13 Essex Street, London WC2R 3AA
Fax 020-7240 5518   Tel 020-7240 5514
Website: www.ansa.it
The leading Italian news agency.

Associated Press (AP)
12 Norwich Street, London EC4A 1BP
Fax 020-7353 8118   Tel 020-7353 1515
Website: www.apweb.com
UK office of the American agency, owned by US media
companies. Supplies international news and picture
services to the UK media, and collects British material
for US and other clients. Also runs the AP-Dow Jones.

Australian Associated Press
12 Norwich Street, London EC4A 1EJ
Fax 020-7583 3563   Tel 020-7353 0153
E-mail: aapnzpa@compuserve.com
Website: www.aap.com.au
Australia's only domestic news agency. Reports on
events in Britain and Europe of interest to Australia and
the South Pacific.

Bellis News Agency
Seabreezes, 14b Kenelm Road, Rhos-on-Sea,
Colwyn Bay LL28 4ED
Fax 01492-543226   Tel 01492-549503
E-mail: bellisd@aol.com
News reporters for most of north Wales .

Bloomberg News
City Gate House, 39-45 Finsbury Square, London
EC2A 1PQ
Fax 020-7392 6000   Tel 020-7330 7500
Website: www.bloomberg.com\uk
Business and financial news.

Bournemouth News & Picture Service
14 Lorne Park Road, Bournemouth BH1 1JN
Fax 01202-553875   Tel 01202-558833
Covers: Hants, Dorset, Wilts. News, features and
photos.

Bridge Information Systems
KR House, 78 Fleet Street, London EC4Y 1NB
Fax 020-7583 0519   Tel 020-7842 4000
Website: www.bridge.com

Bristol & West News Agency
80 Combe Avenue, Portishead, Somerset BS20 6JT
Fax 01275-843899   Tel 01275-842053
Specialises in sports coverage of the region.

Britannia Press Features
1 Pettits Close, Romford, Essex RM1 4EB
Fax 01708-761833   Tel 01708-761186
Provides wide range of features Travel is a speciality.

Cambrian News Agency
PO Box 30, Methyr Tydfil, CF 48
Fax 01685-375190   Tel 01685-382070
Covers: South Wales.

Canadian Press
12 Norwich Street, London EC4A 1EJ
Fax 020-7583 4238   Tel 020-7353 6355
The leading Canadian news agency.

Cassidy & Leigh (Southern News Service)
Exchange House, Hindhead, Surrey GU26 6AA
Fax 01428-606351   Tel 01428-607330
E-mail: southernnews@compuserve.com
News and pictures: Surrey, Sussex, Hants and Kent.

Caters News Agency
Suite 40, Queens Gate, 121 Suffolk Street,
Queensway, Birmingham B1 1LX
Fax 0121-616 2200   Tel 0121-616 1100
                      ISDN 0121-616 2014
Covers: West Midlands.

Cavendish Press
17-19 Whitworth Street, Manchester M1 5WG
Fax 0161-237 5353   Tel 0161-237 1066
                      ISDN 0161-236 1370
Website: www.cavendish-press.co.uk
Covers: North west England. News, features, pictures.

Central News Network
30a Newmarket Street, Falkirk, FK1 1JQ
Fax 01324-630515   Tel.01324-630505

Central Office of Information (COI)
Hercules Road, London SE1 7DU
Fax 020-7928 5037   Tel 020-7928 2345
Website: www.coi.gov.uk/coi
The government press and publicity agency.
  COI South East
  Hercules Road, London SE1 7DU
  Fax 020-7928 6974   Tel 020-7261 8795
  COI Eastern
  Three Crowns House, 72-80 Hills Road, Cambridge
  CB2 1LL
  Fax 01223-316121   Tel 01223-311867
  COI West Midlands
  Five Ways House, 4th floor, Islington Row,
  Middleway, Edgbaston, Birmingham B15 1SL
  Fax 0121-626 2041   Tel 0121-626 2023
  COI East Midlands
  Belgrave Centre, Talbot St, Nottingham NG1 5GG
  Fax 0115-971 2791   Tel 0115-971 2780
  COI North West
  Piccadilly Plaza, Manchester M1 4BD
  Fax 0161-236 9443   Tel 0161-952 4513
  COI Plymouth
  Mast House, Sheppards Wharf, 24 Sutton Road,
  Plymouth PL4 0HJ
  Fax 01752-227647   Tel 01752-635053
  COI South West
  The Pithay, Bristol BS1 2NQ
  Fax 0117-945 6975   Tel 0117-945 6969
  E-mail: bristol@coi.gov.uk
  COI Yorkshire & Humberside
  City House, New Station Street, Leeds, LS1 4JG
  Fax 0113-283 6586   Tel 0113-283 6599
  E-mail: leeds@coi.gov.uk

Central Press Features
Temple Way, Bristol BS99 7HD
Fax 0117-934 3575   Tel 0117-934 3000
E-mail mail@central-press.co.uk.
Website: www.cpost.co.uk
Features syndication worldwide. Specialists in TV
listings, crosswords, puzzles and motoring.

Central Press Lobby
Press Gallery, House of Commons, London SW1A
0AA
Fax 020-7799 1026   Tel 020-7219 3673
Specialists in Parliamentary reporting for regional press
and TV.

Chapman & Page
Denegate House, Amber Hill, Boston,Lincs PE20 3RL
Tel 01205-290477
Syndications agency supplying regular weekly columns
and crosswords plus editorial to support ad features.

Chester News Service
Linen Hall House, Stanley Street, Chester CH1 2LR
Fax 01244-326075   Tel 01244-345562
Covers: Chester local courts, sport and features

Chester Press Bureaus
Riverside Ho, River Lane, Saltney, Chester CH4 8RQ
Fax 01244-678749   Tel 01244-678575
E-mail: smith-davis@smith-davis.co.uk
Provides press agency, PR and contract publishing.

Cotswold & Swindon News Service
101 Bath Road, Swindon, Wilts SN1 4AX
Fax 01793-485462   Tel 01793-485461
Specialist cover of magistates' and crown courts. Also
research, business profiles and features.

Coventry News Service
1st Floor, 3 Queen Victoria Road, Coventry CV1 3JS
Fax 024-7663 4906   Tel 024-7663 3777
E-mail: adent@clara.net

JW Crabtree & Son
43 Cheapside, Bradford, West Yorkshire BD1 4HP
Fax 01274-732937   Tel 01274-732937
Covers: Bradford area for sport and news.

Dee News Service
12 Chester Street, Mold, Clwyd CH7 1EG
Fax 01352-759009   Tel 01352-754016
Covers: NE Wales area, Mold Crown Court, Mold,
Hawarden, Flint magistrates.

Deutsche Presse Agentur
30 Old Queen Street, London SW1H 9HP
Fax 020-7233 3534   Tel 020-7233 2888
German news agency, owned by German media.

Devon News Agency
4 Clifton Road, Exeter, Devon EX1 2BR
Fax 01392-435248   Tel 01392-276338
Covers: Devon and Cornwall.

Dow Jones Newswires
10 Fleet Place, Limeburner Lane, London EC4M 7RB
Fax 020-7842 9361   Tel 020-7842 9900
E-mail: helen.donnellan@cor.dowjones.com
Website: www.dowjones.com
UK office of newswire service owned by Dow Jones &
Co, publishers of the Wall Street Journal. Supplies
international news affecting global financial markets.
Produced in co-operation with AP.

Dragon News & Picture Agency
21 Walter Road, Swansea, SA1 5NQ
Fax 01792-475264   Tel 01792-464800
E-mail: dragon.news@btinternet.com
Website: www.dragon-pictures.com
Covers: South and west Wales.

Dundee Press Agency
10 Victoria Road, Dundee DD1 1JN
Fax 01382-907790   Tel 01382-907700
Covering east and central Scotland.

Elliott News Service
1 Fisher Lane, Bingham, Nottingham NG13 8BQ
Fax 01949-836583   Tel 01949-836566

Essex News Service
121 High Street, Witham, Essex CM8 1BE
Fax 01376-521222   Tel 01376-521222
perfect@essexnews.freeserve.co.uk
Covering all news and features in Essex.

Extel Financial
see AFX News

Features International
Lydeard St Lawrence, Taunton, Somerset TA4 3PS
Fax 01984-623901   Tel 01984-623014
Syndicates internationally newspaper and magazine
features.

Ferrari Press Agency
1A Hurst Road, Sidcup, Kent DA15 9AE
Fax: 020-8302 6611   Tel 020-8302 6622
For pictures telephone 01634-373 572
Covers: South east London and Kent.

First Features Syndicate
39 High Street, Battle, East Sussex.
Fax 01424-870877   Tel 01424-870877
E-mail: first.features@dial.pipex.com
Supplies all types of feature material to press and radio .

Fleet News Agency
Fleet House, 68a Stanfield Road, Bournemouth,
Dorset BH9 2NR
                    Tel 01202-515151
Covers: Bournemouth, Dorset and surrounding area.

Fleetline News Service
1a Bedford Road, London N2 9DB
Fax 020-8444 2313   Tel 020-8444 9183
Covers: London and Home Counties.

Fourth Estate Press Agency
12 North Campbell Avenue, Glasgow G62 7AA
                    Tel 0141-956 1540
Covers: Glasgow and west of Scotland.

Fowlers Press Agency
11 Village Way, London SE21 7AN
Fax 020-7236 8136   Tel 020-7248 6858
Nationwide bankruptcy and liquidation service.

Frank Ryan News Service
Cargenriggs, Islesteps, Dumfries DG2 8ES
Fax 01387-251121   Tel 01387-253700
Covers: South west Scotland - news, features, PR,
photography.

Freemans Press Agency
Raleigh Mill, Lower Raleigh Road, Barnstaple, Devon
EX31 4JQ
Fax 01271-344922   Tel 01271-324000
Covers: News features, PR and pix all SW England.

Front Page News Agency
1st Floor, 67 High Street, Bidford-on-Avon,
Warwickshire B50 4BQ
Fax 01789-490286   Tel 01789-778590
Covers: True life features in the UK.

Gemini News Service
9 White Lion Street, London N1 9PD
Fax 020-7278 0345   Tel 020-7278 1111

Gloucester & County News Service
26 Westgate Street, Gloucester GL1 2NG
Fax 01452-300581   Tel 01452-522270
E-mail: glosnews@mcmail.com

Great North News & Features
Woody Glen, How Mill, Carlisle, Cumbria CA4 9JY
Fax 01228-70381   Tel 01228-70381
E-mail: gnorthnews@aol.com
News from the northern Lake District to southern
Scotland and coverage of Carlisle courts.

Great Scot International
Camerons, Midton Road, Howwood PA9 1AG
Fax 01505-702333   Tel 01505-705656
E-mail: great.scot@glasgow.almac.co.uk
Newspaper, magazine, TV, radio, books. They have
Scottish experts and international medicine specialists.
Close to Glasgow Airport,

Guardian/Observer News Services
119 Farringdon Road, London EC1R 3ER
Fax 020-7837 1192   Tel 020-7278 2332
International syndication services of news and features
from the Guardian and Observer. Most national daily
and Sunday newspapers have similar syndication
operations; contact via their main switchboards.
See also London News Service and Solo Syndication,
below.

Hayter's Sports Agency
146-148 Clerkenwell Road, London EC1R 5DP
Fax 020-7837 2420   Tel 020-7837 7171
E-mail: sport@hayters.com
Website: www.hayters.co.uk
Specialises in sports reporting, features, statistics and
event support.

Hebridean Press Service
1 Maritime Buildings, Stornaway, Isle of Lewis HS1 2XU
Fax 01851-704270   Tel 01851-702737/706060
Covers: Western Isles.

Hill's Welsh Press
58 Lower Cathedral Road, Cardiff CF1 8LT
Fax 029-2022 4947   Tel 029-2022 7606
A news and photographic agency specialising in news,
sport, features, PR. Mac facilities.

Hopkinson News & Feature Service
22 Hallfield Road, Bradford BD1 3RQ
Fax 01274-725565   Tel 01274-725565
Yorkshire and Humberside.

Hull News & Pictures
Room 115, Hull Microfirms Centre, 266-290
Wincolmlee, Hull HU2 0PZ
Fax 01482-210267   Tel 01482-210267
E-mail: hull@hullnews.karoo.co.uk
East Yorkshire and north Linclonshire.

INS News Group
145 Wharfedale Road, Winnersh Triangle, Winnersh,
Reading, Berks RG41 5RB
Fax 01118-922 9404   Tel 0118-944 0600
E-mail: newsdesk@insnews.co.uk

Inter-Continental Features
48 Southerton Road, London W6 0PH
Fax 020-8741 3819   Tel 020-8748 9722
Agents for Universal Press Syndicate and Tribune
Media Services. Syndicated cartoons, features, KRT,
news and graphics and photos on line.

Islamic Republic News Agency (IRNA)
3rd Floor, 390 High Road, Wembley, Middlesex HA9
6AS
Fax 020-8900 0705   Tel 020-8903 1630
E-mail: PAYAM@lrna.co.uk
Website: www.irna.com

Jarrolds Press Agency
68 High Street, Ipswich, Suffolk IP1 3QJ
Fax 01473-218447   Tel 01473-219193
Covers: Suffolk and surrounding area and football
coverage.

Jenkins Group
186 High Street, Rochester, Kent ME1 1EY
Fax 01634-830930   Tel 01634-830888
Covers Kent for news features.

Jiji Press
76 Shoe Lane, London EC4A 3JB
Fax 020-7583 8353   Tel 020-7936 2847
E-mail: jijildn2@ma.kew.net
Japanese news agency.

John Connor Press Associates
57a High Street, Lewes, East Sussex BN7 1XE
Fax 01273-486852   Tel 01273-486851
E-mail: newsdesk@jcpa.freeserve.co.uk
Website: www.jcpa.freeserve.co.uk
News, pictures and features from East and West
Sussex.

Kett's News Service
53 Christchurch Road, Norwich, Norfolk, NR2 3NE
Fax 01603-508055   Tel 01603-508055
Covers news and features in Norfolk and Suffolk.

Kuwait News Agency
150 Southampton Row, London WC1B 5AL.
Fax 020-7278 6232   Tel 020-7278 5445

Kyodo News
Suites 119-130, NW Wing, Bush House, Aldwych,
London WC2B 4PJ
Fax 020-7438 4512   Tel 020-7438 4501
Website: www.kyodo.co.jp
Japanese news agency that covers UK and Scandinavia.

Lakeland Press Agency
Birch Garth, Beemire, Birthwaite Road, Windermere,
Cumbria LA23 1DW
Fax 015394-45128   Tel 015394-45127
Covers: Lake District.

Leicester News Service
Third Floor, 1c Conduit Street, Leicester LE2 0JN
Fax 0116-255 6565   Tel 0116-255 5055
Covers: Leicestershire

London At Large
36 Aybrook Street, London W1M 3JL
Fax 020-7224 4452   Tel 020-7224 4464
E-mail: newsbreaks@londonatlarge.com
A forward planning press agency specialsing in arts and
entertainment.

M & Y News Agency
65a Osborne Road, Southsea, Hants PO5 3LS
Fax 023-9229 1709   Tel 023-9282 0311
Covers: Hants, West Sussex, IoW, Dorset. Specialists in
sport, particularly soccer and cricket.

Masons News Service
Chesterton Mill, French's Road, Cambridge CB4 3NP
Fax 01223-361508   Tel 01223-366996
E-mail: on51@dial.pipex.com
News, photographs and TV packages from eastern
England for national and international news outlets.

Mercury Press Agency
The Cotton Exchange, Old Hall St. Liverpool L3 9LQ
Fax 0151-236 2180   Tel 0151-236 6707
E-mail: mercury@livpool.u-net.com
Covers: north west of England and north Wales, with
news, features and pictures.

MAPA
Second Star on the Right, Land of Green Ginger, Hull
HU1 2EA
Fax 01482-589926   Tel 01482-589900
E-mail: Group@MAPA.demon.co.uk
Formerly Mike Ackroyd Press Agency. Covers Hull area
sport. Produces local publications.

National News Press Agency
109 Clifton Street, London EC2A 4LD
Fax 020-7684 3030   Tel 020-7684 3000
E-mail: national.news@dial.pipex.com
Website: national.pictures-library.com
Court and general news and features in London and the
south east. Also works in partnership with BB TV to
produce short news pieces for home and foreign use.

New Zealand Press Association
12 Norwich Street, London EC4A 1EJ
Fax 020-7583 3563   Tel 020-7353 5430
E-mail: kippyb@hotmail.com
The co-operatively owned national news agency.

Newsflash Scotland
Thistle Industrial Estate, Kerse Road, Stirling FK7 7RW
Fax 01786-446145   Tel 01786-448497/446210
E-mail: newsflash@dial.pipex.com
3 Grosvenor Street, Edinburgh EH12 5ED
Fax 0131-225 9009   Tel 0131-226 5858
E-mail: newsflashed@dial.pipex.com
A news, features and picture agency.

News Team International
Albany House, Hurst Street, Birmingham B5 4BD
Fax 0121-666 6370   Tel 0121-346 5511
Website: www.newsteam.co.uk
News, pictures and features from West Midlands and
Manchester areas. Syndicates for Midland Independent
Newspapers, Manchester Evening News and others.

North Scot Press Agency
18 Adelphi, Aberdeen AB11 5BL
Fax 01224-212163   Tel 01224-212141
News, features and picture coverage of Grampian and
North of Scotland.
North Wales Press Agency
157 High Street, Prestatyn, Denbighshire LL19 9AY
Fax 01745-855534   Tel 01745-852262
North West News & Sports Agency
148 Meols Parade, Meols, Merseyside L47 6AN
Fax 0151-632 5484   Tel 0151-632 5261
Covers: Wirral and Merseyside.
Northants Press Agency
28 Hunter Street, Northampton, Northants NN1 3QD
Fax 01604-638008   Tel 01604-638811
E-mail: crispin@northamptonpress.demon.co.uk
Covers: Northamptonshire, north Beds and north
Bucks for news, features and pictures.
Northern Ireland Information Service
Block B, Castle Buildings, Stormont, Belfast BT4 3SG
Fax 028-9052 8473   Tel 028-9052 0700
11 Millbank, London SW1P 4QE
Fax 020-7210 0254   Tel 020-7210 3000
Website: www.nio.gov.uk
Government information service.
Nottingham News Service
8 Musters Road, West Bridgford, Nottingham NG3
7PL
Fax 0115-982 2568   Tel 0115-982 1697
Novosti
See Russian Information Agency
Orbit News Service
1 Froghall Lane, Warrington, Cheshire WA2 7JJ
Tel 01925-631592
E-mail: orbit@cwcom.net
Website: www.orbit.news.mcmail.com
News and picture service in Cheshire and South
Manchester.
Page One
11 West Avenue,West Bridgford, Nottingham NG2 7NL
Fax 0115-981 3133   Tel 0115-981 8880
E-mail: news@pageone-pa.co.uk
Website: www.pageone-pa.co.uk
Central and east Midlands. Features, news, photos, TV
filming and editing facilities. PR design and corporate
publishing.
Parliamentary & EU News Service
19 Douglas Street, London SW1P 4PA
Fax 020-7821 9352   Tel 020-7233 8283
E-mail: pnspublications@btinternet.com
News on major developments in Parliament and the
EU.

PA News - London
PA News Centre, 292 Vauxhall Bridge Road, London
SW1V 1AE
Fax 020-7963 7192   Tel 020-7963 7000/7146
Pictures: 020-7963 7155
Teletext: 020-7963 7241
Marketing: 020-7963 7511
Website: www.pa.press.net
PA News is the national news agency of the UK and the

Republic of Ireland. Operating 24 hours a day, 365 days
a year, it is the UK's leading supplier of news and sports
editorial, photographs, weather and listings to the print,
broadcast and electronic media. It transmits an average
of 1,500 stories and 100 pictures every day. The PA
News library contains over 14 million cuttings and the
PA News Photo library more than 5 million pictures.
PA News - along with PA Sport, PA Listings and PA
New Media - is part of the Press Association group.
Other subsidiary companies are Tellex Monitors (all
types of media monitoring) and Two Ten
Communications (media information and press release
distribution).
PA News - Leeds
PA NewsCentre, Central Park, New Lane, Leeds
LS11 5DZ
Fax 0113-244 0758   Tel 0113-234 4411
    PA REGIONAL OFFICES
    PA Belfast
    Queen's Buildings, 10 Royal Avenue, Belfast, BT1
    1DB
    Fax 028-9043 9246   Tel 028-9024 5008
PA Birmingham
1st Floor, Charles House, 148/149 Great Charles
Street, Birmingham B3 3HT
Fax 0121-212 3350   Tel 0121-212 3225
PA Bristol
3rd Floor, 66 Queens Road, Clifton, Bristol BS81RE
Fax 0117-922 0493   Tel 0117-922 0560
PA Cardiff
11 Brynawelon Road, Cardiff CF2 6QR3
Fax 029-207 64213   Tel 029-207 64211
PA Dublin
41 Silchester Road, Glenageary, Dublin
Fax 00 353 1 28 04221   Tel 00 353 1 28 00936
PA East Anglia
3 Edieham Cottages, Angle Lane, Shepreth,
Royston SG8 6QJ
Fax 01763 262638   Tel 01763 262638
PA Exeter
143 Sweetbriar Lane, Exeter Devon EX1 3AP
Fax 01392 431166   Tel 01392 431166
PA Glasgow
124 Portman Street, Kinning Park, Glasgow G41
1EJ
Fax 0141-429 1596   Tel 0141-429 0037
PA Liverpool
PO Box 48, Old Hall Street, Liverpool L69 3EB
Fax 0151-472 2411   Tel 0151-472 2548
PA Manchester
5th Floor, 33 Piccadilly, Manchester M1 1LQ
Fax 0161-228 7331   Tel 0161-228 7717
PA Newcastle
16 Shearwater, Whitburn, Sunderland, Tyne-and-
Wear SR6 7SF
Fax 0191-529 5022   Tel 0191-529 5012
E-mail: brain_unwin@bigfoot.com
Website: www.welcome.to/brianunwin
PA Southampton
11 Wembley Way, Fair Oak, Hampshire SO5 7JN
Fax 023- 806 92015 Tel 023- 806 92015

Press Agency (Gatwick)
1a Sunview Valley, Peacehaven, Sussex BN10 8PJ
Fax 01273-589112   Tel 01273-583103
Covers: Gatwick Airport and surrounding area.
Press Gang News
137 Endlesham Road, London SW12 8JN
Fax 020-8673 3205   Tel 020-8673 4229
News, features, pictures and investigations for London
and South East area.
Press Team Scotland
Unit 53 Fountain Business Centre, Ellis Street,
Coatbridge ML5 3AA
Fax 01236-440066   Tel 01236-440077
Covers: Gatwick Airport and surrounding area.
Quicksilver Media
St George Street, Leicester LE1 9FQ
Fax 0116-251 2151   Tel 0116-253 0022
E-mail: news@quicksilvermedia.co.uk
Founded in 1993 by Northcliffe Newspapers and
Westminster Press. It provides national and
international news, sport. and pictures to 33 regional
papers. UK News has reciprocal arrangements with
subscriber newspapers, giving it access to the work of
hundreds of journalists. It also has a team of lobby
journalists based at the House of Commons.
Raymonds Press Agency
Gower Street, Derby DE1 1SD
Fax 01332-386036   Tel 01332-340404
E-mail: ako@raymonds.demon.co.uk
Covers: Central and east Midlands. One of the largest
regional agencies. Provides news, sport, photo and
feature coverage.
Reuters
85 Fleet Street, London EC4P 4AJ
Fax 020-7542 4970   Tel 020-7250 1122
Website: www.reuters.com
The Reuters Television network of more than 70
bureaux around the world provides broadcasters with a
fast, reliable news service. The Reuters Television World
News Service (WNS) delivers news feeds, news flashes,
live coverage and in-depth features via satellite to more
than 200 broadcasters plus their networks and affiliates
in 85 countries 24 hours a day. Reuters is an
independent public company, founded in 1851.
Russian Information Agency - Novosti
3 Rosary Gardens, London SW7 4NW
Fax 020-7244 7875   Tel 020-7370 1162/3002
E-mail: ria@novosti.demon.co.uk
Website: www.rian.ru
Russian news and information service. Soviet/Russian
photo library.
SNS
15 Fitzroy Place, Glasgow G3 7RW
Fax 0141-221 3595   Tel 0141-221 3602
E-mail: scotnews@btinternet.com
Showbusiness and sport, PR, words and photos.
Samuels News & Photo Service
71 Stafford Road, Uttoxeter, Staffs ST14 8DW
Fax 01889-567181   Tel 01889-566996
Saudi Press Agency
18 Cavendish Square, London W1M 0AQ
Fax 020-7495 5074   Tel 020-7495 0418/9

Scarborough News/Ridings Press Agency
19 Hall Garth Lane, Scarborough YO13 9JA
Fax 01723-865054   Tel 01723-863395
News, features, rural, sport and PR.
Scase News Service
Congham, Kings Lynn, Norfolk PE32 1DR
Fax 01485-600672   Tel 01485-600650
E-mail: news@scase.co.uk
Website: www.scase.co.uk
Covers: East Anglia and specialises in news, royal news
and features.
Scottish Office Information Directorate
St Andrews House, Edinburgh EH1 1DG
Fax 0131-244 1721   Tel 0131-244 2709
Website: www.scotland.gov.uk
Government information service.
Scottish News Agency
99 Ferry Road, Edinburgh EH6 4ET
Fax 0131-478 7327   Tel 0131 478 7711
E-mail: scotnews@sol.co.uk
10Victoria Road, Dundee DD1 1JN
Fax 01382-907700   Tel 01382-907790
Scottish news and sports pictures.
Seven Day Press
132 West Nile Street, Glasgow G1 2RQ
Fax 0141-572 0265   Tel 0141-572 0060
E-mail: daypress@aol.com
Covers: Scotland.
Shrewsbury Press Service
1a Victorian Arcade, Hills Lane, Shrewsbury, Salop
SY1 1PS
Fax 01743-247701   Tel 01743-352710
Covers: Shropshire.
Sirius Media Services
Green Farm, Harleston, Stowmarket, Suffolk IP14 3HW
Fax 01449-736894   Tel 01449-736889
E-mail: grnfarm@globalnet.co.uk
Provides a range of editorial features, including
crossword puzzles and quizzes.
Smith Davis Press
8 Westport Road, Stoke-on-Trent, Staffs ST6 4AW
Fax 01782-812428   Tel 01782-812311
E-mail: smith-davis@smith-davis.co.uk
Provides press agency, PR and contract pubishing
services.
Solent News & Photo Agency
21 Castle Way, Southampton SO14 2BW
Fax 023-8023 2983   Tel 023-8022 3217
Covers: Hants, IoW, Wilts and Dorset.
Solo
49-53 Kensington High Street, London W8 5ED
Fax 020-7938 3165   Tel 020-7376 2166
E-mail: solosyndicationltd@btinternet.com
Features and news from Associated Newspapers, The
European, News Limited of Australia. Also archive
library of three million photos including 12,000
Spanish images.
Somerset News Service
43-44 High Street, Taunton, Somerset TA1 3PW
Fax 01823-332862   Tel 01823-331789
Covers: Somerset. News and photo coverage for
national and regional TV, radio and newspapers.

South Bedfordshire News Agency
134 Marsh Road, Luton, Beds LU3 2NL
Fax 01582-493486   Tel 01582-572222
E-mail: south.b@virgin.net
Covers: Herts, Beds and Bucks.

South Coast Press Agency
22 St Peters Road, Bournemouth, Dorset BH1 2LE
Fax 01202-297904   Tel 01202-290199
Covers: Dorset and surrounding counties.

South West News Service
24-30 Hotwell Road, Clifton, Bristol BS8 4UD
Fax 0117-922 6744   Tel 0117-927 6661
E-mail: swnews@hotmail.com
Covers: West Country and South Wales.

South Yorkshire Sport
6 Sharman Walk, Apperknowle, sheffield S18 4BJ
Fax 01246-414767   Tel 01246-414676
E-mail: nicksportl@aol.com
Covers: sport in the South Yorkshire area.

Space Press
Bridge House, Blackden Lane, Goostrey, Cheshire
CW4 8PZ
Fax 01477-535756   Tel 01477-534440/533403
E-mail: scoop2001@aol.com.uk
Covers: Cheshire & surrounding counties, news,
features, photos.

Spanish News Agency (EFE)
5 Cavendish Square, London W1M 0DP
Fax 020-7436 3562   Tel 020-7636 5226
E-mail: agencia@agenciaefe.demon.co.uk
The news agency for Spain and Latin America.

Steve Hill Agency
12 Steep Hill, Lincoln LN2 1LT
Fax 01522 569571   Tel 01522 569595
Covers: Lincolnshire & surrounding counties, news,
features, photos.

Stewart Bonney News Agency
17 St Peter's Wharf, Newcastle-on-Tyne NE6 1TZ
Fax 0191-275 2609   Tel 0191-275 2600
E-mail: powdene@compuserve.com
St Peter's Wharf, Newcastle-upon-Tyne NE6 1TZ
Covers: North east England.

Strand News Service
226 The Strand, London WC2R 1BA
Fax 020-7936 2689   Tel 020-7353 1300
General coverage.

Tartan Tec News Agency
See Great Scot International

Tass/Itar
12-20, Second Floor, Morley House, 320 Regent
Street, London W1R 5AB
Fax 020-7580 5547   Tel 020-7580 5543
London office of the Russian news agency.

Teespress Agencies
15 Baker Street, Middlesbrough, Teeside TS1 2LF
Fax 01642-880744   Tel 01642-880733
Covers: Teeside, North Yorkshire, South Durham.

Tim Wood Agency
11 Village Way, Dulwich, London SE21 7AN
Fax 020-7236 8136   Tel 020-7248 6858
Covers: London courts, including Old Bailey.

Torbay News Agency
45 Lymington Road, Torquay, Devon TQ1 4BG
Fax. 01803-214557   Tel 01803-214555
Covers: Torbay and south Devon.

United Press International (UPI)
2 Greenwich View, Millharbour, London E14 9NN
Fax 020-7538 1051   Tel 020-7675 9967
Covers: Middle East, business, sport, features, news and
political events.

Two-Ten News Network
210 Old Street, London EC1V 9UN
Fax 020-7490 1255   Tel 020-7490 8111
E-mail: info@twoten.press.net
Website: www.twoten.press.net
Transmits news and feature stories direct onto
journalists' screens in 220 newsrooms around the UK.

Wales News Service
Womanby Street, Cardiff CF1 2UD
Fax 029-2066 4181   Tel 029-2066 6366
Covers: Wales and the West.

Warwickshire News & Picture Agency
41 Lansdowne Crescent, Leamington Spa,
Warwickshire CV32 4PR
Fax 01926-424760   Tel 01926-424181
Covers: Warwickshire and West Midlands.
Specialists in features, investigations and a range of
photographic services.

Watson's Press Agency
103 Adelaide Street, Blackpool, Lancs FY1 4LU
Fax 01253-623996   Tel 01253-623996
Covers: Lancashire and South Cumbria.The agency
specialises in local news, sport and feature work.

Welsh Office - Information Division
Cathays Park, Cardiff CF1 3NQ
Fax 029-2082 5508   Tel 029-2082 5648
E-mail: webmaster@wales.gov.uk
Website: www.wales.gov.uk
Government communications agency.

Wessex News & Features Agency
108 High Street, Hungerford, Berkshire RG17 0NB
Fax 01488-686900   Tel 01488-686810
E-mail: news@britishnews.co.uk
          features@britishnews.co.uk
Website: www.britishnews.co.uk
News, features and photos covering England and
Scotland.

West Riding News & Sports Service
Field House, Wellington Road, Dewsbury, West
Yorkshire WF13 1HF
Fax 01924-437564   Tel 01924-437555
Supplies news and features from Huddersfield, Halifax
and Dewsbury. Specialises in soccer and rugby league.

Xinhua News Agency of China
8 Swiss Terrace, Belsize Road, London NW6 4RR
Fax 020-7722 8512   Tel 020-7586 8437
E-mail: xinhua@easynet.co.uk
Covers: foreign and domestic affairs.

Yaffa Newspaper Service
Suite 305-7, 29 Gt Pulteney Street, London W1R 3DD
Fax 020-7439 7318   Tel 020-7437 5133
E-mail: john@yaffa.co.uk
UK representatives of US syndication King Features.

Picture agencies and libraries

KEY CONTACTS

British Association of Picture Libraries and Agencies (BAPLA)
18 Vine Hill, London EC1R 5DX
Fax 020-7713 1211   Tel: 020-7713 1780
E-mail: bapla@bapla.demon.co.uk
Website: www.bapla.org.uk
BAPLA is the trade association representing 350 picture libraries and agencies and provides a referral service for image research. Publishes the industry magazine Light Box, and an annual directory. BAPLA assesses many industry issues including copyright clearance, ethics, pricing, marketing and technology.
Council of Photographic News Agencies
Oak Trees, Burrows Lane, Guildford, Surrey GU5 9QF
Fax 01483-203378   Tel 01483-203378
Represents the UK's six largest press agencies/photo libraries.
Picture Research Association
5a AlvanleyGardens, London NW6 1JD
Fax 020-7431 9887   Tel 020-7431 9886
E-mail: pra@pictures.demon.co.uk
Professional body for all those involved in supplying visual material to all forms of the media. It promotes professional standards and provides a forum for the exchange of information. It publishes a quarterly magazine, monthly newsletter and Freelance Register.
Picture Researchers Handbook
by Hilary & Mary Evans; Pira International
Fax 01372-377526   Tel 01372-802000
The standard reference book to picture sources

Ace Photo Agency
Satellite House, 2 Salisbury Road, Wimbledon, London SW19 4EZ
Fax 020-8944 9940   Tel 020-8944 9944
E-mail: info@acestock.com
Website: www.acestock.com
A wide-ranging colour photo library with material on many subjects.
Action Images
Image House, Station Road, London N17 9LR
Fax 020-8267 2035   Tel 020-8885 3000
E-mail: reception@actionimagescom
Website: www.actionimages.com
Sports pictures with UK and international coverage.
Action Plus
54 -58 Tanner Street, London SE1 3PH
Fax 020-7403 1526   Tel 020-7403 1558
E-mail: info@actionplus.co.uk
Covers over 140 professional and amateur sports worldwide.
Adams Picture Library
156 New Cavendish Street, London W1M 7FJ
Fax 020-7436 7131   Tel 020-7636 1468
Contains the work of more than 500 photographers.

The Advertising Archives
45 Lyndale Avenue, London NW2 2QB
Fax 020-7794 6584   Tel 020-7435 6540
Collection of US and British press ads and magazine covers. Official UK agents for Saturday Evening Post artwork including Norman Rockwell cover illustrations.
Aerofilms
Gate Studios, Station Road, Borehamwood, Herts WD6 1EJ
Fax 020-8207 5433   Tel 020-8207 0666
E-mail: library@aerofilms.com
Aerial photography with library, 1.75 million images, dating back to 1919.
AKG London
10 Plato Place, 72-74 St Dionis Road, London SW6 4TU
Fax 020-7610 6125   Tel 020-7610 6103
Website: www.akg-london.co.uk
London representative of the large Berlin picture library AKG and the Erich Lessing Archive of Fine Art and Culture, Vienna. Specialists in arts and history.
Alan Jones Photos
10 Pelwood Road, Camber, E Sussex TN31 7RU
Tel 01797-225448
Covers: Sussex and Kent. Has ISDN facilities.
Allsport (UK)
3 Greenlea Park, London SW19 2JD
Fax 020-8648 5240   Tel 020-8685 1010
E-mail: lmartin@allsport.co.uk
Website: www.allsportuk.allsport.co.uk
The world's largest specialist sports library, represented in 27 countries. Has over six million images, dating from 1880.
Alpha Photographic Press Agency
63 Gee Street, London EC1V 3RS
Fax 020-7250 1149   Tel 020-7608 2796
E-mail: alphapress@compuserve.com
International photo feature agency and picture library specialising in celebrities.
Andes Press Agency
26 Padbury Court, London E2 7EH
Fax 020-7739 3159   Tel 020-7613 5417
E-mail: photos@andespress.demon.co.uk
Covers social, religious, political, economic and environmental issues around the world, especially in Latin America.
Apex Photo Agency
Priests Court, Main Road, Exminster, Exeter EX6 8AP
Fax 01392-824155   Tel 01392-824024
E-mail: apex@apex-photos.co.uk
Website: www.apex-photos.co.uk
Aquarius Picture Library
PO Box 5, Hastings, East Sussex TN34 1HR
Fax 01424-717704   Tel 01424-721196
E-mail: aquarius.lib@clara.net
Over 1 million film stills, current and archival, dating back to silent days. Also TV, vintage pop, some opera and ballet.

Ardea London
35 Brodrick Road, London SW17 7DX
Fax 020-8672 8787   Tel 020-8672 2067
E- mail: ardea@ardea.co.uk
Wildlife, pets and the environment, worldwide.

Assignments Photographers
1Quaker Court, School Road, Norwich, NR10 4QL
Fax 01603-754767   Tel 01603-754254
ISDN: 01603-754466
E-mail: assignments@paston.co.uk
Covers eastern region in news, features, sport,
commercial and PR photography.

Associated Sports Photography/Headline
21 Green Walk, Leicester LE3 6SE
Fax 0116-231 1123   Tel 0116-232 0310
E-mail: KCW80@dial.pipex.com
National and international coverage. Has ISDN
facilities.

Australia Pictures
38 Carmac Road, Twickenham TW2 6NU
Fax 020-8898 0150   Tel 020-8898 0150
All aspects of Australia (travel, culture, underwater,
tourism). Also Africa, Middle East, Asia.

Autograph
5/25 Scrutton Street, London EC2A 4LP
Fax 020-7729 9400   Tel 020-7739 1777
E-mail: mark@auto.demon.co.uk
Website: www.autograph-abp.co.uk

Barnaby's Picture Library
19 Rathbone Street, London W1P 1AF
Fax 020-7637 4317   Tel 020-7636 6128
E-mail: barnabyspicturelibrary@ukbusiness.com
Webs: www.ukbusiness.com/barnabyspicturelibrary/
A library of over 4 million colour transparencies, b/w
prints. The coverage is worldwide and historic.

Barnardo's Film & Photographic Archive
Tanners Lane, Barkingside, Essex IG6 1QG
Fax 020-8550 0429   Tel 020-8550 8822
500,000 photos dating from 1871, film from 1905,
covering the work of the UK's largest children's charity.

Barratts Photopress
63 Gee Street, London EC1V 3RS
Fax 020-7250 1149   Tel 020-7278 1223/336 0632
E-mail: alphapress@compuserve.com
Has ISDN facilities.

BBC News Stills
Rm B250, TV Centre, Wood Lane, London W12 7RJ
Fax 020-8576 7020   Tel 020-8576 0690
E-mail: picture.desk@bbc.co.uk
A wide range of stills from the BBC News and Current
Affairs collection.

BBC Photograph Library
Rm B116, TV Centre, Wood Lane, London W12 7RJ
Fax 020-8746 0353   Tel 020-8225 7193
Programme stills, mainly comedy, drama and light
entertainment dating back to 1924,

Beken Maritime Services
16 Birmingham Road, Cowes, Isle of Wight PO31 7BH
Fax 01983-291059   Tel 01983-297311
E-mail: beken@aol.com
Marine and stock library, built around the Beken
family's photos. Images from 1888 to the present.

The Bridgeman Art Library
17-19 Garway Road, London W2 4PH
Fax 020-7792 8509   Tel 020-7727 4065
E-mail: info@bridgeman.co.uk
Website: www.bridgeman.co.uk
A specialist source of the world's finest paintings,
drawings, manuscripts, sculpture, antiques and
antiquities; offering large format colour transparencies
and a picture research service.

British Film Institute
21 Stephen Street, London W1P 2LN
Fax 020-7323 9260   Tel 020-7255 1444
E-mail: info@bfi.org.uk
Website: www.bfi.org.uk
Holds 7 million pictures recording the history of
cinema-tography and includes, film, TV and portraits.

British Library Reproductions
British Library, 96 Euston Road, London NW1 2DB
Fax 020-7412 7771   Tel 020-7412 7614
E-mail: bl-repro@bl.uk
Website: portico.bl.uk/repro/
12 million and 5 million other items can be
photographed to order. A 'browsable' picture library
service is now available.

Bruce Coleman Collection
16 Chiltern Business Village, Arundel Road, Uxbridge,
Middlesex UB8 2SN
Fax 01895-272357   Tel 01895-257094
E-mail: info@brucecoleman.co.uk
Website: www.brucecoleman.co.uk
Transparencies on natural history and travel.

Bulletin International Video Library
5-8 Hardwick Street, London EC1R4RB
Fax 020-7278 6349   Tel 020-7278 6070
E-mail: info@bulletin-intl.com
Website: www.bulletin.com
Recent stock footage of industry, commerce, medicine,
leisure, locations; mainly UK, Europe and Asia.

Scottish Media Newspapers Picture Library
195 Albion Street, Glasgow G1 1QP
Fax 0141-553 2642   Tel 0141 553 3209
E-mail: iwatson@cims.co.uk
6 million Scottish photos from 1900 onwards,.

Calyx Multimedia
41 Churchward Avenue, Swindon SN2 1NJ
Fax: 01793-513640   Tel 01793-520131
E-mail: calyx@compuserve.com
Covers: Wiltshire + M4 corridor. Pics, features, PR.

Camera Press
21 Queen Elizabeth Street, London SE1 2PD
Fax 020-7278 5126   Tel 020-7378 1300
Website: www.campress.com
Long-established general picture library of over ten
million items, covering more than a century of news.
Famous photographers include Karsh, Lichfield,
Snowdon and Beaton. Has ISDN facilities.

Capital Pictures
49-51 Central Street, London EC1V 8AB
Fax 020-7253 1414   Tel 020-7253 1122
E-mail: post@capital pictures.demon.co.uk
Specialises in celebrity and personality photos. Also an
extensive film stills collection.

Centrepix
Unit 305, The Custard Factory, Gibb Street, Digbeth, Birmingham B9 4AA
Fax 0121-608 6777   Tel 0121-608 6777/6888
Has ISDN facilities.

Cephas Picture Library
57 Walton Road, East Molesey, Surrey KT8 0DX
Fax 020-8224 8095   Tel 020-8979 8647
E-mail: mickrock@cephas.co.uk
Website: www.cephas.co.uk
Wine and vineyards of the world, spirits, beers and ciders, 100,000+ images. Also food and drink archive.

Christian Aid Photo Library
PO Box 100, London SE1 7RT
Fax 020-7620 0719   Tel 020-7523 2235
E-mail: jcabon@christian-aid.org
Website: www.oneworld.org/christian_aid
Social pictures on community programmes in Africa, Asia and Latin America.

Collections
13 Woodberry Crescent, London N10 1PJ
Fax 020-8883 9215   Tel 020-8883 0083
E-mail: collections@btinternet.com
Website: www.btinternet.com/~collections
The life and landscape of the British Isles. Also child development from pregnancy to adulthood.

Colorific!
Innovation Centre, 225 Marsh Wall, London E14 9FX
Fax 020-7538 3555   Tel 020-7515 3000
E-mail: colorific@visualgroup.com
Large colour photo library of current topics.

Colorsport
44 St Peters Street, London N1 8JT
Fax 020-7226 4328   Tel 020-7359 2714
E-mail: c-sporthq@aol.com
Extensive library of sport photos, including football and cricket history. All other sports date from late 1960s to the present. Has ISDN facilities.

Comstock
21 Chelsea Wharf, 15 Lots Road, London SW10 0QJ
Fax 020-7352 8414   Tel 00800-266786 25
E-mail: info@comstock.co.uk
Website: www.comstock.com
General library with over 5 million pictures. Free catalogues and CD-Roms. Digital and transparencies, rights protected and royalty free picturesavailable.

David Hoffman Photo Library
21 Norman Grove, London E3 5EG
Fax 020-8980 2041   Tel 020-8981 5041
E-mail: lib@hoffmanphotos.demon.co.uk
Website: www.hoffmanphotos.demon.co.uk
Social issues. Policing, drugs, youth, race, housing, environmental demos, waste disposal, energy, industry and pollution. Range of images mainly UK and Europe, also USA, Venezuela and Thailand.

David King Collection
90 St Pauls Road, London N1 2QP
Fax 020-7354 8264   Tel 020-7226 0149
Photos, posters and ephemera covering political/cultural history of Russia, USSR, China, Spanish civil war. Communist leaders. Gulag. Collection of Stalinist falsifications. 250,000 images.

Dobson Photo Agency
6 Mordacks Close, Bridlington, Yorkshire YO16 6ZF
Fax 01723-363661   Tel 01723-363661
E-mail: dobsonzz@aol.com
Covers: Yorkshire coast. Press and PR photographers, broadcast video and 40 year picture library

David Williams Picture Library
50 Burlington Avenue, Glasgow G12 0LH
Fax 0141-337 3031   Tel 0141-339 7823
Specialist Collections of Scotland and Iceland. Smaller collections of Faroe Islands, France, Spain, Canary Islands, Czech Republic, Hungary, Portugal and Western USA. Commissions undertaken, catalogue.

Ecoscene
The Oasts, Headley Lane, Passfield, Liphook, Hants GU30 7RX
Fax 01428-751057   Tel 01428-751056
E-mail: sally@ecoscene.com
Website: www.ecoscene.com
80,000 images on the environment, natural history, industry, energy, agriculture, conservation and recycling.

Empics Sports Photo Agency
26 Musters Road, W Bridgford, Nottingham NG2 7PL
Fax 0115-840 4445   Tel 0115-840 4444
E-mail info@empics.co.uk
Website: www.empics.co.uk
International sports photo agency covering major sports events. ISDN facilities. On-line picture archive.

Environmental Investigation Agency Photo Library
2nd Floor, 69-85 Old Street, London EC1V 9AX
Fax 020-7490 0436   Tel 020-7490 7040
E-mail: eiauk@gn.apc.org
Website: www.pair.com/eia/
Library following the charity's campaigns. Most pictures cover endangered subjects (wild birds, rhinos, whales, tigers, elephants, forests and wildlife trade).

Environmental Images
Finsbury Business Centre, 40 Bowling Green Lane, London EC1R 0NE
Fax 020-7713 6348   Tel 020-7713 6347
E-mail: environmentalimages@compuserve.com
Website: www.environmentalimages.com
Specialises in environmental issues. From road protests to climate change. 60,000 colour images.

Farmers Weekly Picture Library
Quadrant House, The Quadrant, Sutton, Surrey SM2 5AS
Fax 020-8652 4005   Tel 020-8652 4914
E-mail: farmers.library@rbi.co.uk
Website: www.fwi.co.uk
Britain's biggest agricultural picture library holding 250,000 images of all aspects of farming . Has ISDN.

ffotograff
10 Kyveilog Street, Cardiff CF11 9JA
Fax 029-2022 9326   Tel 029-2023 6879
E-mail ffotograff@easynet.co.uk
Website: www.
cf.ac.uk/ccin/main/buscomm/ffotogra/ffoto1.html
Photolibrary, specialising in travel, exploration and the arts and covering the Middle, Far East, and Wales. ISDN

Forest Life Picture Library
231 Corstorphine Road, Edinburgh EH12 7AT
Fax 0131-314 6285   Tel 0131-314 6411
E-mail: n.campbell@forestry.gov.uk
Official image bank of the Forestry Commission. It has comprehensive coverage of tree species, forests, woodland landscapes, timber production and a collection of wildlife and recreation images.

Format Photographers
19 Arlington Way, London EC1R 1UY
Fax 020-7833 0381   Tel 020-7833 0292
E-mail: format@formatphotogs.demon.co.uk
Social documentary library and agency. Includes: education, health, disability, religion and women. UK and abroad. Archive from 70's. Colour and b/w.

Francis Frith Collection
Frith's Barn, Teffont, Salisbury, Wiltshire SP3 5QP
Fax 01722-716881   Tel 01722-716376
E-mail: sales@francisfrith.com
Website: www.francisfrith.com
4,000 British towns and villages taken between 1860 and 1970. Has ISDN facilities.

Frank Spooner Pictures
16-16a Baldwins Gardens, London EC1N 7US
Fax 020-7632 5828   Tel 020-7612 5800
Large general photo library representing Gamma (Paris), for current international material and Roger Viollet for historic. Has ISDN facilities.

Gaze International
39-41 North Road, London N7 9DP
Fax 020-7697 8334   Tel 020-7697 8333
E-mail: info@gaze.co.uk
Website: www.gaze.co.uk
Picture library covers all aspects of gay, lesbian and transgender life and culture for editorial, reportage, features, ad campaigns and health promotions.

GeoScience Features Picture Library
6 Orchard Drive, Wye, Kent TN25 5AU
Fax 01233-812707   Tel 01233-812707
E-mail: gsf@geoscience.demon.co.uk
Website: www.geoscience.co.uk
All aspects of earth sciences and natural history worldwide. Over 330,000 pictures.

Greenpeace UK
Canonbury Villas, London N1 2PN
Fax 020-7865 8200   Tel 020-7865 8294
Email angela.glienicke@uk.greenpeace.org
Website: www.greenpeace.org/gpimages
Holds approximately 60,000 photos of campaigns and environmental issues.

Greg Evans International Photo Library
6 Station Parade, Sunningdale, Ascot, Berks SL5 0EP
Fax 020-7637 1439   Tel 020-7636 8238
E-mail: greg@geipl.demon.co.uk
Website: www.geipl.demon.co.uk
Comprehensive colour photo library.

Guardian/Observer Photo Service
119 Farringdon Road, London EC1R 3ER
Fax 020-7837 1192   Tel 020-7713 4423
International syndication service for all Guardian pictures and for the pre-1989 Observer archive library. Has ISDN facilities.

Hulton-Getty
21-31 Woodfield Road, London NW9 2BA
Fax 020-7266 3154   Tel 020-7266 2662
E-mail: info@getty-images.com
Website: www.hultongetty.com
The Hulton Getty Picture Collection is part of Getty Images. It is one of the world's greatest picture libraries, covering nearly all topics and periods. The overall archive holds more than 50 special collections, including Picture Post, Keystone, Fox, Central Press, Evening Standard and Ernst Haas.

Hutchison Picture Library
118b Holland Park Avenue, London W11 4UA
Fax 020-7792 0259   Tel 020-7229 2743
E-mail: library@hutchinsonpic.demon.co.uk
Half a million worldwide documentary colour transparencies. Subjects include: agriculture, energy, environments, families, festivals, industry, landscape, religion, transport and weather.

ICCE Photo Library
Burcott House, Wing, Leighton Buzzard LU7 0JW
Fax 01296-688245   Tel 01296-688245
E-mail: icceplib@aol.com
Founded by the International Centre for Conservation Education. specialises in wildlife, habitats, conservation and environmental issues worldwide; including acid rain, agriculture, energy, erosion, pollution etc.

Illustrated London News Picture Library
20 Upper Ground, London SE1 9PF
Fax 020-7805 5905   Tel 020-7805 5585
News images from 1842 onwards. Covers all aspects of history; industrial, social and political.

The Image Bank
17 Conway Street, London W1P 6EE
Fax 020-7391 9111   Tel 020-7312 0300
E-mail: info@imagebank.co.uk
Webste: www.imagebank.co.uk
The world's largest source for contemporary and archive photography, illustration and film footage.

Image Bank, Manchester
4 Jordan Street, Manchester M15 4PY
Fax 0161-236 8723   Tel 0161-236 9226

Image Bank, Scotland
57 Melville Street Street, Edinburgh EH3 7HL
Fax 0131-225 1660   Tel 0131-225 1770

Image Bank, Ireland
11 Upper Mount Street, Dubin 2
Fax 3531-676 0873   Tel 3531-676 0872
E-mail: ukmarketing@theimagebank.com
Website: www.imagebank.co.uk

Images of Africa Photobank
11 The Windings, Lichfield, Staffs WS13 7EX
Fax 01543-417154   Tel 01543-262898
E-mail: info@imagesofafrica.co.uk
Wide range of subjects covering 14 African countries from Egypt to South Africa. Excellent on wildlife, habitat, national parks, tourism and traditional peoples.

Impact Photos
26-27 Great Sutton Street, London EC1V 0DX
Fax 020-7608 0114   Tel 020-7251 5091
E-mail: library@impactphotos.demon.co.uk
Worldwide images covering all subjects.

Imperial War Museum
Photograph Archive, All Saints Annex, Austral Street, London SE11 4SL
Fax 020-7416 5355   Tel 020-7416 5333/5338
E-mail: photos@iwm.org.uk
Website: www.iwm.org.uk
National archive of more than six million photos dealing with 20th century warfare, especially the two world wars.

In-Focus
Sitwell Centre, Scarborough, N Yorks YO12 5EX
Fax 01723-503749   Tel 01723 501904
E-mail: in-focus.co.uk
Web: www.in-focus.co.uk
Sport, politics, royals and celebrities.

Insight ACR
10 Lambs Conduit Passage, London WC1R 4RH
Fax 020-7419 7777   Tel 020-7419 0171
E-mail: solutions@insight-visual.com
Website: www.insight-visual.com
Represents photographers working in the advertising, corporate and commercial sectors. Specialist areas include people, reportage, portraits, still life and sports.

Insport International
Home Farm Cottage, Church Lane, Church Langton, Market Harborough LE16 7SX
Fax 01858-545492   Tel 01858-545492
E-mail: INSPORT@compuserve.com
Photolibrary and service covering sporting events.

ITN Archive
200 Grays Inn Road, London WC1X 8XZ
Fax 020-7430 4453   Tel 020-7430 4480
E-mail: archive.sales@itn.co.uk
Website: www.itnarchive.com
Material that spans the century from the ITN and Reuters archives and the historic French Pathé library.

ITV Sport Archive
London Television Centre, Upper Ground, London SE1 9LT
Fax 020-7827 7634   Tel 020-7261 3064
E-mail: itvsportenquiries@lnn-tv.co.uk
Contains approximately 50,000 tapes of sports events shown on the ITV network from the 1960s to the present.

Janine Wiedel Photolibrary
8 South Croxted Road, London SE21 8BB
Fax 020-8761 1502   Tel 020-8761 1502
The photojournalist's coverage of contemporary society.

John Frost Historical Newspaper Service
8 Monks Avenue, New Barnet, Herts EN5 1DB
Fax 020-8440 3159   Tel 020-8440 3159
Over 65,000 British and overseas newspapers, and 100,000 cuttings, relating to outstanding events from 1640 to the present.

Julian Cotton Photo Library
55 Upper Montagu Street, London W1H 1FQ
Fax 020-7724 7555   Tel 020-7723 5800
E-mail: chris@juliancotton.co.uk
Website: www.juliancotton.co.uk
Aerial photography covering Britain, New York, Provence and natural abstracts. Also 100,000 pictures ranging from life style, landscapes to animals and food.

Katz Pictures
Zetland House, 5-25 Scrutton Street, London EC2A 4LP
Fax 020-7377 5558   Tel 0171377 5888
E-mail: katzpictures@katzpictures.com
International photo agency and library covering many topics, including personalities, news and current affairs.

Kevin Fitzpatrick Photography
40 Woodville Drive, Sale, Cheshire M33 6NF
Fax 0161-962 9441   Tel 0161-969 2709
Covering the northwest from south Manchester. News, features, library and wire facilities.

Kobal Collection
184 Drummond Street, London NW1 3HP
Fax 020-7383 0044   Tel 020-7383 0011
Collection of 1 million movie images including portraits and scene stills in colour and b&w, from 1895 to the present.

London Metropolitan Archives
40 Northampton Road, London EC1R 0HB
Fax 020-7833 9136   Tel 020-7332 3820
E-mail: ima@ms.corpotlondon.gov.uk
Half a million photos covering the history and topography of the London area. Run by the Corporation of London.

MacQuitty International Collection
7 Elm Lodge, Stevenage Road, London SW6 6NZ
Fax 020-7385 5606   Tel 020-7385 5606
E-mail: maranda.mcquitty@btinternet.com
Library of 250,000 photos on social life and culture in over seventy countries dating back to the 1920s. Also some archive film.

Magnum Photos
5 Old Street, London EC1V 9HL
Fax 020-7608 0020   Tel 020-7490 1771
E-mail: magnum@magnumphotos.co.uk
Website: www.magnumphotos.co.uk/magnumphotos
International agency and library for leading photo-journalists. Over one million photos cover all aspects of C20 life from the 1936 Spanish Civil War onwards.

Mary Evans Picture Library
59 Tranquil Vale, London SE3 0BS
Fax 020-8852 7211   Tel 020-8318 0034
E-mail: lib@mepl.co.uk
Comprehensive historical archive of prints, engravings, photographs and ephemera. Free brochure.

Max Jones Archive
14 Manor Way, Bognor Regis, Sussex PO22 6LA
Fax 01243-584670   Tel 01243-584670
E-mail: freekout@freeuk.com
Jazz photographs (1920-1980) and memorbilia, plus blues, R&B, psychedelic and underground.

McKenzie Heritage Picture Archive
90 Ardgowan Road, London SE6 1UU.
Fax 020-8697 0147   Tel 020-8697 0147
E-mail: MkHeritage@aol.com
Black African, Afro Caribbean & Asian people in Britain and abroad.

Military Picture Library
28a Station Road, Aldershot, Hants GU11 1HT
Fax 01252 350546   Tel 01252-350547
E-mail: pictures@mpl1.demon.co.uk
Website: www.mpl1.demon.co.uk

Mirror Syndication International
1 Canada Square, Canary Wharf, London E14 5AP
Fax 020-7293 2712   Tel 020-7266 1133
E-mail: desk@mirrorpix-com
Website: www.mirpix.com
Picture agents for Mirror Group Newspapers . It
includes the Picture Goer archive. Has ISDN facilities.
Monitor Syndication
17 Old Street, Clerkenwell, London EC1V 9HL
Fax 020-7250 0966   Tel 020-7253 7071
Picture agency/large library specialising in personalities
from 1959. Also personality file 1870-1930, music hall,
theatre; file on Lotus cars and personalities from 1964.
Motoring Picture Library
John Montagu Building, Beaulieu, Brockenhurst,
Hampshire SO42 7ZN
Fax 01590-612655   Tel 01590-612345
E-mail: nmmt@compuserve.com
Nearly 1,000,000 motoring related images.
Museum of London Picture Library
London Wall, London EC2Y 5HN
Fax 020-7600 1058   Tel 020-7814 5604/5605
E-mail: picturelib@museumoflondon.org.uk
Website: www.museumoflondon.org.uk
London views and life illustrated through paintings,
drawings, historic photographs and exhibitions.
National Maritime Museum
Romney Road, Greenwich, London SE10 9NF
Fax 020-8312 6533   Tel 020-8312 6631/6704
Website: www.nmm.ac.uk
Photos and other visual material covering all maritime
topics as well as the Greenwich sites. CD rom available.
National Monuments Record
National Monuments Record Centre, Kemble Drive,
Swindon, Wilts SN2 2GZ
Fax 01793-414606   Tel 01793-414600
E-mail info@rchme.co.uk
Website: www.english-heritage.co.uk
English Heritage's collection of aerial photos, pictures
of historic buildings, and archaeological sites.
National Museum of Photography
See: Science and Society Picture Library
National Railway Museum
Leeman Road, York, North Yorks YO26 4XJ
Fax 01904-611112   Tel 01904-621261
E-mail: nrm@nmsi.ac.uk
Website: www.nrm.org.uk
4.5 million images relating to all aspects of railway life.
National Remote Sensing Centre
Arthur Street, Barwell, Leicestershire LE9 8GZ
Fax 01455-841785   Tel 01455-849227
E-mail: data-services@nrsc.co.uk
Website: www.nrsc.co.uk
UK's largest archive of satellite and aerial photography.
Neil Setchfield Travel Picture Library
23 Crofters Court, Croft Street, Surrey Quays, London
SE8 5DW
Fax 020-7394 9246   Tel 020-7394 9246
E-mail: neil@setchfield.com
Website: www.setchfield.com
Major cities and travel destinations of the world,
including a collection of images of London.

Network Photographers
3-4 Kirby Street, London EC1N 8RG
Fax 020-7831 4468   Tel 020-7831 3633
E-mail: netphoto@compuserve.com
Group of dedicated photojournalists, with extensive
news collection. Represents Rapho (Paris) and
Bilderberg (Hamburg). Has a library which includes
social documentary, travel and feature stories.
Novosti Photo Library
3 Rosary Gardens, London SW7 4NW
Fax 020-7244 7875   Tel 020-7370 1873
E-mail: photos@novosti.demon.co.uk
Website: www.rian.ru
Russian photo agency with archive and current
material.
Nunn Syndication Library
193 Fleet Street, London EC4A 2AH
Fax 020-7405 7688   Tel 020-7242 5544
Website: www.nunn-syndication.com
British and European royal families and celebrities.
Olympic Television Archive Bureau
Axis Centre, Burlington Lane, London W4 2TH
Fax 020-8233 5354   Tel 020-8233 5353
E-mail: dwilliam@imgworld.com
Archive library of Olympic sporting history.
PA News Photo Library
PA NewsCentre, 292 Vauxhall Bridge Road, London
SW1V 1AE
Fax 020-7963 7066   Tel 020-7963 7000
E-mail: photo-sales@pa.press.net
Over five million news sport and entertainment
pictures from the 1890s to the present day.
Pacemaker Press International
787 Lisburn Road, Belfast, N Ireland BT9 7EX
Fax 028-9068 2111   Tel 028-9066 3191
All Ireland, covering news, sport, politics, current
affairs and PR.
Panos Pictures
1 Chapel High St, Borough High St, London SE1 1HH
Fax 020-7357 0094   Tel 020-7234 0010
E-mail: pics@panos.co.uk
Website: www.panos.co.uk
Documentary library specialising in Third World and
Eastern European photography.
Parachute Pictures
1 Navarino Grove, London Fields, London E8 1AJ
Fax 020-7249 2751   Tel 020-7275 7066
E-mail: info@parachute.co.uk
Website: www.parachute.co.uk
Specialist Third World photo library, with coverage of
narcotics, human rights, children at risk, development
issues and World music.
Pearson Television Stills Library
Teddington Studios, Broom Road, Teddington,
Middlesex TW11 9NT
Fax 020-8614 2250   Tel 020-8781 2789
E-mail: stills.library@pearsontv.com
Website: www.pearsontvarchive.com
Library stores and sells around 1 million programmes
stills from Thames, Grundy and Alomo productions.
Archive research, duplication and private sales.

Photofusion
17A Electric Lane, London SW9 8LA
Fax 020-7738 5509   Tel 0171 738 5774
E-mail: library@photofusion.org
Website: www.photofusion.org
All aspects of contemporary life in Britain, particularly
social issues. Photographers available for commission.
Photonews Scotland
36 Washington Street, Glasgow G3 8AZ
Fax 0141-572 1019   Tel 0141-248 4888
Picture, news and feature agency. Has ISDN facilities.
Picture House Photography
West Leam, Station Road, Baildon, W Yorks BD17 6HS
Fax 01274-531058   Tel 01274-531058
E-mail: wilkinson@picture-house.freeserve.co.uk
Pictor International
30-31 Lyme Street, London NW1 0EE
Fax 020-7267 1396   Tel 020-7482 0478
E-mail: info@london.pictor.co.uk
Website: www.pictor.co.uk
3 million photos on a variety of topics, especially travel,
business and industry. Has ISDN facilities.
Popperfoto
The Old Mill, Overstone Farm, Overstone,
Northampton NN6 0AB
Fax 01604-670635   Tel 01604-670670
E-mail: Popperfoto@msn.com
Website: www.popperfoto.com
One of Britain's leading picture libraries, home to over
13 million images covering 150 years of photographic
history. Collections include photos from Reuters, HG
Ponting, AFP and Bob Thomas Sports Photography.
Powerstock Zefa
Unit G10, 59 Chilton Street, London E2 6EA
Fax 020-7729 7476   Tel 020-7729 7473
E-mail: info@powerstockzefa.com
Web: www.powerstockzefa.com
Lifestyle, business, finance and industry images.
The Press Features Syndicate
9 Paradise Close, Eastbourne, Sussex BN20 8BT
                       Tel 01323-728760
International photo-feature agency and picture library.
Professional Sport International
8 Apollo Studios, Charlton Kings Mews, London NW5
2SA
Fax 020-7482 2441   Tel 020-7482 2311
E-mail: pictures@prosport.co.uk
Website: www.prosport.co.uk
Has ISDN facilities.
Public Record Office Image Library
Ruskin Avenue, Kew, Surrey TW9 4DU
Fax 020-8392 5266   Tel 020-8392 5225
E-mail: image-library@pro.gov.uk
Website: www.pro.gov.uk/imagelibrary/
Source for historical, social and political images from
the national archive. Free CD-Rom available.
RAF Museum
Grahame Park Way, Hendon, London NW9 5LL
Fax 020-8200 1751   Tel 020-8205 2266
E-mail: rafmus@dircon.co.uk
Website: www.rafmuseum.org.uk
Archive of military aviation. Written requests only.

Retrograph Nostalgia Archive
164 Kensington Park Road, London W11 2ER
Fax 020-7229 3395   Tel 020-7727 9378
E-mail: MBreeseggg@aol.com
Website: www.Retrograph.com
Specialist picture library/design source of worldwide
nostalgia.Posters, labels, magazine advertising (1860-
1960). RetroTravel has worldwide travel/tourism
images (1900-1960).
Reaction Photographic
3 Berkley Grove, London NW1 8XY
Fax 020-7586 4500   Tel 020-7586 2370
Organisation of photoshoots and management of
fifteen photographers of celebrities.
Reuters
See Popperfoto.
Rex Features
18 Vine Hill, London EC1R 5DZ
Fax 020-7837 4812   Tel 020-7278 7294
E-mail: rex@rexfeatures.com
Large international picture agency and photo library,
strong on news. Represents the work of over 1,500
photographers. Several million images covering news,
personalities and features. Also handles some
newspaper and magazine syndication.
Robert Harding Picture Library
58-9 Great Marlborough St, London W1V 1DD
Fax 020-7631 1070   Tel 020-7287 5414
E-mail: info@robertharding.com
Over 2 million photos on all topics. ISDN facilities.
Royal Geographical Society Picture Library
1 Kensington Gore, London SW7 2AR
Fax 020-7591 3061   Tel 020-7591 3060
E-mail: pictures@rgs.org
Website: www.rgs.org/picturelibrary
Archive specialising in geographical and explorational
activity from 1830 to the present day (including moving
footage). For commercial and academic use.
Royal Photographic Society
Octagon Galleries, Milsom Street, Bath BA1 1DN
Fax 01225-448688   Tel 01225-462841
E-mail: rps@rps.org
Website: www.rps.org
Founded in 1853 for the advancement and promotion of
the art and science of photography. Arranges many
exhibitions, lectures, seminars and workshops. The
RPS runs its own gallery, museum, photolibrary and
archives. Publishes monthly Photographic Journal and
bi-monthly Imagines Science Journal.
RSPCA Photolibrary
Causeway, Horsham, West Sussex RH12 1HG
Fax 01403-241048   Tel 01403-223150
E-mail: photolibrary@rspca.org.uk
Animal welfare, wildlife and natural history.
SOA Photo Agency
87 York Street, London W1H 1DU
Fax 020-7258 0188   Tel 020-7258 0202
E-mail: info@soa-photoagency.co.uk
Website: www.soa-photoagency.co.uk
Specialising in funny photos, avant garde images and
imagery from and about Germany.

Sally and Richard Greenhill
357 Liverpool Road, London N1 1NL
Fax 020-7607 7151　Tel 020-7607 8549
E-mail: library.greenhill@shadow.org.uk
Website: www.shadow.org.uk/photoLibrary
Scial documentary photos. UK and China.

Science Photo Library
327-329 Harrow Road, London W9 3RB
Fax 020-7286 8668　Tel 020-7432 1100
E-mail: info@sciencephoto.co.uk
Website: www.sciencephoto.com

Science and Society Picture Library
Exhibition Road, London SW7 2DD
Fax 020-7938 9751　Tel 020-7938 9750
E-mail: piclib@nmsi.ac.uk
Website: www.nmsi.ac.uk/piclib
Pictures from the collections of three major museums:
the Science Museum, York's National Railway Museum
and Bradford's National Museum of Photography, Film
and Television. The latter's stock includes important
collections (Frith, Fox Talbot, Sutcliffe, Herschel, Daily
Herald Archive, etc).

Scottish Highland Photo Library
Croft Roy, Crammond Brae Tain, Ross-shire, Scotland
IV19 1JG
Fax 01862-892298　Tel 01862-892298
E-mail: shpl@call.co.uk
Website: www.cali.co.uk/shpl
Images of the Highlands and Islands of Scotland.

SIN
Unit 4, 2 Somerset Road, London N17 9EJ
Fax 020-8808 1821　Tel 020-8808 8660
E-mail: 101457.1516@compuserve.com
Website: www.sin-photo.co.uk
Rock and pop, and youth culture.

Skyscan Photolibrary
Oak House, Toddington, Cheltenham, Glos GL54 5BY
Fax 01242-621343　Tel 01242-621357
E-mail: info@skyscan.co.uk
Website: www.skyscan.co.uk
Collection of 'balloon's-eye' views of Britain, now
extended to cover aircraft, international air to ground
photography, aerial sports, in fact anything aerial.

Sport & General Press Agency
63 Gee Street, London EC1V 3RS
Fax 020-7250 1149　Tel 020-7336 0632
E-mail: alphapress@compuserve.com
One of Britain's oldest press photo libraries,
specialising in sport, also general news stock. Allied to
London News Service.

Sporting Pictures (UK)
7A Lambs Conduit Passage, London WC1R 4RG
Fax 020-7831 7991　Tel 020-7405 4500
E-mail: photos@sportingpictures.demon.co.uk
International library of over 3 million pictures

Sportsphoto
20 Clifton Street, Scarborough, N Yorks YO12 7SR
Fax 01723-500117　Tel 01723-367264
E-mail: stewart@sportsphoto.co.uk
Website: www.sportsphoto.co.uk
Established agency covering sport, entertainment,
politicians and royals at national and international level.

Steve Hill Photography
12 Steep Hill, Lincoln LN2 1LT
Fax 01522-569571　Tel 01522-569595
Lincolnshire-based national and international
photographic service with ISDN facilities.

Stewart Ferguson Photography
11 Moredun Vale Grove, Edinburgh EH17 7QZ
Fax 0131-664 6614　Tel 0131-664 6614
Press and features covering all Scotland.

Still Moving Picture Co
67a Logie Green Road, Edinburgh EH7 4HF
Fax 0131-557 9699　Tel 0131-557 9697
E-mail: stillmovingpictures@compuserve.com
Website: www.stillmovingpictures.com
250,000 images of Scotland including Scottish Tourist
Board's collection. Free CD rom browser.

Still Pictures Whole Earth Photo Library
199 Shooters Hill Road, London SE3 8UL
Fax 020-8858 2049　Tel 020-8858 8307
E-mail: stillpictures@stillpic.demon.co.uk
Website: www.stillpictures.com
Key source on environment, the Third World and nature.

Swift Imagery
Media House, 76 Queen Street, Newton Abbot,
Devon TQ12 2ER
Fax 01626-208014　Tel 01626-208011
E-mail: swift@eurobell.co.uk
Worldwide travel, social documentary and lifestyle.

Sygma
Cairo Studios, 4 Nile Street, London N1 7ZZ
Fax 020-7608 3757　Tel 020-7608 3690
E-mail: london@sygmaltd.demon.co.uk
Website: www.sygma-london.co.uk
London office of the large French photographic agency,
specialising in news, featues, showbusiness and
personalities. Sygma has access to the historical
archives of L'illustration and Keystone Paris.

Syndicated Features
PO Box 33, Edenbridge, Kent TN8 5PB
Fax 01342-850244　Tel 01342-850313
E-mail: admin@topfoto.co.uk
Website: www.topfoto.co.uk
A weekly general and showbiz features service available
by post or internet.

Thames Television Library
See Pearson Television Stills Library

Tony Stone Images
101 Bayham Street, London NW1 0AG
Fax 020-7544 3334　Tel: 020-7544 3333
Website: www.tonystone.com
One of the leading contemporary stock photography
businesses. The company has around 900
photographers constantly updating the collection. The
subjects range from families to wildlife, finance to
science. Part of Getty Images.

Topham Picturepoint
PO Box 33, Edenbridge, Kent TN8 5PB
Fax 01342-850244　Tel 01342-850313
E-mail: admin@topfoto.co.uk
Website: www.topfoto.co.uk
General agency and library, with over seven million
pictures. Includes UPI'scollection from 1932-1970.

Travel Ink Photo & Feature Library
The Old Coach House, 14 High Street, Goring-on-Thames, Berkshire RG8 9AR
Fax 01491-875558   Tel 01491-873011
E-mail: info@travel-ink.co.uk
Website: www.travel-ink.co.uk
All aspects of travel images and information. Worldwide coverage. From classic picture postcard material to cultures, lifestyles and realism.
Tropix
156 Meols Parade, Meols, Wirral CH47 6AN
Fax 0151-632 1698   Tel 0151-632 1698
E-mail: tropixphoto@postmaster.co.uk
Website: www.merseyworld.com/tropix/
Specialists in developing nations and in environment topics worldwide.
TWI Archive
Axis Centre, Burlington Lane, London W4 2TH
Fax 020-8233 5301   Tel 020-8233 5300
Sports images as well as historic scenic and cultural stockshots from around the globe.
United Northern Photographers
2-4 Lower Green, Baildon, Bradford BD17 7NE
Fax 01274 598756   Tel 01274 412222
E-mail: hamlet@unp.co.uk
Website: www.unp.co.uk
Editorial reportage and documentary mainly for nationals and magazines.
Universal Pictorial Press & Agency
29-31 Saffron Hill, London EC1N 8SW
Fax 020-7421 6006   Tel 020-7421 6000
Archive for British and international personalities from 1944 to the present. Digital archive with ISDN facilities.
Waterways Photo Library
39 Manor Court Road, London W7 3EJ
Fax 020-8567 0605   Tel 020-8840 1659
E-mail: watphot39@aol.com
Britain's inland waterways.
Wellcome Centre for Medical Science
210 Euston Road, London NW1 2BE
Fax 020-7611 8577   Tel 020-7611 8588
E-mail: photolib@wellcome.ac.uk
Website: www.wellcome.ac.uk
Over 150,000 images covering the history of medicine and human culture, from ancient times to the present.
Wessex Photos
108 High Street, Hungerford, Berkshire RG17 0NB
Fax 01488-686900   Tel 01488-686810
E-mail: pictures@britishnews.co.uk
Website: www.britishnews.co.uk
Photos for newspapers, magazines and PR.
Windrush Photos
99 Noahs Ark, Kemsing, Kent TN15 6PD
Fax 01732-763285   Tel 01732-763486
Extensive wildlife and landscape collection, specialising in birds, with worldwide coverage.
Woodfall Wild Images
17 Bull Lane, Denbigh, Denbighshire LL16 3SN
Fax 01745-814581   Tel 01745-815903
E-mail: wwimages@btinternet.com
Landscape, environment, conservation, agriculture and wildlife collection with worldwide coverage.

Cuttings agencies

KEY CONTACT

The Newspaper Licensing Agency gathers copyright revenue from organisations that copy and fax newspaper articles. Some charities and schools are exempted.

The NLA was launched in January 1996 by a number of national newspapers and in October 1997 News International joined other newspaper publishers as members. "NI's participation means that companies and other organisations will be able to buy a single licence covering all national newspapers," said Guy MacNaughton, the NLA managing director.

The NLA represents the publications listed below and has granted photocopying licences to the agencies opposite:

Newspaper Licensing Agency
Lonsdale Gardens, Tunbridge Wells, Kent TN1 1NL
Fax 01892-525275   Tel 01892-525274
Licensing   Tel 01892-525273
E-mail: copy@nla.co.uk
Website: www.nla.co.uk
National newspapers: Daily Mail, Mail on Sunday, Evening Standard, Express, Sunday Express, Daily Star, Financial Times, Mirror, Sunday Mirror, People, Daily Telegraph, Sunday Telegraph, Independent, Independent on Sunday, Guardian, The Observer, Times, Sunday Times, Sun, NoW
Other publications: The European, Press & Journal (Aberdeen), International Herald Tribune, The Scotsman, Scotland on Sunday, Daily Record, Sunday Mail, The Sunday Mercury (Birmingham), The Birmingham Post, Birmingham Evening Mail, The Coventry Evening Telegraph, Grimsby Evening Telegraph, The Sentinel (Stoke), Hull Daily Mail, Leicester Mercury, Western Morning News, South Wales Evening Post, Nottingham Evening Post, Derby Evening Telegraph, Scunthorpe Evening Telegraph, Yorkshire Post, Yorkshire Evening Post, The Star (Sheffield, Barnsley, Doncaster, Rotherham editions), Manchester Evening News, Sunday Business, Western Gazette, Evening Post (Bristol), Western Daily Press, Lancashire Evening Post.

CUTTINGS AGENCIES

A-Line-Aberdeen
86 Hilton Drive, Aberdeen AB24 4NL
Fax 01224 276010   Tel 01224 484661
E-mail: Teresa@A-Line.co.uk
Specialist in oil and gas service only.

CIS Information Services
73 Farringdon Road, London EC1M 3JB
Fax 020-7242 5887   Tel 020-7242 5886
E-mail: cisinfo@compuserve.com
Website: www.cisclip.com

Clipability
Chapel Allerton Centre, Harrogate Road, Leeds LS7 4NY
Fax 0113-268 7981   Tel 0113-269 3290
E-mail: info@ClipAbility.co.uk
Website: www.ClipAbility.co.uk

Cutting It Fine
Unit 24, River Road Business Park, Barking, Essex IG11 0EA
Fax 020-8591 5866   Tel 020-8507 0999

Durrants Press Cuttings
Discovery House, 28-42 Banner Street, London EC1Y 8QE
Fax 020-7674 0222   Tel 020-7674 0200

Energy Data Services
200 Great Dover Street, London SE1 4WU
Fax 020-7407 0765   Tel 020-7407 0764
E-mail: edsnews@hubcom.com

Entertainment Press Cuttings Agency
Unit 11.G.2, The Leathermarket, Weston Street, London SE1 3ER
Fax 020-7378 6077   020-7378 6887

Financial Times Information
89 Worship Street, London EC2A 2BE
Fax 020-7377 6103   Tel 020-7377 1742

House of Cuttings
Media House, 66 Sayes Court Road, Orpington, Kent BR5 2PQ
Fax 01689-810050   Tel 01689-817000
E-mail: Alison@hocl.freeserve.co.uk
Website: www.hocl.com
National, regional, consumer and trade press cuttings.

JHA Research Consultancy
9 Parkwood Road, London SW19 7AQ
Fax 020-8287 3492   Tel 020-8241 3355

McCallum Media Monitor
Tower House, 10 Possil Road, Glasgow G4 9SY
Fax 0141-333 1811   Tel 0141-333 1822
E-mail: press_clips@cqm.co.uk
Website: www.press-clips.com

Media Shadowfax Europe
10 Barley Mow Passage, London W4 4PH
Fax 020-8994 9888   Tel 020-8994 6477

MMS Market Movements
Tey House, Market Hill, Royston, Herts SG8 9JN
Fax 01763-245151   Tel 01763-248828
E-mail: sales@marketmovements.com
Website: www.marketmovements.com
Specialist monitoring for financial services companies.

NewsIndex
55 Farringdon Road, London EC1 3JB
Fax 020-7242 6644   Tel 020-7242 4747
E-mail: inquiries@newsindex.co.uk

Paperclip Partnership
Unit 9, The Ashway Centre, Elm Crescent, Kingston-upon-Thames, Surrey KT9 6HH
Fax 020-8547 1646   Tel 020-8549 4857

Precise Press Cuttings
200 Great Dover Street, London SE1 4WU
Fax 020-7407 0765   Tel 020-7407 0764

Press Cutting Partnership
5 Hillgate Street, London W8 7SP
Fax 020-7727 8558   Tel 020-7229 7796

Press Data Bureau
76-78 Rose Street, North Lane, Edinburgh EH2 3DX
Fax 0131-225 4503   Tel 0131-225 4988
E-mail: info@presdata.co.uk

Press Express
53-56 Great Sutton Street, London EC1V 0DE
Fax 020-7251 1412   Tel 020-7689 0123
E-mail: press.express@romeike.com
Website: www.press-select.co.uk

Press Select
151-153 Farringdon Lane, London EC1R 3AS
Fax 020-7278 4488   Tel 020-7278 4433
Website: www.press-select.co.uk

PressScan
12 Cannongate Venture, 5 New Street, Edinburgh EH8 5EH
Fax 0131-557 8737   Tel 0131-557 9010

Prominent Pages
5th Floor, Bear Wharf, 27 Bankside, London SE1 9DP
Fax 020-7203 0101   Tel 020-7620 0600
E-mail: enquiries@prominfo.com
Wbsite: www.prompages.com

Romeike & Curtice
Hale House, 290-296 Green Lanes, London N13 5TP
Fax 020-8882 6716   Tel 020-8882 0155

Smith Willis Communications
The Bond, 18-20 Fazeley Street, Birmingham B5 5SE
Fax 0121-608 0073   Tel 0121-608 0077

Strata Matrix
23-25 North Parade, Aberystwyth, Ceredigion, Dyfed SY23 2JN
Fax 01970-612774   Tel 01970-625552
E-mail: strata.aber@btinternet.com

Tellex Monitors
210 Old Street, London EC1V 9UN
Fax 020-7608 3464   Tel 020-7566 3131
E-mail: sales@tellex.press.net
Website: www.tellex.press.net

Publications about the press

PRESS MAGAZINES

The Author
84 Drayton Gardens, London SW10 9SB
Fax: 020-7373 5768   Tel 020-7373 6642
E-mail: authorsoc@writers.org.uk
Website: www.writers.org.uk/society
Publisher: Society of Authors
Quarterly news magazine. £7 non-members.

The Bookseller
12 Dyott Street, London WC1A 1DF
Fax 020-7420 6013   Tel 020-7420 6000
Publisher: Bookseller Publications
E-mail: letters.to.editor@bookseller.co.uk
Website: www.theBookseller.com
The trade paper of the book industry. It publishes two annual guides -Spring Books and Autumn Books - with details of forthcoming titles. £2.50. Editor: Louis Baum.

Books in the Media
15-Up, East Street, Chesham, Bucks HP5 1HQ
Fax 01494-784850   Tel 01494-792269
E-mail: 100615.1643@compuserve.com
Publisher: Bookwatch
Weekly newsletter keeping bookshops and libraries informed of books appearing in the media. £112 non-members, £102 members.

British Journalism Review
Faculty of Humanities, University of Luton, LU1 3AJ
Fax 01582-743298   Tel 01582-743297
Publisher: University of Luton Press
Scholarly quarterly for discussion of media topics.

British Printer
Sovereign Way, Tonbridge, Kent TN9 1RW
Fax 01732-377362   Tel 01732-364422
E-mail: gward@unmf.com
Website: www.dotprint.com
Publisher: Miller Freeman
Monthly news and features from the printing industry.

Comagazine
Tavistock Road, West Drayton, Middx UB7 7QE
Fax 01895-433602   Tel 01895-433600
Publisher: Comag
Alternate monthly review of the magazine industry.

Communications Law
2 Addiscombe Road, Croydon, Surrey CR9 5AF
Fax 020-8686 3155   Tel 020-8686 9141
E-mail: Rajni_Boswell@tolley.co.uk
Publisher: Tolley Publishing
6xpa. Journal of computer, media and telecomms law.

Financial Times Newsletters
149 Tottenham Court Road, London W1P 9LL
Fax 020-7896 2748   Tel 020-7896 2222
Publisher: FT Telecom & Media Publishing
Newsletters: Asia-Pacific Telecoms Analyst; Business Computing Brief; Music & Copyright; New Media Markets; Screen Finance; and Telecom Markets.

Free Press
8 Cynthia Street, London N1 9JF
Fax 020-8837 8868   Tel 020-7278 4430
E-mail: freepress@cpbf.demon.co.uk
Website: www.cpbf.demon.co.uk
Publisher: CPBF
Members news magazine, with analysis of monopoly media ownership and control, and other issues. 6x pa.

Freelance Market News
7 Dale Street, Manchester M1 1JB
Fax 0161-228 3533   Tel 0161-228 2362
E-mail: fmn@writersbureau.com
Website: www.writersbureau.com
Monthly newsletter with details of markets for the work of freelance writers. Editor: Angela Cox.

Freelance News
7 Wharf Lane, Old Stratford, Milton Keynes MK19 6AD
Fax 01908-267078   Tel 01908-262560
E-mail: fln@northern-light.co.uk
Publisher: Northern Light
Magazine of the freelance division of the Chartered Institute of Journalists.Only available to CIOJ members.

Index on Censorship
33 Islington High Street, London N1 9LH
Fax 020-7278 1878   Tel 020-7278 2313
E-mail: contact@indexoncensorship.org
Website: www.indexoncensorship.org
International magazine for free speech, with interviews, reportage and debates on the important issues of the day. Paperback format. 6x pa.

The Journalist
314 Grays Inn Road, London WC1X 8DP
Fax 020-7837 8143   Tel 020-7278 7916
E-mail: acorn.house@nuj.org.uk
Publisher: National Union of Journalists
For NUJ members. 6x pa.

Journalist's Handbook
2/7 Galt House, 31 Bank Street, Irvine KA12 0LL
Fax 01294-311322   Tel 01294-311322
E-mail: jh@carrickmedia.demon.co.uk
Publisher: Carrick Media
Quarterly journal with articles and a contacts list.
Editor: Fiona MacDonald.

The Magazine Business Weekly Report
Islington Business Centre, 14-22 Coleman Fields, London N1 7AE
Fax 020-7688 6637   Tel 020-7688 6638
E-mail: tmb@dircon.co.uk
Publisher: Register Information Services
Weekly faxed newsletter. Now owned by Duvan.

Magazine News
Queens House, 28 Kingsway, London WC2B 6JR
Fax 020-7404 4167   Tel 020-7404 4166
Website: www.ppa.co.uk
Publisher: Periodical Publishers Association
Mainly for advertisers and agencies. 5x pa.

Media Law Review
200 Aldersgate Street, London EC1A 4JJ
Fax 020-7600 5555   Tel 020-7600 1000
E-mail: jeremy.ison@cliffordchance.com
Website: www.cliffordchance.com
Editor: Jeremy Ison. Newsletter from law firm Clifford Chance and the PPA. 3x pa free.

Media Lawyer
3 Broom Close, Broughton in Furness, Cumbria LA20 6JG
Fax 01229-716621   Tel 01229-716622
A newsletter for media lawyers, trainers, journalists and all concerned with media law. Bi-monthly. £36 pa.

Media Week
Quantum House, 19 Scarbrook Road, Croydon, Surrey CR9 1LX
Fax 020-8565 4394   Tel 020-8565 4200
E-mail: mweeked@qpp.co.uk
Website: www.mediaweek.co.uk
Weekly. News on advertising. £1.85.

New Media Age
50 Poland Street, London W1V 4AX
Fax 020-7970 4899   Tel 020-7970 4000
E-mail: mikeb@centaur.co.uk
Website: www.nma.co.uk
Weekly news title for the new media industry.

New Media Investor
50 Poland Street, London W1V 4AX
Fax 020-7970 4899   Tel 020-7970 4000
E-mail: feliciaj@centaur.co.uk
Website: www.nma.co.uk

PrePress News
111 Upper Richmond Road, London SW15 2TJ
Fax 020-8788 2302   Tel 020-8780 7800
E-mail: prepressnews@forme.com
Website: www.forme.com
Publisher: Forme Communications
News. reviews and features relating to print production.

Press Gazette
19 Scarbrook Road, Croydon, Surrey CR9 1LX
Fax 020-8565 4395   Tel 020-8565 4200
E-mail: pged@qpp.co.uk
Publisher: Quantum Publishing
The old UK Press Gazette. A weekly paper for all journalists with a concentration on newspapers and magazines, plus coverage of television and radio. Editor: Philippa Kennedy.

PrintWeek
174 Hammersmith Road, London W6 7JP
Fax 020-7413 4455   Tel 020-7413 4397
E-mail: printweek@haynet.com
Publisher: Haymarket
The UK's largest circulation printing industry weekly, covering all sectors of the trade. Editor: Jo Francis.

Printing Industries
11 Bedford Row, London WC1R 4DX
Fax 020-7405 7784   Tel 020-7242 6904
E-mail: info@bpif.org.uk
Website: www.bpif.org.uk
Publisher: British Printing Industries Federation
The printers management journal (also known as Pi), published 10x pa.

Printing World
Sovereign Way, Tonbridge, Kent TN9 1RW
Fax 01732-377552   Tel 01732-364422
E-mail: printing.world@unmf.com
Website: www.dotprint.com
Publisher: Miller Freeman Publishers
Weekly covering all aspects of the printing industry and its personalities. Editor: Terry Ulrick. £2.75.

Private Eye
6 Carlisle Street, London W1V 5RG
Fax 020-7437 0705   Tel 020-7437 4017
E-mail: strobes@cix.compulink.co.uk
Website: www.compulink.co.uk/.private-eye/
Publisher: Pressdram
Fortnightly for journalists. It is one of the few mags which does not depend on ads to survive.

Production Journal
2 Avebury Court, Hemel Hempstead, Herts HP2 7TA
Fax 01442-219641   Tel 01442-233656
E-mail: gary@cullumpublishing.co.uk
Website: www.newstech.co.uk
Newspaper Society monthly since 1958, reviewing newspaper and news media technology.

Professional Printer
Clanricarde Road, Tunbridge Wells, Kent TN1 1PJ
Fax 01892-518028   Tel 01892-538118
E-mail: iop@globalprint.com
Website: www.globalprint.com/uk/iop
Publisher: Institute of Printing
Journal of news and articles. Published 6x pa.

Publishing
111 Upper Richmond Road, London SW15 2TJ
Fax 020-8788 2302   Tel 020-8780 7800
E-mail: forme@forme.com
Publisher: Forme Communications
Management monthly on issues affecting the newspaper, book and catalogue market.

Publishing News
39 Store Street, London WC1E 7DB
Fax 020-7419 2111   Tel 020-7692 2900
E-mail: mailbox@publishingnews.co.uk
The weekly newspaper of the book trade.

Retail Newsagent
11 Angel Gate, City Road, London EC1V 2PT
Fax 020-7689 0500   Tel 020-7689 0600
E-mail: contact@newstrade.co.uk
Publisher: Newtrade Publishing
Weekly newspaper, founded 1888.

Secrets
Suite 102, 16 Baldwins Gardens, London EC1N 7RJ
Fax 020-7831 7461   Tel 020-7831 7477
E-mail: admin@cfoi.demon.co.uk
Website: www.cfoi.org.uk
Publisher: Campaign for Freedom of Information
A newspaper which monitors unnecessary official secrecy and its effects on the public and the media.

Spokesman
20 Cardigan Road, London E3 5HU
Fax 020-8981 3779   Tel 020-8981 3779
E-mail: spokesman@mcmail.com
Website: www.spokesman.mcmail.com
Quarterly report on the press and governmant. £120 pa.

SHOCK, HORROR!

Yes, whatever the millennium, *Media Lawyer's* themes don't change. But we're keeping up the tradition of not taking things <u>too</u> seriously

"I WANT TO SUE THE TABLOIDS FOR CALLING ME A DODDERING OLD INEBRIATE ..."

Cartoons by Barry Knowles

Media Lawyer, a bi-monthly newsletter, is for editors, reporters, journalism trainers, lawyers and all concerned with media law. Subscription is £36 a year.

Get a free sample from editor Tom Welsh, at 3 Broom Close, Broughton-in-Furness, Cumbria LA20 6JG

Phone 01229 716622, fax 01229 716621

E-mail media_lawyer@compuserve.com

The Week
5-11 Westbourne Grove, London W2 4UA
Fax 020-7229 0049   Tel 020-7229 0006
E-mail: admin.theweek@dennis.co.uk
Weekly. £1.50. A digest of British and foreign press.

Writers News
PO Box 4, Nairn IV12 4HU
Fax 01667-454401   Tel 01667-454441
Subscription monthly for all writers and would-be
writers. also publishes quarterly Writing Magazine.

Writers' Newsletter
430 Edgware Road, London W2 1EH
Fax 020-7706 2413   Tel 020-7723 8074
E-mail: postie@wggb.demon.co.uk
Website: www.writers.org.uk/guild
Publisher: Writers' Guild of Great Britain
News from the writers' trade union. 6x pa.

PRESS YEARBOOKS

Benn's Media
Riverbank HoUse, Angel Lane, Tonbridge, Kent TN9
1SE
Fax 01732-367301   Tel 01732-362666
Publisher: Miller Freeman Information Services
Contact: Debbie O'Neill
Three vols UK, Europe and the rest of the world.£310,
two vols £290, single vols £145. Benn's has the most
comprehensive listings amongst the general directories.
The UK volume lists 17,000 organisations, publications
and broadcasting stations. Est. 1846.

The Circulation Report
Islington Business Centre, 14-22 Coleman Fields,
London N1 7AE
Fax 020-7688 6637   Tel 020-7688 6638
E-mail: tmb@dircon.co.uk
Publisher: Register Information Services.
Contact: Alan Maacfarlane
£145, bi-annual. Also available on disc. Circulation and
vital statistics on all 450 ABC and independently
audited newstrade magazines.

Directory of Book Publishers, Distributors &
Wholesalers
272 Vauxhall Bridge Road, London SW1V 1BA
Fax 020-7834 8812   Tel 020-7834 5477
E-mail: 100437.2261@compuserve.com
Website: www.booksellers.org.uk
Publisher: Booksellers Association.
Editor: Sydney Davies
£50. Ordering guide/reference for the book trade.

Directory of Publishing
Wellington House, 125 Strand, London WC2R 0BB
Fax 020-7240 8531   Tel 020-7420 5555
E-mail: cassellacad@msn.com
Website: www.cassell.co.uk
Publisher: Cassell & the Publishers Association
Editor: Verona Higgs
£65. The definitive guide to the book publishing
business, with all main publishers, organisations and
agencies detailedin the UK and the Commonwealth.

Encyclopedia of the World Press
310 Regent Street, London W1R 5AJ
Fax 020-7636 6982   Tel 020-7636 6627
E-mail: press@fitzroydearborn.deon.co.uk
Web: www.fitzroydearborn.com/london/press.htm
Publisher: Fitzroy Dearborn
Due out in 2001. An illustrated, two million word A-Z
of the press in 180 countries, its sponsors include the
Newspaper Society, the NPA, the World Association of
Newspapers and the Freedom Forum. The two volumes
will cover the press from Gutenburg to the millennium
and they are tentatively priced at £200. The deadline for
entries is the end of 2000.

Freelance Directory
Acorn House, 134 Grays Inn Road, London WC1X
8DP
Fax 020-7278 1812   Tel.020-7278 7916
E-mail: nuj@mcr1.poptel.org.uk
Publisher: National Union of Journalists
Editor: Don Mackglew
£35, inc p&p. Biennial directory of 1,200 freelance
reporters, photographers, broadcasters, editors, subs,
cartoonists and illustrators.

Freelance Photographer's Market Handbook
Focus House, 497 Green Lanes, London N13 4BP
Fax 020-8886 5174   Tel 020-8882 3315
Publisher: Bureau of Freelance Photographers
Editors: John Tracy, Stewart Gibson
£12.95. How to find markets for photographs, mainly
with magazines.

IPO Directory
PO Box 30, Weatherby, West Yorkshire LS23 7YA
Fax 01937-541083   Tel 020-7261 8527
Publisher: Central Office of Information
£13. The official directory of the information and press
officers in government departments and public
corporations. Bi-annual.

Institute of Printing Handbook
The Mews, Hill House, Clanricarde Road, Tunbridge
Wells, Kent TN1 1PJ
Fax 01892-518028   Tel 01892-538118
E-mail: iop@globalprint.com
Website: www.globalprint.com/uk/iop
Contact: David Freeland
Technical articles about printing and related industries
with a listing of the names and addresses of IOP
members. £100 or free to members.

MDB Magazine Directory
33-39 Bowling Green Lane, London EC1R 0DA
Fax 020-7505 8201   Tel 020-7505 8000
E-mail: andrewn@brad.co.uk
The Magazine Business
Contact: Alan Macfarlane
£17.50 Biannual ad-oriented directory of magazines for
sale in British newsagents.

Media Disc
34 Germain Street, Chesham, Bucks HP5 1SJ
Fax 01494-797217   Tel 01494-797200
E-mail: mediadisc@mediainfo.co.uk
Editor: Nick Elliot
Dial up media info on 15,000 titles and contacts. Label
and check list service. Subs £200/month.

The Media Guide
Media Relations, Communications, Open University,
Walton Hall, Miton Keynes MK7 6AA
Fax 01908-652247   Tel 01908-653343
E-mail: press-office@open.ac.uk
Editor: Sophie Bethune
A guide for the media to the expertise of Open
University academics.
The Media Guide
Fourth Estate, for The Guardian
                Tel 020-7727-8993
Media Pocket Book
Farm Road, Henley on Thames, Oxon RG9 1EJ
Fax 01491-571188   Tel 01491 411000
E-mail: info@ntc.co.uk
Publisher: NTC Publications
Editor: Jeff Curtis
£26. Statistical data for all UK media.
Multimedia & CD Rom Directory
6-14 Underwood Street, London N1 7JQ
Fax 020-7324 2312   Tel 020-7324 2345
E-mail: gbuecker@waterlow.com
Website: www.newmediainfo.com
Publisher: Waterlow New Media Information
Contact: Gesche Beucker
Vol 1 New Media Companies £149, lists 15,000
companies that are active in multimedia industry
worldwide with contact details, description of company,
newsletters, mags and events targetted at multi-media
professionals. Vol 2 New Media Titles £149, lists
28,000 commercially available DVD and CD Rom titles
as well as publishers. Sections of info £49 each.
National Small Press Centre Handbook
NSPC, BM Bozo, London WC1N 3XX
£12.
How to self-publish, from bar codes to distributors.
Pims Media Directories
Mildmay Avenue, London N1 4RS
Fax 020-7354 7053   Tel 020-7226 1000
E-mail: prservices@pims.co.uk
Publisher: Pims UK
Editor: Steve Reed
Pims produces a range of detailed, loose-leaf guides to
editorial media contacts, all regularly updated, aimed
mainly at the public relations sector. Titles include: UK
Media Directory (£365 pa), A-Z Towns Directory (£250)
USA Directory (£215), European Directory(£205).
Printing Trades Directory
Riverbank House, Tonbridge,Kent TN9 1SE
Fax 01732-367301   Tel 01732-362666
E-mail: pleegood@unmf.com
Publisher: Miller Freeman
£112. Listing more than 7,300 print related companies
(printers, manufacturers and suppliers).
Publishers Handbook
Grosvenor Press   Tel 020-7278 7772
£49.95.
Commercial services available for publishers.
Small Press Yearbook
Small Press Group, BM Bozo, London WC1N 3XX
£7.95.
Guide to the many small presses in the UK.

Studies in Newspaper & Periodical History
3 Henrietta Street, London WC2E 8LU
Fax 020-7379 0609   Tel 020-7240 0856
Publisher: Greenwood Publishing
Scholarly look at press history. Formerly published as
the Journal of Newspaper and Periodical History.
Two-Ten Media Directories
Communications House, 210 Old Street, London
EC1V 9UN
Fax 020-7490 1255   Tel 020-7490 8111
E-mail: info@twoten.press.net
Publisher: Two-Ten Communications
Contact: Julie Roberts
UK Media - 6 issues pa - £308
UK Media Town by Town - 2 issues pa - £185
European Media - 4 issues pa - £585
UK Press Directory
32 South Road, Saffron Walden, Essex CB11 3DN
Fax 01799-502665   Tel 01799 502665
E-mail: showell@ukmd.demon.co.uk
Publisher: UK Media Directories
Contact: Simon Howell
£145 for UK, £85 for Republic of Ireland. Financial
profiles and maps of the 125 leading newspaper
publishers in the UK and the 40 in the Republic of
Ireland. The UK directory has a second volume
detailing 90 of the leading subsidiary companies.
Ulrich's International Periodicals Directory
Windsor Court, East Grinstead House, East
Grinstead, West Sussex RH19 1XA
Fax 01342-335612   Tel 01342-326972
E-mail: custserv@bowker-saur.co.uk
Publisher: Bowker-Saur
A five volume £385 American guide to the world's
periodicals, detailing approx 200,000 titles.
Willings Press Guide
Harlequin House, 7 High Street, Teddington,
Middlesex, TWII 8EL
Fax 020-8977 1133   Tel 020-8977 7711
E-mail: willings@hollis-pr.co.uk
Website: www.hollis-pr.co.uk
Contact: Nesta Hollis
Publisher: Hollis Directories
Two vols £205. Alphabetical list detailing over 26,000
newspapers and periodicals worldwide. Available on
CD for £255/£299.63 inc VAT. CD + 2 vols at £287.25
inc VAT.
Writers' & Artists' Yearbook
35 Bedford Row, London W1CR 4JH
Fax 020-7404 7706   Tel 020-7404 5613
E-mail: writers&artists@acblack.co.uk
Publisher: A & C Black
Contact: Christine Robinson
£11.99.A long-established handbook, mainly for writers
and authors.
Writer's Handbook
25 Eccleston Place, London SW1W 9NF
Fax 020-7881 8001   Tel 020-7881 8000
Website: www.macmillan.co.uk
Publisher: Macmillan
Contact: Claire Robinson.£12.99. Covers publishers,
publications, broadcasting, agents, services, prizes, etc.

Press support organisations

MAIN TRADE UNIONS

British Association of Journalists
600 members
Chartered Institute of Journalists
1,500 members
Graphical, Paper and Media Union
200,000 members
National Union of Journalists
29,000 members
Society of Authors
6,000 members

MAIN TRADE ASSOCIATIONS

Newspaper Publishers Association
National papers
Newspaper Society
Local papers
Periodical Publishers Association
Magazines
Scottish Daily Newspaper Society
Scottish dailies and Sundays
Scottish Newspapers Publishers' Association
Scottish regional and local papers

ABC
See Audit Bureau of Circulations
Amalgamated Engineering & Electrical Union (AEEU)
Hayes Court, West Common Road, Bromley, Kent BR2 7AU
Fax 020-8315 8234   Tel 020-8462 7755
E-mail: h.jefferies@headoffice.aeeu.org.uk
Website: www.aeeu.org.uk
Formed from the merger of the Amalgamated Engineering Union the Electrical, Electronic, Telecommunications and Plumbing Union. It has members in newspaper production and broadcasting and publishes quarterly newspaper Contact.
Advance Media Information
226 Strand, London WC2R 1BA
Fax 020-8 286 2482   Tel 020-8 549 0799
E-mail: ami@easynet.co.uk
Web site: www.amiplan.com
AMI supplies Britain's major news organisations with a daily-updated list of future events, with access to extensive background information.
Amnesty International Journalists' Network
99-119 Rosebery Avenue, London EC1R 4RE
Fax 020-7833 1510   Tel 020-7814 6200
E-mail: journos@amnesty.org.uk
Website: www.amnesty.org.uk
Campaigns on behalf of media workers who have been imprisoned, tortured or threatened with death. Holds meetings and publishes a quarterly newsletter.

Article 19, the International Centre Against Censorship
33 Islington High Street, London N1 9LH
Fax 020-7713 1356   Tel 020-7278 9292
E-mail: info@article19.org
Website: www.gn.apc.org/article19
International human rights organisation campaigning for the right to freedom of expression and information. Promotes improved legal standards for freedom of expression and defends victims of censorship. Publishes regular newsletter and a range of country and theme reports, with emphasis on media freedom.
Association of American Correspondents in London
AP, 12 Norwich Street, London EC4A 1BP
Fax 020-7936 2229   Tel 020-7353 1515
The association represents a broad spectrum of 200 American and Canadian journalists. It was founded in 1919. and holds regular lunches.
Association of British Editors
See Society of Editors
Association of British Science Writers
23 Savile Row, London W1X 2NB
Fax 020-7973 3051   Tel 020-7439 1205
E-mail: absw@absw.demon.co.uk
Its aim is to improve standards of science journalism. The association organises meetings with scientists and policy makers, and arranges visits. It publishes a monthly newsletter The Science Reporter.
Association of European Journalists
7a St Albans Grove, London W8 5PN
Fax 020-7937 0025   Tel 020-7376 9998
A pan-European group of individual journalists. Its aim is to increase knowledge of Europe and to defend the freedom of the media.
Association of Golf Writers
c/o M Garrod   Tel 01707-654112
Association of Illustrators
1-5 Beehive Place, London SW9 7QR
Fax 020-7733 1199   Tel 020-7733 9155
E-mail: a-o-illustrators.demon.co.uk
Website: www.aoi.co.uk
Professional association promoting British illustration and supporting illustrators through membership services. Also campaigns and lobbies. Publishes guides and monthly newsletter.
Association of Investigative Journalists
Cedar House, 72 Holloway Road, London N7 8NZ
Fax 08700 882845   Tel 0709-121 6085
Website: www.aij-uk.com
The AIJ has a good web wite and provides a variety of resources for investigative journalists.

Association of Little Presses
25 St Benedict's Close, Church Lane, London SW17 9NX
E-mail: asslp@geocities.com
Website: www.geocities.com/Athens/Oracle/7911
Represents 200 members producing books and magazines on all topics, especially poetry. Publishes newsletter, magazine, Poetry and LittlePress Information bulletins and annual catalogue; organises bookfairs. Does NOT publish any creative writing.

Association of Newspaper & Magazine Wholesalers
Celcon House, 6th Floor, 289-293 High Holborn, London WC1V 7HZ
Fax 020-7405 1128   Tel 020-7242 3458
E-mail: enquiries@anmw.co.uk

Association of Photographers
81 Leonard Street, London EC2A 4QS
Fax 020-7739 8707   Tel 020-7739 6669
E-mail: aop@dircon.co.uk
Website: www.aphoto.co.uk
Trade association for professional fashion, advertising, design and editorial photographers. Publishes monthly magazine Image. Holds annual awards and runs own gallery at address above.

Association of Publishing Agencies (APA)
Queen's House, 55-56 Lincoln's Inn Fields, London WC2A 3LJ
Fax 020-7404 4166   Tel 020-7404 4167
E-mail: hilary@apa.co.uk
Website: www.apa.co.uk
Trade body for customer magazine industry, providing research, training, events and marketing support. It aims to promote awareness of customer magazines as a marketing medium and to act as a central source of information. Affiliated to the PPA.

Association of UK Media Librarians
PO Box 14254, London SE1 9WL
                     Tel 020-7813 6105
Website: www.aukml.org.uk
A network of information professionals keeping pace with technological developments. Publishes quarterly journal Deadline.

Audit Bureau of Circulations (ABC)
Black Prince Yard, 207-209 High Street, Berkhamsted, Herts HP4 1AD
Fax 01442-877407   Tel 01442-870800
E-mail abcpost@abc.org.uk
Website: www.abc.org.uk
Regulatory body for the publishing industry, providing certified circulation data for newspapers and magazines. Also runs Verified Free Distribution, checking distribution claims of publishers of free newspapers. Figures are available via the Internet:

Authors' Licensing & Collecting Society
Marlborough Court, 14-18 Holborn, London EC1 2LE
Fax 020-7395 0660   Tel 020-7395 0600
E-mail alcs@alcs.co.uk
Website: www.alcs.co.uk
Collects and distributes royalties to writers (books, television, radio and film) and campaigns for collective rights schemes.

Birmingham Press Club
100 Hagley Road, Edgbaston, Birmingham B16 8LT
E-mail: andrew@birminghampressclub.co.uk
The world's oldest press club founded in Birmingham in 1865 has nearly 500 members. Visiting press welcome.

Book Trust
Book House, 45 East Hill, London SW18 2QZ
Fax 020-8516 2978   Tel 020-8516 2977
E-mail: jwilliams@booktrust.org.uk
Website: www.booktrust.org.uk
The Book Trust organises and promotes literary prizes, including the Booker Prize and the Orange Prize for fiction, runs Children's Book Week and a Book Information Service. Publishes author profiles and guides to book selection.

British Association of Communicators in Business
42 Borough High Street, London SE1 1XW
Fax 020-7378 7140   Tel 020-7378 7139
E-mail: bacb@globalnet.uk
Webste: www.bacb.org.uk
Formerly the BAIE, the association is for editors of in-house journals. It publishes Crucible 10x pa, the quarterly magazine Communicators in Business and the Editors' Handbook. It runs training programmes and organises an annual convention and awards.

British Association of Journalists
88 Fleet Street, London EC4Y 1PJ
Fax 020-7353 2310   Tel 020-7353 3003
A small non-TUC trade union set up as a rival to the National Union of Journalists in 1992 by some Mirror Group journalists and the former NUJ general secretary Steve Turner. It has over 700 members.

British Association of Picture Libraries and Agencies (BAPLA)
18 Vine Hill, London EC1R 5DX
Fax 020-7713 1211   Tel 020-7713 1780
E-mail: bapla@bapla.demon.co.uk
Webste: www.bapla.org.uk
BAPLA is the trade association that represents 350 libraries. BAPLA provides a referral service for image research. Publishes the industry magazine 'Light Box' and annual directory. As well as valuable work in copyright, BAPLA assesses many industry issues for both picture users and libraries, including copyright clearance, ethics, pricing, marketing and technology.

British Copyright Council
29 Berners Street, London W1P 4AA
Fax 020-7306 4069   Tel 020-7306 4069
Liaison committee for the organisations representing owners of copyright in literary, musical and artistic works. Not an advice service, but will try to answer written queries. Publishes two guides to the law.

British Guild of Travel Writers
Hangersley Hill, Ringwood, Hampshire BH24 3JN
                     Tel 01425-470946
E-mail: adeleevans@compuserve.com
Association of writers, authors, broadcasters and photographers specialising in travel. Publishes monthly internal newsletter, Globetrotter, and annual yearbook with details of 170 members.

British Institute of Professional Photography
Fox Talbot House, Amwell End, Ware, Herts SG12 9HN
Fax 01920-487056   Tel 01920-464011
E-mail: bipp@compuserve.com
Website: www.bipp.com
Founded in 1901, this is the leading professional organisation for photographers. It publishes the respected monthly magazine The Photographer, and the annual Directory of Professional Photography (with details of the 4,000 members).

British Printing Industries Federation
11 Bedford Row, London WC1R 4DX
Fax 020-7405 7784   Tel 020-7242 6904
E-mail: info@bpif.org.uk
Website: www.bpif.org.uk
The BPIF is the business support organisation for employers in the printing, packaging and graphic communications industry. Based in London and with six regional business centres around the country, the BPIF represents more than 3000 member companies. Publishes: Printing Industries (monthly), surveys, Directions (quarterly economic digest) and books.

British Society of Magazine Editors
c/o Gill Branston & Associates, 137 Hale Lane
Edgware Middx HA8 9QP
Fax 020-8959 2137   Tel 020-8906 4664
E-mail: bsme@cix.compulink.co.uk
Professional association for magazine editors and senior editorial staff. The Society organises annual editorial awards and industry forums.

Bureau of Freelance Photographers
497 Green Lanes, London N13 4BP
Fax 020-8886 5174   Tel 020-8882 3315
Gives advice and market information to freelance photographers supplying publishing markets (magazines, newspapers, books, picture agencies, etc). Publishes monthly Market Newsletter and annual Freelance Photographers Market Handbook. Annual membership £40.

Campaign for Freedom of Information
Suite 102, 16 Baldwin Gardens, London EC1N 7RJ
Fax 020-7831 7461   Tel 020-7831 7477
E-mail: admin@cfoi.demon.co.uk
Website: www.cfoi.org.uk
The campaign is pressing for a Freedom of Information Act which would create a general right of access to official records subject to exemptions protecting information whose disclosure would cause real harm to essential interests such as defence, law enforcement and privacy. Campaigns for a public interest defence under the Official Secrets Act. It also seeks disclosure in the private sector on issues of public interest. Publishes briefings and other publications.

Campaign for Press and Broadcasting Freedom
8 Cynthia Street, London N1 9JF
Fax 020-7837 8868   Tel 020-7278 4430
E-mail: freepress@cpbf.demon.co.uk
Website: www.cpbf.demon.co.uk
Campaigns for a democratic, diverse and accountable media, accessible to all. The CPBF opposes monopoly ownership of the press and seeks a Right of Reply. It organises events and publishes 6x pa journal Free Press, occasional pamphlets and the Media Catalogue of mail order books and postcards.

Cartoon Art Trust
7 Brunswick Centre, Bernard Street, London WC1A 1AF
Fax 020-7278 4234   Tel 020-7278 7172
E-mail: skp@escape.u-net.com
Aims to preserve and promote the art of cartooning. Runs an appeal to establish a national museum of cartoon art and is building up a library of cartoon material. Publishes quarterly newsletter and exhibition catalogues. They run the Cartoon Art Trust Awards which are given in November every year.

Cartoonists' Club of Great Britain
46 Strawberry Vale, Twickenham, Middlesex TW1 4SE
Fax 020-8891 5946   Tel 020-8892 3621
E-mail: terryc@axiom.co.uk
The Club is a social one for professional cartoonists. It meets on the first Tuesday of every month at The Cartoonist pub, Shoe Lane, London EC4, publishes the monthly magazine Jester and holds regular exhibitions.

Central Criminal Court Journalists' Association
Press Room, Old Bailey, London EC4N 7EH
Fax 020-7248 0133   Tel 020-7248 3277
Represents media interests in court coverage.

Chartered Institute of Journalists
2 Dock Offices, Surrey Quays Road, London SE16 2XU
Fax 020-7232 2302   Tel 020-7252 1187
E-mail: cioj@dircon.co.uk
Website: www.cioj.dircon.co.uk
Certificated independent trade union concerned with preserving standards and protecting the pay and conditions of its members. It publishes The Journal.

Chartered Society of Designers
1st Floor, 32-38 Saffron Hill, London EC1N 8FH
Fax 020-7831 6277   Tel 020-7831 9777
E-mail: csd@csd.org.uk
Main professional body for designers in all fields, setting and maintaining standards. Organises events, seminars and awards and publishes a newsletter.

Children's Express London Bureau
Exmouth House, 3-11 Pine Street, London, EC1R 0JH
Fax 020-7278 7722   Tel 020-7833 2577
E-mail: enquiries@childrensexpress.btinternet.com
Website: www.childrens-express.org
A charitable organisation which gives children aged between 8 -18 years the opportunity to learn journalism skills, such as reporting and interviewing. Part news agency and part youth club.

Commonwealth Journalists Association
17 Nottingham Street, London W1M 3RD
Fax 020-7486 3822   Tel 020-7486 3844
Fosters interest in Commonwealth affairs, undertakes training of journalists in Commonwealth countries and defends journalists' rights where these are threatened. Publishes newsletter 3x pa and holds international conferences every 3 years.

Commonwealth Press Union
17 Fleet Street, London EC4Y 1AA
Fax 020-7583 6868   Tel 020-7583 7733
E-mail: cpu@compressu.demon.co.uk
Website: www.cpu.org.uk
Association of Commonwealth newspapers, news agencies and periodicals, upholding the ideals and values of the Commonwealth. Activities include press freedom monitoring and extensive training programmes throughout the Commonwealth, fellowships , biennial conferences. Publishes CPU News, bi-monthly.

Copyright Licensing Agency
90 Tottenham Court Road, London W1P 0LP
Fax 020-7631 5500   Tel 020-7631 5555
E-mail cla@cla.co.uk
Website: www.cla.co.uk
Non-profit company looking after the interests of copyright owners in copying from periodicals and books. Collects copying fees and pays them to authors (via Authors Licensing and Collecting Society, 020-7255 2034) and publishers (via Publishers Licensing Society, 020-7829 8486).

Council of Photographic News Agencies
Boswague Cottage, Boswague, Tregony, Cornwall TR2 5ST
Fax 01872-501393   Tel 01872-501393
Represents the UK's six largest press agencies/photo libraries.

Cricket Writers Club
2 Bobble Court, Little Rissington, Glos GL54 2ND
Tel 01451-810435
Represents most cricket writers in newspapers, magazines, TV and radio. It celebrated its 50th anniversary in 1996.

Critics' Circle
c/o Stage Newspaper, 47 Bermondsey Street, London SE1 3XT
Fax 020-7357 9287   Tel 020-7403 1818x106
Organisation of professional critics in theatre, film, music, dance and visual arts.

Defence, Press & Broadcasting Advisory Committee
Room 2235, Main Building, Ministry of Defence, London SW1A 2HB
Fax 020-7218 5857   Tel 020-7218 2206
Aka the D-Notice Committee. The Defence, Press and Broadcasting Advisory Committee oversees the voluntary code which operates between the media and those government departments with responsibilities for national security. The vehicle for this is the DA Notice system, where "advisory notices" are issued to the media at editor level describing sensitive areas.

Directory & Database Publishers Assoc.
PO Box 23034, London W11 2WZ
Tel 020-7221 9089
E-mail: rosemarypettit@msn.com
Website: www.directory-publisher.co.uk
The DPA was established in 1970 for directory and database publishers.

Edinburgh Book Festival
137 Dundee Street, Edinburgh EH11 1BG
Fax 0131-228 4333   Tel 0131-228 5444
E-mail: admin@edbookfest.co.uk
Website: www.edbookfest.co.uk
Organises the annual festival, described by the Guardian as Europe's happiest and largest. 14-30 August 1999.

Edinburgh Press Club
19 Rutland Street, Edinburgh EH1 2AE
No fax.   Tel 0131-229 2800
Social club for the media in the Edinburgh area. Runs Festival of Journalism during the Edinburgh International Festival.

EETPU
See Amalgamated and Electrical Union

Electronic Media Round Table
26 Rosebery Avenue, London EC1R 4SX
Fax 020-7837 8901   Tel 020-7837 3345
E-mail eps@epsltd.demon.co.uk
Independent and informal grouping of publishers, hardware and software manufacturers, developers, integrators, distributors, retailers and other companies and individuals interested in promoting closer working relationships for all forms of electronic publishing activity.

European Society for News Design
28 Holden Road, London N12 8HT
Fax 020-8992 6964   Tel 020-8445 1262
For anyone - not just designers - interested in design in newspapers and magazines, looking at all aspects of the subject.

Federation of Entertainment Unions
1 Highfield, Twyford, Hants SO21 1QR
Fax 01962-713288   Tel 01962-713134
E-mail: harris@interalpha.co.uk
Collective body of trade unions, representing the interests of 140,000 members in the broadcasting and entertainment industries. The unions are: BECTU, Equity, Musicians Union, NUJ, Writers Guild and the AEEU. It provides liaison, lobbying and co-ordination services on issues of common concern.

Financial Journalists' Group
51 Gresham Street, London, EC2V 7HQ
Fax 020-7696 8996   Tel 020-7216 7411
E-mail: financialjournalistsgroup@compuserve.com
Aims to improve the quality of financial journalism by holding group briefings to reporters to help expand their knowledge on a variety of financial topics. Contact - Suzanne Moore

Fleet Street Motoring Group
Elmleigh, Old Perry Street, Chislehurst, Kent BR7 6PP
Fax 020-8300 5694   Tel 020-8300 2140
E-mail: fsmg@bakerdowning.demon.co.uk
Association of motoring correspondents.

Football Writers Association
6 Chase Lane, Barkingside, Ilford, Essex IG6 1BH
Fax 020-8554 2455   Tel 020-8554 2455
Represents members' interests and liaises with football
bodies to improve working conditions at football
grounds.Since 1948 selects the Footballer of the Year.
Foreign Press Association in London
11 Carlton House Terrace, London SW1Y 5AJ
Fax 020-7925 0469   Tel 020-7930 0445
Website: www.foreign-press.org.uk
Founded 1888. Helps London-based foreign
correspondents in their professional work, providing
extensive facilities and assistance at its headquarters.
Arranges briefings and social events. Publishes
newsletter and members list.
Freedom Forum European Centre
Stanhope House Stanhope Place, London W2 2HH
Fax 020-7262 4631   Tel 020-7262 5003
E-mail: freedomforumeurope@compuserve.com
Website: www.freedomforum.org
Provides a forum for debate about the media. Holds
discussions and talks on topical media isues and
photojournalism exhibitions. Has a news library.
Graphical, Paper and Media Union
Keys House, 63-67 Bromham Road, Bedford MK40
2AG.
Fax 01234-270580   Tel 01234-351521
E-mail general@gpmu.org.uk
Website: www.gpmu.org.uk
GPMU is the trade union for the printing, paper and
allied trades industry. Membership covers managerial,
administrative, clerical and production workers in
printing, publishing, papermaking, advertising and
information tchnology. Represents, and negotiates on
behalf of, its 200,000 members in advertising
agencies, art studios, newspapers, general print,
publishing, ink and papermaking and numerous
specialist industries. Provides legal and educational
services, pubishes GPMU Journal free to members ten
times a year.
Guild of Food Writers
48 Crabtree Lane, London SW6 6LW
Fax 020-7610 0299   Tel 020-7610 0299
E-mail: ckthomas@gfw.co.uk
Website: www.gfw.co.uk
Professional association of food broadcasters and
writers. Established in 1984 it has over 300 members.
Independent Publishers Guild
4 Middle Street, Great Gransden, Sandy Beds SG19
3AD
Fax 01767-677069   Tel 01767-677753
E-mail: sheila@ipg.uk.com
Website: www.ipg.uk.com
INK
170 Portobello Road, London W11 2EB
                  Tel 020-7221 8137
The trade association for alternative periodicals.
Institute of Journalists
See Chartered Institute of Journalists

Institute of Printing
The Mews, Hill House, Clanricarde Road, Tunbridge
Wells, Kent TN1 1PJ
Fax 01892-518028   Tel 01892-538118
E-mail: IOP@Globalprint.com
Website: www.globalprint.com/uk/iop
The professional body for the printing industry. Holds
lectures, debates, seminars, conferences and local
branch activities. Publishes journal Professional Printer,
Guide to Educational Courses in the Printing Industry,
Career Guide, Handbook and list of members.
**International Association of Women Sports
  Photographers**
Wayside, White Lodge Lane, Baslow, via Bakewell,
Derbyshire DE45 1RQ
Fax 01246-582227   Tel 01246-582376
E-mail: g.langsley@virgin.net
Aims to attract more women into the profession, help
beginners and raise standards. Produces videos, books,
posters, calendars and exhibitions.
**International Federation of the Periodical
  Press (FIPP)**
Queens House, 55/56 Lincoln's Inn Fields, London
WC2A 3LJ
Fax 020-7404 4170   Tel 020-7404 4169
E-mail: info@fipp.com
Website: www.fipp.com
FIPP works through national associations to establish
and promote worldwide the optimum conditions for
developing periodical publishing. It fosters formal and
informal alliances between publishers to exploit
successful publishing ideas, marketing initiatives and
technological opportunities. Publishes quarterly
Magazine World, holds biennial FIPP World Congress.
JICNARS
See National Readership Surveys
JICREG
Bloomsbury House, 74-77 Great Russell Street,
London WC1B 3DA
Fax 020-7631 5119   Tel 020-7636 7014
E-mail: steve@jicreg.co.uk
Website: www/newspapersoc.org.uk
JICREG provides readership information on regional
and local newspapers with area flexibility, enabling the
readership of papers or schedules to be established
within any marketing or catchment area.
Library Association
7 Ridgmount Street, London WC1E 7AE
Fax 020-7436 7218   Tel 020-7636 7543
E-mail info@la-hq.org.uk
Website: www.la-hq.org.uk
Professional body for librarians which awards
chartership status, sets standards and lobbies
government. It works for freedom of access to
information and against censorship and library cuts.
Publishes monthly magazine Library Association
Record.

LIRE Media Group
BM LIRE, London WC1N 3XX
Fax 020-7267 8003   Tel 020-7267 8003
E-mail: media@easynet.co.uk
Website: www.easynet.co.uk/LIRE/home.htm
A right wing voluntary group set up to research media issues. Organises media conferences, publishes reports and a quarterly newsletter Eyewitness.

London Press Club
c/o Freedom Forum, European Centre, Stanhope House, Stanhope Place, London W2 2HH
Fax 020-7363 4631   Tel 020-7402 2566
E-mail: lpressclub@aol.com
Club for journalists and media in general which makes three annual awards: Scoop of the Year; Edgar Wallace Trophy for outstanding writing; Freedom Award to the journalist or organisaiton doing the most for fredom of the press. Also runs seminars and lectures.

Media Research Group
36 Howland Street, London W1A 1AT
Fax 020-7915 2165   Tel 020-7580 6690
Website: www.mccann.co.uk
Provides forum for debating issues relating to media planning and research. Holds bi-annual conference.

Media Resource Service
Novartis Foundation, 41 Portland Place, London W1N 4BN
Fax 020-7637 2127   Tel 020-7580 0100/631 1634
E-mail mrs@novartisfound.org.uk
Web: www.novartisfound.org.uk/
This service gives journalists free and independent access to experts in medicine, science and technology. It is run by the the Novartis Foundation. A twice yearly newsletter contains news of the MRS and the world of science communication.

Media Society
56 Roseneath Road, London SW11 6AQ
Fax 020-7223 5631   Tel 020-7223 5631
Forum for discussing issues pertinent to the media. Membership includes editors, journalists, pr, media lawyers, MPs and academics. Also submits evidence to appropriate select committees, commissions and enquiries.

Medical Journalists' Association
101 Cambridge Gardens, Ladbroke Grove, London W10 6JE
Fax 020-8968 7910   Tel 020-8960 4382
The MJA aims to improve understanding between health and medical journalists and the health and medical professions. The Association organises awards and social events and publishes directory of members and newsletter.

National Artists Association
234 Cable Street Studios, 566 Cable Street, London E1 9MB
                            Tel 020-7790 6696
E-mail: naa@gn.apc.org
It represents visual artists on UK national and European bodies. Produces quarterly bulletin.

National Association of Press Agencies
41 Lansdowne Crescent, Leamington Spa, Warwickshire CV32 4PR
Fax 01926-424760   Tel 01926-424181
Trade association for news and photographic agenies. A free handbook is available.

National Federation of Retail Newsagents
Yeoman House, Sekforde Street, London EC1R 0HD
Fax 020-7250 0927   Tel 020-7253 4225
E-mail: info@nfrn.org.uk
Website: www.nfrn.org.uk
Represents 28,500 independent retail newsagents in the UK and Ireland. It publishes the weekly journal Retail Newsagent and has 16 regional offices

National Readership Surveys
42 Drury Lane, London WC2B 5RT
Fax 020-7632 2916   Tel 020-7632 2915
E-mail: nrs.co.uk
Website: www.nrs.co.uk
The NRS measures newspaper and magazine readership in the UK. NRS is funded by the IPA, NPAC and the PPA.

National Small Press Centre
BM Bozo, London WC1N 3XX
                            Tel 01234-211606
A self-funding independent organisation for self-publishers. It organises exhibitions, courses and workshops; runs a consultancy service, has a reference library and a collecion of samples.

National Union of Journalists
Acorn House, 314-320 Grays Inn Road, London WC1X 8DP
Fax 020-7837 8143   Tel 020-7278 7916
E-mail: nuj@mcr1.poptel.org.uk
Website: www.nuj.org.uk
The leading trade union representing all editorial sectors of the media, including photographers and freelancers. Membership totals 29,000, including 1,800 student journalists. It provides many services for members, including legal. Campaigns for journalists' rights and freedom of information, and against censorship. Publishes: the prominent and widely read bi-monthly magazine The Journalist; bi-monthly bulletin Freelance, with news for freelancers; Freelance Directory; Freelance Fees Guide; Careers in Journalism guide booklet; comprehensive annual report; the NUJ Code of Conduct; and much other material. Holds conferences, seminars and training sessions.

Newspaper Library (British Library)
Colindale Avenue, London NW9 5HE
Fax 020-7412 7379   Tel 020-7412 7353
E-mail newspaper@bl.uk
Website: www.bl.uk/collections/newspaper
The national collection of UK newspapers, plus a large overseas holding. Open Monday-Saturday, 10am-4.45pm, admission free but only to persons over 18. Arrive before 4pm and take proof of identity.

Newspaper Press Fund
35 Wathen Road, Dorking, Surrey RH4 1JY
Fax 01306-876104   Tel 01306-887511
A charity set up in 1864 to assist member journalists and their dependants in need. Life membership is £50.

Newspaper Publishers Association
34 Southwark Bridge Road, London SE1 9EU
Fax 020-7928 2067   Tel 020-7207 2200
Trade association for the eight publishers of national newspapers. It promotes good relations with the advertising industry and opposes government restraints on the press.
Newspaper Society
Bloomsbury House, 74-77 Great Russell Street, London WC1B 3DA
Fax 020-7631 5119   Tel 020-7636 7014
E-mail: ns@newspapersoc.org.uk
Website: www/newspapersoc.org.uk
Association for the publishers of UK regional and local newspapers. Its work is split into two broad areas: marketing and lobbying. (Current priorities include lobbying on press freedom issues and media ownership regulations, and launching a £3 million generic marketing campaign aimed at growing the industry's share of national advertising.) Editorial services include handling Royal Rota passes and press passes for major sporting events and high profile court cases. The Society also acts as gatekeeper to the UK press card scheme. Publishes Production Journal, monthly and Headlines, 6x a year. Runs a series of conferences and seminars each year.
Director: David Newell
Marketing director: Chris Stanley
Head of legal: Santha Rasaiah
Head of employment: Sandy Park
Head of communications: Lynne Gardiner
Head of finance: Chris Welch
Newspapers in Education
Manchester Evening News
164 Deansgate, Manchester M60 2RD
Fax 0161-839 0968   Tel 0161-211 2591
E-mail: janis.pearson@mcn-evening-news.co.uk
Website: www.manchesteronline.co.uk
NIE provides resources for teachers to help pupils become competent and confident writers and readers.
Paper Federation of Great Britain
Papermakers House, Rivenhall Road, Westlea, Swindon, Wilts SN5 7BD
Fax 01793-886182   Tel 01793-889600
E-mail: fedn@paper.org.uk
Website: www.paper.org.uk
The employers federation for all sectors of the paper industry. Runs the Pulp and Paper Information Centre, supplying data to the media.
Paper Industry Technical Association
5 Frechville Court, Bury, Lancashire BL9 0UF
Fax 0161-764 5353   Tel 0161-764 5858
E-mail: info@pita.co.uk
Website: www.pita.co.uk
For people interested in the technology of the paper industry. Publishes: Paper Technology.
Parliamentary Press Gallery/Lobby Journalists
House of Commons, London SW1A 0AA
                Tel 020-7219 4700

PEN
7 Dilke Street, London SW3 4JE
Fax 020-7351 0220   Tel 020-7352 6303
E-mail: enquiries@pen.org.guk
Website: www.pen.org.uk
English centre of the International association for published writers, with over 130 centres in 100 countries. Fights for freedom of expression and against censorship, and helps imprisoned writers worldwide. Makes annual awards, holds regular meetings and publishes newsletter. PEN stands for Poets, Playwrights, Editors, Essayists and Novelists.
Periodical Publishers Association
Queens House, 28 Kingsway, London WC2B 6JR
Fax 020-7404 4167   Tel 020-7404 4166
E-mail: info1@ppa.co.uk
Website: www.ppa.co.uk
The trade association for magazine publishers, representing nearly 200 companies generating 80 per cent of the industry's revenue. Lobbies on behalf of members, and organises conferences, seminars and awards. Produces many publications, including the journal Magazine News, annual Magazine Handbook with key data on the industry, and industry overviews. The PPA provides secretariats for the Association of Publishing Agencies (customer magazines), the International Federation of the Periodical Press (FIPP) UK Newsletter Publishers' Association and the British Society of Magazine Editors (BSME).
Periodicals Training Council
55/56 Queen's House, Lincoln's Inn Fields, London WC2A 3LJ
Fax 020-7404 4167   Tel 020-7404 4168
E-mail: training@ppa.co.uk
Website: www.ppa.co.uk
The PTC is the training arm of the Periodical Publishers Association. It aims to enhance the performance of the UK magazine industry and act as a focus for training.
Picture Research Association
The Studio, 5a Alvanley Gardens, London NW6 1JD
Fax 020-7431 9887   Tel 020-7431 9886
E-mail: pra@pictures.demon.co.uk
Website: www.pictures.demon.co.uk
Professional body for those involved in visual material for the media. Gives advice to members, organises meetings, quarterly magazine, monthly newsletter and Freelance Register.
Pira International
Randalls Road, Leatherhead, Surrey KT22 7RU
Fax 01372-802244   Tel 01372-802000
E-mail marionc@pira.co.uk
Website: www.pira.co.uk
A Research & Technology Organisation for the packaging, paper, printing, publishing and new media industries worldwide. It provides research, consultancy, information services and comprehensive training events for these industries. It is also one of the UK's largest business to business publishers. The Publishing & New Media Group offers Internet based research, strategic business and management consultancy and marketing services.

Press Complaints Commission
1 Salisbury Square, London EC4 8AE
Fax 0171 353 8355   Tel 020-73531248
E-mail: pcc@pcc.org.uk
Website: www.pcc.org.uk
For complainants about the contents and conduct of newspapers and magazines. Upholds a Code of Practice and advises editors on journalistic ethics.

Press Standards Board of Finance
Olympic House, 142 Queen Street, Glasgow G1 3BU
Fax 0141-248 2362   Tel 0141-221 3957
Co-ordinates and finances self-regulation in the newspaper and magazine publishing industry.

PressWise
25 Easton Business Centre, Felix Road, Bristol BS5 0HE
Fax 0117-941 5848   Tel 0117-941 5889
E-mail: pw@presswise.org.uk
Non-profit making organisation promoting high standards of journalism and aiming to empower those ordinary people who become victims of unfair media intrusion and inaccurate or irresponsible reporting. Also provides media training and briefings on current media policy issues. Appointed to a European forum on the Information Society.

Publishers' Association
1 Kingsway, London WC2B 6XF
Fax 020-7836 4543   Tel 020-7565 7474
E-mail: mail@publishers.org.uk
Website: www.publishers.org.uk
Trade association for UK book publishers, offering a wide range of services, and producing many of its own publications.

Publishers' Publicity Circle
48 Crabtree Lane, London SW6 6LW
Fax 020-7385 3708   Tel 020-7385 3708
E-mail: ppc-@lineone.net
Provides a forum for book publicists to meet and share information. Monthly meetings with members of the media. Publishes directory and monthly newsletter.

St Bride Printing Library
St Bride Institute, Bride Lane, Fleet Street, London EC4Y 8EE
Fax 020-7583 7073   Tel 020-7353 4660
A unique public reference library covering all aspects of printing, with an extensive historical collection including artefacts, archive material, photographs and patents. The collection is strong on newspaper history and is housed in atmospheric surroundings just off Fleet Street. Hours: 9.30am-5.30pm, Monday-Friday.

Scottish Book Trust
Scottish Book Centre, 137 Dundee Street, Edinburgh EH11 1BG
Fax 0131-228 4293   Tel 0131-229 3663
E-mail: scottish.book.trust.scotland@dial.pipex.com
Website: www.webpost.net/bts
Publishes directories of authors, literary guides, resources for schools and parents. Organises readership campaigns, operates a Book Information Service and adminsters the Fidler and Scottish Writer of the Year literary prizes and the Writers in Scotland scheme.

Scottish Daily Newspaper Society
48 Palmerston Place, Edinburgh EH12 5DE
Fax 0131-220 4344   Tel 0131-220 4353
E-mail: info@sdns.org.uk
Trade association for Scottish newspaper publishers.

Scottish Newspaper Publishers Association
48 Palmerston Place, Edinburgh EH12 5DE
Fax 0131-220 4344   Tel 0131-220 4353
E-mail: info@snpa.org.uk
Website: www.snpa.org.uk
Trade association for the Scottish weekly press.

Scottish Print Employers Federation
48 Palmerston Place, Edinburgh EH12 5DE
Fax 0131-220 4344   Tel 0131-220 4353
E-mail: info@spef.org.uk
Website: www.spef.org.uk
The employers' organisation and trade association for the Scottish printing industry.

Scottish Publishers Association
Scottish Book Centre, 137 Dundee Street, Edinburgh EH11 1BG
Fax 0131-228 3220   Tel 0131-228 6866
E-mail: enquiries@scottishbooks.org
Website: www.scottishbooks.org
Trade association working for 68 Scottish publishers. Publishes Directory of Publishing in Scotland (annually) and new books lists. Provides training, advice, marketing and promotion services to members.

Society of Authors
84 Drayton Gardens, London SW10 9SB
Fax 020-7373 5768   Tel 020-7373 6642
E-mail: authorsoc@writers.org.uk
Website: www.writers.org.uk/society/html
An independent trade union, which was founded in 1884, to promote the interests of authors and to defend their rights. The Society gives a personal service to writers, with wide range of facilities including advice on contracts. It arranges conferences, meetings and social events. The Society publishes a quarterly journal, The Author, plus numerous guides and has over 6,000 members.

Society of Editors
University Centre, Granta Place, Mill Lane, Cambridge CB2 1RU
Fax 01223-304090   Tel 01223-304080
E-mail: society@ukeditors.com
Website: www.ukeditors.com
Director: Bob Satchwell
Professional association for local newspaper editors, editorial directors and training editors. It provides a medium for collective consultation and representation on matters of editorial concern and interest. Monthly magazine. Lobbies in defence of press freedom.

Society of Freelance Editors and Proofreaders

Mermaid House, 1 Mermaid Court, London SE1 1HR
Fax 020-7407 1193   Tel 020-7403 5141
E-mail: admin@sfep.demon.co.uk
Website: www.sfep.org.uk
Professional body representing editors, especially freelances, and working to improve editorial standards by providing training, information and advice. Publishes newsletter, directory, conference proceedings and other publications.

Society of Indexers

Globe Centre, Penistone Road, Sheffield S6 3AE
Fax 0114-281 3061   Tel 0114-281 3060
E-mail: admin@socind.demon.co.uk
Website: www.socind.demon.co.uk
Promotes indexing, the quality of indexing and the profession of indexers. Publishes quarterly newsletter, twice-yearly journal The Indexer, and ad hoc papers. Provides open learning course.

Society of Typographic Designers

Chapelfield Cottage, Randwick, Stroud, Gloucester GL6 6HS
Fax 01453-759311   Tel 01453-759311
Promotes high standards of typographic design.

Society of Women Writers & Journalists

110 Whitehall Road, Chingford, London E4 6DW
Tel 020-8529 0886
E-mail: swwriters@aol.com
Founded 1894. Encourages literary achievement and the upholding of professional standards. Organises competitions, social events and monthly meetings. Publishes magazine The Woman Journalist 3x pa.

Sports Writers Association of Gt Britain

c/o English Sports Council, 16 Upper Woburn Place, London WC1H 0QP
Fax 020-7383 0273   Tel 020-7273 1555
Founded 1948 for sports journalists. Now has over 500 members. Organises meetings and social events. Makes awards for the Sportsman, Sportswoman and Sports Team of the Year. Organises the British Sports Journalism Awards and Sports Photographer of the Year Awards in conjunction with the English Sports Council. It appoints the Olympic press attache for the British media.

Talking Newspaper Association

National Recording Centre, Heathfield, East Sussex TN21 8DB
Fax 01435-865422   Tel 01435-866102
E-mail: info@tnauk.globalnet.co.uk
A registered charity that provides 200 national newspapers and magazines on audio cassette, computer disk and E-mail for blind, visually impaired and disabled people. There are over 530 local groups, providing two million tapes of over 900 newspapers and magazines for 200,000 visually impaired people. TNEL is the commercial trading arm of the charity.

Teenage Magazine Arbitration Panel

c/o PPA Queen House, 28 Kingsway, London WC2B 6JR
Tel 020-7405 0819
Website: www.ppa.co.uk

The TMAP was formed in 1996 as part of a self-regulatory system to consider complaints about the editorial content of a sexual nature in magazines which have more than 25 per cent of readers who are young women under the age of 15.

UK Newsletter Association

Premier House, 11 Marlborough Place, Brighton BN1 1UB
Fax 01273-682733   Tel 01273-682733
E-mail: ukna@btinternet.com
UKNA is the organisation of newsletter and subscription publishers in the UK.

Women in Publishing

Information Officer, Publishers Association, 1 Kingsway, Floor 3, London WC2B 6XF
Website: www.cyberiacafe.net/wip/
Provides support and encouragement for women working in publishing and related fields through training courses and monthly meetings . Publishes monthly newsletter, surveys and Women in Publishing Directory.

Women Writers Network

c/o 23 Prospect Road, London NW2 2JU
Helps women writers further their professional development by providing a forum for exchanging information and giving support. Holds monthly meetings, and publishes monthly newsletter and annual directory of members.

Worshipful Company of Stationers & Newspaper Makers

Stationers' Hall, Ave Maria Lane, London EC4M 7DD
Fax 020-7489 1975   Tel 020-7248 2934
E-mail: clerk@stationers.demon.co.uk
City livery company for stationers, printers newspaper makers, publishers, booksellers, paper makers and packagers.

Writers Guild of Great Britain

430 Edgware Road, London W2 1EH
Fax 020-7706 2413   Tel 020-7723 8074
E-mail: postie@wggb.demon.co.uk
Website: www.writers.org.uk/guild
Trade union representing professional writers in film, TV, radio, theatre and books. Has scored many successes in improving terms and conditions. Holds regular meetings and publishes bi-monthly Writers' Newsletter.

Yachting Journalists' Association

3 Friars Lane, Maldon, Essex CM9 6AG
Fax 01621-852212   Tel 01621-855943
E-mail: petercookyja@compuserve.com
Promotes yachting - sail and power - in all its forms, and furthers the interests of its members. Open to writers, broadcasters, photographers and illustrators. Publishes annual directory of members, with media advice for event organisers.

Young Newspaper Executives' Association

Newspaper Society, 74-77 Great Russell Street, London WC1B 3DA
Fax 020-7631 5119   Tel 020-7636 7014
E-mail: ns@newspapersoc.org.uk
Website: www.newspapersoc.org.uk
Focal point for newspaper managers aged under 40.

Press awards 1999

NEWSPAPER AWARDS

British Press Awards
Press Gazette,19 Scarbrook Road, Croydon CR9 1LX
Fax 020-8565 4462   Tel 020-8565 4463
Newspaper: The Guardian
Reporter: Mazher Mahmood
Team reporting award: The Mirror, Omagh bombing
Feature writer: Deborah Ross, Independent
Financial journalist: Alex Brummer
Foreign reporter: John Lichfield, The Independent
Specialist reporter: Brian Deer, The Sunday Times
Business journalist: Neil Bennet, Sunday Telegraph
Columnist: Rebecca Tyrrel, The Sunday Telegraph
Magazine
Scoop: TV drugs fake, The Guardian
Young journalist: Burhan Wazir, The Observer
Photographer: Jeremy Selwyn, Evening Standard
Sports photographer: Ian Rutherford, The Scotsman
Cartoonist: Mac, Daily Mail
Critic: Charles Spencer, The Daily Telegraph
Sports reporter: Michael Calvin, Mail on Sunday
On-line news service award: BBC News Online
Supplement: Meg@, The Times
Gold award: David Chipp, British Press Awards
Chairman 1986-1999

Press Gazette Regional Press Awards
Press Gazette,19 Scarbrook Road, Croydon CR9 1LX
Fax 020-8565 4462   Tel 020-8565 4463
E-mail: sarahsj@qpp.co.uk
Newspaper: Nottingham Evening Post
Weekly newspaper: Westmoreland Gazette
Free newspaper: Enfield Advertiser
Campaign: Evening Chronicle, Newcastle
Evening newspaper: Nottingham Evening Post
Local newspaper week: Nottingham Evening Post
Scoop: Mikaela Sitford, Manchester Evening News
Online news service: The News, Portsmouth
Young journalist: Clara Penn, Western Morning News
Reporter: Andrew Norfolk, Yorkshire Post
Photographer: Simon Dack, Evening Argus, Brighton
Sports photographer: Kirsty Wigglesworth,
Birmingham Post and Mail
Sports journalist: Matthew Reader, Swindon Evening
Advertiser
Columnist: Kate Ironside, Western Morning News
Feature writer: Rachel Lamb, Southern Daily Echo
Specialist reporter: Kathleen Nutt, Edinburgh Evening
News
Gold award: Santha Rasaiah, Newspaper Society

What the Papers Say
Granada Television, Manchester M60 9EA
Fax 0161-953 0291   Tel 0161-832 7211
E-mail: paul.tyrell@granadatv.careof.uk
Editor: Simoon Kelner, Independent
Journalist: Nick Davies, Guardian
Correspondent : David McKittrick, Independent
Columnist: Libby Purves, Times
Gerald Barry award: Anthony Howard, Times
Peter Black award: Jaci Stephen, Daily Mail
Scoop: Guardian, Mandelson's home loan
Front page: Zip Me Up Before You Go, Sun

MAGAZINE AWARDS

Magazines & Business to Business '99 Awards: PPA
Periodical Publishers Association, Queens House, 28
Kingsway, London WC2B 6JR
Fax 020-7404 4167   Tel 020-7404 4166
Next deadline: 28.1.2000
Consumer magazine: Men's Health
Business magazine: Building
International magazine (consumer): Hello!
International magazine (business): International
Investment
Customer magazine: Room (Ikea)
Consumer specialist magazine: Official UK Playstation
Interactive magazine: NME.com
Editor (consumer): Lindsay Nicholson
Editor (business): Sarah Woodhead
Designer (consumer): Robin Harvey
Designer (business): Phil Cheesbrough
Specialist writer (consumer): Ian Belcher
Columnist (business): Jane Salvage
Writer (consumer): Anthony Rowlinson
Writer (business): Alistair Blair
Publisher (for companies with less than 25 employees):
Alexandra Hobson
Publisher (consumer): Marcus Arthur
Publisher (business): Kit Gould
Editorial campaign: Family Circle

PHOTOGRAPHY AWARDS

Nikon
380 Richmond Road, Kingston, Surrey KT2 5PR
Fax 020-8541 4584   Tel 020-8541 4440
Photographers
Press: Paul Hackett, Reuters
Regional: Mark Bickerdike, Yorkshire Post
Royals: John Stillwell, Press Association
Sports: Alex Livesey, Allsport
Arts/entertainment: Dave Hogan, Sun
News: Paul Hackett, Reuters
Features: Tom Stoddart, IPG
Photo essay: Zed Nelson, IPG

Observer David Hodge Award
The Observer, 119 Farringdon Road, London EC1R 3ER
Set up in 1986 in memory of David Hodge, a photographer who died aged 29 of injuries sustained during the Brixton riots. This award for documentary photography is open to amateur, student and professional photographer under 30. First prize is £3,000 and an assignment for the Observer. Best Student wins £1,500 plus runners up. Past winners include Jonathan Olley (Network), Harriet Logan (Network) and Zoe Sinclair.
1999 winner: Gunnar Knechtel

OTHER AWARDS

Guardian Student Media Awards
Press Office, The Guardian, 119 Farringdon Road, London EC1R 3ER
The awards are one of the best established routes for journalists, editors and photographers to a successful career in media. The awards are launched in February and the winners announced in November. The 1998 roll of honour is:
Newspaper: Leeds Student, Leeds University and Leeds Metropolitan University
Magazine: Mustard Magazine, University of East Anglia
Reporter: Helen Briggs, Scan, Lancashire University
Feature writer: Katherine Crockett, Concrete, University of East Anglia
Photographer: Matthew Fearn, Pluto, University of Central Lancashire
Publication design: Richard Turley and James Turrell, Shout, Liverpool John Moore University
Website: Edinburgh Student Newspaper Online, Edinburgh University
Impact award: Heather Tomlinson and Bill Staples, Roar, Kings College London

Industrial Journalism Awards
Industrial Society, Robert Hyde House, 48 Bryanston Square, London W1H 7LNLondon W1H 7LN
Fax 020-7479 2222   Tel 020-7262 2000
Website www.indsoc.co.ukl
Industrial journalist (national): Iain Carson, The Economist
Industrial journalist (regional): Simon Bain, The Herald
Industrial journalist (broadcast): Evan Davis, BBC
Scoop: Antony Barnett, The Observer

TO AWARDS ORGANISERS

UPDATE FOR THE 2001 MEDIA GUIDE

Use this space below to give details of awards in 2001

PHOTOCOPY AND SEND TO: Paul Fisher, Media Guide, The Guardian, 119 Farringdon Road, London EC1R 3ER
E-mail: paulfisher@online.rednet.co.uk

CHINA: This photo won Gunnar Knechtel first prize in the 1999 Observer David Hodge Award

The BBC

"JOLLY EXCITING ..."

29 AUGUST 1998 A BBC ad campaign, broadcast on BBC 1 & 2, began upping the hype for the imminent launch of digital satellite television. Michael Palin delivered the jolly exciting punch line. According to the advert for the advert "the new information film [which] features Martine McCutcheon, Harry Enfield, Gianluca Vialli, Stephen Fry, Ruby Wax, Goldie, Lee Evans, Jeremy Irons ..."

CENTRAL TRAINING

17 SEPTEMBER The BBC opened a central London training centre in 35 Marylebone High Street. A 900 foot TV studio is central to a hardware cornucopia including IT, multimedia and digital workshops, fully equipped editing suites, radio and TV news training rooms, DV cameras and videoconferencing.

RADIO TIMES' 75TH & AGEISM

22 SEPTEMBER The best selling mag formerly known as The Official Organ of the BBC celebrated 75 years of masthead publishing with a poll revealing a readership rooted in nostalgia.

Best ever drama: Cathy Come Home, 1966
Best period drama: I Claudius, 1976
Best comedians: Morecambe and Wise, 1960s-1984
Funniest radio: Hancock, first broadcast in 1954
Top entertainer: Bruce Forsyth circa Dark Ages

"It is a misconception that only pensioners read the magazine," said a 93 year old BBC spokeswoman.

In November a BBC/Age Concern report noted that while 10 per cent of people appearing on TV were over 60, older people comprise over 20 per cent of the audience and - with an average 35 hours telly a week - are the most ubiquitous set of viewers.

PRIVATISED COMPLAINTS/INFO

28 SEPTEMBER The BBC hired the call centre firm Capita to run a new information centre from Spring 1999. From a single phone number running to BBC Northern Ireland, Capita will also field solicited calls and telephone ticket sales for BBC Experience. "In the multi-channel, digital world of the future, we expect the enquiries to become more varied and complex," said Colin Browne, the director of corporate affairs. "The BBC has an important role as a trusted guide to this new world, providing reassurance for the digitally daunted."

PRIVATISED FUNDS

14 OCTOBER In announcing a review of funding arrangements until charter renewal time in 2006, the culture secretary Chris Smith said the BBC may be allowed to tout for advertising and sponsorship on digital channels. "The BBC must be capable of adapting, surviving and prospering in the fragmented modern market," Smith explained.

BAD NEWS WEEK

19-23 OCTOBER Monday: Channel 4 grabbed Test cricket rights. Tuesday: Richard Bacon, a Blue Peter presenter, was sacked after a Sunday paper revealed the "goody-goody was a cocaine snorting sneak" and Chris Evans - a former BBC DJ - stoked up the controversy with his claim that "half the BBC are on drugs". Wednesday: Having lost Barry Norman to Sky, the rights to the Oscars also went to the competition. Thursday: The director-general John Birt got a roasting by MPs at Westminster. Friday: audience figures showed the Radio 4 revamp was a big turn-off for listeners.

PRIVATISED LICENCE COLLECTION

26 OCTOBER The BBC hired Envision - a consortium of Bull Information Systems, WPP Marketing and the Post Office's Subscription Services - to collect the licence fee. The contract to collect £16 billion over the next seven years is worth an estimated £500 million. In December the culture secretary Chris Smith announced a licence rise of £3.50 to £101 as from April 1999. A BBC spokesman called it "a penny-a-day increase".

New scanning technology deployed by the BBC revealed Manchester as the national capital of licence dodgers. The number of licence dodgers caught between September and December was:

5,490	Manchester
5,071	SE London
4,084	Birmingham
3,721	Liverpool
2,997	East London

FUNNY MONEY

25 NOVEMBER The BBC1 controller Peter Salmon announced a £30 million investment in situation comedies for 30 hours of new comedy material. Long running shows like Birds of a Feather, One Foot in the Grave and Men Behaving Badly were scheduled for replacement.

NO TO DEVOLUTION

10 DECEMBER BBC governors decided Scotland, Wales and Northern Ireland will not get their own BBC Six O'Clock News bulletins. Instead they offered a £21 million investment in devolved bulletins on BBC2 and BBC Choice plus a review in a year's time.

FIRST WOMAN TV CONTROLLER

17 DECEMBER Jane Root was promoted from her commissioning job to become controller of BBC2. Other top BBC women are Jane Bennett, director of production; Jenny Abramsky, director of radio; Patricia Hodgson, director of policy and planning; and Sue Farr, marketing and communications director.

BBC1'S DECLINING AUDIENCE

12 JANUARY Viewing figures revealed BBC1's audience share dropped below 30 per cent for the first time in recorded history. "You've got to put the fall in the context of 19 new channels coming on stream and a further 12 doing massive relaunches," said a BBC spokeswoman. "You've also got the first real effect of Channel 5 being felt." The drop in popularity with viewers as a whole coincided with the announcement of a government appointed panel, chaired by the economist Gavyn Davies with the brief to give advice on BBC funding and the future of the license fee.

A NATION MOURNS

25 FEBRUARY Noel's House Party, the Saturday show which started with 15 million ratings and fell to 6 million, was axed. Noel Edmonds insisted the decision to expunge Mr Blobby from national life was his.

PANJANDRUMS' PRONOUNCEMENTS

3 MARCH Lord Hussey (above) - who, as plain Marmaduke, was the BBC chairman who hired John Birt as director-general - told the House of Lords that the BBC should invest more in mainstream channels and less in digital daydreams like News 24. He turned on his protege when he criticised the BBC for "bureaucracy, over-bloated policy units and too much spent on expansion in management" and condemned Birt's merger of radio and TV production. "I don't believe in the amalgamation of radio and television," he said. "They are not the same and I fear for the future of radio against the monster of TV." Sir Christopher Bland, who replaced Lord Hussey as BBC chairman in 1996, condemned the speech for being "woefully inaccurate and out of touch". The emerging BBC party line came in an interview published in the Radio Times on 15 March, when David Dimbleby said: "The BBC has lost the knack of quick decision-making because it relies on endless focus groups ... it is a mistake for the BBC to chase ratings ... you don't have to chase the lowest common denominator."

BIRT'S SUCCESSOR

12 APRIL 1999Interviews began to find a new BBC director general. On 17 April Rupert Murdoch's Times revealed that the leading contender Greg Dyke had made £50,000 contributions to the Labour party. Dyke, who is worth £7 million and was then a Manchester United director, was an outspoken opponent of Murdoch's failed BSkyB bid. On 20 April the bookies' odds for the next DG were:

7-2 Greg Dyke: 51 year old chairman of Pearson TV
4-1 Mark Byford: 40 year old boss of BBC World Service
9-2 Alan Yentob: 52 year old director of BBC TY
5-1 Tony Hall: 48 year old BBC News chief executive
10-1 Richard Eyre: 44 year old ITV chief executive
16-1 David Elstein: 54 year old Channel 5 chief executive
16-1 Patricia Hodgson: 52 year old director of BBC policy and planning
20-1 Matthew Bannister: 42 year old chief executive of BBC Production

JILL DANDO MURDER

26 APRIL Jill Dando's shooting by an unknown assassin was the most hyped death since Princess Di. The 37 year old news/holiday/crime/antiques presenter was so popular that a record 11 million people tuned into the BBC's Six O'Clock News for confirmation of the shooting and every national paper pushed Balkan coverage off their front pages the next day. Serbs were

A MEDIA EVENT: The scene of Jill Dando's murder as crowds gathered outside her house in Fulham

among the first suspects and three other BBC staff - John Humphrys (Radio 4's Today programme), Alan Yentob (BBC TV director) and Tony Hall BBC News chief executive) - were warned of Serbian death threats.
* When the Queen made her tribute to Princess Diana in 1997, 10.6 million watched the Six O'Clock News.

MAKE ME LAUGH

16 APRIL John Birt spoke of his "real concern" at the feebleness of mainstream BBC1 sitcom and its inability to compete with American imports like Friends and Frasier. Meanwhile the BBC1 controller Peter Salmon axed Next of Kin and Prince Among Men. He also said he'd drop One Foot in the Grave but then changed his mind. Ray Galton, who wrote Steptoe, thought the BBC was in thrall to American imports and condemned much recent homegrown sitcom saying: "The trouble is that the scriptwriters seem to have forgotten to put the jokes in."

JOHNNY MORRIS DIES

5 MAY Johnny Morris, the presenter of Animal Magic, died aged 82. "The new BBC is bonkers," he had said recently. "Many mothers who were children when I was presenting come up to me and ask why they don't get more of my sort of programme, which was non-violent, amusing, informative and gentle."

Speaker training

Radio training

Television training

"Are you successfully saying what you mean and expressing how you feel? A convincing conference speech, fluent radio presentation or captivating television performance is a communicative gift. Nurture new skills and revise old skills with BBME Training."

BBME Training - experts in...

Speaker training and Autocue coaching for professional conferencing presentation...

Media training and crisis management...

Television presenter training and showreel production.

Radio presenter training for music and current affairs programming...

BBME

training

COMMERCIAL BREAK

19 MAY 1999 The BBC published Commercial Policy Guidelines to dampen criticism about how it exploits assets built up with licence fee money. Should the BBC spend £40 million on refurbishing Broadcasting House? Should it use so much airtime to promote itself? Should it use cross corporate puffery to promote magazines? Should it try and slice off bits of the internet market? Should BBC World be a £15 million a year loss leader in pursuit of global news provision? Should it abandon non-core services? Yes to the last say myriad commercial interests, but should licence payers take their questions seriously?

DYKE REPLACES BIRT

JUNE BBC governors appointed Greg Dyke as the BBC director general. Criticism of Dyke - orchestrated by newspapers (particularly The Times) anxious to push their proprietors own TV interests, and then amplified by a Tory party desperate to push home any attack it can on Labour - centred on Dyke's £55,000 donation to Labour funds. Dyke had resigned party membership in preparation for his bid for the top job. Commenting on his predecessor John Birt, he said: "John has left a brilliant company, and he isn't really getting credit for it," he said. "He has done the things that needed to be done. You had to put in an internal pricing system, so you knew where the money was going. Anyone would have done that. But the real legacy is what he has done with digital TV and online. Those who criticise him for being ahead of the game would have complained just as much if the BBC was behind the times." When Dyke takes over in April 2000 he's likely to cut down on the £20 million a year cost of business consultants.

BBC FINANCES

17 JUNE The BBC's £2.2 billion annual revenue placed it among the UK's top 50 companies. The finance director John Smith said spending on digital TV would increase from £154 million in 1998 to £200 million. He pointed out that overall costs continue to fall by £105 million. However, BBC execs will continue to push for further licence fee increases.

"BRAINING UP"

23 JUNE Alan Yentob, the BBC director of TV, used the annual review to announce he would gradually axe some populist and daytime shows in favour of "braining up" to a more "distinctive" output. The BBC board of governors said the BBC ought to rise above ratings battles and show the confidence to be an unashamedly public service.

BBC REJECTS DAVIES REPORT

5 AUGUST John Birt attacked the government-comissioned Davies report saying it was not in the "best interests of the licence fee payer". Gavyn Davies' main recommendations are:

* a digital licence supplement should be introduced in April 2000 starting at £24 a year and falling to £12 by 2006
* there should be no advertising, sponsorship or subscription to the BBC's core services
* BBC Worldwide and BBC Resources should be partially privatised
* BBC accounts should be scrutinised by the Office of Fair Trading and the National Audit Office
* the licence fee discount for blind people should be increased to 50 per cent

"The report fails to follow the logic of its own argument," Birt argued. "The level of funding the panel has recommended will not enable the BBC to offer its licence payers the substantial public service choice in the digital era ahead that the panel so clearly desires."

PUBLIC DEMANDS BBC SHAKE-UP

10 AUGUST A Guardian/ICM poll revealed that the public thinks BBC programmes have got worse. The poll also highlighted support for ads on the Beeb and opposition to increased licence fees for digital television. "Loyalty to the BBC was once a general, almost unthinking response across the country," said a Guardian leader. "Not any more. There is more diversity now, and less deference. To maintain its place in the world, to convince its political paymasters that it is worth the money it is asking for, the BBC needs public respect and loyalty. It no longer gets respect as of right; it has to earn it. On ICM's figures, it is not earning it now." Gavyn Davies responded to the poll by saying: "If people are asked to pay for something which they (wrongly) perceive to be "free", it is not surprising they object."

GOOD
MORNING
TELEVISION
For over 25 million viewers*

Independent TV

CHANNEL 4 NEWS

2 SEPTEMBER 1998 Regular weekly political coverage dropped off the Channel 4 menu when the chief exec Michael Jackson confirmed there would be no replacement for A Week in Politics. "I'm not sure it's Channel 4's core job to put more politicians on the airwaves," Jackson said. Meanwhile Channel 4 News pledged £1.25 million a year on "sharper, clearer" news features laced with "dollops of wit".

FOR THE LOVE OF MONEY

4 SEPTEMBER 1998 The first broadcast of ITV's Who Wants To Be A Millionaire?, the Chris Tarrant gameshow offering £1 million to contestants who answer 15 successive questions. Celeador Productions joined the ranks of the rich when average audience figures reached 17 million. In March a contestant was asked "what is the minimum number of strokes with which a tennis player can win a set? 12, 24, 36 or 48?" "24," replied a contestant. Tarrant agreed and cranked the prize up to £64,000. Carlton's switchboards jammed when callers rang to say the real number was 12 because a player could serve four aces in three service games and the opponent could serve 12 double faults.

WHIRLED IN DAMAGES

28 SEPTEMBER Granada's World in Action paid £1.5 million in costs and damages having wrongfully accused three police officers of perjury after a prisoner's death in custody at Hammersmith police station. The previous March Granada paid Marks and Spencer £1.3 million after a World in Action claim that the retailer exploited child labour.

"TV FROM THE HEART"

29 SEPTEMBER In an attempt to rebrand itself for the middle class majority, ITV unveiled a new logo and slogan. John Hardie, marketing and commercial director, maundered about "TV from the heart" and justified a £1 million investment saying ITV needed a symbol like BBC1's balloon or BBC2's number 2.

SPONSORSHIP

OCTOBER ITV execs consoled themselves at predictions of sponsorship deals rising from the current £35 million to £100 million a year. "The creatives don't want to do it," commented Martin Lowde, Granada Media's commercial controller. "They want to do 60-second spot advertising." Yes, to that, say PowerGen which, rather than buy expensive advertising has boosted its public recognition by sponsoring ITV weather since 1989.

CHANNEL 4 CLEARED OF LIBEL

27 OCTOBER Channel's 4's Trial and Error was cleared of libel after the Police Federation failed to convince a jury that one its members, Trevor Gledding of the Gloucester police, had not perjured himself during a murder trial. The Federation, which lost £1.2 million on the case, said the defeat was only the second in the past 100 libel claims against the media. The previous July five officers from Stoke Newington police lost an appeal against the Guardian in a case costing the Federation £900,000.

MASS DEBATE

29 OCTOBER In house censorship by Channel 5 executives cut some of the more explicit scenes in the 13-part Sex and Shopping series. "The aim was to make an intelligent documentary with intelligent argument about pornography. But ..." said Douglas Chirnside, the programme maker "... but you have to show people what the debate is all about." John Wadham, director of the civil rights group Liberty, agreed. "Provided people are not hurt in the making of pornography and there are sufficient warnings, adults should be allowed to watch it. Censoring programmes that begin that debate sends out the wrong message." Channel 5's message in the opening title was: "This will be the most explicit programme you have ever seen." On 19 October the ITC told the government that Channel Bizarre, a satellite service launched in July, "is unacceptable and should be the subject of a proscription order".

THE BEST TV NETWORK IN THE UK.

*The***Guardian** Edinburgh International Television Festival 99

If you're in television and you want to be part of the bigger picture, don't miss the Guardian Edinburgh International Television Festival. With over 50 sessions debating the industry's present and future, you can meet and hear its leading figures at the most important four days in the television calendar. We sold out last year, so make sure you don't miss out and call **0171 379 4519** for further information or visit our website at **arena-digital.co.uk**.

MAJOR SPONSORS

REAUCTION OF PROMISES

25 NOVEMBER 1998 Eight ITV companies were told they could reduce their annual licence fee payments by £90 million. The main beneficiary of the ITC's largesse was GMTV (the breakfast station owned by the Guardian Media Group, Carlton, Granada, Scottish Media Group and Disney) which, having over-bid for the franchise in 1991, had its annual levy cut from £50.5 million to £20 million. Ulster, Border and Central faced increased payments.

HIGH EARNERS

3 DECEMBER Carol Vorderman (pictured above) secured a £5 million Channel 4 contract to present Countdown for the next five years. She is Britain's highest paid daytime broadcaster because the deal also left her free to continue presenting the National Lottery and Points of View for the BBC and Better Home for ITV. Further income will continue accruing from the £1.20 monthly magazine Carol Vorderman's Challenge Puzzle plus a range of maths and science books. She has an IQ of 154 and has been solving puzzles on Countdown (which regularly attracts 4 million teatime viewers) for 16 years. In January the exclusive high earning female presenters' club had more deals to celebrate when Radio 1's Zoe Ball secured a £3.5 million deal to co-produce and present 14 live one hour shows for Channel 4 and Newsnight's Kirsty Wark signed a £3 million three year deal with the BBC.

WORLD INACTION

7 DECEMBER The last episode of World in Action, Channel 3's flagship documentary programme for 35 years. David Leigh, a former World in Action producer, said: "World in Action's half-hour investigations have now become a victim of the same process which has ousted News at 10 from its slot. Bad TV is driving out the good, as the satellite and digital wastelands encroach."

LORD GRADE DIES

13 DECEMBER Lord Lew Grade, who shaped commercial television during his 20 year chairmanship of ATV, died aged 91. "Lew was always such fun," wrote Nancy Banks-Smith. "With him you felt entertainment was entertaining."

THE CONNECTION

18 DECEMBER Carlton's documentary about the Columbian drug trade, which was broadcast in 1996 and won several awards and was then exposed as a fake by the Guardian, ended its history with a record £2 million fine from the ITC. The price of faking it was four times the size of any previous ITC penalty, though a small chunk of Carlton's £340 million pre-tax profits.

XMAS TRADITION

25 DECEMBER Once again ITV's Christmas Day ratings were less than the BBC with only three of the top ten programmes. For the second year running Men Behaving Badly did best with 13.9 million viewers. ITV's Coronation Street came third with 13.5 million viewers - just behind East Enders.

LIBRARY PURCHASE

19 JANUARY 1999 Carlton paid the Canadian drinks and music group Seagram $150 million for the ITC film library. The library, originally built up by Lew Grade, contains more than 300 films and 5,000 hours of TV. Michael Green, the head of Carlton, said: "It gives us even more to sell to the rapidly expanding number of channels world-wide. We have always believed that content is king and the ITC library is a jewel in the crown."

STRIKE VOTE

2 FEBRUARY 1999 Votes cast by the majority of Granada's BECTU, NUJ and AEEU union members supported strike action over pay and job security. Staff, angered that Granada's five executive directors awarded themselves a 14 per cent rise costing £2.67 million, rejected their 3.6 per cent offer and claimed 11 per cent.

SEX AND CHANNEL 5 ...

27 JANUARY The Broadcasting Standards Commission accused Channel 5 of eroding standards by its broadcasts of late night soft porn. C5's Hotlines and Compromising Situation regularly attracts 700,000 viewers and David Elstein, the channel's chief exec, talked of the early Sixties Lady Chatterley trial and called the BSC "anachronistic and patronising". Elspeth Howe, head of the BSC, said: "Our most recent research, Sex and Sensibility, showed clearly that audiences expect sexual portrayal to be justified by its context [which is] in line with ITC research suggesting there is a different expectation about what should be available on free-to-air television."

... AND SEX AND CHANNEL 4

24 FEBRUARY Channel 4's eight part drama Queer as Folk was billed as the first TV drama featuring all-gay central characters. Viewing figures showed that a third of the 2.2 million viewers who tuned in switched channels by the end of the first broadcast. Complaints figures revealed the BSC received 30 protesting phone messages.

SEX AND THE BSC

25 FEBRUARY The Broadcasting Standards Commission said it would ban gratuitous sex scenes from terrestrial TV and make it a pay-for-only experience.

FINAL NEWS AT TEN

8 MARCH After occupying the same slot for 31 years, News at Ten went off the air to be replaced by ITV Evening News at 6.30, an 11pm news bulletin and Tonight, a weekly post-News at Ten current affairs show presented by Trevor MacDonald. In place of the old news came a stockpile of old movies with Goldeneye, the first night replacement, pushing up viewing figures to 47.2 per cent of the total audience. During April - with the Kosovo war at its newsworthy height - viewing fell to 29.8 per cent, 1.2 per cent below April 1998.

GELDOF AID

10 MARCH Bob Geldof (above), the former Boomtown Rat who started the Live Aid pop-stars-do-charity wheeze, sold the Planet 24 TV television production company to Carlton Communications. His third share in the company - which made The Big Breakfast and The Word and launched such luminaries as Chris Evans, Gaby Roslin and Denise Van Outen - made him £5 million. One of his partners, Waheed (aka Lord) Ali, joined Carlton as MD of Carlton Productions.

GRANADA INTO SCOTLAND

23 MARCH Granada paid Mirror Group £110 million for an 18.6 per cent stake in Scottish Media Group which owns Scottish TV, Grampian and a slice of GMTV. Though Granada denied it was preparing an all out bid for SMG, its recent purchase put it ahead of Carlton and United News and Media in what a city analyst called "the endgame which is the final consolidation of ITV". At the end of May SMG recruited Don Cruikshank, the former Oftel telecoms regulator and a critic of the ITC, to boost its defence against predators.

TONIGHT: STEPHEN LAWRENCE

8 APRIL The first edition of Granada's Tonight news programme began with an interview with the five white men accused of murdering the black teenager Stephen Lawrence. "This is just a publicity stunt to try and say they did not kill my son," said Stephen's father Neville Lawrence. "Five men, five interviews and a hundred different opinions," wrote Kamal Ahmed, the Guardian's media editor. "Was it merely a platform for the killers? A legitimate television investigation into the death of a black teenager? A stunt? Or maybe just a useless attempt at getting at some truth that many think is now lost in a fog of lies and police incompetence."

ANALOGUE ERA

15 APRIL The cable and television transmission company NTL agreed payment terms in a deal to guarantee the analogue transmission of ITV and Channel 4 broadcasts until 2012. By then much TV transmission will be digital - and the government will presumably have delivered on its promise to set a date for the ending of analogue television signals.

UNM BUYS US FIRM

29 APRIL United News and Media paid £570 million for CMP, an American technology publishing company with profitable online spin-offs. Though UNM said it remained as committed as ever to Anglia and Meridian TV stations, and Express Newspaper, the deal emphasised its enthusiasm for business-to-business publishing which already accounts for 58 per cent of profits.

GRANADA BUSINESS

9 MAY Granada said it wanted to split its TV and hotel divisions. The chief exec Charles Allen said he wanted an "international partner of choice" to help operate a separate listing of what he sees as Granada's undervalued TV assets. In June, Granada pushed aside concerns about its £100 million ONdigital investment and unveiled increased half-yearly profits and dividends. A £609 million profit on a £1.98 billion turnover was boosted by the sale of Granada's 6 per cent holding in Sky for £347 million.

PERFORMANCE UNRELATED PAY

25 MAY Despite Channel 4's declining audiences, Michael Jackson's boss-class pay rose £120,000 to £478,000 in 1998. That's even more than John Birt's £415,000 BBC stipend.

ITN 24 HOUR NEWS

11 JUNE ITN - whose chief newsreader Trevor MacDonald was knighted in the Queen's birthday honours list - confirmed rumours that it plans a 24 hour news service to compete against the BBC, Sky and CNN. Meanwhile, audience research showed that the demotion of News At Ten was losing ITV its share of news viewers.

GRANADA SPORT

13 JULY The Granada Media Group bought a 10 per cent stake in Liverpool football club for £22 million. Meanwhile Carlton - Granada's partner in ONdigital, was linked with Aston Villa and Arsenal. The cable company NTL already has a 6.3 per cent stake in Newcastle United, though NTL takeover plans were abandoned when the government blocked Sky's £623 million bid for Manchester United.

ITV LOSES VIEWERS

12 AUGUST ITV's share of peaktime viewers fell to 37. 5 per cent during the second quarter of 1999, a critical 1.5 percentage points from the target 39 per cent. More bad news was that prosperous ABC1 adults aged 16-54 - the people valued by advertisers - are the lowest of all audience categories.

TONIGHT: ITV RESCEDULES

14 AUGUST With Tonight audiences dipping to 3.5 million (some 2.5 million fewer than hoped for), ITV executives said their current affairs flagship has "got real problems". An unnamed critic quoted by the Sunday Times said: "Tonight's gone from bad to worse, wallowing in mysterious off-diary investigations that not even regional programmes would touch. You're almost embarrassed for Trevor McDonald ... presiding over sub-Tomorrow's World reports like, 'So driving in fog does increase the risk of road accidents'."

New TV

OVER THE SKY

26 AUGUST 1998 Jimmy Hill - the only man in football to have been a football player, coach, manager, director and club chairman - quit the BBC to join Sky Sports. Having signed on for London Weekend in 1967, he transferred to the BBC in 1973 and put in over 600 Match of the Day appearances.

MAN BITES DOGS

28 AUGUST Peter Bazalgette, an ex-BBC staffer whose production company makes Changing Rooms, used the MacTaggart Memorial Lecture at the Edinburgh TV Festival to attack TV watchdogs. He called Lady Howe, chairwoman of the BSC, the "biggest busybody of them all" and said ITC powers should be curbed. "It should be up to the audience to decide what the audience wants to see," said Bazalgette. "With individual electronic programme guides, we will make our own selections and we will bar our children from material we think unsuitable."

CAT STUCK UP TREE

3 SEPTEMBER "And Channel One is closing two of its stations. But first, tonight's main news about a cat stuck up a tree in Acacia Avenue." So said a Kipper Williams cartoon about the collapse of the cable TV channel for local audiences in London and Bristol. The Daily Mail and General Trust failed to see any return on an estimated £40 million investment and 90 staff, including a vaunted new breed of video-journalists, lost their jobs.

GRANADA SELLS SKY SHARES

13 OCTOBER Granada sold its 6.5 per cent shareholding in BSkyB for £448 million. Granada owns 50 per cent of ONdigital, BSkyB's competitor in digital TV.

BT WANTS A SHARE IN SKY

13 NOVEMBER British Telecom management urged the government to relax regulations barring a deal with BSkyB. The result might be for BT to dominate mobile phone market and see off cable company deals bundling cheap phone charges with their own pay TV services. Sky would benefit by being better able to persuade BT customers into pay TV. BT, which is losing residential phone business, tripled pre-tax profits to £1.9 billion after the £1.1 billion sale of its stake in the US phone company MCI.

GATES TO THE FUTURE

25 JANUARY 1999 Bill Gates' Microsoft bought a 5 per cent stake in the cable company NTL with an option to increase the holding to 6.2 per cent. The £303 million deal marks further expansion of the software company's media interests following Microsoft's $1 billion stake in the US cable company Comcast.

SKY'S 10TH BIRTHDAY

5 FEBRUARY Ten years ago Sky doubled the number of TV channels to eight. Now it is an established part of the TV scene with its most popular channel having a 1.5 per cent audience share - compared to BBC1's 29.5 per cent.

BT GOES ONLINE

10 FEBRUARY British Telecom introduced ClickFree for free connection to the Internet. BT is a shareholder in British Interactive Broadcasting which was set up to launch digital services for BSkyB.

MURDOCH IN EUROLAND

4 MARCH Plans for a £14 billion merger of Europe's two biggest pay TV operators BSkyB and Canal in Italy were cancelled due to worries over EU regulations. A couple of weeks later News Corp said it had been "reinvited" to join alliances formed by Kirch of Germany and Mediaset of Italy. In May News Corp pulled off two sporting deals: it bought media rights for Roma, Lazio, Parma and Fiorentinna football clubs; and in Germany it paid £280 million over four years for German transmission rights to broadcast the European Champions League on tm3, previously a women's channel with 0.6 per cent of the German viewing audience.

KURDISH INCITEMENT

22 MARCH The British based Med-TV, which has sent satellite broadcasts to Kurdish audiences around Europe since 1995, was closed down for 21 days. The ITC issued the punishment for the transmission of programmes "likely to encourage or to incite crime or to lead to disorder". The station's anti-Turkish line had already incurred a £90,000 fine and two warnings for breaching impartiality agreements.

CABLE MERGER/MORE GATES

6 APRIL Cable and Wireless (which owns 53 per cent of Britain's biggest cable company) and Telewest moved towards a merger of residential assets to create a group of 2.6 million customers, enough critical mass to compete head on with British Telecom. This followed speculation that CWC wanted to pull out of the television broadcast elements of Cable and Wireless Communications. Shortly afterwards, Bill Gates' Microsoft took a 29 per cent share in Telewest.

NEW SKY BOSS

14 MAY Tony Ball became BSkyB's fifth chief executive in 10 years. The ex-president of the Fox-Liberty American sports network took over from Mark Booth. Microsoft had offered him a job heading its internet businesses but Murdoch clung on to him by creating a new media company, e*partners, for him to run. Elisabeth Murdoch wasn't considered ready for the job.

NTL EMERGES AS CABLE TOP DOG

26 JULY NTL became Britain's largest cable company when it bought Cable and Wireless Communications' consumer interests for £18.7 billion. NTL's chief executive Barclay Knapp celebrated the deal by making it clear he wanted to buy Telewest, the remaining large rival.(Both companies have Microsoft as a major shareholder.) However, merger talks between Telewest and the newly enlarged NTL were called off halfway through August. Thus the much-hyped future of cable is still uncertain with the consensus among industry analysts that competing cable interests won't be able to compete fully with Sky and British Telecom.

Radio

CULTURAL SOUNDBITE

10 AUGUST 1998 Professor George Steiner said Classic FMs' habit of broadcasting "ten-minute snatches" of classical music was part of the "wind of patronising populism" in British cultural life. Speaking at the annual Radio 3 Proms' lecture, the professor said listeners should be encouraged and supported in discovering complete classical works.

FREQUENCY FINE

3 SEPTEMBER The Radio Authority fined Medway FM £5,000 for the crime of increasing its transmission power above the levels permitted by its licence. "These frequencies are used to guide aircraft towards their destination airfield," the Radio Authority said. In January Severn Sound, Ram FM and GWR FM were each fined £1,000 for unintentional signal deviations.

COMMERCIAL DIGITAL RADIO

12 OCTOBER Digital One Ltd was awarded the first and only national commercial digital multiplex. The contract stipulates that the three existing national commercial services - Classic FM, Virgin Radio and Talk Radio - are guaranteed space on the multiplex with up to five new national stations. The main shareholders are GWR and the cable operator NTL.

CAPITAL RADIO'S 25TH

16 OCTOBER It was 25 years ago that Capital Radio, Britain's first commercial station, began broadcasting with Simon and Garfunkel's Bridge Over Troubled Waters. At first it sailed on troubled waters and in 1976 its chairman Richard Attenborough had to pawn a Degas painting to pay wage bills. However, within the space of ten years Capital was the first radio station to float on the Stock Exchange and in 1990 it outstripped Radio 1's listenership in London. Now Captial's 3 million listeners make it the most popular metropolitan radio station in the world.

AGEISM

27 OCTOBER 1998 The BBC's implicit rejection of older listeners was made explicit in a leaked memo which stated that total audience share would fall from the current 48 per cent to as low as 33 per cent by 2007 if younger listeners are not brought into Radio 2. "Our aim will be to move Radio 2's older listeners to Radio 3 for classical music and Radio 4 for speech."

ALL TALK

28 OCTOBER Kelvin MacKenzie, the former Sun editor and then Mirror deputy chief executive, won control of Talk Radio in a £15 million deal partly backed by Rupert Murdoch. "Because the BBC has dominated speech so much, there are, bizarrely, no broadcasters around. They're all on-the-one-hand-this-other-hand-that," MacKenzie said. "What has to change is that the BBC pays so poorly. Radio is always the third medium. It is ridiculous. In America it's not like that at all."

NEW BBC BOSS

NOVEMBER Jenny Abramsky - whose experience includes founding Radio 5 and editing Radio 4's main news programmes - was appointed BBC director of radio. She got the job ahead of thhe Radio 4 controller James Boyle, 5 Live controller Roger Mosey and the BBC2 controller Mark Thompson.

SPEARING THE MESSENGER

SCENE I, APRIL 1998
Chris Dunkley, the presenter of Radio 4's Feedback asked the Radio 4 controller James Boyle: "What will you do if listeners don't like the changes [to Radio 4]?" Boyle replied: "Obviously, if it doesn't work out, I will have to fall on my sword."
SCENE II, 9 DECEMBER 1998 Radio 4 ratings were still slipping and Dunkley was sacked. His programme's content, according to a BBC spokesman, had nothing to do with it. Said Dunkley: "The BBC is much more centralised these days and Radio 4 is the prime example. Control freakery is the phrase at the back of my mind and Feedback does not fit into the control-freak mentality."

A TALE OF HARASSMENT

7 JANUARY 1999 The Radio Authority fined Virgin Radio £10,000 after Chris Evans, its owner and main presenter, encouraged listeners to "hound" a freelance photographer "until he goes toes up". The photographer, who had allegedly been papping Liam Gallagher, claimed to have received death threats.

MAGIC MARKETING

14 JANUARY Melody Radio in London changed its name to Magic as part of a £3 million Emap rebranding campaign following the £25 million purchase of Melody the previous March. Magic is one of three Emap Radio brands along with Kiss and Big City.

BBC WORLD SERVICE CONTRACTION

17 JANUARY Leaked memos revealed BBC plans to save £20 million and lose 200 jobs by cutting German and Czech operations and reducing Russian and Arabic services.
Two reassurances: 1) "The World Service is certainly going to be a very important priority for us," said Robin Cook, the foreign secretary;
2) "The authority of the World Service will not be reduced ... we are not about to squander a national asset," said the BBC chairman, Sir Christopher Bland.

MEEJA MARRIJ

25 JANUARY: The BRMB radio station in Birmingham arranged a blind date marriage between Gregory Cordell and Carla Germaine. The newly-weds went on a Bahamas honeymoon accompanied by "journalists" from Channel 4 and News of the World. BRMB's tacky stunt was not, however, a world first for a Sydney radio station had pulled the same trick the previous September. Both marriages collapsed within three months.

GWR EXPANSION

28 JANUARY GWR paid £26 million to acquire Orchard Media's channels in Somerset (Orchard FM), Exeter (Gemini FM), SE Devon (Westward) and N Devon (Lantern). GWR, which controls Classic FM, is Britain's second biggest commercial radio owner.

RADIO 3 DEFENDS CORNER

2 FEBRUARY Roger Wright, the new Radio 3 controller, countered dumbing down criticism by announcing increased drama and live classical music. "The network remains the only place you can find such a diversity of top-quality cultural and music programmes," he said.

RADIO 4 TURNS CORNER

4 FEBRUARY RAJAR figures showed Radio 4 had added an extra 260,000 listeners between September and December. In October the audience had dropped 500,000 to below 8 million. Boyle said: "The new schedule is carrying more listeners from one programme to another - clear, strong evidence that the schedule is now succeeding in its objective of encouraging lighter listeners to listen longer."

RADIO REVENUE

4 FEBRUARY An 18.6 per cent increase in advertising revenue during 1998 meant commercial radio was Britain's fastest growing advertising medium. Estimates for growth during 1999 ranged from 7 to 11.5 per cent.

RADIO AUTHORITY CLEARED

3 MARCH Allegations against the Radio Authority, first aired on BBC Newsnight in December, were dismissed by a firm of auditors. Grant Thornton found there had not been "an abuse of power, an act of bad faith and a perversion of good practice" in the granting of a licence to Vibe FM. John Norrington, the Radio Authority's former secretary, had also said that the RA chairman Sir Peter Gibbings had a conflict of interest because his family's charitable trust owned 0.5 per cent of shares in Essex Radio which owns 56 per cent of Vibe. Grant Thornton denied that allegation as well.

SACKED HOWARD AND READ

3 MAY Classic FM used competitive pressure as the excuse to get rid of Margaret Howard and Mike Read. "There are seven brand-new digital radio stations out there and we need to compete," said a spokeswoman. "Margaret Howard brought a sense of gravitas ... but we need to keep increasing our audience share."

GWR GOES DIGITAL

4 MAY GWR, which owns Class FM, pledged a £12 million digital radio investment over the next six years. It was in talks with several telecoms companies to explore techniques of building tiny digital radios into mobile phones.

FIGURES FAVOUR RADIO 4

10 JUNE Listening figures confirmed the renaissance of Radio 4 with the Today flagship getting the highest share of any breakfast show at 15.1 per cent of listeners. Radio 4 captured 9.4 million listeners between January and March 1999, a turn round from the October low of 7.7 million.

RADIO 1 DEVOLVES

10 JUNE Huw Stephens, whose 18th birthday was in May 1999, became the BBC's youngest DJ (Noel Edmonds used to hold the youthful record). Stephens will broadcast to a Welsh audience in July when, for another first, Radio 1 devolves its schedule with other separate shows for England, Northern Ireland and Scotland.

BBC RADIO TO THAMES

18 JUNE BBC executives were revealed to be negotiating for a media centre on London's South Bank. Rumour was that it will house 2,000 radio and World Service journalists The BBC operates from 500 buildings across Britain and aims to concentrate operations.

PAXO vs KISSINGER

28 JUNE Jeremy Paxman used his Monday morning Radio 4 show to ask Henry Kissinger: "Did you feel a fraud accepting the Nobel prize [for the Indo-China peace agreement]?" Kissinger walked off air.

TALK EXPANDS

26 JULY Kelvin MacKenzie's Talk Radio became Britain's fifth largest radio group with the acquisition of nine local radio stations. Talk paid the Radio Partnership a reported £40 million for stations which have a combined 2.5 per cent share of commercial listening and reach nearly 3.5 million people in the north of England and South Wales.

Television: introduction

British television

BBC

Publicly funded via an annual licence fee that raised a total of £2.1 billion in 1998. It is broadcast nationally with regional variations on BBC1 (which spent £752 million in 1998) and BBC2 (£406 million).
See pages 172-179

ITV

The commercial sector which is funded by advertisements to the tune of £2.59 billion in 1998. It is broadcast regionally on 16 Channel 3 stations (£1.8 billion net advertising revenue in 1998), S4C in Wales (£9 million) and nationally on Channel 4 (£553 million) and Channel 5 (£142 million).
See pages 180-193

Digital

The potential is for up to 36 digital terrestrial, over 150 digital satellite and up to 400 digital cable channels. At present there are digital services from the BBC (BBC Knowledge, BBC Choice and BBC Parliament) and Channel 3/4/5 plus ONdigital, SDN, and Digital 3 and 4.
See pages 194-199

Satellite and cable

Funded by £2 billion worth of subscriptions and advertising sales spread over more than 200 TV channels which, mostly, are broadcast nationally.
See pages 200-209

Share of total television audience

BBC 40.2%

ITV (C3) 32.9%

Channel 4   9.9%

Cable   7.4%

Sky   5.0%

Channel 5   4.6%

Point size stands for 1% of audience share.

In 1998 the figures: BBC 41.7%, ITV 32.4%, Channel 4 10.4%, Cable 5.9%, Sky 5.3%

In 1997 Gavyn Davies, the economist called on by the government to make recommendations about BBC funding, wrote Broadcasting, Society and Policy in the Multimedia Age. "Who needs public service broadcasting?" he asked. "The answer is that we all do and that the new technology increases, not decreases, this need. The reasons are, first, that there is a real danger that if broadcasting were left just to the market it would become excessively concentrated; second, that even if this were not the case, commercial broadcasting on its own would fail to produce the form of broadcasting which people individually, or as citizens and voters collectively, require; and, third, that there is no set of rules or regulations or laws which could entirely correct the deficiencies of the commercial system."

Much has changed since 1997 with the rise of the Internet and, more to the point, the consolidation of satellite into 30 per cent of households and the emergence of digital television. It is a matter of government policy that, at some unspecified date, all television will be broadcast digitally but, for now, the much-hyped digital TV is cause for consumer apathy and confusion. An ITC viewer survey in the spring found that 38 per cent of those asked said they were "not at all interested" in going digital at an initial cost of £200. Interest went up when the connection boxes were given away.

More TV equals less audiences per channel and has shifted us from the shared cultural experience of old TV and left programme planners scrabbling

TV - the viewer's view

BBC 1

"Staid, stuffy, establishment and reliable ... like John Major or Queen Victoria."

BBC 2

"An old professor ... a trendy teacher ...a social worker keen to save the world."

ITV

"Jolly, lively and normal ... rather brash with a touch of the second-hand car dealer."

Channel 4

"A channel that does things differently [like] Richard Branson." (Women over 45 think it's the channel the Queen would watch for the documentaries and horse racing.)

Source: Likely to Complain ITC

Share of total audience

CHANNEL	'96-97	'97-98	'98-99
BBC 1	32.20%	30.40%	29.00%
BBC 2	11.70%	11.30%	11.20%
Channel 4	10.30%	10.00%	9.90%
Sky	4.30%	5.30%	5.00%
Central	5.40%	4.80%	4.70%
Channel 5	2.80%	3.20%	4.60%
Granada	4.00%	3.90%	3.90%
Yorkshire	3.40%	3.40%	3.40%
Carlton	3.20%	2.90%	3.00%
Meridian	2.60%	2.50%	2.50%
HTV	2.60%	2.40%	2.30%
Scottish	2.20%	2.10%	2.00%
LWT	2.10%	2.00%	2.00%
Anglia	2.10%	1.90%	1.90%
GMTV	1.80%	1.70%	1.60%
Tyne Tees	1.70%	1.70%	1.60%
Ulster	1.10%	1.00%	1.00%
Westcountry	0.90%	0.90%	0.80%
UK Gold	0.60%	0.60%	0.80%
Cartoon N'work	0.70%	0.80%	0.80%
Nickelodeon	0.50%	0.70%	0.70%
Grampian	0.70%	0.60%	0.60%
Living	0.30%	0.40%	0.60%
Border	0.60%	0.50%	0.50%
MTV		0.30%	0.40%
S4C Wales	0.40%	0.40%	0.30%
Bravo	0.20%	0.30%	0.30%
Discovery	0.20%	0.30%	0.30%
Disney Channel	0.30%	0.30%	0.30%
Eurosport	0.30%	0.30%	0.30%
VH-1	0.20%	0.20%	0.30%
Challenge TV		0.20%	0.20%
Discovery		0.10%	0.20%
Granada Plus	0.10%	0.20%	0.20%
QVC	0.10%	0.10%	0.20%
Sci-Fi Channel	0.10%	0.10%	0.20%
TNT	0.10%	0.10%	0.20%
ZEE TV Europe	0.10%	0.10%	0.20%
BBC News 24			0.10%
The Box	0.10%	0.10%	0.10%
Channel TV	0.10%	0.10%	0.10%
CNN			0.10%
Fox Kids Network	0.10%	0.10%	0.10%
Live TV			0.10%
Network 2	0.10%	0.10%	0.10%
Paramount	0.10%	0.10%	0.10%
RTE 1	0.10%	0.10%	0.10%
Trouble			0.10%
UK Horizons			0.10%

Source: ITC, June 1999

after what they call Event Television. At its most compelling an Event TV event had the vast majority watching programmes usually pegged to a news item like the death of Kennedy, the World Cup Final, the first moon landing, the first Band Aid or Lady Di's funeral. Difficult events for a TV executive to cook up. Event TV also used to be the big soaps plus the BBC and ITV main news broadcasts where nearly everybody shared the same viewing experience. But commercial pressures meant a farewell to News at Ten in 1999. The best recent examples of Event TV, albeit watered down events, are the BBC Lottery shows and Chris Tarrant's Who Wants To Be a Millionaire?.

The results are plain. While competition has brought greater choice of channels, nobody claims content has improved. Instead market forces have forced up the price of sport, forcing armchair fans to pay far more than they ever did in a more regulated environment. In 1998 the BBC1 audience share dropped below 30 per cent for the first time and ITV failed to hit its targets. A good thing too, given that the average viewer has long been habituated to watching 26 hours a week. There isn't time in an average life for any more telly and White Dot, the anti-TV lobbyist, has the solution. "Give up TV and you are doubling your free time," is the advice in White Dot's book Get a Life. "It's a whole extra ten years of your life." The non-viewing view was echoed by John Ryle in the Guardian who wrote: "TV is a drug - anti-social, addictive and bad for you. The TV set is already a kind of hypodermic syringe, offering a quick route to the nervous system. But the use of television in the multi-channel future will be more like crack cocaine - fast-acting and low grade. The channel we really need is the Off Channel, the one that shows a blank screen and tells you to get a life."

Some guilt attaches to TV viewing. A five year study called TV Living - Television Culture and Everyday Life said daytime TV was "seen as a kind of moral weakness". TV is also seen as a friend which helps people through illness and unemployment. The report says older people who, along with children, are the most dedicated viewers are "self conscious" about too much viewing which "stems partly from having grown up in a world where television was part of life".

The current generation of children finds TV central to a life where many parents - their heads filled with boogaloos which probably dance into mind straight from the TV set - are too paranoid to allow their sons and daughters to play out of doors unsupervised. Consequently homes with children have an average 2.6 TV sets and more than a third have a TV in the bedroom. While the proportion of children's drama has fallen to about 15 per cent across the board, there is no shortage of manic cartoons and hyped up presenters desperate to make a break into a proper day job. According to yet more ITC research: 50 per cent of children watch before going to school on weekdays; 75 per cent turn on immediately they get home from school; 40 per cent watch during weekday evenings; and 30 per cent watch during weekend evenings. They read, on average, for 15 minutes a day.

FURTHER READING

Broadcasting, Society and Policy In The Multimedia Age
by Gavyn Davies and Andrew Graham
University of Luton Press
Get a Life!
by David Burke and Jean Lotus of White Dot
Bloomsbury, £12.99
TV Living - TV Culture and Everyday Life
by Annette Hill
Routledge, £15.99
Young People New Media
by Sonia Livingstone
London School of Economics

The TV News

In the early days of television news there was no such thing as a presenter. Instead disembodied voices would read scripts and, even in 1955 when Richard Baker and Robert Dougall first appeared on screen, news readers kept their heads down lest their expressions distracted from objectivity. Things are now moving towards a looks-only recruitment policy of over-hyped personality presenters. Jeremy Paxman, for example, probably commands more column inches than the entire shadow cabinet.

Rather than sitting in austere studios, celebrity news readers appear in logo-decked stage sets which have become items of news in their own right. Thus it must now be put on public record that in May 1999 the BBC's Six o'Clock News replaced cold blue and silver with ivory walls and red carpet. The 1999 fashion for studio rethinks began on 4 January when the two heavyweight news programmes Channel 4 News and Newsnight strutted some new stuff. Jon Snow abandoned his desk for a low pink plinth which was a key part of Channel 4's £3 million relaunch. Free to wonder round the studio, Snow said: "There is nothing between me and the viewer. It is direct communication." Later that night Newsnight presenters appeared in what the BBC described as "a modernist set".

Evidence of TV stupidity emerged in a Granada memo which was part of a successful bid to take over the 60 Minutes current affairs programme. The memo writer wanted to use the discarded World in Action name for a show which "should be presenter-led" and include the following: the hidden angle on a major running story; an irreverent approach to a current controversy; a news-related human interest feature; and (such is telly's reverence for itself) "in the week of Deirdre's conviction in Coronation Street ... news related reportage finding out what it's really like in a women's prison".

The biggest breaking TV news story was at ITV where, at the beginning of 1998, its chief exec Richard Eyre had predicted 40 per cent of the 7pm to 10pm viewing audience to reverse a decline which had been taking place since 1994.

Trevor MacDonald interviewing Tony Blair at 10 Downing Street in one of the new ITV news programmes

Eyre's bid to increase viewing meant kicking News at Ten off the air. After talk of a diminution of public service broadcasting, the Independent Television Commission stalled until November before giving ITV permission to have its way. A Guardian leader said News at Ten had "become part of the bio-rhythms of the nation" and thought it too valuable a brand name to lose. "ITV argues that programming needs to respond to the hundreds of channels thrown up by the digital revolution. But in the digital revolution - including the Internet - strong brands are more important than ever as beacons to guide people in the dark. If the new digital channels - or even the BBC - snatches News at Ten for their own, ITV will have no one but itself to blame." When Sky did the predictable thing and said it might take over the name, ITV responded with a lawyer's letters.

But, finally, after occupying the same slot for 31 years, News at Ten went off the air on 8 March. It was replaced by ITV Evening News at 6.30, a 20-minute 11pm news bulletin and a weekly late night show presented by Trevor MacDonald. In place of the news came old movies with Goldeneye, the first night replacement, pushing viewing figures to 47.2 per cent of the total audience. By the summer Eyre was getting kicked because - with the Kosovo war at its newsworthy height - April

viewing fell to 29.8 per cent, 1.2 per cent below April 1998. This revitalised doubts about the ITV network's financial viability and renewed speculation that Channel 3 companies might merge to consolidate their diminishing strength.

There was also a news review at the BBC which took £200,000 to discover that viewers felt their relationship with the news was child and parent rather than adult to adult. Back in August Peter Sissons, star presenter of the Nine O'Clock News, put the case for his stardom. "We are part of the BBC's assets," he declared with a grown-up's objective modesty. "But its managers have been undermining our stature by giving the impression that we're dispensable. People don't just turn to the BBC, they turn to its presenters. We give the BBC credibility." This man of stature and credibility sneered at what he called a "beauty contest".

On 10 May - amidst the beauty of a new set which its designer Martin Lambie-Nairn called "warmer, clearer, more accessible" - Sissons was in place on a revamped Nine o'Clock News. The truly radical changes were on the top rating Six o'Clock News where the stature and credibility of Martyn Lewis was replaced by the stature and credibility of Huw Edwards. Where Martyn had been instructed to wear orange, purple and black, Huw was decked out in pink, lavender and blue. And that's the end of the news.

BBC Television

The BBC, being the biggest single part of the British media, generates the most media based stories. Where they used to concentrate on the two strands of John Birt's managerial regime, namely the internal reorganisation and the move toward commercialism, the new question is what will the new boss do when he takes charge in April 2000.

The BBC staffers' choice was ABB - Anybody But Birt - but after his appointment Greg Dyke was full of praise for his predecessor. "John has left a brilliant company, and he isn't really getting credit for it," he said. "He has done the things that needed to be done. You had to put in an internal pricing system, so you knew where the money was going. Anyone would have done that. But the real legacy is what he has done with digital TV and online. Those who criticise him for being ahead of the game would have complained just as much if the BBC was behind the times."

Criticism of Dyke - orchestrated by newspapers (particularly the Times) and then amplified by a Tory party desperate to push home any attack it can on Labour - centred on a £55,000 donation to Labour funds. That this amounts to 0.75 per cent of the £7 million fortune Dyke made as head of Pearson TV underlines the old rule that the rich get richer. However Tory complaints were never very convincing, given the historical patterns of political donations and the fact that BBC governors rather than the Department of Culture made the appointment. Meanwhile Dyke resigned his Labour party membership and the Tory party pushed for "special mechanisms" to monitor the BBC's impartiality.

The impartiality story will run and run. However, once he's in post, judgement of Greg Dyke will depend on his ability to maintain the licence fee and stop the slide in ratings. Early talk was that he would make plans for a digital future less of an issue and concentrate on the main analogue game. That implies diverting more money to BBC1 and pushing hard to grab a greater share of Premiership football back from Sky. By sport he'll be judged and Des Lynam's

defection in August 1999 was an early blow. He's also likely to cut down on John Birt's unpopular managerialism and the astonishing £9 million annual expenditure on business consultants. Instead of permanent revolution, there will be a consolidation of the revised corporate structure in a £2 billion a year organisation with 24,000 staff running two terrestrial television channels, five domestic radio networks, a clutch of cable, digital and satellite stations, the World Service and a big presence on the Internet.

The BBC is now into its 77th analogue year. What began as a cartel of radio manufacturers licensed by the government became a public body in 1927 when it was granted a Royal Charter to "provide broadcasting services as public services". That tradition holds and was underlined by the last government which renewed the BBC's Royal Charter for ten years until 2006. For all the fragmentation of viewing, BBC1 is still a force in the land. Audience figures can be presented in ways other than charting a decline and the Annual Report made much of the statistic that 94 per cent of UK households tune into the BBC for more than two hours a week. Indeed, the BBC claims the highest overall ratings and at Christmas 1999, for example, Men Behaving Badly topped the viewing with 13.9 million viewers. And then came the complaints, and a fierce and intense debate about morality which eventually had the BBC saying the "edition of Men Behaving Badly was inappropriate Christmas Day viewing".

The departing director-general is nothing if not a salesman, and at a speech in July 1999 Birt pulled out the superlatives in praise of the organisation he is soon to leave. "The BBC is the world's most successful cultural institution," he told the New Statesman media lecture. "It is one of Britain's great contributions to the 20th century. The BBC fosters a rumbustious, vigorous and informed democracy. In no other country are there such fierce and intense debates about the issues that matter as there are here in the UK."

GREG DYKE, THE NEW BBC DIRECTOR GENERAL, BACKED BY HIS CHAIRMAN SIR CHRISTOPHER BLAND
Following Greg Dyke's appointment in June, Mathew Horsman wrote: "How did the BBC get from Reith to Greg Dyke in such a short period of time in the country's political and cultural development? Is it conceivable that a man like Dyke, the populist, estuary-toned, blunt and socially unschooled TV man, would have been asked to run the BBC in the 1950s? The 1960s? Even the 1980s? The establishment would have been aghast at the prospect. That Dyke has now been chosen is testimony above all to how far the country has come. William Hague might disagree, and the old dinosaurs will harangue, but most of us are willing to wait before we judge him. That is a cultural revolution in itself."

BBC structure

The BBC is split into five directorates:

BBC Broadcast	**175-177**
BBC News	**178**
BBC Production	**178**
BBC Resources	**179**
BBC Worldwide	**179**

BBC MAIN OFFICES

BBC Corporate HQ & BBC Broadcast
Broadcasting House, Portland Place, London W1A 1AA
Tel 020-7580 4468
Website: www.bbc.co.uk
The hub of the BBC and the HQ for BBC Broadcast, including Network radio and Regional Broadcasting.

BBC News, BBC Production, BBC Broadcast - Network Television
Television Centre, Wood Lane, London W12 7RJ
Tel 020-8743 8000
The HQ for BBC News and BBC Production, with the main television production facilities.

BBC Worldwide Television Publishing & Learning
Woodlands, 80 Wood Lane, London W12 0TT
Tel 020-8743 5588
Headquarters of BBC commercial activities.

BBC Resources & BBC Broadcast - Education
BBC White City, 201 Wood Lane, London W12 7TS
Tel 020-8743 5588

BBC World Service
Bush House, London WC2B 4PH
Tel 020-7240 3456

BBC White City
201 Wood Lane, London W12 7TS
Tel 020-8752 5252

BBC Written Archives
Caversham Park, Reading, Berks RG4 8TZ
Tel 01734-472742

BBC PRESS OFFICES

The main BBC press office is at Television Centre. Its opening hours are 8ooam to midnight on weekdays, and 10am to 11pm at the weekend. For specific enquiries, use Publicity numbers after the addresses on the following three pages.

Main press office	020-8576 1865
International press office	020-7557 2941

BBC TOP MANAGEMENT

Day-to-day management is the responsibility of the executive committee, led by the DG. Committee members are recruited by the governors who also set the broad strategy, ensure the BBC complies with the Royal Charter and the law, and keeps high standards. Governors are appointed by the Crown for four years. The Governors consult National Broadcasting Councils about programmes for Scotland, Wales and N Ireland. They also receive advice from the English National Forum, representing Advisory Councils in England.

BBC Board of Governors
Chairman: Sir Christopher Bland (to 31.3.01)
Vice-chairwoman: Baroness Young (31.7.02)
Governor for Scotland: Fabian Monds (31.7.04)
Governor for N Ireland: Sir Robert Smith (31.7.04)
Governor for Wales: Roger Spencer Jones (31.12.01)
Chair English National Forum: Ranjit Sondhi (31.7.02)
Other governors
Dame Pauline Neville-Jones DCMG (31.12.01)
Sir David Scholey (31.10.00)
Adrian White (31.10.00)
Sir Richard Eyre (31.10.00)
Tony Young (31.7.02)
Heather Rabbatts (31.1.04)
BBC Executive Committee
Director general: John Birt (to 04.00)
Director general designate: Greg Dyke
Chief executive, BBC Broadcast: Will Wyatt
Chief executive, BBC Production: Matthew Bannister
Chief executive, BBC News: Tony Hall
Chief executive, BBC Resources: Margaret Salmon
Chief executive, BBC World Service: Mark Byford
Chief executive, BBC Worldwide: Rupert Gavin
Director of personnel: tba
Director of finance: John Smith
Director of policy and planning: Patricia Hodgson CBE
Director of corporate affairs: Colin Browne
Board of Management
The executive committee together with BBC Broadcast
Director of television: Alan Yentob
Director of radio: Jenny Abramsky
Director of nat./regional broadcasting: Mark Thompson
Director of Education: Michael Stevenson
Director of new services & dep. director, television: David Docherty
Director of Online: Nigel Chapman
BBC Production
Director of programmes: Jana Bennett
BBC Technology
Director of technology: Phillip Langsdale
BBC Worldwide
Dep. chief executive & MD, UK Regions: Peter Teague

BBC directorates

BBC BROADCAST

BBC Broadcast HQ
Broadcasting House, London W1A 1AA
Fax: 020-7637 1630   Tel: 020-7580 4468
Chief executive, broadcast: Will Wyatt
Director, finance and business affairs: Tony Dignum
Head of financial control: Carolyn Foxall
Director, marketing and communications: Sue Farr
Controller press & publicity: Sally Osman
Director, broadcasting and presentation: Pam Masters
Controller, personnel: Kate Smith

BBC Television
Almost 14,000 hours of television programmes are broadcast per year on BBC1
and BBC2. The majority of programmes are
commissioned from BBC Production, but
BBC Broadcast has a statutory obligation to
ensure that 25 per cent of network television
programmes are made by independent producers and, further, that a significant proportion are made in the regions outside London.

BBC Regional Broadcasting
About a third of network television and radio
programmes are made outside London and
the south east.

BBC Network Radio
In total BBC Radio broadcasts 33,000 hours
of programming a year on Radios 1, 2, 3 and
4 (Radio 5 Live is part of News Directorate).

BBC Education
BBC Education provides "learning for life
for everyone from early childhood to retire-
ment". In classrooms, schools programmes
cover over 2,000 hours of educational material are broadcast each year, with related
books, videos or audio cassettes. A new digital service BBC Knowledge which is dedicated to learning was launched in June and a
new internet-based service which will guide
people to the learning available inside and
outside the BBC is being developed. Current
projects include interactive software for language learning and a web browser for the
blind.

BBC Television

Television Centre, Wood Lane, London W12 7RJ
Fax 020-7749 7520   Tel 020-8743 8000
General publicity:	020-8576 7921
Drama publicity:	020-8576 1861
Entertainment publicity:	020-8576 1075
Sports publicity:	020-8225 9900
Factual publicity:	020-8752 6435
Specialist programmes:	020-8752 6521
Children's publicity:	020-8576 1860
Feature Films publicity:	020-8576 1868
Daytime, children's & prog acquisition:	020-8576 7350
Religious publicity:	0161-244 4890

Director of television: Alan Yentob
Deputy director of television: David Docherty
Controller, BBC1: Peter Salmon
Controller, BBC2: Jane Root
Controller, television sport: Mike Miller
Controller, press & publicity: Sally Osman
Controller, programme acquisition: Sophie Turner Laing
Head of purchased programmes: Sophie Turner Laing
Controller new services development: Roly Keating
Head, television press & publicity: Vanda Rumney
Head of business and legal affairs: Simon Taylor
Head of independent commissioning group, entertain-
ment: Bill Hilary
Head of independent commissioning, drama: Tessa Ross
Head of children's commissioning: Roy Thompson
Head of daytime commissioning: Jane Lush
Head of programming, BBC Choice: Katharine Everett
Head of programming, UK Gold: Kathryn Mitchell

BBC Network Radio

Broadcasting House, Portland Place, London W1A 1AA
Radio 1 publicity:	020-7765 4575
Radio 2 publicity:	020-7765 5712
Radio 3 publicity:	020-7765 2722
Radio 4 publicity:	020-7765 5337
Radio 5 publicity:	020-7576 4770

Director of radio: Jenny Abramsky
Deputy controller, Radio 1: Andy Parfitt
Controller, Radio 2: Jim Moir
Controller, Radio 3: Roger Wright
Controller, Radio 4: James Boyle
Managing editor, DAB: Glyn Jones
Head of press & publicity: Sue Lynas

BBC National & Regional: general

Central: BBC White City (London HQ)
Broadcasting House. Portland Place, London W1A 1AA

Tel 020-7580 4468
Regional HQ Press office Tel 020-7765 2797
Director of regional broadcasting: Mark Thompson
Financial controller: Peter White
Controller, English regions: Andy Griffee
Head of press and publicity, regional broadcasting: Tim Brassell
Secretary, regional broadcasting: Moyra Tourlamain

BBC Scotland
Broadcasting House, Queen Margaret Drive, Glasgow G12 8DG

Tel 0141-338 2000
Controller, Scotland: John McCormick
Head of broadcasting: Ken MacQuarrie
Head of production: Colin Cameron
Head of drama: Barbara McKissack
Head of news and current affairs: Ken Cargill

BBC Wales
Broadcasting House, Llantrisant Road, Llandaff, Cardiff CF5 2YQ

Tel 029-2032 2000
Controller, Wales: Geraint Talfan Davies
Head of broadcast (Welsh): Gwynn Pritchard
Head of broadcast (English): Dai Smith
Head of production: John Geraint
Head of drama: Pedr James
Head of strategy and channel development: Keith Jones

BBC Northern Ireland
Broadcasting House, Ormeau Avenue, Belfast BT2 8HQ

Tel 028-9033 8000
Controller, Northern Ireland: Pat Loughrey
Head of broadcasting: Anna Carragher
Head of production: Paul Evans
Head of drama: Robert Cooper

BBC National and Regional: TV

The BBC operates ten regional television services across England and three national television services in Wales, Scotland and Northern Ireland. The HQ is in London. Below are regional HQs and TV centres; local radio stations are later on in the book.

BBC National & Regional Broadcasting (London HQ)
Broadcasting House, Portland Place, London W1A 1AA

Tel 020-7580 4468

Birmingham (English Regionsl HQ)
BBC, Pebble Mill, Birmingham B5 7QQ
Fax 0121-432 8634　　Tel 0121-432 8888
Daily news programme: Midlands Today

Nottingham
BBC London Road, Nottingham NG2 4UU
Fax 0115-955 0501　　Tel 0115-955 0500
Daily news programme: East Midlands Today

Norwich
St Catherine's Close, All Saint's Green, Norwich, Norfolk NR13ND
Fax 01603-667865　　Tel 01603-619331
Daily news programme: Look East

Bristol
Broadcasting House, Whiteladies Road, Bristol BS8 2LR

Tel 0117-973 2211
Daily news programme: News West

Elstree
Clarendon Road, Borehamwood, Herts WD6 1JF
Fax 020-8228 8092　　Tel 020-8953 6100
Daily news programme: Newsroom South East

Southampton
Broadcasting House, Havelock Road, Southampton, Hants SO14 7PU
Fax 023-8033 9931　　Tel 023-8022 6201
Daily news progamme: South Today

Plymouth
Broadcasting House, Seymour Road, Mannamead, Plymouth, Devon PL3 5BD
Fax 01752-234595　　Tel 01752-229201
Daily news programme: Spotlight

Manchester (Regional HQ)
New Broadcasting House, PO Box 27, Oxford Road, Manchester M60 1SJ
Fax 0161-244 4999　　Tel 0161-200 2020
Daily news programme: North West Tonight

Leeds

Broadcasting Centre, Woodhouse Lane, Leeds, LS2 9PN
Fax 0113-243 9387   Tel 0113-244 1188
Daily news programe: Look North

Newcastle

Broadcasting Centre, Barrack Road, Newcastle-upon-Tyne NE99 2NE
Fax 0191-221 0112   Tel 0191-232 1313
Daily news programme: Look North.

SCOTLAND

Glasgow (National HQ)

Broadcasting House, Queen Margaret Drive, Glasgow G12 8DG
Fax 0141-334 0614   Tel 0141-338 2000
Daily news programme: Reporting Scotland

WALES

Cardiff (National HQ)

Broadcasting House, Llantrisant Road, Llandaff, Cardiff CF5 2YQ
Fax 029-2032 2576   Tel 029-2032 2000
Daily news programme: Wales Today

NORTHERN IRELAND

Belfast (National HQ)

Broadcasting House, Ormeau Avenue, Belfast BT2 8HQ
Fax 028-9033 8800   Tel 028-9033 8000
Daily news programme: Newsline 6.30

BBC Broadcast Strategy and Channel Management

Broadcasting House. Portland Place, London W1A 1AA
Fax 020-7765 5709   Tel 020-7565 1569
Director of strategy and channel management: Robin Foster
Controller, television strategy: Jane Scott
Head of channel management: Vaughan Williams
Head of strategic projects: Ian Hunter
Head of commissions and development BBC1: Don Cameron
Head of commissions and development BBC2: Jill Pack
Head of scheduling BBC1: Adam MacDonald
Scheduler BBC2: Matthew Tombs
Head of marketing & strategy: Sophie McLaughlin
Head of news services strategy: Jeremy Olivier
Head of strategy, regions: Peter Davies
Head of strategy, education: Mark Collinson
Head of performance analysis: Robin McCron

BBC Education

BBC White City, 201 Wood Lane, London W12 7TS
Fax 020-8752 4398   Tel 020-8752 5252
Press office Tel 020-8752 5152
Director of education: Michael Stevenson
Head of commissioning, adults: Fiona Chesterton
Head of commissioning, education for children: Frank Flynn
Acting head of strategy: Louise Ainsworth
Head of finance: Simon Nunan
Head of policy: Josh Hillman
Head of marketing: Dafna Israeli
Head of commissioning, OU: Paul Gerhardt
Acting head of digital media: George Auckland
Head of learning support: Steve Pollock
Personnel manager: Sue Hillman

BBC NEWS

BBC News is the biggest newsgathering operation in the world. It is a bi-media organisation with journalists reporting for BBC World Service radio and BBC World television as well as the BBC's UK radio and television outlets. BBC News has bureaux in 50 countries and 250 correspondents around the world - the largest network of foreign correspondents of any international broadcaster, and employs some 2,000 journalists in total.

There are four specialist units: foreign affairs; economics and business; politics; and social affairs. News crews are trained in health and safety, including battlefield first-aid, and are taught to minimise personal risk. They are equipped with flak jackets, helmets, medication and, when necessary, armoured vehicles and nuclear, biological and chemical warfare suits. They are trained in satellite and terrestrial broadcasting technology, so that film and audio reports can be transmitted back to the UK quickly and efficiently.

BBC News
Television Centre, Wood Lane, London W12 7RJ
Tel 020-8743 8000
Press office Tel 020-8576 7726
Chief executive, news: Tony Hall
Deputy to chief executive: Richard Ayre
Controller, finance: Peter Phillips
Controller, personnel: Lesley Hopkins
Controller media and public relations: Michele Grant
Head of newsgathering: Richard Sambrook
Head of current affairs: Helen Boaden
Acting head of news programmes: Steve Mitchell
Executive editor TV news: Malcolm Balen
Executive editor TV daily current affairs: Jon Barton
Executive editor radio daily current affairs: Anne Koch
Head of political programmes: Mark Damazer
Deputy head: Alexandra Henderson
Acting controller, continuous news: Roger Mosey
Controller, Radio 5 Live: Roger Mosey
Controller, television news channels: Tim Orchard
Managing editor, news 24: Margaret Budy
Head of production, continuous news: Michele Romaine

BBC PRODUCTION

BBC Production is the programme-making heart of the BBC. The directorate creates programmes for the five BBC Radio Networks, BBC 1, BBC 2, World Service and BBC News 24. It also provides programmes for the new subscription channels in which the BBC has a stake, under the banner of UKTV. BBC Production is increasingly seeking commissions with the BBC's partners abroad, though its exclusive co-production deal for factual programmes with Discovery, as well as co-producing with other major broadcasting organisations throughout the world. Staff are increasingly involved in developing the BBC's online presence, and departments are sited in London, Birmingham, Manchester and Bristol. BBC Production is also responsible for the Open University Production Centre.

BBC Production
Television Centre, Wood Lane, London W12 7RJ
Tel 020-8743 8000
Press office Tel 020-8225 7607
Chief Executive, Production: Matthew Bannister
Director of programmes & deputy chief executive: tba
Director of production: tba
Controller radio production: tba
Controller of talent management: tba
Controller, production: Paula Higson
Controller, multimedia development: Caroline Millington
Controller, finance: Anne Bulford
Controller, personnel: tba
Controller, drama production: Colin Adams
Controller, entertainment: Paul Jackson
Head of editorial compliance: TBA
Head of commercial & business affairs: Chris Pye
Head of communications: Ilse Howling
Head of drama series: Mal Young
Head of films and single drama: David Thompson
Business manager: Kate Pluck
Senior executive, production BBC1 films & serials: Jane Tranter
Executive producer, Birmingham TV drama: Richard Langridge
Open University Production centre: Ian Rosenbloom
Head of radio drama: Kate Rowland
Head of entertainment: Paul Jackson
Head of comedy: Geoffrey Perkins
Head of comedy entertainment: Jon Plowman
Head of factual entertainment: Tony Moss
Head of light entertainment: Mike Leggo
Head of sport: Bob Shennan

Head of science: Glenwyn Benson
Head of natural history unit, Bristol: Keith Scholey
Head of features, Bristol: Jeremy Gibson
Head of network production, Birmingham: Kate Marsh
Head of religion, Manchester: Ernie Rea
Head of arts & classical music: Kim Evans
Head of entertainment features, Manchester: Wayne Garvie
Head of children's: Lorraine Heggessey
Head of education production: Marilyn Wheatcroft
Head of music entertainment: Trevor Dann
Head of documentaries and history: Paul Hamann
Head of classical music: Roger Wright
Head of commercial and business affairs: Chris Pye
Head of features and events: Anne Morrison

BBC RESOURCES

BBC Resources was divided into two enterprises in summer 1998 - BBC Resources Limited, operating as a wholly-owned subsidiary of the BBC, and Production Services Division, which concentrates almost exclusively on BBC activities. Most broadcast facilities were transferred into the company, which operates the main studios, outside broadcast fleet, postproduction facilities and graphic design capability. BBC Resources Limited trades from its London base and its regional centres of Birmingham, Manchester, Bristol, Glasgow, Belfast and Cardiff with both BBC and external customers, working in programme production, corporate and the multimedia marketplaces. In its first eight months of trading (August 1998-March 1999) the company had a turnover of £223m. Production Services Divison supplies the facilities for the BBC's news and local programmes operation, runs the BBC's archive, supplies facilities for radio production, and manages the BBC's outsourced services such as catering and security.

BBC Resources Directorate
201 Wood Lane, London W12 7TS
               Tel 020-8752 5252
Press office Tel 020-8752 4047
Chief Executive: Margaret Salmon
Finance director: David Green
Director of HR: Rob Murdoch
Director of Sales & Marketing: Paula Carter
Company Secretary/Legal Adviser: Rikki Nath
Director, production services division: Mike Lumley

BBC WORLDWIDE

BBC Worldwide was formed in May 1994 to coordinate the BBC's international and commercial activities. It encompasses cable and satellite channels and international programme distribution and publishing.

A joint venture with Flextech led to the the launch of five channels - UK Horizons, UK Arena, UK Style, UK Play - and the relaunch of UK Gold, all under the banner of UKTV. A further joint venture with Discovery was signed in March 1998. This deal has resulted in the launch of BBC America plus two global joint venture channels, Animal Planet and People & Arts. BBC Worldwide's other channel interests are in BBC World, the BBC's 24 hour international news and information channel, available in more than 135 milliion homes in over 200 countries and territories, and BBC Prime, an entertainment channel for Europeand Africa, which has over seven million subscribers. BBC Worldwide is also a 20 per cent shareholder in UK TV, an entertainment subscription channel in Australia, along with Pearson and Foxtel. BBC Worldwide is the UK's third largest consumer magazine publisher with 23 titles, the market leader in audio publication and a significant player in the video and book market.

BBC Worldwide
Woodlands, 80 Wood Lane, London W12 OTT
Fax 020-8749 0538   Tel 020-8576 2000
Press office   Tel 020-8576 2339
Website: www.bbcworldwide.com
Chief executive: Rupert Gavin
Managing director, UK region & deputy chief executive: Peter Teague
Managing director EMIA: Mark Young
Director of finance: David King
Director of international TV: Mike Phillips
Director, new media: Jeremy Mayhew
Managing director, BBC World: Patrick Cross
Director, human resources: Bob McCall
Director, GMBD (global brand development): Jeff Taylor
Director of technology: Gary Richards
Director of communications: Janie Ironside Wood
President and chief executive officer of BBC Worldwide Americas: Peter Phippen
Chief operating officer, BBC sales company (US): Candace Carlisle

Independent TV/ITC

The Independent Television Commission is responsible for licensing non-BBC television in Britain as shown in the chart below.

ITC licensed TV channels:

TYPE	NUMBER
Channel 3 regional	15
Channel 3 national breakfast	1
Channel 4	1
Channel 5	1
Digital terrestrial	5
Restricted services	1
Public teletext	1
Other	1
Commercial additional	2
Satellite	201
Licensable programme (cable)	91
Local delivery (15 years)	41
Local delivery (5 years)	31
Cable diffusion	9
Prescribed diffusion	115
Licensable programme (restricted)	8

The ITC is a regulator as well as a licensor and there are five categories of Channel 3 programmes for which the ITC sets minimum requirements.

Channel 3 broadcast requirements

National and international news

Three programmes each weekday of 20 minutes (lunch), 15 minutes (early evening) and half an hour in peak time

Current affairs

One and a half hours weekly average

Children

Ten hours weekly average

Religion

Two hours weekly average

Regional

Varies from franchise to franchise.

So, in essence, the ITC's job is to limit the independence of independent broadcasters and maintain a balancing act where governments since the mid-1950s have defined the commercial channels as some kind of a public service. The ITC is a statutory corporation which derives its power from the 1990 and 1996 Broadcasting Acts that give a wide-ranging remit to "ensure fair and effective competition in the provision of television programmes".

When licensees fail to comply with ITC conditions - plus a host of others set out in the Broadcasting Act and in individual licences - the ITC imposes penalties ranging from warnings and the requirement to broadcast an apology, to fines and the shortening or revocation of a licence. Carlton got the biggest ever ITC fine and paid a record £2 million (four times the size of any previous ITC penalty) for the faked up scenes which underpinned The Connection documentary on the Columbian drug trade.

Otherwise the ITC has recently been exercising a light regulatory hand and has responded to the Channel 3 boss's grizzles about the increased commercial pressures they face. Firstly, the ITC sanctioned the rescheduling of News At Ten and then it renegotiated the license fees and handed back £90 million to the station owners.

The big five independents

BSkyB

BSkyB has the highest income of all independent TV companies

Granada

Granada is the second largest independent TV company, with an income two thirds of BSkyB, owns Granada TV, LWT and has shares in BDB, Yorkshire TV and BSkyB

Carlton

Carlton has half BSkyB's income. It owns Carlton TV, Central TV and Westcountry Television and has shares in BDB and GMTV

MAI

MAI owns Anglia TV and Meridian TV and has shares in Yorkshire TV, HTV and C5

Channel 4

Channel 4 is two fifths the size of BSkyB

ITC Head Office

33 Foley Street, London W1P 7LB
Fax 020-7306 7800   Tel 020-7255 3000
E-mail: ITC_general@compuserve.com
Website: www.itc.co.uk
Chief executive: Peter Rogers
Director of economic regulation: Sheila Cassells
Director of programmes & cable: Sarah Thane
Deputy director - programmes: Marion Bowman
Deputy director - cable: Anthony Hewitt
Director of advertising and sponsorship: Stephen Locke
Deputy director - advertising and sponsorship: Ian Blair
Director of regions & public affairs: Paul Smee
Director of engineering: Gary Tonge
Secretary and director of administration: Michael Redley

ITC board of members

Chairman: Sir Robin Biggam, chairman of the Fairey Group.
Deputy chairman: Lord Holme of Cheltenham, chairman of Threadneedle Publishing since 1988
OTHER BOARD MEMBERS
Alastair Balls, Chief exec of International Centre for Life
John Beynon, Member of the British Library Advisory Council
Sir Michael Checkland, Non-executive director of Nynex Cablecoms, a trustee of Reuters, and former director general of the BBC

Jude Goffe, venture capitalist and non-executive director of Moorfields Eye Hospital
Maria Moloney, member for Northern Ireland. Director of the Northern Ireland Transport Holding Company.
John Ranelagh, European media consultant and current affairs producer. Former secretary to the board of Channel 4.
Dr Michael Shea, member for Scotland. Writer, broadcaster and professor of journalism and personal and corporate communications at the University of Strathclyde.

ITC National and regional offices:

Northern Ireland	028-9024 8733
Scotland	0141-226 4436
Wales	029-2038 4541
West of England	0117-915 4171
East of England	01603-623533
Midlands - Birmingham	0121-452 5128
Midlands - Nottingham	0115-952 7333
North East England	0114-276 9091
North of England	0191-261 0148
North West England	0161-834 2707
S of England, Winchester	01962-883950
S of England, Plymouth	01752-663031
West of England	029-2038 4541

Complaints about television advertising for 1998

	NUMBER OF COMPLAINTS	NUMBER OF ADVERTS	NUMBER OF COMPLAINTS WHOLLY OR PARTLY UPHELD
Harmful	1,063	455	7
Miscellaneous	657	253	18
Misleading	1,856	1,110	88
Offensive	4,279	742	9
TOTALS	**7,855**	**2,560**	**122**

Source: ITC

Total number of complaints by category for 1998

	NEWS/FACTUAL				FICTION/ENTERTAINMENT			
	ITV	Ch4	Cab/Sat	Ch5	ITV	Ch4	Cab/Sat	Ch5
Accuracy	86	27	11	5	21	2	2	-
Impartiality	18	26	1	-	-	-	-	-
Other unfairness	145	215	1	-	-	-	-	-
Secxual portrayal	15	11	5	6	41	13	18	12
Language	34	7	2	2	115	27	8	10
Violence	32	4	12	2	93	16	9	9
Other taste & decency	484	101	30	35	433	103	42	32
Racial offence	21	9	10	3	41	13	4	1
Religious offence	4	3	1	-	39	5	7	-
Scheduling	103	4	1	2	41	10	16	1
Regionality	-	-	-	-	-	-	-	-
Miscellaneous	92	19	202	3	91	14	53	-
Sub totals	**1034**	**426**	**294**	**68**	**997**	**209**	**162**	**67**

Source: ITC

Channel 3 companies

Channel 3/Independent Television/ITV consists of 15 regional licensees and the GMTV national breakfast station. They divide the UK into 14 regions, all but one of which has a Channel 3 company controlling broadcasting rights. The exception is London which is split between Carlton on weekdays and LWT at weekends.

Current legislation prevents any one company having over 15 per cent of the audience. However those rules could be relaxed and there may be legislative changes to allow just one or two ITV companies. Times have certainly become harder than ITV owners expected when they negotiated their licences in the early Nineties. In 1999 the Channel 4 funding formula - which yielded C3 companies a final tranche of £66 million in 1998 - was finally scrapped. Competition from Channel 4 and 5 plus satellite and digital intensified and viewing figures continued a downward spiral which hasn't finished yet. So, those who had benefitted by appearing as champions of Thatcherite free-market principals went cap in hand to the ITC and renegotiated fees payable until licences are up for renewal in 2003. The new deal, which reduced payments by a total of £90 million, is as follows:

Renegotiated C3 licence fees:

CHANNEL 3	1998	1999
LICENSE FEES		
Anglia	£29.5m	£29.0m
Border	£0.06m	£0.05m
Carlton	£81.5m	£72.0m
Central	£31.5m	£49.0m
GMTV	£50.5m	£20.0m
HTV	£25.5m	£9.0m
Meridian	£64.0m	£58.0m
Tyne Tees	£18.5m	£11.0m
Yorkshire	£52.0m	£35.0m
Ulster	£1.0m	£2.0m
Westcountry	£9.0m	£6.0m

The deal was evidently satisfactory to the licensees because eight of them (with the exception of Anglia, Border and Central) put in for licence renewals.

Channel 3 licensees must originally produce or commission (rather than merely acquire) a minimum 65 per cent of programmes. The majority of TV production is coordinated in a Byzantine arrangement focussed on ITV Network Centre, a subsidiary owned by the ITV companies to commission programmes shown across the network. Channel 3 news is also produced at Network Centre. Independent Television News has a weekly output of some 30 hours, and also supplies Channel 4 and Channel 5 news. In 1997 ITN took over control of Euronews, a pan-European broadcaster which transmits TV news in six languages to 43 countries for 20 hours a day.

The biggest recent ITV news was rescheduling News at Ten from the slot it had occupied for 30 years. ITV has pushed through other changes in the schedules by doubling the amount of factual programming (aka docu-soaps) shown during prime-time. Docu-facts replaced news-facts as a way of tempting younger, aspirational viewers back to ITV with series like From Hell, Pleasure Island, For Better For Worse and Family Life. The annual budget to have people act out their real lives on camera increased from £43 million in 1998 to £55 million in 1999. The other ratings triumph was Chris Tarrant's millionaire programme.

ITV Network Centre
200 Grays Inn Road, London WC1X 8HF
Fax 020-7843 8158   Tel 020-7843 8000
Council of ITV Association chairman: Leslie Hill
Chief executive: Richard Eyre
Children's programmes: Nigel Pickard
Drama: Nick Elliot
Entertainment: Claudia Rosencrantz
Documentary/factual: Grant Mansfield
Head of sport production: Brian Barwick
News/current affairs, religion: Steve Anderson

ITN
200 Grays Inn Road, London WC1X 8XZ
Fax 020-7430 4016   Tel 020-7833 3000
Press office   Tel 020-7430 4700
Website: www.itn.co.uk
ITN's UK television programmes have a total weekly output of 29 hours including News at Ten, Early Evening News, C4 News and Channel 5 News.

Anglia Television

Anglia House, Norwich, Norfolk NR1 3JG
Fax 01603-631032   Tel 01603-615151
E-mail: angliatv@angliatv.co.uk
Website: www.anglia.tv.co.uk
London office: 48 Leicester Square, WC2H 7FB
Fax 020-7493 7677   Tel 020-7389 8555
Regional newsrooms:

Norwich	01603-753400
Cambridge	01223-467076
Chelmsford	01245-357676
Ipswich	01473-226157
Luton	01582-729666
Milton Keynes	01908-691660
Northampton	01604-624343
Peterborough	01733-269440

Covers: East of England.
Owner: United News and Media
Regional news programme: Anglia News East/West.
1993-2002 licence fee: £17.8 million pa.

ITC 1998 Performance Review: "Anglia Television's regional service performed strongly in 1998, aided by a fresh look to its news service and a range of well-made new series. There was welcome progress in the quality of light entertainment programmes, addressing a point in last year's review. The level of co-productions was further reduced and repeats were at a satisfactory level. However while there was a diverse range of arts output, too much of it was concentrated in the last quarter of the year, and there was little coverage of mainstream arts activity in the region. Anglia's network output encompassed a range of daytime talk shows, religious programming, documentaries and peak-time dramas."

Chairman: David McCall.
Managing director: Graham Creelman
Director of programmes and production:
    Malcolm Allsop
Controller of news: Guy Adams
Press and regional affairs: Bob Ledwidge

Border Television

The Television Centre, Carlisle, Cumbria CA1 3NT
Fax 01228-541384   Tel 01228-525101
Website: www.border-tv.com
Newsroom: 01228-829229
Covers: Scottish borders, Lake District and the Isle of Man. Also has local radio involvement.
Owner: Border Television; largest shareholder Cumbrian Newspapers Group (18 per cent).
Regional news programme: Look Around, Border News.
1993-2002 licence fee: £52,000 pa.

ITC 1998 Performance Review: "Border performed well in 1998, providing a regional service that identified closely with the scattered communities of this diverse region. More regional programmes were scheduled in peak-time than in 1997, which was a welcome development. New ideas were introduced to enliven arts output and border maintained its commitment to encouraging new local talent by providing a showcase for drama producers and directors, and broadcasting the results. Regional news coverage was of generally high quality and plans were made for a new opt-out for south west Scotland. a religious documentary series was supplied to the network."

Chairman: James Graham
Chief executive: Paul Corley
Managing director: Peter Brownlow
Controller of programmes: Neil Robinson
Head of news: Ian Proniewicz

CARLTON COMMUNICATIONS

Carlton is the largest commercial terrestrial broadcaster in the UK, holding the ITV licences for London weekday, the Midlands and the south west. Together they reach 38 per cent of the population and account for 34 per cent of ITV advertising revenue. The group comprises two principal businesses - the Carlton Media Group and the Technicolour Group.

Carlton produces almost 3,000 hours of television programmes a year through Carlton Productions, Action Time and Planet 24. Carlton Studios is based in Nottingham, while Carlton 021 is the leading commercial operator of outside broadcast in Europe. Carlton has a library of 18,000 hours of TV programmes and over 2,000 films which it sells to over 100 countries. ONdigital - which is 50 per cent Carlton owned - carries Carlton shows including the Food Network and Cinema channels.

Carlton Communications HQ

25 Knightsbridge, London SW1X 7RZ
Fax 020-7663 6300   Tel 020-7663 6363
Chairman: Michael Green
Chief executive: Steven Cain
Finance director: Bernard Cragg
Executive director: Nigel Walmsley

Carlton Television

101 St Martins Lane, London WC2N 4AZ
Fax 020-7240 4171   Tel 020-7240 4000
E-mail: dutyoffice@carltontv.co.uk
Website: www.carltontv.co.uk
ITC 1998 Performance Review: "Carlton maintained the high quality of its regional programming in 1998, building on the strengths of well-established series a well as offering a diverse range of new programmes. The regional news service continued to be of a high standard, but the main early evening news programme again found ratings success elusive. The minimum licence requirement for regional programmes was well exceeded. Although the supply of programmes to the network dropped sharply (chiefly for reasons outside Carlton's control), the company remained a major supplier in almost every programme category."
Covers: London area, from 0600 Monday to 1715 Friday
Owner: Carlton Communications (100 per cent).
Chairman: Nigel Walmsley
Chief executive: Clive Jones
Director of programmes: Steve Hewlett
Chief executive, Carlton sales: Martin Bowley
Finance director: Mike Green
Controller business affairs: Martin Baker
Controller of regional & public affairs: Hardeep Kalsi
Legal affairs: Don Christopher

Carlton Productions

35-38 Portman Square, London W1H 0NU
Fax 020-7486 1132   Tel 020-7486 6688
Carlton Studios, Lenton Lane, Notts NG7 2NA
Fax 0115-964 5552   Tel 0115-986 3322
Website: www.carltontv.co.uk
Carlton Productions makes regional and network programmes for Carlton Broadcasting and Central Broadcasting.
Director of programmes: Andy Allan
Director of drama and co-production: Jonathan Powell
Entertainment and comedy: John Bishop
Factual programmes: Steve Clark
Children's programmes: Michael Forte
Network affairs: Claire Lummis
Finance director: Martin McCausland
Community programmes unit: Peter Lowe
Commissioning & network business affairs: Tom Betts
Production executive, Carlton Films: William Turner

Carlton Broadcasting

London Television Centre, Upper Ground, London SE1 9LT
Fax 020-7827-7500   Tel 020-7620 1620
Central House, Broad Street, Birmingham B1 2JP
Fax 0121-643 4897   Tel 0121-643 9898
Controller of broadcasting: Coleena Reid
Finance director: Ian Hughes
Promotions: Jim Stokoe
Acquisitions: George McGhee
Presentation, Carlton Broadcasting: Wendy Chapman
Presentation, Central Broadcasting: David Burge

Carlton Studios

Lenton Lane, Nottingham NG7 2NA
Fax 0115-9645552   Tel 0115-9863322
A facilites operation providing studios and related services.
Managing director: Ian Squires
Director of operations: Paul Flanaghan
Production controller: John Revill

Carlton 021

12-13, Gravelly Hill Industrial Estate, Gravelly Hill, Birmingham B24 8HZ
Fax 0121-327 7021   Tel 0121-327 2021
Carlton's outside broadcasting service.
Managing director: Ed Everest
Business manager: Mike McGowan
Head of operations: Rob Hollier
Chief engineer: John Fisher

Central Broadcasting

Central Court, Gas Street, Birmingham B1 2JT
Fax 0121-634 4240   Tel 0121-643 9898
                      Press office 01159-863322
Website: www.centraltv.co.uk

Carlton Studios

Lenton Lane, Nottingham NG7 2NA
Fax 0115-964 5552   Tel 0115-986 3322
Unit 9, Windrush Court, Abingdon Business Park,
Abingdon OX14 1SA
Fax 01235-524024   Tel 01235-554123
Covers: English Midlands
Owner: Carlton Communications
Regional news programme: Central News East/ South/ West.
1993-2002 licence fee: £2,000 pa.

ITC 1998 Performance Review: "Central replaced the familiar globe trademark as part of the on-screen rebranding of its service in 1998 and various improvements were made to programme content. Regional output featured six new series while some established programmes were refreshed. A welcome start was made in introducing more diversity into current affairs, although the ITC is looking for further progress in this area in 1999. The news services for the East, West and South Midlands, reflecting in their different styles of presentation the individuality of the three sub-regions, were also revamped and provided high quality coverage. Central continued to be a major source of network programmes and the award of the live presentation contract for Children's ITV (CITV) was an important development."

Chairman: Nigel Walmsley
Managing director: Ian Squires
Finance director: Ian Hughes
News and operations: Laurie Upshon
Presentation & planning: David Burge
Promotions: Mike Villiers-Stuart
Regional programmes: Mike Blair
Regional affairs: Kevin Johnson
Sport: Gary Newbon
Technical director: Mike Snalam

Channel Television

Television Centre, La Pouquelaye, St Helier, Jersey, Channel Islands JE1 3ZD
Fax 01534-816817   Tel 01534-816816
E-mail: newsroom@channeltv.co.uk
Website: www.channeltv.co.uk
Regional newsrooms:
    Guernsey   01481-41877
    Jersey   01534-816688
Covers: Channel Islands
Owner: Channel Islands Communications (TV), whose largest shareholders are Lapwing Investments (29.9 per cent) and 3i Capital Jersey (6.6 per cent).
Regional news programme: Channel Report
1993-2002 licence fee: £1,000 pa.

ITC 1998 Performance Review: "Channel Television's programme achievements in 1998 were satisfactory but there were fewer individual programmes or series of note than in previous years. This was partly because the loss of several senior staff in 1997 put extra pressure on producers and performers in 1998. The news magazine performed strongly but the amount of regional programming, including first-run material, was less than that achieved in the previous year. However, Channel still broadcast more then the required amount and the service overall provided a wide and valued range of programmes for the 144,000 people of the Channel Islands. Channel Television suffered a setback in May with the death of its long serving and well regarded chairman Major John Riley."

Chairman: Tom Scott
Chief executive: John Henwood
Managing director, licensee: Michael Lucas
Head of programmes: Karen Rankine
Head of resources & transmission: Tim Ringsdore
Head of sales: Gordon de Ste Croix
Financial director: Charles Day

GMTV

London Television Centre, Upper Ground, London SE1 9TT
Fax 020-7827 7001   Tel 020-7827 7000

GMTV took over the ITV network breakfast-time service from TV-am in January 1993. Weekday programmes cover news, topical interviews, live reports, entertainment and lifestyle. Children's programming is provided at the weekend. The Sunday Programme from 0700 to 0800 deals with the week's political issues. In January 1999 GMTV launched its digital service, GMTV2 which broadcasts news, children's and lifestyle programmes seven mornings a week.

Covers: National, breakfast time from 0600-0925 daily.
Owners: Walt Disney (25 per cent), the Granada Group (20 per cent), Scottish TV (20 per cent), Carlton Communications (20 per cent), Guardian Media Group (15 per cent).
1993-2002 licence fee: £20 million pa.
News programme: News Hour.

ITC 1998 Performance Review: "GMTV delivered an attractive and generally high quality service, and maintained its position as the most watched service at this increasingly competitive time of the day. Few changes were made in the scheduling, style or content of programming, but a more consistent and adult-orientated approach to the core weekday service was evident. Last year's review pointed out that GMTV's financial position and the resources available were not all the company would have wished. In 1998, the ITC announced new and more favourable financial terms for GMTV's licence payments. GMTV informed ITC of where its priorities would lie, if greater resources became available for programmes. These included further strengthening of current affairs coverage on weekdays and on Sundays, and better children's factual programmes. These objectives concur with the ITC's own assessment of where developments are most needed."

Commercial director: Simon Davey
Managing director: Christopher Stoddart
Sales and marketing: Clive Crouch
Controller of resources: Rhian Jones
Editor: Peter McHugh
Director of programmes: Peter McHugh
Mananging editor, GMTV: John Scammell
Managing editor, Reuters: Henry Clark
Press and publicity: Sue Brealey
Training and personnel manager: Stephanie Edwards

Grampian Television

Queen's Cross, Aberdeen, Grampian AB15 4XJ
Fax 01224-846800   Tel 01224-846560
Website: www.scottishmediagroup.co.uk
Other production studios:
Seaforth House, 54 Seaforth Road, Stornoway HS1 2SD
Fax 01851-706406   Tel 01851-704433
Regional newsrooms:
   Inverness   01463-242624
   Dundee   01382-591000
Covers: North Scotland
Owner: Scottish Media Group
Regional news programme: North Tonight.
1993-2002 licence fee: £720,000 pa.index-linked

ITC 1998 Performance Review: "This review provides the first opportunity properly to examine and reflect on the effects of the merger between Scottish Television and Grampian which happened in late 1997. Grampian's regional commitments were increased by the ITC in light of the merger to reflect the actual level of service latterly delivered to viewers over and above the minimum licence conditions. As well as the merger, the approach to the first elections to the Scottish Parliament, with a new focus on national and regional identity in Scotland, has inevitably meant that broadcasting in Scotland, like every aspect of the culture and communication, is subject to increased public scrutiny. There has been fierce criticism of Grampian's output in 1998. However, on the basis of all the data analysed by the ITC and of regular monitoring, we do not accept that this was a true reflection of Grampian's regional service overall."

Chairman: Calum Macleod
Controller: Derrick Thomson
Head of news: Bert Ovenstone
Head of currrent affairs: Alan Cowie
Technical manager: A J Macdonald
Production resources manager: Brian Clark
Press and PR: Hilary Buchan

Granada Television

The Granada Group has four businesses in restaurants, hotels, rental and media.

Granada Media Group controls Granada Television, LWT, Yorkshire and Tyne Tees. Granada TV is the ITV's biggest programme supplier.

Granada Television

Quay Street, Manchester M60 9EA
Fax 0161-827 2029   Tel 0161-832 7211
London office:
TV Centre, Upper Ground, London SE1 9LT
Fax 020-7261 3307(press)
   Tel 020-7620 1620
Website: www.granadatv.co.uk
Regional newsrooms:

Blackburn	01254-690099
Chester	01244-313966
Lancaster	01524-60688
Liverpool	0151-709 9393
Manchester	0161-832 7211

Covers: North-west England.
Owner: Granada Group
Regional news programme: Granada Tonight.
1993-2002 licence fee: £9 million pa.

ITC 1998 Performance Review: "Granada's regional service built on the achievements of 1997 and contained more first-run material than in any previous year. There were major changes to the style of regional programming in 1998, but the regional focus and relevance of the service were not in doubt. Granada's network programming was the mainstay of the ITV network service, providing almost a third of new programmes commissioned by the Network Centre and contributing to high quality, especially in drama."

Chairman: Charles Allen
Chief executive: Steve Morrison
MD, Granada TV: Brenda Smith
Joint MDs, Granada Productions: Jules Burns, Andrea Wonfor
Commercial director: Paul Taylor
Chief executive (sales): Mick Desmond
Director of programmes: Simon Shaps
Sales director: Mick Desmond
Controller of comedy: Andy Harries
Controller of entertainment: Duncan Gray
Head of factual programmes: Charles Tremayne
Controller of lifestyle: James Hunt
Head of regional programmes: Sue Woodward
Director of personnel: Philippa Hird
Director of public affairs: Chris Hopson

HTV

HTV (Cymru) Wales, Television Centre, Culverhouse Cross, Cardiff CF5 6XJ
Fax 029-2059 7183   Tel 029-2059 0590
Website: www.htv.co.uk

West

TV Centre, Bath Road, Bristol, BS4 3HG
Fax 0117-972 2400   Tel 01179-972 2722
E-mail: htv@htv.co.uk
Website: www.htv.co.uk
Regional newsrooms:

Cardiff	029-2059 0754
Carmarthen	01267-236806
Colwyn Bay	01492-534555
Newtown	01686-623381

Covers: Wales and Bristol, Gloucestershire, Somerset and Wiltshire plus parts of Devon and Dorset
Regional news programme: HTV News
1993-2002 licence fee: £2.09 million pa and 7% qualifying revenue

ITC 1998 Performance Review: "In 1998 HTV consolidated the extensive restructuring of the company following the take-over by United News and Media in 1997. Under the managing directors for HTV Wales and HTV West a number of senior appointments were made, including two new heads of regional programmes and two new heads of news. The regional programme services were diverse and there was evidence of high quality in most strands. The overall repeat level was acceptable, although the ITC would like to see more new material in some strands: drama, documentaries and features in Wales; drama, religion, adult education and entertainment in the West. Disappointingly , audience ratings for the early evening news in Wales fell well below those attained in 1997. By contrast, there was a significant improvement in the news service in the West following the completion of a new digital Broadcast Centre the previous year, and this was reflected in audience share with HTV West matching the BBC's regional service. Supply to the network increased again, mainly in the children's and drama strands, and there were also some documentary successes."

HTV
Managing director: John Cresswell

HTV Wales
Chairman: Gerald Davies
Managing director: Menna Richards
Light entertainment: Emlyn Penny Jones
Programme planning: Sian Thomas
Press and PR: Mansel Jones

HTV West
Chairman: Louis Sherwood
Managing director: Jeremy Payne
Press and PR: Richard Lister

London Weekend Television (LWT)

London Television Centre, Upper Ground, London SE1 9LT
Fax 020-7261 1290   Tel 020-7620 1620
Newsroom (LNN)   Tel 020-7827 7700
Website: www.lwt.co.uk
Covers: London area, from 1715 Friday until 0600 Monday.
Owner: Granada Group, whose largest shareholder is SG Warburg. LWT splits into LWT Productions, LNN, the London News Network (a joint news gathering and production venture between LWT and Carlton TV), and The London Studios which has production facilities for hire to independent producers and the corporate sector.
Regional news programme: London Today, provided by LNN.
1993-2002 licence fee: £7.59 million pa.

ITC 1998 Performance Review: "The ITV network has relied heavily on LWT at the weekends for many years. In 1998, its 30th year of broadcasting, the company made welcome efforts to bring new entertainment ideas to weekend peak-time slots, although again it was the familiar faces and formats to which the audience responded most strongly. The regional service included some high quality factual programmes and an ambitious community arts initiative for young people. Although increasing demands by the network reduced the number of regular slots available, the company made consistent use, in particular, of the early evening schedule on Fridays and Sundays to show a wide and attractive range of regional programmes."

Chairman: Charles Allen
Chief executive: Steve Morrison
Managing director: Laim Hamilton
Director of programmes: Marcus Plantin
Chairman of LNN: Clive Jones
Managing director of The London Studios:
Brenda Smith
Public affairs: Chris Hopson
Controller of entertainment & comedy: Nigel Lythgoe
Controller of drama: Jo Wright
Controller of arts: Melvyn Bragg
Controller of factual: James Allen

Meridian Broadcasting

Television Centre, Northam, Southampton SO14 0PZ
Fax 023-8033 5050   Tel 023-8022 2555
Website: www.meridian.tv.co.uk
London office: Ludgate House, 245 Blackfriars Road, London SE1 9UY
Fax 020-7579 4435   Tel 020-7579 4400
Regional centres:
   New Hythe, Kent   01622-882244
   Newbury, Berks   01635-522322
Covers: South and south-east England
Owner: United News & Media (76 per cent), Carlton Communications (20 per cent). Meridian took over its region from TVS in January 1993.
1993-2002 licence fee: £36.52 million pa.

ITC 1998 Performance Review: "In many respects 1998 was a very satisfactory year for Meridian. The regional service was popular and high quality. Nineteen new series were introduced along side established programmes and regionality was improved, together with a substantial reduction in co-productions. Although network supply fell in 1998, it included the first of its splendid Hornblower films."

Managing director: Mary McAnally
Controller of corporate & commercial affairs: Martin Morall
Director of public affairs: Simon Albury
Director of finance: Tim Ricketts
Director of broadcasting: Richard Platt
Controller of news: Andy Cooper
Personnel: Peter Ashwood

Scottish Television

Cowcaddens, Glasgow G2 3PR
Fax 0141-300 3030   Tel 0141-300 3000
Website: www.scottishmediagroup.co.uk
London: 20 Lincoln's Inn Field, London WC2A 3ED
Fax 020-7446 7010   Tel 020-7446 7000
Scottish Television continues to achieve the highest
audience share of all broadcasters in Central Scotland at
35.5 per cent, remaining above the ITV national average
and with a lead over its nearest challenger, BBC1.
Covers: Central Scotland and south-west Highlands.
Owner: Flextech (5.95 per cent), Flextech Investments
(13.90 per cent), Scottish Daily Record/Sunday Mail
(19.81 per cent), Chase Nominees (5.38 per cent), FMR
Corp (4.94%).
Regional news programme: Scotland Today.
1993-2002 licence fee: £2,000 pa.

ITC 1998 Performance Review: "In the approach to the
first elections every aspect of Scottish culture and
communication is the subject of intense debate.
Scottish Television has therefore heard criticism of its
output in 1998. Nevertheless, the company has made
strenuous and largely successful efforts to maintain the
general quality of its regional service and a strong
regional identity through its programmes, which
included high quality factual and social action material.
Special efforts were made to reflect Scotland's interest
in the World Cup. Improvements in arts output
broadened its appeal. Gaelic programmes also included
high quality material. A range of programmes was
supplied to the network, more than in 1997."

Chairman: Don Cruickshank
Chief executive: Andrew Flanagan
FinanceDirector: Gary Hughes
Managing director of broadcasting: Donald Emslie
Corporate affairs director: Callum Spreng
Head of news: Paul McKinney
Head of factual programmes & sport: Denis Mooney
Human resources director: Gerry Stevenson

Tyne Tees Television

City Road, Newcastle-upon-Tyne NE1 2AL
Fax 0191-261 2302   Tel 0191-261 0181
E-mail: tttv.regional.affairs@gmg.co.uk
Covers: North East England and North Yorkshire.
Owner: Granada Media Group since 1997
Regional news programmes: North East Tonight.
1999-2009 licence fee: £11 million pa.

ITC 1998 Performance Review: "Tyne Tees Television
produced a strong on-screen performance in 1998 in
terms of regional programmes. This included a
comprehensive news service for the two large sub-
regions as well as innovative new styles of regional
programming in the religious, factual, arts and
entertainment categories. On the network side 1998
was a transitional year. New arrangements and extra
resources were put in place to develop programme
proposals, including drama, but translating these into
commissions was proving difficult. Nevertheless, the
ITC was satisfied with the progress made. The year also
saw a return to the Tyne Tees Television branding
replacing Channel Three North East."

Chairman: Charles Allan
Managing director: Margaret Fay
Director of broadcasting: Graeme Thompson
Managing editor - news: Graham Marples
Editor, current affairs & features: Jane Bolesworth
Head of young people's programmes: Lesley Oakden
Head of network features: Malcolm Wright
Head of sport: Roger Tames
Head of regional affairs: Norma Hope
Personnel manager: Lynda Wadge

UTV (Ulster Television)

Havelock House, Ormeau Road, Belfast BT7 1EB
Fax 028-9024 6695   Tel 028-9032 8122
E-mail: info@utv.live.com
Website: www.utvlive.com
Covers: Northern Ireland.
Owner: Ulster Television. No single holdingover 6%
Regional news programme: UTV Live at Six.
1993-2002 licence fee: £1.03 million pa.

ITC 1998 Review: "Ulster Television responded to events with programming that was both timely and appropriate. It maintained the reputation it has won for accurate and impartial news whilst adding some new and refreshing material to its schedule. UTV Live at Six, the evening news and features magazine and the mainstay of UTV's regional schedule, continued to be the choice of a majority of Northern Ireland viewers. Weaknesses in social action, identified in last year's review, were rectified. A commission from the network was at last won although failure to supply more during 1998 was a disappointment."

Chairman: John McGuckian
Managing director: Desmond Smyth
General manager: John McCann
Controller of programming: Alan Bremner
Operatioons manager: Robert McCourt
Personnel: Mariead Regan

Westcountry Television

Langage Science Park, Plymouth PL7 5BQ
Fax 01752-333444   Tel 01752-333333
E-mail: info@westcountry.co.uk
Covers: Cornwall, Devon, west Dorset, south Somerset
Owner: Carlton Communications
Regional news programme: Westcountry Live.
1993-2002 licence fee: £7.82 million pa.

ITC 1998 Review: "Westcountry Television met its commitments in 1998 with a service of generally high quality. The wide range of programmes - comparable to the achievements of previous years - was well regarded by the ITC's new Viewer Consultative Council (VCC) for the region. In particular, the reporting of events and issues of regional significance was comprehensive and assured. Several hours of factual programmes were supplied to the network."

Chairman: Clive Jones
Managing director: Mark Haskell
Director of programmes: Jane McCloskey
Controller, operations & engineering: Mark Chaplin
Controller of news: Brad Higgins
Controller of features & programme development: CarolineRighton
Controller of public affairs: Mark Clare

Yorkshire Television

Kirkstall Road, Leeds, West Yorks LS3 1JS
Fax 0113-244 5107   Tel 0113-243 8283
Covers: Yorkshire, Humberside, Derbyshire, Notts, Lincs.
Owner: Granada Plc .
Regional news programme: Calendar.
1993-2002 licence fee: £37.7 million pa.

ITC 1998 Performance Review: "1998 was Yorkshire Television's 30th anniversary and the company's first full year as part of the Granada Media Group. However, it continued a sturdily independent style and most regional programmes attracted large audiences with news and the weekday early evening magazine proving particularly popular. More new regional programming was produced than in the previous two years and more than the amount agreed following the takeover. Arts, education and factual material were generally satisfactory and the support for new talent in drama in the region was welcome, but the virtual absence of regional religious programming until October was disappointing. Yorkshire continued as a major supplier to the network in areas where it has long experience - popular drama, children's and factual programmes."

Chairman: Charles Allen
Managing director: Richard Gregory
Documentaries and current affairs: Chris Bryer
Entertainment: David Reynolds
Drama: Keith Richardson
News: Clare Morrow
Director of group corporate affairs: Chris Hopson
Director of programmes: John Whiston

Channel 4

Channel 4 is a minority station by design. Where the BBC must provide something for everybody and ITV must deliver ratings and profits to shareholders, Channel 4 has the compromise remit to deliver innovation, diversity and originality. C4's chief executive Michael Jackson is trying to shift this view, saying: "Channel 4 is no longer a minority channel for minority audiences. Its future lies in being the channel of contemporary culture [which is] ahead of the mainstream." He reasons that C4 must change with the times. "Think about how different Britain is today from when Channel 4 launched 16 years ago," he says. "Numbers in higher education have doubled. Half the population is now classified as middle class." And there, in the young middle class (with their appetite for innovation, diversity and originality), is the channel's core audience.

Jackson inherited a station in fine fettle. His predecessor Michael Grade had seen off threats that C4 might be privatised and had lobbied successfully to do away with a funding formula which, since 1982, had meant some £400 million passed from Channel 4 to Channel 3 companies. All the more confidence and money to fulfil the ITC requirement that 55 per cent of programmes are original commissions.

At the beginning of 1999 Jackson said his goal was to make the channel the most talked about in Britain. Over recent years it had grown over-reliant on American comedy imports like Friends and Frasier but the schedules are livening up with new programmes like the 11 O'clock Show and shows promised from Chris Morris and Armando Iannucci. Nato on Trial provided TV's boldest examination of the Balkan war and Jackson identified Queer as Folk as the series which summed up C4 aspirations. "It's a programme no other broadcaster would have shown," he claimed. "It was funny, truthful and stylish. In the past, this subject would have been handled in a self-conscious manner but in Queer as Folk there are no 'issues'. There are only emotions, unsympathetic gay characters and, shockingly, no safe-sex message."

Channel 4
124 Horseferry Road, London SW1P 2TX
Fax 020-7306 8366   Tel 020-7396 4444
E-mail Channel4.co.uk
Website: www.channel4.com

ITC 1998 Performance Review: "Last year's ITC review commented that Channel 4 had lost some of its drive in respect of innovation. The ITC accepts that the speed of the Channel's response to this will be conditioned by the sometimes long lead-times involved, in commissioning programmes and getting them to the screen. Nevertheless there were some promising developments in 1998, particularly in the autumn. In current affairs there was a new strand of personal political views. There were more innovative approaches to drama and some strong seasons of programmes about the NHS and the Palestine/Israeli conflict. The range of programmes in peak time was generally satisfactory. The volume of UK film investment doubled and the proportion of commissions going to producers outside London increased. There was an effort to address criticism's of science output. However, the requirement for provision of educational programme support material was not met in full. The Channel also failed to respond sufficiently to the criticism that foreign language movies are inaccessibly scheduled."

Chairman: Vanni Treves
Deputy chairman: Barry Cox
Chief executive: Michael Jackson
Managing director: David Scott
Director & general manager: Frank McGettigan
Director of strategy & development: David Brook
Commercial director: Andy Barnes
Director of finance and business affairs: Janet Walker
Director of programmes: Tim Gardam
Head of programmes (nat. & regional): Stuart Cosgrove
Head of corporate affairs: Sue Robertson
Chief executive Film 4: Paul Webster
Head of drama & animation: Gub Neal
Commissioning editor, sport: Mark Sharman
Commissioning editor, schools: Paul Ashton
Commissioning editor, youth: Andi Peters
Commissioning editor, arts: Janey Walker
Commissioning editor, documentaries: Peter Dale
Independent film & video: Adam Barker
Commissioning editor, multicultural: Yasmin Anwar
Religion & features: Janice Hadlow
Head of science, & education: Sara Ramsden
Head of news and current affairs: David Lloyd
Head of entertainment: Kevin Lygo
Commissioning editor of current affairs: Dorothy Byrne
Entertainment: Caroline Leddy, Graham Smith
Commissioning editor, animation: Claire Kitson
Commissioning editor, features: Liz Warner

Sianel Pedwar Cymru S4C

S4C/Sianel Pedwar Cymru/Channel 4 Wales is a public service broadcaster which is regulated by the S4C Authority, whose members are appointed by the Department of Culture. Its direct funding by the Treasury dates back to an appeasement of Welsh Nationalist demands that Welsh got a share of the airwaves. It broadcasts an average of 34 hours per week in Welsh, 10 hours provided by the BBC. The analogue service also carries over 70 per cent of C4's output, mostly rescheduled around the channel's commitment to peak time Welsh language programmes. S4C programmes have won three Oscar nominations - Hedd Wyn (1994), Famous Fred (1998) and The Canterbury Tales (1999) and Pobol Y Cwm, the only daily (Monday-Friday) soap opera in the UK recorded and transmitted within the same week.

S4C Digital (which is available via ONDigital in Wales and satellite throughout the UK) carries all S4C's peak hours service in Welsh, plus a plethora of additional programmes. It broadcasts in Welsh for at least 12 hours per day. S4C International is responsible for the channel's commercial activity - on screen advertising sales and sponsorship, programme co-productions, foreign sales and franchises, videos, books and the licensing of other spin-off merchandise. S4C Digital Networks Limited (SDN), which was awarded the right to operate a digital terrestrial multiplex across the whole of the UK. The Digital College is a joint venture between S4C and BBC Wales - its intention is to offer the people of Wales opportunities to develop work-related skills by using a combination of digital television, traditional learning methods and the Internet.

S4C (Sianel Pedwar Cymru)

Parc Busnes ty Glas, Llanishen, Cardiff CF4 5DU
Fax 029-2075 1457   Tel 029-2074 1458
E-mail: s4c@s4c.co.uk
Website: www.s4c.co.uk
Chairman: Elan Closs Stephens
Chief executive: Huw Jones
Director of production: Huw Eirug
Director of corporate affairs: Iona Jones
Secretary and director of policy: Steve Martin
Head of corporate press and public relations: David Meredith
Director of commercial operations: Wyn Innes
Director of animation: Christopher Grace
Commissioning editors:
  Factual programming: Cenwyn Edwards
  Drama: Angharad Jones
  Children's programmes: Meirion Davies
  Entertainment: Huw Chiswell
  Music consultant: Richard Elfyn Jones

**POBYL Y CWM
The Welsh soap
opera with the
Jones family
celebrating their
National Lottery
winnings**

Channel 5

The ITC's annual pronouncement on Channel 5 began on a kindly note. "Nineteen ninety-eight was a year of consolidation. Audience growth was impressive and achieved through more focused investment in original programmes, sport and better film titles," was the ITC annual report's opening line. The tone harshened with a "considerable scope for further progress" and a "failure to provide much original drama". And then the boot went in. "The substantial rise in compliance issues was a worrying development, as was the tackiness associated with an increased use of low budget erotic drama."

The Journal of the Royal Television Society put it more succinctly. "Nothing exceptional sums up the response to Channel 5 as it evolves from crawling to walking upright." With a reputation as upright as a Neanderthal man, C5 is catching criticism from everybody from the Broadcasting Standards Commission to the Broadcasting Select Committee to the advertisers whose interests it was primarily set up to serve. Faked up outrage about sex aside, advertisers complain that the 16-34 year old viewing is falling and only over-55s tune in with greater frequency.

"Sensationalism ...is designed to grab attention and get people to sample the channel," said Martin Campbell, the media analyst at Capel-Cure. Not so, said the C5 boss David Elstein. "The bizarre and weird have a particular fascination for younger viewers," said the Cambridge double first who must now defend programmes like UK Raw, Sex and Shopping and Compromising Positions. But what do you do when your audience profile gets older and programme finances place your channel somewhere between cable channels and the conventional terrestrial channels?

One answer is that Elstein has worked hard to increase transmission capacity so that 19 million homes can now receive a clear picture. Then he sits tight (a shame that "the cleverest man in Britain" didn't get the top BBC job) and says he is "quietly confident" C5 channel will get its targeted 5 per cent audience share by the end of the year. Another year of consolidation.

Channel 5 Broadcasting

22 Longacre, London WC2E 9LY
Fax 020-7550 5554   Tel 020-7550 5555
Website: www.channel5.co.uk
Value of ITC bid: £22,002,000
Shareholders: United News & Media, CLT ufa, Pearson Television, Warburg Pincus
ITC 1998 Performance Review: "1998 was a year of consolidation for Channel 5. Audience growth was impressive and achieved through more focused investment in original programmes, sport and better film titles. Significant improvements were made in some areas, partly meeting concerns expressed by the ITC in the 1997 review. However, performance was uneven and there remains considerable scope for further progress, particularly in drama (for both adults and children) and entertainment. The failure to provide much original drama for adults was a breach of licence commitments. The substantial rise in compliance issues was a worrying development, as was the tackiness associated with an increased use of low budget erotic drama late in the evening and of various factual programmes on sexual themes including some material that was unacceptable. Although programme budgets were still very tight, the results of ITC monitoring showed that overall the decision to focus resources on fewer original programmes paid off in terms of improvements in quality particularly in the factual, arts and educational areas. The other main changes compared with 1997 were reductions in entertainment and feature programmes in favour of more documentaries, acquired drama and children's information. These were considered acceptable by the ITC. There was a small shortfall against the overall requirement for original productions/commissions; this requirement needs to be met in full in the future."

Chief executive: David Elstein
Director of finance: Damien Harte
Director of legal & business affairs: Colin Campbell
Director of sales: Nick Milligan
Director of marketing & communication: Jim Hytner
Director of programmes: Dawn Airey
Controller, news, current affairs/documentaries: Chris Shaw
Controller, drama: Corinne Hollingworth
Controller, arts and features : Michael Atwell
Controller, entertainment: Alan Nixon
Controller, sport: Robert Charles
Controller, children's: Nick Wilson
Head of regional productions & special events: Adam Perry
Controller, programme planning: Ashley Hill
Controller, acquisitions: Jeff Ford

Digital television

The reasons for digital TV are clear enough: a superior technology means TV consumers can get clearer pictures on wider screens which show more channels; TV business has more product to sell, including a range of interactive services which will bring the long anticipated convergence of computers and TV sets; and, within 15 years when the government switches off TV analogue frequencies, millions of pounds worth of airwaves will be auctioned for such things as mobile telephones. The consumer, once again, will benefit with a cheap telephone for each ear, multi-channel TV for each eye and internet access for every corner of the brain.

Initial consumer apathy about digital TV was countered by ONdigital and Sky giving away the set top boxes necessary to decode digital signals. The problem now is to educate us into a new transmission system which means getting to grips with digital multiplexes delivering increasing numbers of channels plus the choice of terrestrial, satellite or cable reception.

As is always the case when anything is described as digital, the sales talk is of revolution. It's the best way to sell change and the digital priority was John Birt's main justification for his Trotsky-like regime of constant revolution. His eventual reputation may well rest on whether or not history judges an enthusiastic embrace of all things digital to have been a success.

DIGITAL LAUNCHES

BBC
23 SEPTEMBER 1998 BBC transmissions of digital channels began in a terrestrial/satellite trial run of BBC1, BBC2, BBC News 24 and BBC Choice. "The BBC's digital proposition will be available to all, not just to those can afford to pay subscription," said John Birt.

SKY DIGITAL
1 OCTOBER Sky launched satellite digital TV with 140 channels. By April it had 350,000 subscribers, of whom 120,000 were new. Sky froze prices at £29.99 a month, with the exception of pay-per-view movies.

ONDIGITAL
15 NOVEMBER ONdigital launched terrestrial digital with 15 channels. The £10 million advertising campaign said: "Be the first in your street to get ONdigital. The Philips receiver cost £199.99. Subs were between £7.99 and £27.99 per month. By April it had 110,000 subscribers.

ITV2
7 DECEMBER ITV2 started broadcasting free as part of the ON digital package with a programme mix of repeats, soaps, sport, quiz shows and repeats.

NTL
31 MARCH 1999 Cable interest intensified when NTL launched a TV-based interactive services on digital cable and digital terrestrial. It reset existing Internet content "to suit web-on-TV expectations".

CWC
25 JUNE Prices on Cable and Wireless Communciation's digital service started in Manchester priced at £9.98 a month. Trials also began in London with the promise that by the end of 1999 "CWC digital services will be available to over half the homes in CWC franchise areas, approximately 2 million households".

MICROSOFT
15 JULY A Microsoft WebTV trial in London and Liverpool found - on the basis of a sample drawn from 113 families - that "over a third of households would be willing to adopt interactive TV". As a sales pitch for its TVPAK (Platform Adaptation Kit) web TV box, Microsoft claimed that particular interest was shown in two way TV games, home shopping, better TV listings and education. "The Microsoft brand was identified as a key consumer reassurance factor.

The are many other TV players besideas the BBC - notably the Sky and Carlton/Granada ONdigital platforms. The power of publicity harnessed to the logic of technological advance means a multi-channel future is irresistible. Longer term we must look forward to digital cable, because it is the best way of transmitting TV signals and because its greater bandwidth enables the merging of internet and TV. The main influence here is Microsoft - which bought a chunk of Telewest and has been quietly experimenting with WebTV.

CWC's summer 1999 launch into digital TV, though restricted initially to Manchester and only due to be available in its franchise areas, is a launch into a communications future which extends way beyond more and more sillier and sillier TV stations. Interactivity is the word for it, the communicating with the things that also communicate with us to do remote shopping, banking and gaming and accessing data about anything that appears on screen. "Our digital services are more than just TV," said the CWC chief executive Greg Clarke. "With a single connection, customers will get the TV of their choice, best value telephony and access to the world's most sophisticated interactive services including high speed internet through the TV.

There are already seven million PC users in the UK and 3.6 million users online. By 2003, data revenues are expected to treble to nearly £9 billion a year. The internet already accounts for almost 20 per cent of our local call traffic. CWC will exploit this high demand via the television using its fibre optic broadband network, bringing services direct to the TV screen, for the first time opening internet to a mass market."

Persuasive words, but lean back. There's another view, well put by Sky TV's Elisabeth Murdoch in her MacTaggart Lecture at the 1998 Edinburgh Television Festival. "For years now the word convergence has gone side by side with digital as a convenient way of explaining how TVs and PCs will get married and live happily ever after," she said. "Well, I am sorry to be the bearer of bad news, but there has been a divorce. TV will continue to be the dominant medium for 'lean-back' leisure rather than 'lean-forward' interaction. Both pieces of technology will happily sit together in the home of the future, fulfilling different needs for their owners."

Meanwhile, whether you lean backwards of forwards, Microsoft will advance inexorably into new digital media sure in its conviction that "UK consumers are more than happy to tune in and log in at the same time".

Digital TV

Multiplex A	S4C Digital Networks in Wales, and capacity to carry Gaelic programmes in Scotland
Multiplex B	ONdigital, jointly owned by Carlton Communications and the Granada Group
Multiplex C	ONdigital, jointly owned by Carlton Communications and the Granada Group
Multiplex D	ONdigital, jointly owned by Carlton Communications and the Granada Group
BBC Multiplex	BBC 1 & 2, 24 hour news, BBC Choice, BBC Inform
C3/C4 Multiplex	Digital 3 and 4. Channel 3, Channel 4, Teletext, ITV 2, C4 Film Club

NB: Multiplexing combines the signals of several broadcasters into a single stream on a single-frequency channel. The signals are received and decoded by digital receivers within set-top boxes. This means there is no longer a direct one-to-one relationship between a television service and a frequency.

DIGITAL: terrestrial/satellite/cable

DIGITAL TERRESTRIAL

Channels: up to 36

Cost: programmes free from most existing terrestrial broadcasters but some subscription - set top box will cost something over £200

Suppliers: BBC, ITV, On Digital/BDB

DIGITAL SATELLITE

Channels: 150+

Cost: Subscription plus a new dish

Supplier: BSkyB

DIGITAL CABLE

Channels: 100-400

Cost: Probably the same as for existing cable

Supplier: CWC ... and its rival will follow.

New jargon: NVOD or New Video on Demand or the new TV world where there's a movie starting every ten minutes.

BATTLE OF THE DIGITS

BiB

4 AUGUST 1998 British Interactive Broadcasting - intended by its main owners BSkyB and BT to become the main interactive shopping channel - announced its intention to be distributed by its two rivals ONdigital and the cable companies. BiB's chief executive David Hilton made the confident prediction that major retailers would soon be competing to go interactive with his company and he said: "We intend to be on as many platforms as are in existence."

SKY vs BDB

14 AUGUST Sky dropped the threat of legal action against British Digital Broadcasting for BDB's decision to operate a brand of decoder technology which was incompatible with Sky equipment. Sky's new reckoning was that BDB's choice of technology "would highlight the advantages of our box".

LIKE BETAMAX vs VHS

14 AUGUST Adam Singer, the chairman of Flextech, warned that viewers would be dazed by the complexities of multi-channel TV. He said that people had a "folk memory" of the confusions around the Betamax vs VHS video formats and might therefore delay buying new digital kit.

LIKE 405 vs 625 LINES

28 AUGUST The Independent Television Commission warned the Department of Media that the switch from analogue to digital TV will take at least 20 years. The ITC's chief executive Peter Rogers said that the switch from black and white 405 lines to the UHF was mooted in 1960 and only completed in 1985. The fact that modern TVs last longer could further inhibit digital expansion. The ITC also said that ONdigital terrestrial transmission made it analogue TV's natural successor because the Sky satellite could only ever reach 95 per cent of the population.

SKY vs ITV

20 AUGUST Sky took ITV's refusal to allow it to carry ITV2 programming on digital satellite to the Office of Fair Trading. ITV asserted that Sky's services compete for audience share against its own programmes. Sky said that ONdigital's refusal to cooperate would cost it £500 million. ONdigital refused to budge and in March the Independent Television Commission ruled that ONdigital was within its rights and did not have to amend its strategy.

EXCITEMENT vs BOREDOM

29 AUGUST A BBC advertising campaign, broadcast on BBC 1 & 2, began upping the hype for the imminent launch of digital satellite. Michael Palin delivered the "jolly exciting" punchline in what the BBC called a "new information film [which] features Martine McCutcheon, Harry Enfield, Gianluca Vialli, Stephen Fry, Ruby Wax, Lee Evans, Jeremy Irons etc, etc, etc."

CABLE vs VIDEO

OCTOBER Blockbuster video shops said "if we are complacent, we could die". The company faces an uncertain future once cable digital TV allows home film watchers to perm from vast film libraries and order what they want to be piped to them on demand. Sky shows over 7,500 movies a year, a range of choice set to be dwarfed if firms like Video Networks gets off the ground. The firm has David Frost and Lord Owen among its backers, and its founder, Simon Hochhauser, said: "We want to be one of the first home grown new media companies and one of the top UK companies."

QUANTITY vs QUALITY

1 OCTOBER "The BBC spends about £1,100 million a year on BBC1 and BBC2 compared to less than £5 million, on average, for a basic cable or satellite channel," said Sir Christopher Bland, the BBC chairman. He described public service broadcasters as buffers against a tidal wave of cheap programming and added: "Commercial broadcasters promote fierce competition for

audiences and rights, competing with a cheque book. PSBs must compete by our creativity. They make money, we make programmes." In September Sky announceD it would make five feature films, costing between £2 million and £5 million, over the next two years.

ITC vs ITV
20 NOVEMBER The ITC ordered ITV to cancel an anti satellite digital TV campaign. Complaints had been lodged by the BBC, BSkyB, Channels 4 and Flextech. ITV is the only channel not being carried on BSkyB's digital satellite platform while ONdigital, the terrestrial pay TV service, is run by the ITV companies Granada and Carlton.

BBC vs THE REST
APRIL 1999 The BBC director general John Birt hinted at his support for a higher licence fee for those receiving BBC digital programmes. Most of the competition signed a letter to the Times which said: "We urge the government to reject this idea, which would hinder the development of digital TV and operate against the UK's wider industrial interests." The Channel 5 boss David Elstein (who was in the running for Birt's job) disagreed. "Even with a digital supplement of £30 per annum," he said, "the BBC would be running a digital deficit for many years - but it would have created a vital bridgehead between the past and future."

CABLE vs SATELLITE
5 MAY Cable and Wireless announced its plans for transmitting digital television through cables, with summer pilots in Manchester and autumn pilots in London. Those of CWC's customers able to take a digital feed are likely to pay a £17.95 subscription for six channels and an estimated £37.40 for extra movies and sport.

GATES vs THE WORLD
MAY The ambitions of Bill Gates' Microsoft became crystal clear with the purchase of a 29 per cent stake in Telewest. Following the January 1999 purchase of 5 per cent of NTL, that took

Microsoft's cable investment to over £3 billion. The world's richest man is positioning his company to sell software products which are as vital to the new generation of interactive TV as they are to the majority of the world's computers

ITC vs SKY
23 MAY As Sky's success in digital TV became ever more pronounced, the Independent Television Commission emerged as a de facto ONdigital lobbyist. Unattributed ITC voices declared: "There is a real concern that digital terrestrial TV will take a long time to become established and could be seen as the losers' platform which could damage it a lot. It could cost Granada and Carlton a lot. There is still deep unease in the ITC that they may want to pull out if Sky streams ahead and after a year ONdigital is nowhere close to breaking even."

NTL vs CWC/TELEWEST
10 JUNE NTL confirmed a digital cable launch for September 1999 with 200 TV channels, interactive shopping and internet access, thus putting it way ahead of its cable rivals.

MAY PRICE CUTS

SKY
5 MAY Sky intensified the battle for digital viewers by offering free set top boxes which had cost £199 to buy and £40 to install. The cost - which News Corp was in a better position to bear since the failure of it Man United bid - was £315 million. Meanwhile monthly prices of its top of the range subscription rose £2 to £32 and its mid-range option by £1. Sky also offered 40 per cent off phone calls.

ME TOO ONDIGITAL
24 MAY ONdigital followed Sky's handout by offering to connect its own £199 set top boxes for nothing. Costs were estimated at £200 million and Carlton's profits dipped. As with Sky, subscriptions increased and it also offered 40 per cent off phone calls.

DIGITAL TV CONTACTS

BBC Digital TV
Television Centre, Wood Lane, London W12 7RJ
Tel 020-8743 8000
BBC Choice, BBC News 24, BBC Online, BBC
Learning and Digital Radio

British Interactive Broadcasting
BIB (Platform) Company, 47 Cannon Street, London
EC4M 5SQ
Tel 020-7332 7083
Owners: BSkyB (32.5 per cent), British Telecom (32.5
per cent), Midland bank (20 per cent), Matsushita (15
per cent)
Interactive services providing advertising and
information.

British Sky Broadcasting
See Sky Digital

Cable and Wireless
Caxton Way, Watford Business Park, Watford, Herts
WD1 8XH
Tel 020-8528 2000
C&W is developing a range of interactive TV services
and on 1 July 1999 announced 130 channels. It has
made deals with Barclays Bank, British Airways,
Littlewoods/Granada Home Shopping, ITN, Associated
New Media, Flextech Interactive, Bloomberg, Emap
Online, Emap Radio, Scoot, PA Sporting Life, Uproar,
Loot, Live TV, Manchester Evening News and ABC
Connect. As of July further deals were possible with
Discovery Networks Europe, Nickelodeon, QVC, What
Car and First Call.
C&W's main providers:
Flextech Interactive: Nicola Howson   020-7299 5000
Bloomberg: Anna Bateson   020-7330 7758
Emap: Ed Whiting   020-7309 2704
Scoot: Richard Darby   020-7466 5000
PA Sporting Life: David Annat   0113 220 4706
Live TV: Mark Cullen   020-7293 2003
Uproar: Timothy Ewing   020-7292 7150
Loot: Iqtadar Hasnain   020-7625 0266
Manchester Evening News: Tony Whalley
0161-211 2260
ABC Connect: Mike Stevenson   01483 211 430
Discovery Networks Europe: Nick Southall
020-7462 3640

Carlton Entertainment
UK Channel Management, 160 Great Portland Street,
London W1N 5TB
Tel 020-7576 2000
Website: www.cfn.co.uk
Holds an ITC Digital Programmes Service Licence.

The Cartoon Network
Turner Broadcasting systems, 18 Soho Square, London
W1V 5FD
Tel 020-7478 1000
Holds an ITC Digital Programmes Service Licence.

Digital 3 and 4 Ltd
Unit 4, 56 Norwich Road, Wymondham, Norfolk NR18
0NT
Fax 01953-601196   Tel 01953-608040
E-mail: d3and4@btinternet.com

FilmFour
124 Horseferry Road, London SW1P 2TX
Fax 020-7306 8366   Tel 020-7396 4444
Website: www.channel4.com
Holds an ITC Digital Programmes Service Licence.

Flextech Television
160 Great Portland Street, London W1N 5TB
Fax 020-7299 6000   Tel 020-7299 5000
Website: www.flextech.co.uk
Owners: Liberty Media (37 per cent), Cox
Communications (13 per cent), MediaOne (7 per cent),
Capital Group (5 per cent)
The largest provider of basic channels to the UK pay-TV
market via thematic channels to BSkyB and ONdigital.
Also runs UKTV, a joint venture with the BBC using
the corporation's archives. Its channels can be seen on
cable and satellite, in analogue and digital.

GMTV2
The London Television Centre, Upper Ground, London
SE19TT
Tel 020-7827 7000
Holds an ITC Digital Programmes Service Licence.

Granada Sky Broadcasting (DTT)
Franciscan Court, 16 Hatfields, London SE1 8DJ
Tel 020-7578 4040
Website: www.gsb.co.uk
Holds an ITC Digital Programmes Service Licence.

Home Shopping Channel
Sir John Moores Building, 100 Old Hall Street, Liverpool
L70 1AB
Tel 0151-235 2055
Holds an ITC Digital Programmes Service Licence.

ITV2
200 Gray's Inn Road, London WC1X 8HF
Tel 020-7843 8000
Website: www.itv.co.uk
Holds an ITC Digital Programmes Service Licence.

Microsoft
Endeavour House, 189 Shaftesbury Avenue, London
WC2H 8JB
Fax 020-7632 5555   Tel 020-7632 5500
E-mail: Sharonba@microsoft.com
Website: www.microsoft.com/tv

NTL
CableTel House, 1 Lakeside Road, Farnborough,
Hampshire GU14 6XP
Crawley Court, Winchester Hampshire SO21 2QA
Fax 01252 402100   Tel 01252-402000
NTL is both a cable operator and the provider of
conventional transmission services for independent
television. It aims to grow further via TV-based
interactive services.

ONdigital
346 Queenstown Road, London SW8 4DG
Fax 020-7819 8100   Tel 020-7819 8000
Website: www.ondigital.co.uk
Owners: Carlton (50 per cent), Granada (50 per cent)
Primary channels: Carlton Food Network, Cartoon
Network, Breeze, Men and Motors Plus, Euro Sport,
Carlton Cinema, Carlton Kids, Home Shopping
Channel Sky One UK Gold, UK Play UK Style UK
Horizons, Carlton Select, Carlton World
Premium channels: Sky Sports 1, Sky Sports 3, Sky
Premier, Sky Movieman
Free-to-view digital channels: BBC1, BBC2, BBC
Choice, BBC News 24, C4, C5, Teletext, ITV, ITV2
ONdigital was the first company to provide digital pay
television through an ordinary aerial. It provides a
choice of pay channels from programme makers such
as BBC/Flextech, BSkyB and their own shareholders,
Carlton and Granada. It also carries an exclusive
channel - First ONdigital - that is used to show one-off
special events, such as pop concerts and sports. It is in
the process of adding new interactive services such as
email, games and Pay Per View, all through an ordinary
aerial.
Chief executive: Stuart Prebble

SDN
The Media Centre, Culverhouse Cross, Cardiff CF5 6XJ
Fax 01222-405 625   Tel 01222-405 600
Owners: United News and Media, NTL and S4C
The second digital terrestrial broadcaster, using
Multiplex A and broadcasting S4C's digital output.

Select TV Cable
27-35 Mortimer Street, London W1N 7RJ
                            Tel 020-7725 4600
Website: www.cfn.co.uk
Holds an ITC Digital Programmes Service Licence.

Sky Digital
BSkyB, 6 Centaurs Business Park, Grant Way, Isleworth
TW7 5QD
                            Tel 020-7705 3000
Website: www.sky.co.uk
Holds an ITC Digital Programmes Service Licence.

UK Channel Management
160 Great Portland Street, London W1N 5TB
                            Tel 020-7576 2000
Website: www.cfn.co.uk
Holds an ITC Digital Programmes Service Licence.

UK Gold Broadcasting
160 Great Portland Street, London W1N 5TB
                            Tel 020-7576 2000
Website: www.cfn.co.uk
Holds an ITC Digital Programmes Service Licence.

MAIN WEBSITES

BBC: www.bbc.co.uk/digital
Cable & Wireless: www.cwcom.co.uk
ITV: www.itv.co.uk
Microsoft: www.microsoft.com/tv
NTL: www.cabletel.co.uk
ONdigital: www.ondigital.co.uk
Sky: www.sky.co.uk/skytv/digital

HELPLINES

BBC	0345 010 313 &
	0990 118 833
ONdigital	0808 100 0101
Sky	0870 242 4200

Cable

To date, less than a quarter of British households are cable subscribers. For all the digging up of the streets around Britain, cable still passes only just over a half of British households and of the 12 million who could receive cable, only 4.24 million have so far taken the plunge.

However, cable is beginning to achieve the critical mass to start generating a payback on the £10 billion or so being spent on rewiring Britain. As long as cable meant slightly cheaper phone calls and the pick of some irrelevant TV, then interest was small. Its purpose becomes clear with the growing acceptance of both digital TV and the internet, both of which can exploit cable's superior capacity.

Top cable operators		
CABLE OPERATOR	HOMES CONNECTED	HOMES PASSED
Telewest	981,101	4,013,298
CWC	842,692	3,981,578
NTL	943,315	3,361,998
Cable London	96,495	381,833
Microsoft ...	wait for it	

Source: ITC June 1999

The picture of cable suppliers has become clearer with Telewest, Cable & Wireless Communications and NTL having emerged from a host of early runners as the major operators. Received wisdom has it that further mergers are a matter of when and not if. Meanwhile the big players are working together and the picture became clearer again in May 1999 when all three signed a deal with the technology company NCI to supply a set-top box and the associated internet server software. Welcome to the world of television and computer convergence.

The big picture changed when Microsoft bought 5 per cent of NTL in January 1999 and 29 per cent of Telewest the following May. The reason is clear: the world's biggest software company has made its £2 billion cable investment to strengthen a hegemony of computer software which looks likely to migrate

into television sets. The aim is to ensure Microsoft products will be as vital to television as they are to the majority of the world's computers. Microsoft's endorsement of cable has shifted the argument from satellite vs cable to a consideration that Bill Gates' powerful Microsoft will soon set an unassailable de facto standard for distributing internet and data services to the home. If this happens, then Bill Gates looms far more monopolistically ominous over the British media landscape than Rupert Murdoch ever did.

The state of cable		
	1999	1998
Number of franchises	137	132
Homes passed	12.145m	11.037m
Homes connected (TV &/or phone)	4.239m	3.644m
Homes connected (TV)	2.971m	2.469m

Source: ITC, June 1999

CABLE OPERATORS

Independent Television Commission licences for cable operators fall into two groups. Franchised Cable Systems or the Multiple Systems Operators (MSOs) are the first. They have exclusive rights for the licensee to provide multi-channel TV over a large scale purpose-built cable system for 15 years. The licence also allows for telephone services to be supplied and has proved a major stimulant to growth.

The second group is the Unfranchised Cable Systems and these are the cable operators which have been allotted a restricted channel capacity that predates the current franchising arrangement. Unfranchised cable systems operators don't have exclusive rights, are subject to shorter term licences and liable to be superseded by a franchised system.

WORLD DOMINATION

Bill Gates, the Microsoft boss, wrote a book called The Road Ahead where he explains his view of how technology is likely to affect journalism.

Microsoft's media advance

June 1997:
$1 billion for 11.5 per cent of Comcast, US cable provider

August 1997
$425 million for the outright purchase of WebTV Networks, a pioneer integrator of TV programmes and Internet content

December 1998
$200 million for a 1.5 per cent stake in Quest Comms

January 1999
$500 million (£303 million) for 5 per cent of NTL, the third largest cable company in the UK

May 1999
$5 billion on a stake in AT&T, including a £2 billion for 29.9 per cent of Telewest, the largest cable company in the UK

May 1999
$600 million in a tie up with Nexus Communications, a leading American mobile phone company

Bill Gates: "Journalism tends to be inefficient today, for both the journalist and the reader. A reporter spends a considerable amount of time restating past events or in other ways providing context for brand new information. A consumer of news often wastes time wading through a restatement of what she already knows, looking for a new development or a fresh detail. Time is also wasted when the consumer doesn't have enough background inforamtion to make sense of breaking developments. And it can be frustrating to have to wait for a particular news story, whether in printed form or during a broadcast.

"As web-based journalism evolves, reporters will deliver information about new developments and maintain extensive background information for consumers who want to explore the context of the day's breaking story. Journalists won't have to restate information over and over, and consumers won't have to listen to the restatements. Because news will be delivered interactively, consumers will get the degree of detail and background they want, and they'll get it when they want it - no waiting until after the next commercial or until the next hour. Important news stories will be both current and under construction at all times. Readers may be able to check a journalists's source material, from news releases to interview transcripts to public documents, which will promote professionalism in news organisations."

FRANCHISED CABLE

Atlantic Cable
303 King Street, Aberdeen AB24 5AP
Fax 01224-644601　　Tel 01224-646644
E-mail: atlantic@telecom.co.uk
Website: www.atlantic/telecom.co.uk
Franchises: Aberdeen

British Telecommuications (BT)
87/89 Baker Street, London W1M 2LV
　　　　　　　Tel 020-7487 1259/1270
Subsidiaries: BT New Towns Cable TV, Westminster
Cable Company.

Cable & Telecoms (C&T)
Lismirrane Industrial Park, Elstree, Herts WD6 3EA
Fax 020-8236 6449　　Tel 020-8236 6524
Franchises: Carlisle, Central Cumbria, South Cumbria,
Ayr, Northumberland, Dumfries, Galloway
Subsidiaries: Cumbria Cable & Telecoms, South
Cumbria Cable & Telecoms, Ayrshire Cable &
Telecoms, Northumberland Cable & Telecoms.
Owner: US Cable Corporation

Cable & Wireless Communications (CWC)
26 Red Lion Square, London WC1R 4HQ
Fax 020-7528 2181　　Tel 020-7528 2000
Website: www.cwcom.uk
Franchises: E Lancs, Bolton, Totton/Hythe, Chichester,
Bognor Regis, Folkestone, Dartford, Dover, Eastbourne,
Hastings, Brighton, Hove, Shoreham, Worthing,
Bournemouth, Poole, Christchurch, Portsmouth,
Winchester, Southampton, Eastleigh, Chilterns, North
Surrey, Derby, N Yorks & S Co Durham, Bury, Rochdale,
Oldham, Wearside, Stoke-on-Trent, Macclesfield, Leeds,
the Wirral, NE Cheshire, Newcastle-under-Lyme,
Stockport, Manchester, Norwich, Great Yarmouth,
Whittlesey, March, Wisbech, Harrow, Thamesmead,
Epping Forest, S Herts, London Boroughs of: Bromley,
Waltham Forest, Wandsworth, `Lambeth, Southwark,
Newham, Tower Hamlets, Kensington, Chelsea,
Hammersmith, Fulham, Ealing, Havering, London E

Comcast Europe (Comcast)
Network House, Bradfield Close, Woking GU22 7RE
　　　　　　　Tel 01483-880800
Franchises: Managing partner in several London
franchises plus Bury St Edmunds, Stowmarket,
Sudbury, Braintree, Ipswich, Colchester, Clacton,
Cambridge, Stansted, Harlow, Birmingham, Teeside,
Darlington, London Boroughs of Camden, Haringey,
Enfield, Hackney, Islington,
Owner: Comcast, USA.

ComTel (Vision Networks)
Wharfedale Road, Winnersh, Wokingham RG41 5TZ
Fax 0118-954 4001　　Tel 0118-954 4000
Website: www.comtel.co.uk
Franchises: Tamworth, North Warwickshire, Meriden,
Stafford, N.E. Northamptonshire, Coventry,
Northampton, Rugby, Daventry, Nuneaton, Stratford,
West Hertfordshire, Thames Valley, Swindon, Andover,
Oxford, Stafford, Salisbury, Romsey.
Wessex Cable, Oxford Cable, Jersey Cable.

The Convergence Group (Convergence)
Martlet Heights, The Martlets, Burgess Hill, West
Sussex RH15 9NJ
Fax 01444-250550　　Tel 01444-250555
E-mail: tonyb@convergenceholdings.com
Website: www.convergenceholdings.com
Franchises: East Grinstead, Haywards Heath, mid
Sussex, Yeovil
Owner: Convergence Group

Diamond Cable Communications (Diamond)
Diamond Plaza, Daleside Road, Nottingham NG2
3GG
Fax 0115-912 2211　　Tel 0115-912 2240
Website: www.diamond.co.uk
Franchises: Nottingham, Newark, Mansfield,
Grantham, Melton Mowbray, Cleethorpes, Grimsby,
Lincoln, Leicester, Loughborough, Burton-on-Trent,
Coalville, Hinckley, Ravenshead, Chesterfield, Vale of
Belvoir, Scunthorpe, Immingham
Owner: part of NTL

Eurobell
E House, Churchill Court, Manor Royal, Crawley RH10
2PN
Fax 01293-400440　　Tel 01293-400444
Website: www.eurobell.com
Franchises: Gatwick, Crawley, Horley, Tunbridge Wells,
Sevenoaks, Tonbridge, Exeter, Plymouth, Torbay,
Totnes, Newton Abbot.
Subsidiaries: Eurobell (South West), Eurobell (Sussex),
Eurobell (West Kent).
Owner: Detecon

General Cable (General)
37 Old Queen Street, London SW1H 9JA
Fax 020-7393 2800　　Tel 020-7393 2828
Website: www.generalcable.co.uk
Franchises: Windsor, Hillingdon & Hounslow,
Birmingham, Bradford, Sheffield, Doncaster,
Rotherham, Wakefield, Barnsley, Halifax, Brighouse.
Subsidiaries: Cable Corporation, Yorkshire Cable.
Owner: Public Holdings 60%, Compagnie Generale
des Eaux, France 40%.

NTL CableTel
Bristol House, 1 Lakeside Road, Farnborough
Hampshire GU14 6XP
Fax 01252-402100　　Tel 01252 402000
Website: www.ntl.com
Franchises: Glasgow, Paisley, Renfrew, Beasden,
Milngavie, Inverclyde, South Glamorgan, Mid
Glamorgan, Gwent, Glyncorrwg, Newport, Pontypool,
Guildford, Woking, Camberley, Aldershot, Farnham,
Fleet, south Bedford, Hertfordshire, Hampshire,
Huddersfield, Northern Ireland.
Subsidiaries: CableTel Herts & Beds/Glasgow/Kirklees/
Northern Ireland/South Wales/Surrey.
Owner: NTL Inc USA
The third largest franchise holder.

Telewest Communications (Telewest)
Genesis Business Park, Albert Drive, Woking, Surrey
GU21 5RW
Fax 01483-750901 Tel 01483-750900
Website: www.telewest.co.uk
Franchises: One of the two largest operators in UK, with
franchises in north Kent, south Essex, Merton, Sutton,
Kingston, Richmond, Croydon, Newcastle, Gateshead,
Tyneside, the Black Country, Telford, Liverpool,
Southport, Blackpool and Fylde, St Helens, Knowsley,
central Lancashire,Wigan, Falkirk, Livingston,
Edinburgh, Lothian, Fife, Dundee, Perth, Motherwell,
Dumbarton, Falkirk, Cumbernauld, Glenrothes,
Kirkcaldy, Taunton, Bridgewater, Bristol, Bath and area,
Cheltenham, Gloucester, Worcester.
Subsidiaries: Telewest Communications: (London
South), (Midlands), (North East), (North West),
(Scotland), (South East), (South West), Cable
Corporation.
Owners: Principal shareholders are
TeleCommunications Inc and US West Inc (29.8 per
cent each), Cox Comms (10 per cent), SBC Comms (10
per cent. Remainder is public.

UNFRANCHISED CABLE

Gwyneth May Evans
1 West End, Dolrheoyn, Tanygrisiau, Blaenau
Ffestiniog, Gwynedd LL41 3SR
Blaenau Ffestiniog
John Jones
97 Rhosemean Street, Llandeilo, Dyfed, Llandeilo
Metro Cable TV
Unit 12, 23 Park Royal Road, London NW10 7JH
Fax 020-8961 6771 Tel 020-8961 6776
Eastbourne, Hastings, Leicester, Lewes, Rochdale.
Metro South Wales
Bridge Terrace, Gwent MP1 5FE
Fax 01495-246095 Tel 01495-247595
South Wales.
Salford Cable Television
Black Horse House, Basildon, Essex SS14 3BX
Fax 01268-450455 Tel 01268-450450
E-mail: group@cda.co.uk
Salford, Sunnyside Court.
Tawd Valley Cable
82 Sandy Lane, Skelmersdale, Lancashire WN8 8LQ
Fax 01695-51315 Tel 01695-51000
Skelmersdale.
A Thomson Relay
1 Park Lane, Beith, Ayrshire KA15 2FG
Fax 01505-503030 Tel 01505 503441
E-mail: glee40@compuserve.com
Beith, Kilbirnie

CABLE CHANNELS

A

ATM
0161-627 1207
Adam and Eve Channel
Soft porn
020-8961 3335
Afro-Caribbean Channel
020-8802 4576
Airport Television
01753-579660
Andover Now
01264 401402
Arcade channels
01483-750900
Arsenal
020-7704 4000

B

BET on Jazz
020-8814 2357
BVTV*
020-8884 0467
Black Music Television
020-8740 5505
Boro TV
Live football
01483-880800

Bradford Festival News
01274-727488
Bradford Festival TV
01274-884863
BIB Advertising & information
020-7332 7083

C

CSV Media
020-7278 6601
Cable Daily
024-7623 1099
Cable 17
News /info south London
020-8251 5151
Cable 17
Local to Worcester area
01384-838483
Cambridge Interactive TV
01223-567200
The Channel Guide
01902-469238
Channel 10
01224-649444
Christian Channel London
0191-4952244

D

Diamond Cable 7
0115-912 2240

E

East
020-8573 4000
Education Channel
01254-292182
Elmsdale Interactive video-on-demand
020-7462 5600
Epping Forest Community Channel
01923-435000

F

Festival Revue
Live performances from Edinburgh
0131-662 8600
The Food Channel
01562-882633

G

Grapevine London text/graphic service
020-7911 0555

H

Havering Community Channel
01923-435000
Hellenic Television
020-7292 7037

I

Ice TV
020-8476 6000
Interactive Channel
01923-435000

CABLE CHANNELS

L
Learning Channel
0191-515 2452
Leicester Community Channel
0115-912240
Live TV Local Network
020-7293 3900
Local Channel (Tellywest)
01772-902902
Local 8 Peterborough/Norwich
01923-435000

M
Metrovision
020-7935 4400
Multi-Screen channels
Avon, Cotswolds, NE, Scotland, SE
01483-750900

N
NCTV
Brighton & Northern
01923-435000
Natural Health
01384-395654
Network 021
Local - Birmingham
0121-628 1234
Nimrooz Persian channel
020-8748 6676

O
ON TV Local - Hampshire
01252-402677

P
Persian TV
Iranian programming on London
Interconnect
020-8328 1084
Preview Channel
0113-239 2255

R
Redbridge Community Channel
01923-435000
Royal Opera House Channel
020-7240 1200

S
Sheffield Local Cable
0114-281 2661
Silverstone TV*.
020-7487 2641
Swindon Local
01252-402000

T
Take One
Film and event, pay-per-view
01252-402000
Take One Look
01992-500 016

Tawd Valley Cable
01695-51000
TellyWest Avon area
0117-983 9000
Tower Hamlets
01923-435000

V
Videonet Interactive TV
01707-362500
Videotron Channel
01923-435000
Vision Channel
01793-511244

W
WBC Yorkshire
01442-253100
Waltham Forest
01923-435000
Weekend Entertainment
020-7287 2929
Westminster Cable Entertainment
020-7935 4400
Williams Worldwide Television
Home shopping
020-7734 7010

Y
YCTV-Youth Cable Television
020-8964 4646

CABLE AREAS

A
Aberdeen area:
Aberdeen Cable (Devanha)
01224-649444
Andover: Cablevision (IVS)
01264-334607
Avon:
United Artists (TeleWest)
01454-612290

B
Bedfordshire: south, Luton:
Cablevision Beds (CableTel)
01582-401044
Birmingham, Solihull:
Birmingham Cable (Comcast)
0121-628 1234
Bolton:
Cable and Wireless
0161-946 0388
Bradford:
Yorkshire Cable
01274-828282
Brighton, Hove, Worthing,
Shoreham:
Cable and Wireless
01273-880000
Burton-upon-Trent, Swadlincote,
Ashby-de-la-Zouch:
LCL Cable
0116-233 4100

C
Cambridge, Ely, Newmarket,
Huntingdon:
Cambridge Cable (Comcast)
01223-567200
Coventry:
Coventry Cable (Devanha)
024-7650 5345

D
Derby:
Cable and Wireless
01332-200002
Dundee, Perth area:
United Artists (TeleWest)
01382-322220

E
Edinburgh:
United Artists (TeleWest)
0131-539 0002

G
Gatwick, Crawley:
Eurobell
01293-400444
Glasgow area:
CableTel
0141-221 7040
Guildford, W Surrey, E Hants:
CableTel
01483-254000

H
Hampshire: east, Portsmouth,
Gosport:
Cable and Wireless
01705-266555
Harlow, Bishops Stortford, Stansted:
Anglia Cable (Comcast)
01279-867000
Hertfordshire: south:
Jones Cable
01923-464000
Hertfordshire: west:
Telecential
01442-230444
Hinckley, BosworthLCL Cable
0116-233 4100

L
Lancashire: Merseyside:
Cable North West (SBC)
01772-832888
Lancashire: east:
Cable and Wireless
0161-946 0388
Leeds: Jones Cable
0113-293 2000
Leicester, Loughborough: LCL Cable
0116-233 4100
Lichfield, Burntwood, Rugeley
LCL Cable
0116-233 4100

CABLE AREAS

LONDON
East End:
Cable and Wireless
020-7363 2000
  Barnet, Brent, Ealing, Fulham,
Greenwich, Harrow, Kensington,
Lambeth, Lewisham, Southwark:
Cable and Wireless
020-8244 1234
  Bromley:
Cable and Wireless
020-8446 9966
  Camden, Enfield, Hackney,
Haringey, Islington:
Cable London (Comcast/TeleWest)
020-7911 0911
  Croydon to Richmond:
United Artists (TeleWest)
020-8760 0222
  Hillingdon, Hounslow:
Middx Cable (Gen Cable)
01753-810810
Westminster Cable (BT)
020-7935 4400

M
Motherwell, Hamilton, East Kilbride:
United Artists (TeleWest)
01698-322332
N
Northampton: Telecential
01604-643619
Northern Ireland CableTel N Ireland
01483-254000
Norwich: Cable (Cable and Wireless)
01603-787892
Notts, Grimsby, Lincoln, Mansfield:
Diamond Cable
0115-952 2240
P
Peterborough:
Cable and Wireless
01733-371717
S
Southampton, Eastleigh:
Cable and Wireless
023-8031 5000
Surrey: north, north east:
Cable and Wireless
01372-360844

Swansea, Neath, Port Talbot:
CableTel
029-2045 6644
Swindon: Swindon Cable (Telecential)
01793-480483
T
Tamworth, north Warwicks and
Meriden
Tamworth Cable (LCL)
0116-233 4100
Thames Valley, Basingstoke,
Wycombe:
Telecential
01734-756868
Tyneside:
United Artists (TeleWest)
0191-420 2000
W
Windsor, Slough, Maidenhead,
Heathrow:
Windsor TV (Gen Cable)
01753-810810
Wolverhampton, Dudley, Telford:
Cable Midlands (SBC)
01384-838483

Cable and satellite audience figures

CHANNEL	AUDIENCE	CHANNEL	AUDIENCE	CHANNEL	AUDIENCE
Sky 1	2,901,844	**Challenge TV**	1,668,772	**Sky Cinema**	877,760
Channel Guide	2,880,000	**Carlton Food**	1,590,319	**Disney**	876,639
QVC	2,837,775	**Carlton Select**	1,589,232	**Christian Chan.**	848,527
BBC News 24	2,829,345	**UK Horizons**	1,554,919	**ITV2**	777,678
Eurosport	2,707,891	**Bloomberg Info**	1,553,238	**TV Travel Shop**	772,102
Live TV	2,646,238	**History Channel**	1,511,116	**CNBC**	745,862
UK Gold	2,546,314	**Granada Breeze**	1,490,944	**Vision**	723,016
Living	2,287,384	**Performance**	1,385,627	**Animal Planet**	718,511
TNT	2,266,813	**Bravo**	1,375,619	**UK Play**	528,561
Cartoon N'work	2,248,217	**Trouble**	1,366,326	**Asianet**	528,219
VH1	2,239,274	**BBC Parliament**	1,355,300	**TV5**	512,516
Sky News	2,082,075	**UK Style**	1,348,459	**Tara TV**	359,170
Discovery	2,032,883	**UK Arena**	1,293,410	**Euronews**	215,598
The Box	2,026,178	**Fox Kids**	1,072,905	**Landscape**	160,468
Discovery	2,016,369	**Sky Sports 3**	1,067,335	**Bet on Jazz**	113,684
MTV	1,980,215	**Nat. Geographic**	1,036,802	**C1 Liverpool**	92,775
Nickelodeon	1,922,674	**Sky Sports 1**	1,034,520	**ZEE TV**	51,394
Sci-Fi	1,914,417	**Sky Soap**	972,244	**Namaste**	49,500
Granada Men	1,890,651	**Sky Travel**	936,785	**TVX**	40,251
Granada Plus	1,889,282	**Sky Sports 2**	921,622	**Adult Channel**	30,893
CNN	1,804,492	**Sky Premiere**	918,261	**HVC**	29,537
Travel Channel	1,776,793	**Sky Moviemax**	902,254	**Sony TV**	10,494
Paramount	1,690,269	**Rapture**	896,582	Source: ITC June 1999	

Satellite television

Sky Television's success, which generates an annual turnover in excess of £1.4 billion, is built on the popularity that comes from giving people what they want. It has 7.3 million subscribers of which 1.2 million are digital subscribers. In ten years it has expanded from five to 50 channels.and it has made the news since it began broadcasting on 5 February, 1988. Nobody could have anticipated that within a decade it would redefine the TV landscape and make enough money to put in a £600 million bid to buy Manchester United.

Sky started as unofficial competitor to British Satellite Broadcasting, launching itself from Luxembourg using a pirate satellite. Rupert Murdoch, whose News International owns 40 per cent of Sky, put his money where his mouth was and bet his business on the success of satellite. Within a year Sky had absorbed BSB and in August 1992 it had outbid all rivals to buy the rights to broadcast live Premier League football. The soccer deal will run until 2001 and it has pay-TV rights to 90 per cent of Hollywood movies plus a range of other made for TV American imports.

Elisabeth Murdoch, not ready for the Sky top job ... yet

It now controls the majority of pay TV revenue and, once again, has been ahead of the game in leading the digital push. In October 1998 Sky Digital launched itself ahead of its main commercial rivals at ONdigital. Despite ONdigital's advantage of needing no £50 plus dish Sky's immediate lead over the new rival is such that the Independent Television Commission - recalling the earlier battle with British Satellite Broadcasting - is worried there isn't enough competition, for Sky also has a 32.5 per cent share in BIB, the interactive TV outfit.

The meritocratic audacity of Sky is such that it has always been a story in its own right, with repeated questioning of how much Murdoch's 30 per cent ownership of the British press is used as a lever to force the government concessions needed to change TV. Much attention has also focused on its management and a string of five chief executives. Best known was the abrasive Sam Chisholm who took over in 1990. He got the measure of Kelvin MacKenzie who left the Sun editorship to become Sky MD and then quit after seven months. Murdoch forgave his favourite newspaper editor saying: "People go half way round the world not to work for Chisholm."

Chisholm pocketed £4.5 million after Sky's stock market flotation in 1994 and eventually left after Elisabeth Murdoch was given a top job as general manager of broadcasting. "Elisabeth thought Sam would teach her everything but he didn't," said the general manager's Dad. "He tried to cut her out." So much for meritocracy.

In May 1999 Tony Ball became BSkyB's fifth chief executive in 10 years. The former president of the Fox-Liberty American sports network took over from Mark Booth. Microsoft had offered Booth a job heading its internet businesses but Murdoch clung on to him by creating a new media company, e*partners, for him to run. Elisabeth Murdoch wasn't considered ready for the job. Then, in June, Murdoch took over as chairman of Sky for the first time since the early days when the venture into satellite television threatened to bankrupt News International.

Sky's next ten years look less assured. Traditional competition will emerge from a BBC which is likely to bid much higher for sporting rights. New competition will come from cable - a transmission medium which is superior to satellite and which is now the focus of American expansion led by Microsoft and AT&T. While Sky won the early battle for new TV subscribers it may well lose the communications war.

Sky channels

WHOLLY OWNED	JOINTLY OWNED
Sky 1	Nickelodeon UK (50%)
Sky News	QVC (20%)
Sky Travel	Paramount Comedy (25%)
Sky Soap	Granada Plus (49.5%)
Sky Sports 1	Granada Men & Motors (49.5%)
Sky Sports 2	Granada Good Life (49.5%)
Sky Sports 3	History Channel (50%)
.tv (Computer Channel)	National Geographic (50%)
Movie Channel	Sky Music Choice (49%)
Sky Premier	Playboy TV (30%)
Sky Moviesmax	MUTV (33%)
Sky Cinema	

Source: BSkyB.

BSkyB
6 Centaurs Business Park, Grant Way, Isleworth, Middlesex TW7 5QD
Fax 020-7705 3030   Tel 020-7705 3000
Website www.sky.co.uk
This site is one of the most popular in the UK with three million hits a week. It has pages on sport, world news, a TV guide and a Sky shop. Also available is Sky Text and Sky Intertext.
Chairman: Rupert Murdoch
Managing director: Tony Ball
Director of corporate communications: Tim Allan
Managing director, Sky Networks: Elisabeth Murdoch
Head of Sky news: Nick Pollard
Director of sales: Peter Shea
General manager, broadcasting: Bruce Steinberg
Managing director Sky Sports: Vic Wakeling
Director of engineering: Geoff Walters
Chief financial officer: Martin Stewart
Head of pay-per-view: Mark Conneely

FLEXTECH

Flextech's channels account for a quarter of Britain's satellite and cable viewing so, as the other main pay TV provider, it too is listed in this section.
Flextech
160 Great Portland Street, London W1N 5TB
Fax 020-7299 6000   Tel 020-7299 5000
Chairman & chief executive: Adam Singer
Managing director: Brent Harman
Vice president, corporate affairs: Nicola Howson
Flextech owns Bravo, Trouble, Challenge, Living, Screenshop and ScreenOne. Its UKTV joint venture with the BBC gives it half shares of UK Gold, UK Arena, UK Horizons, UK Style and UK Play. The main share holders are: Liberty Media, Cox Communications and Media One

SATELLITE CHANNELS

3+
Scandinavian entertainment
01895-433327

A
Ace TV
Entertainment
020-8947 8841
Adult Channel Porn
020-8581 7000
AMC Asian music
0116-233 5599
Africa Independent TV
News, drama, soaps, sport
020-7233 7965
Al-Rashad
Oriental & western cultures
020-7233 7965
Animal Planet
020-7462 3600
Apna TV Asian entertainment and radio
020-7359 6464
Arab News Network
020-7323 9920
Asianet
020-8930 0930
Atomic TV
Music video entertainment
01622-684463
Auction Channel
020-8788 4429

B
Babylon Blue Porn
020-7287 6623
Bangla TV Bengali speaking service
020-8514 8693
Bar Channel
General entertainment
020-7705 3000
Barker Service
Sky promotional
020-7705 3000
Best Direct TV
24 hour home shopping
020-8868 4355
BET on Jazz International
Jazz
020-8814 2357
Bloomberg Info TV   Financial news
020-7330 7500
The Box   Interactive music
020-7376 2000
Bravo Classic films
020-7813 7000
British Interactive Broadcasting
Services for ads and promo
020-7332 7083
Business Information Channel
01273-728809

C

CNBC
Business programming
020-8600 6600

CNE
News from China, Hong Kong & Taiwan
020-7610 3880

CNN International
International news
020-7637 6700

Caribbean One TV
AfroCaribbea entertainment
020-8653 3512

Carlton Food Network
Cookery & lifestyle
020-7432 9000

Carlton Select
Entertainment
020-7432 9000

Cartoon Network
020-7478 1000

Challenge TV
Interactive
01622-69111

Chand Televsion
Asian programming
01384-291854

Channel One Infotainment
020-7209 1234

Channel 4
020-7396 4444

Channel 5
General entertainment
020-7550 5625

Channel 7 Europe
020-7510 0011

Christian Channel
Christian programming
0191-495 2244

Christian Communication Net
Christian programming
028-90853997

Computer Channel
Education & entertainment
020-7705 3000

Crime Channel
Fact and fiction
020-7573 4580

Cultural Television
Documentaries
01268-775362

D

DBC Cinema Channel
Filmed entertainment
020-7839 4449

Discovery Channels
Documentaries
020-7462 3600

Disney Channel
Family entertainment
020-7605 1300

Dragon
Chinese family entertainment
0161-236 3557

E

EBN
European business news
020-7653 9300

EIN
Infomercials
020-7927 8427

East-West
South Asian news & entertainment
020-8905 5355

Eternal Word UK
Catholic programming
01721- 752625

European Family Christian Net
01442-219525

European Network Broadcasting
Christian programming
020-7287 4908

F

FilmFour
Feature films
020-7396 4444

Fox Kids Network
020-7554 9000

Fresco channel
Cultural channel for EU states
100 New Bridge Road London EC4V 6JA

Front Row
Films and sport
020-7307 2222

G

Goodlife TV
Porn
020-7287 6623

Gospel channel
01249-446210

Granada channels
020-7578 4002

H

HBO
Entertainment for Poland
020-7972 7310

Hallmark Entertainment Network
Horror films
020-8847 4332

History Channel
Historical documentaries
020-7705 3000

Home Shopping Network
020-7705 6800

HVC
Action and horror films
020-8581 7000

I

Image TV
TV for Grimsby & Cleethorpes
01469-515151

Indus Television
Multiracial entertainment
020-7722 2922

International Shopping Network
020-7734 7010

International Media Service
International news
020-8903 7899

Intershop
Home shopping
020-8891 2202

Invention Shop Channel
Home shopping
01732-866356

J

JSTV
Entertainment
020-7426 7330

K

Kanal 5
Entertainment for Sweden
020-7972 7310

Khalsa World Television
Punjabi, Hindu and Urdu
020-7499 1511

K-Tel Home Shopping
020-7499 1511

L

Landscape Channel
Classical music
01424-830688

Le Cinema
Polish, Hungarian, Romanian movies
020-7435 8450

Live TV
Live local network
020-7293 3900

Living
Daytime mangazine
020-7299 5000

M

MED TV
Kurdish, Turkish entertainment
020-7494 2523

MTV Networks
Music video channels
020-7284 7777

MUTV
Manchester United Football TV
0161-834 1111

Mediashop TV
020-7722 0242

Middle East Broadcasting
Arabic entertainment
020-7501 1111

Millennium Channel
Christian channel
020-8461 1618

Minaj Broadcast International
Afro-centric entertainment
020-7491 2393

Mine channel
Afro-Caribbean
020-7281 6996

Movie Channel Subscription filmS
020-7705 3000

Muslim TV Ahmadiyya
020-8870 8517

N

NBC Channels
News and entertainment
020-7352 9205

Namaste
Asian programming
020-8507 8292

Nickleodeon   Children's programming
020-7462 1000

Nickleodeon Scandinavia
Scandinavian children's programming
020-7462 1000

Novashop One/Two   Home shopping
020-7465 1234

P

Paramount Channel
Entertainment
020-7462 1000

Parliamentary Channel
Parliament and political coverage
020-7813 5000

Penthouse Channel
Porn
020-8581 7000

Performance
The performing arts
020-7209 1234

Playboy TV
Porn
020-7287 2223

Promotional Channel
For UK Arena, Horizons, Style channels
020-7765 1959

Punjabi UK TV
Punjabi programmes
0121-558 6600

Q

Q24
Home shopping
020-7465 1234

QVC Deutschland
German language home shopping
020-7705 5600

QVC Shopping Channel
020-7705 5600

Quantum Home Shopping
020-7465 1234

R

Racenet
020-8568 3511

Racing Channel
020-7696 8704

Rainbow Television
Gay entertainment
020-7328 1566

Rapture TV
Infotainment
01603-661188

Regal Shop
Home shopping
020-7434 0567

Relationships Channel
Relationship counselling
020-7732 3521

Revival Channel
Christian
0191-495 2244

Romantica
Polish soap opera
020-7435 8450

S

Satellite Information Services
Racing information
020-7253 1232

Sci-Fi Channel Europe
020-7805 6100

Sell-a-Vision Shopping
020-7465 1234

Setanta Sport Sports service for pubs
020-7930 8926

Sky channels
Entertainment, sports etc
020-7705 3000

Sima TV
Entertainment in Farsi
020-8959 3611

Sony Entertainment
Live educational & business
020-7534 7575

Sportswire
020-7705 3200

STEP-UP
Educational & business
01752-233635

Studio Universal
Theatrical films
020-8250 1651

Style
Women's programmes
020-7478 6900

Supershop
020-7465 1243

T

.tv
About computers
020-7599 8398

TCC Nordic
Children's programming
020-7813 7000

TESUG TV
Satellite industry info
029-2036 1004

TNT Classic Movies
020-7478 1000

TV Land
Middle Eastern entertainment
020-7478 6800

TV Shop
01895-433433

TV3 Denmark
Entertainment for Denmark
01895-433327

TV3 Norway
Entertainment for Norway
01895-433433

TV3 Sweden
Entertainment for Sweden
01895-433327

TVBS Europe
Chinese programmes
020-7636 6818

TV Travel Shop Holiday channel
020-7299 5000

Television Broadcast Services
University of Plymouth
01752-233635

Television X   Soft porn
020-7308 5090

Tell Sell: Home shopping
01784-898109

Travel Channel
020-7636 5401

Travel-Polish
020-7636 5401

Trouble For teenagers
020-7299 5000

U

UK Arena (BBC/Flextech)
Arts, drama, music
020-7765 1959

UK Horizons (BBC/Flextech)
Educational/science
020-7765 1959

UK Channel (BBC/Flextech)
General entertainment
020-7307 1300

UK Gold (BBC/Flextech)
020-7306 6100

UK Play(BBC/Flextech)
Music/comedy for 15-34 year olds
020-7765 1959

UK Style (BBC/Flextech)
Lifestyle
020-7765 1959

V

VH1
Music
020-7284 7491

VT4
Entertainment for Benelux
01707-664555

Visual Arts
General entertainment
020-7307 1350

W

What's in Store
020-7465 1234

Wizja channels
Polish channels
01622-684516

World Health Network
01734-816666

X

X1
German language programming
020-7486 9231

Z

Zee TV
Asian programming
020-8839 4000

ZTV
01895-433327

Local TV: Restricted Service Licences

A new and little-noticed sector of UK went live on 31 October 1998 when TV12 began its local TV broadcasting for the Isle of Wight. It is a product of the 1996 Broadcasting Act 1996 which provides for local terrestrial television through Restricted Services Licences (RSLs). These new licences are available in two forms: the RSL E covers a maximum 56 day festival or sporting event while the RSL L, such as taken out by TV12, is a renewable two year licence.

TV12, which began with a mere £500,000 investment, was followed by Lanarkshire Television, the Oxford Channel and MATV in Leicester. Derry's TVC9 and Edinburgh's Channel 6 began in September 1999. More services are due for Bath, Cardiff, Hertford, Portsmouth, Chichester, Perth, Dundee and Aberdeen. A further 123 towns are having spare analogue frequencies identified by the ITC.

Dave Rushton, of the Local Independent Television Network, says: "Network members are committed to establishing a local form of public service broadcasting and add 'local involvement and participation' to the long-standing PSB objective to 'inform, educate and entertain'. Adopting a PSB remit is entirely voluntary: public service commitment by choice. While the downside for these new services is the limit of a two year licence, the upside is that it will be strong local attachment and a genuine contribution to diversity which decides whether these licences are renewed."

KEY CONTACT

Local Independent Television Network
c/o Community Media Association, 15 Paternoster Row, Sheffield S1 2BX
Fax 0114-279 8976   Tel 0114-279 5219

Channel 6 Broadcasting
PO Box 606, Edinburgh EH7 4YH
Fax 0131-557 8608   Tel 0131-557 8610
Covers: Licences for Edinburgh, Aberdeen, Perth and Stirling with provisional offers of licences for Dundee, Glasgow and Inverness.
Owner: Channel 6 Broadcasting Ltd
Chairman: Dave Rushton
Managing director: David Treadway
Director of Programmes: TBA
Finance director: Michael Dixon

Oxford Channel
Fax 01865-433885   Tel 01865-433775
E-mail: oxfordchannel@compuserve.com
Owner: Oxford Broadcasting Ltd
Chairman: Frank Harding
Managing directors: Deborah Cackler/Thomas Harding

MATV
MPK House, 233 Belgrave Gate, Leicester LE1 3HT
Fax 0116-253 8900   Tel 0116-253 2288
E-mail: mbc.matv@technocom.com
Website: www.matv.co.uk
Owner: V Popat, H Popat, S M Majithia
Chairman: Ashwin Mistry
Managing director: Vinod Popat
Programme controller: Nilesh Thanki

Panjabi TV
174 Kensington Park Road, London W11 2ER
Fax 020-7792 2820   Tel 020-7792 2820
Covers: Slough area
Owner: The Panjabi Centre
Chairman: A K Khera
Managing director: J P S Kundi
Sales and marketing: R S Mangat
Finance director: B S Heera

TV12
The Medina Centre, Fairlee Road, Newport, Isle of Wight PO30 2EW
Fax 01983-521660   Tel 01983-524745
Website: www.tv12.demon.co.uk
Covers: Isle of Wight and Solent region
Chairman: Graham Benson
Managing director: Paul Meade
Director of programmes: Paul Topping
Sales and marketing: Steve Lloyd
Finance director: Adam Humphreys

TVC9
1 Crawford Square, Londonderry BT48 7HR
Fax: 01504-289901   Tel: 01504-289900
E-mail: paulb@tvc9com/
Website: www.tvc9.com
Covers: Greater Londonderry
Owner: Derry Media Access, Honeybee Enterprises, VFG Finance
Chairman: Robert Gavin
Managing director/director of programmes: Paul Boyle
Sales and marketing: Paudrig O'Dwyer
Finance director: John Ward

Teletext

Teletext is written copy broadcast on TV sets. All the main television companies operate a teletext service with bulletins on news, sport, travel, weather and entertainment. The BBC and Channels 3, 4 and 5 provide subtitling for people with hearing difficulties. About a half of all households have teletext decoders and the weekly audience is over 20 million.

The main teletext services are: Ceefax on BBC; Teletext Ltd on ITV; Simple Active on Channel 4; Data Broadcasting International (DBI) which uses spare capacity within the Channel 3 signal to provide commercial services; Sky Text from BSkyB; and 5 Text. Ceefax is an in-house BBC operation which has recently merged with BBC News Online. Its editorial extends beyond text related to BBC TV programming and has recently expanded with a local news, sport, weather, travel and TV listings for each of the BBC's 13 regions.

Teletext Ltd is an ITC-licensed consortium which is 75 per cent owned by the Daily Mail and General Trust. Simple Active has an ITV licence to use spare capacity within the Channel 4 signal to transmit "data packages for provision to a range of professional and consumer markets, with sub-licensing of some capacity to other users". Simple Active shares a senior management with DBI, which has another ITC licensee which "uses spare capacity within the Channel 3 signal and provides commercial services to subscription and to closed user groups". Sky Text has been available on Sky channels since 1992 and the latest Teletext arrival, 5 Text, went live in autumn 1997 carrying news, sport, TV listings, weather, travel and advertising.

Ceefax (BBC teletext)
Room 7013, BBC Television Centre, Wood Lane, London W12 7RJ
Fax 020-8749 6734   Tel 020-8576 1801
E-mail: ceefax@bbc.co.uk
Editor: Peter Clifton

Data Broadcasting International
Allen House, Station Road, Egham, Surrey TW20 9NT
Fax: 01784-438732   Tel: 01784-471515
Website: www.databroadcasting.co.uk
Commercial additional service Channel 3 teletext
Chairman: Peter Mason
Managing director: Justin Cadbury

SimpleActive
Allen House, Station Road, Egham, Surrey TW20 9NT
Fax: 01784-477722   Tel: 01784-477721
Additional commercial service Channel 4 teletext
Chairman: Peter Mason
Deputy chairman: Justin Cadbury

Sky Text
Channel 5 Broadcasting, 22 Long Acre, London WC2E 9LY
Tel: 020-7599 8900
Sky Five Text is jointly owned by BSkyB and Channel 5 Text and has put in a £1,500,557 bid to provide a teletext service on the Channel 5 signal.

Teletext (ITV teletext)
101 Farm Lane, Fulham, London SW6 1QJ
Fax 020-7386 5002   Tel 020-7386 5000
E-mail: dutyed@teletext.co.uk
Website: www.teletext.co.uk
Editorial director: Graham Lovelace
ITC 1998 Performance Review: "At the end of 1998 22 million viewers wre using the service at least once a week compared to 13 million when the service began. Complaints were at a negligible level. A range of services were introduced during the year, notably in the city and finance section and in sport. Following the important improvements made in previous years, the regional news service consolidated its position as a high quality service."

Internet searching

Internet's two main search services are: "search engines", robots which scan website pages to compile indexes; and "directories", where human editors put the websites into useable categories.

Search engines work by automatically reading as many pages on as many websites as possible, and then storing this text in an index. The engine consults its index for whatever words you type and lists them on screen. This is a good way of finding obscure information or carrying out in-depth research, but you can easily be overwhelmed by irrelevant references. The total number of indexable pages on all of internet was estimated at 800 million (and mushrooming) in February 1999, with perhaps the same number of pages inaccessible. In August 1999 FAST Search was the biggest engine, with 200 million pages indexed. The most popular engines are AltaVista and Northern Light. Other major ones are: Excite, FAST Search, Google, HotBot, Infoseek, MSN Search and Netscape Search.

Directories treat internet more like a library of websites than a book of pages. The directories are run by humans, who filter the sites rather than the pages, arrange the sites with themes (like books on library shelves) and create a catalogue of brief comments about each site. Directories are the best places to begin searching, especially for general material. But in detailed research their human, non-robotic editors can miss important sites that engines locate automatically.

The most popular directory by far is Yahoo. Other major ones are: LookSmart, Lycos, Open Directory, Snap and UK Plus.

Most major directories and search engines are now hybrids, offering the other type of service as well as their own. A compromise service is the "metasearch engine", which approaches several search engines and directories with a query and then presents their results in a single list. Copernic, Debriefing, MetaCrawler and SavvySearch are the leaders.

For simple searches, Yahoo and Google are best. In more advanced searches, Northern Light and HotBot score most. For up-to-date data on search engines and directories visit www.searchenginewatch.com. Services below are USA-based, unless otherwise stated. Look for "co.uk" for UK natives and American sites with UK versions.

DIGITAL CONTACTS

AltaVista
www.altavista.com
Generally regarded as the most powerful and useful of all search engines. A favourite with in-depth researchers because of its wide-ranging coverage, advanced search capabilities and many features. Plus directory service from LooSmart. 150 m pages.

AOL NetFind
www.aol.com/netfind
Search engine, basically Excite (cf) under another name.

Ask Jeeves
www.askjeeves.com
Answer service, Child-friendly. Good starting point.

Copernic
www.copernic.com
A metasearch engine that can also be installed on PCs. Access to about 30 search engines.

Debriefing
www.debriefing.com
A quality metasearch engine.

Excite
www.excite.co.uk
One of the most popular search services which is more for general searchers than specialists, it combines a 60 m page search engine (possibly 250 m by late 1999) with a directory of 5,000 sites, many UK. Often ranked as the best of America's UK-specific engines. Parent of AOL, Magellan, Netscape and Webcrawler (cf).

FAST Search
www.alltheweb.com
Claims to be the largest engine, with 200 million pages. Previously called All The Web; relaunched in mid-1999.

GOD (Global Online Directory)
www.god.co.uk
A well-known and interesting global directory, one of the first based in the UK.

Google
www.google.co.uk
One of the most popular search engines, using special methods to find high-quality sites for general searches, rather than advanced searches. It ranks web sites according to their level of use. 85 m pages. Run by Stanford University, USA, with UK version.

GoTo
www.goto.com
A simple search engine, where all you need is a keyword query.

HotBot
www.hotbot.com
A favourite among serious researchers, with a wide variety of search options on almost an equal ranking with Northern Light (cf). Incorporates directory services from Open Directory (cf). 110 million pages.

Infoseek
www.infoseek.co.uk
A popular engine-plus-directory for general searchers rather than specialists. 75m pages, 0.5 m sites. Synonymous with Go Network (www.go.com) which it launched in 1999. American, with UK version.

Inktomi
www.inktomi.com
Not a separate search engine, but a powerful index of 110 m pages which provides enhanced services to some of the biggest engines, including HotBot and MSN (cf).

LookSmart
www.looksmart.co.uk
A directory being a near rival to Yahoo. Powered by Open Directory, it also uses engine facilities from AltaVista (cf). 0.8 m sites. American, with UK version.

Lycos
www.lycos.co.uk
One of the oldest search engines, born 1994, Lycos became a direc-tory as well in 1999, using Open Directory (cf). A good searcher, with advanced search capabilities. Parent of HotBot (cf). 50 m pages. American, with UK version.

Magellan
www.mckinley.com
A directory subsidiary of Excite (cf).

MetaCrawler
www.metacrawler.com
The vintage (1994) metasearch engine, often ranked as the best of its kind. Owned by Go2Net, whose name is also used.

Metaplus
www.metaplus.com/uk.html
A metasearch index of many UK directories, with direct links to many popular sites. American, with UK version.

Mirago
www.mirago.co.uk
UK search engine aimed primarily at UK businesses and families.

MSN Search / Microsoft
http://search.msn.co.uk
Microsoft's Internet Explorer browser defaults to the MSN site, where this, its own, engine is available. Powered by Inktomi. Scheduled for upgrading. American, with UK version.

Netscape Search
http://search.netscape.com
A well-used combination of Excite's search engine and the Open Directory (cf). One of the most popular browsers.

Northern Light
www.northernlight.com
Often ranked as the best of the advanced search engines, with its database and innovatory features. 160 million pages, 5,400 full text sources. American.

Open Directory
http://dmoz.org
Formerly called NewHoo, this is Yahoo's closest directory rival. It is one of the most interesting features of all Internet, being a community-based operation, run by over 12,000 volunteer editors. 800,000 sites. It powers Lycos and Netscape (cf).

SavvySearch
www.savvysearch.com
A popular metasearch engine.

Search Engine Colossus
www.searchenginecolossus.com
Shows what search engines are in which country.

SearchUK
www.searchuk.com
A UK engine and directory, with over 6 m pages, 700,000 sites, and integration into local services.

Snap
www.snap.com
NBC TV and Cnet directory, with over 400,000 sites.

UK Directory
www.ukdirectory.co.uk
A guide to everything UK on the WWW.

UK Index
www.ukindex.co.uk
Wide-ranging directory of UK sites.

UKMax
www.ukmax.com
Mainly for carrying out searches only on pages within the UK domain. Uses Inktomi (cf).

UK Plus
www.ukplus.co.uk
The largest home-brewed UK-specific directory produced by Associated Newspapers. Child-friendly.

Webcrawler
www.webcrawler.com
A simplified Excite (cf), by another name. Easy to use for simple searches, but not the complicated.

Yahoo!
www.yahoo.co.uk
The oldest, biggest and most comprehensive directory, with 1.2 m sites. A good starting point for all types of search, especially simpler ones on a general topic. Launched in late 1994. American, with UK version.

PAPER CONTACTS

Guide to the Internet, 1999 Edition
Jim McClellan
£5.99, Fourth Estate
A good how-to-get-going guide produced from within the Guardian.

u.k. directory
£2.99, UK Directory
The bi-monthly paper version of UK Directory (cf).

Radio and TV news agencies

ABC News Intercontinental
3 Queen Caroline Street, London W6 9PE
Fax 020-8222 2795   Tel 020-8222 5000
London office of the American news network.

APTN - Associated Press Television News
32 Oval Road, Camden Lock, London NW1 7DZ
Fax 020-7413 8302   Tel 020-7410 5200
E-mail: wtnlib@abc.com
Formed from the September 1998 merger of APTV and WTN World Television News, APTN provides a 24-hour satellite service from camera crews in 90 cities to more than a thousand broadcasters. APTN also has one of the most comprehensive film and video archives. Owned by ITN, ABC (USA) and Nine Network (Australia). APTN HQ is in London, with bureaux in 55 other cities.

BBC Parliament
160 Great Portland Street, London W1N 5TB
Fax 020-7299 5300   Tel 020-7299 5000
E-mail: viewer_tpc@flextech.co.uk
Website: www.parlchan.co.uk/
Provides unedited live coverage of daily proceedings in the House of Commons and recorded coverage of the Lords, Parliamentary committees, business statements, the European Union and Question Time. Now run by the BBC, the channel was created by the British Cable Industry.

Bloomberg Television
39-45 Finsbury Square, London EC2A 1PQ
Fax 020-7392 6000   Tel 020-7330 7500
Website: www.bloomberg.com/uk
Covers business and financial news stories with multiscreen format. Broadcasts ten channels around the world in eight languages. Available on cable, satellite and Sky Digital.

CBS News
68 Knightsbridge, London SW1X 7LL
Fax 020-7581 4431   Tel 020-7581 4801
London office of the American news network.

CNN International
19-22 Rathbone Place, London W1P 1DF
Fax 020-7637 6738   Tel 020-7637 6700
Website: www.cnn.com
Cable News Network International, a wholly owned subsidiary of Time Warner Inc., is the world's only global network. Distributing 24-hour news via 15 satellites CNN and CNNI are seen by 224 million households in more than 210 countries. and territories world-wide, and have 36 international bureaux and nearly 700 affiliated TV stations around the world.

Feature Story Productions
40-44 Newman Street, London W1P 3PA
Fax 020-7436 9138   Tel 020-7580 4160
A radio and TV agency that provides customised on-air news coverage.

FT Business News
50 Lisson Street, London NW1 5DF
Fax 020-7723 6132   Tel 020-7402 1011
Business and personal finance news for commercial radio from Unique Broadcasting, FT and ABC Radio.

IRN - Independent Radio News
200 Gray's Inn Road, London WC1X 8X2
Fax 020-7430 4092   Tel 020-7430 4090
News desk   Tel 020-7430 4814
E mail: news@irn.co.uk
Website: wttp://www.irn.co.uk
IRN is Britain's main radio news agency, supplying bulletins and services to over 90 per cent of the commercial radio stations. The news is provided to IRN by ITN, using the resources of ITN at its headquarters in 200 Grays Inn Road. IRN is effectively a commissioning agency acting on behalf of its customers. Its owners are the main radio groups.

ITN
200 Grays Inn Road, London WC1X 8XZ
Fax 020-7833 3000   Tel 020-7833 3000
Press office   Tel 020-7430 4700
E-mail: press.office@itn.co.uk
Website: www.itn.co.uk
ITN produces the daily news programmes for three competing British TV channels: ITV, Channel 4 and Channel 5. Other output includes radio news bulletins, documentaries, educational programmes, Internet websites and archive clips. ITN is also responsible for Euronews, a news channel in six languages which is seen in 43 countries. Founded in 1955 as the news department of ITV, ITN is now owned by a consortium comprising Carlton Communications, the Granada Group, Daily Mail & General Trust, UNM and Reuters.

London News Network
London Television Centre, Upper Ground, London SE1 9LT
Fax 020-7827 7710   Tel 020-7827 7700
Website: www.lnn-tv.co.uk
Jointly set up and run by the London ITV companies Carlton and LWT to provide their local news. Began in January 1992. Also supplies news to GMTV.

News Direct
200 Grays Inn Road, London WC1X 8XZ
Fax 020-7312 8470   Tel 020-7973 1152
Providing a 24-hour rolling news and information service for London with news, traffic, weather, sport, entertainment, city and headlines every 20 minutes..

TUNE IN. CATCH UP.

THE ONLY STATION THAT GIVES YOU THE LATEST NEWS, TRAVEL, BUSINESS AND ENTERTAINMENT.

News as it happens.

NBC News Worldwide
8 Bedford Avenue, London WC1B 3AP
Fax 020-7636 2628   Tel 020-7637 8655
E-mail: nhaw@nbc.com
London office of the American network.

Parliamentary Channel
See BBC Parliament

Reuters Television
85 Fleet Street, London EC4P 4AJ
Tel 020-7250 1122
E-mail: rtv@reuters.com
Reuters Television (RTV) supplies video news material
via satellite 24 hours a day to more than 200
broadcasters, plus their networks and affiliates, in 90
countries.

TV News London
Southbank House, Black Prince Road, Albert
Embankment, London SE1 7SJ
Fax 020-7793 4144   Tel 020-7793 4013
E-mail: roz@tvnews.ftech.co.uk
London news agency supplying stories about events in
the capital to regional broadcasting companies. Started
in 1992.

Unique Entertainment News
50 Lisson Street, London NW1 5DF
Fax 020-7724 5373   Tel 020-7453 1650
E-mail: anna.burles@unique.co.uk
Website: www.unique.co.uk
Entertainment news for commercial radio.

Worldwide Television News (WTN)
See APTN

WRN (World Radio Network)
Wyvil Court, 10 Wyvil Road, London SW8 2TG
Fax 020-7896 9007   Tel 020-7896 9000
E-mail: online@wrn.org
Website: www.wrn.org
WRN operates a 24 hour-a-day network with news,
current affairs and feature programmes from 28 of the
world's public service broadcasters. WRN has three
language streams: English, German and Mulit-lingual,
for listeners across Europe, Africa, the Middle East,
Asia, the Pacific and North America. WRN 's European
English-language stream is available live via the
Internet and is also transmitted on DAB in both
London and Warsaw.

Film libraries

KEY CONTACT

Researcher's Guide to British Film and TV Collections
British Universities Film and Video Council, 77 Well
Street, London W1P 3RE
Tel: 020-7393 1500
E-mail: bufvc@open.ac.uk
Website: www.bufvc.ac.uk

A19 Film and Video
21 Foyle Street, Sunderland, SR1 1LE
Fax 0191-565 6288   Tel 0191-565 5709
Documentary makers, focussing on the north-east.

Archive Film Agency
21 Lidgett Park Avenue, Leeds LS8 1EU
Fax 0113-266 2454   Tel 0113-266 2454
Specialists in early newsreel, documentary, fiction. With
a current stock shot library covering the world.

Archive Films
17 Conway Street, London W1P6EE
Fax 020-7391 9123   Tel 020-7312 0300
E-mail: imorris@theimagebank.com
Website: www.imagebank.co.uk
30,000 hours of historical entertainment footage
including silent films, feature films, newsreels and
documentaries.

BBC Worldwide Television Library Sales
Woodlands, 80 Wood Lane, London W12 0TT
Fax 020-8576 2939   Tel 020-8576 2861
E-mail: ukls@bbcfootage.com
The BBC has Britain's largest library of film and
videotape, with over 400 million feet of film.

Beulah
66 Rochester Way, Crowborough, Sussex TN6 2DU
Fax 01892-652413   Tel 01892-652413
E-mail: beulah@enterprise.net
Website: www.homepages.enterprise.net/beulah
Films and stills library of transport and social history
subjects.

British Film Institute
21 Stephen Street, London W1P 2LN
Fax 020-7436 7950   Tel 020-7255 1444
E-mail: helpdesk@bfi.org.uk
Website: www.bfi.org.uk
300,000 titles. BFI Collections also handles sales from
the 7 million images in Stills, Posters and Designs.

British Movietone News
North Orbital Road, Denham, Middlesex UB9 5HQ
Fax 01895-834893   Tel 01895-833071
Website: www.movietone-com
1929-79 newsreel, including the Look at Life collection.

British Pathe
4th Floor, 60 Charlotte Street, London W1P 2AX
Fax 020-7436 3232 Tel 020-7323 0407
E-mail: pathe@enterprise.net
Website: www.britishpathe.com
50m feet of historical film footage from 1895 to 1970.

Carlton International Media
35-38 Portman Square, London W1H 0NV
Tel 020-7224 3339
E-mail: wnqiries@carltonint.co.uk
300 films and 5,000 hours of television which Carlton bought from Seagram for $150 million in January 19999. Formerly the ITC film library, aka Polygram Film and Entertainment Library.

Central Office of Information Footage File
4th Floor, 184-192 Drummond Street, London NW1 3HP
Fax 020-7383 2333 Tel 020-7383 2288
E-mail: filmimages@compuserve.com
40,000 Crown Copyright titles from the government's News and Information archives spanning over 75 years of British industrial, political, social and sporting history.

Channel 4 Clip Library
Channel 4 International, 124 Horseferry Road, London SW1P 2TX
Fax 020-7306 8363 Tel 020-7306 8490
E-mail: caustin@channel4.co.uk
Website: www.chanel4.com

East Anglian Film Archive
University of East Anglia, Norwich NR4 7TJ
Fax 01603-458553 Tel 01603-592664
E-mail: eafa@uea.ac.uk
Web: www.uea.ac.uk/eafa/
Non-profit archive of moving images relating to Beds, Cambs, Essex, Herts, Norfolk and Suffolk from 1896 to the present.

Educational & Television Films
247a Upper Street, London N1 1RU
Fax 020-7226 8016 Tel 020-7226 2298
E-mail: ginny@etvltd.demon.co.uk
Soviet Union, Eastern Europe, China, Vietnam and Cuba.

Energy Film Library
101 Bayham Street, London NW1 0AG
Fax 020-7544 3400 Tel 020-7544 3410
E-mail: energy@getty-images.com
Website: www.digital-energy.com
Stock film library. Short production 35mm footage.

Environmental Investigation Agency
69-85 Old Street, London EC1 9HX
Fax 020-7490 0436 Tel 020-7490 7040
E-mail: eiauk@gn.apc.org
Website: www.pair.com/eia/
Video archive devoted to illegal trade in wild life.

Film Archive Management & Entertainment
See Beulah

Film Images
See Central Office of Information Footage File

Film Research
177-183 Regent Street, London W1R 8LA
Fax 020-7734 8017 Tel 020-7734 1525
E-mail: frps@aol.com.
Provides a research service for footage for all media purposes.

GMTV Library Sales
The London Television Centre, Upper Ground, London SE1 9TT
Fax 020-7827 7043 Tel 020-7827 7363
E-mail: librarysales@gmtv.co.uk
UK and worldwide news, showbiz, fashion and feature items and stockshots from October 1992 to present day.

Huntley Film Archives
78 Mildmay Park, London N1 4PR
Fax 020-7241 4929 Tel 020-7923 0990
E-mail: films@huntleyarchives.com
Website: www.huntleyarchives.com
Adverts, animation, art, dance, education, fashion, features, food, geography, history, industry, media, medicine, music, nature, personalities, places, royalty, science, social history, sport, stills, transport, war.

Image Bank Film
17 Conway Street, London W1P 6EE
Fax 020-7391 9123 Tel 020-7312 0300
E-mail: ukmarketing@theimagebank.com
Website: www.imagebank.co.uk
The largest source of film imagery in the world with footage available from 75 offices worldwide.

Imperial War Museum Film Archive
Lambeth Road, London SE1 6HZ
Fax 020-7416 5299 Tel 020-7416 5291
E-mail: film@iwm.org.uk
Holds material covering all aspects of conflict from the Boer War to Bosnia. Totals 120 million feet of film and 6,000 hours of videotape.

Index Stock Shots
12 Charlotte Mews, London W1P 1LN
Fax 020-7436 8737 Tel 020-7631 0134
E-mail: index@msn.com
Stock footage on 35mm film and tape, including extremes of nature and world climate, time-lapse and aerial photograhy, cities, aircraft and wildlife.

IVN Entertainment
500 Chiswick High Road, London W4 5RG
Fax 020-8956 2339 Tel 020-8956 2454
E-mail: ivnentuk@aol.com
Website: www.ivn.com
Travel, including Reader's Digest and Lonely Planet footage. Free loan of BITC VHS.

ITN Archive
200 Grays Inn Road, London WC1X 8XZ
Fax 020-7430 4453   Tel 020-7430 4480
E-mail: archive.sales@itn.co.uk
Website: www.itnarchive.com
Material spanning the century from the ITN and
Reuters television archives in the UK and the historic
French Pathe´ library.

ITV
The ITV companies have libraries of material:
Anglia	01603-615151
Central	0121-643 9898
Channel Four	020-7396 4444
Granada	0161-827 2207
HTV	029-2059 0590
LWT	020-7620 1620
Meridian	023-8022 2555
Scottish	0141-300 3000
Ulster	028-9032 8122
Yorkshire - Tyne Tees	0113-243 8283

The London Film Archive
78 Mildmay Park, London N1 4PR
Fax 020-7241 4929   Tel 020-7923 4074
London images from 1895 to the present day, including
streets, landmarks, housing, education and the arts.

London Stockshots Library
London News Network, London TV Centre, Upper
Ground, London SE1 9LT
Fax 020-7827 7579   Tel 020-7827 7784
E-mail: lnn-tv.co.uk
Website: www.lnn-tv.co.uk
LNN library of London region coverage during the
nineties.

North West Film Archive
The Manchester Metropolitan University, Minshull
House, 47-49 Chorlton Street, Manchester M1 3EU
Fax 0161-247 3098   Tel 0161-247 3097
E-mail: n.w.filmarchive@mmu.ac.uk
Website: www.nwfa.mmu.ac.uk
Documentary collection about life in the North West
region dating from 1896 to the present. Contact the
commercial access assistant for enquiries.

Nova Productions
11a Winholme, Armthorpe, Doncaster DN3 3AF
                    Tel 01302-833422
Production company with a social documentary archive
of shopping, transport and ways of life. Also runs the
Doncaster Film & Video Archive.

Oxford Scientific Films
Lower Road, Long Hanborough, Oxon OX8 8LL
Fax 01993-882808   Tel 01993-881881
E-mail: enquiries@osf.uk.com
Website: www.osf.uk.com
Natural history films, commercials, non-broadcast film
and extensive stills and footage resources.

Pearson Television International Archive
1 Stephen Street, London W1P 1PJ
Fax 020-7691 6080   Tel 020-7691 6232
E-mail: archive@pearsontv.com
Website: www.pearsontvarchive.com
Footage library dates back to mid-fifties and includes
Thames, Grundy, ACI, Alomo and All American
productions with total of 15,000 hours of programming.

Polygram Film and Television Library
See Carlton International Media

Reuters Television
85 Fleet Street, London EC4P 4AJ
                    Tel 020-7250 1122
TV news archive with over 26,000 hours of material.

Ronald Grant Archive
The Master's House, The Old Lambeth Workhouse, 2
Dugord Way, off Renfrew Road, London SE11 4TH
Fax 020-7840 2299   Tel 020-7840 2200
E-mail: martin@cinemamuseum.org uk
Images of cinema and film from 1896 to present day.

RSPB Film Library
The Lodge, Sandy, Beds SG19 2DL
Fax 01767-692365   Tel 01767-680551
E-mail: birds@rspb.demon.co.uk
Natural history footage (not just birds).

Scottish Film & Television Archive
1 Bowmont Gardens, Glasgow G12 9LR
Fax 0141-377 7413   Tel 0141-337 7400

Sky News Library Sales
Grant Way, Isleworth TW7 5QD
Fax 020-7705 3201   Tel 020-7705 2872/3132
E-mail: libsales@bskyb.com
Website: www.skynewslibsales.co.uk
Sky News, current affairs and entertainment footage
from 1989. Held on-site, available 24 hours a day.

Sports Video Library
TWI, Axis Centre, Burlington Lane, London W4 2TH
Fax 020-8233 5301   Tel 020-8233 5500
E-mail: twiarchive@imgworld.com
Video library of TWI sports programming.

Universal Television International
Oxford House, 76 Oxford Street, London W1N 0HQ
Fax 020-7307 7501   Tel 020-7307 7500
The ATV/ITV libraries from 1955-1981.

Wales Film & Television Archive
Unit 1, Science Park, Cefn Llan, Aberystwyth SY23 3AH
Fax 01970-626008   Tel 01970-626007
E-amil: sgrin@sgrinwales.demon.co.uk
Website: www.sgrinwales.demon.co.uk

Wessex Film & Sound Archive
Sussex Street, Winchester, Hants SO23 8TH
Fax 01962-878681   Tel 01962-847742
E-mail: sadedm@hants.gov.uk

Independent TV producers

KEY CONTACT

Pact
45 Mortimer Street, London W1N 7TD
Fax 020-7331 6700
Tel 020-7331 6000
E-mail: enquiries@pact.co.uk
Website: www.pact.co.uk

123 Productions	020-7263 4199
1A Productions	01360-620855
2.4 Media	01562-822099
3BM Television	020-7439 2664
3Di TV Software	0113-274 4933
400 Company	020-8746 1400
421 Productions	015395-31507

A

A19 Film & Video	0191-565 5709
A38 Films	01822 833955
Aardman Animation	0117-984 8485
Abbey Films	01865-725015
About Face Media	028-9089 4555
Absolutely Productions	020-7930 3113
ABTV	020-7351 7070
Acacia Productions	020-8341 9392
Achievement Concepts	01584-890893
Action Cuts	34 68 150702
Action Time (North)	0161-236 8999
Adams Wooding TV	01453-885700
Addictive Television	020-8960 2233
Adventure Pictures	020-7613 2233
Afro Wisdom Films	020-7490 8386
After Image	020-7737 7300
Age Film & Video	01763-852128
Agenda Television	01792-510635
Agran Barton TV	020-7351 7070
Aimimage Productions	020-7916 3734
Airship Films	0191-233 2001
Alan Torjussen	01222 624669
Alcibiades	020-89688873
Alfalfa Entertainments	020-7284 3275
Alhambra Films	01505 874111
Alive Productions	020-7384 2243
Amirani Films	020-7328 7057
Amy International	01295-760256
Anchor Marine	01548-561511
Andrea Florence	020-7794 3787
angel eye film & tv	020-7437 0082

Animation Partnership	020-7636 3300
Annalogue	020-8743 3630
Annex (Films)	020-7734 4471
Antelope	020-7209 0099
Antelope South	01273-648800
Antidote	01225-722262
Antonine Films	0141-420 3410
Apex TV	01223-872900
Aphrodisia Films	0191-281 7289
Approaching Fish	020-8960 6616
Apt Film & TV	020-7284 1695
Arcadia Films	020-7235 5935
Arcadian Productions	01484-515123
Ardent Productions	01276-456000
Aries Productions	01372-457724
Ark Productions	020-8788 8762
Armac Films	0141-337 2322
Armadillo Films	020-7439 0400
Arrowhead Productions	020-7376 8222
Arts Council Films	020-7333 0100
ASD Films	020-7437 3898
Asylum Pictures	0131-270 5069
At It Productions	020-7287 6616
Atlantic Eye	020-7403 8528
Atlantic Productions	020-7371 3200
Atlas Adventures	0117 970 6756
Attic Productions	01423-504386
Atticus TV	020-8876 0406
Aurora Productions	0117-924 3320
Automatic Pictures	01752-344551
Automatic Pilot	020-7494 0544
Available Light	0117-929 1311
Avalon TV	020-7598 7280
AVC Media	01224-248007
Avie Littler Assoc	020-7794 2742
Avonbridge Film	0131-478 4439

B

B&T Productions	020-8525 7812
Bachaks Productions	020-7624 8455
Back2Back TV	020-7431 0202
Bailey Partnership	01727-861449
Baker Tilly	020-7413 5100
Balcony Productions	0141-332 1440
Bamboo Film & TV	020-7916 9353
Bandung	020-7482 5045
Bangaw Cyf	029-2059 0225
Banshee	020-7287 7330
Bard Entertainments	020-7689 4289

Bare Faced Productions	020-7242 3816
Barraclough Carey	020-7258 6800
Barraclough Carey (North)	0161-827 2073
Barrass Company	020-8749 3527
Bazal	020-7462 9000
Beach, The	020-7437 6957
Beach House	020-7240 3385
Beckett Communications	020-8669 8730
Beckmann Productions	01624-816585
Bell TV	01206-240192
Benchmark Fil & TV	01753-630666
Berwick Universal Pictures	020-7923 1998
Besom Productions	01504-370303
Beyond International	020-7636 9611
Beyond the Frame	020-7487 1320
BFI Production	020-7636 5587
Big Bear Films	020-7229 5982
Big Events Co	020-8946 0056
Big Eye Film & TV	0161-832 6111
Big 'H' Productions	01753-501506
Big Idea Productions	020-7224 5100
Big Issue Film Unit	020-7418 0425
Big Strand	020-8876 7047
Big Table Film Co, The	020-7793 4125
Big Talk Productions	020-7255 1131
BigWig Productions	01462-635966
Bitcom International	01483-574545
Bitter & Twisted	020-7254 7737
Black Bear	0131-447 7448
Black Coral	020-8880 4860
Black Hill Productions	01981-240161
Black Lion TV	020-7225 1449
Black Star Films	028-9046 3636
Blackbird Productions	020-7352 4882
Blackstone Pictures	020-7243 3565
Blackwatch Productions	0141-341 0033
Blakeway Productions	020-8743 2040
Blast! Films	020-7267 4260
Blenheim TV Films	01491-614288
Blizzard	020-7488 9098
Blow By Blow Productions	01522-754901

Blue BillieProductions 020-7323 6778
Blue Heaven Productions 020-7404 4222
Blueprint Productions 020-7287 6623
Blue Water Films 020-7609 1362
Boa Picture Co 01252-783385
Bob Godfrey Films 020-7278 5711
Boot 020-7243 3555
Bounds Away 01892-521373
Boxclever Productions 020-7619 0606
Bramble Production 01569-731980
Branded Entertainment 020-7437 4736
Brass Monkey Company, The 020-7229 8893
Break Future 020-8444 3303
Breathing Canyon 020-7437 1309
Brechin Productions 020-8876 2046
Brenda Rowe Productions 0117-973 0390
Brian Waddell Productions 028-9042 7646
Bright Thoughts Co 01934-642732
Brighter Pictures 020-7738 4048
Britt Allcroft Group, The 023-8033 1661
British Car Films 020-7281 2859
British Pathe 020-7323 0407
British Screen 020-7323 9080
Britt Allcroft Company 023-8033 1661
Broad Productions 01505-842840
Broadbent Partnership 0141-332 2042
Broadsword TV 01603-762211
Bronco Films 0141-287 6817
Bronson Knight 020-7734 7042
Brook Lapping Productions 020-7428 3100
Brookside Productions 0151-722 9122
Buena Vista 020-8222 1000
Buffalo Pictures 020-7439 0401
Bumper Films 01934-418961
Buxton Raven 020-7296 0012

C
Cactus Television 020-7465 6232
Cadiz Films 020-8977 7752
Cafe Productions 020-7460 4700
Caledonia, Sterne & Wyld 0141-353 3153
Callister Commuications 01846-673717
Cambrensis 029-2025 7075

Cambridge Film & TV 01223-236007
Cambridge Video 01223-553416
Canopus Communications 020-8318 4707
Canvasback Productions 020-8940 6710
Capital Group Studios 020-8874 0131
Capron Productions 020-8871 5107
Carlton Productions 020-7612 7441
Carlton UK 020-7486 6688
Carlyle TV 020-7439 8967
Carnival Films 020-8968 1818
Carol Gould 020-7266 1953
Carpe Diem Productions 0131-557 0960
Carte Blanche TV Productions 020-7684 0400
Case TV 020-7296 0010
Castle Haven Digital 01557-870366
Cat's Eye 020-7722 9065
Catalist Films 0141-942 5621
Catalyst TV 020-7603 7030
Catherine Bailey 020-7483 2681
Cause n Effect PH 020-7490 0390
CBTV 01434-602867
Celador Productions 020-7240 8101
Celtic Films 020-7637 7651
Celtic Productions 029-2075 2532
Central Reservation 0141-337 3537
Century Films 020-7378 6106
Chain Production 020-7229 4277
Chameleon Television 0113-244 4486
Channel X 020-7387 3874
Chapman Films 020-7287 5416
Chapter One 020-7580 8636
Chariot Productions 0191-230 4449
Charisma Films 020-7610 6830
Charlotte Metcalf Productions 020-7371 2389
Chatsworth 020-7734 4302
Cheeky Ideas 01923-859692
Cheerful Scout 020-7287 0076
Cheerleader Productions 0171 258 6800
Cheriton Enterprises 01963-350113
Children's Film/TV Foundation 020-8953 0844
Children's Film Unit 020-8785 0350
Childsplay Productions 020-7328 1429
Chistera Productions 028-9061 5573
Choi & Co 01904-470787

Christmas TV & Film Co 020-7733 0110
Christopher Swann Assocs 020-8749 9056
Christopher Sykes Production 020-8748 8748
Christopher Young Films 0141-339 1112
Chrysalis Sport 020-7284 2288
Chrysalis Television 020-7465 6353
Chrysalis Visual Entertainment 020-7221 2213
Cicada Films 020-7266 4646
Cin & Beannie 020-8675 7739
Cinar Europe 020-7591 7500
Cine Electra 020-7586-2780
Cine Europe 020-8743 6792
Cinecam Productions 01638-500888
Cinecontact 020-7323 1690
Cinecosse 01358-722150
Cinema Verity 020-7460 2777
Cinesite(Europe) 020-7973 4000
Cinnabar Films 020-8348 0918
City Broadcasting 01565-634083
Clanvisions 028-9042 1232
Clarioncall Film & TV 01943-607553
Clark 020-7388 7700
Class Productions 01462-742914
Classic Film 020-7323 5333
Clear Definition 020-7636 0366
Clearwater Films 020-8995 1308
Cobbetts 0161-833 3333
Coleridge 01752-761138
Columbia Pictues 020-7533 1000
Comedy House 020-7304 0047
Comedy Unit, The 0141 353 1500
Common Features 0191-477 5532
Communicopia 01273-384900
Company Pictures 020-7388 9277
Compulsive Viewing 020-7836 8330
Connections Communications 020-8741 1767
Contrast Films 020-8472 5001
Convergence Productions 020-8993 3666
Cool Beans Productions 0114-267 0704
Cool Crew Company 01292-267281
Cormorant Productions 0131-657 3393
Cornerstone Films 07000-843367
Cosgrove Hall Films 0161-882 2500
Cottonwood Films 020-7385 4323
Couch Potato TV 020-8960 5676
Counterpoint Films 020-7700 4933
Countrywide Films 023-8023 0286

Courtyard Productions 01732-700324
Covent Garden Pioneer 01753-789661
Cowboy Films 020-7287 3808
Creation Company, The 020-7586 7012
Creation Video 0800 7312945
Creative Alliance 020-7637 2927
Creative Film Productions 020-8447 8187
Creative Law 01732-460592
Crew Cut Productions 01738-630815
Crewed Up 0161-442 0603
Crinkle Cut Motion Pictures 0191-284 4073
Cronk Dromgoole 020-7287 4441
Crucial Films 020-7229 8899
Cruickshank Cazenove 020-7735 2933
Crux Productions 01730-894720
Crystal Media 0131-558 8766
CSV Media (Midlands) 0121-683 1800
CTVC 020-8950 4426
Cultural Partnerships 020-7254 8217
Cunliffe & Franklyn 01243-532531
Curtis & Freud 020-7221 9434
Cutting Edge 020-8780 1476
Cyclops Vision 020-7385 5119

D

Dakota Films 020-7287 4329
Dan Films 020-7916 4771
Dancing Fleas 020-7713 1330
Dark Horse Productions 01874-665435
Darlow Smithson Productions 020-7428 7027
Dashwood Productions 01308-420672
Dave Knowles Films 023-8084 2190
Davenhall 01565-653369
David Hickman 020-8995 8016
David Wickes Productions 020-7225 1382
Dawkins Associates 01622-741900
Day-Lewis Productions 01278-671334
Daylight Productions 020-7254 5604
Debonair 020-7251 4451
Deco Films & TV 020-8748 0448
Decoupage Films 01287-633038
Deep Water 0410-095581
Deepwater Productions 01865-450343

Demaine Associates 020-7376 1739
Denham Productions 01752-345444
Dennis Woolf Productions 0161-442 8175
Desmond Wilcox 020-8743 7431
Diamond Time 020-8203 3303
Dibb Directions 020-8748 1579
Dime Goch TV 029-2048 0222
Diplomat Films 0161-929 1603
Direct TV 01865-437878
Disckit 020-8964 2077
Disruptive Element Films 0114-268 1350
Distant Horizon 020-7813 3134
Diva Pictures 020-8567 6655
Diverse Production 020-7603 4567
DLD Films 01707-664063
DLT Entertainment 020-7631 1184
DNA Films 020-7485 4411
Domaine 020-7437 3084
Domino Films 020-7582 0393
Double Band Films 028-9024 3331
Double E Productions 020-8993 2394
Double Exposure 020-7490 2499
Double Take 020-8788 5743
Double-Band Films 028-9024 3331
Douglas Chirnside 020-7287 7027
DOX Productions 020-7602 3094
DPTV 01436-820084
Dragonhorse Productions 020-8549 7149
Drama House 020-7388 9140
Dramatic Productions 0118-975 0754
Dreamchaser 0118-975 0754
Dreug Productions 0141-644 4327
Driftwood Films 020-8332 6365
Duchess Productions 020-7436 8230

E

Eagle & Eagle 020-8995 1884
Eagle Dancer Productions 020-7379 8800
Eagles Productions 0141-639 4217
East Wind Films 01603-628728
ECM Productions 020-7727 5752
Ecosse Films 020-7371 0290
Eden Productions 020-7794 1533
Edinburgh Film 01968-672131
Edinburgh Film & Video 01968-672131
Edinburgh Film Workshop 0131-557 5242
Educational & TV Films 020-7226 2298

Educational Broadcasting 020-7765 5023
EFS TV Production 020-8950 8394
Eight Syndicate 020-8883 9929
Electric Sky 01273-384208
Element Films 01747-851448
Element Productions 0117-973 8799
Elephant Productions 01932-562611
Elgin Productions 020-7727 9174
Elm Road Entertainment 0117-923 2324
Elmgate Productions 01932-562611
Elstree Production Co 01932-572680
Emme Productions 020-7602 2595
Endboard Productions 0121-429 9779
English & Pockett 020-7287 1155
Enigma Productions 020-7222 5757
Enterchoice 020-7373 6796
Entertainment Film Production 020-7439 1606
Eo teilifis 353 91 553500
Eolas 01851-705638
Eon Productions 020-7493 7953
Eos Media 0161-428 6900
EPA International 020-7267 9198
Epicflow Films 020-7328 8768
Equilibrium Films 020-8898 0150
Erik Knudsen Films 01706-813742
Ernst & Young 020-7931 4822
Esta's TV Company 020-8741 2843
Euphoria Films 020-7226 4224
EuroArt Media 020-7221 4162
Euroarts-Primetime 020-7935 9000
Evans Woolfe 020-8287 4445
Excalibur Productions 01422-843871
Excelsior Group Productions 01737-812673
Extreme Film & TV 01247-888900
Eye Eye 020-7485 6924
Eye Film & TV 01379-870083
Eye to Eye TV 020-7498 5335

F

Fabulous Fruits	0131-229 5370
Face Films International	020-8898 6328
Faction Films	020-7608 0654
Fair Game Films	020-7286 8602
Fairline	0141-331 0077
Fairwater Films	029-2057 8488
Farnham Film	01252-710313
Farthings Productions	020-8974 8060
Fat Chance Productions	0117-972 2725
Fat Pictures	020-7267 9535
Feature Films	01202-736666
Feelgood Fiction	020-8746 2535
Felgate Media	020-7624 1525
Feline Films	01225-461138
Festival Film & TV	020-8297 9999
Fflic	029-2040 9000
Field Illeray	01360-770805
Fierce Bird Films	020-8767 8397
Figment Films	020-7287 3209
Fillum	028-9031 4826
Film Bakery	020-8449 1128
Film Company, The	020-7586 3686
Film Education	020-7976 2291
Film Form Productions	020-7794 6967
Film Four International	020-7306 8602
Film & General Productions	020-7221 1141
Film Master Film	39 6 5925926
Film Video Multimedia	01708-250870
FilmFair Animation	020-8960 6415
Filmhouse	020-7734 7743
Filmit	020-7738 4175
FilmNOVA	0191-402 0017
Films Of Record	020-7286 0333
Filmworks	020-8741 5631
Final Draft Films	020-7386 7010
Fine Art Productions	020-7321 0011
Finetake Productions	020-7359 5786
First Avenue Films	01663-733684
First Choice Productions	020-7485 5000
First Circle Films	020-7221 3737
First City Features	020-7437 3344
First Day Productions	020-8692 8691
First Film Company	020-7439 1640
First Freedom Productions	020-7916 9355
First Growth	020-7434 3655
First Light Films	01273-327344

First Light Productions	0141-226 2255
First Take Films	01603-615151
Firstmile	020-8785 9268
Flashback Communication	0141-554 6868
Flashback Television	020-7490 8996
Flicker Films	020-7289 7964
Flipside Films	020-8788 2102
Flying Brick Films	020-7249 7440
Flying Dutchman Co, The	020-7223 9067
Flying Elephant	020-8230 6920
Flying Fox Films	028-9024 4811
Focus Films	020-7435 9004
Focus International TV	020-7493 8801
Focus Productions	01789-298948
Folio Productions	020-7258 6800
Footage Productions	028-9023 7326
Footprint Films	07002-366877
Footstep Productions	020-7836 9990
Forget About It Films	029-20319377
Formation Films	020-8960 1647
Forward Films/Altogether Now	020-8881 9006
Foundation TV	01622-691111
Foundry Productions	020-7793 9976
Fountain TV	020-8900 1188
Fragile Films	020-7287 6200
Frances Anderson	0121-693 3505
Fred Wolf Films	353 1 478 3199
Frantic Productions	020-8866 2430
Free Spirit Films	0117-924 3595
Freeform Productions	020-8986 3425
Freelance Film Partners	020-7328 8202
Freeway Films	020-7937 9114
Fremantle Productions	020-7284 0880
Fresh Air Productions	0161-491 0700
Friday Productions	020-7730 0608
Front Page Films	020-7329 6866
Frontier Films	353 1 497 7077
Frontrunner Films	020-7436 5373
Fugitive Group	020-7242 6969
Fuji International	020-7734 8888
Fulcrum Productions	020-7253 0353
Full On Films	0961-361823
Fulmar West TV & Film	029-2045 5000
Furlong & Power	0151-283 1132

G

GM Productions	0141-357 5066
Gabriel Productions	01225-311194
Gabriela Productions	020-8993 3158
Gael Media	353 91-592 888
Gainsborough Productions	01753-651700
Galafilm	1 514 987 9972
Garfield Kennedy Co	0141-353 0456
Gauntlet Pictures	01225-481199
Gauvain Productions	01508 532682
Gavin Weightman	020-7704 2452
Geestor Productions	020-8985 7726
Geofilms	01235-537400
Getzels/Gordon	01865-512556
Gimlet Productions	020-7350 2878
Ginger	020-7663 2000
Giro Rosso	01865-308 397
Glasgow Film & Video Workshop	0141-553 2620
Glasgow Film Office	0141-287 0424
Glass Pictures	020-7609 3360
Glasshead	020-8876 7598
Glen Wilhide	020-7261 3079
Global Arts	020-8731 6811
Global Productions	0117-946 6110
Global Sports Productions	020-7610 6444
GM Partnership, The	0161-929 8339
GMG Endemol Ent	020-7462 9000
GMTV	020-7827 7000
GNU Productions	020-7267 3399
Gold Productions	01723-366582
Goldcrest Films & TV	020-7437 8696
Golden Eagles Production	0141-331 0525
Golden Square Pictures	020-7446 0080
Goldhawk Media	01494-729777
Goldwyn Films	020-7333 8877
Gordon Getzels	01865-512556
Gorilla Entertainment	020-7792 9364
Gosh! Films	0141-353 0456
Grade Company, The	020-7409 1925
Granada Film Productions	0161-827 2090
Granite Film & TV	020-7354 3232
Grant Naylor Productions	01932-572175
Grant Thornton	020-7229 9181
Graphite Film & TV	020-8994 6617

Grasshopper Productions
020-7229 1181
Green House Productions
020-8780 5960
Green Inc Productions
028-9057 3000
Green Umbrella 0117-973 1729
Greenlit Productions
020-7439 6969
Greenpark Productions
01566-782178
Greenpoint Films 020-7437 6492
Gruber Films 020-7436 3413
Gwynhelek Productions
01736-762132

H
Halcyon Films 020-7352 0209
Half Way Production House
020-8673 7926
Halo Productions 020-7379 7398
Hamilton TV 01298-79424
Hammer Film Productions
020-8207 4011
Hand Pict Productions
0131-558 1543
HandMade Films 020-7434 3132
Hanrahan TV Productions
01789-450182
Hanson TV 020-7371 8381
Harbottle & Lewis 020-7629 7633
Harcourt Films 020-7267 0882
Hart Ryan Productions
020-7403 6363
Hartswood Films 020-8607 8736
HarumScarum Films
01225-329400
Harvest Films 0117-974 4823
Hasan Shah Films 020-7722 2419
Hat Trick Productions
020-7434 2451
Hawkshead 020-7462 9555
Hayes Bolton 020-7209 2244
HD Thames 020-7437 2737
HEADflicks 020-7494 2329
Headlightvision 020-7287 1953
Healthcare Productions
020-7721 7150
Heart of England Productions
01789-298100
Heavy Entertainment
020-8960 9001
Helen Langridge Associates
020-7299 1000
Hewland International
020-7916 2266
Hexagon Productions
020-7437 1552
Hibbert Ralph Entertainment
020-7240 5787

Highflyer Productions
01653-658599
Hightimes Prods 020-8892 2724
Hindi Picture 020-8245 2534
Hit Entertainment 020-7224 1717
Hobson's Production Co
020-8742 7118
Holdings Ecosse 0131-557 2678
Hollyoaks Productions
0151-722 9122
Hollywood Reporter, The
020-7323 6686
Holmes Associates 020-7813 4333
Horrod & Harris 020-7430 1014
Horsepower Films 020-7287 7322
Hot Formats 020-7434 2122
Hot Property Films 020-7323 9466
Hot Shot Films 028-9031 3332
Hourglass Pictures 020-8540 8786
Hungry Horse Pictures
020-7734 7979
Hunkydory 34 68 150702
Hunter Productions 0141-943 2226
Hutchins Film Co 020-7636 2104
Hyphen Films 020-7734 0632

I
Iambic Productions 020-7487 1334
Icon Entertainment 020-7543 4300
Icon Films 0117-924 8535
Ideal World Productions
0141-353 3222
IKG Productions 020-7384 3381
Illuminations Films 020-7226 0266
Illuminations TV 020-7226 0266
Illustra TV 020-7437 9611
Images First 020-8579 6848
Imagicians 020-7287 5211
Imagination 020-7323 3300
Imago Productions 01603-752684
INCA 020-8255 6255
Independent Image 020-7292 4300
Independent Production Co
020-7245 1288
Index Entertainment 020-7240 9494
Indica Films 020-7287 4228
Indigo Television 020-7486 4443
Initial 020-7462 9999
INP 020-7229 1265
Inside Broadcast 020-7689 8899
Insight Films 020-7252 5328
Insight Productions 01647-432686
Interesting Television
01926-844044
Interim films 020-7482 2635
Intermedia Film 0115-955 6909
International Films 01732-874784
International News Productions
020-7229 1265
Intrepid Films 020-7435 9590

Intrinsica Films 020-7923 7070
Invideo Productions 0131-557 2151
Invincible Films 020-8237 1150
InVision Productions
020-7371 2123
IPCA 0117-942 8582
IPH 020-7207 2965
Ipso Facto Films 0191-230 2585
IPTV 0131-659 6566
Iron Bridge/No Cake
020-8444 9574
Isis Productions 020-8748 3042
IWT TV 020-7460 1106

J
J & M Entertainment
020-7723 6544
Jacaranda Productions
020-8741 9088
Jane Balfour Films 020-7267 5392
Jane Walmsley Productions
020-7290 2676
January Films 0141-339 5504
Jay TV 0191-201 2131
Jeremy Isaacs Productions
020-7240 9920
Jerusalem 020-7410 7038
Jim Henson Productions
020-7428 4000
Jo and Co 020-8878 5455
Jo Lustig 01223-461001
Jo Manuel Productions
020-8930 0777
John Adams TV 01453-885700
John Cary Studios 020-7637 4760
John Gau Productions
020-7381 8182
John Lawrence Enterprises
020-8933 8414
John Peel Productions
01697-371703
Jon Blair Film Co 020-7839 3444
JT Fleming 020-8207 2041
Judy Counihan 020-7287 4329
Julian Seddon 020-7831 3033
Junction Five 020-8758 8673
Juniper 020-7722 7111
Just Television 020-7404 6744

K

Kai Productions	020-8673 4550
Karma Productions	01455-202278
Kayfay Productions	020-7485 9352
Kazan River Productions	
	01603-872336
Kelnat	020-8582 1960
Kennedy Mellor	020-7483 3241
Keo Films	020-7490 3580
Kestrel Film Company	
	020-8788 6244
Keystone (Ealing)	020-8993 7441
Kilroy Television	020-8943 3555
Kinetic Film	020-7610 6619
King Rollo Films	01404-45218
Kingfisher TV Productions	
	0115-964 5226
Kingsfire Services	020-7584 1664
KPA TV	0121-248 3900
Kudos Productions	020-7580 8686

L

L&M Productions Ireland	
	353 1 670 9389
La Plante Productions	
	020-7734 6767
Lake Productions	020-7388 9277
Lambent Productions	
	020-7609 3881
Landmark Productions	
	01962-734227
Landseer Film & TV	020-7485 7333
Langham Productions	
	020-8743 7431
Large Door	020-7978 9500
Last Ditch TV	01986-892549
Lateral Productions	020-7372 7566
Lauderdale Productions	
	020-8780 0072
Laurel Productions	020-7267 9399
Lauriston Film & TV Production	
	020-7485 6302
Lawless Films	020-8566 0993
Lawson Productions	
	04-046 9497
Leading Ladies Film Co	
	020-7229 5529
Learning Media	020-8332 9984
Leda Serene	020-8969 7094
Lee-Wright Productions	
	01494 446429
Left Handed Pictures	
	020-7735 2933
Legacy Films	020-8341 1911
Legend Productions	
	020-8940 8285
Leila Films	020-8291 6339
Leisure Time Midlands	
	01564-742520

Leisure Time Productions	
	020-7837 8777
Leman Productions	0131-447 1082
Lexington Films	020-7328 6337
Liba Productions	020-8904 8136
Libra Films	020-7385 8899
Lichen Films	0131-667 4110
Lifesize Pictures	0114-249 2211
Lifetime Group	020-7577 7500
Lighthouse Films	01406-351522
Lightyears Films	0191-259 5408
Like Minds	0121-523 1212
Lilyville Productions	020-7371 5940
Lime Street	0151-236 7636
Limited Company Limited	
	020-7439 4277
Lindley Stone	020-7379 8664
Line TV	020-7792 8480
Link Entertainment	020-8996 4800
Lion TV	020-8735 4000
Lionhead Productions	
	020-8749 6071
Lionheart Contracts	01932-761079
Lionsgate Media	020-8977 3252
Little Bird Co	020-7434 1131
Little Dancer Films	020-8653 9343
Living Tape Productions	
	020-7439 6301
Lluniau Lliw Cyf	029-2025 5630
Loaded Productions	
	0141-337 3025
Lodestar Productions	
	020-7287 3302
Lomond TV	0141-420 3132
London Film & Video Dev.	
	020-7383 7755
London Post	020-7439 9080
London Weekend TV	
	020-7620 1620
Longbow Productions	
	01822-610210
Longeye	020-7624 5444
Look Lively TV	023-8069 5550
Loose Arrangement Film & TV	
	020-8995 5833
Loose Moose	020-7287 3821
Loud Mouse Productions	
	020-7371 9429
Loud Productions	020-7359 0275
Louise Panton Productions	
	020-7284 2870
Lucas Media	0870-707 0870
Lucida Productions	020-8699 5070
Lucinda Broadbent	0141-332 2042
Lucky World Productions	
	020-8883 3900
Lunchtime Productions	
	020-7316 1827

Lusia Films	0171436 3050
Luther Pendragon	020-7353 1500

M

ML International Pictures	
	020-7460 6465
MASC Productions	020-8769 2286
MacHeath Productions	
	01952-201212
MacIntyre & Co	020-7242 0242
Macmillan Media	028-9068 3800
Magic Lantern Productions	
	020-8769 6116
Magic Stone	0141-569 1489
Mair Golden Moments	
	020-8743 7152
Makar Productions	0131-226 7077
Malachite Productions	
	01790-763538
Malavan Media	020-7794 5509
Mallinson Film	0141-332 0589
Mallory Films	01396-830160
Malone Gill Productions	
	020-7460 4683
Man Alive Group	020-8743 7431
Man-Made	020-7736 7110
March Hare Productions	
	01884-820877
Marchmont Films	0131-228 1562
Marie Hoy Film	020-7493 3345
Mark 4 Film & TV	01932-227675
Mark Forstater Productions	
	020-7624 1123
Mark Patterson & Associates	
	01895-673610
Mars Productions	020-7792 8584
Martin Gates Productions	
	020-7580 8440
Martin Pope Productions	
	020-7734 6911
MASC Productions	020-8769 2286
Matinee Films	020-7739 7528
Maverick Enterprises	
	020-8459 3858
Maverick Television	0121-771 1812
Maya Vision	020-7836 1113
Mayfair Entertainment	
	020-7304 7911
Mayfair Productions	020-7491 4585
MBC Midlands	0121-233 9944
MBC North	0161-827 2073
McConnell Film Assoc	
	0141-337 1414
McDougall Craig	020-7240 7272
McGuffin Films	020-8672 7089
McKenna & Co	020-7606 9000
Media Circus	020-7341 9752
Media Europe	020-8449 1128
Media Pictures	01746-781068

Meditel Productions 020-7833 4959
Melrose Film Productions
　020-7627 8404
Memoir Film Productions
　0191-265 2215
Mental Health Media
　020-7700 8131
Mentorn Barraclough Carey
　020-7258 6800
Mentorn Films　020-7734 7067
Mentorn Midlands　0121-233 9944
Merchant Ivory Productions
　020-7437 1200
Merlin Films　0191-414 7995
Mersey Television　0151-722 9122
Mersham Productions
　01233-503636
Metamedia Productions
　020-7287 6690
Michael Cole Productions
　020-8994 4821
Michael Howes Productions
　020-7928 7851
Michael Weigall Productions
　020-7229 5725
Michael White　020-7734 7707
Michaelides & Bednash
　020-7468 1168
Middlemarch Films　020-7371 4596
Midlantic Films Inc UK
　020-7240 9823
Migrant Media　020-7254 9701
Mike Mansfield TV　020-7580 2581
Millar Movies　020-7370 1830
Mills Video Company
　0151-709 9822
Mintai　029-2048 9813
Miramax Hal Films　011-535 8300
Mirror Image Productions
　0976-794418
Mirus Production　020-8740 5505
MJW Productions　020-7713 0400
MKP　01223-843277
ML International Pictures
　020-7460 6465
MNE TV　0141-353 3135
Mogul TV　01344-622140
Molehill Productions 023-8061 5688
Molitor Productions 020-7491 3985
Momentum Video　020-7729 3536
Monogram Productions
　020-7734 9873
Moonbase Alpha Productions
　020-7493 6707
Moondance Films & TV
　020-7323 6458
Moondog Productions
　028-9057 2500
Moonstone Films　020-8998 6016

Mosaic Films　01594-530708
Mosaic　01594-530708
Mostly Movies　020-8788 6120
Move On Up　01381-600777
Moving Image Development
　0151-708 9858
Moving Still Productions
　353 1 670 9275
Multi Media Arts　0151-476 6050
Multi-Story Productions
　01483-416336
Music Box　020-7478 7300
Music Mall　020-7534 1444
Music House (International)
　020-7434 9678
Music on Earth　020-8998 5675
Muso　020-7240 1140

N

Naked Ape　0117-973 2775
Naked Film　0131-478 1111
National Film & TV School
　01494-671234
Nautilus Films　020-8348 6683
NCTV　01224-492020
Nebraska Productions
　020-8444 5317
Nelvana Enterprises 020-7287 2770
Network Five TV　01902-640014
Never Summer Productions
　07071-222171
New Era TV　020-7927 8817
New Media TV　01904-621331
New Street Productions
　0121-248 2425
NFH　020-7584 7561
Nicholas Claxton Productions
　020-8956 2261
Nick Patten Productions
　0121-693 7117
NMTV　01904-621331
Noble Films　020-7655 1177
Nobles Gate　020-8994 8161
Noel Gay Motion Picture Co
　020-8600 5200
NoHo Digital　020-7299 3434
Normal Films　020-7437 6413
North South Productions
　020-7388 0351
Northern Exposure TV Co
　0161-839 9394
Northlight Productions
　01224-646460
Northridge Entertainment
　020-8455 7125
Notre Dame Films　020-7370 7653
Nova Inc Fim & TV　0151-474 9176
Nova Productions　01302-833422
NVC Arts　020-7388 3833

O

Oaklawn Entertainment
　020-8946 4748
Oasis Media　020-7450 9050
Objective Productions
　020-8348 5899
Ocicat　020-8995 8991
Octagon Pictures　020-7834 0088
October Films　020-7916 7198
Oil Factory　020-7837 0007
Old Street Films　01865-722357
ON TV　01235-537400
One Lung Productions
　020-7490 4433
One Way Film　020-7978 6788
Open Eye Productions
　020-7287 4177
Open Media　020-7229 5416
Open Mike Productions
　020-7434 4004
Open Mind　020-7437 0624
Optomen TV　020-7967 1234
Opus TV　01222 -223456
OR Media　020-8987 1000
Orbit Media　020-7221 5548
Oriana Production　020-8964 8221
Origami Films　01572-747692
Orlando TV Productions
　01608-683218
Orpheus Productions
　020-8892 3172
Otmoor Productions
　01865-331445
Outrider International
　020-7723 6021
Oxford Scientific Films
　01993-881881
Oxford Television Company
　020-7483 3637
Oxymoron Films　020-7437 5905
Oyster Productions 020-8960 0108

P

Pacific 1	020-7287 2233
Pagnamenta Assoc	020-7727 9960
Pagoda Film & TV	020-7534 3500
Palace Gate Productions	020-7584 3025
Paladin Pictures	020-8956 2260
Palindrome Productions	020-7262 7484
Palm Tree Productions	0141-552 3774
Panache Pictures	020-8809 7465
Parallax Pictures	020-7836 1478
Parallel Pictures	020-8758 8603
Paramount Pay TV	020-8563 4158
Parisio Productions	020-7250 3630
Parker Mead	020-8579 1082
Parkside Productions	01268 472242
Partners in Production	020-7490 5042
Partridge Films	0117-972 3777
Passion Pictures	020-7323 9933
Pathe Productions	020-7323 5151
Pathway Productions	0131-447 3531
Paul Berriff Productions	01482-641158
Paul Martingell	020-8893 3743
Paul Trijbits Productions	020-7439 4343
Pauline Muirhead Productions	0131-476 9598
PDP	01465-871219
Peakviewing Productions	01452 863217
Pearl Catlin Associates	01483-567932
Pearson TV	020-7691 6991
Pelicula Films	0141-287 9522
Pendragon Productions	020-7353 1500
Peninsula Films	020-8964 2304
Pentagon Communications	01482-226298
Penumbra Productions	020-7328 4550
Pepper's Ghost	020-8481 6700
Performance Films	01494-670505
Periwinkle Productions	01489-572009
Perx Productions	0113-274 2379
Peter Batty Productions	020-8942 6304
Peter Sasdy Productions	020-8783 1147
Peter Williams TV	01622-684545
Peters Fraser	020-7344 1000

PGTV	0 411 275220
Phoenix TV Productions	020-7386 5810
Photoplay Productions	020-7722 2500
Picasso Pictures	020-7437 9888
Pictorial Heroes	0141-550 0875
Picture Factory	020-8347 9233
Picture House Productions	0117-973 8859
Picture Palace Films	020-7586 8763
Picture This Independent Film	0117-972 1002
Picturehead	01962-865454
Pierrot Productions	020-8858 0846
Pilgrim Films	0191-230 3930
Pillarbox Productions	020-7700 0505
Pilot Film & TV Productions	020-8960 2771
Pineapple Productions	020-7234 0050
Pioneer Film & TV Productions	01753-650500
Piotrowska Films	020-8748 4518
Pirate Productions	0141-337 1333
Pizazz Pictures	020-7434 3581
Planet 24	020-7512 5328
Planet Wild	0151-288 8000
Platform Films & Video	020-7278 8394
Platinum Film & TV	020-7916 9091
PMA	020-8893 3743
PM Murphy Productions	01865-553717
Point Sound & Vision	020-7616 8100
Pola Jones Film	020-7439 1165
Polite Company	020-8567 0437
Polkadot Productions	020-7831 4002
Polygram Film	020-7307 1300
Pomegranate Pictures	020-7935 3400
Poolbeg	353-1 676 2521
Poorhouse Productions	020-7439 2637
Popular Films	020-7419 0722
Portman Entertainment	020-7468 3440
Portobello Pictures	020-7379 5566
Poseidon Productions	020-7734 4441
Post Raphaelite Productions	01189-505352
Pozzitive	020-7734 3258
Praxis Films	01472-398547
Precise Media	0870-607 1254

Premiere Productions	020-7255 1650
Presentable Productions	029-2055729
Pressure Cooker	020-7722 9314
ProBRO Int	01757-288201
Primetime Television	020-7935 9000
Princess Productions	020-7261 3384
Principal Media Group	020-7928 9882
Prisma Sports	020-7291 8800
Producers Productions	020-7636 4226
Projector Productions	020-7434 1110
Promenade Film Productions	020-7813 0208
Prominent Features	020-7497 1100
Propeller Productions	029-2037 7128
Prospect Cymru Wales	029-2070 0580
Prospect Pictures	020-7636 1234
Pueblo Productions	020-8969 2134
Pukka Films	020-7437 4220
Pulse Productions	020-7794 1514
Puppetoon Productions	020-7636 2000
Purple Frog	01273-735475

Q

Quadrant Broadcast	029-2023 7333
Quadriga	020-8614 2339
Quadrillion	01628-487522
Quality Duo	0467-785683
Quality Time TV	01672-540281
Quanta	01666 826366
Quicksilver Films	020-7603 8339
Quintessence Films	01626-770750

R

Radix	020-7437 8696
Ragdoll Productions	01753-631800
Raphael Associates	020-7265 1620
Rapid Eye Movies	020-7613 0010
Rapido TV	020-7229 9854
Raw Charm	029-2064 1511
Raw Nerve Productions	01504-260562
Rawle Partnership	01702-353359
Ray Fitzwalter Associates	0161-832 3337
RDF Television	020-7887 7500
RD Productions	020-8780 3819
Real Life Productions	0113-234 7271

Real Radio & Television
01275-375861
Real World Pictures 020-7978 1178
Really Animated Productions
01625-612459
Really Useful Video Production Co
020-7240 0880
REB Productions 020-8891 4225
Rebecca Television 020-7923 7166
Recorded Delivery 020-7431 0064
Recorded Picture Co
020-7636 2251
Red Door Productions
020-7637 3220
Red Galaxy Pictures 020-7622 2230
Red Green and Blue Company
020-8746 0616
Red Letter Productions
01442 833126
Red Production Co 0161-798 9644
Redlight Productions
0141-337 3269
Redwave Films 020-7753 7200
Reel Life Television 020-7713 1585
Reel Scoop 0141-632 3345
Reg Grundy Productions
020-7691 6000
Regent Productions 020-8789 5350
Reiner Moritz Associates
020-7439 2637
Remote Films 020-7738 2727
Renegade Films 020-7637 0957
Replay 020-8672 0606
Resource Base 023-8023 6806
Retribution Films 020-8874 3457
Reuters Television 020-7250 1122
Revere Entertainment
020-7304 0047
Revolution Films 020-7242 0372
rgo Communications
020-8968 9992
Richard Butler 020-7247 6555
Richmond Films & TV
020-7734 9313
Richmond Light Horse
020-7937 9315
Ricochet Films 020-7251 6966
Ritefilms 01303-252335
Riverfront Pictures 020-7481 2939
RM Associates 020-7439 2637
R One Productions 0141-570 1425
Roadhouse 020-7793 4200
Roadshow Productions
020-7584 0542
Roberts & Wykeham Films
020-7602 4897
Rock Sound films 020-8746 1566
Rocket Pictures 020-8741 9090
Rodney Read 020-8891 2875

Roger Bolton Productions
020-7209 2244
Rohan-Asher Media 020-8968 1696
Rooftop Productions
020-7523 2403
Rose Bay Film Productions
020-8600 5200
Rosetta Pictures 020-7647 5900
Rosso Productions 01843-823992
Rough Sea Productions
0410 064632
Rubyred Films 020-7820 9703
Rugby Vision Cyffro 01222 666800
Rum tree 01723-871255

S

SATV 0131-558 8148
Safe and Sound Productions
01789-450182
Safir Films 020-8423 0763
Saffron Productions 01440-785200
Sally Head Productions
020-8607 8730
Salsa Rock Productions
01932 856102
Salt Island Productions
028-9057 3000
Samba Films 020-8674 0141
Samuelson Productions
020-7236 5532
Sandercock Films 020-8874 3457
Sands Films 020-7231 2209
Sankofa Film & Video
020-7485 0848
Sarah Radclyffe Productions
020-7437 3128
Saunders & French Productions
020-7344 1010
Scala Productions 020-7734 7060
Science Pictures 01462-421110
Scimitar Films 020-7603 7272
Scope Productions 0141-332 7720
Scorer Associates 0117-946 6838
Scottish Screen 0141-302 1700
Screen First 01825-712034
Screen Partners 020-7247 3444
Screen Resource 01865-744451
Screen Ventures 020-7580 7448
ScreenAge Pictures 020-7225 1783
Screenhouse Productions
0113-242 4900
Secret Garden 01993-831904
September Films 020-7494 1884
Serendipity Picture Company
0117-929 0417
Seventh Art Productions
01273-777678
Seventh House Films
01603-749068

Severn Pictures 01886-884745
SFTV 01844-202027
Shaker Films 020-8968 4278
Sharp Image Productions
020-8674 2466
Sharpshooter Films 020-8743 4237
Shart Bros 020-7263 4435
Shattered Images 020-8946 9865
Shed Productions 020-7359 7655
Sheffield Independent Film
0114-249 2204
Sherbet 020-7636 6435
Shipleys 020-7312 0000
Shona Tribe 020-7460 1960
Shooting Star 020-7409 1925
Shorna Productions 0115-956 5070
Showplay 020-7371 3234
Sigma Films 0141-339 1241
Signals 01206-560255
Siguy Films 020-7437 2890
Silvercreek 01666-503908
Simkins Partnership 020-7631 1050
Sindibad Films 020-7823 7488
Siriol mm 029-2048 8400
Skreba 020-7437 6492
Skreba-Creon Films 020-7437 6492
Skyline Films 020-8354 2236
Skyline Productions 0131-557 4580
Skyscraper Films 020-7625 6465
Smith & Watson Productions
01803-863033
Smoke & Mirrors 020-7468 1003
Snap Productions 020-8346 9310
SohoCommunications
020-7637 5825
Soho Images 020-7437 0831
SOI Film & TV 020-7267 4373
Solid Productions 020-7267 9479
Songbird 020-7249 1477
Soul Purpose Productions
020-8625 1625
South Productions 020-8297 2195
South West Media Development
0117-927 3226
Southern Star 020-7636 9421
Souvenir Productions
0141-423 3835
Spafax 020-7906 2001
Speakeasy Productions
01738-828524
Specific Films 020-7580 7476
Spelthorne 020-8979 6215
Spider Pictures 0171 287 6707
Spike Island 0117-929 7299
Spire Films 01865-371979
Spirit Films 020-7734 6642
Spitfire Films 020-7221 2005
Splash Productions 020-7730 9641
Split Screen 029-2059 0562

Spoken Image (Broadcast)	0161-236 7522
Spot Films	01869-331685
Sprocketeers	0131-553 3935
St Elmo Films	020-8741 7373
St Pancras Films	020-7385 2094
Stagescreen Productions	020-7497 2510
Stampede	020-7729 7174
Stand & Deliver Productions	020-7465 6249
Stark Films	020-7287 3229
Starlock Pictures	020-7734 0535
Stephinson TV	01457-820820
Stikeman	020-7378 0880
Stirling Film	028-9033 3848
Stockbridge Films	07771-921234
Stone City Films	020-7240 8789
Stone House Pictures	01932-571044
Stone Ridge	353-1 8723922
Stories	020-7734 4080
Storm TV	0161-236 6006
Storyland	01334-472542
Storyline	0191-232 2050
Straight Forward Productions	028-9042 6298
Straight TV	0161-228 2228
Strawberry Productions	020-8994 4494
Strawberry Vale Film & TV	020-7494 1399
Stray Cat Motion Pictures	0141-338 6662
Streetwise TV	020-7470 8825
Studio Arts TV	0191-261 2023
Suffolk Films	01986-875875
Suitcase Productions	1-212 863 9702
Sundog Media	01752 265562
Sunstone Films	020-7485 2884
Supervision	020-8251 9500
Susan Young	020-7928 7977
SVC Screen Entertainment	020-7460 6060
Swanlind Communication	0121-616 1701
Sweaterheads Productions	0141-204 2864
Swingbridge Video	0191-232 3762

T

Table Top Productions	020-8742 0507
Taft TV Associates	020-7223 0906
Takeaway Media	020-7267 0166
Talent Television	020-7434 1677
Talisman Films	020-7603 7474
Talkback	020-7323 9777
Tall Order Productions	0121-766 5911
Tall Stories	020-7357 8050
Tandem Television	020-7465 6365
Tangent Films	020-8749 5549
Tapecraft Productions	01986-782266
Tapson Steel Films	020-7287 7244
Taylored Productions	0141-334 1462
TC TV	01962-714359
Telemagination	020-7828 5331
Television Company, The	020-7837 0789
Television Junction	0121-248 4466
Television Sport & Leisure	020-7820 0700
Teliesyn	029-2030 0876
Tell-A-Vision TV	0131-556 3743
Tell-Tale Productions	020-8324 2308
Tempest Films	020-8340 0877
Tern Television Productions	01224-211123
Terra Firma Film Productions	020-7261 0885
Testimony Films	0117-925 8589
That 70's Co	020-8614 2579
Thin Man Films	020-7734 7372
Third Eye Productions	020-8969 8211
Thomas Gray Productions	01865 284236
Thura Film	020-8735 0828
Tiger Aspect	020-7434 0672
Tiger Lily Films	020-7580 0633
Tigervision	020-7383 2267
Tigress Productions	020-7434 4411
Tilt Films	020-7502 7085
Tin Fish Films	020-8874 0342
Titanic	01268-531905
TKO Communications	01273-550088
TNTV	020-7483 3526
Toledo	020-7485 4411
Tomboy Films	020-7436 3324
Tonic Pictures	020-7229 2512
Top Left	0141-357 3657
Topaz Productions	020-8749 2619
Topical TV	023-8071 2233

Total Communications	01983-752326
Touch Productions	01747-828030
Touchdown Films	020-7917 2871
Track 29	0141-424 1124
Trans World International	020-8233 5400
TransAtlantic Films	020-8735 0505
Transmedia Productions	020-7580 6655
Tricorn Associates	020-8995 3898
Triffic Films	01908-261234
Trijbits Productions	020-7439 4343
Triple Echo Productions	01503-272428
True Corner Productions	0151-281 0741
True TV and Film	0141-554 1196
True Visions Productions	020-8742 7852
Try Again	01225-862705
Tucker Partnership	01245-260307
Tullstar Productions	01786-825587
Tumble Hill Productions	029-2059 4044
Turn On Television	020-7729 2611
Turnround	01242-224360
Tu-Tone Productions	020-7221 2213
TV Cartoons	020-7388 2222
TV Choice	020-7379 0873
TV 6	020-7610 0266
TV 6 Scotland	0131-319 2333
TV21	020-7258 6800
TVF	020-7837 3000
Twelfth House	020-7287 2276
Twentieth Century Fox	020-7437 7766
Twenty Twenty Television	020-7284 2020
Two Four Productions	01752-345424
Two Sides TV	020-7439 9882
Ty Gwyn Films	01286-881235
Tyburn Productions	01753-651700

U

Uden Associates	020-7351 1255
Ugly Duckling Productions	0802-774100
Umbrella Entertainment	020-7267 8834
Umbrella Productions	0141-429 1750
Unexpected Producions	020-7209 4661
Unhooked Prods	020-8208 0947
Unicorn Organisation	020-7229 5131
Union Pictures	020-7287 5110
Union Productions	020-8563 0734
United Artists	020-8741 9288
United Peoductions	020-7389 8555
United Broadcasting	020-7389 8654
United Television Artists	020-7831 4433
Universal Pictures	020-8563 4329
Up 'N' Under	01222 255630
Upfront Televison	020-7836 7702
Uptown Films	020-7833 1153

V

Ventura Productions	01926-844066
Vera Productions	020-7436 6116
Vicarious Productions	020-7228 0679
Victor Film Co	020-7494 4477
Victoria Real	01273-702007
Video Arts	020-7637 7288
Video Assignments	020-8343 2513
Video Visuals	020-7384 2243
Videotel Productions	020-7439 6301
Vidfilm Europe	01895-835555
Virtual TV Company	020-7580 9895
Vis Television Services	0116-233 5599
Visage Productions	020-7487 2641
Visible Ink TV	01968-661291
Visible Jazz	020-7403 9333
Visionworks	028-9024 1241
Viz	01383-412811
Vobavision	01903-217567
Volcano Films	020-7424 0146
Vortex TV	020-7485 5326
Voyager Television	01865-407474

W

Wall to Wall Television	020-7485 7424
Waller Film Co	020-8675 0947
Walnut Partnership	0113-245 6913
Wark, Clements & Co	0141-429 1750
Warner Brothers	020-7465 4830
Warner Sisters Film	020-8960 3550
Watchmaker Productions	020-7465 6000
Watchword	020-7381 2168
Watermark Films	020-7243 0259
Watermark Productions	0181746 1634
Wayward Films	020-7587 1007
Weigall Productions	020-7229 5725
West Heath Productions	01730-816062
West Highland Animation	01877-384671
Westbourne Films	020-7221 1998
Westerley Productions	01752-830522
Westmorland Film	01539-624927
Westway Film Production	01504 308383
Whitby Davison Productions	020-8579 3811
White Magic	07000 784707
Whitehorse Films	020-7586 8940
Whitehouse & Co	020-8964 8035
Whole Films	020-7402 3323
Wide Eye Pictures	020-7636 1918
Wild Dream Films	029-2066 6311
Wild & Fresh Productions	020-8440 7889
Wildcard Film and Television	01752 262968
Wild Dream Films	029-2066 6311
Wild Films	020-8672 2489
Wildcat Films	01434 381772
Wildflower Productions	020-7234 0330
Wildtrack TV	0151-330 2081
Winchester TV	020-7434 4374
Windfall Films	020-7637 2666
Wink Productions	07000 788898
Winklemania	01608-644444
Wishbone Productions	020-7642 1755
Wobbly Picture Productions	020-8870 6369
Women Now Films	020-8830 5156
Women's Ind. Cinema House	0151-707 0539
Wonderworks Productions	020-8423 6507

Woodfilm Productions	020-7243 8600
Word-Pictures	01494-481629
Workhouse TV	01962-626400
Working Title Films	020-7307 3000
World of Wonder	020-7737 2222
World Productions	020-7734 3536
World Television	0117-930 4099
World Wide Pictures	020-7434 1121
WorldWide Entertainment News	020-7287 4545
Worldmark Productions	0171 792 9800
WoW Productions	020-8838 2566
Wrench & Franks	020-7250 3026
Writers Republic	020-7613 4705

X

Xanadu Productions	020-7404 2225
Xanthe Film & TV	0131-667 9960
XL Entertainment	07000 953953
XYTV	0113-237 1199

Y

YI Productions	0191-281 2256
Yorkshire Film Co	0113-244 1224
Yorkshire International	0161-827 2887
Yorkshire-Tyne Tees TV	0113-243 8283

Z

Zanzibar Film Productions	01425-472892
ZCZ Films	020-7284 0521
Zebra Film Productions	0117-970 6026
ZEF Productions	01273-384210
Zenith Entertainment	020-7224 2440
Zenith North	0191-261 0077
Zep Tepi/Wiggin O'Neal Films	020-74370551
Zephir Films	020-7431 1534
Zephyr Films	020-7221 8318
Zin Zan Productions	01734-503816
ZKK	020-7482 5885
Zoo Gang	020-8947 2404
Zooid Pictures	020-7281 2407

Radio: Introduction & BBC

British radio is divided between the licence-funded BBC and a growing number of profit making companies. The latter are overseen by the Radio Authority, the statutory equivalent of the Independent Television Commission. Radio companies operate under licence to the Radio Authority which was set up by the 1990 Broadcasting Act. Where the BBC once had a monopoly, the UK now has some 240 radio services, nearly 200 of them provided by commercial broadcasting. The average listener can receive 15 radio stations, six from the BBC and nine from commercial radio. In London, listeners can hear 24 services, of which six are BBC.

There's no doubting the ubiquity of radio. It's the most popular form of broadcasting until 4pm each day and the average person spends more time listening to the radio than reading newspapers and magazines. In the typical British household there are no fewer than six radio sets and every year 12 million more - portables, car stereos, hi-fi tuners and now a sprinkling of digital radios - are sold.

New methods of audience calculation used by Rajar recently revealed that no less than 89 per cent of the population listen to radio at least once a week. "This is a quite extraordinary achievement in a multimedia age," said Jenny Abramsky, the BBC's new director for radio. "Radio listening is extremely healthy and central to people's lives."

Radio bands

	MHz88-90.2	90.2-92.4	92.4-94.6	94.9 London	95.1	95.8	97.3	97.6-99.8
FM	Radio 2	Radio 3	Radio 4	GLR	GMR	CapitalFM	London News	Radio 1
	Light music	Classical	Talk	Pop/talk	All talk	Pop	News	Pop/rock

	194m	206m	1332/1413	1341	247m	261m	275/285	290m
	1548kHz	1458kH	1305kHz	873kHz	1215kH	1152kHz	1089/1053kHz	1035kHz
AM	Capital Gold	Sunrise	Premier	Radio Ulster	Virgin	LBC	Talk Radio	Country
	Oldies/sport	Asian	Christian	General	Pop/rock	Talk/news	Talk/news	C&W

Listening figures

'98 figures in ( )	WEEKLY REACH		AVERAGE HOURS PER LISTENER		SHARE OF LISTENING	
ALL RADIO	42.63m	(40.29)	22.4	(20.7)	100%	(100%)
ALL BBC	30.50m	(26.61)	15.8	(14.7)	50.3%	(46.8%)
BBC Radio 1	10.84m	(9.36m)	8.7	(8.4)	9.8%	(9.5%)
BBC Radio 2	9.67m	(8.79m)	12.7	(12)	12.8%	(12.6%)
BBC Radio 3	2.27m	(2.54m)	5.8	(4)	1.4%	(1.2%)
BBC Radio 4	9.47m	(8.25m)	11.6	(10.4)	11.4%	(10.3%)
BBC Radio 5 Live	5.83m	(5.22m)	6.8	(5.9)	4.2%	(3.7%)
BBC Local/regional	10.20m	(8.59)	9.9	(9.3)	10.6%	(9.6%)
ALL COMMERCIAL	31.48m	(28.65m)	14.4	(14.9)	47.5%	(51.5%)
All national commercial	12.34m	(11.83m)	7.3	(7.2)	9.4%	(10.2%)
Atlantic 252	2.28m	(2.97m)	4.3	(4.9)	1.0%	(1.7%)
Classic FM	6.03m	(5.05m)	6.8	(6.1)	4.3%	(3.7%)
Talk Radio	2.32m	(2.38m)	7.3	(6)	1.8%	(1.8%)
Virgin Radio	3.52m	(3.36m)	6.5	(7.4)	2.4%	(3%)
All local commercial	26.37m	(23.84m)	13.8	(14.3)	38.1%	(40.8%)

Source: Rajar, March 1999

The BBC runs five national networks and 38 local radio stations serving England and the Channel Islands, and national regional radio services in Scotland, Wales and Northern Ireland, including Welsh and Gaelic language stations. This is a vast operation but one which nonetheless often seems a subsidiary to the BBC's main preoccupation with television and its digital futures.

In November 1998, against her own and others expectations, Jenny Abramsky was appointed BBC director of radio. It put the top job into popular and experienced hands and the woman who launched Radio 5 and who has edited all Radio 4's top news programmes identified two main tasks. First was "repairing" the divide between programme commissioners and producers, second to answer the critics who say Radio 3 is going for audience-grabbing

Jenny Abramsky, the new BBC director of radio

Ball added 500,000 listeners to the vital breakfast show and trumped Chris Evans, her even more mouthy rival over at Virgin Radio who only managed an to secure an extra 63,000 listeners. Radio 5 Live had its strongest year yet with 5.2 million regular listeners. Radio 2's

100 London			102.2			
102.-Manchester	100.7 Midlands	100-101.9	100.4	105.4	105.8 London/SE	106.2 London
KissFM	Heart	Classic FM	JazzFM	Melody	Virgin	Heart
Dance	Adult pop	Classical	Jazz/blues	Light music	Pop/rock	Adult pop

330/433m			417/1500m (lw)	463m
909/693kHz	882kHz	810kHz	720/198kHz	648kHz
Radio 5 Live	Radio Wales	Radio Scotland	Radio 4	World Service
News/sport	General	General	Talk/general	General

inanities. Her solution here isn't to go for audience share but to encourage "quality and intelligence" and to let licence payers "know how their licence fee is being spent".

Abramsky has been fortunate in taking over a ship that has sailed out of some choppy waters, including a move to west London from the wonderful ship-shaped BBC building in Portland Place. A year after the spring 1998 Radio 4 revamp, the schedule changes finally began yielding increased audience figures after falling to an autumn low of 7.68 million. For once, the spring 1999 Rajar figures told an encouraging story. Middle England had swallowed the moving of the Archers and the axing of Sport on Four, Kaleidoscope and Week Ending. James Boyle, the station controller who said he would quit if his overhaul failed, was not obliged to "fall on [his] sword". On Radio 1 Zoe

expanded audience held fast with its forty something diet of "popular music with lyrics people can remember". Radio 2's support of old acts like Blondie and Aerosmith managed to propel some oldies back into the pop charts. And even Radio 3 was able to attract an extra 130,000 listeners.

A notable voice of dissent - and one who remains a regular Radio 4 presenter- is Libby Purves who used her column in the Times to say: "TV people have always despised radio, and now they have power over it. Those at the top of the BBC think of themselves as running a television service, and radio is a distraction. They have no feeling for it. This is the heart of the problem, and those who want Britain to keep its unique service of crafted speech radio should not be distracted by the Rajar-Boyle-dumbdown business."

BBC NATIONAL RADIO

Administratively, Radio 1, 2, 3 and 4 belong the BBC's Broadcast directorate while Radio 5 comes under the BBC News directorate.

BBC Radio HQ
Broadcasting House, Portland Place, London W1A 1AA
Publicity office: 020-7765 4990
Director of radio: Jenny Abramsky
Managing Editor, digital radio: Glyn Jones

Radio 1
Broadcasting House, Portland Place, London W1A 1AA
Publicity office: 020-7765 4575
Controller, Radio 1: Andy Parfitt
Managing editor: Ian Parkinson

Radio 2
Broadcasting House, Portland Place, London W1A 1AA
Publicity office: 020-7765 4330
Controller, Radio 2: Jim Moir
Managing editor: Lesley Douglas

Radio 3
Broadcasting House, Portland Place, London W1A 1AA
Publicity office: 020-7765 2722
Controller, Radio 3: Roger Wright
Managing editor: Brian Barfield

Radio 4
Broadcasting House, Portland Place, London W1A 1AA
Publicity office: 020-7765 5337
Controller, Radio 4: James Boyle

Radio 5 Live
Television Centre, Wood Lane, London W12 7RJ
Publicity office: 020-7765 4990
Controller, Radio 5 Live: Roger Mosey
Controller, radio sports rights and deputy controller, Radio 5 Live: Mike Lewis

BBC LOCAL RADIO: SOUTH

BBC Radio Bristol
PO Box 194, Bristol BS99 7QT
Tel 0117-974 1111
BBC Radio Cornwall
Phoenix Wharf, Truro, Cornwall TR1 1UA
Tel 01872-275421
BBC Radio Devon
Broadcasting House, Seymour Road, Mannamead, Plymouth PL3 5BD
Fax 01752-234599   Tel 01752-260323
BBC Radio Gloucestershire
London Road, Gloucester GL1 1SW
Tel 01452-308585
BBC GLR 94.9 (London)
PO Box 94.9, 35c Marylebone High Street, London W1A 4LG
Tel 020-7224 2424
BBC Radio Guernsey
Commerce House, Les Banques, St Peter Port, Guernsey GY1 2HS
Tel 01481-728977
BBC Radio Jersey
18 Parade Road, St Helier, Jersey JE2 3PL
Tel 01534-870000
BBC Radio Kent
Sun Pier, Chatham, Kent ME4 4EZ
Tel 01634-830505
BBC Radio Solent
Havelock Road, Southampton SO1 7PW
Tel 023-8063 1311
BBC Somerset Sound
14-15 Paul Street, Taunton TA1 3PF
Tel 01823-252437
Southern Counties Radio (Sussex & Surrey)
Broadcasting House, Guildford GU2 5AP
Tel 01483-306306
BBC Thames Valley (Oxon & Berkshire)
PO Box 952, Oxford OX2 7YL
PO Box 954, Slough SL1 1BA
PO Box 1044, Reading RG30 1PL
Tel 01645-311444
Wiltshire Sound
Broadcasting House, Prospect Place, Swindon, Wilts SN1 3RW
Tel 01793-513626

BBC RADIO: MIDLAND/EAST

BBC Asian Network
Epic House, Charles Street, Leicester LE1 3SH
Tel 0116-251 6688
Pebble Mill Road, Birmingham B5 7SD
Tel 0121-414 8484
BBC Radio Cambridgeshire
Broadcasting House, 104 Hills Road, Cambridge CB2 1LD
Tel 01223-259696
BBC Radio Derby
PO Box 269, Derby DE1 3HL
Tel 01332-361111

BBC Radio Essex
198 New London Road, Essex CM2 9XB
Tel 01245-616000
BBC Hereford & Worcester
Hylton Road, Worcester WR2 5WW
Tel 01905-748485
BBC Radio Leicester
Epic House, Charles Street, Leicester LE1 3SH
Tel 0116-251 6688
BBC Radio Lincolnshire
PO Box 219, Newport, Lincoln LN1 3XY
Tel 01522-511411
BBC Radio Norfolk
Norfolk Tower, Surrey Street, Norwich NR1 3PA
Tel 01603-617411
BBC Radio Northampton
Abington Street, Northampton NN1 2BH
Tel 01604-239100
BBC Radio Nottingham
York House, Mansfield Road, Nottingham NG1 3JB
Tel 0115-955 0500
BBC Radio Shropshire
2-4 Boscobel Drive, Shrewsbury, Shropshire SY1 3TT
Tel 01743-248484
BBC Radio Stoke
Cheapside, Hanley, Stoke-on-Trent, Staffs ST1 1JJ
Tel 01782-208080
BBC Radio Suffolk
St Matthews Street, Ipswich, Suffolk IP1 3EP
Tel 01473-250000
BBC Three Counties Radio (Beds, Herts & Bucks)
PO Box 3CR, Hastings Street, Luton LU1 5XL
Tel 01582-441000
BBC Radio WM (West Midlands)
PO Box 206, Birmingham B5 7QQ
Tel 0121-414 8484

BBC LOCAL RADIO: NORTH

BBC Radio Cleveland
PO Box 95FM, Broadcasting House, Newport Road, Middlesbrough, Cleveland TS1 5DG
Tel 01642-225211
BBC Radio Cumbria
Annetwell Street, Carlisle, Cumbria CA3 8BB
Tel 01228-592444
BBC GMR Talk (Manchester)
PO Box 951, Oxford Road, Manchester M60 1SD
Tel 0161-244 3002
BBC Radio Humberside
9 Chapel Street, Hull, N Humberside HU1 3NU
Tel 01482-323232
BBC Radio Lancashire
26 Darwen Street, Blackburn, Lancs BB2 2EA
Tel 01254-262411
BBC Radio Leeds
Broadcasting House, Woodhouse Lane, Leeds, West Yorks LS2 9PN
Tel 0113-244 2131
BBC Radio Merseyside
55 Paradise Street, Liverpool L1 3BP
Tel 0151-708 5500

BBC Radio Newcastle
Barrack Road, Newcastle-upon-Tyne NE99 1RN
Tel 0191-232 4141
BBC Radio Sheffield
60 Westbourne Road, Sheffield S10 2QU
Tel 0114-268 6185
BBC Radio York
20 Bootham Row, York YO3 7BR
Tel 01904-641351

WALES, SCOTLAND & NI

BBC Radio Wales
Cardiff CF5 2YQ
Tel 029-2057 2888
BBC Radio Cymru
Broadcasting House, Llantrisant Road, Llandaff, Cardiff CF5 2YQ
Tel 029-20572888
BBC Radio Scotland
Broadcasting House, Queen Margaret Drive, Glasgow G12 8DG
Fax 0141-334 0614   Tel 0141-338 2000
BBC Radio Nan Gaidheal
7 Culduthel Road, Inverness IV2 4AD
Tel 01463-720720
BBC Radio Ulster
Broadcasting House, Ormeau Avenue, Belfast BT2 8HQ
Tel 028-9033 8000
BBC Radio Foyle
8 Northland Road, Londonderry, Northern Ireland BT48 7NE
Tel 028-7126 2244

INTERNATIONAL RADIO

BBC World Service - HQ
Bush House, The Strand, London WC2B 4PH.
Publicity Office   020-7557-2941
BBC World Service has been the world's most trusted - and freely available - source of news and analysis for more than six decades. Its output is equally valued in media-rich societies and countries where news is far from free. Broadcasts are funded through the Foreign and Commonwealth office by a Parliamentary Grant in Aid. Operating under the BBC's Royal Charter, World Service has editorial and managerial independence from commercial or political pressures.
Chief executive: Mark Byford
Deputy chief executive: Caroline Thompson
Director, news and programmes: Bob Jobbins
Director, World Service regions: Andrew Taussig
Controller, resources and technology: Chris Gill
Controller, personnel: Lesley Granger
Finance and commercial director: Andrew Hind
BBC Monitoring
Caversham Park, Reading, Berks RG4 8TZ
Fax 01734-463823   Tel 01734-469289
BBC Monitoring reports on foreign broadcasts to the BBC and the government. This information is also sold to the press, businesses, academia and public bodies.
Director: Andrew Hills

Independent radio

Local independent radio has come a long way since Capital and LBC began broadcasting 25 years ago. It is now a confident £420 million a year business which - in spite of the Eighties advertisers' jibe calling it the "2 per cent medium with 1 per cent attitude" - now has 5.3 per cent of the national advertising spend. The Nineties has been commercial radio's decade and, although the competition at the BBC has recently done well in the struggle for ratings, the long term trend favours the independents. By 2010 they will have built on the current 50 per cent plus audience ratings and, with the launch of multi-channel digital radio, will have reached nearer 70 per cent.

At commercial radio's twentyfifth birthday celebration Chris Smith, the culture secretary, said: "I am convinced that technology - particularly digital radio - will enhance the pleasure we gain from traditional radio services but radio's 'killer application', to use the jargon of the new technology, will largely remain what it has been - transportable audio entertainment."

The sector is licensed by the Radio Authority, a statutory body established by the 1990 Broadcasting Act. The Act allowed for three national licenses - Classic FM, Talk Radio and Virgin - and these, plus a lighter regulatory touch lightened further by the 1996 Broadcasting Act, have ensured ad-funded radio's prosperity. The Authority reported a busy year with the award of 23 more analogue licenses (more than granted in any previous year) to take the total to 226. The Radio Authority also has regulatory powers and upheld 59 of 951 viewer complaints and fined seven licensees.

There is resentment among commercial operators at the imposition of a controlling government hand and Chris Smith faces both ways on this issue. Sometimes he says: "My preference - and that of the government - is for deregulation where possible." And on other occasions he says: "It is questionable whether the free market can fairly determine radio output ... [and] complete deregulation runs the risk that too much effort will be spent on a

**Chris Smith, the culture secretary:
"Complete deregulation runs the
risk that too much effort will be
spent on [the] mainstream rather
than ... seeking different niches."**

mainstream audience rather than broadcasters seeking different niches." Meanwhile the bigger issue for commercial radio owners is whether they can mimic their American counterparts and diversify into other media. Chris Evans, the boss of Virgin, had a go at the end of 1998 with a publicity seeking bid for the Daily Star. Capital has diversified into Radio Cafés, the internet and the Wild Star record label; GWR has also gone for the internet plus the Classic FM magazine and record label; Scottish Radio Holdings has invested in poster advertising and local newspapers; and Chrysalis is plumping for TV production and music production.

Radio Authority
Holbrook House, 14 Great Queen St, Holborn,
London WC2B 5DG.
Fax 020-7405 7062   Tel 020-7430 2724
Chairman: Sir Peter Gibbings
Deputy chairman: Michael Moriarty
Chief executive: Tony Stoller
Head of development and deputy chief exec: David Vick
Head of finance: Neil Romain
Head of programming and advertising: Martin Campbell
Head of engineering: Mark Thomas
Chief press officer: Tracey Mullins
Head of legal services: Eve Saloman

NATIONAL FRANCHISES

Until 1992 the only national radio channels belonged to the BBC. The Broadcasting Act changed all that and gave the Radio Authority power to issue licenses for three new Independent National Radio (INR) networks. Only INR1 could be on an FM frequency and the other two had to be on AM. The Act also said that INR1 should concentrate "wholly or mainly, in the broadcasting of music which ... is not pop music" and that the first AM service could offer any programming that did not duplicate INR1. INR3 would have to be primarily speech-based. Hence the arrivals of Classic FM, Virgin 1215 and Talk Radio.

Classic FM - INR1
PO Box 2834, London W1A 5NT
Fax 020-7344 2700   Tel 020-7343 9000
E-mail: enquiries@classicfm.co.uk
Starting date: 7.9.92
Dial: 100-102 FM

Talk Radio - INR3
76 Oxford Street, London W1N 0TR
Fax 020-7636 1053   Tel 020-7636 1089
Parent company: TalkCo. (Holdings)
Starting date: 14.2.95
Dial: 1053/1089/1107 kHz AM

Virgin 1215 - INR2
1 Golden Square, London W1R 4DJ.
Fax 020-7434 1197   Tel 020-7434 1215
E-mail: virgin@vradio.co.uk
Parent company: Ginger Media Group
Starting date: 30.4.93
Dial: Nationally: 1215 and 1197 - 1260 AM/MW;
London: 105.8 FM

Atlantic 252
Mornington House, Trim, County Meath
Fax 00353 4636688   Tel 00353 4636655
Website: www.atlantic252.com
Atlantic 252 broadcasts from Southern Ireland without a British government licence, but is effectively a national station due to a 10 per cent national audience share garnered from two-thirds of the UK, north and west of a line from the Wash to Dorset.
Parent company: CLT UFA
Starting date: 1.9.89
Dial: 252 kHz LW

MAIN OWNERS

Border Radio Holdings
Border Television, Carlisle CA1 3NY
Fax 01228-511193   Tel 01228-525101
E-mail: Radio@century105.com
Stations: Century `Radio, Century 105/106, Sun FM

Capital Radio
30 Leicester Square, London WC2H 7LA
Fax 020-7766 6100   Tel 020-7766 6000
Website: www.capitalradio.co.uk
Subsidiaries: Capital Radio London, Ocean Radio Group, Southern Sound Group, Invicta Radio, BRMB Radio, Red Dragon Radio, Fox Radio.
Stations: BRMB-FM, Capital FM, Capital Gold, Invicta FM, OceanFM, PowerFM, S Coast Radio, Southern FM.

Chrysalis Radio
Chrysalis Building, Bramley Road, London W10 6SP
Fax 020-7221 6341   Tel 020-7221 2213
E-mail: (name)@heart1062.co.uk
Stations: Galaxy, Heart.

DMG Radio
Northcliffe House, 2 Derry Street, London W8 5TT
Fax 020-7766 6100   Tel 020-7766 6000
Website: www.dmgt.co.uk
Stations: Breeze, Essex FM, KFM, Mercury FM, Oasis FM, Ten 17, Vibe FM.

Emap Radio
97 Tottenham Court Road, London W1P 9HF
Fax 020-7504 6001   Tel 020-7504 6000
E-mail: emaponair@emaponair.com
Shares: Owns over 50% of Radio City, 19% of East Anglian Radio and 10% of Essex Radio.
Stations: broadcast on 17 FM and AM frequencies and cover London, Wales, Liverpool, Manchester, Preston, Leeds, Sheffield, Hull, Newcastle Upon Tyne and Stockton on Tees, Hallam FM, Great North, Great Yorkshire, Metro FM, The Pulse, TFM, Viking FM.

GWR Group
PO Box 2345, Swindon, Wiltshire SN5 7HF
Fax 0118-928 4310   Tel 0118-928 4300
Website: www.gwrgroup.musicradio.com
Subsids: Mid-Anglia Radio .Chiltern Radio Network
Stations: Beacon, Brunel Classic Gold, CN FM, Gem-AM, GWR FM, Hereward, Leicester Sound, Mercia FM/Classic Gold, Ram FM, 1332, Trent FM/Gem AM, 2CR FM/Classic Gold, 2Ten FM/Classic Gold, WABC, B97/Classic Gold, Broadland 102/Amber Radio, Chiltern FM/Classic Gold, FM 103-Horizon, Northants 96, Q103 FM, SGR Colchester/Amber Radio, 102.4 Severn Sound, Radio Wyvern.

Independent Radio Group
The Lodge, Orrell Road, Orrell Wigan WN5 8HJ
Fax 01942-777657   Tel 01942-777666
Stations: Scot FM, Lite 1458 AM, 96.3 QFM, 102.4 Wish FM, Wire FM 102.7, Discovery 102 FM

Local Radio Company
Cross Keys House, 22 Queen Street, Salisbury SP1 1EY
Fax 01772 335032   Tel 01772 413188
E-mail: TLRC@dial.pipex.com
Stations: Cat FM, IoW Radio, Th NRG, Spire FM, Win 107FM, Wessex FM, Vale FM

Marcher Radio Group
The Studios, Mold Road, Wrexham LL11 4AF
Fax 01978 759701   Tel 01978 759701
Website: www.mfmradio.co.uk
Stations: The Buzz, Champion FM, Coast FM, Marcher Gold, MFM.

Murfin Music International
Old Smithy, Post Office Lane, Kempsey, Worcester WR5 3NS
Fax 01905 820015   Tel 01905 820659
Website: www.capitalradio.co.uk
Stations: Classic Gold 954/1530, Kix 96, Radio Maldwyn, Sunshine 855.

Scottish Radio Holdings
Clydebank Business Park, Clydebank, Glasgow G81 2RX
Fax 0141-565 2322   Tel 0141-565 2202
Website: www.srh.org.uk
Stations: Clyde 1 FM, Clyde 2, Downtown FM, Cool FM, Forth FM/AM, Westsound FM/ AM, Tay FM, Northsound 1/2, Radio Tay, Borders 69%, Carlisle 40%, Moray Firth 97%.

Sunrise Radio Group
Sunrise House, Merrick Road, Southall, Middlesex UB2 4AU
Fax 020-8813 9800   Tel 020-8574 6666
Stations: Sunrise Radio London, Sunrise FM Yorkshire

Tindle Radio
Weavers Yard, 6 West Street, Farnham, Surrey GU9 7DN
Fax 01252 734007   Tel 01252 735667
Stations: Channel 103, Dream 100, Island FM, The Beach

UKRD Group
Dolphin House, North Street, Guildford, Surrey GU1 4AA
Fax 01483 454443   Tel 01483 306156
Website: www.ukrd.com
Stations: Active FM, County Sound, Delta FM, The Eagle, Bristol Community Radio, Pirate FM, Star FM

The Wireless Group
76 Oxford Street, London W1N 0TR
Fax 020-7636 1053   Tel 020-7636 1089
Stations: Talk Radio, The Pulse, Signal , The Wave and Swansea Sound, Valleys Radio, The Wave (Blackpool).

LOCAL RADIO STATIONS

2CR FM
5 Southcote Road, Bournemouth, Dorset BH1 3LR
Fax 01202-255244   Tel 01202-259259
Website: www.2crfm.co.uk
Parent company: GWR Group
Starting date: 15.9.80   Area: Dorset, west Hampshire
Dial: 102.3 MHz (2CR FM) 828 kHz (Classic Gold)

2-Ten FM
PO Box 2020, Reading, Berks RG31 7FG
Fax 0118-928 8433   Tel 0118-945 4400
E-mail: musicmix@2tenfm.musicradio.com
Website: www.2-TENFM.co.uk
Parent company: GWR Group   Starting date: 8.3.76
Area: Reading, Basingstoke, Andover
Dial: 97.0 & 102.9 FM, 103.4 FM

96.7 FM
PO Box 77, 18 Blackfriars Street, King's Lynn, Norfolk PE30 1NN
Fax 01553-767200   Tel 01553-772777
E-mail: klfmradio.co.uk
Area: west Norfolk

Active 107.5 FM
7 Western Road, Romford, Essex, RM1 3LD
Fax 01708-731643   Tel 01708-730383
E-mail: sales@activefm.co.uk
Web: www.activefm.co.uk
Starting date: 18.5.98   Area: Havering

96.3 Aire FM
51 Burley Road, Leeds, West Yorkshire LS3 1LR
Fax 0113-283 5501   Tel 0113-283 5500
E-mail: airefm@airefm.co.uk
Website: www.airefm.co.uk
Parent company: Emap
Starting date: 1.9.81
Area: Leeds   Dial: 96.3 MHz

Alpha 103.2
11 Woodland Road, Darlington DL3 7BJ
Fax 01325-255551   Tel 01325-255552
E-mail: admin@alpharadio.demon.co.uk
Area: Darlington and Newton Aycliffe.
Dial: 103.2 FM

Amber Classic Gold
PO Box 4000, Norwich NR3 1DB
Fax 01603-666353   Tel 01603-630621
Parent company: GWR Group
Starting date: 24.9.95
Area: Great Yarmouth & Norwich   Dial: 1152 KHz

Argyll FM
Unit 6, Old Quay, Campbelltown, Argyll PA28 6ED
Fax 01586 551888   Tel 01586 551800
Starting date: 11.99
Area: Kintyre, Islay, Jura

107.8 Arrow FM
Priory Meadow Centre, Hastings, East Sussex, TN34 1PJ
Fax 01424-422 622   Tel 01424-461 177
E-mail: info@arrowfm.co.uk
Web: www.arrowfm.co.uk
Start date: 10.4.98
Area: Hastings

Asian Sound
Globe House, Southall Street, Manchester M3 1LG
Fax 0161-288 9000   Tel 0161-288 1000
E-mail: asiansound@aol.com
Area: East Lancashire   **Dial:** 1377, 963 AM

B97 Chiltern FM
55 Goldington Road, Bedford MK40 3LT
Fax 01234-218580   Tel 01234-272400
E-mail: studio@b97fm.musicradio.com
Parent company: GWR Group
Area: Bedfordshire, Hertfordshire, Cambridgeshire
Dial: 96.9 FM

Bath FM
4 Queen Square, Bath BA1 2HA
Fax 01225 339737   Tel 01225 339661
Starting date: 11.99   **Area:** Bath

The Bay
PO Box 969, George's Quay, Lancaster LA1 3LD
Fax 01524-848787   Tel 01524-848747
E-mail: thebay.co.uk
Starting date: 1.3.93
Policy: classic hits, local news, community information
Area: North Lancashire & south Cumbria.
Dial: 96.9, 102.3 & 103.2 FM

The Beach
PO Box 103.4 Lowestoft, Suffolk
Fax 07000 001036   Tel 07000 001035
E-mail: 103.4@thebeach.co.uk
Website: www.thebeach.co.uk
Parent company: Tindle Newspapers
Starting date: 29.9.96
Area: Great Yarmouth & Lowestoft   **Dial:** 103.4 FM

Beacon FM/WABC Classic Gold
267 Tettenhall Road, Wolverhampton WV6 0DQ
Fax 01902-838266   Tel 01902-838383
E-mail: steve.martin@beaconfm.musicradio.com
Parent company: GWR Group
Starting date: 12.4.76; Shrewsbury & Telford 14.7.87
Area: Wolverhampton & Black Country, Shrewsbury & Telford   **Dial:** 97.2 & 103.1 MHz/990&1017 AM

FM 102 The Bear
Guard House Studios, Banbury Road, Stratford upon Avon, Warwicks CV37 7HX
Fax 01789-263102   Tel 01789-262636
Starting date: 24.5.96   **Area:** Stratford upon Avon

Beat 106
PO Box 25061, Glasgow G3 7WW
Starting date: 10.99
Area: Central Scotland   **Dial:** 105.7 MHz, 106.1 MHz

The Breeze
Clifftown Road, Southend-on-Sea, Essex SS1 1SX
Fax 01702-333686   Tel 01702-333711
E-mail: studios@breeze.co.uk
Website: www.breeze.co.uk
Starting date: 16.7.89
Dial: 1431 kHz (Southend), 1359 kHz (Chelmsford)

96.4 FM BRMB
9 Brindley Place, Broad Street, Birmingham B1 2BL
Fax 0121-359 1117   Tel 0121-359 4481
Website: www.brmb.co.uk
Parent company: Capital Radio   **Starting date:** 19.2.74
Area: Birmingham.   **Dial:** 96.4 FM

Bristol Community Radio
PO Box 242, Springfield House, West Street, Bristol BS99 5BF
Starting date: 11.99   **Area:** Bristol

Broadland
47 Colegate, Norwich, Norfolk NR3 1DB
Fax 01603-666252   Tel 01603-630621
E-mail: sales@broadland102.co.uk
Website: www.broadland102.co.uk
Parent company: GWR Group
Starting date: 1.10.84 **Area:** Norwich/Great Yarmouth.
Dial: 102.4 MHz, 1152kHz

Brunel Classic Gold
PO Box 2000, Bristol BS99 7SN
Fax: 0117-984 3202   Tel 0117-984 3200
E-mail: reception@gwrfm.musicradio.com
Website: www.gwrfm.musicradio.com
Parent company: GWR Group   **Starting date:** 25.11.88
Dial: 1260 kHz (Bristol), 936 kHz (west Wilts), 1161 kHz (Swindon)

The Buzz
Media House, Claughton Rd, Birkenhead CH41 6EY
Fax 0151-647 5427   Tel 0151-650 1700
Website: www.thebuzz971.co.uk
Parent company: Marcher Radio Group
Starting date: 31.3.89
Area: The Wirral   **Dial:** 97.1 MHz

Cambridge Red Radio
PO Box 492, Cambridge CB1 2BW
Fax 01223 577686   Tel 01223 722300
E-mail: 9name)@redradio.co.uk
Website: www.redradio.co.uk
Parent company: Dawe Media **Starting date:** 20.03.98
Area: Cambridge   **Dial:** 107.9 MHz

Capital FM/Capital Gold
30 Leicester Square, London WC2H 7LA
Fax 020-7766 6100   Tel 020-7766 6000
Parent company: Capital Radio
Starting date: 16.10.73 (FM), 28.11.88 (Gold)
Area: London.
Dial: 95.8 MHz (Capital FM), 1548 kHz (Capital Gold)

Capital Gold, Birmingham
9 Brindley Place, Broad Street, Birmingham B1 2BL
Fax 0121-359 1117   Tel 0121-359 4481
Website: www.brmb.co.uk
Area: Birmingham   **Dial:** 1152 AM

Capital Gold, Brighton
Radio Ho, Franklin Road, Portslade BN41 2SS
Fax 01273-430098   Tel 01273-430111
E-mail: info@southernradio.co.uk
Parent company: Capital Radio
Starting date: 29.8.83 (Brighton), 10.3.91 (Portsmouth & Southampton)
Area: Brighton, Southampton, Portsmouth
Dial: 1323 kHz (Brighton), 1170, 1557 kHz (Portsmouth, Southampton)

107.5 Cat FM
Regent Arcade, Cheltenham, Glos, GL50 1JZ
Fax 01242-699 666   Tel 01242-699 555
E-mail: catfm@netcomuk.co.uk
Web: www.catfm.co.uk
Start date: Sept 1998   **Area:** Cheltenham

Central FM
201-203 High Street, Falkirk FK1 1DU
Fax 01324-611168   Tel 01324-611164
Starting date: 4.6.90
Area: Stirling an Falkirk.   **Dial:** 103.1 MHz

Centre FM
5-7 Aldergate, Tamworth, Staffs B79 7DJ
Fax 01827 318002   Tel 01827 318000
E-mail: studioone@centrefm.co.uk
Website: www.airefm.co.uk
Starting date: 01.06.98
Area: SE Staffordshire   **Dial:** 101.6 MHz, 102.4 MHz

Century Radio
Century Ho, PO Box 100, Gateshead NE8 2YX
Fax 0191-477 15600   Tel 0191-477 6666
E-mail: reception@centurynortheast.com
Parent company: Border Media
Starting date: 1.9.94
Area: North East   **Dial:** 100.7, 101.8 & 96.2 MHz

Ceredigion
Alexandra Road, Aberystwyth, Dyfed SY23 1LF
Fax 01970-627206   Tel 01970-627999
Starting date: 14.12.92
Area: Ceredigion.   **Dial:** 103.3 & 96.6 MHz, 97.4FM

CFM
PO Box 964, Carlisle, Cumbria CA1 3NG
Fax 01228-818444   Tel 01228-818964
E-mail: traffic@cfmradio.com
Starting date: 14.4.93   **Area:** Carlisle.
Dial: 96.4 Penrith, 102.2 Whitehaven

Champion FM
Llys-y-Dderwen, Parc Menai, Bangor LL57 4BN
Fax 01248 671971   Tel 01248 671888
Website: www.championfm.co.uk
Parent company: Marcher   **Starting date:** 11.12.98
Area: Caernarfon   **Dial:** 103 MHz

Channel 103 FM
6 Tunnel Street, St Helier, Jersey JE2 4LU
Fax 01534-887799   Tel 01534-888103
E-mail: radio@103fm.itl.net
Website: www.103fm.itl.net
Starting date: 25.10.92
Area: Jersey.   **Dial:** 103.7 MHz

Channel Travel Radio
PO Box 2000, Folkestone, Kent CT18 8XY
Fax 01303 283874   Tel 01303-283873
Starting date: 20.4.95
Area: along the M20 towards the Kent Channel ports

107.7 Chelmer FM
Cater House, High Street, Chelmsford, CM1 1AL
Fax 01245 259558   Tel 01245 259400
E-mail: mail@chelmerfm.co.uk
Website: www.chelmerfm.co.uk
Parent company: Mid-Essex   **Starting date:** 18.10.98
Area: Chelmsford   **Dial:** 107.7 MHz

Chiltern FM/ClassicGold 792 & 828
Chiltern Road, Dunstable, Beds LU6 1HQ
Fax 01582-676241   Tel 01582-676200
Parent company: GWR Group
Starting date: 15.10.81 (Chiltern FM); 15.7.90 (Classic Gold)   **Area:** Bedford, Luton.
Dial: 97.6 MHz Chiltern FM, 792 & 828 kHz Gold

Choice FM
291-299 Borough High Street, London SE1 1JG
Fax 020-7378 3911   Tel 020-7378 3969
Website: www.choice96.9fm.co.uk
Starting date: 31.3.90
Area: Brixton.
Dial: 96.9 MHz

Chrysalis Radio North East
Chrysalis Building, Bramley Road, London W10 6SP
Tel 0191-273 2772
Parent company: Chrysalis Group
Area: Tyne & Wear, Cleveland, Durham

City Beat 96.7
46 Stranmills Embankment, Belfast BT9 5DF
Fax 028-9020 0023   Tel 028-9020 5967
E-mail: citybeat96.7@bnet-co.uk
Starting date: 6.9.90
Area: Belfast   **Dial:** 96.7 MHz

Clan FM
PO Box 9083, Dalziel Workspace, Motherwell ML1 1YU
E-mail: clanradio@aol.com
Starting date: 11.99   **Area:** North Lanarkshire

Classic Gold 828
5 Southcote Road, Bournemouth, BH1 3LR
Fax 01202-255244   Tel 01202-259259
Website: www.classicgold828.co.uk
Parent company: GWR Group
Area: Dorset, west Hampshire   **Dial:** 828

Classic Gold 1332
PO Box 2020, Queensgate, Peterborough PE1 1LL
Fax 01733-281445   Tel 01733-460460
E-mail: tima@musicradio.com
Parent company: GWR Group
Starting date: 14.4.92
Area: Peterborough.   **Dial:** 1332 kHz

Classic Gold 1359
Hertford Place, Coventry CV1 3TT
Fax 024-7686 8202   Tel 024-7686 8200
E-mail: mercia@musicradio.com
Parent company: GWR   **Area:** Coventry, Warwickshire

Classic Gold 1431
PO Box 2020, Reading, Berks RG31 7FG
Fax 0118-925 4456   Tel 0118-945 4400
E-mail: musicmix@twotenfm.musicradio.com
Website: www.2-tenfm.co.uk
Parent company: GWR Group   **Starting date:** 8.3.76
Area: Reading.   **Dial:** 1431 kHz

Clyde 1/Clyde 2
Clydebank Business Park, Glasgow G81 2RX
Fax 0141-565 2265   Tel 0141-565 2200
E-mail: clydenews@srh.co.uk
Website: www.radioclyde.co.uk
Parent company: Scottish Radio   **Starting date:** 31.12.73
Dial: Clyde 1, 102.5 MHz (Glasgow), 97.0 MHz (Vale of Leven), 103.3 MHz (Firth of Clyde). Clyde 2, 1152 kHz

Coast FM
Media Hse, 41 Conwy Road, Colwyn Bay LL28 5AB
Fax 01492 535248   Tel 01492 533733
Website: www.coastfm.co.uk
Parent company: Emap   **Starting date:** 27.08.93
Area: North Wales Coast   **Dial:** 96.3 MHz

Connect FM
Church Street, Wellingborough, Northants, NN8 4XX
Fax 01933-442 333   Tel 01933-224972
Web: www.web-uk.com/connectfm
Start date: 12.4.98
Area: Wellingborough   Dial: 97.2 FM

Cool FM
PO Box 974, Belfast BT1 1RT
Fax 01247-814974   Tel 01247-817181
E-mail: music@coolfm.co.uk
Website: www.coolfm.co.uk
Starting date: 7.2.90
Area: Belfast.   Dial: 97.4 MHz

Country 1035 (formerly Ritz)
33-35 Wembley Hill Road, Middlesex HA9 8RT
Fax 020-8733 1393   Tel 020-8733 1300
Starting date: 1.9.94
Area: Greater London.   Dial: 1035 kHz

County Sound Radio 1476AM
Dolphin House, North Street, Guildford GU1 4AA
Fax 01483-531612   Tel 01483-300964
E-mail: eagle@countysound.co.uk
Website: www.cableol.net/ukrd/
Parent company: UKRD Group
Starting date: 4.9.95 Area: W Surrey and NE Hampshire
Dial: 1476 KHz

Crash FM
27 Fleet STreet, Liverpool, L1 4AR
Fax 0151-707 3109   Tel 0151-707 3107
E-mail: info@107crashfm.com
Web: www.107crashfm.com
Start date: 27.3.98
Area: 107.6 FM
Dial: 107.6 FM

CTFM
16 Lower Bridge Street, Canterbury, Kent CT1 2HQ
Fax 01277-785106   Tel 01277-789106
E-mail: firstname.surname@ctfm.co.uk
Website: www.ctfm.co.uk
Starting date: 21.9.97
Area: Canterbury, Whitstable, Herne Bay

Delta FM 97.1
65 Weyhill, Haslemere, Surrey GU27 1HN
Fax 01428-658971   Tel 01428-651971
E-mail: delta@ukrd.com
Website: www.countysound.co.uk/delta
Parent company: UKRD Group   Starting date: 9.5.96
Area: Haslemere   Dial: 97.1 MHz

Delta FM 102
Prospect Place, Mill Lane, Alton, Hants GU34 2SY
Fax 01420-544044   Tel 01420-544444
E-mail: studio@delta102.freeserve.co.uk
Website: www.cableol.net/ukrd/
Parent company: UK Radio Development
Starting date: 22.11.92
Area: NE Hampshire   Dial: 101.6 & 102 MHz

Discovery 102
8 South Tay Street, Dundee DD1 1PA
Fax 01382 900999   Tel 01382 901000
Parent company: Independent Radio Group
Starting date: summer 1999
Area: Dundee   Dial: 102 MHz

Downtown Radio
Newtownards, Co Down, Northern Ireland BT23 4ES
Fax 01247-818913   Tel 01247-815555
E-mail: programmes@downtown.co.uk
Website: www.downtown.co.uk
Parent company: MaxAM
Starting date: 16.3.76
Dial: 1026 kHz (Belfast), 102.4 MHz (Londonderry),
96.4 MHz (Limavady), 96.6 MHz (Enniskillen)

Dream 100 FM
Northgate Hse, St Peters Street, Colchester CO1 1HT
Fax 01206-715102   Tel 01206-764466
E-mail: info@dream100.com
Website: www.dream100.com
Starting date: 7.10.90
Area: Tendring   Dial: 1557 kHz

107.9 Dune FM
The Power Station, Victoria Way, Southport PR8 1RR
Fax 01704-502540   Tel 01704-502500
E-mail: dunefm@aol.com
Website: www.dunefm.co.uk
Starting date: 12.10. 97
Area: North Merseyside and west Lancashire
Dial: 107.9 fm

96.4 The Eagle
Dolphin House, North Street, Guildford GU1 4AA
Fax 01483-531612   Tel 01483-300964
E-mail: eagle@countysound.co.uk
Website: www.cableol.net/ukrd/
Parent company: UKRD Group
Starting date: 4.1.96
Area: W Surrey and NE Hampshire
Dial: 96.4 MHz

eleven SEVENTY AM
PO Box 1170, High Wycombe, Bucks HP13 6YT
Fax 01494 447272   Tel 01494 446611
E-mail: elevenseventy@pipex.dial
Starting date: 31.12.93
Area: High Wycombe.   Dial: 1170 kHz

Essex FM
Clifftown Road, Southend, Essex SS1 1SX
Fax 01702-345224   Tel 01702-333711
E-mail: studios@essexfm.co.uk
Website: www.essexfm.co.uk
Parent company: Essex Radio, a subsidiary of DMG
Radio
Starting date: 12.9.81
Dial: 96.3 MHz (Southend), 102.6 MHz (Chelmsford)

FM 107 The Falcon
Brunel Mall, London Road, Stroud, Glos GL5 2BP
Fax 01453 757107   Tel 01453 767369
E-mail: info@thefalcon.org
Website: www.thefalcon
Parent company: UKRD
Starting date: 29.1.98
Area: Stroud   Dial: 107.2 MHz, 107.9 MHz

Fame 1521
Radio Mercury, The Stanley Centre, Kelvin Way,
Crawley, W Sussex RH10 2SE
Fax 01293-565663   Tel 01293-519161
Parent company: DMG Radio
Starting date: 4.5.92   Area: Reigate & Crawley

FLR 107.3
Astra House, Arklow Road, New Cross, SE14 6WA
Fax: 020-8691 9193   Tel 020-8691 9202
E-mail: enquiries@ukrd.com
Web: www.ukrd.com/flr
Start date: Autumn 1998
Area: Lewisham

FM 103 Horizon
Broadcast Centre, Crownhill, 14 Vincent Avenue,
Milton Keynes, Bucks MK8 0AB
Fax 01908-564893   Tel 01908-269111
E-mail: morning crew@fm103.musicradio.com
Website: www.mkweb.co.uk
Area: Milton Keynes

Forth FM/Forth AM
Forth House, Forth Street, Edinburgh EH1 3LF
Fax 0131-558 3277   Tel 0131-556 9255
Parent company: Scottish Radio Holdings
Starting date: 22.1.75
Area: Edinburgh, Lothian & Fife
Dial: 97.3/97.6, 102.2 FM, 1548 AM

Fosseway Radio
Suite 1, 1 Castle Street, Hinckley, Leicestershire, LE10 1DA
Fax 01455-616888   Tel 01455-614151
E-mail: fosseway@fosseway.co.uk
Web: www.fossewayradio.co.uk
Start date: Spring 1999
Area: Hinckley and SW Leicestershire
Dial: 107.9 FM

FOX FM
Brush House, Pony Road, Oxford OX4 2XR
Fax 01865-871036   Tel 01865-871000
E-mail: fox@foxfm.co.uk
Starting date: 15.9.89.
Area: Oxford, Banbury.
Dial: 102.6 & 97.4 MHz

Fresh AM
Gargrave Road, Skipton, N Yorks BD23 1yd
Fax 01756 799711   Tel 01756 799991
Starting date: 4.5.97
Area: Yorkshire Dales
Dial: 1413 KHz

Galaxy 101
Millennium House, 26 Baldwin Street, Bristol BS1 1SE
Fax 0117-901 4555   Tel 0117-901 0101
E-mail: FirstinitialSurname@Galaxy101.co.uk
Parent company: Chrysalis Group
Starting date: 4.9.94
Area: South Wales and the West
Dial: 101 MHz & 97.2 MHz

Galaxy 102
PO Box 102, Manchester M60 1GJ
Fax 0161-228 1020   Tel 0161-228 0102
Parent company: Chrysalis Group
Starting date: 16.10.94
Area: Greater Manchester.   **Dial:** 102 MHz

Galaxy 102.2
1 The Square, Broad Street, Birmingham B15 1AS
Fax 0121-696 1007   Tel 0121-695 0000
Starting date: 1.1.99
Area: Birmingham.   **Dial:** 102.2 MHz

Galaxy 105
Joseph's Well, West Gate, Leeds LS3 1AB
Fax 0113-213 1055   Tel 0113-213 0105
Parent company: Chrysalis Group
Starting date: 14.2.97
Area: Yorkshire
Dial: 105 MHz

Gem-AM
29-31 Castle Gate, Nottingham NG1 7AP
Fax 0115-912 9333   Tel 0115-952 7000
E-mail: direct@gemam.musicradio.com
Parent company: GWR Group
Starting date: 4.10.88
Area: Nottingham and Derby.   **Dial:** 999 & 945 kHz

Gemini FM/Westword Radio
Hawthorn House, Exeter Business Park, Exeter,
Devon EX1 3QS
Fax: 01392-444433   Tel 01392-444444
Parent company: GWR Group
Starting date: 1.1.95
Area: Exeter, east Devon and Torbay.
Dial: 96.4/97.0/103 Mhz, 666/954 kHz

GWR FM
PO Box 2000, Bristol, Avon BS99 7SN
Fax 0117-984 3202   Tel 0117-984 3200
E-mail: reception@gwrfm.musicradio.com
Website: www.gwrfm.musicradio.com
Parent company: GWR Group
Starting date: 27.10.81 (Bristol), 22.5.87 (Bath)
Dial: 96.3 MHz (Bristol), 103.0 MHz (Bath)

GWR-FM Wiltshire
PO Box 2000, Swindon SN4 7EX
Fax 01793-842602   Tel 01793-842600
Parent company: GWR Group
Starting date: 12.10.82
Dial: 97.2 MHz (Swindon), 102.2 MHz (west Wilts),
96.5 MHz (Marlborough)

Hallam FM
900 Herries Road, Sheffield S6 1RH
Fax 0114-285 3159   Tel 0114-285 3333
E-mail: programmes@hallamfm.co.uk
Website: www.hallamfm.co.uk
Parent company: EMAP
Starting date: 1.10.74
Dial: 97.4 MHz (Sheffield), 102.9 MHz (Barnsley),
103.4 MHz (Doncaster)

100.7 Heart FM/Galaxy 102.2
1 The Square, 111 Broad Street, Birmingham B15 1AS
Fax 0121-696 1007   Tel 0121-626 1007
E-mail: addressee@heartfm.co.uk
Parent company: Chrysalis
Policy: Soft adult contemporary music
Starting date: 7.9.94
Area: West midlands, Warwickshire
Dial: 100.7 MHz

Heart 106.2 FM
Chrysalis Building, Bramley Road, London W10 6SP
Fax 020-7470 1095   Tel 020-7468 1062
E-mail: kpalmer@heart1062.co.uk
Parent company: Chrysalis Group
Starting date: summer 1995
Area: Greater London. **Dial:** 106.2 MHz

Heartland FM
Lower Oakfield, Pitlochry, Perthshire PH16 5HQ
Fax 01796-474007   Tel 01796-474040
Some Gaelic and mixed language output.
Starting date: 21.3.92
Area: Pitlochry and Aberfldy.
Dial: 97.5 MHz

102.7 Hereward FM
PO Box 225, Queensgate, Peterborough,
Cambridgeshire PE1 1XJ
Fax 01733-281444   Tel 01733-460460
Parent company: GWR Group
Starting date: 20.7.80
Area: Peterborough
Dial: 102.7 MHz

Huddersfield FM
The Old Stableblock, Brewery Drive, Lockwood Park,
Huddersfield, HD1 3UR
Fax 01484-311107   Tel 01484-321107
Start date: 1.3.98
Area: Huddersfield   **Dial:** 107.9 FM

Invicta FM/Capital Gold
Radio House, John Wilson Business Park, Whitstable,
Kent CT5 3QX
Fax 01227-771557   Tel 01227-772004
E-mail: info@invictaradio.co.uk
Parent company: Capital Radio
Starting date: Invicta FM: 1.10.84, Capital Gold 27.3.89
Dial: Invicta FM 103.1 MHz (Maidstone & Medway),
102.8 MHz (Canterbury), 95.9 MHz (Thanet), 97.0
MHz (Dover), 96.1 MHz (Ashford). Capital Gold 1242
kHz (west Kent), 603 kHz (east Kent)

Island FM
12 Westerbrook, St Sampsons, Guernsey GY2 4QQ
Fax 01481-249676   Tel 01481-242000
E-mail: vikki@islandfm.guernsey.net
Website: www.islandfm.guernsey.net
Starting date: 15.10.92
Dial: 104.7 MHz (Guernsey), 93.7 MHz (Alderney)

Isle of Wight Radio
Dodnor Park, Newport, Isle of Wight PO30 5XE
Fax 01983-822109   Tel 01983-822557
E-mail: admin@iwradio.co.uk
Website: www.iwradio.co.uk
Starting date: 15.4.90
Area: Isle of Wight   **Dial:** 107 & 102 MHz

Isles FM
PO Box 333, Stornaway, Isle of Lewis HS1 2PU
Fax 01851 703322   Tel 01851 703333
E-mail: islesfm@radiolink.net
Website: www.listen.to/islesfm
Starting date: 7.3.98
Area: Western Isle   **Dial:** 103 MHz

Jazz FM
Exchange Quay, Manchester M5 3EJ
Fax 0161-877 1005   Tel 0161-877 1004
E-mail: jazzfminfo@jazzfm.com
Website: www.jazzfm.com
Parent company: Golden Rose Communications
Starting date: 1.9.94
Area: North west   **Dial:** 100.4 MHz

Jazz FM 102.2
26 Castlereagh Street, London W1H 6DJ
Fax 020-7723 9742   Tel 020-7706 4100
E-mail: info@jazzfm.com
Website: www.jazzfm.com
Parent company: Golden Rose Communications.
Starting date: 4.3.90
Area: Greater London.   **Dial:** 102.2 MHz

KCBC
PO Box 1074, Kettering, Northants NN16 8PU
Fax 01536-517390   Tel 01536-412413
E-mail: 107.4@kcbc.co.uk
Website: www.kcbc.co.uk
Parent company: TLRC
Starting date: 6.4.90
Area: Kettering, Corby.
Dial: 107.4 FM

107.6 Kestrel FM
2nd Floor, Paddington House, The Walks Shopping
Centre, Basingstoke, RG21 7LJ
Fax 01256-694111   Tel 01256-694000
Start date: 18.5.98
Area: Basingstoke

Key 103
Castle Quay, Castlefield, Manchester M15 4PR
Fax 0161-288 5151   Tel 0161-288 5000
Website: www.key103fm.com
Parent company: Emap Radio
Starting date: 3.9.88
Area: Manchester
Dial: 103MHz

KFM
1 East Street, Tonbridge, Kent TN9 1AR
Fax 01732-369201   Tel 01732-369200
Starting date: 8.7.95
Area: Tonbridge, Tunbridge Wells and Sevenoaks
Dial: 96.2 Hz (south), 101.6 MHz (north)

Kiss 100 FM
80 Holloway Road, London N7 8JG
Fax 020-7700 3979   Tel 020-7700 6100
Website: www.kiss100.com
Parent company: Emap
Starting date: 1.9.90
Area: Greater London.
Dial: 100 MHz

Kix 96
Watch Close, Spon Street, Coventry CB1 4XX
E-mail: kix96@aol.com
Fax: 024-7655 1744   Tel 024-7652 5656
Website: www.indiscrete/kix96
Starting date: 28.8.90
Area: Coventry. **Dial:** 96.2 MHz

KL-FM
18 Blackfriars Street, Kings Lynn, Norfolk PE30 1NN
Fax 01553-766453   Tel 01553-772777
E-mail: nigels@klfmradio.co.uk
Parent company: Dawe Media
Starting date: 1.7.92
Area: Kings Lynn.
Dial: 96.7 MHz

Lantern FM
The Lighthouse, 17 Market Place, Bideford, North Devon EX39 2DR
Fax 01237-423333   Tel 01237-424444
Starting date: 19.10.92
Area: North Devon.
Dial: 96.2 MHz

LBC 1152AM
200 Gray's Inn Road, London WC1X 8XZ
Fax 020-7312 8565   Tel 020-7973 1152
Website: www.lbc.co.uk
Britain's first commercal station, LBC had its 25th anniversary on October 8 1998. Relaunched in its current format in July 1996, the station provides 24 hour news and comment for London with phone-ins.
Parent company: London News Radio
Starting date: July 1996
Area: Greater London
Dial: 1152 am

Leicester Sound
Granville House, Granville Road, Leicester LE1 7RW
Fax 0116-256 1303   Tel 0116-256 1300
E-mail: leicestersound@musicradio.com
Parent company: GWR Group
Starting date: 7.9.84
Area: Leicester.
Dial: 105.4 MHz

963/972AM Liberty Radio
Trevor House, 100 Brompton Road, London SW3 1ER
Fax 020-7893 8965   Tel 020-7893 8966
E-mail: liberty963@aol.com
Parent company: Liberty Publishing
Starting date: 3.7.95
Area: Greater London
Dial: 963 + 972 AM

Lincs FM
Witham Park, Waterside South, Lincoln LN5 7JN
Fax 01522-549911   Tel 01522-549900
E-mail: contact@lincsfm.co.uk
Starting date: 1.3.92
Area: Lincolnshire

1458 Lite AM
Quay West, Trafford Park Manchester M17 1FL
Fax 0161-872 0206   Tel 0161-872 1458
Website: www.crazyprices.com/liteam/
Starting date: 20.6.94
Area: Greater Manchester. **Dial:** 1458 kHz

Lite FM
5 Church Stree, Peterborough PE1 1XB
Fax 01733 898107   Tel 01733 898107
E-mail: admin@litefm.co.uk
Website: www.litefm.co.uk
Starting date: 24.7.99
Area: Peterborough
Dial: 106.8 MHz

Lochbroom FM
Mill Street, Radio House, Ullapool, Rossshire IV26 2UN
Fax 01854-613132   Tel 01854-613131
Starting date: 97
Area: West Ross
Dial: 102.2 MHz

London Greek Radio
Florentia Village, Vale Road, London N4 1TD
Fax 020-8800 8005   Tel 020-8800 8001
E-mail: lgrhgc@globalnet.co.uk
Website: www.lgr.co.uk
Music, news and info for Greek speaking listeners
Starting date: 13.11.89
Area: Haringey.
Dial: 103.3 MHz

London Turkish Radio
185b High Road, Wood Green London N22 6BA
Fax 020-8881 5151   Tel 020-8881 0606
E-mail: gbn54@1.pipex.com
Music for the Turkish community
Starting date: summer 1995
Area: north London, Haringey.
Dial: 1584 kHz

Magic AM
900 Herries Road, Sheffield S6 1RH
Fax 0114-285 3159   Tel 0114-285 2121
E-mail: programmes@magicam.co.uk
Website:www.magicam.co.uk
Parent company: EMAP
Starting date: 12.2.97
Dial: 990 kHz, 1305 kHz, 1548 kHz

Magic 105.4
180 Brompton Road, London SW3 1HF
Fax 020-7581 7000   Tel 020-7581 1054
Website: www.melody.co.uk
Starting date: 9.7.90
Area: Greater London.
Dial: 105.4 MHz

Magic 828
PO Box 2000, 51 Burley Road, Leeds LS3 1LR
Fax 0113 283 5501   Tel 0113 283 5500
E-mail: MAGIC 828@firstnet.co.uk
Website: www.magic 828.co.uk
Parent company: Emap
Starting date: 17.7.90
Area: Leeds, west Yorkshire
Dial: 828 kHz

Magic 1152
Newcastle-upon-Tyne NE99 1BB
Fax 0191-488 0933   Tel 0191-420 3040
Parent company: Emap Radio
Starting date: 8.4.89
Area: Tyne & Wear, Northumberland & Durham
Dial: 1152AM

Magic 1152 Manchester
Castle Quay, Castlefield, Manchester M15 4PR
Fax 0161-288 5151   Tel 0161-288 5000
Parent company: Emap Radio
Starting date: 2.4.99
Area: Manchester
Dial: 1152 kHz

Magic 1161
Commercial Road, Hull HU1 2SG
Fax 01482-587067   Tel 01482-325141
E-mail: magic1161.co.uk
Parent company: Emap Radio
Starting date: 13.9.93
Dial: 1161 kHz

Magic 1548
8-10 Stanley Street, Liverpool L1 6AF
Fax 0151-471 0330   Tel 0151-227 5100
Website: www.radiocity967.com
Parent company: Emap
Starting date: 21.10.74
Area: Merseyside
Dial: 1548 kHz
Radio Maldwyn
Studios, The Park, Newtown, Powys SY16 2NZ
Fax 01686-623666   Tel 01686-623555
E-mail: radio.maldwyn@ukonline.co.uk
Starting date: 1 .7.93
Area: Montgomeryshire.   **Dial:** 756 kHz
Manx Radio
PO Box 1368, Broadcasting House, Douglas, Isle of
Man IM99 1SW
Fax 01624-682604   Tel 01624-661066
E-mail: postbox@manxradio.com
Starting date: 5.6.64   **Area:** Isle of Man.
Marcher Coast FM
The Studios, 41 Conway Road, Colwyn Bay, Conway
Fax 01492-535248   Tel 01492-533733
E-mail: info@coastfm.co.uk
Website: www.coastfm.co.uk
Area: North Wales
Marcher Gold
The Studios, Mold Road, Wrexham LL11 4AF
Fax 01978-759701   Tel 01978-752202
E-mail: mfm.radio@ukonline.co.uk
Website: www.marchergold.co.uk
Starting date: 5.9.83
Area: Wrexham, Chester, Deeside and Wirral.
Dial: 1260 kHz
Medway FM
Berkeley House, 186 High Street, Rochester ME1 1EY
Fax 01634-841122   Tel 01634-841111
E-mail: studio@medwayfm.co.uk
Website: www.medwayfm.com
Starting date: 1.9.97
Area: Medway towns   **Dial:** 107.9MHz, 100.4MHz
Mercia FM/Classic Gold 1359
Hertford Place, Coventry, W Midlands CV1 3TT
Fax 024-7686 8203   Tel 024-7686 8200
E-mail: reception@merciafm.musicradio.com
Parent company: GWR
Starting date: 7.3.94 (Mercia Classic Gold), 23.5.80
(Mercia FM)
Area: Coventry, Warwickshire.
Dial: 1359 kHz Mercia Classic Gold, 97.0 & 102.9 Hz
Mercia FM
Mercury FM/Fame 1521
The Stanley Centre, Kelvin Way, Crawley, West Sussex
RH10 2SE
Fax 01293-565663   Tel 01293-519161
E-mail: news@mercuryfm.co.uk
Website: www.mercuryfm.co.uk
Parent company: Independent Radio
Starting date: 20.10.84 (Mercury FM East), 4.5.92
(GRP. Fame 1521)
Area: Reigate, Crawley
Dial: 102.7 MHz (Mercury FM) 1521 kHz (Fame 1521)

Metro FM
Newcastle-upon-Tyne NE99 1BB
Fax 0191-488 0933   Tel 0191-420 3040
E-mail: steph@metromk.ace.co.uk
Website: www.metrofm.co.uk
Parent company: Emap Radio
Starting date: 15.7.74
Areas: Tyne & Wear, Northumberland & Durham
Dial: 97.1 MHz (Tyne & Wear)103.2 MHz (Tyne
Valleyo, 102.6 Alnwick
MFM
The Studios, Mold Road, Wrexham LL11 4AF
Fax 01978-759701   Tel 01978-752202
E-mail: contact@mfmradio.co.uk
Website: www.mfmradio.co.uk
Starting date: 31.8.89
Area: Wrexham, Chester, Deeside and Wirral
Dial: 97.1 & 103.4 MHz
Millennium Radio
Harrow Manor Way, Thamesmead, London SE2 9XH
Fax 020-8312 1930   Tel 020-8311 3112
mfm@greenwichuk.com
Starting date: 18.3.90
Area: Thamesmead
Dial: 106.8 MHz
Minster FM
PO Box 123, Dunnington, York YO1 5ZX
Fax 01904-488811   Tel 01904-488888
E-mail: minsterfm@demon.co.uk
Starting date: 4.7.92
Area: York.
Dial: 104.7 & 102.3 MHz
Mix 96
Friars Square Studios, 11 Bourbon Street, Aylesbury,
Bucks HP20 2PZ
Fax 01296-398988   Tel 01296-399396
E-mail: mix@mix96.demon.co.uk
Website: www.mix96.demon.co.uk
Starting date: 15.4.94
Area: Aylesbury Vale, Thame, Tring, Leighton Buzzard
Dial: 96.2 MHz
Moray Firth
PO Box 271, Inverness IV3 8UJ
Fax 01463-243224   Tel 01463-224433
E-mail: moray.firth.radio@mfr.uk.com
Starting date: 23.2.82
Area: Inverness   **Dial:** 97.4 & 96.6 MHz, 1107 kHz
NECR
Town House, Kintore, Inverurie, Aberdeenshire AB51
0US
Fax 01467 632969   Tel 01467 6329090
E-mail: airefm@airefm.co.uk
Starting date: 6.6.94
Area: Inverurie   **Dial:** 102.6 MHz
Neptune Radio 96.4 & 106.8FM
PO Box 1068, Dover CT16 1GB
Fax 01304-212717   Tel 01304-202505
E-mail: neptuneradio@btinternet.com
Website: www.neptuneradio.co.uk
Starting date: 29.9.97
Area: Dover & Folkestone
Dial: 106.8 MHz Dover, 96.4 MHz Folkestone

Nevis Radio
Inverlochy, Fort William PH33 6LU
Fax 01397 701007   Tel 01397-700007
E-mail: nevisradio@lochaber.sol.co.uk
Website: www.nevisradio.demon.co.uk
Starting date: 1.8.94
Area: Fort William
Dial: 96.6 & 102.3 MHz

News Direct 97.3FM
200 Grays Inn Road, London WC1X 8XZ
Fax 020-7312 8470   Tel 020-7973 1152
Providing a 24-hour rolling news and information
service for London with news, traffic, weather, sport,
entertainment, city and headlines every 20 minutes..
Parent company: London News Radio
Starting date: December 1996
Area: Greater London
Dial: 97.3FM

Northants 96/Classic Gold 1557
19-21 St Edmunds Road, Northampton NN1 5DY
Fax 01604-795601   Tel 01604-795600
E-mail: reception@northants96.musicradio.com
Parent company: GWR Group
Starting date: 1.10.86
Area: Northampton
Dial: 96.6 MHz, 1557 AM

NorthSound One/Two
45 Kings Gate, Aberdeen, Grampian AB15 4EL
Fax 01224-637289   Tel 01224-337000
E-mail: northsound@srh.co.uk
Parent company: Scottish Radio Holdings
Starting date: 27.7.81
Area: Aberdeen. Dial: 96.9, 97.6, 103 MHz (One),1035
kHz (Two)

The NRG
PO Box 1234, Bournemouth BH 3YH
Fax 01202 318110   Tel 01202 318100
E-mail: office@the-nrg.co.uk
Website: www.the-nrg.co.uk
Starting date: 26.6.99
Area: Bournemouth and Poole
Dial: 107.6 MHz

107 Oak FM
7 Waldron Court, Prince William Road,
Loughborough, Leics LE11 5GD
Fax 01509 246107   Tel 01509 211711
E-mail: info @oakfm.co.uk
Website: www.oakfm.co.uk
Starting date: 14.2.99
Area: Loughborough
Dial: 107 MHz

Oasis FM
9 Christopher Place, Shopping Centre, St Albans,
Herts AL3 5DQ
Fax 01727-834456   Tel 01727-831966
E-mail: general@oasisfm.co.uk
Parent company: Essex Radio
Starting date: 22.10.94
Area: St Albans & Watford
Dial: 96.6 FM

Oban FM
132 George Street, Oban PA34 5NT
Fax 01631-570530   Tel 01631-570530
E-mail: us@oban-fm.freeserve.co.uk
Starting date: 1.7.96
Area: Oban

Ocean FM
Radio House, Whittle Avenue, Segensworth West,
Fareham PO15 5SH
Fax 01489-589453   Tel 01489-589911
E-mail: oceanfm.com
Parent company: Capital Radio
Starting date: 12.10.86
Area: Portsmouth, Soton and Winchester
Dial: 96.7, 97.5 MHz

Orchard FM
Haygrove House, Taunton, Somerset TA3 7BT
Fax 01823-321044   Tel 01823-338448
E-mail: orchard@orchardfm.co.uk
Website: www.orchardfm.co.uk
Starting date: 26.11.89
Area: Yeovil and Taunton.
Dial: 96.5, 97.1, 102.6 MHz

Oxygen 107.9
Suite 41, Westgate Centre, Oxford OX1 1PD
Fax 01865-726161   Tel 01865-724442
E-mail: mail@oxygen.demon.co.uk
Website: www.oxygen.demon.co.uk
Parent company: The Local Radio Company (49%),
Oxford Student Radio (51%)
Starting date: 14.2.97
Area: Oxford
Dial: 107.9 MHz

Peak 107 FM
Radio House, Foxwood Road, Chesterfield, S41 9RF
Fax 01246-269933   Tel 01246-269107
E-mail: info@peak107.co.uk
Web: www.peak107.co.uk
Start date: 1.10.98
Area: Chesterfield

Pirate FM 102
Carn Brae Studios, Wilson Way, Redruth, Cornwall
TR15 3XX
Fax 01209 314345   Tel 01209-314400
E-mail: piratefm102.co.uk
Website: www.piratefm102.co.uk
Starting date: 3.4.92
Area: Cornwall, W Devon, Isles of Scilly
Dial: 102.2 MHz (east Cornwall, west Devon), 102.8
(west Cornwall, Isle of Scilly)

Plymouth Sound AM/FM
Earls Acre, Plymouth, Devon PL3 4HX
Fax 01752-670730   Tel 01752-227272
E-mail: mail@plymouthsound.com
Web: www.plymouthsound.com
Starting date: 19.5.75
Area: Plymouth
Dial: 1152 kHz (AM), 97.0, 96.6 MHz (FM)

Power FM
Radio House, Whittle Avenue, Segensworth,
Fareham, Hampshire PO15 5PA
Fax 01489-589453   Tel 01489-589911
E-mail: info@powerfm.com
Parent company: Capital Radio
Starting date: 4.12.88
Area: Portsmouth, Southampton and Winchester
Dial: 103.2 MHz

Premier Radio (Christian)
Glen House, Stag Place, London SW1E 5AG
Fax 020-7233 6706   Tel 020-7233 6705
E-mail: premier@premier.org.uk
Website: www.premier.org.uk
Starting date: 10.6.95
Area: Greater London   **Dial:** 1305, 1332 & 1413 kHz

The Pulse (FM) Classic Gold (AM)
Forster Square, Bradford, W Yorkshire BD1 5NE
Fax 01274-203130   Tel 01274-203040
E-mail: general@pulse.co.uk
Parent company: The Radio Partnership
Starting date: 31.8.91
Area: Bradford, Halifax, Huddersfield
Dial: 97.5 FM Bradford, 102.5 FM Huddersfield &
Halifax, 1278 AM Bradford, 1530 AM Huddersfield &
Halifax

96 3 QFM
26 Lady Lane, Paisley, Strathclyde PA1 2LG
Fax 0141-887 0963   Tel 0141-887 9630
E-mail: requests@qfmclassichits.co.uk
Starting date: 1.9.92
Area: Paisley. **Dial:** 96.3 MHz

Q102.9 FM
Old Waterside Railway Station, Duke Street,
Waterside, Londonderry BT47 6DH
Fax 01504-311177   Tel 01504-344449
E-mail: q102@iol.ie.
Website: www.q102-fm.com
Starting date: 21.10.93
Area: Londonderry, north west
Dial: 102.9 MHz

Q103 FM
PO Box 103, Vision Park, Chivers Way, Histon,
Cambridge CB4 9WW
Fax 01223-235161   Tel 01223-235255
E-mail: reception@Q103.musicradio.com
Parent company: GWR Group
Area: Cambridge, Newmarket

Quay West Radio
Harbour Studios, The Esplanade, Watchet, Somerset
TA23 0AJ
Fax 01984-634811   Tel 01984-634900
Area: west Somerset and Exmoor
Dial: 102.4 FM

Radio Borders
Tweedside Park, Galashiels, Borders TD1 3TD
Fax 01896-759494   Tel 01896-759444
Website: www.radioborders.co.uk
Parent company: Scottish Radio Holdings
Starting date: 22.1.90
Area: Scottish Borders, north Numberland
Dial: 96.8, 97.5, 103.1 & 103.4 MHz

Radio City 96.7/Magic 1548
8-10 Stanley Street, Liverpool LI 6AF
Fax 0151-471 0333   Tel 0151-227 5100
Website: www.radiocity967.com
Parent company: Emap
Starting date: 21.10.74
Area: Merseyside.
Dial: 96.7 MHz

Radio Mansfield
The Media Suite, Brunts Business Centre, Samuel
Brunts Way, Mansfield, Notts, NG18 2AH
Fax 01623-660606   Tel 01623-646666
E-mail: philsmith.radman@btinternet.com
Web: www.nottingham-online.co.uk
Start date: 1.10.98
Area: Mansfield and Ashfield
Dial: 103.2FM

Radio XL 1296 AM
KMS House, Bradford St,Birmingham B12 0JD
Fax 0121-753 3111   Tel 0121-753 5353
For the Asian community in the West Midlands
Starting date: 30.5.95
Area: Birmingham   **Dial:** 1296 kHz

Ram FM
The Market Place, Derby DE1 3AA
Fax 01332 292229   Tel 01332 292945
E-mail: reception@ramfm.musicradio.com
Parent company: GWR Group
Starting date: 3.3.87
Dial: 102.8 MHz

Red Dragon FM
Radio House, West Canal Wharf, Cardiff CF1 5XL
Fax 029-2038 4014   Tel 029-2038 4041
E-mail: mail@rdfm.co.uk
Parent company: Capital Radio
Starting date: 11.4.80 (Cardiff), 13.6.83 (Newport)
Area: south east Wales
Dial: 103.2 MHz (Cardiff), 97.4 (MHz (Newport)

Red Rose Gold/Red Rose Rock FM
St Pauls Square, Preston, Lancashire PR1 1XS
Fax 01772-201917   Tel 01772-556301
Website: www.rockfm.co.uk
Parent company: Emap
Starting date: 1.6.90
Area: Blackpool, Preston **Dial:** 999kHz (Gold),
97.4 Hz (Rock FM)

Revolution
PO Box 877, Oldham, Lancs OL8 1US
Fax 0161-627 0905   Tel 0161-628 8787
Starting date: 9.99
Area: Oldham

Ridings FM
PO Box 333, Wakefield WF1 5YN
Fax 01924 367133   Tel 01924 367177
Starting date: 12.99
Area: Wakefield   **Dial:** 106.8 MHz

Rock FM
PO Box 974, Preston, Lancs PR11XS
Fax 01772 201917   Tel 01772 556301
Starting date: 5.10.82
Area: Preston, Blackpool
Dial: 97.4 MHz

RTL Country
33-35 Wembley Hill Road, Wembley, Middlesex HA9 8RT
Fax 020-8733 1393   Tel 020-8733 1300
Starting date: 1.9.94
Area: Greater London
Dial: 1035 kHz

Rutland Radio
Rutland Business Centre, Gaol Street, Oakham, Rutland, LE15 6AQ
Fax 01572-757744   Tel 01572-757868
E-mail: enquiries@rutlandradio.co.uk
Start date: Autumn 1998
Area: Rutland and Stamford
Dial: 107.2 & 97.4 FM

Sabras Sound
63 Melton Road, Leicester LE4 6PN
Fax 0116-266 7776   Tel 0116-261 0666
24 hour music, news and info service to Asian communities.
Starting date: 7.9.95
Area: Leicester, Nottingham, Derby and the east Midlands
Dial: 1260 kHz

Scot FM
Number 1 Shed, Albert Quay, Leith EH6 7DN
Fax 0131-554 2266   Tel 0131-554 6677
Starting date: 16.9.94
Policy: Speech and adult contemporary music
Area: Central Scotland
Dial: 100.3 & 101.1 MHz

Severn Sound FM/Classic Gold
Bridge Studios, Eastgate Centre, Gloucester GL1 1SS
Fax 01452-313213   Tel 01452-313200
E-mail: reception@severnfm.musicradio.com
Parent company: Chiltern Radio Network
Starting date: 23.10.80
Area: Gloucester and Cheltenham
Dial: 102.4 & 103 MHz (Severn Sound), 774 kHz (SuperGold)

SGR FM Bury
Radio House, Alpha Business Park, Whitehouse Road, Ipswich, Suffolk IP1 5LT
Fax 01473-741200   Tel 01473-461000
Website: www.sgrfm.co.uk
Parent company: GWR
Starting date: 6.11.82
Area: Bury St Edmunds
Dial: 96.4 MHz, 1251 kHz

SGR Colchester
9 Whitewell Road, Colchester CO2 7DE
Fax 01206-561199   Tel 01206-575859
E-mail: prog.col@sgrfm.co.uk
Website: www.sgrfm.co.uk
Parent company: East Anglian Radio
Starting date: 17.10.83
Area: Colchester **Dial:** 96.1 MHz

SGR FM Ipswich
Radio House, Alpha Business Park, Whitehouse Road, Ipswich, Suffolk IP1 5LT
Fax 01473-741200   Tel 01473-461000
E-mail: chris@sgrfm.co.uk
Website: www.sgrfm.co.uk
Parent company: GWR
Starting date: 28.10.75
Area: Ipswich
Dial: 97.1 MHz

SIBC
Market Street, Lerwick, Shetland ZE1 0JN
Fax 01595-695696   Tel 01595-695299
E-mail: info@sibc.co.uk
Website: www.sibc.co.uk
Starting date: 26.11.87
Area: Shetland Islands
Dial: 96.2 MHz

Signal 104.9/96.4
Regent House, Heaton Lane, Stockport, Greater Manchester SK4 1BX
Fax 0161-285 1010   Tel 0161-285 4545
E-mail: signal@signal1049.com
Parent company: The Radio Partnership
Starting date: 17.2.90
Area: south Manchester & Cheshire
Dial: 104.9 - south Manchester, 96.4 Cheshire

Signal 1/Signal 2
Stoke Road, Stoke-on-Trent, ST4 2SR
Fax 01782-744110   Tel 01782-747047
E-mail: recipient@signalradio.com
Website: www.signalradio.com
Parent company: The Radio Partnership
Starting date: 5.9.83 (1)14.9.92 (2),
Area: Cheshire, Staffordshire
Dial: 102.6 & 96.9 FM(1)1170 AM(2),

Silk FM
Radio House, Bridge Street, Macclesfield, Cheshire, SK11 6DJ
Fax 01625-269010   Tel 01625-268000
E-mail: mail@silkfm.com
Web: www.silkfm.com
Start date: 25.5.98
Area: Macclesfield
Dial: 106.9 FM

107 SouthCity FM
City Studios, Marsh Lane, Southampton SO14 3ST
Fax 02380 220060   Tel 02380 220020
E-mail: info@southcityfm.co.uk
Website: www.southcityfm.co.uk
Starting date: 12.99
Area: Southampton
Dial: 107.8 MHz

South West Sound
Campbell House, Bankend Road, Dumfries DG1 4TH
Fax 01387-265629   Tel 01387-250999
E-mail: cameron@srh.co.uk
Parent company: West Sound Radio
Starting date: 21.5.91
Area: Dumfries and Galloway
Dial: 97 FM, 96.5 FM, 103 FM

Southern FM
Radio Ho, Franklin Road, Portslade BN41 2SS
Fax 01273-430098   Tel 01273-430111
E-mail: info@southernradio.co.uk
Parent company: Capital Radio
Starting date: 29.8.83 (Brighton), 12.2.88 (Eastbourne)
Area: Brighton, Newhaven, Eastbourne and Hastings
Dial: 103.5 MHz (Brighton), 96.9 MHz (Newhaven), 102.4 MHz (Eastbourne), 102.0 MHz (Hastings)

South Hams Radio
Brook House, South Milton, Kingsbridge, Devon TQ73JQ
Fax 01548 561414   Tel 01548 561414
Starting date: soon
Area: South Hams

Sovereign Radio
14 St Mary's Walk, Hailsham, East Sussex BN27 1AF
Fax 01323 440643   Tel 01323 442700
E-mail: steve@1075SovereignRadio
Website: www.SovereignRadio.co.uk
Parent company: East Sussex Radio
Starting date: 17.11.97
Area: Eastbourne
Dial: 107.5 MHz

Spectrum Radio
204-206 Queens Town Road, London SW8 3NR
Fax 020-7627 3409   Tel 020-7627 4433
E-mail: Spectrum@spectrum558am.co.uk
Music, news and information for ethnic communities
Starting date: 25.6.90
Area: London
Dial: 558 kHz

Spire FM
City Hall Studios, Malthouse Lane, Salisbury, Wiltshire SP2 7QQ
Fax 01722-416688   Tel 01722-416644
E-mail: admin@spirefm.co.uk
Website: www.spirefm.co.uk
Starting date: 20.9.92
Area: Salisbury
Dial: 102.0 MHz

Spirit FM
Dukes Court, Bognor Road, Chichester, West Sussex PO19 2FX
Fax 01243-786464   Tel 01243-773600
E-mail: spiritfm@argonet.co.uk
Website: www.spiritfm.net
Starting date: 21.4.96
Area: Chichester & Bognor Regis
Dial: 96.6 MHz & 102.3 MHz

Star FM
Observatory Shopping Centre, Slough, Berks SL1 1LH
Fax 01753-512277   Tel 01753-551066
E-mail: onair@starfm.co.uk
Website: www.starfm.co.uk
Starting date: 21.5.93
Area: Windsor, Slough, Maidenhead
Dial: 106.6 MHz

97.2 Stray FM
PO Box 972, Station Parade, Harrogate HG1 5YF
Fax 01423-522922   Tel 01423-522972
E-mail: mail@97.2strayfm.co.uk
Starting date: 4.7.94
Area: Harrogate
Dial: 97.2 FM

Sun FM
PO Box 1034, Sunderland SR1 3YZ
Fax 0191-548 7171   Tel 0191-548 1034
E-mail: mail@sun-fm.com
Website: www.sun-fm.com
Music, local news, sport and information.
Parent company: Border Radio Holdings
Area: Sunderland, Washington, South tyneside and Co Durham.
Dial: 103.4MHz

Sunrise Radio
Sunrise House, Merrick Road, Southall, Middlesex UB2 4AU
Fax 020-8813 9800   Tel 020-8574 6666
Music, news and information for the Asian community
Parent company: Sunrise Group
Starting date: 5.11.89
Area: Greater London and SE England
Dial: 1458 AM

Sunrise FM
30 Chapel Street, Little Germany, Bradford BD1 5DN
Fax 01274-728534   Tel 01274-735043
Music, news and information for the Asian community
Starting date: 9.12.89
Area: Bradford
Dial: 103.2 MHz

Sunshine 855
Sunshine House, Waterside, Ludlow, Shropshire SY8 1GS
Fax 01584-875900   Tel 01584-873795
Starting date: 18.10.92
Area: Ludlow, south Shropshire   **Dial:** 855 kHz

Surf 107.7
PO Box 107, Brighton, BN1 1QG
Fax 01273-273107   Tel 01273-386107
Web: www.surf107.co.uk
Start date: 27.3.98
Area: Brighton
Dial: 107.2 FM

Swansea Sound (1170) Sound Wave 964
Victoria Road, Gowerton, Swansea, West Glamorgan SA4 3AB
Fax 01792-511171   Tel 01792-511170
E-mail: sales@swanseasound.co.uk
Website: www.swanseasound.co.uk
Some Welsh language broadcasting
Parent company: The Radio Partnership
Starting date: 30.9.74
Area: Swansea
Dial: 96.4 MHz, 1170 kHz

Tay FM/Radio Tay AM
6 North Isla Street, Dundee, Tayside DD3 7JQ
Fax 01382-423252   Tel 01382-200800
E-mail: tayfm@srh.co.uk and tayam@srh.co.uk
Parent company: Scottish Radio Holdings
Starting date: 17.10.80 Radio Tay AM, 9.1.95 Tay FM
Area: Dundee, Perth
Dial: 102.8 MHz (Dundee), 96.4 MHz (Perth) Tay FM/
1161 kHz (Dundee), 1584 kHz (Perth), Radio Tay AM

107.4 Telford FM
PO Box 1074, Telford TF3 3WG
Fax 01952 2080010   Tel 011952 280011
Starting date: 3.5.99
Area: Telford   **Dial:** 107.4 MHz

Ten 17
Latton Bush Centre, Harlow, Essex CM18 7BL
Fax 01279-445289   Tel 01279-432415
E-mail: studios@ten17.co.uk
Website: www.ten17.co.uk
Parent company: DMG Radio   **Starting date:** 1.5.93
Area: Harlow.   **Dial:** 101.7 MHz

TFM
Yale Crescent, Stockton-on-Tees, TS17 6AA
Fax 01642-868290   Tel 01642-888222
Parent company: Emap Radio
Starting date: 24.6.75
Area: Teesside.
Dial: 96.6 MHz

107.8 FM Thames Radio
Brentham House, 45 High Street, Kingston, Surrey KT1 4DG
Fax 020 8288 1312   Tel 020 8288 1300
E-mail: mail@thamesradio.co.uk
Website: www.thamesradio.co.uk
Starting date: 1.3.97
Area: Kinsgston-upon-Thames
Dial: 107.8 MHz

Thanet Local Radio
Imperial House, 2-14 High Street, Margate, Kent CT9 1DH
Fax 01843-299666   Tel 01843-220222
E-mail: general@tlrfm.co.uk
Starting date: 17.01.98
Area: Thanet, east Kent
Dial: 107.2 MHz

TLR
Imperial House, 2-14 High Street, Margate, Kent CT9 1DH
Fax 01843 299666   Tel 01843 220222
E-mail: tlr@tlrfm.co.uk
Website: www.tlrfm.co.uk
Starting date: 17.1.98
Area: Thanet
Dial: 107.2MHz

Touch AM
West Canal Wharf, Cardiff CF1 5XL
Fax 029-2038 4014   Tel 029-2023 7878
E-mail: mail@rdfm.co.uk
Website: www.rdfm.co.uk
Parent company: Capital Radio
Starting date: 15.7.90
Dial: 1359 kHz (Cardiff), 1305 kHz (Newport)

Tower FM
The Mill, Browlow Way, Bolton BL1 2RA
Fax 01204 534065   Tel 01204 387000
E-mail: info@towerfm.co.uk
Website: www.towerfm.co.uk
Starting date: 20.3.99
Area: Bolton, Bury   **Dial:** 107.4 MHz

Trax FM
PO Box 444, Worksop, Notts, S81 9YW
Fax 01909-500445   Tel 01909-500611
E-mail: enquiries@traxfm.co.uk
Start date: Autumn 1998
Area: Bassetlaw   **Dial:** 107.9 FM

Trent FM
29 Castle Gate, Nottingham NG1 7AP
Fax 0115-912 9302   Tel 0115-952 7000
E-mail: admin@trentfm.musicradio.com
Parent company: GWR Group
Starting date: 3.7.75
Area: Nottingham.   **Dial:** 96.2 MHz

97.4 Vale FM
Longmead, Shaftesbury, Dorset SP7 8QQ
Fax 01747 855722   Tel 01747 855711
E-mail: studio@valefm.co.uk
Website: www.valefm.co.uk
Starting date: 25.6.95
Area: Shaftesbury   **Dial:** 97.4 MHz

Valleys Radio
Festival Park, Victoria, Ebbw Vale NP3 6XW
Fax 01495-300710   Tel 01495-301116
Starting date: 23.11.96
Area: Heads of south Wales valeys.
Dial: 999 & 1116MW

Radio Victory
Media House, Tipner Wharf, Twyford Avenue, Portsmouth PO2 8PE
Fax 023-9235 8863   Tel 023-9235 8853
E-mail: info@radiovictory.co.uk
Website: www.victory.fm
Starting date: soon
Area: Portsmouth
Dial: 107.4 MHz

Vibe FM
Reflection House, Olding Road, Bury St Edmunds, Suffolk IP33 3TA
Fax 01284-718839   Tel 01284-718800
E-mail: studios@vibefm.co.uk
Website: www.vibefm.co.uk
Parent company: Essex Radio, subsidiary of DMG Radio
Starting date: 22.11.97
Area: East of England
Dial: 106.4 MHz(Suffolk), 105.6 MHz(Cambridge), 106.1 MHz(Norwich), 107.7 MHz(Peterborough)

Viking FM
Commercial Road, Hull, HU1 2SG
Fax 01482-587067   Tel 01482-325141
Website: www.vikingfm.co.uk
Parent company: Emap Radio
Starting date: 17.4.84
Area: Yorkshire-Lincolnshire
Dial: 96.9 MHz

Virgin Radio London
1 Golden Square, London W1R 4DJ
Fax 020-7434 1197   Tel 020-7434 1215
E-mail: reception@ginger.com
Website: www.virginradio.co.uk
Parent company: Ginger Media Group
Starting date: 30.4.93   Area: National radio
Dial: 1215 AM nationwide, 105.8 FM London/south east

96.4 FM The Wave
PO Box 964, Victoria Road, Gowerton SA4 3AB
Fax 01792 511965   Tel 01792 511964
E-mail: info@athewave.com
Website: www.thewave.co.uk
Starting date: 30.9.96
Area: Swansea
Dial: 96.4 MHz

The Wave
965 Mowbray Drive, Blackpool, Lancs FY3 7JR
Fax 01253-301965   Tel 01253-304965
E-mail: sales@thewavefm.co.uk
Website: www.thewave.co.uk
Starting date: 25.5.92
Area: Blackpool and the Fylde coast
Dial: 96.5 MHz

Waves Radio Peterhead
Blackhouse Industrial Estate, Peterhead AB42 1BW
Fax 01779 490802   Tel 01779 491012
E-mail: waves@radiophd.freeserve.co.uk
Starting date: 6.12.97
Area: Peterhead
Dial: 101.2 MHz

Wessex FM
Radio House, Trinity Street, Dorchester, Dorset DT1 1DJ
Fax 01305-250052   Tel 01305-250333
E-mail: admin@wessexfm.co.uk
Website: www.wessexfm.co.uk
Starting date: 4.9.93
Area: Dorset
Dial: 97.2 MHz & 96.0 MHz

West FM
54a Holmston Road, Ayr KA7 3BE
Fax 01292-283665   Tel 01292-283662
E-mail: westfm@srh.co.uk
Starting date: 1.1.97
Area: Ayrshire, Arran, the Cumbraes
Dial: 96.7 FM

West Sound
54a Holmston Road, Ayr KA7 3BE
Fax 01292-283662   Tel 01292-283662
E-mail: westsound@srh.co.uk
Web: www.west-sound.co.uk
Starting date: 16.10.81
Area: Ayrshire, Arran, the Cumbraes
Dial: 1035 AM

107.7 WFM
11 Beaconsfield Road, Weston-Super-Mare BS23 1YE
Fax 01934 629922   Tel 01934 624455
Website: www.breeze107.com
Starting date: 23.10.99
Area: Weston-Super-Mare

Win 107.2
PO Box 107.2, The Brooks, Winchester, Hants SO23 8FT
Fax 01962 841079   Tel 01962 841071
E-mail: info@win1072.com
Website: www.win1072.com
Starting date: 9.99
Area: Winchester
Dial: 107.2 MHz

107.2 Wire FM
Warrington Business Park, Long Lane, Warrington, WA2 8TX
Fax 01925 657705   Tel 01925-445545
E-mail: mail@wirefm.com
Web: www.wirefm.com
Start date: Sept 1998
Area: Warrington

Wish 102.4
Orrell Lodge, Orrell Road, Orrell, Wigan WN5 8HJ
Fax 01942-620222   Tel 01942-761024
E-mail: general@wishfm.net
Parent company: Independent Radio Group
Starting date: 1.4.97
Area: Wigan, St Helens, Skelmersdale
Dial: 102.4 MHz

107.7 The Wolf
10th Floor, Mander House, Wolverhampton WV1 3NB
Fax 01902-571079   Tel 01902-571070
E-mail: studio@thewolf.co.uk
Website: www.thewolf.co.uk
Starting date: 7.10.97
Area: Wolverhampton   Dial: 107.7 MHz

Wyvern FM/Classic Gold
5 Barbourne Terrace, Worcester WR1 3JZ
Fax 01905-613549   Tel 01905-612212
Area: Hereford, Worcester, Kidderminster
Dial: 97.6 Mhz (Hereford), 102.8 MHz (Worcester), 96.7 Mhz (Kidderminster); Classic Gold - 954 Khz (Hereford), 1530 Khz (Worcester)

X-Cel FM
46 Camel Road, Littleport, Cambridgeshire CB6 1EW
Fax 01353 865105   Tel 01353 865102
E-mail: (name)@xcelfm.co.uk
Website: www.xcelfm.co.uk
Starting date: 3.10.99
Area: Fenland   Dial: 107.5 MHz

Xfm
PO Box 1049, London WC2H 7XX
Fax 020-7766 6601   Tel 020-7766 6600
Starting date: 9.97
Area: Greater London   Dial: 104.9 MHz

Radio XL
KMS House, Bradford Street, Birmingham B12 0JD
Fax 0121-753 3111   Tel 0121-753 5353
Starting date: 30.5.95
Area: Birmingham   Dial: 1296 kHz

Yorkshire Coast Radio
PO Box 962, Scarborough, Yorkshire YO12 5YX
Fax 01723-501050   Tel 01723-500962
Parent company: Minster Sound Radio
Starting date: 7.11.93
Area: Scarborough   Dial: 96.2 & 103.1 MHz

CABLE RADIO

BCB (Bradford Comunity Broadcasting)
2 Forster Square, Bradford, West Yorkshire BD1 1DQ
Fax 01274-771680   Tel 01274-771677
E-mail: timbo@bcb.yorks.com
Website: www.bcb.yorks.com
Community radio for Bradford. Special event RSL broadcaster. Broadcasts full time from website. Radio production skills training.
Area: Bradford
Dial: 104 FM on the Yorkshire Cable Network 107.4 FM or 1566 AM during RSL broadcasts.

Birmingham's BHBN
Dudley Road, Birmingham B18 7QH
Fax 0121-554 2255   Tel 0121-554 5522
Hospital info, music, local news and features
Starting date: 5.9.94

Cable Radio Milton Keynes
14 Vincent Avenue, Milton Keynes MK8 0AB
Fax 01908-564893   Tel 01908-265266
Community radio for Milton Keynes
Starting date: 3.79
Area: Milton Keynes

Forth FM
Forth House, Forth Street, Edinburgh EH1 3LF
Fax 0131-558 3277   Tel 0131-556 9255
Pop
Starting date: 22.1.75
Dial: 96.8 MHz

Gemini FM
Hawthorn House, Exeter Business Park, Exeter, EX1 3QS
Fax 01392-444433   Tel 01392 444444
Start date: 1.1.95
Area: Eurobell South West Network
Dial: 99.6 FM on Eurobell South West Network

Music Choice Europe
16 Harcourt Street, London W1H 2AU
Fax 020-7724 0404   Tel 020-7724 9494
E-mail: sales@musicchoice.co.uk
Website: www.musicchoice.co.uk

Radio City
Singleton Hospital, Sketty Lane, Swansea SA2 8QA
                              Tel 01792-205666 x 5264
Starting date: 31.12.66

Radio Phoenix
Neath General Hospital, Neath SA11 2LQ
                              Tel 01639-762029/762333
Starting date: 25.3.88
Area: Neath & Port Talbot

Town FM
125 Fore Street, Edmonton, London N18 2XF
Fax 020-8373 1074   Tel 020-8373 1073
Community radio for North London
Starting date: 28.6.97
Dial: Cable London Channel 48 and 107.1 hook up

Radio Verulam
PO Box 396, St. Albans, Herts, AL3 6NE
Tel 01442 398099
Start date: 24.2.96
Area: West Herts

SATELLITE RADIO

ASDA FM (National in-store radio)
Suite 2, the Old Nick, Stanley Road, Walkden, Manchester M28 3DT
Fax 0161-703 8180   Tel 0161-703 8530
E-mail: asdafm@hampson.co.uk
Website: www.hampson.co.uk

Asian Sound Radio
Globe Hall, Southall Street, Manchester M3 1LG
Fax 061-288 9000   Tel 0161-288 1000
Asian community radio.
Starting date: 3.6.98
Dial: Transponder 26 of the Astra 1B satellite

Bloomberg News Radio
City Gate House, 39-45 Finsbury Square, London EC2A 1PQ
Fax 020-7256 5326   Tel 020-7256 7500
Dial: Astra 1B, transponder 31

Radio Caroline
426 Archway Road, London N6 4JH
Fax 020-8340 3075   Tel 020-8340 3831
Carrying on a legitimised pirate tradition with some relgion thrown in.
Dial: Astra 1c, transponder 35

CMR (Country Music Radio via MNO)
PO Box 42, Alton, Hampshire GU32 4YU
Fax 01252-724312   Tel 01252-724891
E-mail: cmr@ukonline.co.uk

Costcutter Satellite Radio
PO Box 123, York YO1 5ZX
Fax 01904 488811   Tel 01904 488888
Supermarket service.
Dial: Astra 10876.5 MHz

Cross Rhythms
PO Box 1110, Stoke-on-Trent ST4 8JR
Fax 01782 641121   Tel 01782 642444
Christian music and teaching.
Dial: Astra 1B 7.38 MHz

FEM FM/BHS Radio
29-30 Windmill Street, London W1P 1HG
Fax 020-7692 0201   Tel 020-7692 0200
Music, news etc for women.
Dial: Eutelsat TX46- 12588.56 Digital

Gfm
29-30 Windmill Street, London W1P 1HG
Fax 020-7692 0201   Tel 020-7692 0200
Music and news for the motorway traveller
Dial: Astra 1c, transponder 33

Homebase FM
29-30 Windmill Street, London W1P 1HG
Fax 020-7692 0201   Tel 020-7692 0200
Music and information for the home improver
Dial: Eutelsat TX46 12589.64 Digital

MBC FM
204-206 Queentown Road, London SW8
Fax 020-7501 1025   Tel 020-7501 1000
E-mail: 100635.1314@compuserve.com

Student Broadcast Network
49 Princes Place, London W11 4QA
Fax 020-7727 0009   Tel 020-7229 5667
Provides programming and support services to student radio stations across the UK. Programmes include the national student radio chart show, the sesion show and the best student-produced shows.
Dial: Astra 1c, transponder 15

Sunrise Radio
Sunrise Road, Southall, Middlesex UB2 4AU
Fax 020-813 9800   Tel 020-8574 6666
Asian community radio
Dial: Astra 2 5850 SW

Tamil Radio and Television (TRT)
727 London Road, Thornton Heath, Surrey CR7 6AU
Fax 020-8683 4445   Tel 020-8689 7503
Tamil language community radio

UCB (United Christian Broadcasters)
Hanchurch Christian Centre, Hanchurch Lane, Stoke-on-Trent ST4 8RY
Fax 01782-641121   Tel 01782-642000
E-mail: ucb@ucb.co.uk
Website: www.ucb.co.uk/.
Starting date: 4.93

Virgin Radio
1 Golden Square, London W!R 4DJ
Fax 020-7434 1197   Tel 020-7434 1215
Starting date: 30.4.93
Rock

World Radio Network
Wyvil Court, Wyvil Road, London SW8 2TG
Fax 020-7896 9007   Tel 020-7896 9000
News from over 20 international public sector broadcasters.
Dial: Astra 1B, 11.538 GHz

INDEPENDENT RADIO PRODUCERS

Independent Association of Radio Producers
29 Foley Street, London W1P 7LB
Fax 020-736 0132   Tel 020-7402 1011

A

Above theTitle Prods	020-7916 1984
Aggelon Radio	01278-732848
All Out Productions	020-7255 2525
Andy Jordan	020-8963 9171
Armada Theatre	020-7831 1814
Arthur Johnson	020-8202 0274
Audio Movies	020-8743 2677

B

BGB	020-7385 4501
Black Box Prods	01225-868148
Blanket Productions	020-8342 9700
Bona Lattie	01843-290944
Business Sound	01483-898868

C

Celador Productions	020-7240 8101
Children's Voices	01364-642787
CSA Telltapes	020-8960 8466

D

David Ness	0131-556 4764
Davina Greenspan	020-7372 6311

E

Excalibur Productions	01422-843871

F

The Fiction Factory	020-8853 5100
First Writes	01223-264 129
Floating Earth	020-8997 4000
Forsyth Productions	0131-667 9573

G

Gilmour B'casting	01303-840024
Greeh Audio	020-7240 3456
Green Mann Productions	020-8341 6754

H

Harry Schneider	020-8959 1695
Heavy Entertainment	020-8960 9001
Human Horizons	020-7704 8583

J

Jo Phillips	01227-455618
Jon Glover Partnership	09932-864426
Jude Habib	020-8455 6431
Just Radio	020-7404 6744

K

K & TL Productions	020-7735 8139
Kirsten Lass	020-8996 9960

L

Ladbroke Productions	020-7580 8864
Leisure Time Productions	020-7837 8777
Liba Productions	020-8904 8136
Loftus Productions	020-8740 4077
Louise Armitage	020-7243 0456
Louise Lawson	020-8801 0650

M

Mandy Wheeler	020-7437 8121
Mediatracks	01254-691197

P

Palace Radio	020-7415 7136
Partners in Sound	020-7485 0873
Peartree Productions	01905-351748
Pier Productions	01273-691401
Planet 24	020-7345 2424
Pratima Parker	020-7258 1140
Presentable	029-20575729
Printz P Holman	01298-27975

Q

Quantum Radio	020-8875 9999

R

Radio Star	020-7717 1257
Revolution Recordings	01603-433566
Rewind Productions	020-7577 7772
Robin Quinn	01892-669346
Rosemary Hartill	01665-578 543
Ruth Prince	01633-450351

S

Screen Play	01273-708610
Somethin Else Sound Direction	020-7613 3211
Stationhouse	020-7602 9906
Sound Visual	01380-726831

T

Testbed Productions	020-7436 0555
Track Record	020-7431 3834
Tumble Hill Productions	029-20594044

U

Unique Broadcasting	020-7402 1011

V

VERA	020-7436 6116
The Vocal Suite	020-7437 2455

W

Watchmaker	020-7456 6000
Watermill Productions	01784-442625
Weigall Productions	020-7229 5725
Whirlwind	024-76382633
Wise Buddah	020-7307 1600
WKD Productions	020-8748 1413

Digital radio

Digital radio is much talked up in the Radio Authority, in government and at the BBC. But even the BBC - which is investing something like £20 million for digital radio transmission - estimates that less than half the population will own a digital set in 2009. The costs are considerable for consumers too and we will have to pay some £500 for the first generation of digital audio broadcast receivers. As well as giving CD-quality reception, they will also be able to receive audio data on a small screen which will offer a potential for interactivity. There is thus the odd prospect of radio gradually converging with TV and the internet. Teldios or raynet or whatever the new boxes get called will be boosted by a government commited to switch off radio's existing analogue frequencies to free them for mobile telephones and the like. The 1996 Broadcasting Act provides for the licensing of at least 12 digital radio services on two national multiplexes, with at a multiplex for local services in most parts of Britain. Transmissions start towards the end of 1999.

The BBC has had an experimental digital radio broadcast covering 60 per cent of the country since September 1995. Digital One - a consortium made up of GWR (57 per cent), NTL Digital Radio (33 per cent) and Talk Radio (10 per cent) - was awarded the only national commercial digital multiplex licence in October 1998. Digital One will run new music, sports and news channels plus relaying output from Classic FM, Virgin and Talk Radio.

Digital One
Classic FM, 7 Swallow Place, London W1R 7AA
Tel: 020 7518 2600
Its ten proposed channels are as follows:
24 hours/day: Classic FM; Virgin Radio; Talk Radio; Classic Gold Rock; Soft AC; Teen and Chart Hits.
1900-0600: Club Dance
0600-1900: Plays/Books/Comedy
0600-0000: Rolling News
1900-000: weekdays & **1200-1900:** weekend Sports Channel

In March 1999 there were three applicants for the Greater London digitial multiplex licence

CE Digital
Capital, 30 Leicester Square, London WC2H 7LA
Tel: 020 7766 6288
Emap Radio, the Network Building, 97 Tottenham Court Road, London W1P 9HF
Tel 020-7504 6010
It is proposing: Contemporary hit radio; Gold: Dance;Soft & melodic; Rolling news and information; Modern rock; Asian; News, views & entertainment; Hot adult contemporary.

MXR London
Chrysalis Radio, The Chrysalis Building, Bramley Road, London W10 6SP
Tel: 020 7470 1057
Border Radio Holdings, Television Centre, Carlisle, Cumbria CA1 3NT
Tel 01228-829241
It is proposing: Melodic adult contemporary; Rhythmic hits; Music & talk; Jazz; Afro-Caribbean; Top 40; Mature rock & pop; Phone-in/debate; Rolling news.

Switchdigital
Talk Radio, 76 Oxford Street, London W1N 0TR
Tel: 020 7636 1089
Ginger Media Group, 1 Golden Sq, London W1R 4DJ
Tel 020-7434 1215
It is proposing: Chart hits; Soft adult contemporary; Asia service; Classic rock & sport; Jazz/blues; City/business; Saga radio; Modern rock; Classic soul.

THE TECHNOLOGY

A conventional FM/AM transmitter sends radio waves into the air modifying them in a way which directly mimics the original sounds sent by the radio studio. Radios interpret this modulation and reproduce the original electronic mimicry of a microphone or other sound source to drive a speaker. Instead of using electronic circuits to mimic sounds directly, digital radio translates sounds into a rapid sequence of binary digits. These are converted back to analogue prior to hitting the radio speakers. The older methods of transmission are prone to distortion and interference, whereas digital radio listeners will either get a clear signal or nothing at all. The advantage to listeners, once they have invested in decoders, is reception quality to match a CD.

The principles for broadcasting digitally is like digital TV, where multiplexing combines the signals of several broadcasters into a single stream on a single-frequency channel. There is no longer a direct one-to-one relationship between a programme service and a frequency.

Publications about broadcasting

BROADCAST MAGAZINES

Airflash
15 Paternoster Row, Sheffield S1 2BX
Fax 0114-279 8976   Tel 0114-279 5219
E-mail cma@commedia.org.uk
Website: www.commedia.org.uk
Publisher: Community Media Association
Editor: Nicky Edmonds
£1.00. Quarterly journal about community media.

Ariel
Room 123, Henry Wood House, 3 Langham Place,
London W1A 1AA
Fax 020-7765 3621   Tel 020-7765 3623
E-mail: ARIEL@bbc.co.uk
Publisher: BBC
Internal weekly staff magazine of the BBC.

Asia Image
6 Bell Yard, London WC2A 2JR
Fax 020-7520 5226   Tel 020-7520 5244
Publisher: Cahners
Editor: Constance Soh
Monthly magazine for people in broadcasting,
production and post production in Asian TV.

Audio Media
Atlantica House, 11 Station Road, St Ives, Cambs
PE17 4BH
Fax 01480-461550   Tel 01480-461555
E-mail: mail@audiomedia.com
Website: www.audiomedia.com
Publisher: AM Publishing
£3.80. A monthly publication aimed at audio
professionals in the fields of recording, broadcast, post-
production, live sound and multi-media.

AV Magazine
Quantum House, 19 Scarbrook ROAd, Croydon CR9
1LX
Fax 020-8565 4282   Tel 020-8565 4224
E-mail: peterl@av-magazine.co.uk
Publisher: Quantum
Editor: Peter Lloyd
£3.90. Monthly news on the audio-visual business.

BBC On Air
Bush House, Strand, London WC2B 4PH
Fax 010-7240 4899   Tel 020-7557 2875
E-mail: on.air.magazine@bbc.co.uk
Website: www.bbc.co.uk/worldservice/onair
Publisher: BBC World Service
£2. Monthly programme guide to the BBC World
Service radio, and BBC World and BBC Prime TV.

Better Satellite
57 Rochester Place, London NW1 9JU
Fax 020-7331 1241   Tel 020-7331 1000
E-mail: bettersat@aol.com
Website: www.members@aol.com/bettersat
Publisher: WV Publications
Editor: Mark Newman
£2.50. Quarterly for consumers of satellite products.

Books in the Media
15-Up, East Street, Lewins Yard, Chesham, Bucks
HP5 1HQ
Fax 01494-784850   Tel 01494-792269
E-mail: 100615.1643@compuserve.com
Publisher: Bookwatch
£102 p.a. members, £112 non-members. Weekly
resource newsletter keeping bookshops and libraries
informed of books appearing in the media. Bookwatch
carries out book-related research for newspapers, TV
and radio.

Braille Radio/TV Times
RNIB PO Box 173, Peterborough, Cambs PE2 6WS
Fax 01733-371555   Tel 01733-370777
Publisher: Royal National Institute for the Blind.
Radio Times: 24p UK discount, 63p UK cost. TV Times:
42p UK discount, £1.30 UK cost.

British Journal of Photography
39 Earlham Street, London WC2H 9LD
Fax 020-7306 7017   Tel 020-7306 7000
E-mail: bjp@benn.co.uk
Website: www.bjphoto.co.uk
Publisher: Timothy Benn Publishing
£1.50. The leading weekly professional photographic
magazine which was established 1854.

British Journalism Review
University of Luton Press, University of Luton,
75 Castle Street, Luton LU1 3AJ
Fax 01582-743298   Tel 01582-743297
E-mail: ulp@luton.ac.uk
Publisher: University of Luton Press
Scholarly quarterly, providing a critical forum for
discussion of media topics.

Broadcast
33-39 Bowling Green Lane, London EC1R 0DA
Fax 020-7505 8050   Tel 020-7505 8014
E-mail bcasted@media.emap.co.uk
Publisher: Emap Media.
£2.30. The leading weekly newspaper on the TV and
radio industry, with news, features and comments.
Emap also publishes: Production Solutions, covering
key technological areas of production; Screen
International for the international film business;
Production Guide and TV World.

CGI
3 St Peters Steet, London N1 8JD
Fax 020-7226 8586   Tel 020-7226 8585
E-mail: joeo@mdi-uk.com
Publisher: Media Directories International
£3.95. monthly. Art technology and ideas, a monthly
guide to the latest in digital content creation.

Cable Guide
172 Tottenham Court Road, London W1P 0JJ
Fax 020-7419 7299   Tel 020-7419 7300
Publisher: Cable Guide
Editor: Robin Jarossi
£3.25 monthly. Monthly cable listings magazine with
editorial coverage of film, drama and sports events.

Cable & Satellite International
2 Queensway, Redhill, Surrey RH1 1QS
Fax 01737-855470   Tel 01737-768611
E-mail: jarmitage@cmg.co.uk
Web: www.dmg.co.uk
Monthly mag for management with purchasing power
working in cable and satellite technology industry.

Cable & Satellite Europe
149 Tottenham Court Road, London W1P 9LL
Fax 020-7896 2256   Tel 020-7896 2700
Website: www.media.ft.com
Publisher: FT Media & Telecommunications
£99. The journal of satellite and cable comms.

Channel 21
25 Phipp Street, London EC2A 4NP
Fax 020-7729 7416   Tel 020-7729 7460
E-mail: info@c21media.net
Publisher: David Jenkinson
International television trade monthly

Commonwealth Broadcaster
17 Fleet Street, London EC4Y 1AA
Fax 020-7583 5549   Tel 020-7583 5500
E-mail: elizabeth@cba.org.uk
Website: www.oneworld.org/cba
The magazine of the Commonwealth Broadcasting
Association

Convergence
University of Luton Press, 75 Castle Street, Luton,
Beds LU1 3AJ
Fax 01582-743298   Tel 01582-743297
E-mail: convergence@luton.ac.uk
Quarterly. Journal on new media tech and research.

Creation
3 St Peters Street, London N1 8JD
Fax 020-7226 8586   Tel 020-7226 8585
E-mail: clarem@mdi-uk.com
Publisher: Media Directories International
£2.95. monthly. Mag for people in film/TV/new media.

Crosstalk
PO Box 124, Westcliff on Sea, Essex SS0 0QU
Fax 01702-305121   Tel 01702-348369
E-mail: office@caclb.org.uk
Website: www.caclb.org.uk
Publisher: CACLB
Editor: Jeff Bonser
Quarterly bulletin about churches and broadcasting.

Cuts Magazine
48 Carnaby Street, London W1V 1PF
Fax 020-7437 3259   Tel 020-7437 0801
E-mail: CUTS@compuserve.com
Website: www.demon.co.uk/interactive/cuts/
Publisher: Sound & Vision Publishing.
Editor: George Jarrett
£35 p.a.European TV and film production monthly.

Eyepiece
Studio 15, 65 Maygrove Road, London NW6 2EG
Fax 020-7372 8319   Tel 020-7328 2210
E-mail: ffilm+video@studio22ten.demon.co.uk
Publisher: Guild of British Camera Technicians
Editors: Kerry Anne Burrows, Charles Hewitt
Magazine for film and TV people featuring location
reports, equipment reviews and interviews.

Financial Times Business
Maple House, 149 Tottenham Court Road, London
W1P 9LL
Fax 020-7896 2256   Tel 020-7896 2072
Website: www.media.ft.com
Publisher: FT Media & Telecoms Publishing.
Produces the following newsletters: Asia-Pacific
Telecoms Analyst; Mobile Communications; Music &
Copyright; New Media Markets; Screen Finance;
Telecom Markets and related management reports.

Free Press
8 Cynthia Street, London N1 9JF
Fax 020-8837 8868   Tel 020-7278 4430
E-mail: freepress@cpbf.demon.co.uk
Publisher: Campaign for Press and Broadcasting
Freedom.
£1 non-members. Free members news magazines.
Published six times a year.

Historical Journal of Film, Radio and
Television
PO Box 25, Abingdon, Oxfordshire OX14 3UE
Fax 01235-401550   Tel 01235-401000
E-mail: enquiries@carfax.co.uk
Website: www.carfax.co.uk
Publisher: Carfax Publishing
Quarterly academic journal.

HotShoe International
Fairmeadow, Maidstone, Kent ME14 1NG
Fax 01622 757646   Tel 01622-687031
E-mail: hotshoe@datateam.co.uk
Website: www.datateamc.o.uk
Publisher: Datateam Publishing
Editor: Chris Townsend
£2.95. bi-monthly. Magazine for the upper echelons of
creative professional photography.

Image
81 Leonard Street, London EC2A 4QS
Fax 020-7739 8707   Tel 020-7739 6669
E-mail: aop@dircon.co.uk
Publisher: Association of Photographers.
£2.00. High quality, monthly photography magazine,
with news, reviews, events and ads. Also published is
The Awards Book, an annual of top advertising and
editorial photography.

Image Technology
63-71 Victoria House, Vernon Place, London WC1B
4DA
Fax 020-7405 3560   Tel 020-7242 8400
E-mail: movimage@bksts-demon.co.uk
Website: www.bksts.demon.co.uk
Publisher: BKSTS.
Monthly technical journal for members of the British
Kinematograph Sound and TV Society. Also publishes
Cinema Technology.

Information World Review
Woodside, Hinksey Hill, Oxford OX1 5BE
Fax 01865-736354   Tel 01865-388000
E-mail: iwr@learned.co.uk
Website: www.iwr.vnu.co.uk
Publisher: Learned Information.
Monthly newspaper on the information industry, for
users and producers of electronic information services.

Inside Cable & Telecoms Europe
PO Box 5 Church Stretton, Shropshire SY6 6ZZ.
Fax 01694-724135 Tel 01694-722504
E-mail: editor@dflair.demon.co.uk
Website: www.inside-cable.co.uk
Free-access web-news service covering the European cable TV and telecoms industry. Also maintains key data and statistics files on cable industry.

InterMedia
Tavistock House South, Tavistock Square, London WC1H 9LF
Fax 020-7380 0623 Tel 020-7388 0671
E-mail: martin@iicom.org
Website: www.iicom.org/
Publisher: International Inst of Communications
Discussion journal covering issues affecting international telecommunications, broadcasting and media. 6x pa.

International Broadcast Engineer
Queensway House, 2 Queensway, Redhill, Surrey RH1 1QS
Fax 01737-855470 Tel 01737-768611
E-mail: 100553.151@compuserve.com
Website: www.dmg.co.uk/ibex
Publisher: DMG Business Media
Looking at broadcast technology, for senior engineering and operational staff. 9x pa.

Journal of Educational Media
37 Monkgate, York YO31 7PB
Fax: 01904-639212 Tel 01904-639212
E-mail: josie.key@etma.u-net.com
Website: www.etma.org.uk
Publisher: Carfax Publishing Co..
Academic journal providing forum for discussing developments in TV and related media in education.

Kagan World Media
524 Fulham Road, London SW6 5NR
Fax 020-7371 8715 Tel 020-7371 8880
E-mail: kwmresearch@kagan.com
Website: www.pkbaseline.com
Kagan is an international company specialising in analysis of the media and communications industries. It publishes a range of Europe-oriented monthly newsletters, covering topics around TV, cable, video and radio, and special reports.

Line Up
27 Old Gloucester Street, London WC1N 3XX
Fax 01323-491739 Tel 01323-491739
Publisher: Institute of Broadcast Sound.
Journal mixing technical information, news and articles by practitioners in sound. 6x pa.

Media, Culture & Society
6 Bonhill Street, London EC2A 4PU
Fax 020-7374 8741 Tel 020-7374 0645
E-mail: market@sagepub.co.uk
Website: www.sagepub.co.uk
Publisher: Sage Publications.
Quarterly, £45 individual sub, £225 for company. An international forum for the presentation of research concerning the media within their political, economic, cultural and historic context.

Media Education Journal
c/o Scottish Screen, 249 West George Street, Glasgow G2 4RB
Fax 0141-302 1711 Tel 0141-302 1700
E-mail: info@scottishscreen.com
Website: www.scottishscreen.com
Publisher: Association for Media Education in Scotland.
2x pa. Educational journal covering media theory, and ideas for teaching from primary one to adult. Also teaching packs and newsletters.

Media Track
Aztec Media Systems, 10-12 John Marshall House, 246-254 High Street, Sutton, Surrey SM1 1PA
Fax 020-8288 9793 Tel 020-8288 9795
E-mail: info@mediatrack.com
Web: www.mediatrack.com
Published every 12 weeks on CD-ROM. More than 90,00 entries in 800 categories, covering advertising, film, television, print, multimedia, radio and music.

Media Week
Quantum Ho, 19 Scarbrook Road, Croydon CR9 1LX
Fax 020-8565 4394 Tel 020-8565 4200
E-mail: mweeked@qpp.co.uk
Website: www.mediaweek.co.uk
Publisher: Quantum
£1.85. Weekly news magazine linking media and advertising .

Middle East Broadcast & Satellite
Chancery House, St Nicholas Way, Sutton , Surrey SM1 1JB
Fax 020-8642 1941 Tel 020-86421117
E-mail: farah@icompub.com
Website: www.icompub.com
Publisher: Icom Publications Ltd.
£65. 9x.pa magazine on broadcast in the Middle East & S Asia. Also publishes Middle East Communications.

Moving Pictures International
34-35 Newman Street, London W1P 3PD
Fax 020-7636 7379 Tel 020-7637 0651
E-mail: mopix@compuserve.com
Website: www.filmfestivals.com
Publisher: Moving Pictures International
Monthly coverage of the international film, televsion and video industry.

Off-Air
5 Market Place, London W1N 7AH
Fax 020-7255 2020 Tel 020-7255 2010
E-mail: info@radacad.demon.co.uk
Website: www.radacad.cemon.co.uk
Publisher: The Radio Academy.
Monthly journal of the Radio Academy.

The Pact Magazine
3 St Peters Street, London N1 8JD
Fax 020-7226 8586 Tel 020-7226 8585
E-mail: michaelt@mdi-uk.com
Publisher: Media Directories International
Members magazine for the Producers Alliance for Cinema and Television.

The Photographer
Fox Talbot House, Amwell End, Ware, Herts SG12 9HN
Fax 01920-487056   Tel 01920-464011
E-mail: bavister@easynet.co.uk
Website: www.bipp.com
Publisher: British Institute of Professional Photography.
Editor: Steve Bavister
£2.75, free to members. 10 issues p.a. The British Institute of Professional Photography's journal of professional images and imaging technology.

Post Update
3 St Peters Street, London N1 8JD
Fax 020-7226 8586   Tel 020-7226 8585
E-mail: rebeccah@mdi-uk.com
Publisher: Media Directories International
£3.50. monthly. The European post-production magazine, features regular, detailed product reviews and technology updates.

Production Solutions
33-39 Bowling Green Lane, London, EC1R 0DA
Fax 020-7505 8076   Tel 020-7505 8000
E-mail: catherinew@media.emap.co.uk
Monthly magazine aimed at people working in television, production and film. Covers new technology, film issues, training and features a buyers guide to technology . Cover price £5.00

The Radio Magazine
25 High Street, Rothwell, Northants NN14 6AD
Fax 01536-418539   Tel 01536-418558
radiomazine-goldcrestbroadcasting@btinternet.com
Website: www.theradiomagazine.co.uk
Publisher: Goldcrest Broadcasting.
Editor: Howard Rose
£72. p.a.Weekly, glossy on the radio world.

Radio Review
PO Box 46, Romford RM7 8AY
Newsletter about Radio Caroline, Radio London, Dutch radio, pirate sations etc.

Radio Times
Woodlands, 80 Wood Lane, London W12 0TT
Fax 020-8576 3160   Tel 020-8576 2000
E-mail: radio.times@bbc.co.uk
Website: www.rtguide.beeb.com
Publisher: BBC Worldwide
Editor: Sue Robinson
Weekly, 79p. The BBC's money-spinning mag detailing all TV programmes, plus radio.

Satellite TV Europe
531-3 Kings Road, London SW10 0TZ
Fax 020-7352 4883   Tel 020-7351 3612
E-mail: stv1@compuserve.com
Website: www.satellite-tv.co.uk
Publisher: Millenium Consumer Magazines
£2.50. Monthly.
Satellite TV listings.

Satellite Times
The Stable Block, West Hill Grange, North Road, Horsforth, Leeds LS18 5HG
Fax 0113-258 9745   Tel 0113-258 5008
E-mail: stimes@cix.co.uk
Publisher: Everpage
£2.20. Monthly listings for satellite, cable and digital tv.

Screen Digest
38 Georgiana Street, London NW1 0EB
Fax 020-7580 0060   Tel 020-7482 5842
E-mail: editorial@screendigest.com
Website: www.screendigest.com
Publisher: Screen Digest.
Editor: David Fisher
£325 p.a. Monthly round-up of news, research and stats on film, video, multimedia and TV aimed at executives.

Screen International
33 Bowling Green Lane, London EC1R 0DA
Fax 020-7505 8117   Tel 020-7505 8080
E-mail: screeninternational@compuserve.com
Publisher: Emap Media
International editor: Patrick Frater
£2.10. Weekly on the international cinema business.

Short Wave Magazine
Arrowsmith Court, Broadstone, Dorset BH18 8PW
Fax 01202-659950   Tel 01202-659910
E-mail: kevin@pwpublishing.ltd.uk
Website: www.publishing.ltd.uk
Publisher: PW Publishing.
£2.99. Monthly for enthusiasts of all types of listening.

Shots
33 Bowling Green Lane, London EC1R 0DA
Fax 020-7505 8490   Tel 020-7505 8487
E-mail: info@shots.net
Website: www.shots.net
Publisher: Emap Media
£467.50 + VAT. Bi-monthly video mag on DVD, with advertising, music promos and post production.

Sight & Sound
21 Stephen Street, London W1P 1PL
Fax 020-7436 2327   Tel 020-7255 1444
Publisher: British Film Institute.
E-mail s&s@bfi.org.uk
Editor: Nick James
£2.95. Leading monthly covering the film world.

Stage, Screen & Radio
111 Wardour Street, London W1V 4AY
Fax 020-7437 8268   Tel 020-7437 8506
E-mail: bectu@geo2.poptel.org.uk
Website: www.bectu.org.uk
Publisher: BECTU.
£2, free to members. 10x p.a. Journal of the largest trade union in film and broadcasting.

The Stage (incorporating Television Today)
47 Bermondsey Street, London SE1 3XT
Fax 020-7357 9287   Tel 020-7403 1818
E-mail: info@thestage.co.uk
Website: www.thestage.co.uk
90p. Weekly newspaper of the entertainment industry - theatre, dance, opera, TV and radio. The publishers also produce Showcall, a light entertainment directory.

Television
100 Grays Inn Road, London WC1X 8AL
Fax 020-7430 0924   Tel 020-7430 1000
E-mail: info@arts.org.uk
Website: www.rts.org.uk
Publisher: Royal Television Society
Editor: Peter Fiddick
9x pa, £76 pa. Covers all aspects of the TV industry.

Television
Quadrant House, Sutton, Surrey SM2 5AS
Fax 020-8652 8111   Tel 020-8652 8120
E-mail: tessa winford@rbi.co.uk
Publisher: Reed Business Information
Editor: John Reddihough
£2.70. Specialist monthly. Technical news and features for the TV/video servicing engineer.

Television Asia
6 Bell Yard, London WC2A 2JR
Fax 020-7520 5226   Tel 020-7520 5244
E-mail: janet@tvasia.com.sg
Publisher: Cahners Publishing
Editor: Patricia Lee
Monthly glossy magazine looking at the TV business across Asia.

Televisual
49-50 Poland Street, London W1V 4AX
Fax 020-7970 6733   Tel 020-7970 6666
E-mail: televisual@centaur.co.uk
Publisher: Centaur Communications
Editor: Mundy Ellis
£2.95. Monthly business magazine for independent producers, facility providers and the TV industry.

TV Quick
Shirley House, 25-27 Camden Road, London NW1 9LL
Fax 020-7241 8066   Tel 020-7241 8000
E-mail: lorimiles@tvquick.demon.co.uk
Publisher: H Bauer Publishing
62p. Weekly witty TV listings magazine geared to women's interests.

TV & Satellite Week
Kings Reach Tower, Stamford Street, London SE1 9LS
Fax 020-7261 7525   Tel 020-7261 7534
E-mail: TVandSatweek@ipc.co.uk
Website: www.ipc.co.uk
Publisher: IPC Magazines.
80p. Weekly consumers guide to what's on satellite, terrestrial and cable TV.

TV Times
Kings Reach Tower, Stamford Street, London SE1 9LS
Fax 020-7261 7777   Tel 020-7261 5000
E-mail: tvtimes@ipc.co.uk
Website: www.ipc.co.uk
Publisher: IPC Magazines.
Weekly details of television programmes. Sales of the TV Times have now been overtaken by IPC's mass-market magazine What's On TV, operating out of the same offices.

TV Zone
9 Blades Court, Deodar Road, London SW15 2NU
Fax 020-8875 1588   Tel 020-8875 1520
E-mail: tvzone@visimag.com
Website: www.visimag.com
Publisher: Visual Imagination
Longest running magazine dedicated to cult television. Monthly plus 4 quarterly specials with features and interviews on past and current TV with an emphasis on science fiction and fantasy.

UK Press Gazette
See Press Gazette

UK Radio Guide & Directory
Crown House, 25 High Street, Rothwell, Northants NN14 6AD
Fax 01536-418539   Tel 01536-418558
radiomazine-goldcrestbroadcasting@btinternet.com
Website: www.theradiomagazine.co.uk
Publisher: Goldcrest Broadcasting.
Editor: Paul Boon
£20. p.a.6 monthly. Radio audience update on all RAJAR participating stations, plus directory.

Vertigo
20 Goodge Place, London W1P 1FN
Fax: 020-7631 1040   Tel 020-7436 3050
E-mail: vertigo.insia@lineone.net
Editor: Kimberley Cooper
£3.75, bi-annual. Vertigo gives independent film, video and television works outside the mainstream the attention they deserve.

Viewfinder
77 Well Street, London W1P 3RE
Fax 020-7393 1555   Tel 020-7393 1500
E-mail: bufvc@open.ac.uk
Website: www.bufvc.ac.uk/
Publisher: British Universities Film & Video Council
News and features published three times a year by the British Universities Film/Video Council, which exists to promote the production, study and use of film, TV and related media for higher education and research.

Voice of the Listener & Viewer
101 Kings Drive, Gravesend, Kent DA12 5BQ
Fax 01474-351112   Tel 01474-352835
E-mail: vlv@btinternet.com
Website: www.vlv.org.uk
Publisher: Voice of the Listener and Viewer.
Quarterly newsletter of the independent watchdog, which bills itself as "the citizen's voice in broadcasting and the only consumer body speaking for listeners and viewers on the full range of broadcasting issues".

What Satellite TV
57 Rochester Place, London NW1 9JU
Fax 020-7331 1241   Tel 020-7331 1000
E-mail: wwhatsat@aol.com
Website: www.wotsat.com
Publisher: WV Publications
Editor: Geoff Bains
£2.95. Monthly consumer magazine with news on "the equipment to buy and the programmes to watch".

World Media
BBC Worldwide Monitoring, Caversham Park, Reading, Berks RG4 8TZ
Fax 0118-946 3823   Tel 0118-946 9289
E-mail: marketing@mon.bbc.co.uk
Website: www.monitor.bbc.co.uk
Weekly, also available via Internet, containing news of the international broadcasting scene, reporting on satellite, cable and terrestrial radio and TV. Annual subscription £410.

Zerb
                              Tel 01608-810954
E-mail: samps@easynet.co.uk
Web: www.easyweb.easynet.co.uk/~guildtvc
Publisher: Guild of TV Cameramen.

BROADCAST YEARBOOKS

BAPLA Directory
18 Vine Hill, London EC1R 5DX
Fax 020-7713 1211   Tel 020-7713 1780
E-mail: bapla@bapla.org.uk
Website: www.bapla.org.uk
Publisher: British Association of Picture Libraries & Agencies
Contact: Linda Royles
£20. An invaluable guide to picture sources by Britain's leading association. With full details of all members, a description of their stock, a subject index and hints for library users.

Benn's Media
Riverbank House, Angel Lane, Tonbridge, Kent TN9 1SE
Fax 01732-367301   Tel 01732-377591
E-mail: bennsmedia@unmf.com
Website: www.mfuk.com/mfinfo
Publisher: Miller Freeman Information Services
3 vols £310, 2 vols £290, 1 vol £145.
Benn's has the most comprehensive listings amongst the general media directories. It comes in three volumes, covering the UK, Europe and the rest of the world.

Blue Book of British Broadcasting
Communications House, 210 Old Street, London EC1V 9UN
Fax 020-7566 3142   Tel 020-7490 1447
E-mail: publications@tellex.press.net
Publisher: Tellex Publications Dept.
A contacts book for radio, TV and satellite containing thousands of names, addresses and phone numbers. Also publish the Burgundy Book of European Broadcasting at £95.

Bowkers Complete Video Directory
Bowker-Saur, Reed Bsiness Information, Windsor Court, East Grinstead House, West Sussex RH19 1XA
Fax 01342-336198   Tel 01342-326972
E-mail: custserv@bowker-saur.co.uk
Website: www.bowker-saur.co.uk
£210, three vols.
Only source of info covering over 107,000 video titles.

British Film Institute Film and Television Handbook
21 Stephen Street, London W1P 2LN
Fax 020-7436 7950   Tel 020-7255 1444
E-mail: helpdesk@bfi.org.uk
Website: www.bfi.org.uk
Publisher: BFI
£18.99. Combines hundreds of film and broadcasting facts and figures with an extensive directory of thousands of contacts and addresses.

Cable & Satellite Yearbook
Maple House, 149 Tottenham Court Road, London W1P 9LL
Fax 020-7896 2749   Tel 020-7896 2700
E-mail: info@ftmedia.com
Website: www.media.ft.com
Publisher: FT Media & Telecoms
£295 for yearbook, £295 for TV Business International Both on CD £595. Comprehensive details of the industry in all European countries, covering manufacturers, distributors and broadcasters, plus a breakdown of each nation. Also published is: TV Business International, with all the world's TV stations and prices.

Cable TV & Telecom Yearbook
Forum Chambers, the Forum, Stevenage, Hertfordshire SG1 1EL
Fax 01438-740154   Tel 01438-742424
E-mail: sandymaclean@dial.pipex.com
Website: the-philips-group.com
Publisher: Philips Business Information
Contact: Karen Milton
£95.
Industry facts, figures analysis and information.

Commonwealth Broadcasters' Directory
17 Fleet Street, London EC4Y 1AA
Fax 020-7583 5549   Tel 020-7583 5550
E-mail: cba@cba.org.uk
Website: www.oneworld.org/cba
Publisher: Commonwealth Broadcasting Assocation
£25. non-members, UK; £28 non-members Europe. Details of Commonwealth broadcasting organisations, with names of top executives, phones, faxes and addresses.

Directors' Guild Directory
15-19 Great Titchfield Street, London W1P 7FB
Fax 020-7436 8646   Tel 020-7436 8626
E mail: guild@dggb.co.uk
Website: www.dggb.co.uk
Publisher: Directors Guild of Great Britain
£20.
A-Z of Britain's TV, film, radio and theatre directors.

Directors and Producers Directory
111 Wardour Street, London W1V 4AY
Fax 020-7437 8268   Tel 020-7437 8506
E-mail: bectu@geotv.poptel.org.uk
Website: www.bectu.org.uk
Publisher: BECTU
Free to members .Contains the names and addresses of over 1,000 producers and directors who are members of the London Production Division of the main broadcasting trade union BECTU.

Directory of British Film & TV Producers
PACT, 45 Mortimer Street, London W1N 7TD
Fax 020-7331 6700   Tel 020-7331 6000
Publisher: Pact
£30.Full details of PACT members.

Directory of International Film & Video Festivals
11 Portland Place, London W1N 4EJ
Fax 020-7389 3041   Tel 020-7389 3065
E-mail: paul.howson@britcounc.org
Website: www.britfilms.com
Publisher: British Council
£12
Lists all international film and video festivals.

The Edinburgh Handbook
24 Neal Street, London WC2H 9PS
020-7836 0702   Tel 020-7379 4519
E-mail: geitf@festival.demon.co.uk
Publisher: Edinburgh International Television Festival
£7.99.
Published to tell people of the profusion of programmes and programme-making issues arising at the annual August festival in Edinburgh.

Encyclopedia of Television
                     Tel 020-7636 6627
£200

IPO Directory
PO Box 30, Wetherby, West Yorkshire LS23 7YA
Fax 01937-541083   Tel 01937-541010
£13 annual subscription.
The official directory of the information and PRs in government departments and public corporations. Published bi-annually.

Kays UK Production Manual
8 Golden Square, London W1R 3AF
020-7437 0884   Tel 020-8749 1214
Publisher: Kays Publishing
£70.
With its Crew Directory, this is one of the most comprehensive and reliable manuals of people and organisations in the production side of the film, TV and broadcast industry. Contains 15,000 names and addresses in over 250 classifications. Also available is its European equivalent the European Production Manual (£85), plus the Art Diary (£30) listing the art business.

Kemps Film, TV & Video Yearbook
34-35 Newman Street, London W1P 3PD
Fax 020-7580 5559   Tel 020-7637 3663
E-mail: odlin@aol.com
Publisher: Variety Media Publications
£35 UK; £75 International
Long-established directory of the film and television production industries in nearly every country.

The Knowledge
E-mail: knowledge@unmf.com
Website: www.knowledge.com
Publisher: Miller Freeman Information Services
Book £90; CD rom £90; book and CD £105
The leading guide to the products and services of the UK film, TV and video industry. Over 15,000 listings of companies and freelance crew. Also industry information, charts and maps. Book includes portable version in A-Z format for use on location.

The Media Guide
Fourth Estate, for The Guardian
                     Tel 020-7727-8993
Bingo.

Multimedia and CD-ROM Directory
6-14 Underwood Street, London N1 7JQ
Fax 020-7324 2312   Tel 020-7324 2345
E-mail: gbuecker@waterlow.com
Website: www.newmediainfo.com
Publisher: Waterlow Publishing
Contact: Gesche Beucker
Vol 1. Media Companies- £149,Vol 2. Media Titles - £149; both £249

Pims Media Directories
Pims House, Mildmay Avenue, London N1 4RS
Fax 020-7354 7053   Tel 020-7226 1000
E-mail: press@pims.co.uk
Website: www.pims.co.uk
Publisher: Pims International
Contact: Susan Mears
Pims produces a range of detailed, loose-leaf guides to editorial media contacts, all regularly updated, aimed mainly at the public relations sector. Titles include: UK Media Directory £365 for 12 p.a., A-Z Towns Directory £250 for 4 p.a. and several USA/European directories.

The Production Guide
33-39 Bowling Green Lane, London EC1R 0DA
Fax 020-7505 8293   Tel 020-7505 8000
E-mail: lukes@media.emap.co.uk
Publisher: Emap Media
Contact: Doug Marchall
£79
Details of technical contacts, services and equipment.

Programme News
32-38 Saffron Hill, London EC1N 8SH
Fax 020-7430 1089   Tel 020-7405 4455
E-mail: info@profilegroup.co.uk
Website: www.profilegroup.co.uk
Publisher: The Profile Group
From £574 p.a. with monthly bulletins. An information service in directory format. Independent broadcast listings. The UK industry guide for advance broadcast planning.

Radio Academy Yearbook
5 Market Place, London W1N 7AH
Fax 020-7255 2029   Tel 020-7255 2010
E-mail: info@radacad.demon.co.uk
Website: www.radacad.demon.co.uk/
Publisher: The Radio Academy.
£25.00. Annual directory/listings guide of the radio industry's leading professional society.

Radio Advertising Handbook
77 Shaftesbury Avenue, London W1V 7AD
020-7306 2505   Tel 020-7306 2500
E-mail: rab@rab.co.uk
Website: www.rab.co.uk
Publisher: Radio Advertising Bureau
Free
Handbook of radio advertising, providing an overview
of the commercial radio industry, with masses of data
and listings information.

Radio Authority Pocket Guide
Holbrook House, 14 Great Queen Street, London
WC2B 5DG
Fax 020-7405 7062   Tel 020-7430 2724
E-mail: info@radioauthority.org.uk
Website: www.radioauthority.org.uk
Publisher: Radio Authority
Free
Annual reference book tlisting all independent radio
stations and other radio related organisations.

Radio Listener's Guide
PO Box 151 Abingdon, Oxon OX13 5DP
                     Tel 01865-820387
E-mail: clive@radioguide.demon.co.uk
Publisher: PDQ Publishing
Editor: Clive Woodyear
£4.95.
Pocket guide to all the UK radio stations, detailing
which wavelengths they are on, and explaining clearly
how to tune in. This is an invaluable aid to those trying
to find their way around the radio dial.

Royal Television Society Handbook
100 Grays Inn Road, London WC1X 8AL
Fax 020-7430 0924   Tel 020-7430 1000
E-mail: publications@rts.org.uk
Website: www.rts.org.uk
Publisher Radio Television Society
Editor: Sue Griffith
£8
Guide to the society, with freelance directory.

Television Business International Yearbook
Yearbooks Dept., Maple House, 149 Tottenham Court
Road, London W1P 9LL
Fax 020-7896 2710   Tel 020-7896 2700
Website: www.media.ft.com
Publisher: FT Media and Telecoms
£295.
Handbook for international TV executives.

University of Manchester Broadcasting Symposia
75 Castle Street, Luton LU1 3AJ
Fax 01582-743298   Tel 01582-743297
E-mail: ulp@luton.ac.uk
Publisher: University of Luton Press
£14.95
Each year all sides of the broadcasting industry meet for
a symposium organised by the University of
Manchester. The proceedings are published later in
book form. The latest publication is Youth and the
Media.

The White Book
The White Book
                     Tel 01932-572622
£50.
The key international production directory.

Who's Who in Cable & Satellite UK
Forum Chambers, The Forum, Stevenage,
Hertfordshire SG1 1EL
Fax 01438-740154   Tel 01438-742424
E-mail: sandymaclean@dial.pipex.com
Website: www.the-philips-group.com
Publisher: Philips Business Information
Contact: Karen Milton
Single edition £39.95; years sub £59.95
Contact details for more than 3000 key personnel from
over 1100 companies. Published in January and July.

Who's Who in Cable & Satellite Europe
Forum Chambers, The Forum, Stevenage,
Hertfordshire SG1 1EL
Fax 01438-740154   Tel 01438-742424
E-mail: sandymaclean@dial.pipex.com
Website: www.the-philips-group.com
Publisher: Philips Business Information
Contact: Karen Milton
Single edition £34.95; years sub £64.95
Covers over 30 countries, more than 4000 key
personnel from over 1900 cmpanies. Published in
April and October.

World Radio & TV Handbook
23 Ridgmount Street, London WC1E 7AH
Fax 020-7323 2314   Tel 020-7323 6686
E-mail: bevans@bpicomm.com
Website: www.billboard.com
£21.50.
World broadcasting stations, by frequency, time and
language.

World Satellite Yearly
24 River Gardens, Purley, Reading RG8 8BX
Fax 0118-9414468   Tel 08365-82785
E-mail: vincentbay@hotmail.com
Website: www.baylin.com
Publisher: Baylin Publications
£59.
American technical manual and guide to satellites.

Broadcast support organisations

All-Party Media Group
Old Queen Street, London SW1H 9JA
Fax 020-7222 4189   Tel 020-7222 4179
Cross party forum of 100 MPs and peers with an interest in media issues.

AMARC
15 Paternoster Row, Sheffield, Yorkshire S1 2BX
Fax 0114-279 8976   Tel 0114-221 0592
E-mail: europe@amarc.org
Website: www.amarc.org
AMARC, the World Association of Community Radio broadcasters, is a world-wide network of local radios which operate for social purposes and are independent of governments and large media corporations.

Amnesty International: Journalists' Network
102 Mansfield Road, Nottingham NG1 3HX
Fax 0115-924 5055   Tel 0115-924 5100
E-mail: nottrn@amnesty.org.uk
This division of Amnesty International campaigns on behalf of media workers who have disappeared, been imprisoned, tortured or threatened with death. It holds meetings and publishes a quarterly newsletter.

Amsat-UK
70 Downsview, Small Dole, West Sussex BN5 9YB
Fax 01273-492927   Tel 01273-495733
E-mail: g6ziu@amsat.org
National society specialising in amateur radio satellite matters. Publishes Oscar News 6x pa.

Article 19, Centre Against Censorship
Lancaster House, 33 Islington High Street, Islington, London N1 9LH
Fax 020-7713 1356   Tel 020-7278 9292
E-mail: info@article19.org
International human rights organisation campaigning for the right to freedom of expression and information. The organisation promotes improved legal standards for freedom of expression and defends victims of censorship. It publishes newsletters plus country and theme reports, with emphasis on media freedom.

Aslib
Staple Hall, Stone House Court, London EC3A 7PB
Fax 020-7903 0011   Tel 020-7903 0000
E-mail: members@aslib.co.uk
Website: www.aslib.co.uk/aslib/
The Association for Information Management is the leading corporate membership information management association. It gives advice on information sources and strategy. There is also a network of special interest groups.

Association of Broadcasting Doctors
PO Box 15, Sindalthorpe House, Ely, Cambridge CB7 5SG
Fax 01353-688451   Tel 01353-688456
E-mail: soundpean@dial.pipex.com
Represents practising doctors who also broadcast, providing training, data and media liaison. Publishes monthly newsletter and briefings. Contact point for broadcasters seeking medical contributors.

Association of Independent Radio Companies
See Commercial Radio Companies Association

Association of Smallscale Scottish Broadcasters
Struan House, The Square, Aberfeldy, Perthshire PH15 2DD
Fax 01887 820038   Tel 01887 820956
E-mail: wwright@sol.co.uk
For those interested in small-scale radio and TV broadcasting, RSLs and workshops in Scotland.

Audio Visual Association
156 High Street, Bushey, Hertfordshire WD2 3DD
Fax 020-8950 7560   Tel 020-8950 5959
Website: www.thebiz.co.uk/ava.htm
Special interest group of the British Institute of Professional Photography representing people working to sub-broadcast standard in audio visual and multi-media. The association evolves with new technical developments.

Barb
See Broadcast Audience Research Board

British Academy of Film and Television Arts
195 Piccadilly, London W1V 0LN
Fax 020-7734 1792   Tel 020-7734 0022
BAFTA North   Tel 0161-831 9733
BAFTA Scotland   Tel 0141-357 4317
BAFTA Wales   Tel 029-2022 3898
Website: www.bafta.org
BAFTA was formed in 1947 and promotes high creative standards in film and television production, and encourages experiment and research. It organises awards ceremonies for film, television, children's films and programmes and interactive entertainment and has an extensive programme of seminars, lectures etc. It has 3000 members and provides screenings and previews and publishes a monthly newsletter. It also offers a range of educational and training initiatives.

British Academy of Composers & Songwriters
The Penthouse, 4 Brook Street, London W1Y 1AA
Fax 020-7629 0993   Tel 020-7629 0992
E-mail: info@britishacademy.com
Represents the interest of songwriters and composers across all genres, providing advice on professional and legal matters. It administers the Ivor Novello awards. and publishes a quarterly magazine, The Works.

British Amateur Television Club
Church Road, Harby, Notts NG23 7ED
Fax 01522-703348   Tel 01522-703348
E-mail: secretary@batc.org.uk
Website: www.batc.org.uk
Founded in 1948 to inform, instruct, co-ordinate and represent the activities of television enthusiasts in the UK and worldwide. Publishes quarterly technical magazine CQ-TV

British Board of Film Classification

3 Soho Square, London W1V 6HD
Fax 020-7287 0141   Tel 020-7439 7961
E-mail: webmaster@bbfc.co.uk
Website: www.bbfc.co.uk
The body responsible for classifying publicly shown films:

U (Universal)
PG (Parental Guidance)
12 (age 12 and over only)
15 (age 15 and over only)
18 (age 18 and over only)
R18 (restricted to premises barred to under 18s)

British Film Commission

70 Baker Street, London W1M 1DJ
Fax 020-7224 1013   Tel 020-7224 5000
E-mail: press@britfilmcom.co.uk
Website: www.britfilmcom.co.uk

Bath Film Office	01225-477711
Cardiff Film Comm	029-2059 0240
Central England Screen Commission	
East Midlands Office	01159-527870
Eastern Screen	01603-767077
Edinburgh and Lothian	
Screen Industries	0131-622 7337
N Wales Film Comm	01286 679685
Isle of Man Film Commission	
	01624-685864
Lancashire Film & Television Office	
	01772-203020
Liverpool Film Office	0151-291 9191
London Film Commission	
	020-7387 8787
Manchester Film Office	
	0161-238 4537
North West Commission	
	0151-330 6666
N Ireland Film Commission	
	028-9023 2444
Northern Screen Commission	
	0191-204 2311
Scottish Screen Locations	
	0141-302 1700
Sgrin	029-2033 3300
SW Film Commission	01752 841199
SW Scotland Screen Commission	
	01387-263666
Southern Screen Commission	
	023-9265 0779
Yorkshire Screen Commission	
	01142-799115

Set up by the government in 1991, the BFC is funded through the Department of Culture, Media and Sport. It promotes the UK as an international production centre and provides support to those filming in the UK. BFC publications include Check Book, a UK production guide for overseas film-makers and the newsletter Framework. The BFC also participates in trade events abroad and helps foreign film makers in the UK. It works with the UK Film Commission Network.

British Film Institute

21 Stephen Street, London W1P 2LN
Fax 020-7436 7950   Tel 020-7255 1444
Website: www.bfi.org.uk.
The BFI is Britain's leading moving image resource. It encourages the development of film, TV and video, both as an art and as a medium of record. The BFI includes the National Film and Television Archive, the National Film Theatre, the BFI London Imax Cinema, the Museum of the Moving Image, the London Film Festival and Sight and Sound magazine. The institute also runs a library and information service (BFI National Library), the New Directors Scheme (run in conjunction with Channel 4), provides training advice and oranises events. A catalogue of its publications can be obtained from BFI Publishing. Support for regional and local film theatres and societies is also administered by the institute. BFI funding comes party from commercial activities and partly from the Department of Culture, Media and Sport.

British Interactive Multimedia Association

5-6 Clipstone Street, London W1P 7EB
Fax 020-7436 8251   Tel 020-7436 8250
E-mail: enquiries@bima.co.uk
The trade body for the multimedia industry. Publishes directory of members and newsletter. Meets ten times year.

British Kinematograph, Sound and Television Society (BKSTS)

63-71 Victoria House, Vernon Place, London WC1B 4DA
Fax 020-7405 3560   Tel 020-7242 8400
E-mail: movimage@bksts.demon.co.uk
Website: www.bksts.com
BKSTS was founded in 1931 and is the only European society covering all technical aspects of film, television, sound and associated industries. It plays a leading role in the development and implementation of technical standards. The main aim is to keep members abreast of the continually changing technology in the industry an its implications. The society achieves this through its journals, Cinema Technology and Image Technology (10x pa) and by holding seminars and conferences. Many training courses are held.

British Library National Sound Archive

96 Euston Road, London NW1 2DB
Fax 020-7412 7441   Tel 020-7412 7440
E-mail: nsa@bl.uk
Website: www.bl.uk/collections/sound-archive
The national collection of sound recordings, covering a topics since the 1890s. Provides library, information, listening and transcription services. Publishes newsletter Playback and range of print and audio titles.

British Radio & Electronic Equipment Manufacturers' Association

Landseer House, 19 Charing Cross Road, London WC2H 0ES
Fax 020-7839 4613   Tel 020-7930 3206
E-mail: @brema.org.uk
Trade association for consumer electronics manufacturers.

British Screen Advisory Council
9 Cavendish Square, London W1M 9AB
Fax 020-7306 0329   Tel 020-7499 4177
E-mail BSACouncil@aol.com.
Independent, industry funded, advisory body to
government and policy makers at national and
European level. It provides a forum for the audiovisual
industry to discuss major issues. It commissions
research and organises conferences and seminars.

British Screen Finance
14 -17 Wells Mews, London W1P 3FL
Fax 020-7323 0092   Tel 020-7323 9080
E-mail: info@britishscreen.co.uk
A private company partly financed by grants through
the Department of Culture, Media and Sport and by
lottery money through the Arts Council of England.
Provides investment in development and production of
feature films aimed at the commercial cinema
marketplace. Manages the European Co-production
Fund and the Greenlight Fund.

British Society of Cinematographers
11 Croft Road, Gerrards Cross, Bucks SL9 9AE
Tel 01753-891486   Tel 01753-888052
E-mail: BritCinematographers@compuserve.com
Society of motion picture cinematographers. Arranges
technical meetings, social events, film shows etc.
Publishes directory biennially.

Broadcasters Audience Research Board (Barb)
Glenthorne House, Hammersmith Grove, London W6
9ND
Fax 020-8741 1943   Tel 020-8741 9110
Website: www.barb.co.uk
Barb provides information to all elements of the TV
industry, broadcasters, advertising/media buying
agencies and advertisers. Barb uses professional
research suppliers to conduct and report on audience
research. It produces statistical research on TV
audiences for its subscribers. Audiences for TV
programmes are measured by electronic meters
attached to television sets in 4,485 homes. This panel,
which is one of the largest of its kind in the world,
includes some 10,500 people. The meters record the
state of each TV set or video. The information is
transmitted automatically each night by telephone into
a central computer and is used to calculate the size of
the audience. Since 1991, the meters have been able to
record video playbacks.

Broadcasting Complaints Commission
Merged with Broadcasting Standards Commission

BECTU: Broadcasting, Entertainment, Cinematograph and Theatre Union
111 Wardour Street, London W1V 4AY
Fax 020-7437 8258   Tel 020-7437 8506
E-mail: bectu@geo2.poptel.org.uk
Website: www.bectu.org.uk
Midlands office	Tel 0121-632 5372
North west office	Tel 0161-274 3174
Scottish office	Tel 0141-248 9558
Wales office	Tel 029-2066 6557

BECTU is the main trade union for workers in
broadcasting, film, theatre and other sectors of the
entertainment and media industry. It offers a Student
Link-up Scheme to arts and media students, and a
special introductory membership rate to course
graduates. It can give some careers advice (SAE please)
but works with Skillset, regional training consortia and
FT2 in promoting acess, opportunity, training and
employment prospects. Publishes a journal Stage,
Screen & Radio.

Broadcasting Press Guild
Tiverton, The Ridge, Woking, Surrey GU22 7EQ
Fax 01483-765882   Tel 01483-764895
Association of 90+ journalists writing about the media
in the national and trade press. Membership by
invitation. Holds monthly lunches addressed by top
broadcasting executives. Each spring it presents the
BPG TV and Radio Awards.

Broadcasting Research Unit
see Voice of the Listener and Viewer

Broadcasting Standards Commission
7 The Sanctuary, London SW1P 3JS
Fax 020-7233 0397   Tel 020-7233 0544
E-mail: bsc@bsc.org.uk
Website: www.bsc.org.uk
The BSC is the statutory body for both standards and
fairness in broadcasting. It is the only organisation
within the regulatory framework of UK broadcastng to
cover all tv and radio. this includes BBC and
commercial broadcasters as well as text, cable, satellite
and digital services. As an independent organisation
representing the interests of the consumer, the
Broadcasting Standards Commission considers the
portrayal of violence, sexual conduct and matters of
taste and decency. As an alternative to a court of law it
provides redress for people who believe they have been
unfairly treated or subjected to unwarranted
infringement of privacy. Its three main tasks are set out
in the 1996 Broadcasting Act:
* to produce codes of practice relating to standards and
  fairness;
* to consider and adjudicate on complaints;
* to monitor, research and report on standards and
  fairness in broadcasting

Campaign for Freedom of Information
Suite 102, 16 Baldwins Gardens, London EC1N 7RJ
Fax 020-7831 7461   Tel 020-7831 7477
E-mail: admin@cfoi.demon.co.uk
Website: www.cfoi.org.uk
The campaign is pressing for a Freedom of Information
Act which would create a general right of access to
official records subject to exemptions protecting
information whose disclosure would cause real harm to
essential interests such as defence, law enforcement
and privacy. Campaigns for a public interest defence
under the Official Secrets Act. It also seeks disclosure
in the private sector on issues of public interest. It
publishes the newspaper Secrets, plus briefings and
other publications.

Campaign for Press and Broadcasting Freedom
8 Cynthia Street, London N1 9JF
Fax 020-7837 8868   Tel 020-7278 4430
E-mail: freepress@cpbf.demon.co.uk
Website: www.cpbf.demon.co.uk
Campaigns for a democratic, diverse and accountable
media, accessible to all. The CPBF opposes monopoly
ownership of the press and seeks a Right of Reply. It
organises events and publishes 6x pa journal Free
Press, occasional pamphlets and the Media Catalogue
of mail order books and postcards.

Celtic Film and Television Festival Company
1 Bowmont Gardens, Glasgow G12 9LR
Fax 0141-342 4948   Tel 0141-342 4947
E-mail: mail@celticfilm.co.uk
Organises the annual International Celtic Festival of
Film and Television, peripatetic in Scotland, Wales,
Cornwall, Ireland and Brittany, including awards and
conference. It supports development of TV and film in
Celtic nations and indigenous languages.

Children's Film & Television Foundation
Elstree Film Studios, Borehamwood, Herts WD6 1JG
Fax 020-8207 0860   Tel 020-8953 0844
E-mail: annahome@cftf.onyxnet.co.uk
Non-profitmaking organisation which funds script
development for quality television projects aimed at 5-12
year old children. Holds an extensive film library, with a
wide range of films made for children/family viewing.
Founded 1951.

Churches Advisory Council for Local Broadcasting (CACLB)
PO Box 124, Westcliffe-on-Sea, Essex SS0 0QU
Fax 01702-305121   Tel 01702-348369
E-mail: office@caclb.org.uk
Website: www.caclb.org.uk
A charity bringing together the main Christian
churches for the advancement of Christianity through
radio and TV. Has an Association of Christian
broadcasters, quarterly news bulletin, annual
conference and awards.

Cinema and TV Benevolent Fund
22 Golden Square, London W1R 4AD
Fax 020-7437 7186   Tel 020-7437 6567
Trade charity for retired and serving employees and
their dependents needing caring help, support and
financial aid.

Commercial Radio Companies Association
77 Shaftesbury Avenue, London W1V 7AD
Fax 020-7470 0062   Tel 020-7306 2603
E-mail: info@crca.co.uk
Website: www.crca.co.uk
The trade body for UK commercial radio. It represents
commercial radio to Government, the Radio Authority,
Copyright Societies and other organisations concerned
with radio. CRCA gives advice to members and acts as
clearing house for radio information. The CRCA jointly
owns Radio Joint Audience Research (RAJAR) with the
BBC, owns the Network Chart Show and is a member
of the Association of European Radios which lobbies
European institutions on behalf of commercial radio.

Commonwealth Broadcasting Association
17 Fleet Street, London EC4Y 1AA
Fax 020-7583 5549   Tel 020-7583 5550
E-mail: cba@cba.org.uk
Website: www.oneworld.org/cba
Non-profit association of broadcasters with a
commitment to public service broadcasting in
Commonwealth countries. Activities include training
programmes and conferences.

Communication Workers Union
150 The Broadway, Wimbledon, London SW19 1RX
Fax 020-8971 7437   Tel 020-8971 7200
E-mail: LQuinn@cwu.org
Website: www.cwu.org
The largest trade union in posts, telecommunications
and financial services. The CWU Voice is published
monthly.

Community Media Association
15 Paternoster Row, Sheffield, S Yorks S1 2BX
Fax 0114-279 8976   Tel 0114-279 5219
E mail: cma@commedia.org.uk
Website: www.commedia.org.uk
London Development Unit: The Resource Centre, 35
Holloway Road, London N7 6PA
Fax 020-7700 0099   Tel 020-7700 0100 x 234
UK membership body, developing and campaigning for
community-based media. It offers information, advice,
training and consultancy, holds conferences and events
and publishes the quarterly journals Airflash and
London News.

Confederation of Aerial Industries
Fulton Road, Wembley Park, Middlesex HA9 0TF
Fax 020-8903 8719   Tel 020-8902 8998
E-mail: office@cai.org.uk
Trade association for aerials and satellite dish manufacturers.

CSV Media
237 Pentonville Road, London N1 9NJ
Fax 020-7278 7912   Tel 020-7278 6601
E-mail 100141.3615@compuserve.com
CSV Media, part of the national charity Community Service Volunteers, specialises in social action broadcasting, media support services and media training. Services range from TV and radio programme production, broadcast back-up , including telephone helplines and training in TV and radio production.

Deaf Broadcasting Council
70 Blacketts Wood Drive, Chorleywood, Rickmansworth, Herts WD3 5QQ
Fax 01923-283127
E-mail dmyers@cix.co.UK
Website: www.waterlow.com/dbc
An umbrella organisation to which all the major national bodies for and on behalf of deaf, deafened and hard of hearing people are affiliated. Ensures that TV companies and broadcasters are aware of their needs. Publishes newsletter Mailshot 3-4x pa.

Different Voices
108 Portnall Road, London W9 3BG
Fax 020-8968 0991   Tel 020-8969 0109
E-mail: voices@twiza.demon.co.uk
Website: www.twiza.demon.co.uk/
Non-profit making information and support network working for greater cross-cultural understanding and wider media access for under-represented groups. Different Voices is a OneWorld online partner.

Directors Guild of Gt Britain
15-19 Great Titchfield Street, London W1P 7FB
Fax 020-7436 8646   Tel 020-7436 8626
E-mail: guild@dggb.co.uk
Website: www./dggb.co.uk
Union for directors in all media, including TV, film, theatre and radio. Issues an advised schedule of rates, code of practice and contract guides. Gives contractual advice and holds workshops, conferences, public events and social events. Publishes a magazine, Direct and an annual directory of all members.

Directors and Producers' Rights Society
15-19 Great Titchfield Street, London, W1P 7FB
Fax 020-7631 1019   Tel 020-7631 1077
E-mail: dprs@dial.pipex.com
A collecting society which administers authorial rights payments on behalf of British film and television directors.

Eclipse
18-20 Highbury Place, London N5 1QP
Fax 020-7354 8106   Tel 020-7354 5858
Website: www.irseclipse.co.uk
Provides information on industrial relations practice, health and safety legislation and employment law as well as publishing journals and reports.

Equity
Guild House, Upper St Martins Lane, London WC2H 9EG
Fax 020-7379 7001   Tel 020-7379 6000
E-mail: equity@easynet.co.uk
Website: www.equity.org.uk/equity
British Actors' Equity Association is the trade union for actors, stage managers, opera singers, dancers, directors, designers, choreographers, variety artistes and stunt performers working in theatre, film, television, radio and variety venues. The union publishes the quarterly magazine Equity which is distributed to the membership of 35,000.

Euronews
60 Chemin des Moules, BP 161, 69131 Lyon, France
Fax: 0033 4 72 18 93 71 Tel: 0033 4 72 18 80 00
Website: www.euronews.net
A pan-European broadcaster which trasnmits TV news in six languages to 43 countires and is controlled by ITN.

FACT
7 Victory Business Centre, Worton Road, Isleworth, Middlesex TW7 6DB
Fax 020-8560 6364   Tel 020-8568 6646
FACT, Federation Against Copyright Theft, is an investigative organisation funded by its members to combat counterfeiting piracy and misuse of their products.

Federation of Communication Services
Keswick House, 207 Anerley Road, London SE20 8ER
Fax 020-8778 8402   Tel 020-8778 5656
E-mail: fcs.london@dial.pipex.com
Website: www.fcs.org.uk
The FCS is the representative body for the UK mobile communications industry. It is the focus for developments, issues and legislation affecting moblie communications.

Federation of the Electronics Industry
Russell Square House, 10-12 Russell Square, London WC1B 5EE
Fax 020-7331 2040   Tel 020-7331 2000
E-mail feedback@fei.org.uk
Website: www.fei.org.uk/fei
Trade association for information technology, electronics, communications, business technology and office furniture. Represents the industry's interests on major European and international standards and regulatory bodies, satellite and broadcasting groups. It publishes annual statistics on electronic components.

Federation of Entertainment Unions

1 Highfield, Twyford, near Winchester, Hants SO21 1QR
Fax 01962-713288   Tel 01962-713134
E-mail: harris@interalpha.co.uk
Collective body of trade unions, representing the interests of 150,000 members in the broadcasting and entertainment industries. The unions are: BECTU, Equity, Musicians Union, NUJ, Writers Guild, AEEU. It provides liaison, representation, lobbying and co-ordination services on issues of common concern.

Film Artistes Association

111 Wardour Street, London W1 4AY
Fax 020-7287 8984   Tel 020-7437 8506
E-mail: bactu@geo2.poptel.org.uk
The trade union representing crowd artistes, stand-ins and doubles.

FOCAL International: Federation of Commercial Audio Visual Libraries

Pentax House, South Hill Avenue, Northolt Road, South Harrow HA2 0DU
Fax 020-8423 5853   Tel 020-8933 4826
E-mail anne@focalltd.demon.co.uk
Website: www.focalltd.demon.co.uk/
FOCAL is the international trade association for audio visual libraries, researchers and producers. It promotes the use of library footage, stills and sound in programming and holds regular seminars and meetings.

405-Line Group

71 Falcutt Way, Northampton, Northants NN2 8PH
Fax 01604-821647   Tel 01604-844130
E-mail midshires@cix.compulink.co.uk
Promotes the study of television history. Publishes quarterly magazine 405 Alive and holds occasional displays of old TV equipment.

Gaelic Broadcasting Committee

4 Harbour View, Cromwell St Quay, Stornoway, Isle of Lewis HS1 2DF
Fax 01851-706432   Tel 01851-705550
E-mail: comataidh@compuserve.com
Website: www.ccg.org.uk
Statutory body grant-funding Gaelic television sound programmes, development and training.

Guardian Edinburgh International TV Festival

24 Neal Street, London WC2H 9PS
Fax 020-7836 0702   Tel 020-7379 4519
E-mail: GEITF@festival.demon.co.uk
Britain's biggest international forum for the TV industry attracts prominent speakers, many delegates and widespread interest. Held over the English August bank holiday, for four days, during the Edinburgh Festival. Publishes an annual magazine.

Guild of British Animation

26 Noel Street, London W1V 3RD
Fax 020-7434 9002   Tel 020-7434 2651
E-mail: afvpa@easynet.co.uk
The Guild represents the interests of the growing number of British animation companies.

Guild of British Camera Technicians

5-11 Taunton Road, Metropolitan Centre, Greenford, Middlesex UB6 8UQ
Fax 020-8575 5972   Tel 020-8578 9243
The Guild represents film and video camera technicians working in the UK entertainment industry. It publishes the bimonthly news magazine Eyepiece.

Guild of British Film Editors

Travair, Spurlands End Road, Great Kingshill, High Wycombe, Bucks HP15 6HY
Fax 01494-712313   Tel 01494-712313
E-mail: cox.gbfe@btinternet.com
The Guild of British Film Editors organises film shows and technical visits for its members. It presents awards for film and sound editing. It maintains a dialogue with other technical guilds at home and abroad, publishes newsletters.

Guild of Local Television

c/o The Food Channel, Hagley Hall, Stourbridge, W Midlands
Fax 01562-883386   Tel 01562-882633
Promotes locally-originated TV, and supports groups and individuals involved in local TV. Organises conferences, seminars, workshops and publications. Promotes the skills of its members and undertakes research on their behalf. Aims to identify and accredit training opportunities.

Guild of Television Cameramen

1 Churchill Road, Tavistock, Devon PL19 9BU
Fax 01822-615785   Tel 01822-614405
Website: www.easyweb.easynet.co.uk/~guildtvc
Professional association aiming to preserve the working status of TV camera operators. Publishes bi-annual Zerb Magazine and newsletter. Holds regular workshops.

Hospital Broadcasting Association

PO Box 2481, London W2 1JR
Fax 01324-612225   Tel 01324-611996
E-mail: hba@nahbo.demon.co.uk
Website: www.nahbo.demon.co.uk
The HBA is the national representative association for hospital broadcasting. It is responsible for providing advice and support to hospital radio stations, and for promoting hospital broadcasting nationwide.

Independent Media Distribution

10 John Princes Street, London W1M 0AH
Fax 020-7468 6869   Tel 020-7468 6868
E-mail: info@imd.plc.uk
Distributes commercials, short form programmes and new music releases to all radio stations in the UK and Ireland.

Independent Television Commission (ITC)

HQ: 33 Foley Street, London W1P 7LB
Fax 020-7306 7800 Tel 020-7255 3000
Kings Worthy Court, Kings Worthy, Winchester, Hants SO23 7QA.
Fax 01962-886141 Tel 01962-848600
E mail: publicaffairs@itc.org.uk
Website: www.itc.org.uk

National and regional offices:

Northern Ireland	028-9024 8733
Scotland	0141-226 4436
Wales	029-2038 4541
East of England	01603-623533
Midlands - Birmingham	0121-452 5128
Midlands - Nottingham	0115-952 7333
North East England	0191-261 0148
North of England	0114-276 9091
North West England	0161-834 2707
S of England, Winchester	01962-883950
S of England, Plymouth	01752-663031

The ITC is the public body responsible for licensing and regulating commercially funded television services provided in and from the UK. These include Channel 3 (ITV), Channel 4, Channel 5, public teletext and a range of cable, local delivery, satellite and digital television services. They do not include services provided by the BBC or by S4C, the fourth channel in Wales. The ITC replaced the Independent Broadcasting Authority and the Cable Authority in 1991.

ITC Engineering/Research/Finance:

Kings Worthy Court, Kings Worthy, W i n c h e s t e r, Hants SO23 7QA
Fax 01962-886141 Tel 01962-848600

Institute of Broadcast Sound

27 Old Gloucester Street, London WC1N 3XX
Fax 020-8887 0167 Tel 01923-270888
E-mail: info@ibs.org.uk
Website: www.ibs.org.uk
Professional body for people responsible for the sound broadcast on TV and radio. Publishes the industry's bi-monthly trade magazine Line Up.

Institute of Local Television

13 Bellevue Place, Edinburgh EH7 4BS
Fax 0131-557 8608 Tel 0131-557 8610
E-mail: instituteoflocaltv@msn.co.uk
Aims to increase local TV programming and maintain high quality local service on cable.Through research and consultancy supports development of the new resticted service TV licence and the introduction of local digital TV. Runs courses and conferences. Launched Channel 6 as first local terrestrial TV service in Edinburgh in spring 1997.

International Broadcasting Trust

2 Ferdinand Place, London NW1 8EE
Fax 020-7284 3374 Tel 020-7482 2847
E-mail: ibt@gn.apc.org
An independent TV company with charitable status specialising in making programmes on development, environment and human rights issues. Its aim is to promote a wider understanding of these issues through the use of the media. IBT is backed by a consortium of 70 aid and development agencies, educational bodies, churches and trade unions. It publishes the bi-annual newsletter Fast Forward and a range of back-up material.

International Institute of Communications

Tavistock House South, Tavistock Square, London WC1H 9LF
Fax 020-7380 0623 Tel 020-7388 0671
E mail: enquiries@iicdm.org
Website: www.iicom.org
Promotes the open debate of issues in the communications field worldwide, in the interest of human and social advancement. Specialises in broadcasting, telecommunications and communications policy. It publishes books, bimonthly journal Intermedia, newsletter, reports, etc.

International Visual Communications Association

5-6 Clipstone Street, London W1P 8LD
Fax 020-7436 2606 Tel 020-7580 0962
E-mail: info@ivca.org
A trade association representing the users and suppliers of the corporate visual communications industry. It publishes magazine and guides and organises regular professional and social events. Provides legal and information help.

ITV Association

200 Grays Inn Road, London, WC1X 8HF
Fax 020-7843 8155 Tel 020-7843 8000
The corporate political arm for the ITV. It lobbies MPs about broadcasting standards and seeks to improve or amend broadcasting bills.

ITV Network Centre

200 Grays Inn Road, London WC1X 8HF
Fax 020-7843 8158 Tel 020-7843 8000
Represents the interests of the regional ITV companies. Set up in late 1992 to commission and schedule ITV's networked programmes from 1 January 1993, as required by the 1990 Broadcasting Act. Also responsible for research, programme acquisitions and financial, legal and business matters for ITV. The Centre also clears advertisements prior to transmission.

Local Independent Television Network

c/o Community Media Association, 15 Paternoster Row, Sheffield S1 2BX
Fax 0114-279 8976 Tel 0114-279 5219
The trade body for those operating ITC Restricted Service Licences.

London Film Commission
20 Euston Centre, Regent's Place, London NW1 3JH
Fax 020-7387 8788   Tel 020-7387 8787
E-mail: lfc@london-film.co.uk
The Commission encourages and assists film and TV production in London and holds databases of locations, personnel and facilities. Funded by government, the film industry and other private sector sponsors, it works to promote London as a first choice destination for overseas film makers.

MDA
22-24 Worple Road, London SW19 4DD
Fax 020-8947 9042   Tel 020-8947 5991
E-mail: mda@dial.pipex.com
The Mobile Data Association was formed to increase awareness of mobile data amongst users and their advisers. It also aids its members in communication with the DTI. the Radiocommunications Agency and Oftel.

Mechanical-Copyright Protection Society
41 Streatham High Road, London SW16 1ER
Fax 020-8769 8792   Tel 020-8664 4400
E mail: corpcomms@mcps.co.uk
Websitew: www.mcps.co.uk
Organisation of music publishers and composers, collecting and distributing royalties from the recording of copyright music onto CDs, cassettes, audio-visual and broadcast material. The society's National Discography, a database of commercial music and records, offers a wide range of music information. Publishes On the Right Track (a guide to starting in the music business) and the magazine For the Record.

Media Antenna Scotland
74 Victoria Crescent Road, Glasgow G12 9JN
Fax 0141-357 2345   Tel 0141-302 1777
E-mail: louisescott@dial.pipex.com
Office in Scotland for the European Commission's media programme.

Media Research Group
Telmar,46 Chagford Street, London NW1 6EB
Fax 020-7723 5265   Tel 020-7224 9992
Website: www.telmar.co.uk
Provides forum for debating issues relating to media planning and research. Holds bi-annual conference.

MediaTel
52 Poland Street, London W1V 4LQ
Fax 020-7734 0940   Tel 020-7439 7575
E-mail: info@mediatel.co.uk
Website: www.mediatel.co.uk
MediaTel is an on-line media news and information database. There is free access to daily media news and walkthrough screens but the media databases are only available on an annual company subscription.

Media Trust
3-7 Euston Centre, Regents Place, London NW1 3JG
Fax 020-7874 7644   Tel 020-7874 7600
E-mail: info@mediatrust.org
Website: www.mediatrust.org
The Trust builds partnerships between the media and the voluntary sector. It provides information, training services, and on-line material. It also runs Media Resource to match voluntary organisations with skills and resources donated by the media.

Mobile Data Association
Russell Square House, 10-12 Russell Square, London WC1B 5EE
Fax 020-7331 2040   Tel 020-7331 2022
E-mail: mda@mda-mobiledata.org
Website: www.mda-mobiledata.org
Association for the mobile data industry, representing manufacturers, vendors, resellers and end users.

Museum of the Moving Image
South Bank, Waterloo, London SE1 8XT
Fax 020-7815 1419   Tel 020-7815 1331
E-mail: wendy.taylor@bfi.org.uk
Website: bfi.org.uk/museum/
The national museum of TV and cinema including pre-cinema film, TV, video and new technologies. It is run by the British Film Institute. It hosts exhibitions, screenings, press previews and photocalls.

Musicians' Union
60-62 Clapham Road, London SW9 0JJ
Fax 020-7582 9805   Tel 020-7582 5566
The trade union which looks after the interests all styles of musician. It publishes the quarterly journal Musician plus a range of leaflets on the music biz.

National Communications Union
See Communication Workers Union

National Film and Television Archive
21 Stephen Street, London W1P 2LN
Fax 020-7436 7950   Tel 020-7255 1444
Founded in 1935 as a division of the British Film Institute. It acquires, preserves, catalogues and makes permanently available for study, research and screening a national and international collection of moving images of all kinds. Now holds over 350,000 titles, starting from 1895. Covers TV, documentary and feature films. The J Paul Getty Jnr Conservation Centre, in Berkhamsted is the location for the Archive's preservation work and for storage.

National Film Theatre
South Bank, Waterloo, London SE1 8XT
Fax 020-7815 1419   Tel 020-7815 1327
E-mail: brian.robinson@bfi.org.uk
Three cinemas owned by the British Film Institute (cf) showing the widest possible range of film and television from around the world.

National Sound Archive
See British Library National Sound Archive

National Viewers and Listeners Association

All Saints House, High Street, Colchester, Essex CO1 1UG
Fax 01206-766175   Tel 01206-561155
E-mail: info@nvala.org
Organisation founded by Mary Whitehouse. It campaigns to make the Obscene Publications Act 1959 and 1964 effective, and encourages discussion and debate about the effects of the media on individuals, family and society. Publishes reports and the magazine The Viewer & Listener x3 p.a.

Networking

Vera Media, 30-38 Dock Street, Leeds, West Yorks LS10 1JF
Fax 0113-245 1238   Tel 0113-242 8646
E mail: networking@vera-media.demon.co.uk
Membership organisation for women involved in any way, or hoping to work in film, video or television. Media departments, libraries,careers offices are welcome. It publishes a newsletter and contacts index and provides information and advice.

NTL

Crawley Court, Winchester, Hants SO21 2QA
Fax 01962-822378   Tel 01962-823434
Website: www.ntl.com
Provides the transmission service for ITV, Channel 4, S4C, Channel 5 and most independent radio stations. Services include mobile radio communications and satellite uplinking (including Occasional Services).

OneWorld Online

Hedgerley Wood, 4 Red Lane, Chinnor Oxon OX9 4BW
Fax 01494-481751   Tel 01494-481629
E-mail: justice@oneworld.org
Website: www.oneworld.org
OneWorld is a community of over 100 websites devoted to human rights and sustainable development. It includes a library, a discussion forum, a news wire and a radio station offered free to local communities for rebroadcasting.

Pact (Producers Alliance for Cinema & Television)

45 Mortimer Street, London W1N 7TD
Fax 020-7331 6700   Tel 020-7331 6000
E-mail: enquiries@pact.co.uk
Website: www.pact.co.uk
Trade association and employers' body for feature film and independent TV producers. Formed in 1991 from the Independent Programme Producers Association and the British Film and TV Producers Association. Provides a range of services, including information and production advice.

Production Managers Association

Ealing Studios, Ealing Green, London W5 5EP
Fax 020-8758 8647   Tel 020-8758 8699
E-mail: pma@pma.org.uk
Website: www.pma.org.uk
Offers a professional voice for both freelance and permanently employed production managers. Provides regular workshops, training courses and an employment register.

Radio Academy

5 Market Place, London W1N 7AH
Fax 020-7255 2029   Tel 020-7255 2010
E-mail: radacad@radacad.demon.co.uk
Website: www.radacad.demon.co.uk
Professional membership organisation for the radio industry. Organises the industry's annual conference, the Radio Festival plus seminars and workshops. Regional centres organise their own programme of events. Makes a number of awards for outstanding contributions to the radio industry.

Radio Advertising Bureau

77 Shaftesbury Avenue, London W1V 7AD
Fax 020-7306 2505   Tel 020-7306 2500
Website: www.rab.co.uk
The RAB is the marketing arm of the commercial radio industry. It aims to increase the levels of familiarity and favourability towards commercial radio as an advertising medium.

Radio Advertising Clearance Centre

46 Westbourne Grove, London W2 5SH
Fax 020-7229 0352   Tel 020-7727 2646
E-mail: adclear@racc.co.uk
Clears advertisements for radio.

Radio Authority

Holbrook House, 14 Great Queen Street, London WC2B 5DG
Fax 020-7405 7062   Tel 020-7430 2724
Statutory body licensing and regulating independent radio (all non-BBC services). Started in 1991, replacing part of the Independent Broadcasting Authority (see also Independent Television Commission). Publishes the annual Radio Authority Pocket Book, detailing the independent radio stations, and The Radio Authority complaints leaflet 'How Do I Complain'.

Radio

PO Box 14880, London NW1 9ZD
Radio 020-7428 0541   Tel 020-7485 0873
A recently-formed trade body representing independent radio producers. It is a lobbying organisation that negotiates with the radio network, government and the unions. One of its aims is to increase the BBC's quota of independently produced programmes from around 10 per cent to some 25 per cent of output.

RAJAR: Radio Joint Audience Research

Collier House, 163-169 Brompton Road, London SW3 1PY
Fax 020-7589 4004   Tel 020-7584 3003
Joint body involving the BBC and commercial radio which is responsible for controlling a system of audience research for radio in the UK.

Radio Society of Great Britain
Lambda House, Cranborne Road, Potters Bar, Herts
EN6 3JE
Fax 01707-645105   Tel 01707-659015
E-mail: ar.dept@rsgb.org.uk
The leading national organisation for amateur radio
enthusiasts, offering a range of services to members.
The society publishes: the monthly magazine Radio
Communication, full of news, features, etc; and the
annual Yearbook, a comprehensive guide to all
organisations and the holder of every G call-sign.

Radiocommunications Agency
New King's Beam House, 22 Upper Ground, London
SE1 9SA
Fax 020-7211 0507   Tel 020-7211 0211
E-mail: library@ra.gtnet.gov.uk
Website: www.open.gov.uk/radiocom/
An executive agency of the DTI. It is responsible for the
management of the civilian radio spectrum within the
UK. It also represents UK radio interests
internationally. Publishes an annual report and many
useful information sheets on radio-related topics.

RAJAR
See Radio Joint Audience Research

Reel Women
57 Holmewood Gardens, London SW2 3NB
Fax 020-8678 7404   Tel 020-8678 7404
E-mail: rawlinj@uwest.ac-uk
Brings together women working in television,film and
video for discussions, seminars, screenings and
workshops.

Researcher's Guide to British Film and Television Collections
British Universities Film and Video Council, 77 Wells
Street, London W1P 3RE
                             Tel: 020-7393 1500
E-mail: bufvc@open.ac.uk
Website: www.bufvc.ac.uk

Royal Television Society
100 Grays Inn Road, London WC1X 8AL
Fax 020-7430 0924   Tel 020-7430 1000
E-mail: info@rts.org.uk
Website: www.rts.org.uk
Promoting the art and science of television
broadcasting, the Society provides a unique forum
where all branches of the industry can meet and discuss
major issues. Organises conferences, lectures,
workshops, masterclasses and awards ceremonies. The
RTS has regional centres, each running their own
programme of events. Publishes Television magazine
nine times a year and an annual handbook.
Membership £60 pa, students £20.

Satellite & Cable Broadcasters' Group
64 West End, Northwold, Thetford, Norfolk IP26 5LG
Fax 01366-727411   Tel 01366-728795
Association of cable and satellite TV programme
providers.

Satellite Media Services
Lawford Heath, Rugby, Warwickshire CV23 9EU
Fax 01788-523001   Tel 01788-523000
E mail info@sms.co.uk
SMS uses its dedicated lines, digital satellite and ISDN
networks to distribute commericals, programmes, IRN
and PA news services and record releases to
independent commercial radio. It is also active in retail
broadcasting, data communications networks and other
commercial services distributed via satellite.

Scottish Association of Smallscale Broadcasters
Struan House, The Square, Aberfeldy, Perthshire
PH15 2DD
Fax 01887-820038   Tel 01887-820956
E-mail: wwright@sol.co.uk
Co-operative umbrella for all individuals and
organisations concerned with smallscale broadcast
operations, RSLs (restricted service licences), training
workshops, etc. Publishes quarterly newsletter.
Formerly called the Scottish Community Broadcasting
Group, set up in 1985.

Scottish Screen
249 West George Street, Glasgow G2 4RB
Fax 0141-302 1711   Tel 0141-302 1700
E-mail: info@scottishscreen.com
Website: www.scottishscreen.com
Scottish Screen is responsible to the Scottish
Parliament for developing all aspects of screen industry
and culture in Scotland. This includes script and
company development, short film production,
distribution of National Lottery finance and the Scottish
Film and Television Archive.

Services Sound and Vision Group
Chalfont Grove, Gerrards Cross, Bucks SL9 8TN
Fax 01494-872982   Tel 01494-874461
Website: www.ssvc.com
Broadcasts radio and TV to the British armed forces via
BFBS (British Forces Broadcasting Service) around the
world. TLI (Teleport London International) provides
satellite services and Visua gives audiovisual and
multimedia help.

Sgrin - Media Agency for Wales
The Bank, 10 Mount Stuart Square, Cardiff Bay,
Cardiff CF10 5EE
Fax 029-2033 3320   Tel 029-2033 3300
E-mail: sgrin@sgrinwales.demon.co.uk
Website: www.sgrinwales.demon.co.uk
The Welsh national information centre for European
audiovisual funding and policy in Wales. It promotes
the EU action programme for the audiovisual industry.

Society of Cable Telecommunication Engineers

Fulton House Business Centre, Fulton Road, Wembley Park, Middlesex HA9 0TF
Fax 020-8903 8719   Tel 020-8902 8998
E-mail: office@scte.org.uk
Technical body aiming to raise the standards of cable telecommunication engineering, improve the status of cable engineers and offer members opportunities to attain further skills. Publishes journal Cable Telecommunication Engineering.

Society of Television Lighting Directors

Tel 0973-249432
The Society promotes discussion on techniques and on the use and design of equipment. It organises meetings and produces a journal: Television Lighting.

Student Radio Association

c/o The Radio Academy, 5 Market Place, London W1N 7AH
Fax 020-7255 2029   Tel 020-7255 2010
E-mail: sra-exec@studentradio.org.uk
Website: www.studentradio.org.uk
The SRA is the representative body for student radio. Run by an elected committee drawn from its 70 member stations. It holds three conferences and organises the Lee Student Radio Awards with Radio 1.

Telecommunications Users' Association

Woodgate Studios, 2-8 Games Road, Cockfosters EN4 9HN
Fax 020-8447 4901   Tel 020-8449 8844
E-mail: tua@dial.pipex.com
Website: www.tua.co.uk
An independent organisation representing its members interests within the world's telecommunications companies. Membership includes a help line, consultancy, training, workshops and publications.

Television & Radio Industries Club

2 Duckling Lane, Sawbridgeworth, Herts CM21 9QA
Fax 01279-723100   Tel 01279-721100
Founded 1931 to promote goodwill amongst those engaged in the audio, visual and allied industries. Its primary role is arranging social events and it also publishes a yearbook and organises annual Celebrity Awards.

Television Trust for Scotland

The Retreat, Manse Road, Dirleton, East Lothian EH39 5EP
Fax 01620-850408   Tel 01620-850408
E-mail: 101501.110@compuserve.com
Local charity set up to provide training for TV access via restricted television services and cable.

3WE (Third World & Environmental Broadcasting Project)

2 Ferdinand Place, London NW1 8EE
Fax 020-7284 3374   Tel 020-7482 2847
E-mail: ibt@gn.apc.org
3WE works for sustained and imaginative coverage of global affairs on UK TV on behalf of Oxfam, WWF, Amnesty International and a consortium of other leading voluntary agencies.

Voice of the Listener and Viewer

101 King's Drive, Gravesend, Kent DA12 5BQ
Tel.01474-352835
E-mail: vlv@btinternet.com
Non-profit making, independent society representing the citizen's voice in broadcasting. The only consumer body speaking for viewers and listeners on all broadcasting issues. Publishes quarterly newsletter, reports and briefings on broadcasting developments. Arranges public seminars, debates and conferences throughout the UK. Holds the archives of the former Broadcasting Research Unit and British Action for Children's Television.

White Dot

PO Box 2116, Hove, East Sussex BN3 3LR
E-mail: whitedot@mistral.co.uk
A campaign against television which encourages people to get a life and turn off their sets. It organises an annual Turn Off TV Week.

Wireless Preservation Society

52 West Hill Road, Ryde, Isle of Wight PO33 3LN
Fax 01983-564708   Tel 01983-567665
The society and the linked Communications and Electronics Museum preserve a reference collection of radio, TV and other electronic equipment in Museums at Arreton Manor and Puckpool on the Isle of Wight and at Bletchley Park, near Milton Keynes.

Women in Film and Television

11-15 Betterton Street, London WC2H 9BP
Fax 020-7379 1625   Tel 020-7379 0344
E-mail wftv@easynet.co.uk
Professional membership organisation for women working in the film and TV industries. Provides information and support to members. Campaigns and lobbies on issues pertinent to membership. Publishes a quarterly magazine and runs a programme of events and an annual awards ceremony.

The Writers' Guild of Great Britain

430 Edgware Road, London W2 1EH
Fax 020-7706 2413   Tel 020-7723 8074
E-mail: postie@wggb.demon.co.uk
Website: www.writers.org.uk/guild
The writers' union. It has agreements with Pact, BBC, ITV, ITC, TMA and TAC. Provides support for members, organises events and publishes a bi-monthly magazine.

Broadcast awards 1999

BAFTA Performance Awards (TV Section)
British Academy of Film and Television Arts, 195 Piccadilly, London W1V 0LN
Fax 020-7734 1792   Tel 020-7734 0022
Best single drama: A Rather English Marriage, BBC2
Best drama series: Cops
Best drama serial: Our Mutual Friend
Best factual series: The Human Body
Best light entertainment: Who Wants to be a Millionaire
Best comedy: Father Ted
Best news/current affairs: Inside the Animal Liberation Front, Dispatches, C4
Best live OB: Channel 4 Racing - Derby Day
Best actress: Dame Thora Hird, Waiting for the Telegram
Best actor: Tom Courtenay, A Rather English Marriage
Best light entertainment performance: Michael Parkinson, Parkinson
Best comedy performance: Dermot Morgan, Father Ted
Best arts programme: The Brian Epstein Story, Arena, BBC2
Best documentary: After Lockerbie, ITV
Best original music: A Rather English Marriage, BBC2
Best soap: East Enders
Best feature: Back to the Floor, BBC2
Best make-up and hair: Our Mutual Friend, BBC2
Best photography (factual tv): 42 Up, BBC1
Best photography (entertainment tv): Far From the Madding Crowd, ITV
Best costume: A Respectable Trade, BBC1
Best graphic design: The Human Body, BBC1
Best sound: Our Mutual Friend, BBC2
Best editing: Lockerbie: A Night ot Remember C4
Best design: Our Mutual Friend, BBC2
Originality award: The Human Body, BBC1
International award: the Larry Sanders Show, BBC2
Most popular TV (audience vote): Goodnight Mr Tom, ITV
Outstanding creative achievement: Jimmy Mulville & Denise O'Donoghue
Contribution to factual television: Trevor McDonald
Dennis Potter award: David Renwick
Special award: Richard Curtis

Broadcast Production Awards
33-39 Bowling Green Lane, London EC1R 0DA
Fax 020-7505 8050   Tel 020-7505 8014
E-mail: bcast@media,emap.co.uk
Cable or satellite programme: Dream Team, Hewland International for Sky One
Children's programme: The Fame Game, BBC Scotland for Children's BBC and Bill's New Frock, Tetra Films for Channel 4
Drama: Jonathan Creek, BBC Entertainment for BBC1
Documentary programme: True Story - Orphans of War, Hart Ryan Productions for Channel 4
Documentary series: 42 Up, Granada for BBC1
News programme: Newsline - Good Friday Agreement, BBC Northern Ireland

Comedy: I'm Alan Partridge, Talkback Productions for BBC2
Light entertainment: Who Wants to be a Millionaire?, Celador Productions for ITV
Sports programme: World Cup 1998, BBC Sport
Popular factual programme: Hotel, Lion Television for BBC1
New programme: Who Wants to be a Millionaire?, Celador Productions for ITV
Independent production company: Tiger Aspect
Post production house: Blue Post Production
Studio facilities: Fountain Television

Broadcasting Press Guild Awards
Tiverton, The Ridge, Woking, Surrey GU22 7EQ
Fax 01483-765882   Tel 01483-764895
Best single drama: A Rather English Marriage, Wall to Wall Productions for BBC2
Best drama series: Our Mutual Friend, BBC2
Best documentary series: The Life of Birds, BBC1
Best single documentary: 42 Up, Granada for BBC1
Best entertainment: Cold Feet, Granada Television for ITV and Goodness Gracious Me, BBC2
Best actor: Timothy Spall, Our Mutual Friend
Best actress: Daniela Nardini, Undercover Heart
Best performer: Michael Parkinson, BBC1
Writer's award: Caroline Aherne, Craig Cash and Henry Normal, The Royle Family, Granada for BBC2
Radio programme of the year: Food Programme, R4
Radio broadcaster: John Peel, Home Truths, Radio 4
Outstanding contribution: News At Ten, ITN for ITV

The Indies
Single Market Events, 23-24 George Street, Richmond, Surrey TW9 1HY
Fax 020-8332 0495   Tel 020-8948 5522
The Indie: Who Wants to be a Millionaire? Celador Productions
Hat Trick Pioneer: Bazal Productions
Drama: Playing the Field, Tiger Aspect
Light entertainment: Who Wants to be a Millionaire? Celador Productions
Music and arts: Jo Whiley, At It Productions
Factual: Time Team, The Picture House
News: Chris Patten's East & West, Oxford Television Company
Documentary: The Clinton's Marriage of Power, Mentorn Barraclough Carey
Animation: The Adventures of Captain Pugwash, John Cary Studios
Sport: F1 coverage, Chrysalsis Sport
Cable and satellite: Dream Team, Hewland International
Digital cinematography: The Queen's Nose, Film & General Productions
Archive award: The Cold War, Jeremy Isaacs Productions
Children: Teletubbies, Ragdoll Productions
The Indie-vidual award: Beryl Vertue

Rory Peck Award

Rory Peck Trust, 7 Southwick Mews, London W2 1JG
Fax 020-7262 2162   Tel 020-7262 5272
E-mail: rptrpa@dial.pipex.com
Website: www.oneworld.org/rorypeck
Honours the initiative, courage and skill of freelance
cameramen and women in TV newsgathering and
documentaries worldwide. The award is named after
Rory Peck a freelance cameraman killed whilst filming
the Moscow revolt in October 1993.
Winner 1998: Miguel Gil (on assignment for APTN)
Kosovo

Royal Television Society Awards

Holborn Hall, 100 Grays Inn Road, London WC1X
8AL
Fax 020-7430 0924   Tel 020-7430 1000
Journalist of the year: David Loyn, BBC News
Young journalist of the year: Peter Lane, 5 News - ITN
Daily news magazine: London Tonight, London News
Network for Carlton Television
Regional current affairs: Frontline Scotland-The Ghost
of Piper Alpha, TV6 Production for BBC Scotland
News (home): Drumcree-Portadown Divided, GMTV/
Reuters
News (international): Nine O'Clock News, The
Massacre at Drenica, BBC News
Current affairs (home): Dispatches, Inside the ALF,
David Monaghan Prductions for Channel 4
News event: Good Friday Agreement, BBC News
Television technician of the year: Nikki Millard, BBC
News
Interview of the year: Dermot Murnaghan interviews
Peter Mandelson, ITN News on ITV
Production award: Live broadcasts from the Gulf, BBC
News Resources Location Facilities
Judges award: World in Action, Granada
Sports award: Sky Sports football production team
Sports news: World Cup Trouble, News at Ten, ITN
News on ITV
Sports documentary: The Man Who Jumped to Earth,
BBC Wales for BBC1
Regional sports news: Meridian Tonight, Meridian
Broadcasting
Regional sports documentary: Bred for the Red, Home
Truths, BBC Northern Ireland
Sports presenter: Des Lynam
Sports commentator: Clive Tyldesley, ITV Sport
Judges award: Jimmy Hill

One World '99

One World Broadcasting Trust, 3-7 Euston Centre,
Regent's Place, London NW1 3JG
Fax 020-7383 4238   Tel 020-7383 4248
E-mail: owbt@oneworld.org
TV news: BBCNewsnight, Education Crisis in Tanzania
UNICEF: Dispatches, Apartheid's Children
TV documentary: When Good Men Do Nothing, Steve
Bradshaw
Best NGO campaign: Jubilee 2000: Debt Free Start for
a Billion People
Radio news: The Human Chain, Felix Broadcasting

Radio documentary: A Mission to Civilise? Gabon, the
Oil-rigged State, Radio 4
National press: New Slavery (debt relief), Guardian

Online Journalism Awards

Milverton Wallace, Journalism Department, City
University, London EC1 0HB
Fax 020-7477 8594   Tel 020-7477 8233
E-mail: m.s.wallace@city.ac.uk
Website: www.jour.city.ac.uk/olja99/index.html
Best overall journalism service: IWPR Online
Internet jornalist of the year: John West, Out There
News
Sports: Scotland Online
Best entertainment: Film Unlimited
Best business: BBC News Online
Best general news: BBC News Online
Science and technology: BBC Online
Best news design and navigation: Guardian Unlimited

Sony Radio Awards

Zafer Productions, 47-48 chagford Street, London
NW1 6EB
Fax 020-7724 6163   Tel 020-7723 0106
E-mail: zafer@compuserve.com
UK station of the year (upto 500,00 listeners): Moray
Firth Radio
UK station of the year (500,00-12 mil listeners): Clyde 2
UK station of the year (to UK): Radio 2
Talk or news broadcaster: Tim Hubbard, BBC Radio
Cornwall
News gold award: Farming Today, BBC Birmingham for
BBC Radio 4
Sony gold award: Zoë Ball
Event gold award: The Enthronement of 7th Bishop,
BBC Radio Merseyside
Daytime talk or news gold award: Between Ourselves,
BBC Birmingham for BBC Radio 4
DJ award: Mark Lamarr, Shake, Rattle and Roll, BBC
Radio 2
Breakfast music award: The Adam Cole Breakfast
Show, Galaxy 102
Breakfast talk award: 5 Live Breakfast, BBC Radio 5 Live
Daytime music: The Mark Radcliffe Show, BBC
Entertainments and Features, Manchester for Radio 1
Drivetime music: Simon James, Aire FM
Comedy gold award: Old Harry's Game, BBC Radio
Light Entertainment for BBC Radio 4
Sport gold award: Metro Sport, Two Wembley finals
Late night talk: Up All Night, BBC Radio 5 Live

Voice of the Listener and Viewer Awards

101 King's Drive, Gravesend, Kent DA12 5BQ
                              Tel 01474-352835
Best television contributor: Alan Bennett
Best radio contributor: Chris Dunkley
Best radio programme: In the Psychiatist's Chair, BBC
Radio 4
Best television programme: Life of Birds, BBC 1
Best new television programme: Local Heroes, BBC2
Best new radio programme: Home Truths, Radio 4
Special award: John Dunn

Ethnic media

The UK's population is 55 million, of which just over three million - some 5.5 per cent - belong to an ethnic minority. As the two tables show, these proportions are not reflected in the best known parts of the media.

A report into ethnic minority employment in broadcasting called this a "national disgrace". More Colour in the Media, which was written by Jim Pines of Luton University, revealed that throughout the entire ITV network there are fewer than 100 ethnic minority staff employed in programme departments. At the BBC, the latest figures show that in London - where most employees live - the proportion of ethnic minorities fell from 7.5 per cent in 1996-97 to 7.4 per cent in 1997-98.

Despite over 20 per cent of the London population belonging to an ethnic minority, only 1.5 per cent of London-based national press journalists are ethnic and the imbalance is greater on locals.

*Thanks to the Commission for Racial Equality for the bulk of the listings. Its number is:
CRE: 020-7828 7022

Ethnic Multicultural Media Awards

Hearsay Communications, 67-69 Whitfield Street, London W1P 5RL
Fax 020-7636 1255   Tel 020-7468 3527
E-mail: comms@hearsay.co.uk
Website: www.emma.co.uk
Best written feature: Maya Jaggi, The Guardian
Best graphic design: Phillip Basi, Eastern Mix
Best female media newcomer: Jennifer Jones, Who What, When
Best male media newcomer: Ravi Vadgama, Sky News
Best marketing campaign: Shubhankar Ray, CAT
Best advertising campaign: Prince Naseem, Adidas UK
Best PR campaign: Ola Wright, Cohn & Wolfe
Best music presenter,radio: Clive Patterson, ChoiceFM
Best music production: Beverley Knight, Parlophone Rhythm
Best TV production: Trevor Philips, Windrush
Best print journalist: Michael Edoba, New Nation
Beat audio journalist: Henry Bonsu, freelance
Best visual journalist: Farah Durrani, BBC News
Ethnic minority charity: Daniel De-Gale, Afro-Caribbean Leukaemia Trust
Politician/public figure: Doreen and Neville Lawrence
Business personality: Sir Anwar Parveez, chairman of Best Way
Media professional/personality: Ian Wright, LWT
Lifetime Achievement Award: Muhammad Ali

Ethnic minorities in broadcast editorial

BBC Home Services	7.4%
BBC World Service	11.4%
BBC Scotland	1.3%
BBC Wales	1.5%
BBC North	3.0%
BBC South	2.8%
BBC Midlands/East	5.1%
Anglia	1.7%
Border	0.9%
Carlton	8.1%
Central	3.2%
Channel	2.3%
Grampian	1.1%
Granada	3.1%
HTV	2.9%
LWT	7.7%
Meridian	2.2%
Scottish	2.1%
Tyne Tees	1.3%
Ulster	0.4%
Westcountry	0.5%
Yorkshire	1.5%
GMTV	4.6%
Channel 4	9.5%
Channel 5	6.5%

Source: More Colour in the Media

Minorities in national paper editorial

PAPER	EMPLOYEES
Daily Mail/MoS	2
Daily/Sunday Telegraph	2
Express/EoS	6
Financial Times	6
Guardian/Observer	10
Independent/IoS	5
Mirror/Sunday Mirror	2
News of the World	1
People	2
Sun	1
Times/Sunday Times	5
Nos of nat journalists	**3,000**
Proportion of ethnic	**1.4%**

Source: Guardian survey, March 1999

JIM PINES, AUTHOR OF COLOUR IN THE MEDIA

PETER PRESTON, GUARDIAN EDITORIAL DIRECTOR

"The broadcasting industry is not simply an economic or market-driven sector, it is central to the cultural life. In a wide sense, culture could be described as people's lived experience expressed through the arts and media. As every society is different, and as all the groups that make up a society have different experiences, it is important that cultural media reflect diversity.

"A society needs this vehicle in order to explore issues of importance to it, for the people within that society to communicate with each other ... and to extend and develop the democratic process which depends upon information and participation. The effect of locking out a section of society from this process makes them invisible to the rest of society. It has already led to less tolerance of and higher unemployment within marginalised communities.

"But for the cultural product to reflect cultural diversity, the creators of that product have also to reflect that. And this is why the abysmal statistics concerning ethnic employment within British broadcasting are not only economically unfair, but are also dangerous to the development of society and the nation's democracy."

"National newspapers - locked in competition - depend on a flow of talent along familiar routes. Most typically: from university on to a local or regional paper where you can learn the ropes of survival. It's not fair to anybody to pitch them into a reportorial dogfight without the skills they need for survival. Those skills have to be experienced: they can't be merely taught.

"The crux, then, is to persuade A-level children from ethnic minorities to think of journalism as a career; to get them to university and to the post-graduate journalism courses which are at the heart of training, certainly so far as nationals are concerned; then to have jobs in the regions, and on magazines, available for them as they emerge. It needs - particularly at the Afro-Caribbean end, where the shortage is greatest - to be a natural path of aspiration and advancement.

"The growth of a vibrant ethnic press is great news, but you don't want to recruit journalists only as specialists in their communities - that's an artificial constraint on their career development. You want them, one great day, to be able to edit a national for the whole of society."

ETHNIC PRESS

Ad-Diplomasi News
PO Box 138, London SW3 6BH
Fax 020-7266 1479   Tel 020-7286 1372
E-mail: ad-diplomasi@easynet.co.uk
Website: www.easyweb.easynet.co.uk/~ãd-diplomasi
Arabic, weekly.
Editor: Raymond Ataliah

The African
25 Hester Road, London N18 2RF
Fax 020-8351 0516   Tel 020-8350 0684
Bi-monthly.
Editor: Zaya Yeebo

Akhbar-e-Watan
Chamber House, 306-308a Hoe Street, London E17 9PX
Fax 020-8925 0446   Tel 020-8923 9222
E-mail: watan@wavenet.co.uk
Website: www.wavenet.co.uk/users/watan
Urdu.
Editor: Taj Javaid

Al Ahram International
203-209 North Gower Street, London NW1 2NJ
Fax 020-7388 3130   Tel 020-7388 1155
Arabic daily.
Editor: Abdalla Attia

Al-Alaam
Banner House, 55-57 Banner Street, London EC1Y 8PX
Fax 020-7608 3581   Tel 020-7608 3454
E-mail: al.alaam@btinternet.com
Arabic weekly.
Editor: Dr Sead Mahamed Shehabi

Al Arab
159 Acre Lane, London SW2 5UA
Fax 020-7326 1783   Tel 020-7274 9381
Website: www.alarab.co.uk
Arabic daily.
Editor: M Kabarday

Al Hayat
66 Hammersmith Road, London W14 8YT
Fax 020-7602 4963   Tel 020-7602 9988
Website: www.alhayat.com
Arabic daily.
Editor George Semaan

Al Muhajir
146 Kilburn High Road, London NW6 4JD
Fax 020-7372 6703   Tel 020-7624 6366
Arabic fortnightly.
Editor: M Assou

Amar Deep Hindi
36 Trent Avenue, London W5 4TL
Fax 020-8579 3180   Tel 020-8840 3534
Weekly.
Editor: J M Kaushal

Ananda Bazar Patrika
37 Lawns Court, The Avenue, Wembley Park, Middx HA9 9PN
Fax 020-8908 2625   Tel 020-8904 2533
Bengali/English weekly.
Editor: Shrabani Basu

Asharq Al Awsat (Arab News)
Arab Press House, 184 High Holborn, London WC1V 7AP
Fax 020-7405 7892   Tel 020-7831 8181
E-mail: admin@arab.net
Editor: Abdul Rahaman Al Rashid

Asian Age
Dolphin Media House, Spring Villa Park, Spring Villa Road, London HAB 7EB
Fax 020-8951 4839   Tel 020-8951 4401
Daily.
Editor: S Bhatia

Asian Convenience Retailer/Asian Voice
8-16 Coronet Street, London N1 6HD
Fax 020-7739 0358   Tel 020-7729 5453
E-mail: gujarat@samachar.com
Fortnightly.

Asian Entertainment Guide
18 Molyneux Street, London W1H 5HU
Fax 020-7724 2971   Tel 020-7723 6797
Weekly.
Editor: N Gosai

The Asian Express
211 Piccadilly, London W1V 9LD
Fax 020-7537 2141   Tel 020-7439 8985
Fortnightly.
Editor: Vallabh Kaviraj

Asian Hotel & Caterer
Garavi Gujarat House, 1 Silex Street, London SE1 0DW
Fax 020-7261 0055   Tel 020-7928 1234
E-mail: caterer@gujarat.demon.co.uk
Monthly.
Editor: Ramniklal Solanki

The Asian News
192b Stoney Lane, Birmingham B12 8AN
Fax 0121-449 1725   Tel 0121-449 1725
Editor: M Shafique

Asian Telegraph
21a Park Road, London NW1 6XN
Fax 020-7607 6705   Tel 020-7723 5042
Wesite: www.telegraph.com
Editor: Jafar Raza

Asian Times
1st floor, 148 Cambridge Heath Road, `London E1 5QJ
Fax 020-7702 7937   Tel 020-7702 8012
E-mail: name@eeye.demon.co.uk
Weekly.
Editor: Burhan Ahmad

Asian Trader
1 Silex Street, London SE1 0DW
Fax 020-7261 0055   Tel 020-7928 1234
E-mail: jaravi@gujarat.co.uk
English/Gujarati/Urdu. Fortnightly.
Editor: R C Solanki

Asian Voice (Scotland)
51 Forth Street, Glasgow G41 2SP
Fax 0141-420 6833   Tel 0141-420 6811
Weekly
Editor: Ian Stewart

Awaaz Asian Voice
PO Box 15, Batley, West Yorkshire WF17 7YY
Fax 01924-510513   Tel 01924-510512
E-mail: awaaz@pop3.poptel.org.uk
Monthly, English/Gujarati/Urdu.
Editor: Maria Bottomley

Awaze Quam
5b, Booth Street, Smethwick, Birmingham B66 2PF
Fax 0121-555 6899   Tel 0121-555 5921
E-mail: 106004,1160@compuserve.com
Weekly.
Editor: Mr Grewal

Black Perspective
PO Box 246, London SE13 7DL
Fax 020-8692 6986   Tel 020-8692 6986
E-mail: editor@blackperspective.free-online.co.uk
Website: www.blackperspective.free-online.co.uk
Quarterly.

Caribbean Times
148 Cambridge Heath Road, London E1 5QJ
Fax 020-7702 7937   Tel 020-7702 8012
E-mail: name@eeye.demon.co.uk
Weekly.
Editor: Michael Eboda

Cineblitz
Dolphin Media, Spring Villa Road, Edgware HA8 7EB
Fax 020-8381 1177   Tel 020-8381 1166
Monthly, Indian cinema news.
Editor: Rita Mehta

Cipher
184 Bridgewater Road, Alperton, Middlesex HA0 1AR
Fax 020-8795 0502   Tel 020-8903 6350
E-mail: ciphermag@aol.com
Bimonthly.
Editor: Joan Smith

Cronica Latina
PO Box 1269, London SW9 9RN
Fax 020-7793 1743   Tel 020-7582 0943
Spanish monthly.
Editor: Juan Toledo

Cubi Si
Red Rose, 129 Seven Sisters Road, London N7 7QG
Fax 020-7561 0191   Tel 020-7263 6452
E-mail: cubasc@gn.apc.org.com
Quarterly magazine by the Cuban Solidarity Campaign.

Cypriots Review & Advertiser
Kinetic Business Centre, Theobald Street, Boreham
Wood, Herts WD6 4PJ
                        Tel 020-8953 9119
Weekly.

Daily Deshbarta
170 Brick Lane, London E1 6RU
Fax 020-7247 9299   Tel 020-7377 1584
Bengali.
Editor: Shariful Hasan Khan

Daily Jang
1 Sanctuary Street, London SE1 1ED
Fax 020-7378 1653   Tel 020-7403 5833
E-mail: jan@globalnet.co.uk
English and Urdu daily.
Editor: Zhoor Niazi

Daily Millat
2 Baynes Close, Enfield, Middlesex EN1 4BN
Fax 020-8367 6941   Tel 020-8366 5082
E-mail: MUS77SMI@aol.com
Press correspondent: S Mustafa

Des Pardes
8 The Crescent, Southall, Middlesex UB1 1BE
Fax 020-8571 2604   Tel 020-8571 1127
Weekly, news concerning Indian people, in Punjabi.
Editor: G Virk

The Diary
32 Bell Lane, London NW4 2AD
Fax 020-8922 5473   Tel 020-8922 5437
Monthly. Jewish listings.

The East
65 North Acton Road, London NW10 6PJ
Fax 020-8838 6122   Tel 020-8838 6300
Weekly.
Editor: Shahid Khan

Eastern Eye
148 Cambridge Heath Road, London E1 5QJ
Fax 020-7702 7937   Tel 020-7702 8012
E-mail: eeye@demon.co.uk
Weekly news for the Asian community.
Editor: Siddartha Shivdasani

Eikoku News Digest
8-10 Long Street, London E2 8HQ
Fax 020-7256 0363   Tel 020-7739 2802
Weekly news in Japanese.
Editor: Tokuko Hashimoto

EU Japan Business News
Unit 10, 1 Benjamin Street, London EC1M 5QL
Fax 020-7251 1493   Tel 020-7251 1492
Japanese quarterly.
Editor: Tomoo Oba

The Examiner
19 Angel Road, Harrow, Middlesex HA1 1JX
                        Tel 020-8520 8397
Irish news.
Editor: Aidan Hennigan

The Filipino
28 Brookside Road, London NW11 9NE
Fax: 020-8458 1055   Tel 020-8731 7195
E-mail: philmedia@avnet.co.uk
Bimonthly.   **Editor**: Mrs B Foronzan

Garavi Gujarat
1-2 Silex Street, London SE1 0DW
Fax 020-7261 0055   Tel 020-7928 1234
E-mail garavi@Gujaratdemon.co.uk
English/Gujarati. Bi-monthly.
Editor: R C Solanki

The Gleaner
220-223 Elephant & Castle, London SE1 6TE
Fax 020-7277 1734   Tel 020-7277 1714
Website: www.jamaica-gleaner.com
Weekly Jamaican and Caribbean news.
Editor: Colette Hibbert

Greek Review
59 Stroud Green Road, London N4 3EG
Fax 020-7272 7274   Tel 020-7272 2722
Monthly news in English.

Gujarat Samachar/Asian Voice/Asian Business
8-16 Coronet Street, London N1 6HD
Fax 020-7739 0358   Tel 020-7729 5453
Website: www.gujarat-samachor.com
Gujarati/English weekly.

Hurriyet
35 D'Arblay Street, London W1V 3FE
Fax 020-7287 3101   Tel 020-7734 1211
E-mail: zabaltd@.aol.com
Turkish daily.
Editor: Aysegul Richardson

Impact International
233 Seven Sisters Road, London N4 2BA
Fax 020-7272 8934   Tel 020-7263 1417
E-mail: impact@globalnet.co.uk
Fortnightly Muslim news.
Editor: Ahmad Irfan

India Abroad Newspaper
Flat 1, 2 Kendrick Place, London SW7 3HF
                              Tel 020-7581 5244
Editor: Sanjay Suri

India-Home and Abroad
1 Park Close, London NW2 6RQ
Fax 020-8452 4182   Tel 020-8452 4182
Quarterly.
Editor: K K Singh

India Link International
42 Farm Avenue, North Harrow, Middx HA2 7LR
Fax 020-8723 5250   Tel 020-8866 8421
Monthly.
Editor: Krishan Ralleigh

India Monitor
PO Box 25165, London SW1V 3WH
                              Tel 0956-568394
E-mail: MathurRak@aol.com
Website: www.ukindia.com
Editor: Rakesh Mathur

India Times
90 Ascot Gardens, Southall UB1 2SB
Fax 020-8575 7336   Tel 020-8575 0151
Weekly, Asian magazine.
Editor: Ram Kumar

India Today
13 John Princes Street, London W1
                              Tel 020-7493 0351

India Weekly
105 St John Street, London EC1M 4AS
Fax 020-7251 3289   Tel 020-7251 3290
E-mail: email@indiaweekly.co.uk
Website: www.indiaweekly.co.uk
Weekly.
Editor: Premen Addy

Indian Express
117 Fortress Road, London NW5 2HR
Fax 020-7428 9798   Tel 020-7428 9798
Editor: Shekar Gupta

Irish Independent
Vigilant House, 120 Wilton Road, London SW1V 1JZ
Fax 020-7808 7100   Tel 020-7353 4325
Editor: Bernard Purcell

Irish Post
Cambridge House,Cambridge Grove, London W6 0LE
Fax 020-8741 3382   Tel 020-8741 0649
E-mail: irishpost@irishpost.co.uk
Website: www.irishpost.co.uk
Weekly.
Editor: Norah Casey

Irish Times
76 Shoe Lane, London EC4A 3JB
Fax 020-7353 8670   Tel 020-7353 8970
Website: www.irish-times.com
Editor: Frank Millar

Irish World
934 North Circular Road, London NW2 7RJ
Fax 020-8208 1103   Tel 020-8453 7800
E-mail: the-editor@theirishworld.com
Website: www.theirishworld.com
Weekly.   Editor: Damien Gaffney

Janomot
Unit 2, 20b Spelman Street, London E1 5LQ
Fax 020-7247 0141   Tel 020-7377 6032
E-mail: janomot@easynet.co.uk
Bengali weekly.
Editor: Syed Samadul Haque

Jewish Chronicle
25 Furnival Street, London EC4A 1JT
Fax 020-7405 9040   Tel 020-7415 1616
E-mail: jcadmin@jchron.co.uk
Website: www.jchron.co.uk
Editor: Barry Toberman

Jewish Quarterly
PO Box 2078, London W1A 1JR
Fax 020-7629 5110   Tel 020-7629 5004
Culture and Jewish life. Editor: Matthew Reisz

Jewish Recorder
199 Pershore Road, Birmingham B5 7PF
                              Tel 0121-249 1997
Editor: Doctor S Abudarham

Jewish Tribune
95-97 Stamford Hill, London N16 5DN
Fax 020-8800 5000   Tel 020-8800 6688
Weekly.   Editor: J Bentov

The Journal
370 Cold Harbour Lane, London SW9 8PL
Fax 020-7733 7982   Tel 020-7738 7034
Editor: Mike Best

The Leader
2 Baynes Close, Enfield, Middlesex EN1 4BN
Fax 020-8367 6941   Tel 020-8366 5082
E-mail: MUS77SMI@aol.com
Editor: Syed Mustafa

London Irish Press
Unit 8, Concord Business Centre, London W3 0TR
Fax 020-8896 3654   Tel 020-8752 1202
Editor: Michael Hennessy

London Jewish News
28 St Albans Lane, London NW11 7QE
Fax 020-8731 8815   Tel 020-8731 8814
E-mail: news@lgn.co.uk
Fortnightly.
Editor: Stuart Brodkin

London/Midland/Northern Asian/Black African/Caribbean
10a Ellington Road, London E8 3PA
Fax 020-8525 1171   Tel 020-8985 4070
Quarterly.
Editor: Peter Patel

Mauritian International
PO Box 4100, London SW20 0XN
Fax 020-8947 1912   Tel 020-8947 1912
E-mail: jaclee@compuserve.com
Website: www.mauritiusworld.com
Quarterly.
Editor: Jacques K Lee

Mauritius News
583 Wandsworth Road, London SW8 3JD
Fax 020-7627 8939   Tel 020-7498 3066
E-mail: editor@mauritius-news.co.uk
Website: www.mauritius-news.co.uk
Monthly.
Editor: Peter Chellen

Melting Pot
PO Box 13258, London E1 2RR
Fax 020-8503 1555   Tel 020-8503 1414
Bi-monthly. Magazine for the multicultural society.

Milap Weekly
Masbro Centre, 87 Masbro Road, London W14 0LR
                        Tel: 020-7385 8966
Urdu weekly.   **Editor**: R Soni

The Muslim News
PO Box 380, Harrow, Middlesex HA2 6LL
Fax 020-7608 1232   Tel 020-7608 2822
E-mail: musnews@webstar.co.uk
Website: www.webstar.co.uk/~musnews
Monthly.
Editor: Ahmad J Versi

The Nation
96c Ilford Lane, Ilford, Essex IG1 2LD
Fax 020-8478 6200   Tel 020-8478 3200
E-mail: msarwar@thenation.demon.co.uk
Website: www.thenation.demon.co.uk
English/Urdu.
Editor Mr M Sarwar

Navin Weekly
Masbro Centre, 87 Masbro Rd, London W14 0LR
                        Tel: 020-7385 8966
Hindi weekly.
Editor: Ramesh Kumar

New Horizon
16 Grosvenor Crescent, London SW1X 7EP
Fax 020-7245 9769   Tel 020-7245 0404
E-mail icis@iibi.demon.co.uk
Website: www.islamic-banking.com
Monthly Muslim news, Islamic banking.
Editor: Ghazanfar Ali

New Impact Journal
Anser House, Courtyard Offices, 3 High Street,
Marlow, Bucks SL7 1AX
Fax 01628-475570   Tel 01628-481581
Website: www.newimpact.co.uk
Bi-monthly on "enterprise and diversity".
Editor: Elaine Sihera

New Nation
1st Floor, 148 Cambridge Heath Road, London E1 5QJ
Fax 020-7702 7937   Tel 020-7702 8012
Weekly.
Editor: Michael Eboda

New World
234 Holloway Road, London N7 8DA
Fax 020-7607 6706   Tel 020-7700 2673
Fortnightly news on local and international affairs.
Editor: Dhiren Basu

The News
Jang Publications, 1 Sanctuary Street, London SE1 1ED
Fax 020-7378 1653   Tel 020-7403 5833
Editor: Mr Z Niazi

Nigerian News
23 Aberdeen Court, Maida Vale, London W9 1AF
Fax 020-7266 4057   Tel 020-7266 4564
Fortnightly.
Editor: Olubiyi Ayodeji

North West Asian News
Observer Buildings, Drake Street, Rochdale OL16 1PH
Fax 020-7634 1595   Tel 020-7635 7086
Monthly.
Editor: Steve Hammond

Noticias Latin America
59 St Martin's Lane, London WC2N 4JS
Fax 020-7928 9858   Tel 020-7928 0315
E-mail: noticias@dial.pipex.com
Spanish language monthly.
Editor: Marcela Sariego

Notun Din
Room 5, Brady Centre, 192-196 Hanbury Street, London E1 5HU
Fax 020-7247 2280   Tel 020-7247 6280
E-mail: nd@nahas.demon.co.uk
Bengali, weekly.
Editor: M Chowdhury

Parikiaki
534a Holloway Road, London N7 6JP
Fax 020-7281 0127   Tel 020-7272 6777
Weekly, Greek.
Editor: George Georgiou

Perdesan Monthly
478 Lady Margaret Rd, Southall, Middlesex UB1 2NW
Fax 020-8575 8695   Tel 020-8573 8272
Monthly.
Editor: G K Bedi

Pride Magazine
Hamilton House, 55 Battersea Bridge Road, London SW11 3AX
Fax 020-7288 3130   Tel 020-7228 3110
E-mail: rachel@pridemagazine.com
Monthly for women of colour.
Editor: Dionne Sainthill

Probashi Samachar
20 Orchard Avenue, London N14 4ND
                        Tel 020-8886 4231
Bengali quarterly.   **Editor**: S Mazumdar

Punjab Mail International
66 Dames Road, London E7 0DR
Fax 020-8522 0901   Tel 020-8522 0901
Monthly magazine written in Punjabi and English "to promote culture and heritage".
Editor: Gurdip Singh Sandhu

Punjab Times International
24 Cotton Brook Road, Derby DE23 8YJ
Fax 01332 372833   Tel 01332 372851
E-mail: punjabtimes@aol.com
Weekly.
Editor: Harjinder Singh Mandair

The Punjabi Guardian
Soho News Building, 129 Soho Road, Handsworth, Birmingham B21 9ST
Fax 0121-507 1065   Tel 0121-554 3995
Monthly.
Editor: Inder Jit Singh Sandhu

Q News, The Muslim Magazinel
Dexion House, 2-4 Empire Way, Wembley HA9 0EF
Fax 020-8903 0820   Tel 020-8903 0819
E-mail: qnews@aapi.co.uk
Website: www.aapi.co.uk/q-news
News, views and reviews for British Muslims of all nationalities.
Fortnightly.
Editor: Fuad Nahdi

Ravi Asian News Weekly
Ravi House, Legrams Lane, Bradford BD7 1NH
Fax 01274-721227   Tel 01274-721227
Urdu weekly.
Editor: Farida Sheikh

Ri-ra Magazine
Cambridge House, Cambridge Grove, London W6 0LE
Fax 020-8741 3382   Tel 020-8741-0649
E-mail: ri-ra@ri-ra.com
Free magazine for London Irish.
Editor: Micheal Coughlan

Sada Urdu Monthly
PO Box 630, Croydon CR0 2WN
Fax 020-8251 8689   Tel 020-8684 9429
Editor: Athar Raz

Salaam!
Unit 6, 5 Rockware Avenue, Greenford UB6 0AA
Fax 020-8930 2066   Tel 020-8357 0056
Monthly.
Publisher: Khan Iqbal Khan

2nd Generation
Unit 401a, Mon Marche Centre, 444 Brixton Road, London SW9 8EJ
Fax 020-7924 9988   Tel 020-7924 9966
Bi-monthly.
Editor: Imran Khan

Shang Ye Xian Feng
194 Old Brompton Road, London SW5 0AW
Fax 020-7370 6245   Tel 020-7835 2183
E-mail: info@shangmagazine.com
Chinese bimonthly.
Editor: Emile Bekheit

The Sikh Courier International
88 Mollinson Way, Edgware, Middlesex HA8 5QW
Fax 020-8257 0359   Tel 020-8257 0359
Quarterly.
Editors: A S Chatwal

The Sikh Messenger
43 Dorset Road, London SW19 3EZ
Fax 020-8540 4148   Tel 020-8540 4148
Quarterly.
Editor: Indarjit Singh

Sing Tao (UK)
46 Dean Street, London W1V 5AP
Fax 020-7734 0828   Tel 020-7287 1525
E-mail: singtaoeu@yahoo.com
Website: www.singtaoeu.com
Chinese daily.
Editor: S T Wan

Spice Magazine
420 Kingstanding Road, Birmingham B44 9SA
Fax 0121-350 9618   Tel 0121-350 9190
E-mail: enquiries@spice-magazine.demon.co.uk
Website: www.spice-magazine.demon.co.uk
Monthly.
Editor: Parminder Garbha

Surma
40 Wessex Street, London E2 0LB
Fax 020-8981 8829   Tel 020-8980 5544
E-mail: surma@netmatters.co.uk
Bengali weekly.
Editor: M E H Chowdhury

Ta Nea
8-10 Stamford Hill, London N16 6XS
Fax 020-8806 0160   Tel 020-8806 0169
Fortnightly.
Editor: Louis Vrakas

Teamwork
5 Westminster Bridge Road, London SE1 7XW
Fax 020-7928 0343   Tel 020-7928 7861
E-mail: wiscorgan@aol.com
Bimonthly.
Editor: Mr W Trant

Times of India
54 Sydney Road, London W13
Fax 020-8840 3493   Tel 020-8840 3838
Representative: Umesh Chandrasekhar

Toplum Postasi
117 Green Lanes, London N16 9OA
Fax 020-7354 0313   Tel 020-7354 4424
E-mail: toplum.postasi@btinternet.com
Turkish weekly.
Editor: Artun Goksan

Touch Magazine
1st Floor, 51 Hoxton Square, London N1 6PB
Fax 020-7739 6504   Tel 020-7739 5727
E-mail: touchzine@aol.com
Monthly.   Editor: Vincent Jackson

Untold Magazine
Stratford Workshops, Burford Road, London E15 2SP
Fax 020-8739 6504   Tel 020-8519 1920
Bi-monthly.
Editor: Peter Akinti

La Voce Degli Italiani
20 Brixton Road, London SW9 6BU
Fax 020-7793 0385   Tel 020-7735 5164
E-mail ziliotto@dircon.co.uk
Fortnightly.
Editor: Giandomenico Ziliotto

The Voice
370 Coldharbour Lane, London SW9 8PL
Fax 020-7274 8994   Tel 020-7737 7377
E-mail: veeteea@gn.apc.org
Weekly for Black British.
Editor: Matthew Griffiths

Watan Weekend
Chamber Ho, 306-308a Hoe Street, London E17 9PX
Fax 020-8925 0446   Tel 020-8923 9222
E-mail: watan@wavenet.co.uk
Website: www.wavenet.co.uk/users/watan
Urdu.   **Editor:** Taj Javaid

Weekly Des Pardes
8 The Crescent, Southall, Middlesex UB1 1BE
Fax 020-8571 2604   Tel 020-8571 1127
Weekly, Punjabi.   **Editor:** Mr Virk

Weekly Potrika
218 Jubilee Street, London E1 3BS
Fax 020-7423 9122   Tel 020-7423 9270
Bengali, weekly.
Editor: Abdur Raqib

EHTNIC RADIO

Asian Sound Radio
Globe House, Southall Street, Manchester M3 1LG
Fax 0161-288 9000   Tel 0161-288 1000
Head of programmes: Shujat Ali

Choice FM
291-299 Borough High Street, London SE1 1JG
Fax 020-7378 3936   Tel 020-7378 3969
Programme director: Patrick Berry

Choice FM
95 Broad Street, Birmingham B15 1AU
Fax 0121-616 1011   Tel 0121-616 1000
Contact: Stuart Reed

Galaxy 105
Joseph's Well, Westgate, Leeds LS3 1AB
Fax 0113-213 1054   Tel 0113-213 1053
Contact: Nick Walshe

Kiss 100 FM
Kiss House, 80 Holloway Road, London N7 8JG
Fax 020-7700 3979   Tel 020-7700 6100
Programme director: Matthew Matthews

Kiss 102
PO Box 102, Manchester M60 1GJ
Fax 0161-228 1020   Tel 0161-226 3102

Kiss 105
Kiss House, Joseph's Well, Westgate, Leeds LS3 1AB
Fax 0113-213 1054   Tel 0113-213 1053
News editor: Pete Wilson

London Greek Radio
Florentia Village, Vale Road, London N4 1TD
Fax 020-8880 8005   Tel 020-8880 8001
Programme controller: G Gregoriou

London Turkish Radio
185b High Road, London N22 6BA
Fax 020-8881 5151   Tel 020-8881 0606
Programme controller: Umit Dandul

Radio Ceredigion
Yr Hen Ysgol Gymraeg, Fford Alexandra, Aberystwyth, Dyfed SY23 1LF
Fax 01970-627206   Tel 01970-627999
Programme controller: Geraint Lloyd

Radio XL
KMS House, Bradford Street, Birmingham B12 0JD
Fax 0121-753 3111   Tel 0121-753 5353
Programme director: Barry Curtis

Sabras Sound
Radio House, 63 Melton Road, Leicester LE4 6PN
Fax 0116-268 7776   Tel 0116-261 0666
Contact: Emma Carson

Spectrum Radio
204-206 Queenstown Road, London SW8 3NR
Fax 020-7627 3409   Tel 020-7627 4433
Contact: Wolfgang Bucci

Spectrum Chinese Programmes
PO Box 2JT, London W1A 2JT
Fax 020-7434 2836   Tel 020-7434 2835

Sunrise Radio
Merrick Road, Southall, Middlesex UB2 7AU
Fax 020-8893 5090   Tel 020-8893 5900
Chief executive: Avtar Lit

Sunrise Radio
Sunrise House, 30 Chapel Street, Bradford BD1 5DN
Fax 01274-728534   Tel 01274-306666
Programme controller: Ushar Parmar

ETHNIC TV STATIONS

Asia Net
Elliott House, Victoria Road, London NW10 6NY
Fax 020-8930 0546   Tel 020-8930 0930
Chief executive: Dr Barnard Viswanath

Asia Net TV
PO Box 38, Greenford, Middlesex UB6 7SP
Fax 020-8810 5555   Tel 020-8566 9000
Contact: Luxmi Ghosh

Chinese News & Entertainment
Marvic House, Bishops Road, London SW6 7AD
Fax 020-7610 3118   Tel 020-7610 3880
Editor: Poon Sui Mui

Helenic TV
50 Clarendon Road, London N8 0DJ
Fax 020-8292 7042   Tel 020-8292 7037
General manager: Takis Sellas

Middle East Broadcasting
80 Silverthorne Road, London SW8 3XA
Fax 020-7501 1231   Tel 020-7501 1253
Chief executive: Ali Al-Hadaithi

Zee TV
Unit 7, Belvue Business Centre, Belvue Road, Northolt UB5 5QQ
Fax 020-8841 9550   Tel 020-8841 5112
Contact: Anita Anand

Republic of Ireland media

Much Irish Republic media comes from overseas. Nearly half its television programmes originate in the UK, and a third of the Sunday papers plus half the dailies are based in London. There is, however, a thriving indigenous media which is most heavily Irish where it's for the best educated. A well educated readership in a booming economy ensures the Irish Independent and Irish Times do well, despite VAT and competition from cheaper British rivals. The two leading Irish broadsheets have a combined daily circulation of over 250,000 for a population of four million. Of the two, the Irish Independent has the bigger sale with a large farming readership making it the stronger outside Dublin. The Irish Times is close in spirit to the Guardian, for it too is liberal left, urban and owned by a trust.

Approximately one in 14 of Irish people buys a heavyweight daily, compared with one in 24 in the UK and - for another mark of a nation which takes its media seriously - the daily broadsheets outsell the tabloids. The tabloid part of the market belongs to UK interests, with a lightly regionalised Sun and Mirror and a radically reorganised Dublin-based Daily Star outselling Irish owned and produced rivals. The Sunday market is led by the Sunday Independent and the Sunday World with the Ireland on Sunday

gaining readers from the Sunday Independent. Next come Rupert Murdoch's News of the World and Sunday Times.

Tony O'Reilly, the ex-international rugby star and ex-Heinz star executive, owns Independent Newspapers which accounts for two thirds of Irish national morning and evening papers, 95 per cent of the home-produced Sundays, plus ten local papers with average sales of 10,000. This makes for a national press which is more heavily dominated by one owner than in any other liberal democracy. O'Reilly's reputation is based on marketing acumen and he made his commercial name by dispelling British prejudice about Irish food and making Kerrygold butter an acceptable brand name. Having taken control of the Independent and Independent on Sunday in London in March 1997, his business talent has been apparent in their turnaround in fortunes. His marketing reputation is now on the line with the extraordinary appointment of Janet Street-Porter as IoS editor in June 1999.

The demise of the Irish Press saw several old local newspapers fold in 1995. Other than that the market for locals is defined by longevity, stability and family ownership. In magazines, Magill and the satirical magazine Phoenix are must-reads. The RTÉ TV guide is the biggest

Irish national newspaper circulations

DAILIES	1988	1996	1997	1998
1 Irish Independent	153,054	158,712	160,137	163,967
2 Evening Herald	108,702	115,983	112,546	103,583
3 Irish Times	87,855	101,841 1	107,839	111,729
4 The Star	69.819	85,976	88,840	89,938
5 Examiner	58,227	55,194	56,628	60,173
6 Evening Echo	32,450	25,697	26,520	27,022
SUNDAYS				
1 Sunday World	360,138	296,085	307,162	312,402
2 Sunday Independent	230,794	339,501	327,153	310,505
3 Sunday Tribune	96,871	77,817	86,766	95,058
4 Ireland on Sunday			66,863	63,476
5 Sunday Business Press		37,429	43,698	47,232

Source: ABC

selling magazine and its listings have a British feel with TV listings including cabled transmissions of BBC 1 and 2, plus Channels 4 and 5 and Sky.

While there is little sale of Belfast papers in Dublin (and vice versa) there is a clear demand for cross border television with UTV being the state's de facto third channel. UTV - which now favours initial letters for its title instead of the more politically loaded Ulster TV - has over 10 per cent of the Republic's viewing figures and is in the unique position of having more viewers outside its franchise area than in. As in Britain, broadcasting is highly regulated. The 1960 Broadcasting Act established Radio Telefis Eireann (RTÉ) as a licence fee and advertising revenue hybrid. RTÉ runs two English language TV stations (RTÉ 1 and Network 2), three national English language radio stations (Radio 1, 2FM, FM 3), a Gaelic TV station (Teilifis Na Gaeilge or TNAG) and a Gaelic radio station (Raidio Na Gaeltachta). TV3 started broadcasting

late in 1998 as the first fully commercial Irish television station. Its major shareholder is CanWest, the Canadian cable and entertainment conglomerate company which is the world's biggest purchaser of Hollywood movies. CanWest also has a stake in UTV and its strategy is to build upon an island of Ireland commercial TV tradition.

Republic of Ireland radio divides into three sections: first, the state-owned radio channels from RTÉ; second, the commercial channels which are led by Today FM (formerly 100FM) plus over 20 local stations which came into existence after the 1988 Broadcasting Act; and thirdly, community radio for which the Independent Radio and Television Commission started awarding licences in spring 1998. As in Britain, commercial radio has proved successful and secured itself nearl half the listening market. The stations have far more talk than their UK counterparts and thus provide sought after political platforms.

UK newspaper circulations in the Republic of Ireland

DAILIES	Jul-Dec 96	Jul-Dec 97	Jul-Dec 98
1 Sun	89,942	75,522	92,694
2 Mirror	66,218	42,365	51,778
3 Daily Mail	4,497	6,127	7,268
4 Times	16,970	5,811	5,898
5 Financial Times	3,454	3,826	5,050
6 Express	4,017	4,307	3,854
7 Daily Telegraph	6,636	3,979	3,876
8 Guardian	4,974	3,015	3,157
9 Independent	4,405	2,307	2,085
10 Daily Record	1,480	1,189	1,418
SUNDAYS			
1 News of the World	181,038	153,532 -	164,833
2 Sunday Times	89,864	76,018	81,872
3 Sunday People	120,138	73,689	62,106
4 Sunday Mirror	88,188	46,783	43,586
5 Mail on Sunday	10,499	10,483	11,389
6 Express on Sunday	9,806	9,540	8,039
7 Observer	17,861	9,038	7,998
8 Independent on Sunday	13,527	7,049	6,033
9 Sunday Telegraph	8,166	4,370	3,837

Source: ABC

Share of TV audience

	1997	1998
RTE	34%	33%
Network 2	19%	18%
UTV/HTV	11%	10%
BBC1	10%	10%
C4/S4C	6%	6%
Sky1/Sky News		6%
BBC2	5%	4%
TnaG	1%	1%
Others	15%	10%

Source: AC Nielsen for 12 months to December 1998

Share of radio audience

	1997	1998
Independents	43%	43%
RTE Radio 1	31%	31%
2FM	22%	20%
Today FM	2%	6%

Adult listeners tuned in between 7am-7pm

Source: JNLR/MRBI

NATIONAL NEWSPAPERS

Evening Echo
Academy Street, Cork
Fax 00-353 21-275112 Tel 00-353 21-272722
Editor: Brian Feeney
Deputy editor: Maurice Gribbins
Arts editor: Declan Hassett
Features editor: Vincent Power
News editor: Ailin Quinlan
Picture editor: Brian Lougheed
Political editor: Liam O'Neill
Sports editor: Mark Woods
Advertisement manager: Paudraig Mallon
Head of marketing : Nigel O'Mahony
Owner: Examiner Publications

Evening Herald
Middle Abbey Street, Dublin 1
Fax 00-353 1-873 1787 Tel 00-353 1-873 1666
E-mail: herald.letters@independent.ie
Editor: Paul Drury
Deputy editor: Noirin Hegarty
Arts editor: Maurice Haugh
Features editor: David Robbins
Finance editor: Ken Curran
News editor: Martin Brennan
Picture editor: Liam Mulcahy
Political editor: Kate Hannon
Sports editor: David Courtney
Advertisement manager: Karen Preston
Marketing manager: Barry Brennan
Owner: Independent Newspapers (Ireland)

The Examiner
PO Box 21, Academy Street, Cork
Fax 00-353 21-275112 Tel 00-353 21-272722
Dublin office: 96 Lower Baggot Street, Dublin 2
Fax 00-353 1-661 2737 Tel 00-353 1-661 2733
Editor: Brian Looney
Associate editor (content): Tim Vaughan
Associate editor (design): Jack Power
Night editor: Ann Cahill
Arts editor: Declan Hassett
Features editor: Dan Buckley
Finance editor: Kevin Mills
News editor: Eamonn Timmins
Picture editor: Norma Cuddihy
Political editor: Liam O'Neill
Sports editor: Tony Leen
Head of advertising: Paudraig Mallon
Head of marketing: Nigel O'Mahony
Owner: Examiner Publications

Irish Independent
Middle Abbey Street, Dublin 1
Fax 00-353 1-873 1787 Tel 00-353 1-873 1333
Website: www.independent.ie
Editor: V Doyle
Deputy editor: Michael Wolsley
Arts editor: Tom Brady
Business editor: F Mulrennan
Features editor: John Spain
Finance editor: Brendan Keenan
News editor: P Molloy
Picture editor: Padraig Beirne
Political editor: Chris Glennon
Sport editor: PJ Cunningham
Advertisement manager: Brendan McCabe
Marketing manager: Barry Brennan
Owner: Independent Newspapers (Ireland)

The Irish Times
PO Box 74, 11-15 D'Olier Street, Dublin 2
Fax 00-353 1-677 2130 Tel 00-353 1-679 2022
E mail: postmaster@irish-times.ie
lettersed@irish-times.com
Website: www.irish-times.com
Editor: Conor Brady
Managing editors: Pat O'Hara, Eoin McVey
Arts editor: Victoria White
Chief news editor: Don Buckley
Finance editor: Cliff Taylor
Features editor: Sheila Wayman
Foreign editor: Paul Gillespie
News editor: Niall Kiely
Night editors: John Armstrong, Eugene McEldowney
Picture editor: Dermot O'Shea
Political editor: Geraldine Kennedy
Sports editor: Malachy Logan
Sales manager: Maeve Donovan
Chief executive: Louis O'Neill
Owner: Irish Times Trust

The Star
62A Terenure Road North, Dublin 6W
Fax 00-353 1-490 2193   Tel 00-353 1-490 1228
E mail: news@the-star.ie
Editor: Gerard O'Regan
Deputy editor: Danny Smyth
Features editor: Danny Smyth
Finance editor: F McMillan
News editor: D O'Connell
Picture editor: Bernard Phelan
Political editor: John Donlon
Sports editor: Des Gibson
Advertising manager: Ken Grace
Marketing manager: Conner Mahon
Owner: Irish Independent

SUNDAY NEWSPAPERS

Ireland on Sunday
50 City Quay, Dublin 2
Fax 00-353 1-671 8882 Tel 00-353 1-671 8255
E mail: news@ios.iol.ie
Editors: Liam Hayes, Cathal Dervan
Features editor: Fiona Ryan
Finance & business editor: Dara Doyle
News editor: Michael Clifford
Picture editor: Fiomuala McCarthy
Political editors: Mairead Karey, Ken Wheelan
Sports editor: Cathal Dervan
Advertising & marketing manager: Kari Louwrens
Owner: Title Media

Sunday Business Post
80 Harcourt Street, Dublin 2
Fax 00-353 1-679 6496 Tel 00-353 1-679 9777
E-mail: sbpost@iol.ie
Website: www.sbpost.ie
Editor: Damien Kiberd
Deputy editor: Aileen O'Toole
Arts & features editor: Darie O'Brien
Finance editor: Ruth Marchard
News editor: Aileen O'Toole
Picture editor: Brian Walshe
Political editor: Mark O;Connell
Advertising manager: Deidre Hughes
Marketing manager: Fiachra O'Riordan

Sunday Independent
Middle Abbey Street, Dublin 1
Fax 00-353 1-873 1787 Tel 00-353 1-873 1333
E-mail: sunday.letters@independent.ie
Website: www.independent.ie
Editor: Aengus Fanning
Deputy editor: Anne Harris
Arts editor: Ronan Farren
Features editor: Anne Harris
Finance editor: Shane Ross
News editor: Willie Kealy
Deputy news editor: Liam Collins
Picture editor: Brian Farrell
Political editor: Joseph O'Malley
Sports editor: Adhmhain O'Sullivan
Owner: Independent Newspapers (Ireland)

Sunday Tribune
15 Lower Baggot Street, Dublin 2
Fax 00-353 1-661 5302 Tel 00-353 1-661 5555
E-mail: news@tribune.ie
Website: www.tribune.ie-classroom
Editor: Matt Cooper
Deputy editor: Paddy Murray
Arts editor: Cieran Carty
Business editor: Brian Carey
Features editor: Rosaline Dee
News & finance editor: Miriam Dionhoe
Northern editor: Ed Moloney
Political correspondent: Stephen Collins
Sports editor: Paul Howard

Sunday World
Newspaper House, Rathfarnham Road, Dublin 6
Fax 00-353 1-490 1838 Tel 00-353 1-490 1980
Editor: Colm MacGinty
Deputy editor: J P Thompson
Deputy editor (content): John Sheils
Arts editor: Val Sheehan
Features editor: John Sheils
Finance editor: Aileen Hickie
News & political editor: Sean Boyne
Picture editor: Val Sheehan
Sports director: Pat Quigley
Advertising manager: Gerry Lennon
Marketing manager: Joey McGettigan
Owner: Sunday Newspapers

IRISH MAGAZINES
When phoning from the UK, Republic of Ireland telephone numbers begin: oo-353

A
Accountancy Ireland	1-668 0400
Administration	1-269 7011
Afloat Magazine	1-284 6161
Aisling Magazine, The	99-61245
Amnesty International	1-677 6361
AMT Magazine	1284 7777
Arena	1661-5588
Aspect	1-676 0774
Astronomy & Space	1-459 8883

B
Bakery World	1-280 0000
Big Issue, The	1-855 3969
Books Ireland	1-269 2185
An Bord Altranais News	1-676 0226
Bulletin	1-838 4167
Business & Finance	1-676 4587
Business Contact	1-855 0477
Buy & Sell	1-6080707

C
Car Driver Magazine	1-2600899
Cara	1-662 3158
Catholic Standard	1-8555619
Celtic Journey	1-296 0000
Checkout Magazine	1-280 2933
CIF Blue Pages	1-667-2885

CIRCA Art Magazine	1-676 5035
CIS Report	1-668 9494
Clar na nOg	1-478 4122
Comhar	1-678 5443
Commercial Law Practitioner	1-873 0101
Communications Today	1-284 7777
Communications Worker	1-836 6388
ComputerScope	1-830 3455
Construction	1-671 9244
Consumer Choice	1-668 6836
An Cosantoir	1-804 2690
CPA Journal of Accountancy	1-676 7353
Cuba Today	1-676 1213

IRISH MAGAZINES

D

Decision 1-283 6466
Doctor Desk Book
1-492 4034

E

Economic & Social Review
1-667 1525
Economic Series 1-661 3111
Education Today 1-872 2533
Employment Law Reports
1-873 0101
Engineers Journal 1-855 0477
Environmental Management
Ireland 1-872 0734

F

Feasta 1-475 7401
Finance 1-660 6222
Finance Dublin 1-660 6222
Forum 1-280 3967
Futura 1-283 6782

G

Gaelic Sport 1-837 4311
Gaelic World 1-679 8655
Gaelsport Magazine
1-478 4322
Garda Review 1-830 3533
Gay Community News
1-671 9076
Golfers Companion
1-2804077
Grocer's Magazine 1-2809466
Guidelines 1-676 1975

H

Health & Safety 1-671 3500
Health Service News
1-668 6233
History Ireland 1-453 5730
Hot Press 1-679 5077
Hotel & Catering Review
1-280 0000

I

IMAGE 1-280 8415
IMPACT News 1-855 0873
In Dublin 1-478 4322
Industrial Relations News Report
1-497 2711
Industry & Commerce
1-671 3500
Inside Business 1-855 0477
Inside Ireland 1-493 1906
Insight Magazine 1-205 7200
IPA Journal 1-671 3500

IPU Review 1-493 1801
Ireland of the Welcomes
1-602 4000
Ireland's Eye 44-48868
Ireland's Own 53-22155
Iris Oifigiuil 1-661 3111

Irish Architect 1-295 8115
Irish Banking Review, The
1-671 5299
Irish Building Services News
1-288 5001
Irish Catholic 1-8555169
Irish Criminal Law Journal
1-873 0101
Irish Current Law Monthly Digest
1-873 0101
Irish Dental Association, Journal of
1-283 0496
Irish Electrical Review
1-283 6755
Irish Emigrant, The 91-569158
Irish Farmers' Journal
1-450 1166
Irish Farmers' Monthly
1-289 3305
Irish Field, The 1-679 2022
Irish Food 1-289 3305
Irish Geography 1-708 3938
Irish Hardware Magazine
1-280 0000
Irish Homes Magazine
1-878 0444
Irish Journal of European Law
1-873 0101
Irish Marketing Journal
1-295 0088
Irish Medical Journal
1-676 7273
Irish Medical News 1-296 0000
Irish Medical Times1-4757461
Irish Pharmacy Journal
1-660 0551
Irish Racing Calender 45-441599
Irish Skipper, The 1-296 0000
Irish Social Worker 1-677 4838
Irish Travel Trade News
1-450 2422
IT 1-6623158

J

Journal, The 1-478 4141

L

LAN 1-872 0734
Law Society Gazette
1-671 0711
Licensing World 1-280 0000
Local Authority Times
1-668 6233

M

Marketing 1-280 7735
Medico-Legal Journal of Ireland
1-873 0101
Motoring Life 1-878 0444

N

New Music News 1-661 2105
Newmarket Business Report
1-668 9494
NODE News 1-475 1998
North County Leader
1-840 0200

O

Off Licence 1-280 0000

P

PC Live! 1-830 3455
Phoenix 1-661 1062
Plan-The Business of Building
1-295 8115
Poetry Ireland Review
1-671 4632
Provincial Farmer 46-21442
Public Sector Times
1-286 9111
Public Service Review
1-676 7271

R

Retail News 1-671 9244
RTE Guide 1-208 3111
Running Your Business
1-296 2244
Runway Airports 1-704 4170

S

Saol na nOilean 99-75096
Shelflife 1-284 7777
Socialist Voice 1-671 1943
Sporting Press 52-21422
Sportsworld 1-878 0444

T

Taxi News 1-855 5682
Technology Ireland
1-808 2287
Tillage Farmer, The
503-31487
Today's Farm 1-668 8188
Trade-Links Journal
1-454 2717
Tuarascail 1-872 2533

U

U Magazine 1-662 3158
Unity 1-671 1943
Updata 1-872 8800

V

Visitor 1-296 0000

W

WHERE Killarney 64-31108
Wicklow Times 1-286 9111
Wings 1-280 4322
Woman's Way 1-662 3158

LOCAL PAPERS

CAVAN
The Anglo-Celt Weekly w
00-353-49-31100

CARLOW
Nationalist and Leinster Times w
00-353-503-31731
The Carlow People w
00-353-503-41877

CLARE
Clare Champion w
00-353-65-28105

CORK
The Corkman w
00-353-66-21666
Southern Star w
00-353-28-21200

DONEGAL
Derry People and Donegal News w
00-353-74-21014
Donegal Democrat w
00-353-72-51201
Donegal People's Press w
00-353-74-28000

CO. DUBLIN
Inner City News f 6xpa
00-353-1-836 3832
Local News Publications
00-353-1-453 4011

GALWAY
The Connacht Sentinel w
00-353-91-567251
The Connacht Tribune w
00-353-91-567251
Galway Advertiser w
00-353-91-567077
Tuam Herald w
00-353-93-24183

KERRY
The Kerryman w
00-353-66 21666
Kerry's Eye w
00-353-66-23199

KILDARE
Kildare Nationalist
00-353-45-432147
Leinster Leader w
00-353-45-897302
Liffey Champion
00-353-1-624 5533

KILKENNY
Kilkenny People w
00-353-56-21015

LEITRIM
Leitrim Observer w
00-353-78-20025

LEIX
Laois Nationalist w
00-353-502-60265
Leinster Express w
00-353-502-21666

LIMERICK
Limerick Chronicle w
00-353-61-315233
Limerick Leader 4xw
00-353-61-315233
Limerick Post
00-353-61-413322

LONGFORD
The Longford Leader w
00-353-43-45241
Longford News w
00-353-43-46342

LOUTH
Drogheda Independent w
00-353-41-38658
Dundalk Democrat w
00-353-42-34058

MAYO
Connaught Telegraph w
00-353-94-21711
Mayo News w
00-353-98-25311
The Western People w
00-353-96-21188

MEATH
Meath Chronicle w
00-353-46-21442
Cavan and Westmeath Herald w
00-353-46-21442
Meath Topic w
00-353-44-48868

MONAGHAN
Northern Standard w
00-353-47-81867

OFFALY
The Midland Tribune w
00-353-509-20003
Offaly Express w
00-353-506-21744
Offaly Topic w
00-353-506-41182
Tullamore Tribune w
00-353-506-21152

ROSCOMMON
Roscommon Champion w
00-353-903-25051
Roscomon Herald w
00-353-79-62622

SLIGO
Sligo Weekender
00-353-71-42140

TIPPERARY
Nationalist Newspaper w
00-353-52-22211
Nationalist & Munster Advertiser
00-353-52-22211
Nenagh Guardian w
00-353-67-31214
Tipperary Star w
00-353-504-21122

WATERFORD
Dungarvan Leader and Southern Democrat w
00-353-58-41203
Dungarvan Observer and Munster Industrial Advocate w
00-353-58-41205
The Munster Express wx2
00-353-51-872141
Waterford News & Star e
00-353-51-874951

WESTMEATH
The Westmeath Examiner w
00-353-44-48426
Westmeath Independent
00-353-902-72003
Westmeath Topic w
00-353-44 48868

WEXFORD
The Echo w
00-353-54-33231
Enniscorthy Guardian w
00-353-53-22155
Gorey Echo w
00-353-54-33231
The Guardian w
00-353-54-33833
New Ross Echo w
00-353-54-33231
New Ross Standard
00-353-514-21184
The People w
00-353-53-22155
Wexford Echo w
00-353-54-33231

WICKLOW
Wicklow People w
00-353-404-67198
Bray People w
00-353-1-286 7393

IRISH TELEVISION

RTE - Radio Telefis Eireann
Donnybrook, Dublin 4
Fax 00-353 1-208 3080 Tel 00-353 1-208 3111
Website: www.rte.ie
RTE is the Irish national broadcasting organisation. It is a statutory corporation, created under the Broadcsting Authority Act, 1960. There are separate but interlinked divisions catering for radio and television programmes, news, engineering, sales and marketing, personnel, finance and public affairs. RTE's expenditure is funded from television licence fee income and from commercial revenue.
Director-general: Bob Collins
MD - organisation and development: Liam Miller
Managing director - television: Joe Mulholland
Managing director - commercial: Conor Sexton
Director of radio: Helen Shaw
Director of news: Edward Mulhall
Director of finance: Gerard O'Brien
Director of public affairs: Kevin Healy
Director of corporate affairs/secretary: Tom Quinn

Province 5 Television
Clogherboy House, Commons Road, Navan, Co Meath
Fax 00-353 46-27880   Tel 00-353 46-27880
Province 5 Television is a voluntary orgarnisation and is Ireland's only community television station. It operates under Cable Management in the Meath and north Dublin area. It provides 12 hours of local television and a 24 hour 7 day text service. The station is funded by sponsorship and fund-raising activities.
Station director: Kevin Mac Namidhe

TV3
Westgate Business Park, Ballymount, Dublin 24
Fax 00-353 1-419 3317 Tel 00-353 1-419 3333
TV3 is Ireland's first independent national broadcaster. TV3 began broadcasting in September 1998 as an advertiser supported, national, free-to-air, entertainment and information service. TV3 is a full service broadcast network, providing news and information, sport, entertainment, comedy, movies, drama, documentaries and children's programming.
Chief exec/Managing director: Rick Hetherington
Chief financial officer: Ken Scott
Director of programming: Michael Murphy
Director of news: Andrew Hanlon
Director of sales: Pat Kiely
Director of operations: Peter Ennis

RADIO

3R Productions
36 Lower Leeson Street, Dublin 2
Fax 00-353 1-676 2984   Tel 00-353 1-676 8408
96 FM
Broadcasting House, Patrick's Place, Cork
Fax 00-353 21-551500 Tel 00-353 21-551596
E-mail: opinion@96fm.ie
Website: www.96fm.ie
103 FM
Mallow, Co Cork
Fax 00-353 22-42488   Tel 00-353 22-42430
103FM
Bandon, co Cork
Fax 00-353 23-44294   Tel 00-353 23-43103
Anna Livia FM
Griffith College, South Circular Road, Dublin 8
Fax 00-353 1-473 4445 Tel 00-353 1-677 8103
Area: Dublin   **Dial:** 103.8FM
Atlantic 252
Radio Tara, Mornington House, Summerhill Road, Trim, co Meath
Fax 00 353 46-36644   Tel 00 353 46-36655
E-mail: studio@atlantic252.com
Website: www.atlantic252.com
CKR FM-Carlow Kildare Radio
Lismard House, Tullow Street, Carlow
Fax 00-353 503-41047 Tel 00-353 503-41044
ACC House, 51 South Main Street, Naas, Co Kildare
Fax 00-353 45-897611 Tel 00-353 45-879666
Area: Leinster   **Dial:** 97.3FM, 97.6FM 107.4FM
Clare FM
The Abbeyfield Centre, Francis Street, Ennis, Co Clare
Fax 00-353 65-29392   Tel 00-353 65-28888
Classic Hits 98 FM
The Malt House, Grand Canal Quay, Dublin 2
Fax 00-353 1-670 8969 Tel 00-353 1-670 8970
Website: www.98fm.ie
Community Radio Castlebar
Market Square, Castlebar, Co Mayo
Fax 00-353 94-25989   Tel 00-353 94 25555
Area: Castlebar   **Dial:** 102.9 FM
Community Radio Youghal
League of the Cross Hall, Catherine Street, Youghal, Co Cork
Fax 00-353 24-91199   Tel 00-353 24-91199
E-mail: ycradio@iol.ie
Website: www.iol.ie/~ycradio
Area: Youghal   **Dial:** 105.1 FM
Connemara Community Radio
Connemara West Centre, Letterfrack, co Galway
Fax 00-353 95-41628   Tel 00-353 95- 41616
Area: North west Connemara **Dial:** 106.1 FM, 87.8 FM
Cork Campus Radio
Level 3, Aras na MacLeinn, UCC, Cork
Fax 00-353 21-903108 Tel 00-353 21-902008
E-mail: radio@ucc.ie
Website: www.ucc.ie/ccr/
Area: Cork city   **Dial:** 97.4 FM

Donegal Highland Radio
Pinehill, Letterkenny, Co Donegal
Fax 00-353 74-25344   Tel 00-353 74-25000
E-mail: highland@infowing.ie
Website: www.infowing.ie-donegal

Dublin South Community Radio
Old School, Loreto Avenue, Rathfarnham, Dublin 14
Fax 00-353 1-493 0520 Tel 00-353 1-493 0377
Area: Dublin S, Dun Laoghaire W   Dial: 104.9 FM

Dublin Weekend Radio
Dublin City University, Glasnevin, Dublin 11
Fax 00-353 1-704 5968 Tel 00-353 1-704 5203
Area: Dublin city and county   Dial: 102.2 FM

East Coast Radio
9 Prince of Wales Terrace, Bray, Co Wicklow
Fax 00-353 1-286 1219 Tel 00-353 1-286 6414
E-mail: seanashmore@eatcoastradio.fm
Website: www.eastcoastradio.net

Flirt FM
c/o The Porter's Desk, Concourse, NUI, Galway
Fax 00-353 91-525700 Tel 00-353 91-750445
Area: Galway city   Dial: 105.6 FM

FM 104
3rd Floor, Hume House, Pembroke Road, Dublin 2
Fax 00-353 1-668 9401 Tel 00-353 1-668 9689
E-mail: sinead@fm104.ie
Website: www.fm104.ie

Galway Bay FM
Sandy Road, Galway
Fax 00-353 91-752689 Tel 00-353 91-770000
E-mail: gbfm@glaway.net
Website: www.gbfm.galway.net
Area: Galway   Dial: 95.8, 96.0, 96.8, 97.4 FM

Independent Network News
62 Lower Mount Street, Dublin 2
Fax 00-353 1-662 9556 Tel 00-353 1-662 9563

Limerick 95
Norwich Union Buildings, 17 Patrick Street, Limerick
Fax 00-353 61-419890 Tel 00-353 61-319595
E-mail: radiol@tinet.ie

LMFM Radio
Boyne Centre, Drogheda, Co Louth
Fax 00-353 41-32957   Tel 00-353 41 32000
E-mail: info@lmfm.tinet.ie

Long Wave Radio Atlantic 252
Mornington House, Summmerhill Road, Trim, Co Meath
Fax 00-353 46 36644   Tel 00-353 46 36655
E-mail: studios@atlantic252.com
Webiste: www.atlantic252.com

Mid and North West Radio
Abbey Street, Ballyhsunis, Co Mayo
Fax 00-353 907-30285 Tel 00-353 907-30553
E-mail: mwr@iol.ie
Area: Connaught, Donegal

Midlands Radio 3
the Mall, William Street, Tullamore, Co Offaly
Fax 00-353 506-52546 Tel 00-353 506-51333
E-mail: mr3@iol.ie
Area: Westmeath, Laois, Offaly

N.E.A.R 101.6FM
The Development Centre, Bunratty Drive, Dublin 17
Fax 00-353 1-848 6111 Tel 00-353 1-848 5211
Area: North east Dublin   Dial: 101.6 FM

Radio County Sound
Broadcast House, Patricks Place, Cork, Co Cork
Fax 00-353 21-551500 Tel 00-353 21-551596
E-mail: opinion@96fm.ie
Website: www.96fm.ie
Area: Cork city and county   Dial: 96-103FM

Radio Kilkenny
Hebron Road, Kilkenny
Fax 00-353 56-63586   Tel 00-353 56-61577
E-mail: onair@radiokilkenny.tinet.ie
Area: Kilkenny city/county   Dial: 96.6, 96, 106.3 FM

Radio Kerry
Maine Street, Tralee, Co Kerry
Fax 00-353 66-7122282   Tel 00-353 66-7123666
Area: Kerry and SW   Dial: 97, 97.6, 96.2, 96.6 FM

Radio Telefis Eireann
Donnybrook, Dublin 4
Fax 00-353 1-208 3080 Tel 00-353 1-208 3111
Website: www.rte.ie.radio

Radio na Gaeltachta
Cashla, Co Galway
Fax 00-353 91-506666 Tel 00-353 91-506677
Area: National   Dial: 92-94 agus, 102.7 FM

Radio na Life 102 FM
7 Merrion Square, Dublin 2
Fax 00-353 1-676 3966 Tel 00-353 1-661 6333
E-mail: rnl102@iol.ie
Website: www.iol.ie-~rnl102

South East Radio
Custom House Quay, Wexford
Fax 00-353 53-45295   Tel 00-353 53-45200
E-mail: wexford@iol.ie
Website: www.southeastradio.ie

Tipp FM
Co Tipperary Radio, Davis Road, Clonmel, Co Tipperary
Fax 00-353 52-25447   Tel 00-353 52-25299
E-mail: brettm@indigo.ie
Area: Tipperary   Dial: 97.1 FM, 103.9FM

Tipperary Mid-West Radio
St Michael's Street, Tipperary Town
Fax 00-353 62-52671   Tel 00-353 62-52555
E-mail: 1tipperarymidwest@tinet.ie
Dial: 104.8 FM

West Dublin Community Radio
Ballyfermot Road, Dublin 10
Fax 00-353 1-626 1167 Tel 00-353 1-626 1160
Area: Dublin west   Dial: 104.9 & 96 FM

Wired FM
c/o Mary Immaculate College, South Circular Road, Limerick
Fax 00-353 61-315776 Tel 00-353 61-315103
E-mail: wiredFM@mic.ul.ie
Area: Limerick city   Dial: 96.8 FM

WLR FM
The Radio Centre, George's Street, Waterford
Fax 00-353 51 856731 Tel 00-353 584 3951
Website: www.wlr.tinet.ie

SUPPORT ORGANISATIONS

Association of Advertisers in Ireland
Rock House, Main Street, Blackrock, Dublin
Fax 00-353 1-278 0488 Tel 00-353 1-278 0499
Advisory and information service for advertisers, to
ensure the highest ethical standards.
Broadcasting Complaints Commission
PO Box 913, Dublin 2
                                Tel 00-353 676 7571
The Broadcasting Complaints Commission was
established in 1977. The objectives of the comission are
to deal with complaints relating to news, current affairs,
ministerial prohibitions, invasion of privacy, advertising
and published matters broadcast by RTE and local radio
stations.
Cable Link
10 Pembroke Place, Dublin 4
Fax 00 353 668 6766   Tel 00-353 1-799 8400
Website: www.cablelink.ie
**The Independent Radio and Television
  Commission**
Marine House, Clanwilliam Place, Dublin 2
Fax 00-353 1-676 0948 Tel 00-353 1-676 0966
Website: www.irtc.ie
The objectives of the Independent Radio and Television
Commission (IRTC) are to ensure the creation, and
monitoring of independent broadcasting. There are 21
local/regional stations operating in the country as well
as a community/special interest radio station and an
Irish language radio station in the Dublin area.
Working with the stations' management, the IRTC
seeks to ensure compliance with the laws of the land
and the maintenance of broadcasting and advertising
standards. The IRTC is a self-financing agency, drawing
its income from the levies paid by franchised stations.
**Institute of Advertising Practioners
  in Ireland**
8 Upper Fitzwilliam Street, Dublin 2
Fax 00-353 1-661 4589 Tel 00-353 1-676 5991
E-mail: info@iapi.com
Website: www.iapi.ie
Professional body representing advertising agencies,
providing a members advisory and information service.
Available to non-members.
Public Relations Institute of Ireland
62 Merrion Square, Dublin 2
Fax 00-353 1-6764562 Tel 00-353 1-6618004
E-mail: prii@iol.ie
Website: www.prii.ie
Publicity Club of Ireland
c/o Jemma Publications, Marino House, 52 Glasthule
Road, Sandycove, Co Dublin
Fax 00-353 1-280 1818 Tel 00-353 1-280 0000
E-mail: bmcIntyr@NCIR.ie
Regional Newspapers Advertising Network
33 Parkgate Street, Dublin 8
Fax 00-353 1-677 9144 Tel 00-353 1-677 9049
E-mail: info@rnan.ie

**Regional Newspapers Association of
  Ireland**
33 Parkgate Street, Dublin 8
Fax 00-353 1-677 9144 Tel 00-353 1-677 9049
E-mail: info@rnan.ie
Windmill Lane Pictures
4 Windmill Lane, Dublin 2
Fax 00-353 1-671 8413 Tel 00-353 1-671 3444
E-mail: info@windmilllane.com
Ireland's leading independent television facility and
interactive media company.

NEWS AGENCIES

AP-Dow Jones News Wires
Longphort House, Earlsfort Centre, Dublin 2
Fax 00-353 1-676 2189 Tel 00-353 1-662 1389
E-mail: dmarks@ap.org
BBC Dublin Office
36 Molesworth Place, Dublin 2
Shane Harrison
Fax 00-353 1-662 5712 Tel 00-353 1-662 5500
Belfast Telegraph Press Office
156 Vernon Avenue, Clontarf, Dublin 3
Fax 00-353 1-833 3771 Tel 00-353 1-833 3771
Financial Times
20 Upper Merrion Street, Dublin 2
Fax 00-353 1-676 2125   Tel 00-353 1-676 2071
The Independent (London)
90 Middle Abbey Street, Dublin 1
Fax 00-353 1-705 5792 Tel 00-353 1-705 5710
E-mail: independent.news@independent.ie
Website: www.independent.ie
Independent Network News (INN)
62 Lower Mount Street, Dublin 2
                                Tel 00-353 1-662 9555
National news syndicate for local radio stations.
Ireland International News Agency
51 Wellington Quay, Dublin 2
Fax 00-353 1-679 6586 Tel 00-353 1-671 2442
E-mail: iina@indigo.ie
PA News
41 Silchester Road, Glenageary, co Dublin
Fax 00-353 1-280 4221   Tel 00-353 1-280 0936
Reuters Ireland
Kestrel House, Clanwilliam Place, Lower Mount Street
Dublin 2
Fax 00-353 1-676 9783   Tel 00-353 1-661 3377
E-mail: reuters.ireland@reuters.iol.ie

DIGITAL
PHOTOGRAPHY
HOW TO CAPTURE,
MANIPULATE AND'
OUTPUT IMAGES

Still the best guide on the market
For express mail order
telephone 01483 268 888

A **Guardian Book**

PUBLISHED BY FOURTH ESTATE AT £15.99

Department for Culture, Media & Sport

The Department for Culture, Media and Sport has kept on going with a media policy which, apart from matters digital, is laid back to the point of anonymity.

As far as the press goes, DCMS has merely reiterated the line that effective self-regulation is preferable to statutory control or a law of privacy. Of non-digital broadcasting, the DCMS 1999 annual report gave itself a pat on the back for: extending the list of protected events that must be shown on free-to-air television; phasing out the Channel 4 funding formula so that more money is available for domestic programmes and film-making; and establishing the Gavyn Davies review panel to consider the future funding of the BBC. The panel's recommendations will influence a decision about the BBC licence fee to 2007. Tthe other piece of news to look for in 2000 is a joint DCMS and Department of Trade proposal for new broadcasting and communications regulation.

Which leaves digital broadcasting where the DCMS approach is as follows: "Digital broadcasting will increase the level of choice for the consumer, provide opportunities for new broadcasters to enter the market, and enable more efficient use of the UK's broadcasting spectrum." The annual report lists digital first and promises - or warns - that: "The government wants to announce a switch-off date for analogue services as soon as is practicable."

Department for Culture, Media and Sport
2-4 Cockspur Street, London SW1Y 5DH
DCMS: main number   020-7211 6000
Website   www.culture.gov.uk
Public enquiries   020-7211 6200
Secretary of State: Chris Smith
Ministers for: Art: Alan Howarth
Film, Tourism, Broadcasting: Janet Anderson
Sport: Kate Hoey

DCMS press office:
Fax 020-7211 6270   Tel 020-7211 6269/6267
Head of division:
Melanie Leech   020-7211 6463
General policy branch
(includes broadcasting appointments, BSC and broadcasting standards, sports rights):
Harry Reeves   020-7211 6461
International policy branch:
Carolyn Morrison   020-7211 6444
Commercial broadcasting branch :
Abigail Thomas: 020-7211 6456
Pubic service broadcasting:
Paul Heron   020-7211 6468
Head of media division:
Janet Evans   020-7211 6424
Policy on press freedom & regulation, cross media ownership:
Mark McGann   020-7211 6432
Films branch, UK film industry and film culture:
Alan Sutherland   020-7211 6447
National film and television school, film industry training, British Film Commission, media & media programmes:
Jon Zeff   020-7211 6434

OFFICIAL MEDIA GUIDES

Department for Culture Media and Sport 1999 Annual Report
The government's expenditure plans for the Department of National Heritage, the Office of the National Lottery and the Charity Commission.
Media Ownership Regulations
Details of the 1996 Broadcasting Act cross media ownership rules with definitions of control of an enterprise.
Digital Broadcasting
Licencing arrangements and the role of the multiplex provider.
The latter two are available on the Internet at:
http://www.heritage.gov.uk

Freedom of Information

This is not a press fight for private profit," said the ex-Sunday Times editor Harold Evans. "It is everyone's fight." He was commenting on how the May 1999 Freedom of Information bill fell short of what was implied in the 1998 white paper.

While the bill promises a freedom of information ombudsman and offers new legal rights of access to mounds of official paperwork, it changed an earlier government suggestion (made by the sacked junior minister David Clark) that "substantial harm" should be the test for maintaining secrecy. Instead it summoned the more catch-all notion that public bodies need only cite "prejudice" to conceal information and proposed that any legal right to know will be fettered by some 20 exemptions, 20 areas for maintaining a government right to secrecy.

The exemptions include: all work done by MI5, MI6 and GCHQ; defence, communications with the royal family; political advice; international relations; dealings between the new national parliaments; the economy; court records; commercial and personal information supplied do the government in confidence; and police investigations. Thus, for one recent example, much salient information about the bungled investigation into Stephen Lawrence's murder would remain secret.

The government - its arteries of liberal-mindedness hardened by the experience of power - faced a barrage of criticism, including a few off-message Labour MPs. Mark Fisher, the sacked arts minister, called the bill "deeply flawed". Llew Smith, Labour MP for Blaenau Gwent, said: "The key changes needed are reversing the bias towards accepting commercial confidentiality as a justification for continued secrecy; and a more sensible definition of national security." Ian Gibson, Labour MP for Norwich North, said: "I am particularly concerned about the secrecy in hospitals and universities. A recent death in a secure mental health clinic has shown how hard it is to get information."

A Daily Telegraph leader declared: "The bill is

Harold Evans: "Freedom of Information is not a press fight for private profit. It is everyone's fight."

a step backwards. Its divergence from the proposals in white paper will confirm the impression that no government is willing to play the political game with transparent playing cards." Maurice Frankel, director of the Campaign for Freedom of Information said: "In 1996 Tony Blair argued that the Scott report "has made the case for a freedom of information act absolutely unanswerable". But this bill addresses none of the Scott report's concerns. Anyone probing arms to Iraq might arguably do better under the Tory code, with its substantive public interest test."

In June 1999 a Guardian/ICM poll showed the public backed a freedom of information bill but does not believe ministers should be trusted to decide what file should and shouldn't be released. By the end of June, it looked as if the pressure was paying off with ministers saying they would investigate a non-disclosure test based on what would *"substantially* prejudice", a phrase midway between the bill's "prejudice" and the white paper's original idea of "substantial harm".

Law and the media

The media operates under many legal restraints. Broadcasters are governed by several statutory controls specific to them and operated via the Broadcasting Standards Council, the BBC Charter, the ITC and the Radio Authority. Although newspapers and magazines are not so tightly regulated as TV and radio, all forms of media must prepare material within five legally defined boundaries. These are:

DEFAMATION
OBSCENE PUBLICATION
INCITEMENT TO RACIAL HATRED
BLASPHEMY
SEDITION

DEFAMATION is the aspect of law which most affects journalists and it covers a multitude of sins. A statement is defamatory if it damages reputation by exposing a person to hatred, contempt, shame or ridicule or makes a person likely to be avoided or shunned. It is defamatory to attack a person's honour, to injure them (or a company) in following their trade. It is also defamatory to wrongly accuse somebody of criminal activity, dishonesty, cruelty, hypocrisy, incompetence, inefficiency or stupidity.

There are two sorts of defamation: slander is non-published and libel is published. There are five defences to accusations of defamatory libel:
   justification/truth
   fair comment
   privilege
   "innocent" defamation
   apology
Justification: truth is the first defence against a libel action. It is for the journalist to prove that what has been published or broadcast is true, rather than for a plaintiff to disprove it. Therefore, keep notes and background material for at least three years, after which libel claims are barred by statute through lapse of time.

Fair comment: this is a journalist's genuinely held opinion and one which is held without malice and in good faith on a matter of public interest. Malice means dishonest or improper motives as well as personal spite.

Privilege: defamation laws are, under certain circumstances, suspended. These are reports of public judicial proceedings; statements made in Parliament; and public meetings. To avoid libel a court would need to be convinced that a report of a privileged event was fair accurate and contemporaneous.

"Innocent" defamation: the mere absence of an intention to defame is not defence enough against a charge of libel. However the 1952 Defamation Act allows journalists the defence of saying they did not know the circumstance which make a statement libellous. An offer of a correction and apology is a key to this defence.

Apology: this admits a libel without malice or gross negligence and offers recompense via a published apology and sometimes a payment. It originates from the mid-19th century, and is a dangerous defence which must be met to the letter if a court is not to move immediately to its own assessment of damages.

OBSCENE PUBLICATION legislation makes it illegal to publish material which will tend to deprave and corrupt persons who are likely to read, see or hear it. The 1950 Obscene Publications Act allows expert evidence to be given using artistic, literary, scientific or other merits as a defence.

INCITEMENT TO RACIAL HATRED legislation is framed in the 1986 Public Order Act forbids publication of material likely to incite hatred against any racial group.

BLASPHEMY- aka blasphemous libel - only applies where a piece of work is "so scurrilous and offensive as to pass the limit of decent controversy and to outrage Christian feeling". Under this law, only Christians can be outraged.

SEDITION is a little used catch-all to bar publication of material which either incites contempt or hatred for Parliament or the Monarch, or promotes reforms by violent or otherwise unconstitutional means.

media law

your guide

is

OLSWANG

Solicitors

90 Long Acre, London
WC2E 9TT, United Kingdom
T: +44 20 7208 8888
F: +44 20 7208 8800
E: olsmail@olswang.co.uk

www.olswang.co.uk

MEDIA LAW FIRMS

Allen & Overy
One New Change, London EC4M 9QQ
Fax 020-7330 9999   Tel 020-7330 3000
Website: www.allenovery.com
Defamation; TV carrier.
Clients include: Independent Television Commission.

Anderson Strathern WS
48 Castle Street, Edinburgh EH2 3LX
Fax 0131-226 7788   Tel 0131-220 2345
Website: www.andersonstrathern.co.uk
Entertainment and media.

Ashurst Morris Crisp
Broadwalk House, 5 Appold Street, London EC2A 2HA
Fax 020-7972 7990   Tel 020-7638 1111
E-mail: postbox@ashurst.com
Website: www.ashurst.com
TV carrier.

Baker & McKenzie
100 New Bridge Street, London EC4V 6JA
Fax 020-7919 1999   Tel 020-7919 1000
Website: www.bakerinfo.com
Digital mixed media.

Bannatyne Kirkwood France & Co
16 Royal Exchange Square, Glasgow G1 3AG
Fax 0141-221 5120   Tel 0141-221 6020
E-mail: martin@b-k-f.demon.co.uk
Entertainment and media. Clients include: Associated Newspapers, Scotsman Publications, Equity.

Beachcroft Wansbroughs
10-22 Victoria Street, Bristol BS99 7UD
Fax 0117-929 1582   Tel 0117-926 8981
Entertainment and media.

Bell & Scott WS
16 Hill Street, Edinburgh EH2 3LD
Fax 0131-226 7602   Tel 0131-226 6703
E-mail: maildesk@bellscott.co.uk
Entertainment and media.

Berwin Leighton
Adelaide House, London Bridge, London EC4R 9HA
Fax 020-7760 1111   Tel 020-7760 1000
Website: www.berwinleighton.com
TV carrier; TV content. Clients include: UNM, Walt Disney, Dream Works SKG, Endemol, Sovereign Pictures, Miramax, London Weekend TV, Telewest.

Bevan Ashford
35 Colston Avenue, Bristol BS1 4TT
Fax 0117-929 1865   Tel 0117-923 0111
Website: www.bevanashford.co.uk
Entertainment and media.

Biddle
1 Gresham Street, London EC2V 7BU
Fax 020-7606 3305   Tel 020-7606 9301
E-mail: law@biddle.co.uk
Website: www.biddle.co.uk
Defamation. Clients include: Vanity Fair.

Bindman & Partners
275 Grays Inn Road, London WC1X 8QF
Fax 020-7837 9792   Tel 020-7833 4433
Defamation

Bird & Bird
90 Fetter Lane, London EC4A 1JP
Fax 020-7415 6111   Tel 020-7415 6000
Website: www.twobirds.com
Defamation, digital mixed media, publishing and literary, entertainment and media, TV content, TV carrier, intellectual property and computer games.

Bristows
3 Lincolns Inn Fields, London WC2A 3AA
Fax 020-7400 8050   Tel 020-7400 8000
E-mail: info@bristows.co.uk
Website: www.bristows.com
Computer games, digital mixed media, publishing, TV.

Burness Solicitors
50 Lothian Road, Festival Square, Edinburgh EH3 9WJ
Fax 0131-473 6006   Tel 0131-473 6000
E-mail: edinburgh@burness.co.uk
Entertainment,media, defamation, intellectual property, publishing. Clients include: BBC Scotland, The Big Issue in Scotland, Clyde & Forth Press, Greenock Telegraph, BSkyB, Insider Publications.

Campbell Hooper
35 Old Queen Street, London SW1H 9JD
Fax 020-7222 5591   Tel 020-7222 9070
E-mail: ch@campbell-hooper.co.uk
Website: www.campbell-hooper.co.uk
TV carrier; TV content. Clients include: Virgin TV.

Charles Russell
8-10 New Fetter Lane, London EC4A 1RS
Fax 020-7203 0200   Tel 020-7203 5000
Website: www.charlesrussell.co.uk
TV carrier; TV content.

Clifford Chance
200 Aldersgate Street, London EC1A 4JJ
Fax 020-7600 5555   Tel 020-7600 1000
Website: www.cliffordchance.com
Defamation, digital mixed media, TV carrier.
Clients include: Reuters, Carlton, TeleWest.

Crockers Oswald Hickson
10 Gough Square, London EC4A 3NJ
Fax 020-7353 0743   Tel 020-7353 0311
Website: www.c-o-h.co.uk
Defamation. Clients include: Birmingham Post, The Economist, FT, Hello!,International Herald Tribune, Jewish Chronicle, Liverpool Echo, Magnum,Observer, Telegraph Group.

Davenport Lyons
1 Old Burlington Street, London W1X 2NL
Fax 020-7437 8216   Tel 020-7468 2600
E-mail: dl@davenportlyons.com
Website: www.davenportlyons.com
Defamation; TV content; publishing and literary.
Clients include Private Eye, Telegraph, Express, MGN.

David Price & Co
5 Great James Street, London WC1N 3DA
Fax 020-7916 9910   Tel 020-7916 9911
Defamation.

Denton Hall
5 Chancery Lane, Clifford's Inn, London EC4A 1BU
Fax 020-7404 0087   Tel 020-7242 1212
Website: www.dentonhall.com
Digital mixed media, TV carrier, TV content, publishing/literary.

DJ Freeman
43 Fetter Lane, London EC4A 1JU
Fax 020-7353 7377   Tel 020-7583 4055
E-mail: nal@djfreeman.co.uk
Website: www.djfreeman.co.uk
Digital media/defamation. Clients include: Channel 4,
Channel 5, Carlton, Reed Publishing, the Post Office.

Dundas & Wilson CS
20 Castle Terrace, Edinburgh EH1 2EN
Fax 0131-228 8888   Tel 0131-228 8000
Entertainment and media.

Edwards Geldard
Dumfries House, Dumfries Place, Cardiff CF10 3ZF
Fax 029-2023 7268   Tel 029-2023 8239
Intellectual property.

Eversheds
Fitzalan House, Fitzalan Road, Cardiff CF12 1XZ
Fax 029-2046 4347   Tel 029-2047 1147
Website: www.eversheds.com
Intellectual property.

Eversheds
85 Queen Victoria Street, London EC4V 4JC
Fax 020-7615 8080   Tel 020-7615 8000
Defamation, TV, publishing and literary.

Farrer & Co
66 Lincoln's Inn Fields, London WC2A 3LH
Fax 020-7831 9748   Tel 020-7242 2022
E-mail: media@farrer.co.uk
Defamation, intellectual property. Clients include: Sun,
News of the World, Haymarket, Sunday Telegraph.

Field, Fisher, Waterhouse
41 Vine Street, London EC3N 2AA
Fax 020-7488 0084   Tel 020-7 481 4841
E-mail: info@ffwlaw.com
Clients include BBC.

Foot & Bowden
Pynes Hill, Rydon Lane, Exeter EX2 5AZ
Fax 01392-203981   Tel 01392-203980
E-mail: arj@foot-bowden.co.uk
Defamation, contempt, court secrecy, challenges,
promotions. Clients include: Northcliffe Newspapers,
regional newspapers, publishers.

Freshfields
65 Fleet Street, London EC4Y 1HS
Fax 020-7832 7001   Tel 020-7936 4000
E-mail: email@freshfields.com
Website: www.freshfields.com
TV carrier, publishing, on-line services, new media, e-
commerce

Garrett & Co
180 Strand, London WC2R 2NN
Fax 020-7438 2518   Tel 020-7344 0344
Website: www.arthuranderson.com
Digital mixed media.

Goodman Derrick
90 Fetter Lane, London EC4A 1PT
Fax 020-7831 6407   Tel 020-7404 0606
E-mail: info@goodmanderrick.co.uk
Defamation; TV carrier; TV content; publishing and
literary. Clients include: Carlton, Central, Yorkshire,
Granada, ITV Network, ITV2, BSkyB, Channel 5.

Hammond Suddards
7 Devonshire Square, Cutlers Gardens, London
EC2M 4YH
Fax 020-7655 1001   Tel 020-7655 1000
Website: www.hammondsuddards.co.uk
TV content, publishing and literary, intellecttual
property, entertainment and media.

Harbottle & Lewis
14 Hanover Square, London W1R 0BE
Fax 020-7667 5100   Tel 020-7667 5000
Website: www.harbottle.co.uk
Defamation, digital mixed media, TV/film/theatre,
publishing/literary.

Hempsons
33 Henrietta Street, London WC2E 8NH
Fax 020-7836 2783   Tel 020-7836 0011
E-mail: london@hempsons.co.uk
Website: www.hempsons.co.uk
Defamation.

Henderson Boyd Jackson WS
19 Ainslie Place, Edinburgh EH3 6AU
Fax 0131-225 1103   Tel 0131-226 6881
E-mail: hlog@hbj.co.uk
Website: www.hbj.co.uk
Entertainment and media.

Henry Hepworth
5 John Street, London WC1N 2HH
Fax. 020-7242 7998   Tel 020-7242 7999
E-mail: hh@medialaw.co.uk
Defamation; digital mixed media; entertainment and
media; TV carrier; TV content; publishing and literary.
Clients include: BBC, BFI, Express Newspapers, John
Wiley & Sons, Mirror Group Newspapers, S4C,
Yorkshire Tyne Tees Television, Zenith Productions.

Herbert Smith
Exchange House, Primrose Street, London EC2A
2HS
Fax 020-7374 0888   Tel 020-7374 8000
E-mail: enquiries@herbertsmith.com
Defamation; TV carrier.
Clients include: WHSmith, Washington Post,
International Herald Tribune, BSkyB.

Hobson Audley Hopkins & Wood
7 Pilgrim Street, London EC4V 6LB
Fax 020-7450 4545   Tel 020-7450 4500
E-mail: lawyers@hobsonaudley.co.uk
Website: www.hobsonaudley.co.uk
Defamation, publishing, literary, electronic commerce.

Lee & Thompson
Green Garden House, 15-22 St Christopher's Place,
London W1M 5HD
Fax 020-7486 2391   Tel 020-7935 4665
E-mail: leeth@globalnet.co.uk
TV content, media, entertainment, film.

Lewis Silkin
50 Victoria Street, London SW1H 0NW
Fax 020-7222 4633   Tel 020-7227 8000
E-mail: info@lewissilkin.com
Defamation, publishing and literary digital mixed
media, entertaiment. Plaintiff/defendant newspaper to
include contempt.

Media lawyers with digital connections

Establishing an internet share trading service
Advising book publishers on film rights
Winning high profile copyright cases
Giving legal clearance to news items minutes before they're broadcast
Dealing with defamation on the internet

All in a day's work at Biddle.co.uk

For more information contact us at
1 Gresham Street London EC2V 7BU
Telephone 0171 606 9301
e-mail kim.walker@biddle.co.uk
www.biddle.co.uk

Biddle

Lovell White Durrant
65 Holborn Viaduct, London EC1A 2DY
Fax 020-7248 4212   Tel 020-7236 0066
Website: www.lovellwhitedurrant.com
Defamation; digital media; TV content;
publishing/literary. Clients include the Guardian.

Manches
Aldwych House, 81 Aldwych, London WC2B 4RP
Fax 020-7430 1133   Tel 020-7404 4433E-mail:
manchesmedia@manches.co.uk
Website: www.manches.com
Computer games, defamation, digital mixed media, TV
and film, publishing and literary, intellectual property.

Marriott Harrison
12 Great James Street, London WC1N 3DR
Fax 020-7209 2001   Tel 020-7209 2000
TV carrier; TV content.

Masons
30 Aylesbury Street, London EC1R 0ER
Fax 020-7490 2545   Tel 020-7490 4000
Website: www.masons.com
Digital mixed media, e-commerce, online games.

McGrigor Donald
Pacific House, 70 Wellington Street, Glasgow G2 6SB
Fax 0141-204 1351   Tel 0141-248 6677
E-mail: enquiries@mcgrigors.com
Website: www.mcgrigors.com
Entertainment and media.

Mishcon de Reya
21 Southampton Row, London WC1B 5HS
Fax 020-7404 5982   Tel 020-7440 7000
E-mail: postmaster@mischon.co.uk
Defamation; digital mixed media; TV content;
publishing and literary.

Morgan Cole
Princess House, Princess Way, Swansea SA1 3JL
Fax 01792 634500   Tel 01792-634634
E-mail: emyrlewis@morgan-cole.com
Film and TV production and financing, animation, TV
content. Clients include: HIT Entertainment, Agenda
Group, Aaargh! Animation

Nellen & Co
19 Albemarle Street, London W1X 3HA
Fax 020-7493 0146   Tel 020-7499 8122
E-mail: nellenco@compuserve.com
Specialists in buying and selling magazines. Authors of
PPA publication Guidelines for buying and Selling
Magazine Titles - The Legal Framework.

Norton Rose
35-37 Cammomile Street, London EC3A 7AN
Fax 020-7283 6500   Tel 020-7283 6000
Website: www.nortonrose.com
Computer games, telecommunications.

Olswang
90 Long Acre, London WC2E 9TT
Fax 020-7208 8800   Tel 020-7208 8888
Website: www.olswang.co.uk
Defamation; digital mixed media; TV carrier; TV
content; publishing, intellectual property. Clients
include: Guardian, Associated Newspapers, Daily
Mirror, Daily Telegraph, IPC Magazines, MTV, Warner
Bros, C4, Granada, Nickleodeon, BBC Worldwide.

Osborne Clarke
50 Queen Charlotte Street, Bristol BS1 4HE
Fax 0117-927 9209   Tel 0117-923 0220
26 Old Bailey, London EC4M 7HS
Fax 020-7809 1005   Tel 020-7809 1000
Apex Plaza, Reading RG1 1AX
Fax 0118-925 0038   Tel 0118-925 2000
E-mail: info@osborne-clarke.co.uk
Website: www.osborne-clarke.co.uk
Entertainment and media, marketing services,
interactive media, IT and telecoms.
Clients include: Activision, Carlton Screen Advertising,
Manning Gottlieb Media, Yahoo!

Peter Carter-Ruck & Partners
76 Shoe Lane, London EC4A 3JP
Fax 020-7353 5553   Tel 020-7353 5005
E-mail: lawers@carter-ruck.com
Website: www.carter-ruck.com
Defamation, media litigation, copyright, data base
rights and on-line services, literary trusts and estates,
sports media. Clients include: Express Newspapers,
Hello, National Magazines, Pearson Education, high
profile sporting, media and political individuals.

Phil Fisher Waterhouse
35 Vine Street, London EC3N 2AA
Fax 020-7488 0084   Tel 020-7481 4841
E-mail: info@pfwlaw.com
TV carrier; TV content.
Clients include: BBC.

PricewaterhouseCoopers
1 Embankment Place, London WC2N 6NN
Fax 020-7822 4652   Tel 020-7583 5000
Digitiation, content management, royalty rights
management, globalisation, shareholder value
enhancement, internet assurances and post-merger
integration.

Reid Minty & Co
19 Bourdon Place, Bourdon Street, London W1X 9HZ
Fax 020-7318 4445   Tel 020-7318 4444
Website: www.reidminty.co.uk
Defamation.

Reynolds Porter Chamberlain
278-282 High Holborn, London WC1V 7HA
Fax 020-7242 1431   Tel 020-7242 2877
E-mail: rpc@rpc.co.uk
Media and technology department headed by Liz
Hartley.

Richards Butler
15 St Botolph Street, London EC3A 7EE
Fax 020-7247 5091   Tel 020-7247 6555
Defamation; TV content.
Clients include: BBCWorldwide, Turner Broadcasting.

Rowe & Maw
20 Black Friars Lane, London EC4V 6HD
Fax 020-7248 2009   Tel 020-7248 4282
Website: www.roweandmaw.co.uk
Publishing and literary.

Russell Jones & Walker
324 Gray's Inn Road, London WC1X 8DH
Fax 020-7837 2941   Tel 020-7837 2808
Website: www.rjw.co.uk
Defamation.

Russells
1-4 Warwick Street, London W1R 6LJ
Fax 020-7494 3582   Tel 020-7439 8692
E-mail: media@russells.co.uk
TV content.
Schilling & Lom
Royalty House, 72-74 Dean Street, London W1V 6AE
Fax 020-7453 2600   Tel 020-7453 2500
E-mail: legal@schillinglom.co.uk
Entertainment and media, defamation; TV content.
Clients include: LWT, Granada, Carlton, Yorkshire.
Sheridans
14 Red Lion Square, London WC1R 4QL
Fax 020-7831 1982   Tel 020-7404 0444
E-mail: general@sheridans.co.uk
Website: www.sheridans.co.uk
Digital mixed media.
The Simkins Partnership
45-51 Whitfield Street, London W1P 6AA
Fax 020-7436 2744   Tel 020-7631 1050
E-mail: simkins@simkins.com
Defamation; digital media; TV content;
publishing/literary. Clients include: C4, FT.
Simmons & Simmons
21 Wilson Street, London EC2M 2TX
Fax 020-7628 2070   Tel 020-7628 2020
Website: www.simmons-simmons.com
TV carrier. Clients include: NYNEX, General Cable,
Rapture Channel.
Simons Muirhead & Burton
50 Broadwick Street, London W1V 1FF
Fax 020-7734 3263   Tel 020-7734 4499
Defamation. Clients include: Time Out, Random
House.
SJ Berwin & Co
222 Grays Inn Road, London WC1X 8HB
Fax 020-7533 2000   Tel 020-7533 2222
E-mail: info@sjberwin.com
Website: www.sjberwin.com
Digital mixed media; TV carrier; TV content.
Steedman Ramage WS
6 Alva Street, Edinburgh EH2 4QQ
Fax 0131-260 6610   Tel 0131-260 6600
E-mail: info@srws.co.uk
Entertainment and media.
Stephens Innocent
21 New Fetter Lane, London EC4A 1AP
Fax 020-7353 4443   Tel 020-7353 2000
Defamation, world wide web, registration of media, TV
content, publishing. Clients include: Wall Street
Journal, Washington Post, Society of Authors, ITN.
Swepstone Walsh
9 Lincolns Inn Fields London WC2A 3BP
Fax 020-7404 1493   Tel 020-7404 1499
E-mail: swepstone@compuserve.com
Defamation
Tarlo Lyons
Watchmaker Court, 33 St John's Lane, London EC1M
4DB
Fax 020-7814 9421   Tel 020-7405 2000
Website: www.tarlo-lyons.com
TV content.

Taylor Joynson Garrett
50 Victoria Embankment, London EC4Y 0DX
Fax 020-7936 2666   Tel 020-7353 1234
E-mail: enquiries@tjg.co.uk
Website: www.tjg.co.uk
Digital mixed media; TV carrier; TV content; publishing
and literary, entertainment and media, defamation.
Clients include: Associated Newspapers.
Theodore Goddard
150 Aldersgate Street, London EC1A 4EJ
Fax 020-7606 4390   Tel 020-7606 8855
E-mail: info@theodoregoddard.co.uk
Defamation; TV carrier; TV content, digital mixed
media, media litigation, publishing. Clients include:
HTV, Granada, Sky Broadcasting, News Group, UTV.
Titmuss Sainer Dechert
2 Serjeants' Inn, London EC4Y 1LT
Fax 020-7353 3683   Tel 020-7583 5353
Website: www.titmus-sainier-dechert.com
Defamation; digital mixed media.
Tods Murray WS
66 Queen Street, Edinburgh EH2 4NE
Fax 0131-624 7170   Tel 0131-226 4771
E-mail: richard.findlay@todsmurray.co.uk
Entertainment and media.
Wiggin & Co
The Quadrangle, Imperial Square, Cheltenham,
Gloucestershire GL50 1YX
Fax 01242-224223   Tel 01242-224114
E-mail: law@wiggin.co.uk
3 Albany Courtyard, Piccadilly, London W1V 9RA
Fax 020-7287 8628   Tel 020-7287 8833
Entertainment and media, defamation, digital mixed
media, TV carrier, TV content, publishing and literary.

LEGAL PUBLICATIONS

**The Incorporated Council of Law Reporting
for England & Wales**
3 Stone Buildings, Lincoln's Inn, London WC2A 3XN
Fax 020-7831 5247   Tel 020-7242 6471
E-mail: postmaster@iclr.co.uk
The Council publishes the Weekly Law Reports etc and
produces law reports for The Times, The Law Society
Gazette and other titles.
The Legal 500
28-33 Cato Street, London W1H 5HS
Fax 020-7396 9300   Tel 020-7396 9292
Website: the_legal_500@link.org
The definitive guide to British law firms.
Media Lawyer
3 Broom Close, Broughton, Cumbria LA20 6JG
Fax 01229-716621   Tel 01229-716622
Newsletter for media lawyers and all concerned with
media law. Bi-monthly. £36 pa.
Nellen & Co
19 Albemarle Street, London W1X 3HA
Fax 020-7493 0146   Tel 020-7499 8122
E-mail: nellenco@compuserve.com
Authors of PPA publication Guidelines for Buying and
Selling Magazine Titles - The Legal Framework.

WILD
About
media

Serious

When you're focused on the project in hand,

about

the last thing you need to worry about

Insurance

is your insurance cover.

Our media business policies are specifically designed to provide full protection against the risks in your particular environment. We understand the different dangers faced by Advertising Agencies; Media Buyers; Marketing Consultancies; Publishers; Broadcasters; Independent TV, Commercials & Film Production Companies; Market Researchers and Graphic Designers - and build in protection for your business and its reputation accordingly. Each policy gives truly global cover, including all the new risks associated with the Internet.

Our policies include access to the most specialised legal advice within the media industry. And our media claims-handling team really understands the issues you're likely to face. Yet premiums are extremely competitive.

Products include:

Professional Indemnity

Production Insurance

Cyberliability

Employment Practices Liability

All this means Hiscox can offer you the most comprehensive range of insurance cover you could possibly want. Ever.

So either contact your broker, call us on 0171 448 6000, or visit our website www.hiscox.com. And relax.

HISCOX

LIBEL INSURANCE

Two pieces of news from Peter Carter-Ruck and partners - the firm which charges up to £350 an hour for its services. At least it did until it announced a no-win, no-fee option for defamation cases. "We have long believed that everyone should be able to defend themselves against a libellous statement," said Alasdair Pepper, a Carter-Ruck partner. "Because legal aid has not been available in defamation cases, the principle of justice for all has been blighted."

The second news line came from the firm's main man at the first Hugh Cudlipp memorial lecture at the London Press Club. Carter-Ruck said the British press suffers unfairly from libel laws and he called for a statutory defence for newspapers publishing public interest stories which turn out to be untrue. "If the article can be shown to have been written in good faith, without malice and based upon evidence reasonably believed to be true, then there should be a defence," he said.

Libel damages have fallen recently for several reasons. Since 1990 the Court of Appeal has been able to substitute what a jury has awarded as happened, for example, when Elton John's original £350,000 libel award from the Mirror was reduced on appeal to £75,000. On a more general level the Court of Appeal has also ruled that juries may be directed to bear in mind the £50,000 to £125,000 awards for pain and suffering in cases of bodily injury. Another factor is a decision by the European Court of Human Rights that the £1.5 million award in 1995 to Lord Aldington against Nikolai Tolstoy over allegations that he sent Cossacks and Yugoslavs to their death in 1945, breached the freedom of expression guarantee in the European Convention on Human Rights.

While the days of the £1 million are probably over, existing libel laws are still an obstacle to investigative journalism. The Guardian editor Alan Rusbridger says there should be three changes. First, that judges should not be allowed to dismiss the jury and make the final decision, as happened in Jonathan Aitken's action against the Guardian. Second, that the innocent-until-guilty principle should apply instead of the defence having to prove its case. And third, the withdrawal of qualified privilege, which in some circumstances allows individuals to speak without fear of a defamation action.

Meanwhile libel insurance is a booming business. The coverage typically provided within a media or libel policy includes libel, slander, malicious falsehood, passing off, infringement of copyright and trademark, false attribution of authorship, breach of confidence, trespass and invasion of privacy. Optional coverage may include withdrawal costs, errors and omissions or negligent statement and commercial printing exposures. Policies can be written either on a claims made basis or occurrence wording with limits in the aggregate or on an each and every event basis. Professional indemnity underwriters normally give a libel and slander extension where publishing or broadcasting is incidental to the main business of the Insured. However, specific libel policies are provided by the following insurers.

LIBEL INSURERS

Denham Syndicate ((Lloyd's Syndicate 990)
Holland House, 1-4 Berry Street, London EC3A 5HT
Fax 020-7623 8223   Tel 020-7283 0045
E-mail: denhamdirect@compuserve.com
ERC Frankona
7/8 Philpot Lane, London EC3M 8BQ
Fax 020-7617 6860   Tel 020-7617 6800
Website: www.ercgroup.com
Hiscox Underwriting Limited
1 Great St Helen's, London EC3A 6HX
Fax 020-7448 6900   Tel 020-7448 6000
Website: www.hiscox.co.uk
Media/Professional Insurance Agency
16 St Helen's Place, London EC3A 6DF
Fax 020-7680 1177   Tel 020-7772 4700
Website: www.mediaprof.com
RE Brown & Others (Lloyd's Syndicate 702)
84 Fenchurch Street, London EC3M 4BY
Fax 020-7480 6920   Tel 020-7265 0071
Robert Fleming Professional and Financial Risks
Staple Hall, Stone House Court, 87-90 Hounsditch, London EC3A 7AX
Fax 020-7623 6175   Tel 020-7621 1263
Royal & Sun Alliance
1 Leadenhall Street, London EC3V 1PP
Fax 020-7337 5922   Tel 020-7283 9000
Website: www.royal-and-sunalliance.com

Advertising, PR and media analysts

PRESS

Advertising in newspapers, magazines, posters, the cinema and direct mail is regulated by the Advertising Standards Authority, which is funded by a levy on display ads. It aims to enforce standards through a code which says ads should be: legal, decent, honest and truthful; prepared with a sense of responsibility to the consumer and society; and fair competition as generally accepted in business. The Authority's main sanction is to recommend that the ads it considers in breach of its code are not published. This is normally enough to make sure an offending ad is quashed. The Authority publishes monthly reports on the results of its investigations and, as a final resort, refers misleading adverts to the director general of fair trading who has the power to seek injunctions to prevent publication.

BROADCASTING

The advertising rules for broadcasting are more complex than for the press. Advertising is allowed on independent television and radio, subject to controls laid down by the ITC and the Radio Authority. Both can impose heavy penalties on companies failing to comply with their codes. Advertisers are not allowed to influence programme content and their ads must be distinct from programmes. TV advertising is limited to an average seven minutes an hour during the day and seven and a half minutes in the peak evening period. Ads are forbidden in religious and school broadcasts, though religious ads are now permitted. Political advertising is prohibited and gambling ads are restricted to the football pools and the National Lottery. All tobacco ads are banned on TV (with the exception of ones that just happen to appear on Formula One racing cars) and cigarette ads are banned on radio.

1997 advertising expenditure by type

TYPE	PERCENTAGE
Television	31.50%
Press display	33.80%
Press classified	26.80%
Outdoor	4.30%
Radio	3.40%
Cinema	0.80%

Source: Advertising Statistics Yearbook

Percentage of total by medium and type

	1989	1993	1995	1997
Total press	65.1%	61.8%	60.7%	60.1%
Press classified	27.2 %	25.2%	25.5%	26.8%
Press display	37.9%	36.5%	35.2%	33.3%
Television	29.0%	31.6%	31.7%	31.5%
Outdoor	3.4%	3.6%	3.8%	4.3%
Radio	2.0%	2.4%	3.0%	3.4%
Cinema	0.4%	0.6%	0.7%	0.8%
Total display	72.8%	74.8%	74.5%	73.2%
TOTAL	100.0	100.0	100.0	100.0

Source: Advertising Statistics Yearbook

Current advertising prices £m

	1989	1993	1995	1997
Total press	5,131	5,085	5,979	6,967
Press classified	2,143	2,078	2,515	3,107
Press display	2,987	3,008	3,463	3,860
Television	2,288	2,604	3,125	3,651
Outdoor	271	300	378	500
Radio	159	194	296	393
Cinema	35	49	69	88
Direct mail	758	907	1,135	1,540
Total display	6,498	7,061	8,466	10,032
TOTAL	£8.6b	£9.2b	£12b	£13.1b

Source: Advertising Statistics Yearbook

WHATEVER THE MEDIA, WHEREVER IT IS...

● *Over 44,000 listings* ● *Three Volumes* ●
● *The whole World* ●

Benn's Media is the essential reference source to media in the UK, Europe and throughout the world. It will provide you with comprehensive and accurate information on the press, television, radio and other media related organisations.

The UK Volume:
● 16,000 entries

The European Volume:
● 11,500 entries

The World Volume:
● 17,000 entries

●**Advertising and editorial contact details including:**

✔ e-mail numbers
✔ advertising rates
✔ readership data
✔ frequency and circulation data

● ***Benn's Media Guide*** is the *complete* guide to national, regional and international newspapers, consumer and business periodicals, reference publications and broadcasting.

.. BENN'S MEDIA HAS IT COVERED.

AD/PR CONTACTS

AC Nielsen.MEAL
7 Harewood Avenue, London NW1 6JB
Fax 020-7393 5088   Tel 020-7393 5070
E-mail: john.purcell@acnielsen.co.uk
AC Nielsen.MEAL has provided the ad industry's
standard measure of above-the-line advertising
expenditure since 1968, with electronic data available to
1986 on TV, press, radio, cinema and outdoor media.

Advertising Association
Abford House, 15 Wilton Road, London SW1V 1NJ
Fax 020-7931 0376   Tel 020-7828 2771
E-mail: aa@adassoc.org.uk
Website: www.adassoc.org.uk
Promotes and protects the rights, responsibilities, and
role of advertising. It is committed to upholding the
freedom to advertise in the UK and to uphold standards
and principles of self-regulation. Publishes information,
research and statistics on the advertising business.

**Advertising Film & Videotape Producers
Association**
26 Noel Street, London W1V 3RD
Fax 020-7434 9002   Tel 020-7434 2651
E-mail: afvpa@easynet.co.uk
TV commercials' production companies trade body.

Advertising Standards Authority
2 Torrington Place, London WC1E 7HW
Fax 020-7631 3051   Tel 020-7580 5555
Website: www.asa.org.uk
Promotes and enforces standards in non-broadcast
ads.via the British Codes of Advertising and Sales
Promotion. It is financed by a levy on advertising space.

Broadcast Advertising Clearance Centre
200 Grays Inn Road, London WC1X 8HF
Fax 020-7843 8154   Tel 020-7843 8265
E-mail: info@itv.co.uk
Website: www.itv.co.uk
Ensures that TV commercials comply with ITC codes
on behalf of the ITV and satellite companies.

CARMA International
Station Road, Godalming, surrey GU7 1JD
Fax 01483-427528   Tel 01483-419121
E-mail: info@carma.co.uk
Website: www.carma.com
Computer Aided Research & Media Analysis conduct
PR research tracking the evolution of issues in the
media and building profiles of sources, publications
and journalists. Nine offices worldwide.

Direct Marketing Association
1 Oxendon Street, London SW1Y 4EE
Fax 020-7321 0191   Tel 020-7321 2525
E-mail: dma@dma.org.uk
Website: www.dma.org.uk
Trade association for direct marketers which publishes
leaflets, a members' directory and a code of practice.

Granada Media International
TV Centre, Upper Ground, London SE1 9LT
Fax 020-7261 8162   Tel 020-7737 8603
Website: www.sales.granadamedia.com
Sells programmes worldwide for Granada, LWT and
Yorkshire.

History of Advertising Trust
Hat House, 12 Raveningham Centre, Raveningham,
Norwich, Norfolk NR14 6NU
Fax 01508-548478   Tel 01508-548623
E-mail: hat@uea.ac.uk
Website: www.lib.uea.ac.uk/HAT/
An archive of advertising material from the beginning
of the nineteenth century to the present day. The
collection contains over one million items.

Incorporated Society of British Advertisers
44 Hertford Street, London W1Y 8AE
Fax 020-7629 5355   Tel 020-7499 7502
E-mail: info@isha.org.uk
Website: www.isba.org.uk
Association representing major advertisers' interests
across the industry on marketing communication
issues.

Institute of Practitioners in Advertising
44 Belgrave Square, London SW1X 8QS
Fax 020-7245 9904   Tel 020-7201 8211
E-mail: tessa@ipa.co.uk
Website: www.ipa.co.uk
Trade and professional body for UK ad agencies.

Institute of Public Relations
15 Northburgh Street, London EC1V 0PR
Fax 020-7490 0588   Tel 020-7253 5151
E-mail: info@ipr.org.uk
Website: www.ipr.org.uk
The main professional association for all working in PR.

Market Research Society
15 Northburgh Street, London EC1V 0AH
Fax 020-7490 0608   Tel 020-7490 4911
E-mail: mrs@dial.pipex.com
Website: www.marketresearch.org.uk
Publishes a monthly magazine called the Journal of
Market Research Society and runs trainingcourses and
seminars, and holds an annual conference every March.

**National Newspapers Mail Order Protection
Scheme (MOPS)**
16 Tooks Court, London EC4A 1LB
Fax 020-7404 0106   Tel 020-7269 0520
Website: www.mops.org.uk
Reimburses readers of member newspapers who lose
money when approved mail order advertisers enter
liquidation or bankruptcy, or cease to trade.

Public Relations Consultants' Association
Willow House, Willow Place, London SW1P 1JH
Fax 020-7828 9797   Tel 020-7233 6026
E-mail: chris@prca.org.uk
Website: www.prca.org.uk

Radio Advertising Bureau
77 Shaftesbury Avenue, London W1V 7AD
Fax 020-7306 2505   Tel 0171 306 2500
E-mail: rab@rab.co.uk
Website: www.rab.co.uk
Marketing company set up by the commercial radio
industry for advertisers and advertising agencies.

Radio Advertising Clearance Centre
46 Westbourne Grove, London W2 5SH
Fax 020-7229 0352   Tel 020-7727 2646
E-mail: adclear@racc.co.uk
Clears radio ad scripts and ensures compliance with the
Radio Authority's Advertising Code.

AD/PR MAGAZINES

Campaign
174 Hammersmith Road, London W6 7JP
Fax 020-8267 4914   Tel 020-8267 4656
Website: www.campaignlive.com
Publisher: Haymarket.
£2.10. Weekly news for the advertising industry.

Creative Review
50 Poland Street, London W1V 4AX
Fax 020-7970 4498   Tel 020-7439 4222
Website: www.creativereview.com
Publisher: Centaur Communications.
Monthly looking at the best in advertising and design.

Marketing
Haymarket,174 Hammersmith Road, London W6 7JP
Fax 020-7413 4504   Tel 020-7943 5000
E-mail: editor@marketing.haynet.com
Website: www.marketing.haynet.com
£2.30. The weekly business newspaper for marketing.

Advertising Age International
Crain Communications, New Garden House, 78
Hatton Garden, London EC1N 8LD
Fax 020-7216 0053   Tel 020-7457 1419
Monthly media and marketing magazine.

Media & Marketing Europe
Emap,33-39 Bowling Green Lane, London EC1R 0DA
Fax 020-7505 8320   Tel 020-7505 8312
E-mail traceyt@media-emap.co.uk
£5.00. Monthly mag for advertising & marketing execs.

Media Week
Quantum, 19 Scarbrook Road, Croydon CR9 1LX
Fax 020-8565 4444   Tel 020-8565 4200
Weekly news magazine linking media and advertising .

New Media Age
50 Poland Street, London W1V 4AX
Fax 020-7970 4899   Tel 020-7970 4000
E-mail: mikeb@centaur.co.uk
Website: www.nma.co.uk
Weekly subscription news for the new media industry.

PR Week
Haymarket,174 Hammersmith Road, London W6 7JP
Fax 020-7413 4509   Tel 020-7413 4429
E-mail: prweek@haynet.com
Website: www.prweekuk.com
£1.70. The weekly news magazine for the PR industry.

AD/PR YEARBOOKS & GUIDES

Advertisers Annual/Blue Book
Harlequin House, 7 High Street, Teddington,
Middlesex TW11 8EL
Fax 020-8977 1133   Tel 020-8977 7711
Website: www.hollis-pr.co.uk
Publisher: Hollis Directories
Contact: Gary Zabel
£210. An ad directory from same stable as Willings
Press Guide. Covers: Agencies/advertisers; UK media;
Overseas media.

ALF
33-39 Bowling Green Lane, London EC1R 0DA
Fax 020-7505 8336   Tel 020-7505 8458
E-mail: joe@brad.co.uk
Website: www.brad.co.uk
Publisher: Emap Media
Contact: Jo Ellis
Monthly directory of 1,500 agencies, 1,000 advertisers -
all linked to 9,000 brands. All personnel are linked to
brands. £790 for 12 issues, £220 1 vol.

Benn's Media
Riverbank House, Angel Lane Tonbridge, Kent TN9
1SE
01732-367301   Tel 01732-362666
E-mail: bennsmedia@unmf.co,
Website: www.mfuk.com/mfinfo
Publisher: Benn Business Information Services
Contact: Debbie O'Neil
3 vols £310, 2 vols £290, 1 vol £145
Benn's has the most comprehensive of media listings.
Its three volumes, cover the UK, Europe and the rest of
the world. Established 1846.

BRAD (British Rate & Data)
33-39 Bowling Green Lane, London EC1R 0DA
Fax 020-7505 8336   Tel 020-7505 8458
E-mail: judithm@brad.co.uk
Website: www.brad.co.uk
Publisher: Emap Media
Contact: Judith Mellor
Monthly guide to advertising in the UK. Over 12,000
media outlets covered. £495 for 12 issues, £260 1 vol.

Editors
34 Germain Street, Chesham Bucks HP5 1SJ
Fax 01494-797224   Tel 01494-797224
E-mail: editors@mediainfo.co.uk
Website: www.mediainfo.co.uk
Contact: James Scott
6 volumes for £495 pa.subscription
Directory of media contacts for the PR industry.

Hollis Press & PR Annual
Harlequin House, 7 High Street, Teddington,
Middlesex TW11 8EL
Fax 020-8977 1133   Tel 020-8977 7711
E-mail: hollis@hollis-pr.demon.co.uk
Website: www.hollis-pr.co.uk
Publisher: Hollis Directories
Contact: Gary Zabel
£92.50.Contacts throughout industry plus voluntary
organisations, PR consultancies and major media titles.

Institute of Public Relations Handbook
120 Pentonville Road, London N1 9JN
Fax 020-7837 6348   Tel 020-7278 0433
E-mail: kpinfo@kogan-page.co.uk
Publisher: Kogan Page
Contact: Don Edwards
£135. List of over 5,000 IPR members, plus other information and articles.

LENA
33-39 Bowling Green Lane, London EC1R 0DA
Fax 020-7505 8336   Tel 020-7505 84458
E-mail: joe@brad.co.uk
Website: www.brad.co.uk
Publisher: Emap Media
Contact: Joe Ellis
Quarterly guide to the top 2,000 national advertisers. Annual sub £580 for 4 issues, £310 1 vol.

Media Pocket Book
Farm Road, Henley-on-Thames, Oxfordshire RG9 1EJ
Fax 01491-571188   Tel 01491-574671
Publisher: Advertising Association
£26, each July. Key facts and figures on the media and advertising, from newspaper circulations to TV ownership. Other titles in this series, are the Marketing, Retail and Lifestyle Pocket Books.

PR Planner UK & Europe
34 Germain Street, Chesham Bucks HP5 1SJ
Fax 01494-797224   Tel 01494-797224
E-mail: prplanner@mediainfo.co.uk
Website: www.mediainfo.co.uk
Loose-leaf guide to contacts in all media. The UK edition is updated monthly and costs £370 pa, also available on CD. The Euro edition is updated every other month and costs £425 pa for Trade and Technical and £250 the Consumer.

UK Media Yearbook
63-65 Bishops Bridge Road, London W2 1LA
Fax 020-7298 6902   Tel 020-7224 8500
E-mail: publications@zenithmedia.co.uk
Website: www.zenithmedia.com
Publisher: Zenith Media
£250. Facts and figures on the UK's advertising media with commentary and analysis.

Willings Press Guide
Harlequin House, 7 High Street, Teddington, Middlesex, TW11 8EL
Fax 020-8977 1133   Tel 020-8977 7711
E-mail: willings@hollis-pr.co.uk
Website: www.hollis-pr.co.uk
Contact: Nesta Hollis
Publisher: Hollis Directories
Two vols £205. Alphabetical list detailing over 26,000 newspapers and periodicals worldwide. Available on CD for £255/£299.63 inc VAT. CD + 2 vols is £287.25 inc VAT.

World Advertising Trends
Farm Road, Henley on Thames, Oxfordshire RG9 1EJ
Fax 01491-571188   Tel 01491-574671
Publisher: Advertising Association
Contact: Toby Howard
£125. Statistical analysis of ad spends from 57 countries.

ADVERTISING AGENCIES

Top 30 ad agencies, by billings

1	Abbott Mead Vickers BBD
2	Saatchi & Saatchi
3	J. Walter Thompson
4	Ogilvy & Mather
5	Publicis
6	BMP DDB
7	TBWA GGT Simons Palmer
8	McCann-Erickson (London)
9	DMB&B
10	M&C Saatchi
11	Bates Dorland
12	Grey Advertising
13	Lowe Howard-Spink
14	Euro RSCG Wnek Gosper
15	WCRS
16	Leo Burnett
17	Ammirati Puris Lintas
18	Bartle Bogle Hegarty
19	Young & Rubicam
20	HHCL & Parters
21	Rainey Kelly Campbell Roalfe
22	Leagas Delaney
23	FCB
24	FCA!
25	Collett Dickenson Pearce
26	BDH TBWA
27	Banks Hoggins O'Shea
28	Delaney Fletcher Bozell
29	McCann-Erickson (Manchester
30	St Luke's

Source: Campaign , Feb 1999

Abbott Vickers BBDO
151 Old Marylebone Road, London NW1 5QE
Fax 020-7616 3600   Tel 020-7616 3500
Website: www.amvbbdo.co.uk
Clients include: BT, Cellnet, Granada, Kiss FM
Ammirati Puris Lintas
25 Soho Square, London, W1V 5FJ
Fax 020-7534 5001   Tel 020-7534 5000
Web: www.apl.co.uk
Banks Hoggins O'Shea
54 Baker Street, London, W1M 1DJ
Fax 020-7314 0001   Tel 020-7314 0000

Bartle Bogle Hegarty
60 Kingly Street, London, W1R 6DS
Fax 020-7437 3666   Tel 020-7734 1677
Bates Dorland
121-141 Westbourne Terrace, London, W2 6JR
Fax 020-7724 3075   Tel 020-7262 5077
Web: www.bates-dorland.co.uk
Collett Dickenson Pearce
33-34 Soho Square, London, W1V 6DP
Fax 020-7292 4010   Tel 020-7292 4000
Web: www.cdp-uk.com
Delaney Fletcher Bozell
25 Wellington Street, London, WC2E 7DA
Fax 020-7240 8729   Tel 020-7836 3474
Web: www.london.bozell.com
DMB&B
123 Buckingham Palace Road, London, SW1W 9DZ
Fax 020-7630 0033   Tel 020-7630 0000
Web: www.dmbb.com
Euro RSCG Wnek Gosper
11 Great Newport Street, London, WC2H 7JA
Fax 020-7465 0552   Tel 020-7240 4111
E-mail: info@eurorscg.co.uk
Web: www.eurorscg.co.uk
FCA!
103 Wigmore Street, London, W1H 9AB
Fax 020-7314 2601   Tel 020-7314 2600
FCB
110 Saint Martin's Lane, London, WC2N 4DY
Fax 020-7240 5500   Tel 020-7240 7100
Grey
215-227 Great Portland Street, London W1N 5HD
Fax 020-7637 7473   Tel 020-7636 3399
Website: www.greyen.com
HHCL & Partners
Kent House, 14-17 Market Place, Great Titchfield
Street, London, W1N 7AJ
Fax 020-7436 2677   Tel 020-7436 3333
E-mail: postbox@hhcl.com
Web: www.hhcl.com
J Walter Thompson
40 Berkeley Square, London W1X 6AD
Fax 020-7493 8432   Tel 020-7499 4040
E-mail: amanda.fisher@jwt.com
Website: www.jwt.com
Leagas Delaney
233 Shaftsbury Avenue, London, WC2H 8EZ
Fax 020-7240 9005   Tel 020-7836 4455
Web: www.leagas.co.uk
Leo Burnett
The Leo Burnett Building, 60 Sloane Avenue, London,
SW3 3XE
Fax 020-7591 9126   Tel 020-7591 9111
Web: www.leoburnett.com

Lowe Howard-Spink
Bowater House, 68-114 Knightsbridge, London, SW1X
7LT
Fax 020-7584 9557   Tel 020-7584 5033
Web: www.lowehoward-spink.co.uk
M&C Saatchi
36 Golden Square, London W1R 4EE
Fax 020-7543 4501   Tel 020-7543 4500
Website: www.mcsaatchi.com
Clients include: British Airways, Dixons, Whiskas
McCann-Erickson
36 Howland Street, London W1A 1AT
Fax 020-7323 2883   Tel 020-7580 6690
Website: www.mcann.co.uk
Ogilvy and Mather
10 Cabot Sq, Canary Wharf, London E14 4QB
Fax 020-7345 9000   Tel 020-7345 3000
Website: www.ogilvy.com
Publicis
82 Baker Street, London W1M 2AE
Fax 020-7487 5351   Tel 020-7935 4426
Clients include: Asda, Renault, United Biscuits
Rainey Kelly Campbell Roalfe
4th Floor, Middlesex House, 34-42 Cleveland Street,
London, W1P 5SB
Fax 020-7637 7395   Tel 020-7637 7393
Saatchi and Saatchi
80 Charlotte Street, London W1A 1AQ
Fax 020-7637 8489   Tel 020-7636 5060
Website: www.saatchi-saatchi.com
St Luke's
22 Dukes Road, London, WC1H 9AD
Fax 020-7 380 8899   Tel 020-7380 8888
Web: www.stlukes.co.uk
TBWA GGT Simons Palmer
76-80 Whitfield Street, London, W1P 5RQ
Fax 020-7573 6667   Tel 020-7573 6666
Young & Rubicam
Greater London House, Hampstead Road, London,
NW1 7QP
Fax 020-7611 6570   Tel 020-7387 9366
Web: www.yr.com
WCRS
5 Golden Square, London, W1R 4BS
Fax 020-7806 5099   Tel 020-7806 5000

MEDIA AGENCIES

Top twenty media agencies by billings

1 **Zenith Media**
2 **TMD Carat**
3 **Mediavest (London)**
4 **BMP Optimum**
5 **Mediapolis**
6 **Universal McCann**
7 **Initiative**
8 **New PHD**
9 **Mediacom**
10 **CIA Medianetwork**
11 **The Media Business Group**
12 **The Network (now MindShare)**
13 **Leo Burnett**
14 **Optimedia UK**
15 **JWT (now MindShare)**
16 **BBJ Media Services**
17 **Western International Media**
18 **IDK Media**
19 **Motive**
20 **Manning Gottlieb Media**

The advertising market used to be controlled by the advertising agencies, but has since been broken down into divisions. The media agency emerged to specialise in buying advertising space leaving the creative side to the advertising agencies.

Media agencies negotiate prices with media owners and buy advertising space on television, press, radio, cinema and outdoor.

All Response Media
2 Dean Street, London, QW1V 5RN
Fax 020-7878 2851   Tel 020-7878 2850
AMS Advertising
52 Doughty Street, London, WC1N 2LS
Fax 020-7404 3511   Tel 020-7404 9292
E-mail: mail@amcom.co.uk
Clients include Red Bull and Fred Perry
Austin West Media
New Premiere House, 150 Southampton Row, London, WC1B 5AL
Fax 020-7278 0238   Tel 020-7278 7878
Clients include Brittany Ferries and Select Appointments
BBJ Media Services
Orion House, 5 Upper St Martins Lane, London, WC2H 9EA
Fax 020-7497 1177   Tel 020-7379 9000
Clients include Cable and Wireless and Audi.

BJK&E Media
25 Wellington Street, London, WC2E 7DA
Fax 020-7240 0792   Tel 020-7379 8080
Web: www.london.bozell.com
Clients include Financial Times and Triumph
BMP OMD
16 Bishops Bridge Road, Paddington, London, W2 6AA
Fax 020-7258 4545   Tel 020-7893 4189
Website: www.bmpomd.co.uk
Formerly known as BMP DDB. Clients include Barclaycard, Boots and Alliance and Leicester.
BMP Solutions in Media Group
16 Bishops Bridge Road, Paddington, London, W2 6AA
Fax 020-7893 4111   Tel 020-7893 4082
Clients include Pepsi, Halfords and Boots
Carat
Parker Tower,43-49 Parker Street, London, WC2B 5PS
Fax 020-7430 6155   Tel 020-7430 6000
Website: www.carat.com
Clients include Cadburys, American Express and Courts.
CDP Media Company
33-34 Soho Square, London, W1V 6DP
Fax 020-7292 4010   Tel 020-7292 4000
Clients include Honda and Switch
CIA Medianetwork
1 Paris Garden, London, SE1 8NU
Fax 020-7803 2080   Tel 020-7633 9999
Clients include Odeon, Early Learning Centre.
Collins Partnership
11 Calico House, Plantation Wharf, London, SW11 3TN
Fax 020-7738 0014   Tel 020-7738 0177
Dixon Moutrie Silkstone
49-51 Carnaby Street, London, W!v 1PF
Fax 020-7437 1287   Tel 020-7437 1317
Clients include Thomas Cook, Bic and Hertz
Griffin Bacal Advertising
20-22 Stukeley Street, London, WC2B 5LR
Fax 020-7831 0567   Tel 020-7831 4555
Clients include Burberrys and Hasbro
IDK Media
1 Paris Garden, London, SE1 8NU
Fax 020-7803 2086   Tel 020-7803 2400
Website: www.tempusgroup.com
Clients include Microsoft, Lego and DHL.
Initiative Media
84 Ecclestone Square, London, SW1V 1PX
Fax 020-7663 7003   Tel 020-7663 7000
Clients include Calvin Klein, Christian Dior and Peugeot
John Ayling and Associates
Level 2, 27 Soho Square, London, W1V 5FL
Fax 020-7437 8473   Tel 020-7439 6070
E-mail: jaa@jaa-media.co.uk
Clients include Dairycrest and Savacentre

Lavery Rowe Advertising
69-71 Newington Causeway, London, SE1 6BD
Fax 020-7407 4612   Tel 020-7378 1780
E-mail: sales@laveryrowe.demon.co.uk

Leagas Delaney
233 Shaftsbury Avenue, London, WC2H 8EL
Fax 020-7240 9005   Tel 020-7836 4455
Web: www.leagas.co.uk
Clients include Addidas and Fanta

Leo Burnett
60 Sloane Avenue, London, SW3 3XE
Fax 020-7591 9126   Tel 020-7591 9111
Clients include McDonalds and Kellogg's.

Manning Gottlieb Media
Seymour Mews House, Wigmore Street, London,
W1H 0AA
Fax 020-7412 0244   Tel 020-7470 5300
Clients include Eurostar, Nike and Virgin Direct.

Matters Media
25 Gosfield Street, London, W1P 7HB
Fax 020-7637 9364   Tel 020-7637 9363
E-mail: matters@mattersmedia.co.uk
Clients include Easyjet and Carphone Warehouse

MBS Group
84 Grovesnor Street, London, W1X 0LD
Fax 020-7409 0965   Tel 020-7493 1616

Media Shop
14-16 Regents Street, London, SW1Y 4PH
Fax 020-7766 5050   Tel 020-7766 5000

MediaCom TMB
180 North Gower Street, London NW1 2NB
Fax 020-7874 5999   Tel 020-7874 5500
E-mail: nick.lawson@mediacomtmb.com
Clients include BP, Mars, Procter & Gamble, Direct
Line and Universal.

Media Junction
18 All Saints Road, London, W11 1HH
Fax 020-7460 9209   Tel 020-7460 9206
E-mail: advertising@mediajunction.co.uk
Advertising, management, PR. Clients include Avalon
Promotions, MTV, ZTT, Olivetti Computers Worldwide.

Mediapolis
Commonwealth House, 1-19 New Oxford Street,
London, WCA 1NQ
Fax 020-7393 2525   Tel 020-7393 9000
E-mail: dstead@mediapolis.co.uk
Clients include Colgate, Mercedes Benz and Our Price.

Mediavest
123 Buckingham Palace Road, London, SW1W 9DZ
Fax 020-7233 5677   Tel 020-7233 5678

MindShare
40 Strand, London, WC2N 5HZ
Fax 020-7969 4000   Tel 171-969 4040
Website: www.wpp.com
The product of JWT and The Network merger. Clients
include Kelloggs, Ford and Nestle Rowntree.

Motive
24-27 Great Pulteney Street, London, W1R 3DB
Fax 020-7437 2401   Tel 020-7453 4444
Website: www.bbh.co.uk
Clients include Levi Strauss, Golden Wonder and
Electrolux.

New PHD
5 North Crescent, Chenies Street, London, WC1E
7PH
Fax 020-7446 7100   Tel 020-7446 0555
E-mail: contact@newphd.co.uk
Clients include Midland Bank, BT and Toshiba.

Optimedia UK
84-86 Baker Street, London, W1M 1DL
Fax 020-7486 1985   Tel 020-7935 0040
Clients include Renault and British Airways.

Roose & Partners
100 Gray's Inn Road, London, Wc1X 8AU
Fax 020-7831 8761   Tel 020-7831 7400
Clients include Nestle Rowntree

RPM3
William Blake House, 8 Marshall Street, London, W1V
2AJ
Fax 020-7439 8884   Tel 020-7734 9041
E-mail: post@rpm3.co.uk
Clients include Mitsubishi Motors

Saatchi & Saatchi
80 Charlotte Street, London, W1A 1AQ
Fax 020-7637 8489   Tel 020-7636 5060
Web: www.saatchi-saatchi.com

TCS Media Group
35 Garway Road, London, W2 4QF
Fax 020-7221 0460   Tel 020-7221 7292
E-mail: media@tcsmedia.co.uk
Web: www.tcsmedia.co.uk
Clients include Unijet

Total Media
125 Kensington High Street, London, W8 5SF
Fax 020-7937 7015   Tel 020-7937 3793

Walker Media
36 Golden Square, London, W1R 4EE
Fax 020-7543 4501   Tel 020-7447 7500
Web: www.mcsaatchi.com
Clients include British Airways, RAC and Quantas

Universal McCann
36 Howland Street, London, W1A 1AT
Fax 020-7323 2883   Tel 020-7436 7711
Website: www.mccann.co.uk
Clients include Coca-Cola, Post Office and Black &
Decker.

Western International Media
Bowater House, 68-114 Knightsbridge, London,
SW1X 7LT
Fax 020-7823 7115   Tel 020-7581 1455
E-mail: western@wim.co.uk
Clients include Vauxhall and Smirnoff.

Zenith Media
63-65 North Wharf Road, London, W2 1LA
Fax 020-7706 4028   Tel 020-7224 8500
Website: www.zenithmedia.co.uk
Clients include BMW, Rover and B&Q.
Zenith is jointly owned by Saatchi & Saatchi and
Cordiant Communications. It is the largest buyer of
media in the UK and has offices in 25 countries across
Europe. Publishes various media guides including UK
Media Yearbook, Top 50 European Media Owners,
Digital Media and Television in Europe to 2007.

PR AGENCIES

Top 30 PR agencies, by billings

1 International Public Relations
2 Bell Pottinger Communications
3 Citigate Dewe Rogerson
4 Hill and Knowlton (UK)
5 Burson-Marsteller
6 Countrywide Porter Novelli
7 Charles Barker BSMG
8 Ketchum
9 Edelman PR Worldwide
10 Euro RSCG International Comms
11 Grayling Group
12 Text 100
13 Medical Action Communications
14 GCI/APCO
15 Freud Communications
16 College Hill Associates
17 Cohn and Wolfe
18 Fishburn Hedges
19 Key Communications
20 Harrison Cowley
21 Harvard Public Relations
22 Brodeur A Plus
23 Firefly Communications
24 The Shire Hall Group
25 Richmond Towers
26 Beattie Media
27 Holmes and Marchant
28 Nexus Choat
29 Manning, Selvage and Lee
30 QBO

Source: PR Week

Avalon Publicity
4a Exmoor Street, London W10 6BD
Fax 020-7598 7223   Tel 020-7598 7222
E-mail: jamesh@avalonuk.com
Beattie Media
18 Glasgow Road, Uddington, G71 7AS
Fax 01698 787879   Tel 01698-787878
Web: www.beattiemedia.co.uk
Bell Pottinger Communications
7 Hertford Street, London W1Y 8LP
Fax 020-7629 1277   Tel 020-7495 4044
Brodeur A Plus
New Tithe Court, 23 Datchet Road, Slough, Berks,
SL3 7PT
Fax 01753-790701   Tel 01753-790700
Web: www.brodeurapluc.com

Burson-Marsteller
24-28 Bloomsbury Way, London WC1A 2PX
Fax 020-7430 1033   Tel 020-7831 6262
Website: www.bm.com
Clients include: Unilever, World Bank, McDonalds
Charles Barker
110 St Martins Lane, London WC2N 4DY
Fax 020-7841 5777   Tel 020-7841 5555
Website: www.charles.co.uk
Citigate Dewe Rogerson
3 London Wall Buildings, London EC2M 5SY
Fax 020-7628 3444   Tel 020-7638 9571
E-mail: info@citigatedr.co.uk
Website: www.citigate.com
Cohn and Wolfe
30 Orange Street, London, WC2H 7LZ
Fax 020-7331 9088   Tel 020-7331 5300
Web: www.cohnwolfe.com
College Hill Associates
29 Gresham Street, London, EC2V 7AH
Fax 020-7248 3295   Tel 020-7457 2020
Countrywide Porter Novelli
South Bar House, Banbury, Oxfordshire OX16 9AD
Fax 01295-224444   Tel 01295-224400
Website: ww.countrywidepn.co.uk
Edelman PR Worldwide
28-29 Haymarket, London SW1Y 4SP
Fax 020-7344 1222   Tel 020-7344 1200
E-mail: central@edeluk.com
Website: www.edelman.com
Euro RSCG International Communications
69 Monmouth Street, London, WC2H 9DG
Fax 020-7497 8915   Tel 020-7497 3001
Financial Dynamics
30 Furnival Street, London EC4A 1JE
Fax 020-7831 6038   Tel 020-7831 3113
Firefly Communications
25 Unit 4, The Coda Centre, 189 Munster Road,
London, SW6 6AW
Fax 020-7385 4768   Tel 020-7381 4505
Web: www.firefly.co.uk
Fishburn Hedges
1 Northumberland Avenue, Trafalgar Square, London,
WC2H 7LZ
Fax 020-7839 2858   Tel 020-7839 4321
Freud Communications
19-21 Mortimer Street, London, W1N 8DX
Fax 020-7637 2626   Tel 020-7580 2626
Web: www.freud.co.uk
GCI
1 Chelsea Manor Gardens, London, SW3 5NS
Fax 020-7352 6244   Tel 020-7351 2400
Email: gcilondon@graynet.com
Web: www.gcilondon.com
Golin Harris International
Paragon Golin Harris, Film House, 142 Wardour
Street, London, W1V 4LL
Fax 020-7437 6085   Tel 020-7734 6030
Web: www.golinharris.com
Grayling Group
4 Bedford Square, London WC1B 3RA
Fax: 020-7631 0602   Tel: 020-7255 1100

Harrison Cowley
Dragon Court, 27 Macklin Street, London, WC2B 5LX
Fax 020-7404 6888   Tel 020-7404 6777
Web: www.harrisoncowley.com

Harvard Public Relations
Summerhouse Lane, Harmansworth, Middx UB70AW
Fax 020-8 897 3242   Tel 020-8759 0005
Web: www.harvard.co.uk

Hill and Knowlton
5 Theobalds Road, London WC1X 8SH
Fax 020-7413 3111   Tel 020-7413 3000
E-mail: info@hillandknowlton.com
Website: www.hillandknowlton.com

Holmes and Marchant
15-17 Huntsworth Mews, London, NW1 6DD
Fax 020-7706 4732   Tel 020-7402 2272
Web: www.holmes-marchant.com

Ketchum
8-14 Southampton Street, London, WC2E 7HA
Fax 020-7836 3695   Tel 020-7836 6666
Web: www.ketchum.com

Key Communications
Kings Court, 2-16 Goodge Street, London, W1P 1SF
Fax 020-7580 0333   Tel 020-7580 0222
Web: www.keycommunications.co.uk

Manning, Selvage and Lee
123 Buckingham Palace Road, London, SW1W 9SH
Fax 020-7878 3030   Tel 020-7878 3000
Web: www.mslpr.com

Medical Action Communications
Medical Action House, Crabtree Office Village,
Eversley Way, Surrey, TW20 8RY
Fax 01784-431323   Tel 01784-434353
Email: team@medicalaction.co.uk
Web: www.medicalaction.co.uk

Nexus Choat
126-128 Cromwell Road, London, SW7 4ET
Fax 020-7373 3926   Tel 020-7373 4537

QBO
22 Endell Street, London, WC2H 9AD
Fax 020-7379 7259   Tel 020-7379 0304
Web: www.qbo.com

Richmond Towers
26 Fitzroy Square, London, W1P 6BT
Fax 020-7388 7761   Tel 020-7388 7421

Shandwick International
15 Queen Street, London, EC4N 1TX
Fax 020-7950 2001   Tel 020-7950 2000
Email: mmurphy@shandwick.com
Web: www.shandwick.com

The Shire Hall Group
3 Olaf Street, London, W11 4BE
Fax 020-7229 2989   Tel 020-7229 9922
Email: info@shirehall.co.uk Web: www.shirehall.co.uk

Text 100
Ariel Way (off Wood Lane), London, W12 7SL
Fax 020-8735 3215   Tel 020-8242 4100
Web: www.text100.co.uk

The Weber Group
2 Endell Street, Covent Garden, London, WC2H 9BL
Fax 020-7240 6195   Tel 020-7240 6189
Web: www.webergroup.com

MEDIA ANALYSTS

Capel-Cure Sharp
The Registry, Royal Mint Court, London EC3
Fax 020-7481 3798   Tel 020-7488 4000
Media analyst: Martin Campbell

Credit Lyonnais Laing
Broadwalk House, 5 Appold Street, London, EC2A 2DA
Fax 020-7214 5752   Tel 020-7588 4000
Media analyst: Colin Rothwell

CS First Boston
1 Cabot Square, London, E14 4QJ
Fax 020-7888 1600   Tel 020-7888 1616
Media analyst: Michael Picken

Goldman Sachs
Peterborough Court, 133 Fleet Street, EC4A 2BB
Fax 020-7774 5289   Tel 020-7774 1000
Media analyst: Guy Lamming

Henderson Crosthwaite
2 Gresham Street, London EC2V 7QP
Fax 020-7597 5090   Tel 020-7597 5000
Media analyst: Matthew Horsman

Kleinwort Benson
20 Fenchurch Street, London, EC3P 3DB
Fax 020-7475 2690   Tel 020-7623 8000
Media analyst: Michael Hilton

Merrill Lynch
Ropemaker Place, 25 Ropemaker Street, London,
EC2Y 9LY
Fax 020-7772 2614   Tel 020-7867 2000
Media analyst: Neil Blackley

Panmure Gordon
New Broad Street House, 35 New Broad Street,
London, EC2M 1SQ
Fax 020-7920 9305   Tel 020-7638 4010
Media analyst: Lorna Tilbian

Pricewaterhouse Coopers
Southwark Towers,32 London Bridge Street, London,
SE1W 9SY
Fax 020-7378 0647   Tel 020-7939 3000
Head of entertainment and media: Ed Straw

Salomon Smith Barney
Victoria Plaza, 111 Buckingham Palace Road,
London, SW1W 0SB
Fax 020-7222 7062   Tel 020-7721 2000
Media analyst: Richard Dale

SBC Warburg Dillon Read
100 Liverpoool Street London EC2M 2RH
Fax 020-7568 4800   Tel 020-7567 8000
Media analyst: Colin Tennant

Schroder
120 Cheapside, London, EC2V 6DS
Fax 020-7658 4032   Tel 020-7658 6000
Media analyst: Patrick Wellington

MEASURING THE EFFECTIVENESS OF YOUR

INTERNET ADVERTISING

SHOULDN'T BE WISHFUL THINKING.

For many companies, the Internet represents both an enormous opportunity as well as an equally large risk. For those charged with investing advertising pounds responsibly, measuring results can be challenging. At PricewaterhouseCoopers, we're working with our clients to pioneer the development of new services and tools which not only enhance the integrity of web advertising, but the accountability as well. So advertisers know what's working for them on the web, what's not, and why. If this is something you might be interested in, you can reach us on our website. (That way we'll also know how effective this ad has been.) For further information, please contact Richard Hartley on 0171 804 2780.   **www.pwcglobal.com/uk**

PRICEWATERHOUSE COOPERS 🖎

Join us. Together we can change the world.

How to complain about the media

For trivial complaints, write to the journalist who has caused offence. More serious complaints warrant a phone call to the editor responsible for the article or broadcast. They will most likely ask for the complaint in writing and a decently phrased letter has a good chance of being printed. With small complaints about a TV or radio programme, try going to journalists and then producers. If these direct routes are closed, try one of the BBC numbers on this page. Likewise with minor complaints about ITV programmes: try the producers, then the ITC. More serious complaints should go to the Broadcasting Standards Commission.

The BBC has recently introduced a new Information Centre in Belfast. A customer service team in London is responsible for gathering material about programmes and briefing the Belfast team. London also handles more complex inquiries. Information and guidance on technical inquiries about analogue and digital services will be handled separately by BBC Reception Advice. There is also a BBC Audience Lines service (formerly Radio Helpline) in Glasgow, which supplies follow-up advice and information on specific radio programmes. And BBC Information will sell tickets over the telephone for BBC Experience.

PRESS COMPLAINTS

Advertising Standards Authority
2 Torrington Place, London WC1E 7HW
Fax 020-7323 4339   Tel 020-7580 5555
For complaints about newspaper and magazine ads.
National Newspapers Mail Order Protection Scheme (MOPS)
16 Tooks Court, London EC4A 1LB
Fax 020-7404 0106   Tel 020-7269 0520
For repaying victims of mail order rip-offs.
Press Complaints Commission
1 Salisbury Square, London EC4 8AE
Fax 020-7353 8355   Tel 020-73531248
E-mail: pcc@pcc.org.uk
Website: www.pcc.org.uk
For complaints about the contents and conduct of newspapers and magazines. Upholds a Code of Practice and advises editors on journalistic ethics.

BROADCAST COMPLAINTS

BBC Information
BBC Information, PO Box 1116, Belfast BT2 7AJ
08700 100 222*
08700 100 212 (Minicom)
Website: www.bbc.co.uk/info/   Ceefax: page 695
For comments and enquiries.
BBC Reception Advice
BBC Television Centre, London W12 7RJ
08700 100 123*
(8am - 7pm weekdays)
08700 100 212(Minicom)
Website: www.bbc.co.uk/reception/
Ceefax: page 695 & 698
For TV and radio reception advice.
*Calls charged at national rate.
BBC Programme Complaints Unit
BBC Broadcasting House, London W1A 1AA
If you think a programme has included specific and serious injustice, a serious invasion of privacy, a specific and serious inaccuracy or serious breach of accepted broadcasting standards, write to Fraser Steel at the above address.
British Board of Film Classification
3 Soho Square, London W1V 6HD
Fax 020-7287 0141   Tel 020-7439 7961
Responsible for classifying publicly shown films:
  U (Universal)
  PG (Parental Guidance)
  12 (age 12 and over only)
  15 (age 15 and over only)
  18 (age 18 and over only)
  R18 (restricted to premises barred to under 18s)
Broadcasting Standards Commission
7 The Sanctuary, London SW1P 3JS
Fax 020-7222 3172   Tel 020-7233 0544
E-mail: bsc@bsc.org.uk
Website: www.bsc.org.uk
The 1996 Broadcasting Act established the BSC to replace the Broadcasting Complaints Commission and the Broadcasting Standards Council. It starts work on 1 April 1997 for those complaining of a breach of privacy or unjust or unfair treatment on radio or TV.
Independent Television Commission
33 Foley Street, London W1P 7LB
Fax 020-7306 7800   Tel 020-7255 3000
E-mail: publicaffairs@itc.org.uk
Complaints about ITV, C4, C5 and licensed cable, satellite or digital television.
Radio Authority
14 Great Queen Street, London WC2B 5DG
Fax 020-7405 7064   Tel 020-7430 2724
E-mail: info@radioauthority.org.uk
Website: www.radioauthority.org.uk
Complaints about commercial radio. Ask for the RA leaflet titled How Do I Complain.

Media training and education

A recent survey revealed that half of all students - yes, one in every two - said some kind of job in journalism would be their favoured career. That desire is reflected in the numbers applying for a plethora of courses which have sprung up to meet this demand. A decade ago students of journalism picked from 100 courses whereas there are now more like 1,500. In consequence the number doing journalism and media studies courses has increased from 6,000 in 1990 to nearly 35,000 today. The job market has not expanded in proportion and the National Union of Journalists estimates there are about four times as many accepted at the institutions listed in the next pages as can possibly expect work in anything remotely connected to the media. So, be warned.

To earn a living in print journalism requires no compulsory qualifications and thus journalism is not really a profession. Once you've got started many - perhaps most - editors hire on the basis of hunch and evidence of past work. Formal qualifications don't count for much. The problem is getting started and a vocational postgraduate course - not a media studies first degree - is increasingly the best way to start, particularly in local papers or magazines. Local papers are once again a good place to start a career. Half run their own training departments, as do many magazine companies. The national papers hardly pay lip service to formal training and are more than happy to draw in the most talented recruits from magazines and locals.

Broadcasting demands specific technical skills which are not taught during a normal education. A more coherent and universally recognised training structure, which is coordinated by Skillset, is therefore in place. The best way into broadcasting is via one of the BBC or ITV in-house courses. Competition for places is intense and intensifies when even the best qualified are looking for work in an area where only about 5,000 people make a living as broadcast journalists. The BBC receives 80,000 enquiries a year about broadcasting jobs, and takes on around 2,000 a year at all grades. That said, the increase in channels is creating new jobs.

At the non-university end of the scale are National Vocational Qualifications, the closest the media has come to a start-off educational standard. NVQs are awarded by the RSA Examinations Board in partnership with the Newspapers Qualifications Council for newspapers, the Periodicals Training Council for magazines and Skillset in partnership with the Open University for broadcast journalism. They are open to those without formal qualifications (hence the nickname Not Very Qualified) and, being based on practical work and continual assessment, can be done at the candidate's pace. NVQs come in five levels. In newspaper journalism NVQs are at Level 4 in writing, production and press photography, and Level 3 in graphics journalism; in magazine journalism they are at Level 4 for writing and subbing; in broadcast journalism there is a single Level 4.

Then there are media studies degrees. Some take the line they are valuable because they give systematic study to the way information mutates during the process of mediation. Within a business led by people who graduated - in what they regard as more rigorous liberal arts degrees during the seventies and eighties - "media studies" is a phrase to evoke an automatic sneer. Most journalists over 30 tend to agree with Roger Scruton who said: "Media studies course content is sub-Marxist gobbledegook and courses are taught by talentless individuals who can't get jobs in the media, so they teach instead. There's nothing really to learn except by way of apprenticeship on the job."

Whether trained in some way or not, the iron law of the trade is that you are only as good as your last by-line. The best places for a first by-line are school and university newspapers, or by making a close study of the stories your local paper runs and offering them something similar for nothing. Ditto your favourite magazines. The rule in all cases is that the smaller the publication, the better the chance of a byline. Aspiring journalists will find a degree in any subject is more or less mandatory. After that the ways into employment are many and vague, usually mundane, and always badly paid.

TRAINING GUIDES

Skillset Careers Pack
Skillset, free　　　　　　Tel 020-7534 5300
Website: www.skillset.org
The full directory is on the internet.
Media Courses UK 2000
BFI, £12.99　　　　　　Tel 020-7255 1444
Careers in Journalism
NUJ　　　　　　　　　Tel 020-7278 7916
How to be a Journalist
Newspaper Society　　　Tel 020-7636 7014
Includes lists of accredited courses.
A Listing of Short Courses in Media & Multi-media
Compiled by Lavinia Orton
BFI, £3　　　　　　　　Tel 020-7255 1444
Lights, Camera, Action!
BFI, £10.99　　　　　　Tel 020-7255 1444
A useful book.
BFI Film and Television Handbook 2000
BFI, £20　　　　　　　Tel 020-7255 1444
Education, Training and Working in Film, Television and Broadcasting
BKSTS, free　　　　　　Tel: 020-7242 8400
The Big Official Guide to University and College Entrance
UCAS, £19.95　　　　　020-7702 9799
Book and CD Rom
Courses in Radio Training
Commercial Radio Companies Association
　　　　　　　　　　　Tel 020-7306 2603
A computer database of radio training opportunities.
The BFI and Skillset Training Database
At Arts Council Regional Arts Boards:
London Film and Video　020-7383 7755
South East Arts Board　01892-515210
Southern Arts Board　　01962-855099
South West Arts Board　01392-218188
Eastern Arts Board　　　01223-215355
East Midlands Arts Board
　　　　　　　　　　　01509-218292
Virgin 1999 Alternative Guide to British Universities
Virgin　　　　　　　　020-7388 3374

RECOMMENDED READING

McNae's Essential Law for Journalists
Tom Welsh and Walter Greenwood, Butterworth
Journalists' legal bible

Modern Newspaper Practice
FW Hodgson, Focal Press
Everything from style to page planning to freedom of the press

News Journalism
Nick Varley, Fourth Estate
One of a range of career guides and a good solid intro.

TRAINING CONTACTS

BBC Training and Development:
Production Training
35 Marylebone High Street, London W1M 4AA
Fax 020-7765 0006　Tel 020-7765 0005
E-mail: training@bbc.co.uk
Website: www.bbctraining.co.uk
BBC Operations and Engineering Training
Wood Norton, Evesham, Worcestershire WR11 4TB
Fax 01386-420145　Tel 01386-420216
E-mail: woodnorton@bbc.co.uk
Website: www.bbctraining.co.uk
BBC Training and Development offers training services in all production, operations and engineering skills. Training can be tailored to clients' requirements and is provided at a dedicated training centres (including Wood Norton), or at clients' premises. Places for freelances on some courses are subsidised by Skillset. BBC Training and Development ISonly available to professionals already working in the industry.
British Kinematograph Sound and TVSociety
Victoria House, Vernon Place, London WC1B 4DA
Fax 020-7405 3560　　Tel 020-7242 8400
E-mail: movimage@bksts.demon.co.uk
Website: www.bksts.com
The BKSTS publishes a regularly updated collection of documents called Education, Training and Working in Film, Television and Broadcasting. It accredits courses and runs its own courses.
British Film Institute
21 Stephen Street, London W1P 2LN
Fax: 020-7436 7950　　Tel 020-7255 1444
E-mail: helpdesk@bfi.org.uk
Website: www.bfi.org.uk
The BFI has an Education Department who also publisheS the career books listed opposite.
British Universities Film & Video Council
77 Wells Street, London W1P 3RE
Fax 020-7393 1555　　Tel 020-7393 1500
E-mail bufvc@open.ac.uk
Website: www.bufvc.ac.uk
The Council promotes the study, production and use of TV film and related media in higher education. It runs an information service, has editing facilities and organises conferences, courses and research facilities. It publishes the Researcher's Guide to British Film and TV Collections, the Researcher's Guide to British Newsreels. Film and Television Collections in Europe: The MAP-TV Guide and the magazine Viewfinder.
Broadcast Journalism Training Council
39 Westbourne Gardens, London W2 5NR
Fax 020-7727 9522　　Tel 020-7727 9522
E-mail: secretary@bjtc.org.uk
Website: www.bjtc.org.uk
The BJTC promotes professional standards in training broadcast journalists. It is a charity whose subscribers come from all sides of the radio and TV industry, the NUJ and colleges offering broadcast journalism. courses. It advises those hoping to become broadcast journalists and developers of BCTJ-recognised courses.

BECTU: Broadcasting Entertainment Cinematograph & Theatre Union

111 Wardour Street, London W1V 4AY
Fax 020-7437 8258   Tel 020-7437 8506
E-mail: bectu@geo2.poptel.org.uk
Website: www.bectu.org.uk
BECTU is the trade union for workers across the entertainment and media industry. It offers a Student Link-up Scheme to arts and media students, and an introductory membership rate to course graduates. It can give some careers advice (s.a.e. please), but works with Skillset, regional training consortia and FT2 in promoting access, equality of opportunity, quality training, trainees' safety and optimum employment prospects once training has ended. It publishes a journal. Stage Screen & Radio, ten times a year.

Cyfle

Gronant, Penrallt Isaf, Caernarfon, Gwynedd LL55 1NS
Fax 01286-678831   Tel 01286-671000
E-mail: cyfle@cyfle-cyf.demon.co.uk
Website: www.cyfle-cyf.demon.co.uk
Training for the Welsh film and TV industry.

Educational Television and Media Assoc.

37 Monkgate, York, YO31 7PB
Fax 01904-639212   Tel 01904-639212
E-mail Josie.key@etma.u-net.com
Website: www.etma.org.uk
Brings together organisations and individuals using TV and other media for education and training. Holds annual conference and video competition. Publishes newsletter and academic-oriented Journal of Educational Media. New members welcome.

Film Education

27-31 Charing Cross Road, London WC2H 0AU
Fax 020-7839 5052   Tel 020-7976 2291
E-mail: postbox@filmeducation.org
Website: www.filmeducation.org
Film Education is a registered charity supported by the UK film industry. Its aims are to develop the use of film in the school curriculum and to facilitate the use of cinemas by schools. To this end it publishes a variety of free teaching materials, produces educational television programmes, organises screenings and runs a range of workshops, events and In Service Training courses.

FT2 - Film and Television Freelance Training

Warwick House, 9 Warwick Street, London W1R 5RA
Fax 020-7287 9899   Tel 020-7734 5141
E-mail: info@ft2.org.uk
Website: www.ft2.org.uk
FT2 provides new entrant training in the junior construction, production and technical grades for the freelance sector of the film and television industry. It is funded by the Skillset Freelance Training Fund, European Social fund and C4 and runs three projects:
FT2 New Entrant Technical Training A two year course for young people to become technical assistants.
FT2 Setcrafts Apprenticeship Training Scheme For young people to enter the freelance features and commercials as carpenters, plasterers and set painters.
FT2 Freelance Access to Skillset NVQ Assessment To enable existing freelances to undertake subsidised assessments against the Skillset NVQs.

First Film Foundation

9 Bourlet Close,London W1P 7PJ
Fax 020-7580 2116   Tel 020-7580 2111
Development and training provider for new writing, producing and directing talent working on feature film projects. Schemes include a pan-European screen writers programme and the promotion of new British directors to the New York and LA film industries. The Foundation offers a script feedback service.

Institute of Communications Studies

University of Leeds, West Yorkshire LS2 9JT
Fax 0113-233 5820   Tel 0113-233 5820
E-mail: office3@ics-server.novell.leeds.ac.uk
Website: www.leeds.ac.uk/ics
Britain's oldest media research body looking mainly at the role of TV in political communications, now also a teaching department. Three year BA in Broadcasting Studies, three year BA in Broadcast Journalism, degree schemes in association with the BBC and a three year broadly based BA in Communications. MAs in communications and international communications.

National Association for Higher Education in the Moving Image (NAHEMI)

Yossi Bal, NAHEMI, Chair, Sir John Cass Department of Art, c/o London Guildhall University, Central House, 59-63 Whitechapel High Street, London E1 7PF
Tel 020-7320 1000 x 1956
Forum for debate on all aspects of film, video and TV education. Fosters links with industry, the professions and government. Represents all courses offering a major practical study in film, video or TV at higher education level.

National Council for the Training of Journalists

Latton Bush Centre, Southern Way, Harlow, Essex CM18 7BL
Fax 01279-438008   Tel 01279-430009
E-mail: NCTJ@itecharlow.co.uk
Website: www.itecharlow.co.uk/nctj/
The NCTJ is a charity which runs the most widely accepted independent training schemes for print journalists. It accredits courses at universities and colleges and should be the first point of contact for those who need to know more of the pre-entry, block and day release options for formal training. The NCTJ has three standard textbooks - Essential Law for Journalists, published by Butterworths, Essential Local Government for Journalists, and Essential Central Government for Journalists published by LGC Communications - and provides a mail order service of recommended books on many aspects of journalism. The Council's short course department has provided over 500 open courses for more than 7,000 journalists and distance courses for those not able to attend full time at college.

National Union of Journalists

Acorn House, 314-320 Grays Inn Road, London WC1X 8DP
Fax 020-7837 8143   Tel 020-7278 7916
Website: www.gn.apc.org/media/nuj.html
The NUJ's Careers in Journalism is recommended.

NCTBJ
See Broadcast Journalism Training Council

Newspaper Society
Bloomsbury House, 74-77 Great Russell Street,
London WC1B 3DA
Fax 020-7631 5119   Tel 020-7636 7014
E-mail: ns@newspapersoc.org.uk
Website: www.newspapersoc.org.uk
The Society takes a broad interest in local newspaper
training acting as industry training organisation and
lead body. Although the Society leaves course
accreditation to the NCTJ, it is a prime source of
information on all aspects of newspaper training and its
leaflet Training to be a Journalist, is recommended.

OCR
Westwood Way, Coventry CV4 8JQ
Fax 024-7642 1944   Tel 024-7647 0033
Website: www.ocr.org.uk
The vocational and academic awarding body.

Periodicals Training Council
55/56 Queen's House, Lincoln's Inn Fields, London
WC2A 3LJ
Fax 020-7404 4167   Tel 020-7404 4168
E-mail: training@ppa.co.uk
Website: www.ppa.co.uk
The PTC is the training arm of the Periodical
Publishers Association. It aims to enhance the
performance of the UK magazine industry and act as a
focus for training. It has recently been active in setting
up magazine NVQs and has accredited the vocational
courses in periodical journalism listed below. The
Council publishes PPA Training Programme,which has
full listings of all the courses run throughout the year at
the PPA; also A Career in Magazines, which is available
free.

Scottish Daily Newspaper Society
48 Palmerston Place, Edinburgh EH12 5DE
Fax 0131-220 4344   Tel 0131-220 4353
E-mail: info@sdns.org.uk
The major training co-ordinator in Scotland.

Scottish Newspaper Publishers Association
48 Palmerston Place, Edinburgh EH12 5DE
Fax 0131-220 4344   Tel 0131-220 4353
E-mail: info@snpa.org.uk
Website: www.snpa.org.uk
Contact point for SVQ, the Scottish version of NVQs.

Society of Editors
University Centre, Granta Place, Mill Lane, Cambidge
CB2 1RU
Fax 01223-304090   Tel 01223-304080
Professional association for national, regional and local
newspaper editors, and their counterparts in
broadcasting. Lobbies and campaigns on media
freedom issues, self regulation of the press and
training. Publishes monthly journal.

WAVES
4 Wild Court, London WC2B 4AU
Tel 020-7242 2765   Fax 020-7430 1076
Runs practical and theoretical training courses for
women in broadcast video and new digital media.

Skillset
91-101 Oxford Street, London W1R 1RA
Fax 020-7534 5333   Tel 020-7534 5300
E-mail: info@skillset.org
Website: www.skillset.org
The National Training Organisation for broadcast, film,
video and multi media. Recognised by Government as
the voice of the industry in training. Operates at a
strategic level to improve training and education policy
and provision. Publishes a careers pack, plus
employment and labour market trends, professional
standards and qualifications and much more. Set up in
1993, Skillset is managed and funded by Advertising
Film and Videotape Producers Association (AFVPA),
BBC, Channel 4, Channel 5, the Federation of
Entertainment Unions (FEU), International Visual
Communications Association (IVCA), ITVA and the
Producers Alliance for Film and Television (PACT).

Skillset Midlands:
Midlands Media Training Consortium
Studio 11, the Nottingham Fashion Centre,
Huntingdon Street, Nottingham NG1 3LF
Fax 0115-993 0151   Tel 0115-993 0151
Website: www.training@mmtc.co.uk
The Big Peg, 120 Vyse Street, The Jewellery
Quarter, Birmingham B18 6NF
Fax 0121-248 1616   Tel 0121-248 1515

Skillset North East:
Broadcasting Centre, Barrack Road, Newcastle U
Tyne NE99 2NE
Fax 0191-232 8871   Tel 0191-232 5484
E-mail: marion-mediaskill@watermans.net

North West Media Training Consortium
Campus Manor, Childwall Abbey Road,Liverpool
L16 0JP
Fax 0151-722 6839   Tel 0151-722 9122

Skillset Northern Ireland:
Northern Ireland Film Commission
21 Ormeau Avenue, Belfast BT2 8HD
Fax 028-9023 9918   Tel 028-9023 2444
E-mail: info@nifc.co.uk

Scottish Screen Training:
74 Victoria Crescent Road, Glasgow G12 9JN
Fax 0141-302 1715   Tel 0141-302 1761
E-mail: training@scottishscreen.demon.co.uk
Website: www.scottishscreen.demon.co.uk

Skillset South West:
59 Prince Street, Bristol BS1 4QH
Fax 0117-925 3511   Tel 0117-925 4011
E-mail: skillsetsw@bfv.co.uk

Skillset Wales
Broadcast Training Wales, Gronant, Penrallt
Isaf, Caernarfon, Gwynedd LL55 1NS
Fax 01286-678890   Tel 01286-671000
or: Mount Stuart Square, Cardiff CF1 6EE
Fax 029-2046 3344   Tel 029-2046 5533
E-mail: btw.cyfle@virgin.net
Website: www.cyfle-cyf.demon.co.uk

Skillset Yorkshire
30-38 Dock Street, Leeds LS10 1JF
Fax 0113-294 4989   Tel 0113-294 4410
E-mail: info@ymtc.co.uk

PRESS COURSES

Newspaper training courses are accredited by the National Council for Training of Journalists, and magazine courses are accredited by the PPA's training wing, the Periodical Training Council. Both these trade bodies support NVQs.

Bell College of Technology
Almada Street, Hamilton, Lanarkshire ML3 0JB
Fax 01698-282131   Tel 01698-283100
E-mail: enquiries@bell.ac.uk
Website: www.bell.ac.uk
NCTJ accredited two year Higher National Diploma.

Bournemouth University
Talbot Campus, Poole, Dorset BH12 5BB
Fax 01202-595099   Tel 01202-595431
E-mail: macugrad@bournemouth.ac.uk
Website: www.bournemouth.ac.uk
NCTJ accredited degree course in multi-media and journalism & PTC.

Brighton College of Technology
Pelham Street, Brighton BN1 4FA
Fax 01273-667703   Tel 01273-667788
E-mail: info@bricoltech.ac.uk
Website: www.bricoltech.ac.uk
NCTJ accredited

Cardiff University
See University of Wales

University of Central Lancashire
Department of Journalism, Preston PR1 2HE
Fax 01772-892907   Tel 01772-894732
E-mail: n.atkinson@uclan.ac.uk
NCTJ and BJTC accredited courses: undergraduate BA (Hons) course, multi-media two years,print, broadcast or dissertation final year. New media option for '99. Separate one year postgraduate diploma courses in newspaper and broadcast journalism. New media postgraduate diploma course in '99. IPR recognised undergraduate BA (Hons) course in public relations. Joint honours undergraduate BA (Hons) courses in journalism and public relations.

Centre for Journalism Studies
See University of Wales

City University
Department of Journalism, Northampton Square, London EC1V 0HB
Fax 020-7477 8594   Tel 020-7477 8221
E-mail: journalism@city.ac.uk
Web: www.city.ac.uk/journalism
PTC postgraduate diploma in Periodical Journalism. Runs a BJTC accredited broadcast and journalism course, masters in International Journalsim and Electronic Publishing and PG Dip in Newspaper Journalism.

Cornwall College
Centre for Arts, Media & Social Sciences, Redruth, Cornwall TR15 3RD
Fax 01209-718802   Tel 01209 712911
E-mail: enqiries@cornwall.ac.uk
BJTC-accredited postgraduate diploma in broadcast journalism.

Darlington College of Technology
Cleveland Avenue, Darlington, Co. Durham DL3 7BB
Fax 01325-503000   Tel 01325-503050
Website: www.darlington.ac.uk
E-mail: enquire@darlington.ac.uk
NCTJ accredited pre-entry academic year, pre-entry calendar year and block release courses.

De Montfort University
The Gateway, Leicester LE1 9BH
Fax 0116-255 0307   Tel 0116-255 1551
E-mail: andiz@dmu.ac.uk
Website: www.dmu.ac.uk
One-year postgraduate Diploma in Journalism, NCTJ accredited.

The Editorial Centre
Hanover House, Marine Court, St Leonards on Sea, East Sussex TN38 0DX
Fax 01424-445547   Tel 01424-435991
E-mail:editorial_centre@hinge.mistral.co.uk
Offers a wide range of journalism courses including pre-entry NVQ, starting 3 times a year.

Gloucestershire College of Arts & Technology
Brunswick Campus, Brunswick Road, Gloucester GL1 1HU
Fax 01452-426601   Tel 01452-426602
E-mail: postman@bgloscat.demon.co.uk
NCTJ accredited pre-entry academic year course.

Goldsmiths College
Department of Media and Communications, University of London, New Cross, London SE14 6NW
                    Tel 020-7919 7616
E-mail: media-comms@gold.ac.uk
Website: www.goldsmiths.ac.uk
MA in Journalism. BAs in Media and Communications; Anthropology and Communitation and Communications and Sociology.

Greenhill College
Lowlands Road, Harrow, Middlesex HA1 3AQ
Fax 020-8423 5183   Tel 020-8869 8600
E-mail: enquiries@harrow.greenhill.ac.uk
NCTJ accredited college for pre-entry print journalism. Full time one year course.

Gwent Tertiary College
The Rhadyr, Usk NP15 1XJ
Fax 01495-333526   Tel 01495-333333
Website: www.gwent-tertiary.ac.uk
NCTJ accredited pre-entry academic year course in newspaper journalism. BTEC Media, two years, full time. HND/HNC Graphic Design, a range of full and part time courses. BTEC photography and photo-media, GNVQ in media also HND and A level courses.

arlow College
elizy Avenue, Town Centre, Harlow, Essex CM20 3LH
ax 01279-868260   Tel 01279-868000
mail: learninglink@harlow-college.ac.uk
ebsite: www.harlow-college.ac.uk
st graduate journalism in newspapers, 18-20 weeks,
CTJ accredited; post graduate journalism in
riodicals, 18-20 weeks, PPA/PTC accredited; post A-
vel journalism in newspapers; HND journalism 2
ars with one year 'top up' to BA.

ighbury College, Portsmouth
hool of Media & Journalism, Dovercourt Road,
osham, Portsmouth, Hants PO6 2SA
ax 023-9237 8382   Tel 023-9231 3287
mail: glenne.martin@highbury.ac.uk
CTJ and PTC accredited courses in newspaper
urnalism (20 weeks) and magazine journalism.

ournalism Training Centre
nit G, Mill Green Business Park, Mill Green Road,
itcham, Surrey CR4 4HT
ax 020-8640 6266   Tel 020-8640 3696
mail: nvq@journalism-training-centre.co.uk
vel IV NVQ Foundation Skills Certificate in
urnalism. PTC accredited. NUJ approved. 3 courses
er year, duration 14 weeks.

ambeth College
auxhall Centre, Belmore Street, Wandsworth,
ondon SW8 2JY
ax 020-7501 5490   Tel 020-7501 5424
ebsite: www.lambethcollege.ac.uk
CTJ accredited pre-entry academic year course. One
ear post-graduate. Also run Access to Journalism
ourse and Print Journalism course.

eeds Trinity and All Saints College
rownberrie Lane, University of Leeds, Leeds LS18
HD
ax 01132-837200   Tel 01132-837100
ebsite: www.tasc.ac.uk
CTJ approved 10 month PG diploma in print
urnalism.

iverpool Community College
ournalism Unit, 9 Myrtle Street, Liverpool L7 7JA
ax 0151-707 8528   Tel 0151 707 8528
mail: livcolnews@aol.com
ne year postgraduate diploma in print journalism; one
ear pre-entry course in print journalism; one year day
lease programme for junior reporters.

ondon College of Fashion
0 John Princes Street, London W1M 0BJ
ax 020-7514 7484   Tel 020-7514 7400
ebsite: www.lcf.linst.ac.uk
TC accredited fashion promotion degee with
urnalism, public relations and broadcast options.

ondon College of Printing
hool of Media, 10 Back Hill, Clerkenwell, London
C1 5EN
ax 020-7514 6848   Tel 020-7514 6500
mail: t.bodenham@lcpdlt.linst.ac.uk
TC accredited BA and HND journalism courses and
edia courses.

Napier University
Department of Print Media, Publishing and
Communications. Craighouse Campus, Craighouse
Road, Edinburgh EH10 5LG
                    Tel 0131-455 6150
E-mail: d.brand@napier.ac.uk
Four year BA (Hons) programme in Journalism.
MA/postgraduate diploma in Newspaper Journalism,
Periodical Journalism, Electronic Journalism and
International Journalism.

PMA Training
PMA House, Free Church Passage, St Ives,
Cambridgeshire PE17 4AY
Fax 01480-496022   Tel 01480-300653
E-mail: admin@pma-group.com
Website: www.pma-group.co.uk
PMA training was founded in 1980. It maintains close
links with the Periodicals Training Council and now
supplies most of the editorial training for the industry.
PMA is based in Clerkenwell, central London. PMA is
officially approved by the PTC, the Newspaper Society
and the BACB. The five training rooms are registered as
an NVQ assessment centre, and workshops are geared
to NVQs. There are over 500 workshops per year
covering editorial, internet, desktop publishing, law,
design, new technology, marketing, PR, production,
advertising, direct mail, radio and publishing
management. PMA also runs a nine week post
graduate course in magazine journalism every summer.

School of Communication
See University of Westminster

Sheffield College
Norton Centre, Dyche Lane, Sheffield S8 8BR
Fax 0114-2602 301   Tel 0114-2602 600
E-mail: mail@sheffcol.ac.uk
Website: www.sheffcol.ac.uk
NCTJ accredited block release, pre-entry academic year
and January-December courses. 18 week "fast-track"
graduate course. Also photojournalism and press
photography.

Training Direct International
Matlock, Derbyshire DE4 5AW
Fax 01629 534116   Tel 01629 534826
E-mail: bissell@trainingdirect.demon.co.uk
A new non-profit NGO for the training and education
of journalists, broadcasters, photojournalists and media
personnel worldwide. Not yet accredited.

University of Sheffield
Department of Journalism, 171 Northumberland
Road, Sheffield S10 2TZ
Fax 0114-266 8918   Tel 0114-222 2500
E-mail: jnlstudies@sheffield.ac.uk
NCTJ accredited. BA in Journalism Studies, masters
programme in Journalism Studies with pathways in
print and broadcast.

South East Essex College
Carnarvon Road, Southend-on-Sea, Essex SS2 6LS
Tel 01702-220400
E-mail: learning@se-essex-college.ac.uk
BSc (hons) media production and technology - 3 years.
BSc (Hons) multimedia technology - 3 years. BTEC/
GNVQ broadcast media -2 years; print media.2 years.
NCTJ pre-entry one year news journalism certificate.

Strathclyde University
26 Richmond Street, Glasgow G1 1XH
Fax 0141-552 3493   Tel 0141-553 4166
E-mail: gordon.j.smith@strath.ac.uk
NCTJ accredited one year postgradute course.

Surrey Institute of Art and Design
Falkner Road, Farnham, Surrey GU9 7DS
Fax 01252-733869   Tel 01252-722441
E-mail: registry@surrart.ac.uk
Website: www.surrart.ac.uk
BECTU and BKSTS degrees in film and video, media
studies and in animation. BJTC recognised first degree
with radio and print options. BA (Hons) in journalism.

Sutton Coldfield College
Lichfield Road, Sutton Coldfield, B74 2NW
Fax 0121-355 0799   Tel 0121-355 5671
E-mail: SCSE@sutcol.ac.uk
NCTJ accredited.

Training Direct International
Matlock, Derbyshire DE4 5AW
Fax 01629 534116   Tel 01629 534826
E-mail: peterhiscocks@tvtraining.freeserve.co.uk
A new non-profit NGO for the training and education
of journalists, broadcasters, photojournalists and media
personnel worldwide. Not yet accredited.

University of Wales
School of Journalism, Media and Cultural Studies,
Centre for Journalism Studies, Bute Building, King
Edward V11 Avenue, Cardiff CF10 3NB
Fax 029-2023 8832   Tel 029-2087 4041
E-mail: jomec@cardiff.ac.uk
Website: www.cf.ac.uk/uwcc/jomec/index.html
NCTJ recognised postgraduate diploma in newspaper
journalism; BJTC recognised course in broadcast (bi-
media) journalism; PTC recognised course in magazine
journalism, IPR recognised course in public and media
relations. Course in photojournalism. Euro MA course.

University of Westminster
School of Communication, Harrow Campus, Watford
Road, Northwick Park, Harrow HA1 3TP
Fax 020-7911 5972   Tel 020-7911 5000
E-mail: barrata@wmin.ac.uk
PTC postgraduate diploma in periodical journalism for
ethnic minorities. Part-time MA in Journalism Studies.

Warrington Collegiate Institute
Padgate Campus, Warrington WA2 0DB
Fax 01925-816077   Tel 01925-814343
E-mail: wci@warr.ac.uk
Website: www.warr.ac.uk
NCTJ accredited.

Wulfrun College
Paget Road, Wolverhampton WV6 0DU
Fax 01902-423070   Tel 01902-317700
Day-release/pre-entry. NCTJ, C &G and BTEC courses.

GROUP TRAINING (PRESS)

These are the in-house courses run by the local
newspaper companies:

Johnston Training Centre
Upper Mounts, Northampton NN1 3HR
Fax 01604-250186   Tel 01604-231528

Midland News Association
Rock House, Old Hill, Tettenhall Wolverhampton, West
Midlands WV6 8QB
Fax 01902-759478   Tel 01902-742126
NCTJ accredited. Takes a few non-company trainees.
Couses start March and end September.

Regional Independent Media
Wellington Street, Leeds, West Yorks LS1 1RF
Fax 0113-242 1814   Tel 0113-243 2701
E-mai: vicky.blades@rim.co.uk
Accredited courses: Diplomas in Journalism and News
Writing to NVQ level

Trinity Editorial Training Centre
Thomson House, Groat Market, Newcastle upon Tyne
NE1 1ED
Fax 0191-201 6014   Tel 0191-201 6043
E-mail: editorial@trinity-training.co.uk
Website: www.trinity-training.co.uk

Trinity PLC
Kingsfield Court, Chester Business Park, Chester,
CH4 9RE
Fax 01244-687100   Tel 01244-350555
E-mail: trinity@trinity.plc.uk
Website: www.trinity.plc.uk

TV/RADIO COURSES

BBME Training, The Radio and Television School
7-9 The Broadway, Newbury, Berkshire RG14 1AS
Fax 01635-38802   Tel 016635-232800
E-mail: info@bbme.co.uk
Website: www.radiotvschool.co.uk
Short courses in radio and TV presentation to the public and corporate sector. Not yet accredited.

Bell College of Technology
Almade Street, Hamilton, Lanarkshire ML3 0JB
Fax 01698-282131   Tel 01698-283100
E-mail: enquiries@bell.ac.uk
Website: www.bell.ac.uk
BJTC recognised postgrad diploma in radio journalism.

Bournemouth & Poole College of Art & Design
See The Arts Institute at Bournemouth

The Arts Institute at Bournemouth
Wallisdown, Poole, Dorset BH12 5HH
Fax 01202-537729   Tel 01202-533011
E-mail: general@arts-inst-bournemouth.ac.uk
Website: www.arts-inst-bournemouth.ac.uk
BKSTS accredited HND in film and TV. BA (Hons) Film & Animation; Audio Visual Production; postgraduate diploma in Feature Film Production.

Bournemouth University
Fern Barrow, Poole, Dorset BH12 5BB
Fax 01202-595099   Tel 01202-524111
E-mail: emcallis@bournemouth.ac.uk
Website: www.bournemouth.ac.uk
Degrees in Media Production, TV & Video Production. BJTC, NCTJ & PTC endorsed Multi-media journalism degree. Postgrad in TV and Video Production. Post graduate courses in Radio Production and Multi-Media Journalism.

University of Bradford
Richmond Road, Bradford BD7 1DP
Fax 01274-235340   Tel 01274-232323
E-mail: publlic-relations@bradford.ac.uk
Website: www.brad.ac.uk/index.html
BSc in electronic imaging and media communications.

University of Bristol
Woodland Road, Bristol BS8 1UP
Fax 0117-928 8251   Tel 0117-928 7838
Website: www.bristol.ac.uk

University of Central England in B'ham
Dept. of Media and Communication, Perry Bar, Birmingham B42 2SU
Fax 0121-331 6501   Tel 0121-331 5719
E-mail: rod.pilling@uce.ac.uk
Website: www.uce.ac.uk
BJTC postgraduate course in broadcast journalism.

University of Central Lancashire
Department of Journalism, Preston PR1 2HE
Fax 01772-892907   Tel 01772-893730
E-mail: l.j.williamsl@uclan.ac.uk
Website:
www.uclan.ac.uk/facs/lbs/depts/journ/index.htm
NCTJ and BJTC accredited courses: undergraduate BA (Hons) course, multi-media two years,print, broadcast or dissertation final year. New media option for '99. Separate one year postgraduate diploma courses in newspaper and broadcast journalism. New media postgraduate diploma course in '99. IPR recognised undergraduate BA (Hons) course in public relations. Joint honours undergraduate BA (Hons) courses in journalism and public relations.

Centre for Journalism Studies
See University of Wales

City University
Department of Journalism, Northampton Square, London EC1V 0HB
Fax 020-7477 8594   Tel 020-7477 8221
E-mail: journalism@city.ac.uk
Web: www.city.ac.uk/journalism
BJTC postgrad diploma in broadcast journalism.

Falmouth College of Arts
Woodlane, Falmouth, Cornwall TR11 4RH
Fax 01326-212261   Tel 01326-211077
E-mail: reception@falmouth.ac.uk
BJTC recognised courses. Postgraduate diploma in Boadcast Journalism and Broadcast Television. BA Hons in Broadcasting Studies. Plus English with Media Studies and Journalism Studies.Plus a postgrad diploma in Professional Writing and Online Journalism.

Goldsmiths College
Department of Media and Communications, University of London, New Cross, London SE14 6NW
                    Tel 020-7919 7616
E-mail: media-comms@gold.ac.uk
Website: www.goldsmiths.ac.uk
MAs in TV Journalism; TV Documentary; TV Drama; Radio and Image and Communication. BAs in Media and Communications; Anthropology and Communitation and Communications and Sociology.

Gwent Tertiary College
The Rhadyr, Usk NP15 1XJ
Fax 01495-333526   Tel 01495-333333
Website: www.gwent-tertiary.ac.uk
BTEC Media, two years, full time. Emphasis on digital and linear TV/video. HND/HNC Graphic Design, a range of full and part time courses. BTEC photography and photo-media; GNVQ in media also HND and A level courses.

Highbury College, Portsmouth
School of Media & Journalism, Dovercourt Road, Cosham, Portsmouth, Hants PO6 2SA
Fax 023-9237 8382   Tel 023-9231 3287
E-mail: glenne.martin@highbury.ac.uk
BJTC recognised post-graduate diploma in broadcast journalism.

Leeds Trinity and All Saints College
University of Leeds, Leeds LS18 5HD
Fax 01132-837321   Tel 0113-2837100
Website: www.tasc.ac.uk
BJTC recognised postgraduate diploma in bi-media journalism, radio/television. Professional/practical studies within BA (Hons) joint subject programmes.

University of Leeds
Institute of Communications Studies, Roger Stevens building, University of Leeds, Leeds LS2 9JT
Fax 0113-233 5809   Tel 0113-233 5814
E-mail: j.stamper@leeds.ac.uk
BA in Broadcast Journalism.

London College of Printing
10 Back Hill. Clerkenwell, London EC1R 5EN
Fax 020-7514 6848   Tel 020-7514 6500
E-mail: s.cornes@lcp.linst.ac.uk
Website; www.lcp.linst.ac.uk
BJTC diploma in Broadcast Journalism.

London International Film School
24 Shelton Street, London WC2H 9HP
Fax 020-7497 3718   Tel 020-7836 9642
E-mail: lifs@dial.pipex.com
Website: www.lifs.org.uk

University of London
Goldsmith's College, London SE14 6NW
Tel 020-7919 7611
E-mail: t.crook@gold.ac.uk
Website: www.gold.ac.uk
BJTC recognised course. MA Radio covering journalism, drama and new sound technology.

National Film and Television School
Beaconsfield Studios, Bucks HP9 1LG
Fax 01494-674042   Tel 01494-671234
E-mail: cad@nftsfilm-tv.ac.uk
10 full-time post graduate/post experience courses in all aspects of film and television arts and scienes.

Nottingham Trent University
York House, Nottingham NG1 3JB
Fax 0115-948 6632   Tel 0115-948 6677
E-mail: gillmoore@ntu.ac.uk
Website: www.ntu.ac.uk
BJTC recognised degree in broadcast journalism; and industry led MA in investigative journalism. Also MAs in Online Journalism and Television Journalism.

Plymouth College of Art and Design
Tavistock Place, Plymouth PL4 8AT
Fax 01752-203444   Tel 01752-203434
E-mail: enquiries@pcod.plym.ac.uk
BKSTS accredited HND course in film and TV with optional one year top up to BA (Hons). Plus BIPP accredited Advanced Professional Diploma in Photography, Film and Television.

Ravensbourne College of Design & Comms.
Walden Road, Chislehurst, Kent BR7 5SN
Fax 020-8325 8320   Tel 020-8289 4900
E-mail: info@rave.ac.uk
Website: www.rave.ac.uk
Full-time HND programmes in Technical Operations, Production and Engineering. Degree courses in Professional Broadcasting, Broadcast Engineering and Communication and Technology.

Salisbury College
Southampton Road, Salisbury, Wilts SP1 2LW
Fax 01722-344345   Tel 01722-344344
E-mail: @salcol.com
BKSTS accredited HND in film and TV and BA (Hons) degree in film and TV.

Sheffield Hallam University
Northern Media School, The Workstation, 15 Paternoster Row, Sheffield S1 2BX
Fax 0114-225 4606   Tel 0114-225 4648
E-mail: a.kinsey@shu.ac.uk
Website: www.shu.ac.uk
BJTC post-graduate diploma in broadcast journalism.

South East Essex College
Carnarvon Road, Southend-on-Sea, Essex SS2 6LS
Tel 01702-220400
E-mail: learning@se-essex-college.ac.uk
BSc (hons) media production and technology - 3 years.
BSc (Hons) multimedia technology - 3 years.
BTEC/GNVQ broadcast media -2 years; print media.2 years.

South Thames College
Wandsworth High Street, London SW18 2PP
Fax 020-8918 7136   Tel 020-8918 7000
Website: www.souththamescollege.ac.uk
BKSTS accredited HNCs in TV production and AV.

Southampton Institute
East Park Terrace, Southampton SO14 0YN
Fax 023-8033 4441   Tel 023-8031 9555
E-mail: sef@solent.ac.uk
BSc (Hons) Media Technology.

The Surrey Institute of Art and Design, University College
Falkner Road, Farnham, Surrey GU9 7DS
Fax 01252-892616   Tel 01252-722441
E-mail: registry@surrart.ac.uk
Website: www.surrart.ac.uk
BECTU and BKSTS accredited degrees in film, video and animation. BJTC recognised first degree with radio and print options. There is a BA (Hons) in Journalism.

University of Wales
School of Journalism, Media and Cultural Studies, Centre for Journalism Studies, Bute Building, King Edward V11 Avenue, Cardiff CF10 3NB
Fax 029-2023 8832   Tel 029-2087 4786
E-mail: jomec-diploma@cardiff.ac.uk
Website: www.cf.ac.uk/uwcc/jomec/jomec
NCTJ recognised postgraduate diploma in newspaper journalism; BJTC recognised course in broadcast (bi-media) journalism; PTC recognised course in magazine journalism, IPR recognised course in public and media relations. Course in photojournalism. Euro MA course.

University of Westminster
School of Communication, Harrow Campus, Watford Road, Harrow HA1 3TP
Fax 020-7911 5939   Tel 020-7911 5000/5943
E-mail: barrata@wmin.ac.uk
BJTC accredited postgraduate diploma with periodical and broadcast pathways. Many other courses available.

West Herts College
Hempstead Road, Watford, Herts WD1 3EZ
Fax 01923-812667   Tel 01923-812662
E-mail: viscom@westherts.ac.uk
BKSTS accredited course in media production.

MEDIA STUDIES ETC

This final listing in the media education and training section is of universities offering degree courses in media studies and related subjects like communications, journalism, publishing, broadcasting and cultural studies. It has been taken from UCAS official guide.

UCAS 2000 Entry: the big guide

Sheed and Ward, 14 Coopers Row, London EC3N 2BH   Tel 020-7702 9799

Anglia Polytechnic University
East Road, Cambridge, CB1 1PT
Fax 01223-576156   Tel 01223-363271

University of Wales, Bangor
Bangor, Gwynedd LL57 2DG
Fax 01248-370451   Tel 01248-382017

Barnsley College
Old Mill Lane Site, Church Street, Barnsley S70 2AX
Fax 01226-216613   Tel 01226-730191

Bath Spa University College
Newton Park, Bath BA2 9BN
Fax 01225-875444   Tel 01225-875875

University of Birmingham
Edgbaston, Birmingham B15 2TT
Fax 0121-414 3850   Tel 0121-414 3697

Bournemouth University
Studland House, 12 Christchurch Road,
Bournemouth, Dorset BH1 3NA
Fax 01202-503869   Tel 01202-524111

University of Bradford
Richmond Road, Bradford, West Yorkshire BD7 1DP
Fax 01274-236260   Tel 01274-233081

University of Brighton
Mithras House, Brighton, East Sussex BN2 4AT
Fax 01273-642825   Tel 01273-600900

University of the West of England, Bristol
Frenchay Campus, Coldharbour Lane, Bristol BS16 1QY
Fax 0117-976 3804   Tel 0117-965 6261

Brunel University
Uxbridge UB8 3PH
Fax 01895-203167   Tel 01895-274000

Bucks Chilterns University College
High Wycombe, Bucks HP11 2JZ
Fax 01494-524392   Tel 01494-522141

Canterbury Christ Church University College
North Holmes Road, Canterbury, Kent CT1 1QU
Fax 01227-470442   Tel 01227-767700

Cardiff University of Wales
PO Box 494, Cardiff CF1 3YL
Fax 029-2087 4130   Tel 029-2087 4404

University of Central England in B'ham
Academic Registry, Perry Barr, Birmingham B42 2SU
Fax 0121-331 6706   Tel 0121-331 6650

University of Central Lancashire
Foster Building, Preston, Lancashire PR1 2HE
Fax 01772-892935   Tel 01772-892400

Cheltenham and Glos College of Higher Ed
The Park, Cheltenham, Gloucstershire GL50 2QF
Fax 01242-256759   Tel 01242-532824

University College Chichester
Bishop Otter Campus, Chichester, Sussex PO19 4PE
Fax 01243-816080   Tel 01243-816000

City University
Northampton Square, London EC1V 0HB
Fax 020-7477 8995   Tel 020-7477 8028

Colchester Institute
Sheepen Road, Colchester, Essex CO3 3LL
Fax 01206-563041   Tel 01206-518777

Coventry University
Priory Street, Coventry CV1 5FB
Fax 024-7683 8311   Tel 024-7663 1313

Cumbria College of Art & Design
Brampton Road, Carlisle, Cumbria CA3 9AY
Fax 01228-514491   Tel 01228-400300

De Montfort University
The Gateway, Leicester LE1 9BH
Fax 0116-257 7515   Tel 0116-255 1551

Doncaster College
Waterdale, Doncaster DN1 3EX
Fax 01302-553559   Tel 01302-553718

University of East Anglia
Norwich, Norfolk NR4 7TJ
Fax 01603-458596   Tel 01603-592216

University of East London
Longbridge Road, Dagenham, Essex RM8 2AS
Fax 020-8839 3438   Tel 020-8849 3443

Edge Hill College of Higher Education
Ormskirk, Lancashire L39 4QP
Fax 01695-579997   Tel 01695-584274
University of Essex
Wivenhoe Park, Colchester, Esssex CO4 3SQ
Fax 01206-873423   Tel 01206-873778

Falmouth College of Arts
Woodlane, Falmouth, Cornwall TR11 4RA
Fax 01326-212261   Tel 01326-211077

Farnborough College of Technology
Boundary Road, Farnborough, Hampshire GU14 6SB
Fax 01252-407041   Tel 01252-407028

University of Glamorgan
Pontypridd, Mid Glamorgan CF37 1DL
Fax 01443-482925   Tel 01443-482684

Glasgow Caledonian University
City Campus, Glasgow G4 0BA
Fax 0141-331-3449   Tel 0141-331 3334

Goldsmiths College
University of London, New Cross, London SE14 6NW
Fax 020-7919 7509   Tel 020-7919 7281

University of Greenwich
Wellington Street, Woolwich, London SE18 6PF
Fax 020-8331 8145   Tel 0800-005 006

University of Hertfordshire
College Lane, Hatfield, Hertfordshire AL10 9AB
Fax 01707-284870   Tel 01707-284800

University of Huddersfield
Queensgate, Huddersfield, West Yorkshire HD1 3DH
Fax 01484-516151   Tel 01484-422288

King Alfred's Winchester
Winchester, Hampshire SO22 4NR
Fax 01962-827406   Tel 01962-841515

University of Wales, Lampeter
College Street, Lampeter, Ceredigion SA48 7ED
Fax 01570-423423   Tel 01570-423530

Lancaster University
University House, Lancaster LA1 4YW
Fax 01524-846243   Tel 01524-65201

University of Leeds
Leeds LS2 9JT
Fax 0113-233 2334   Tel 0113-233 2332

Leeds, Trinity & All Saints College
Brownberrie Lane, Horsforth, Leeds LS18 5HD
Fax 0113-283 7321   Tel 0113-283 7123

Leeds Metropolitan University
Calverley Street, Leeds LS1 3HE
Fax 0113-283 3114   Tel 0113-283 3113

University of Leicester
Leicester LE1 7RH
Fax 0116-252 2447   Tel 0116-252 5281

University of Lincolnshire & Humberside
Cottingham Road, Kingston upon Hull HU6 7RT
Fax 01482-463532   Tel 01482-440550

University of Liverpool
Liverpool L69 3BX
Fax 0151-708 6502   Tel 0151-794 2000

Liverpool John Moores University
Roscoe Court, 4 Rodney Street, Liverpool L1 2TZ
Fax 0151-231 3194   Tel 0151-231 5090

London Guildhall University
133 Whitechapel High Street, London E1 7QA
Fax 020-7320 1163   Tel 020-7320 1616

London Institute
65 Davies Street, London W1Y 2DA
Fax 020-7514 6131   Tel 020-7514 6129

Loughborough University
Ashby Road, Loughborough, Leicestershire LE11 3TU
Fax 01509-223905   Tel 01509-263171

University of Luton
Park Square, Luton, Bedfordshire LU1 3JU
Fax 01582-489323   Tel 01582-489286

Manchester Metropolitan University
Academic Division, All Saints, Manchester M15 6BH
Fax 0161-247 6871   Tel 0161-247 2966

Middlesex University
White Hart Lane, London N17 8HR
Fax 020-8362 5649   Tel 020-8362 5898

Napier University
219 Colinton Road, Edinburgh EH14 1DJ
Fax 0131-455 4329   Tel 0131-444 2266

University of Newcastle
10 Kensington Terrace, Newcastle-on-Tyne NE1 7RU
Fax 0191-222 6139   Tel 0191-222 6138

NE Wales Institute of Higher Education
Plas Coch, Mold Road, Wrexham LL11 2AW
Fax 01978-290008   Tel 01978-290666

University of North London
166-220 Holloway Road, London N7 8DB
Fax 020-7753 2677   Tel 020-7753 3355

University College Northampton
Park Campus, Northampton NN2 7AL
Fax 01604-713029   Tel 01604-735500

University of Northumbria
Ellison Place, Newcastle upon Tyne NE18ST
Fax 0191-227 3009   Tel 0191-227 4064

Nottingham Trent University
Burton Street, Nottingham NG1 4BU
Fax 0115-848 6063   Tel 0115-941 8418

Oxford Westminster College
Oxford OX2 9AT
Fax 01865-251847   Tel 01865-247644

Oxford Brookes
Gipsy Lane Campus, Headington, Oxon OX3 0BP
Fax 01865-483983   Tel 01865-483040

University of Paisley
High Street Paisley PA1 2BE
Fax 0141-848 3623   Tel 0141-848 3859

University of Portsmouth
Winston Churchill Avenue, Portsmouth PO1 2UP
Fax 023-9284 3082   Tel 023-9287 6543

Queen Margaret University College
Clerwood Terrace, Edinburgh EH12 8TS
Fax 0131-317 3248   Tel 0131-317 3247

College of Ripon & York St John
Lord Mayor's Walk, York YO3 7EX
Fax 01904-716921   Tel 01904-716850

Robert Gordon University
Schoolhill, Aberdeen, Scotland AB10 1FR
Fax 01224-262147   Tel 01224-262105

Roehampton Institute London
Roehampton Lane, London SW15 5PU
Fax 020-8392 3220   Tel 020-8392 3000

Royal Holloway, University of London
Education Office, Egham, Surrey TW20 0EX
Fax 01784-471381   Tel 01784-443399

University of Sheffield
14 Favell Road, Sheffield S3 7QX
Fax 0114-222 8032   Tel 0114-222 8019

Sheffield Hallam University
City Campus, Pond Street, Sheffield S1 1WB
Fax 0114-253 4023   Tel 0114-253 3490

Southampton Institute
East Park Terrace, Southampton SO14 0YN
Fax 023-8033 4161   Tel 023-8031 9039

University of Southampton
Highfield, Southampton SO17 1BJ
Fax 023-8059 3037   Tel 023-8059 5000

South Bank University
103 Borough Road, London SE1 0AA
Fax 020-7815 8273   Tel 020-7815 8158

St Helen's College
Brook Street, St Helens, Merseyside WA10 1PZ
Fax 01744-623400   Tel 01744-623338

St Martins College
Bowerham Road, Lancaster LA1 3JD
Fax 01524-384567   Tel 01524-384444

St Mary's, Strawberry Hill
Waldegave Road, Twickenham TW1 4SX
Fax 020-8240 4255   Tel 020-8240 4000

Staffordshire University
College Road, Stoke on Trent ST4 2DE
Fax 01782-292740   Tel 01782-292752

University of Stirling
Stirling FK9 4LA
Fax 01786-466800   Tel 01786-467044

Suffolk College
Ipswich IP4 1LT
Fax 01473-230054   Tel 01473-255885

University of Sunderland
Edinburgh Building, Chester Road, Sunderland SR1 3SD
Fax 0191-515 3805   Tel 0191-515 3000

Surrey Institute of Art & Design
Falkner Road, Farnham, Surrey GU9 7DS
Fax 01252-892624   Tel 01252-892608

University of Sussex
Undergraduate Admissions, Sussex House, Brighton BN1 9RH
Fax 01273-678545   Tel 01273-678416

Swansea Institute of Higher Education
Mount Pleasant, Swansea SA1 6ED
Fax 01792-481085   Tel 01792-481094

University of Teesside
Middlesborough TS1 3BA
Fax 01642-384201   Tel 01642-218121

Thames Valley University
911 University House, Ealing Green, London W5 5ED
Fax 020-8231 2744   Tel 020-8279 5000

Trinity College Carmarthen
College Road, Carmarthen SA31 3EP
Fax 01267-676766   Tel 01267-676767

University of Ulster
Cromore Road, Coleraine, County Londonderry BT52 1SA
Fax 01265-323005   Tel 01265-44141

University College Warrington
Padgate Campus, Crab Lane, Warrington WA2 0DB
Fax 01925-494289   Tel 01925-494494

West Herts College
Hempstead Road, Watford, Hertfordshire WD1 3EZ
Fax 01923-812540   Tel 01923-812565

University of Westminster
Metford House, 115 New Cavendish Street, London W1M 8JS
Fax 020-7911 5858   Tel 020-7911 5000

Wirral Metropolitan College
Borough Road, Birkenhead, Merseyside L42 9QD
Fax 0151-551 7401   Tel 0151-551 7472

University of Wolverhampton
Compton Road West, Wolverhampton WV3 9DX
Fax 01902-323744   Tel 01902-321000

University College Worcester
Henwick Grove, Worcester WR2 6AJ
Fax 01905-855132   Tel 01905-855111

Balkan war coverage

NATO's war against Serbia began on 24 March with the bombing of a barracks in Pristina. On 4 June - 72 days later - the Serbs agreed to all NATO demands

RADIO B92 CLOSED

24 MARCH Serbian authorities shut down the independent radio station B92 in Belgrade. The offices were sealed but the B92 staff continued broadcasting via the net on www.B92.net.

THE FIRST INTERNET WAR

26 MARCH "The people who have the Internet print information out and distribute it. People in Serbia are news hungry," said Julia Glyn-Pickett, UK spokesman for B92 radio. "The Net brings the information out," said John Owen of the Internet campaign group Freedom Forum. "The more important issue is bringing it back in."

VIDEO EVIDENCE

4 APRIL Milaim Bellanica, a 31 year old Kosovan refugee, presented the BBC with a video of corpses murdered by Serbs in his village of Velika Krusa. "I have done this so the next generation will never forget what the Serbs have done to my people."

JOURNALISTS IN BELGRADE

9 APRIL Among the handful of journalists who remained in Belgrade a fortnight after bombing began were Massimo Calabresi (Time), Julian Manyon (ITN), Tim Marshall (Sky), Maggie O'Kane (Guardian), Brent Sadler (CNN) John Simpson (BBC) and Tom Walker (Times).

PR MAN IN BRUSSELS

16 APRIL Alastair Campbell, the prime minister's personal PR man, was called to NATO headquarters to advise on how to improve performance of the military's press campaign. Jamie Shea, head of NATO PR, pointed out he'd had similar consultations with other government PRs such as the US State Department's James Rubin. "He [Alastair Campbell] is a key player," Shea said. "We want to ensure we have good lines of communication with key players in all Allied countries."

SERBIAN EDITOR MURDERED

11 APRIL Slavko Curuvija, editor of the newspaper Dnevni Telegraf, was murdered. He had called the Serbian government of "gangsters and near-profiteers" who were "pushing the country to disaster." His paper had continued in defiance of press laws which had effectively closed down four of Belgrade's 11 newspapers.

NO TO BOMBING SERB TV ...

12 APRIL The NATO spokesman Jamie Shea said the Serb state television station Radio Televizija Srbija (RTS) was not a target. He made the distinction between transmitters "integrated into military ... communications" and normal broadcasting facilities.

... TV STATION BOMBED

23 APRIL The Belgrade office of RTS was bombed with the reported loss of 30 lives. "The propaganda machine is prolonging the war and it is a legitimate target," said Clare Short. The European Broadcasting Union argued that even a distorted news establishment should be left in place and John Foster, secretary of the NUJ said: "It's barbarity. Killing journalists does not stop censorship, it only brings more oppression."

FEEBLE PRESS

16 APRIL The Campaign for Press and Broadcasting Freedom condemned the British press for Balkan coverage, saying most jounralists "have abandoned what should be, in a democracy, their proper role as critical independent watchdogs. Nato sources are routinely parroted and pro-war voices outnumber those critical of the conduct of the conflict." The CPBF said the following issues were being ignored: the illegality of the NATO operation; tensions in the alliance; the effects of NATO action on the future credibility of the UN; the underlying motives of US foreign policy in the region; and the US attitude to the UN.

MILOSEVIC'S PCC COMPLAINT

16 APRIL Slobadan Milosevic lodged a complaint with the PCC alleging media harassment. Milosevic - aka Dan - has lived in Ilford, Essex for 19 years and told the PCC he wished to "state categorically" he wasn't related to the Yugosalve president.

TV STATION SEIZED

25 APRIL Studio B, Serbia's final remaining independent TV station, was occupied by Serb troops following repeated broadcasts of interviews with Slobodan Milosevic's deputy prime minister Vuk Draskovic. He'd called for a peace deal which allowed UN troops into Kosovo.

BBC BASHING

26 APRIL Foreign Office officials quoted from an old battle script when they said: "The newspapers have been very supportive but we are getting massacred by the broadcasters." The complaint was levelled at John Simpson in Belgrade and John Humphrys on Radio 4's Today. As well as his broadcast reports, Simpson had written a Sunday Telegraph article saying "I'm sorry the war isn't working." Humphrys said the war was a mess. "Look," replied George Robertson the defence secretary, "can you imagine if during the Second World War you had the opportunity, day after day, of questioning the ministers in that government and asking what if we are defeated at D-Day?" Ben Bradshaw, the BBC reporter turned Labour MP, said: "I believe it is a mistake to allow BBC correspondents to write regular opinioned columns in the newspapers."

STOP THE WAR

1 MAY The independent TV producer TV Choice distributed an anti-war video which gave a platform to anti-war voices like John Pilger, Tony Benn, Tariq Ali and Germaine Greer. "Stop the War gives an eye-opening account of what's really happening is Kosovo," said TV Choice's Norman Thomas. "The film shows the terrible human impact of the NATO bombing: innocent people who have died in the most horrific circumstances imaginable."

BATTLE FATIGUE

10 MAY "Once you have reported one mass rape, the next one's not so newsworthy," Tony Blair told a Newspaper Society luncheon. The prime minister said the British media was beginning to suffer "refugee fatigue", a view perhaps confirmed by ABC newspaper circulation figures showing sales had dropped during April. Anne Robinson and Nigella Lawson used their newspaper columns to say they could not bear any more Balkan coverage.

CNN COUNTS COSTS

14 MAY CNN's president Chris Cramer claimed that $1.1 million of equipment had been stolen, confiscated, damaged or destroyed. "Our revenue does not increase, even though ratings go up," Cramer said. "There's not a great amount of dollars in this war."

THE GUARDIAN

15 MAY Ian Mayes, the Guardian reader's editor, wrote: "On many days there have been 100 or so letters about the war in an average post of 300. The letters' editor says they are overwhelmingly against the NATO action and therefore against the paper's editorial line. A selection of them has been published regularly throughout the war."

FEEBLE RADIO

17 MAY Nicholas Wheeler, editor of ITN Radio, excoriated independent radio for its failure to report on Kosovo. "Is it that the news resource of commercial radio has been so diminished in the pursuit of profit that there's no one left with authority to make the case for breaking news?"

MEDIA ROLE CENTRAL

21 MAY The media played a central role in the Balkan war, according to Richard Holbrooke the US special envoy to former Yugoslavia. The Index on Censorship published a speech where Holbrooke said: "For policy makers, what is reported and what isn't matters profoundly .... I think journalists have done their job ... they should do less spinning and the less over-reacting, but that's something that one can't change ... Milosevic's view on this is well known: he thinks it's a media plot."

Fakes and the media

This has been a vintage year for media fakery, with more notable fakes than ever before. A British Film Institute survey of 450 TV producers, published in May 1999 blamed cost cutting. The respondents also pointed to a TV culture that puts gripping footage ahead of accuracy. "Some felt that bowing to pressures for exciting and entertaining programmes had become almost habitual within factual programming," the report said.

Though many fakes seem comical when they are discovered, they undermine public trust. This point was confirmed by a British Social Attitudes survey showing that only 15 per cent of readers trust national newspaper journalists to pursue the truth above getting a good story. "A dismal figure," commented the Guardian editor Alan Rusbridger at a Preston University journalism lecture. "If I were a press baron, I would care about whether or not my papers were trusted. I think the whole issue of trust will become more important and will have commercial implications for everyone working in the media."

But just about every journalist knows the feeling of faking up more interest in a subject than they actually feel and then compounding small acts of bad faith by using journalistic technique to convert dross into an attention grabbing story. The story's the thing. That's the trade and the trade is changing with a growing number of low budget outlets, especially in TV. There is therefore less time and money to be spent per story and an increasing reliance on freelances with no strong allegiance to a single paymaster. Above all the need for an audience and a hunger for cheap stories nudges the media along from faked interest to outright fakery. And then - how ever much the public scowls at cheats - there's a pleasure, which extends beyond the ranks of journalists, in pulling a fast one and turning a coin while enjoying the limelight, the minute of fame and all the other faked up clichés of a media-obsessed culture.

SURVIVAL

6 AUGUST 1998 Hugh Miles, a wildlife television cameraman, admitted that tame animals are sometimes used in pretend natural settings. When commenting on allegations that Anglia TV's Survival series had used what he called "habituated" hyenas, porcupines and wild cats, he said: "It's a common technique when you need to capture a particular piece of behaviour that is vital for the story you are telling,"

JERRY SPRINGER

10 AUGUST The ITV and UK Living continued broadcasting fight-filled footage from the American import Jerry Springer Show despite well-attested claims that participants had been urged to fake up aggression and fighting. The ITC commented: "Typically the entrance of a new participant was a cue for a physical attack, including one assault which appeared to draw blood." Real blood.

LOOK, NO WHEELCHAIR

11 AUGUST The Sun apologised for taking the image of a woman in a wheelchair out of a picture showing the England cricket team celebrating a rare victory. "It was a genuine mistake and not an attempt to distort the picture in any shape or form," said the Sun's sports editor.

RACING POST

24 AUGUST The Racing Post editor Alan Byrne called the police when he found his paper's greyhound results had been falsified for a betting scam estimated to have cost bookies £15,000. A member of the Mirror Group's sports desk was charged with conspiracy to steal and false accounting. The pedigree of this sort of media fraud goes back at least a century when, on 1 August 1898, bookies paid out real money for a non-existent race which the Sporting Life and the Sportsman had publicised as taking place on a fictitious course called Trodmore.

DADDY'S GIRL

2 SEPTEMBER Channel 4 withdrew a £100,000 documentary made by Blast Films when it emerged that 19-year old Victoria Greetham and her father Marcus were not what they seemed. The programme about fathers and daughters was scuppered when Victoria's real father, Geoff, saw a trailer and phoned C4 to claim true paternity.

WATCHDOG

18 SEPTEMBER The BBC faced a Broadcasting Standards Commission enquiry when viewers complained that scenes of building works alleged to have disrupted a holiday in Madeira had been faked up.

15 TO 1

19 NOVEMBER Regent Productions won an action against Trevor Montague after he had appeared on their game show 15 to 1 under two different names. Mr Montague had to return a £3,000 prize won on his second appearance, plus £500 expenses and court costs.

THE CONNECTION

18 DECEMBER Carlton's documentary about the Columbian drug trade, which was broadcast in 1996 and won several awards and was then exposed as a fake by the Guardian, ended its shabby history with a record £2 million fine from the ITC. The price of faking it was four times the size of any previous ITC penalty, though a small chunk of Carlton's £340 million pre-tax profits.

STARS IN THEIR EYES

28 DECEMBER The ITV programme for gifted amateurs was exposed as employing professionals of 30 years standing. "I can see the temptation for performers is huge, but it is extremely worrying," said Jocelyn Hay of the Voice of the Listener and Viewer. "Once viewers lose trust in programmes, it is impossible to win it back."

STAYING LOST

6 JANUARY 1999 Channel 4 and October Films faced High Court action when Nottingham Council accused it of inducing youngsters to fake scenes of prostitution for a heart tugging documentary. Nottingham Council said the film makers were "undermining our efforts to care for and bring up vulnerable children".

AUTO EXPRESS

15 JANUARY Jaguar cars criticised Auto Express magazine for doctoring a publicity shot and substituting the photographed driver with a journalist driver. Misleading? Not at all said the Auto Express editor David Johns. "The picture was altered purely for the protection of the Jaguar employee."

TRISHA

12 FEBRUARY The ITV big-name morning talk show host Trisha Goddard was revealed as paying fake guests including a fat actress who was commissioned to appear with the brief to say she was happy about her weight.

TV CON MAN

15 FEBRUARY The Mirror exposed lazy TV producers of habitually relying on a publicity crazed disc jockey called Max Bennett to say things like:

"I lost count at 250 one-night stands," on Central Weekend.

"I'm repulsed by fat women," on Thursday Night Live.

"I've had 400 women," on Central Weekend.

"I hate women drivers," on The Time The Place.

"I left a woman for putting her friends first," on Kilroy.

"I'm a control freak. I tell women what to wear and eat," on Kilroy.

"I will take Viagra for days of sex fun," on Central Weekend.

"I'm a sex addict. I can't be faithful for over a fortnight," on Vanessa.

COUNTDOWN

19 FEBRUARY Matthew Parris revealed that celebrities (like him) who sat in C4's Countdown Celebrity Corner were fitted with earpieces to help them make wittier suggestions than the contestants. "Just a helping hand to add to their own ideas," said a Channel 4 spokeswoman. "I wouldn't say countdown is fixed."

CHICKENS

26 FEBRUARY Channel 4 paid a £500,000 ITC fine for faking documentary footage of Glasgow rent boys setting up meetings with clients.

RIGHT TO REPLY

5 MARCH Nick Martin-Clark, a freelance journalist, accused Channel 4's Right to Reply of manufacturing false outrage. He said he'd been phoned by a researcher who had invited him to fume against the Monica Lewinsky interview. "We are a viewer-led programme," replied the researcher. "We will sometimes call back people who have called us in the past. If they don't hold an opinion, they won't come on." Well, if you ask me, I'd reply that I think it's, um ...

GUNS ON THE STREET

23 MARCH Yet another Channel 4 programme, this one a documentary about gang warfare in Manchester which was broadcast in March 1996, was uncovered as a fix. The Guardian alleged a reporter had posed as a concerned citizen, that two reporters were given false names, and scenes of underworld sleaze were generally faked.

PIERS MORGAN

The Mirror editor exposed the Vanessa fake and said: "Desperate researchers put under pressure by shrieking producers descend on any fly-by-night member of the public who will tell the right sob story for £75. It's corrupt, it's wrong , and everybody in TV land knows it's been going on for ages. It's not good enough hiding behind this ridiculous charade that you've all been the victims of cruel hoaxers. Nobody believes that for a minute."

"The BBC has to maintain both its distinctiveness and its reputation," said a leader in the Independent."When audiences watch Jerry Springer or Blind Date they know it is all nonsense; with Vanessa they may know it's rubbish, but they expect it to be true rubbish."

BEAST OF BODMIN

16 APRIL Steve Grayson, the former News of the World photographer who passed off a caged puma as the Wild Beast of Bodmin, lost his claim against ufair dismissal. He'd alleged there was a culture of fabrication on the News of the World, but an industrial tribunal ruled this wasn't so.

GMTV

3 JUNE In the Lorraine's Live slot of GMTV's good morning show, Lorraine Kelly had Anna Cartwright tell of the benefits of the Transform Clinic's lysonix ultra-sound lipoplasty. What the two both knew, but didn't say, is that Ms Cartwright was no disinterested punter but rather employed by Transform's marketing department.

THE VANESSA SHOW

10 JUNE The Vanessa Show, the BBC's confessional daytime audience grabber, was scrapped - five months after Vanessa Feltz and her producers had paid actresses to pretend to be battered wives and feuding sisters.

EVERYMAN

27 JUNE The BBC cancelled Addicted to Love, a £75,000 edition of Everyman with clips of a barmaid detailing her obsessions to camera. She was a Sun reporter, Andrea Busfield, and the BBC sued, saying she had signed an honesty clause. "The BBC failed to follow the most basic rules of journalism," said the Sun. The BBC replied: "Ms Busfield's investigation was a calculated and lengthy deception [which] goes beyond reasonable limits."

Sport and the media

Rupert Murdoch's attempt to buy Manchester United mixed blended four of this decade's most potent proper nouns into the tastiest of news recipes. The Murdoch United mix - which combined a fascination about football and the media's fascination with its own doings - was made all the richer by a thick political sauce.

Sky's £525 million bid in early September 1998 was a test of how much Blair's New Labour felt it owed Murdoch's News Corp for favourable election coverage. While the Man Utd directors wanted to take the money and run, Labour faced a test of integrity which was a sport in itself; the then trade secretary Peter Mandelson was friends with Sky's MD Elisabeth Murdoch; the former Downing Street deputy press secretary Tim Allen was now Sky's spin meister; Gavyn Davies, chief economist of Murdoch's deal makers at Goldman Sachs was married to Gordon Brown's aide Sue Nye; Greg Dyke, who was lining himself up for the BBC director general's job, was a Manchester United director, a contributor to Labour party funds. (Before landing the BBC job in June 1999 Dyke had resigned from Man Utd, though not before he had attracted much criticism, especially from the Murdoch press.)

Anyway, in October Sky's bid was increased to £625 million and Mandelson was said to be backing the sale. It was referred to the Monopolies and Mergers Commission which, with Mandelson well off the political park by the following April, decided to prevent the deal saying it "would damage the quality of British football by reinforcing the trend between the larger richer clubs and the smaller, poorer ones." An odd judgment- a sort of Quality Commission decision - which nonetheless prevented Sky from further monopolising televised football.

As ever, other media companies followed where Rupert Murdoch had led. Carlton and then United News and Media chased Arsenal, the cable company NTL put in a bid for Newcastle United, Central TV courted Aston Villa and the Mirror Group sniffed around after a share of Heart of Midlothian FC in Scotland.

Though none of these deals quite materialised, the groundwork has been laid for a US pattern of the media owning sport interests. Stayed tuned - though you might have to pay to view.

Meanwhile the results of the BBC putting digital TV investment above sport worked to the detriment of licence payers. ITV carried all the games on Man Utd's route to a famous European Cup victory and the FA Cup was also no longer the BBC's. Then the BBC was stumped by Channel 4's £103 million deal to show Test cricket over the next four years. The BBC's £15 million deal to cover UK athletics was some kind of consolation but then came the defection of Des to ITV.

Des Lynam's departure from the BBC in July 1999 made it more difficult for Greg Dyke - the new director general - to cut a new sporting dash

SPORTS COUNCILS

English Sports Council	020-7273 1500
Sports Council for Wales	01244-822600
Scottish Sports Council	0131-317 7200
Sports Council for N Ireland	028-9038 1222

Rupert Murdoch - a year in the life of

SEPTEMBER 1998

Rupert's estranged wife Anna left the board of News Corp with her ex-husband's words of praise. "Anna's support has been enormously helpful to me in what I must admit has been a demanding and turbulent career." ... BSkyB bid £525 million to buy Manchester United

OCTOBER

BSkyB upped the Man Utd bid to £625 million ... Hong Kong politicians recruited Murdoch as an adviser on how to attract foreign finance ... 67 year old Rupert, who is worth an estimated £2.1 billion, was photographed with his new lover, the 31 year old six foot tall Wendy Deng

NOVEMBER

More happy family news when Lachlan, Rupert's 27 year old son and heir apparent, announced his engagement to Sarah O'Hare, an Australian Wonderbra model ... Rupert told a Channel 4 interviewer: "I've been demonised by the Guardian-reading British chattering classes."

DECEMBER

To Beijing where Rupert met the Chinese leader Jiang Zemin who praised him for "presenting China objectively and cooperating with the Chinese press over the past two years" ... Star TV satellite channel reaches 36 million Chinese.

JANUARY 1999

Wendy Deng's role as Mrs Murdoch II was confirmed in a magazine run by Lachlan Murdoch ... Rupert said he had no plans to retire. "My children are not ready yet, even though they might not agree with that. I'm planning to make them wait a few more years."

FEBRUARY

Lachlan moved to America as head of News Corp's press ... BSkyB, in an attempt to get into European digital TV, was in talks with the French TV and film group Canal Plus. "You've got to follow the money," Rupert had said. "A joint venture in Europe is the way forward."

MARCH

Allegations emerged that Newscorp "has paid no UK tax since 1988". The Economist said that despite making £1,387 billion in British profits since 1988, corporation tax amounted paid amounted to nothing. One in 12 of Newscorp's 775 firms is based in tax havens.

APRIL

Anna Murdoch's Californian divorce lawyers concentrated on a $12.7 billion family trust fund as a source of alimony ... Man U was saved from BSkyB ownership when the Monopolies and Mergers Commission ruled against Sky's bid....

MAY

The Office of Fair Trading ruled that Times' price cutting was anti-competitive. The OFT's director-general John Bridgeman said: "News International deliberately made a loss on the Times and that this affected competition in the national daily market."

JUNE

A busy month for Rupert. He took over the chair of BSkyB in a move interpreted as showing a worry that his British pay-TV interests are much threatened by ONdigital. A fortnight later he married Wendy Deng in a yacht which, at the time, was sailing round the Statue of Liberty.

JULY

Rupert flew into London to announce a string of net ventures via E-Loan. An alliance of News Corp and the Japanese investment firm Softbank are part of a $150 million investment to bring online mortgages to Britain.

AUGUST

Jean-Marie Messier emerged as a new - and perhaps unwelcome - man in Rupert's packed life. The boss of the French utilities and leisure group Vivendi paid Pearson and Granada £825 million for a 7.5 per cent of BSkyB. This gives Vivendi a 24.5 per cent holding - and increased control over Rupert's Euro expansion plans.

2000 news lines

The year starts and ends with Millennial stories. In between are big sporting occasions of the Euro 2000 football championships and the Sydney Olympic Games, plus elections for a new president in America and a new mayor in London and the possible birth of the first human clone ...

JANUARY

1 JANUARY 2000Millennium baby boom expected. Italian doctor Severino Antinori of the International Associated Research Centre For Human Reproduction Infertility Unit in Rome aims to deliver world's first test-tube millennium babies by Cesarean section starting just after midnight - has implanted fertilized eggs into 14 women in preparation ... Millennium Dome opens to public 12.00. New Millennium Experience press 020-7808 8200 ... European Commission directive banning leaded petrol comes into force in UK with tougher new rules on engine emissions. European Commission press 020-7973 1992 Department of Environment, Transport & Regions press 020-7890 3395

25 JANUARY Whitbread Book of the Year awards. Nicky Stanton, Whitbread 020-7606 4455, or Karen Earl PR 020-7243 0064.

26 JANUARY The fiftieth anniversary of India's becoming an independent republic within the Commonwealth. Indian High Commission 020-7836 8484.

27 JANUARY Annual meeting of the World Economic Forum at Davos, Switzerland, until 1 February. World Economic Forum press 0041 22 869 1212.

FEBRUARY

Human Genome Project first working draft. Noorece Ahmed/Catherine Nestor, Wellcome Trust press 020-7611 8540/8846.

5 FEBRUARY Chinese New Year - Year of the Dragon. Chinese Embassy 020-7431 8279

27 FEBRUARY Worthington Cup Final, Football League 01772-325800

29 FEBRUARY Leap Year.

MARCH

FIFA Executive votes on venue for 2006 World Cup. FIFA 0041 1 384 9595

1 MARCH Competition Act comes into force allowing Office of Fair Trading to fine companies up to 10 per cent of turnover for breaches of competition law. OFT 020-7211 8900/8901/

9-12 MARCH Crufts Dog Show at NEC, Birmingham. Kennel Club 020-7 518 1008

14-16 MARCH Cheltenham Gold Cup. Cheltenham Racecourse 01242 513014

16 MARCH-9 APRIL Ideal Home Exhibition Earl's Court. Rachael Doff, 020-8515 2000

26 MARCH Oscar awards ceremony. Leslie Unter, Academy of Motion Pictures, Arts & Sciences, 001 310 247 3000.

31 MARCH BSE inquiry report submitted to ministers. BSE Press 020-7261 8377/8383.

APRIL

1 APRIL Joint-Service command controlling RAF, Army & Navy helicopters becomes fully operational, Wilton, Wiltshire. Ministry of Defence, press officer Martin Flannigan 020-7218 3258.

2 APRIL
Sunday Times list of the UK's 1000 wealthiest people. Sunday Times 020-7782 5000.

5 APRIL Tax relief for payers of maintenance payments to divorced spouses abolished, although maintenance payments will continue to be treated as non-taxable income for recipients. Inland Revenue press 020-7438 6692.

6 APRIL Islamic New Year 1421 (may be 5 April 5 depending on sighting of moon in March.) London Central Mosque 020-7724 3363.

12 APRIL David Cassidy 50.

16 APRIL Flora London Marathon. Marathon office 020-7620 4117.

24 APRIL 100th anniversary of Daily Express. Daily Express 020-7928 8000.

MAY

1 MAY Start of Around the World in 80 Days Motor Challenge from Tower Bridge, at 12.30 - vintage & classic cars. Classic Rally Association 01235 851291.

4 MAY Elections For Mayor of London. Dept of Environment, Transport & Regions press 020-7890 4721 or Government Office for London 020-7217 3422.

10 MAY Author of the Year, Amsterdam. Jill Cronin, Bookseller Association 020-7834 5477.

20 MAY FA Cup final. Football Association 020-7262 4542/402 7151

22 -27 MAY Chelsea Flower Show. Caroline Hall, Royal Horticultural Society 020-7834 4333.

26 MAY-4 JUNE Hay-on-Wye Literature Festival. Kate Phillips, press 01497 821217 or Nicole Beecroft, Midas PR 020-7584 7474.

JUNE

10 JUNE-2 JULY The Euro 2000 Football Championships, Holland and Belgium. UEFA 0041 2299 444444.

21 JUNE Prince William's 18th birthday. Buckingham Palace press 020-7930 4832

24 JUNE Glastonbury Festival. Organisers 01749 890254/470

25 JUNE 50th anniversary of Korean War. George Lakey, Korean Veterans Association 01923 227080.

JULY

Queen's Birthday Honours List. Buckingham Palace press 020-7 930 4832 or 10 Downing Street 020-7 930 4433

1 JULY France takes over European Union presidency from Portugal ... In-service date for first of 67 Apache Longbow helicopters. Marcus Deville, MoD press 020-7218 2661.

3 JULY Mayor of London takes up post. DETR press 020-7890 4721 or Government Office for London 020-7217 3422.

9 JULY
Wimbledon Men's Singles Final. Press contacts: Broadcasters Leslie Lorimer, Newspapers Francis Crane, All England Lawn Tennis & Croquet Club 020-8944 1066 .

12 JULY Orange Lodge marches to mark Battle of the Boyne. Northern Ireland Office 01232 520700 or Grand Order Of The Orange Lodge 01232 322801.

AUGUST

4 AUGUST Queen Mother 100. Buckingham Palace press 020-7930 4832.

5-12 AUGUST Royal National Eisteddfod of Wales, in Llannelli. Eisteddfod office 029-20 763777 or 01248 722999.

13 AUGUST-2 SEPTEMBER Edinburgh International Festival. Press 0131 473 2020.

27 AUGUST Notting Hill Carnival. Stephanie Harwood 01342-851001, or Notting Hill Carnival Organisers 020-8964 0544.

SEPTEMBER

A-Level changes mean students can take up to five subjects in first year sixth form via new Advanced Subsidiary exam. Also, introduction of national appraisal system for teachers including plans for performance-related pay. Department of Education & Employment press 020-7925 5105 ... Dr Richard Seed's wife Gloria, 59, may give birth to world's first human clone (of herself) in Riverside, Illinois this autumn.

15 SEPTEMBER Sydney Olympic Games. International Olympic Committee 0041 21 621 6111, Australian High Commission 020-7379 4334

OCTOBER

4 OCTOBER 150th anniversary of the Bowler hat.

18-23 OCTOBER Frankfurt Book Fair. Press 0049 69 21020.

NOVEMBER

This month Nigel MacKnight attempts new water speed record in Quicksilver on Coniston Water, Lake District (site of Donald Campbell's 1967 fatal crash), subject to gaining the necessary approvals. Tel: 01400 281741

1 NOVEMBER Fox Hunting season opens. Paul Latham, Countryside Alliance Press 020-7582 5432, Hunt Saboteurs Association 01273 622827.

7 NOVEMBER The American presidential election. Contact the US Embassy press office on 020-7499 5261 or the US State Department on 001 202 647 2492.

12 NOVEMBER Remembrance Sunday at the Cenotaph in Whitehall. Royal British Legion 020-7973 7200.

DECEMBER

8 DECEMBER The twentieth anniversary of John Lennon's murder in New York.

10 DECEMBER Nobel Prize awards ceremony, Oslo. Contants the Nobel Institute 0047 2244 3680

29 DECEMBER The twenty-fifth anniversary of the Sex Discrimination Act and Equal Pay Act. Equal Opportunities Commission 020-7222 1110

31 DECEMBER 100th anniversary of first Australian cabinet on eve of Commonwealth of Australia being formed. Australian High Commission 020-7379 4334.

31 DECEMBER Sailing: The Race, international non-stop circumnavigation event begins. Pierre Giboire, Mer & Media Press 0033 2 99 84 64 64 ... The Real Millennium - last day of 20th century. Millennium Commission press 020-7880 2007.

Advance Media Information
226 Strand, London WC2R 1BA
Fax 020-8 286 2482   Tel 020-8 549 0799
E-mail: ami@easynet.co.uk
Web site: www.amiplan.com
Thanks to the AMI forward planning service for this sample of forthcoming events. AMI supplies Britain's major news organisations with a daily-updated list of future events, with access to extensive background information.

2000 anniversaries

All events listed here took place in multiples of five years ago. 2000 is the:

25th anniversary of 1975
50th anniversary of 1950
75th anniversary of 1925

JANUARY

1 First issue of The Times published, 1785 (it was originally called the Daily Universal Register). The opening of the Trans-Siberian Railway, 1905. Age of majority reduced from 21 to 18 by the British government, 1970. Broadcasting's new Cable Authority assumes its full powers, 1985; and then closes end of 1990. Launch of the World Trade Organisation, succeeding GATT, 1995. The alleged serial killer Frederick West, who was accused of killing 12 young women, found dead in his cell in Winson Green Prison, Birmingham, 1995; his wife Mary stood trial and is jailed for life on 22 November 1995.

3 Mussolini assumes full dictatorial control of Italy, 1925.

5 The Radio Corporation of America is formed for world broadcasting, 1920. FM radio first demonstrated in the USA, 1940.

8 Birth of the USA's top rock star Elvis Presley, 1935.

9 Labour MP Ron Brown fined £1,000 for vandalising the flat of his ex-mistress, 1990. The government gives £2.2 million for special research into BSE, the new "mad cow disease" spreading rapidly, 1990.

10 The computer pioneer Sir Clive Sinclair - who brought us the pocket calculator and the Z80 personal computer - starts marketing his unique electric trike, the C5, 1985; but production soon stops.

13 Radio 1's key breakfast show DJ Steve Wright resigns and is replaced on 24 April by Chris Evans, 1995; he became famous as presenter of Channel 4's Breakfast Show.

15 The first known telephone directory is published, by Bell's company, covering its three London exchanges and 16 provincials, 1880. Labour-backed newspaper Daily Citizen closes, 1915. Robert Maxwell, MGN owner, sells his 15 per cent of shares in Express newspaper group Fleet Holdings to United Newspapers, allowing their 14 October takeover bid, 1985.

16 Start of popular BBC radio children's programme Listen with Mother, 1950.

17 The BBC radio station CWR (Coventry and Warwickshire) goes on-air, 1990.

18 ITA formally approves the setting up of a news company owned and operated by the ITV companies, 1955; ITN is subsequently incorporated on 4 May 1955.

19 Police arrest 21 animal rights protestors in Brightlingsea as they try to stop the export of live sheep, 1995.

20 Boer War, South Africa: Britons defeat Dutch-origin Boers at Spion Kop, 1900; followed by British victories at Ladysmith 28 February, Bloemfontein 13 March, Mafeking 17 May, Orange Free State 24 May, Pretoria 5 June, Johannesburg 31 August and Transvaal 25 October. British government abandons its plan to build a Channel Tunnel, 1975.

21 Launch by author Charles Dickens of the newspaper Daily News, a Liberal rival to the Morning Chronicle, 1845. Death of influential English writer George Orwell, 1950. The government says pirate radio stations should be replaced by "community" stations, 1985; police raid several leading London stations on 4 February.

22 A senior civil servant is jailed for six months for selling confidential Ministry of Defence information to the Observer, 1985. An Oxford cinema owner is fined £1,000 for not taking a large fibreglass shark off the roof of his house, 1990. Yugoslavia's Communist Party votes to end its post-World War Two controlling of the country, 1990.

23 The first jumbo jet Boeing 747 lands at Heathrow, 1970. First televising of House of Lords proceedings, with a debate on unemployment, 1985. Moscow announces its Red Army will be leaving Hungary, which it has dominated for 45 years, 1990.

24 Death of former prime minister Sir Winston Churchill, 1965. Alan Rusbridger replaces Peter Preston as editor of the Guardian, 1995; Andrew Jaspan takes over from Jonathan Fenby as Observer editor on 7 February.

25 Hurricane-force winds, gusting over 100 mph, kill 47 people in southern Britain, 1990.

27 World War Two: Soviet troops liberate the Nazis' largest factory of death, Auschwitz, in Poland, where 1.5 million Jews were killed, 1945. Death of famous international journalist James Cameron, 1985, age 73. Manchester United's French star Eric Cantona is banned from football for the rest of the season for launching a kung-fu style kick at a fan on the Crystal Palace terrace, 1995.

28 The 1868 Telegraph Act is implemented, bringing the inland telegraph system under state control, and thereby giving Whitehall ، a monopoly in telegraphic communication in the UK, 1870. Launch of the Independent on Sunday, 1990.

29 Death of King George III in 1820, then in his 60th year as monarch. The UK's first trunk telephone line is opened, between Leeds and Bradford, 1880. Margaret Thatcher refused an honorary degree by Oxford University, 1985.

30 Start of the BBC2 daily Newsnight, 1980 Sunday Times editor Andrew Neil is awarded £1,000 damages after the Sunday Telegraph implies he is unfit to edit because of his affair with alleged call-girl Pamella Bordes, 1990.

FEBRUARY

1 Labour exchanges open for the first time, 1910. The animal rights protestor Jill Phipps, 31, killed after flinging herself in front of a lorry carrying live veal calves into Coventry Airport for export, 1995; Brigitte Bardot was among those at her funeral.

2 Death of 97-year old liberal philosopher Bertrand Russell, 1970.

6 Three thousand soldiers and police clear 150 anti-nuclear demonstrators from the Molesworth cruise missile site in Cambridgeshire, 1985.

7 Soviet Communist Party votes to end its power monopoly, opening the way to democratic elections, 1990; in this year many eastern states have their first democratic votes or actions for decades. Pearson, publisher of the Financial Times, donates £25,000 to Labour Party funds, a landmark gesture in the acceptance of New Labour by the big business world, 1995.

9 Dwight Davis creates the Tennis Cup, 1900.

11 American, British and Soviet leaders meet together at Yalta, Crimea, to erect the Iron Curtain and divide the world in post-war decades, 1945. Margaret Thatcher MP, 49, becomes the first woman leader of a major British political party, 1975. Senior civil servant Clive Ponting acquitted of an Official Secrets Act offense for releasing details of the sunken Argentine warship General Belgrano, 1985. African National Congress leader Nelson Mandela freed from South African prison after 27 years in captivity, 1990.

EASTENDERS ON AIR: 19 FEBRUARY 1985
Lesley Grantham and Anita Dobson begin their
screen lives as Den and Angie on Eastenders

14 World War Two: Dresden bombed by Allies, 1945. Perrier withdraws its entire worldwide stock of 160 million bottles of mineral water after traces of the cancer-inducing chemical benzine are found in it, 1990. Britain's first national commercial speech radio station, Talk Radio, goes on air at 6am, 1995.

15 Soccer match between England and Irish Republic ends in riot, with 43 arrests (40 English) and 20 people seriously injured, 1995.

16 The Beeching Report details the forthcoming sacrifice of the British rail network to the road transport lobby, 1965.

18 A new planet is discovered beyond Neptune, 1930; it is named Pluto.

19 First radio service for farmers is broadcast by the BBC (market prices), 1925. Broadcasting of the first episode of the BBC's soap opera EastEnders, 1985. The IBA bans Channel Four from broadcasting a programme alleging MI5 is breaking the law with its trade union surveillance methods, 1985.

20 Angela Rippon breaks through a glass ceiling and becomes the first woman to read the news on BBC2, 1975 (see also 20 June and 23 September).

21 Black activist and Muslim leader Malcolm X shot dead in USA, 1965.

23 Chinese troops occupy Tibet, forcing Dalai Lama to flee, 1910. The Marconi Company begins Britain's first public radio broadcasts (more than a decade before the BBC is created), 1920; twice a day it transmits from Chelmsford half hour programmes of news and music. Technology marched ever onwards and forty years later the the first UK general election results were televised by the BBC, 1950.

26 Barings, Britain's oldest merchant bank, collapses when staff member Nick Leeson runs up debts of £860 million, 1995; he is jailed for 6 years on 2 December.

27 British Labour Party is founded officially, with Ramsay MacDonald as secretary, 1900. Birth of Liberal Democrat Party leader Paddy Ashdown, 1940. The new Cable Authority advertises its first five franchises, 1985. The government announces plans for building an M3 motorway addition across Twyford Down, near Winchester, sparking Britain's strongest antimotorway movement until then, 1990.

28 Vietnam War: Major escalation as USA announces it will carry out sustained bombing of North Vietnam, 1965; this and massive troop deployments in coming weeks signal the start of direct American military action. The London Underground experiences its worst accident so far when 34 train passengers are killed at Moorgate Station, 1975. IRA kills nine RUC members in mortar bomb attack on a County Down police station, 1985.

29 Bunny girls enter the public consciousness when Hugh Hefner opens the first Playboy Club, in Chicago, 1960.

MARCH

1 The new Official Secrets Act comes into force, 1990.

2 Sustained US bombing of North Vietnam begins, 1965.

3 Coal miners admit they have lost their year-long, anti-government strike, and they vote to return to work, 1985; this has been the most important trade union action since the 1970s, and the defeat signals the end of coal-mining and of UK union strength. In Los Angeles a 27-year old man who stole a piece of pizza is jailed for 25 years because he had previous offenses, 1995.

4 The radio station Jazz FM goes on-air, 1990.

7 World War Two: Allied forces cross the Rhine, 1945. Start of the popular BBC radio comedy series Round the Horne, 1965.

8 French Baroness de Laroche becomes the first woman pilot, 1910. Vietnam War: First combat unit of US Marines lands in South Vietnam, 1965; followed by first full battalion of Army troops on 19 March. The duopoly of programme publishing operated by the Radio Time and TV Times is going to end, says the government, 1990. The number of people in Britain with Aids goes over 3,000 for the first time, 1990.

9 BBC starts its Regional Scheme offering alternative radio programmes, 1930.

10 Anti-European sentiment enflamed when Spain sends a gunboat to protect its trawlers over-fishing off the coast of Newfoundland, Canada, 1995.

12 Britain brings in its first 30 mph speed limit, for urban areas, 1935.

14 Launch of the Sunday Pictorial, to become the Sunday Mirror, 1915.

15 Iranian government executes British journalist Farzad Bazoft, born in Iran, for so-called spying action, 1990.

16 In a Mail group case, the House of Lords rules it is not unlawful for bosses to withhold pay rises from employees who refuse to sign personal contracts giving up their NUJ bargaining rights, 1995.

18 Opening of Robert Stevenson's Britannia railway bridge over the Menai Strait, in North Wales 1850. Russian cosmonaut Alexei Leonov becomes the first person to walk in space, 1965.

19 Sheerness lifeboat rescues four pirate radio men from the pirate radio ship Radio Caroline, 1980.

20 A nerve gas attack by religious extremists on the Tokyo subway in the height of the rush-hour leaves 10 people dead and 5,500 injured, 1995.

21 Sharpeville Massacre: 69 black people shot dead and 186 wounded by police in South Africa, 1960. ITV regulations are changed to allow football pools to advertise on screen, 1995. Bank of England deputy governor Rupert Pennant-Rea (the former editor of The Economist magazine) resigns after the Sunday Mirror reveals he has been having an extra-marital affair involving sex in his office and official car, 1995.

25 First public demonstration of television, given by John Logie Baird daily for three weeks in Selfridges store, Oxford Street, 1925. In an early outbreak of jargon which would have warned John Birt's heart, the BBC officially adopts the word "televiewer", 1935; it is later shortened to "viewer". BSB launches its five-channel service (including Galaxy and the Movie Channel), at first via cable, then on satellite, 1990. Independent on Sunday editor Ian Jack resigns because of unhappiness over the way the Mirror Group runs the paper, 1995; he is replaced by Peter Wilby.

26 Grand National horse race televised for first time, by BBC, 1960.

27 An oil platform in the North Sea capsizes, killing 100 people on board, 1980.

28 The world's largest bank is created by the merger of the Bank of Tokyo and the Mitsubishi Bank, with assets of $819 billion, 1995.

30 First transmission of 30-line television with synchronised sound and vision, 1930; the 30-line service closes 11 September 1935.

31 Ramsay MacDonald becomes the first British prime minister to own a TV set, 1930. Serious riot in London by many protestors against the new poll tax, starting in England tomorrow, 1990; the Old Bailey on 6 April orders several newspapers and TV companies to give the police unpublished material on the events.

APRIL

1 The Times publishes the first weather forecast, 1875. Nazi Party formed in Germany, 1920. Britain's longest-ever prison riot begins at Strangeways, Manchester, 1990 (until 25th); buildings seriously damaged.

2 The world's first weather satellite is launched by the US from Cape Canaveral, 1960.

3 Three days before Scottish local elections, a Panorama interview of prime minister John Major promising two tax-cutting budgets is banned following legal action by opposition parties, 1995.

4 The BBC radio channels 2, 3 and 4 are relaunched in new formats: 2 light entertainment, 3 serious music, 4 news and current affairs, 1970.

6 A film is shown to air passengers for the first time, on an Imperial Airways flight from London, 1925. The BBC 2LO radio transmitter is moved from Marconi House in the Strand to the roof of Selfridges in Oxford Street, 1925. Anthony Eden becomes Tory prime minister, replacing Winston Churchill, 1955. The first commercial satellite (Intelsat 1 - Early Bird) is launched, 1965; it makes the first transAtlantic TV programme relay on 2 May, 1965.

9 American Civil War: the Confederates surrender, 1865; the war formally ends 26 May. A judge decides there is no public right of way giving access to Stonehenge, 1905. World War Two: Germany invades Norway and Denmark, 1940; followed by Netherlands, Belgium and Luxembourg on 10 May. The Beatles announce they are splitting up, 1970.

10 Bill Goodwin, trainee journalist on the Engineer, is fined £5,000 for refusing to disclose his sources of certain published information, 1990. The Guardian and World in Action reveal the business activities of Treasury minister Jonathan Aitken, 1995; he begins long-running and unsuccessful legal action.

11 The Daily Express becomes the first newspaper to publish daily television programme details, 1930.

12 BBC Radio Suffolk goes on-air, 1990.

14 Murder of USA president Abraham Lincoln in Washington theatre, 1865. Launch of the Daily Express, by Arthur Pearson, in rivalry to Arthur Harmsworth's Daily Mail, 1900.

18 Death of famous scientist Albert Einstein, 1955.

19 The first hostilities take place in the American Revolution, 1775, ending in 1783 with the setting up of the United States of America. A car bomb left outside a Federal government office block in Oklahoma City by two survivalist fruitcakes murders 158 people, 1995.

20 First sighting of south-east Australia by James Cook, 1770. "Cash for questions" emerges as a parliamentary phrase de nos jours when two Tory MPs are suspended from the House of Commons for taking cash from a journalist, 1995.

22 Birth of VI Lenin, the first leader of post-revolutionary Russia, 1870.

23 BBC Radio Shropshire goes on-air, 1985.

24 Joshua Slocum sets sail from Boston in America in his yacht for the first ever single-handed navigation of the world, 1895. The USA abandons its pretence of supplying "advisers" and officially designates Vietnam as a "combat zone" for American forces, 1965.

25 World War One: Allied troops (mainly recruited from Australia and New Zealand) land in Gallipoli, a large-scale military disaster, 1915. The United Nations is created, 1945.

26 The announcement that the Churchill family is to receive £12 million worth of lottery funding in return for handing over Sir Winston's archives arouses widespread anger, as many people see the material as public property, 1995.

28 World War Two: Italy's leader, fascist Benito Mussolini, is executed by Italian partisans, 1945.

29 Captain Cook lands in Botany Bay, Australia, 1770; he names the region New South Wales. The first ever television interview is held, involving actress Peggy O'Neill at the Ideal Home Exhibition, 1930. The "cat's eyes" glass reflectors are used on UK roads for the first time, 1935. British Satellite Broadcasting launches its unsuccessful TV service, 1990; it merges with Sky TV to form BSkyB on 2 November, 1990. Tony Blair's new Labour Party ditches its 77-year old commitment to nationalisation, 1995.

30 Hawaii officially becomes US territory, 1900. World War Two: German leader Adolf Hitler commits suicide, 1945. Britain abandons the Blue Streak missile project, 1960. Vietnam War: US and South Vietnam forces launch 63-day attack on Cambodia, 1970. The last American troops leave Saigon, ending the Vietnam War, 30 April 1975.

MAY

1 Five Cato Street men excuted by government for apparent political plot against the Cabinet, 1820. First postage stamps go on sale in Britain, 1840. British labour movement celebrates May Day for first time, with huge London demonstration, 1890. An American U-2 reconnaissance plane is shot down over the USSR, 1960. The BBC renames its General Overseas Service as the BBC World Service, 1965.

2 First public VHF broadcasting introduced to Britain, 1955. First satellite TV programme is broadcast to international countries, 1965.

3 Aberdeen Cable becomes the first UK cable franchise to start operations, 1985.

4 Vietnam War: Four anti-war protest students are killed by military forces at Kent State University, Ohio, 1970, prompting major international protests.

5 World War One: German submarine torpedoes and sinks the liner Lusitania off Ireland, killing 1,400 people, 1915. Live television shows the SAS storming the Iranian embassy in Kensington to free hostages held by terrorists, 1980.

6 Death of King Edward VII, 1910. London life becomes a tad more complcated when telephone codes change from 01 to 071 for inner and 081 for outer London, 1990.

7 Launch of Nelson's flagship HMS Victory, 1765 (now in Portsmouth Dockyards).

8 World War Two: Street parties like Britain never saw before or since on VE Day as the war officially ends in Europe, 1945.

11 Winston Churchill becomes British prime minister, 1940; replaced 26 July 1945 by Labour's Clement Attlee. Fire at Bradford City football ground during match causes death of 55 people in panic run, 1985. New weekly newspaper The European is first published, by Robert Maxwell, 1990.

15 The premiere performance of Mozart's opera The Marriage of Figaro at the Drury Lane theatre is interrupted by a member of the audience trying to shoot King George III, 1800; he escapes unharmed.

17 Boer War: Seven-month siege by the Boers of the tiny British settlement of Mafeking comes to an end, 1900; this long fight is of little military significance but symbolically is crucial.

20 Government announces the closure of 405-line transmission over about four years from 1982, replaced by 625-line, 1980.

21 Opening of the BBC's Lime Grove studios at Shepherds Bush, 1950.

24 Death of Harold Wilson, 1995; Labour's prime minister from 1964-76.

26 World War Two's petrol rationing ends, opening the gates to the growth of the car culture, 1950.

27 Russo-Japanese War: The Russian naval travels half way round the globe and fleet is annihilated by the Japanese, 1905.

29 Liverpool football fans at Brussels match largely blamed for 38 foreign deaths and 454 injuries when wall collapses, 1985; the Football Association later bans all English matches in Europe in 1986. Superman film star Christopher Reeve severely paralysed in a fall from his horse in at a riding competition in Virginia, 1995.

31 Start of the Boxer rebellion of China's anti-imperialist militia volunteers, 1900; combined forces from abroad hit back, defeating the Boxers in Peking on 14 August. Girl Guide movement created by the Baden-Powell family, 1910. A state of emergency is declared because of the worsening effects of the national rail and dock strikes, 1955; but both strikes end within a month.

JUNE

1 World War One: Zeppelin airships carry out their first bombing of London, 1915.

2 News Chronicle created by merging two other papers, 1930. Battle of the Beanfield: riot police ambush a convoy of travellers' vehicles on their way to celebrate the summer solstice at Stonehenge, 1985; the police wreck 80 vehicles and arrest 420 people; ITN record the police violence.

3 Dr David Owen officially winds up the middle-of-the-road political party the SDP, 1990.

4 English Civil War: Oliver Cromwell returns to England from Ireland, having spend a year there bringing the country totally under English control, 1650. World War Two: Dunkirk evacuation ends today, saving 338,000 British and French troops, 1940.

5 Britain's first-ever referendum has 67 per cent of the public voting to stay in the EEC, 1975. Suez Canal reopens, eight years after being closed during the Six Day War, 1975.

7 The BBC broadcasts the first episode of The Archers on radio, 1950; it is still one of the most popular Radio Four shows. The first NHS hearing aids are issued, 1960.

8 Launch of the Sheffield Daily Telegraph, 1855.

9 Death of the novelist Charles Dickens, aged 58, at his home near Rochester in Kent, 1870. The House of Commons broadcasts its proceedings live on the radio for the first time, 1975.

11 Launch of the Evening Standard, 1860. Motor racing sport is rethought after 80 people are killed in the worst-ever disaster, at a race in Le Mans, France, 1955. Black gold comes on stream as British North Sea oilfields pump ashore their first oil, 1975.

12 Launch of the Mirror Group's £30 million cable television channel Live TV, 1995. Sara Nathan becomes the first woman to be appointed editor of a British network television news service when she takes charge of Channel 4 News, 1995.

14 English Civil War: Royalist King Charles loses crucial Battle of Naseby in Northants to Parliamentary forces, 1645.

15 The Magna Carta is stamped with the royal seal by King John, at Runnymede, 1215. British newspapers are made more publicly affordable by the abolition of the official Stamp Duty, 1855.

16 The Marconi company makes one of the first national radio broadcasts. with opera singer Dame Nellie Melba sponsored by the Daily Mail, 1920 (see 23 November).

18 Britain defeats the French at the Battle of Waterloo (Wellington vs Napoleon), 1815. The government announces an alcohol limit is to be set for drivers, 1965.

19 General election brings surprise victory to the Tories, led by Ted Heath, defeating Labour led by Harold Wilson, 1970.

20 Nan Winton becomes the first woman to read the national television news for the BBC, 1960 (see also 20 February and 23 September). National Union of Railwaymen calls off its national rail strike after gaining a 30 per cent pay rise, 1975; many other trade unions are seeking rises of 25 per cent or more because is inflation is around 27 per cent. Shell abandons its plan to sink a giant old oil platform in the North Sea, following Greenpeace campaign against it, 1995; later Greenpeace apologises for over-estimating the size of the pollution risk.

TED HEATH WINS ELECTION: 19 JUNE 1970
Harold Wilson accepts defeat and there is a new Tory prime minister for a new decade

21 As a response to growing unease about gutter journalism, the publication of the government's first Calcutt report, threatening more laws against the press for intruding into privacy and scandals, 1990.

22 In a surprise move designed to see off the growing Euro-sceptic influence in his party, the prime minister John Major resigns as leader of the Conservatives, 1995; he wins the leadership election.

23 Rupert Murdoch signs a £366 million television deal with rugby-playing nations in the southern hemisphere, 1995.

24 The birth of WH Smith, the founder of today's leading newspaper and magazine retailing business, 1825. The British Army puts down major Londonderry riots, part of the two-year civil war in Northern Ireland, 1920. BBC Radio Bedfordshire goes on-air, 1985.

25 The three-year Korean War begins, with the invasion of USA-backed South Korea by China-supported North Korea, 1950. London's Tory-oriented Carlton Club bombed by the IRA, 1990.

26 Northern Ireland's leading civil rights leader Bernadette Devlin is jailed, 1970.

27 Opening of London Underground's Central Line, 1900. Widespread anti-Tsar movement in Russia sparks mutiny on the battleship Potemkin, 1905; officers are killed and the crew sails it round the Black Sea, then surrendering to Rumania.

29 Daily Telegraph first published, 1855. The Automobile Association - the AA - is formed by 50 motorists in a London restaurant, 1905. Opening of the new BBC Television Centre, on a 13 acre site near Shepherds Bush, 1960.

30 World War Two: Germany occupies the UK's Channel Islands, 1940.

JULY

1 Maiden flight of airship built by Count von Zeppelin, 1900.

2 Salvation Army is created by William Booth at a meeting in London, 1865. The state opening of Parliament is broadcast in colour for first time, 1970. Start of ITV's Oracle teletext service, 1975.

3 Launch of the first radio station aimed specifically at women, Viva!, 1995. Death of Bert Hardy, chief photographer on the pioneering post-war magazine Picture Post, 1995.

7 Start of BBC 1's popular science and inventions programme Tomorrow's World, 1965. Former Labour leader Michael Foot wins "substantial" damages from the Sunday Times for suggesting he was a KGB agent at the height of the Cold War, 1995.

9 Start of the pioneering BBC TV series Dixon of Dock Green, 1955; it lasted 21 years. French naval commandos seize the Greenpeace ship Rainbow Warrior II when it sails into French waters off Mururoa Atoll in the South Pacific in protest at nuclear tests, 1995. The Canadian veteran newspaper publisher the Thomson Corporation announces it is selling all its UK titles, 1995; it once owned the Times and Sunday Times.

10 English Civil War: Parliamentarian victory at the Battle of Langport, 1645. World War Two: Start of the Battle of Britain, the key conflict between German and British airplanes, 1940. Greenpeace's ship the Rainbow Warrior sunk off the coast of New Zealand by French secret service agents, 1985; a crew member dies.

11 Launch of the long-running children's TV series Watch with Mother, 1950; the first programme is Andy Pandy. Inflation hits record level of 25 per cent, prompting new Labour government rules, 1975. Cable Authority awards its 135th and last franchise, 1990.

12 President Wilson opens the USA's Panama Canal, 1920.

13 A global audience totalling 1.5 billion tune into Bob Geldof's Band Aid TV rock concert at Wembley benefiting African famine victims, 1985.

14 The first play is televised by the BBC: The Man with the Flower in His Mouth, 1930.

16 World War Two: The world's first atomic bomb test is carried out, at Alamogordo in New Mexico, 1945. Labour leader Tony Blair is guest speaker at a News International conference on an Australian island off the coast of Queensland, 1995; this appearance in the company of Rupert Murdoch is seen as a landmark in New Labour becoming acceptable to Old Capitalism. The cable television industry celebrates signing up its one millionth UK subscriber, 1995.

18 The first of the Disneyland alcohol-free amusement parks opens in Anaheim, California, 1955; another one in Orlando, Florida follows 12 years later.

19 Sinking of Henry VIII's leading battleship Mary Rose in the Solent, with 700 deaths, 1545; its remains are now on display in Portsmouth Dockyard. MPs approve the televising of proceedings in the House of Commons, 1990.

20 Professional football legalised in Britain, 1875. Two BBC film makers are arrested while working on a freelance project about secret military establishments in Britain, 1990. London's Stock Exchange badly damaged by IRA bomb, 1990.

26 Labour Party wins the first post-war general election, with the election pledge to set up a welfare state, 1945; Clement Attlee becomes prime minister. Whitehall 1212 is no more as the government announces that telephone dialling codes in future will only consist of numerals, 1965.

27 Edward Heath elected leader of the Conservative Party after Sir Alec Douglas-Home resigns, 1965.

28 The High Court bans publication of Courting Disaster, a book about life in Buckingham Palace, 1990.

29 Launch of the BBC's Light Programme, replacing the Forces Programme, 1945 (it became Radio 2 in 1967). Start of the BBC series This is Your Life, 1955.

30 Ship-to-shore radio is used for the first time in solving a crime when police are waiting at the dockside to arrest Dr Crippen for the murder of his wife, 1910. The first Penguin paperback book is published - Ariel, by Andre Maurois - starting a sales revolution in the book trade, 1935. The Conservative MP Ian Gow is killed outside his East Sussex home by the IRA, 1990.

31 J Sainsbury opens the first British self-service grocery store, forerunner of the supermarket, 1950. Constitutional crisis at the BBC when its governors give in to the government and postpone broadcast of a Northern Ireland documentary film, 1985.

AUGUST

1 The transportation of UK convicts to New South Wales, Australia, is ended, 1840. British Communist Party founded, reflecting support for the Russian communist revolution, 1920. The advertising of cigarettes on television is banned by the government, 1965.

2 British troops in Belfast use rubber bullets for first time, 1970. Iraqi troops invade Kuwait, 1990, starting the run-up to the 1991 Gulf War with the West.

3 Opening of the last TV 405-line VHF transmitting station, at Newhaven, East Sussex, 1970; all future transmitters are 625-line UHF.

4 Birth of Queen Elizabeth the Queen Mother, 1900.

5 A meeting of two Welsh nationalist groups in Pwllheli is announced as the first meeting of the new Plaid Cymru, 1925.

6 World War Two: The first ever atomic bomb is used in warfare, on Japan's city Hiroshima, 1945; Nagasaki is bombed 9 August.

7 BBC journalists go on strike because the government has forced the cancellation of a TV interview with Sinn Fein's Martin MacGuiness, 1985.

9 BBC Radio 4 correspondent John Schofield is shot dead by snipers in Bosnia, 1995.

12 The world's first comms satellite is launched from Florida, 1960. The world's worst air tragedy occurs in Japan, with 520 people killed in a Boeing 747 disaster, 1985.

14 World War Two: the dawning of nuclear diplomacy as Japan surrenders, bringing the war to an end, 1945.

15 The Observer reveals that MI5 is vetting senior staff being recruited by the BBC, 1985.

16 The UK colony Cyprus becomes independent after five years internal conflict, 1960.

18 The first oral contraceptive is marketed by the Searle Drug Company, in the US, 1960.

19 Former world heavyweight boxing champion Mike Tyson regains the title in his first match following his release from prison after serving a two year sentence for raping a teenage beauty queen, 1995.

21 Murder in Mexico of Soviet revolutionary Leon Trotsky, 1940.

22 Plane crash at Manchester Airport kills 55 passengers, 1985.

24 Captain Matthew Webb swims the English Channel, the first person ever, 1875.

27 Television signals are passed across the Channel for the first time, using the submarine electricity cable, 1950; the BBC televises a 60-minute programme from Calais. Twenty years later, the BBC launches its new radio network Radio Five, and Radio Two becomes the first national network to go out on FM only, 1990.

29 The Rugby League is created at a club meeting in Huddersfield, 1895.

30 Islambard Kingdom Brunel's revolutionary ship Great Britain sails from Liverpool to become the first propeller-driven iron vessel to cross the Atlantic, 1845; it is now in Bristol.

31 A taste of the Real Thing as Coca-Cola goes on sale in Britain for first time, 1900. Almost 4.8 million television licences have been issued three weeks before ITV starts, 1955; the BBC then only broadcasts from 3pm to around 11pm daily.

SEPTEMBER

1 Launch of Belfast Evening Telegraph, 1870; becomes Belfast Telegraph 1918. Kiss FM radio station goes on-air, 1990.

2 Ho Chi Minh declares independence for Vietnam, 1945.

4 BBC Radio Bristol goes on-air, 1970. The Marxist Dr Salvador Allende is democratically elected as President of Chile, 1970; he is assassinated in a coup on 11 September 1973 and shortly after General Pinochet assumes power.

5 World War Two: Start of Germany's bombing raid on London, the Blitz, 1940; ends May 1941. The BBC acquires its new White City building, 1990.

8 Snooker broadcast on television for the first time, by BBC, 1950 (Walter Donaldson vs Joe Davis).

9 The 11-month struggle around Sebastapol in the Crimean War ends in British victory as the Russians evacuate, 1855. BBC Radio Manchester goes on-air, 1970. Major civil riots occur in Handsworth, Birmingham, 1985; they spread to Brixton on 28 September, to Liverpool on 1 October and, most dramatically and violently, in Tottenham, north London, 6 October.

11 The football FA cup is stolen in Birmingham and melted down to make coins, 1895. BBC Radio Norfolk goes on-air 1980. After a well-publicised bust up with Kelvin MacKenzie, the all-round media personality Janet Street-Porter quits Live TV, the Mirror Group's cable service she herself founded on 1 June, 1995.

2 The first independent TV studios are finished in the run-up to the start of ITV, 1955; the site is the old RAF building in Kingsway, London. Arab guerrillas blow up three airliners, one British, in Jordan, 1970. Independent Television Commission cable statistics show the cable industry has reached one million TV subscribers and one million telephone lines, 1995.

15 World War Two: Climax of the Battle of Britain, 1940; Germany fails, and the battle ends on 31 October.

18 The death from a drug overdose of the world's best ever guitar player, Jimi Hendrix, 1970.

19 BBC shifts its traditional 9-o'clock radio news to 10-o'clock, 1960. Start of the popular Fawlty Towers series on BBC2, starring John Cleese, 1975. Senior staff at the BBC have been vetted by MI5 for many years, the corporation admits, 1985. Earthquake devastates Mexico City, killing 20,000 people,1985. Yorkshire Water's managing director, Trevor Newton, who is trying to encourage his 500,000 customers to accept rationing, says he has not had a bath or shower for three months, 1995.

21 Bonnie Prince Charlie and his Jacobite army defeat the English at the Battle of Prestonpans, Scotland, 1745.

22 Independent TV goes on air for the first time at 7.15pm today, a Thursday, 1955, covering a 70 mile radius around London. The first ITV programme - an early example of media fascination with its own navel - is its official launching ceremony at the Guildhall; the BBC broadcasts The Donald Duck Story at the same time. The first ITV advert is for Gibbs SR toothpaste, broadcast for 90 seconds at 8.12pm. Christopher Chataway presents the first news bulletin, for ITN (12 minutes long, at 10.00pm). The first ITV station is Associated Rediffusion, for London on weekdays; ATV begins on 24 September for London weekends.

23 Barbara Mandell becomes the first woman to read the news regularly on television, 1955; on ITV she reads the ITN noon bulletin, but this is soon scrapped (see also 20 February and 20 June).

24 English Civil War: A notable parliamentarian victory at the Battle of Rowton Moor, 1645. ITV puts out its first Saturday afternoon sports programme, a half-hour of results, 1955.

26 Humphrey, the cat resident at 10 Downing Street, returns after disappearing for three months, 1995.

27 The world's first public passenger steam railway service begins, between Stockton & Darlington in County Durham, 1825. The European Court of Human Rights condemns the killing of three IRA members in Gibraltar in 1988 by the SAS, 1995.

28 The national anthem God Save the King is sung for the first time at London's Drury Lane Theatre, 1745. ITV gives its first outside broadcast of live sport at a Wigan vs Huddersfield rugby league match, 1955. Cue for the voice of Eddie Waring.

29 The BBC launches its Come Dancing television programme, the world's longest-running TV musical series, 1950.

30 BBC makes its first television broadcast from the air, 1950. Young American film star James Dean killed in car crash, 1955.

OCTOBER

1 Serious riots in Toxteth, Liverpool, highlight inner city decay problems, 1985.

2 British television inventor John Logie Baird in his Soho laboratory televises the first-ever recognizable image of a human face, 1925. Start of the full-scale invasion of Ethiopia by Italy, led by Mussolini, 1935; takes full control in May 1936.

3 New Housing Act by the Tory government allows council tenants to buy their homes from today, 1980. Unemployment reaches 3,3446,198, its highest-ever level, 1985. East and West Germany reunited with public support, after 45 years apart, 1990. USA "trial of the century" ends when the sport and film star OJ Simpson is acquitted of murdering his ex-wife and her friend, 1995.

4 Two women members of the suffrage movement refuse to pay fines for assaulting the police and are sent to jail, the first to be imprisoned, 1905. Start of the BBC television series Pick of the Pops, 1955. BBC radio begins its World at One news programme, 1965.

5 Giant British airship the R101 crashes in France, killing 48 people, 1930.

6 BBC Radio London (later renamed GLR) goes on-air, 1970. The police-connected death of a black woman in Tottenham prompts a large-scale riot, resulting in the death of PC Keith Blakelock, 1985.

7 Opening of London's Post Office Tower, then the tallest building in Britain, 1965.

9 Start of Today in Parliament on BBC radio, 1945.

10 BBC starts experimental transmissions of colour TV from London's Alexandra Palace after successful laboratory research, 1955. UK colony Fiji becomes independent, 1970.

11 IBA rejects a takeover bid by Carlton Communications for Thames TV, 1985. Canon Eric James says he will stop contributing to Radio Four's Thought for the Day because his scripts were being edited for political reasons, 1990.

14 United Newspapers succeeds in its long-term bid to take over the old Beaverbrook newspaper empire Fleet Holdings, publishers of the Daily Express and Sunday Express, 1985; cost £317 million.

15 The first British Motor Show is held, at Tunbridge Wells, 1895. World War Two: Bomb explodes in Broadcasting House during 9 o'clock news, killing 7 people, 1940. World War Two's key Battle of Britain reaches climax today, 1940. Vietnam War: The first nationwide protest demonstrations in USA are held, 1965. Boxer James Murray dies two days after being knocked out in a British bantamweight title fight in a Glasgow hotel, 1995.

16 A state of emergency is declared by the government as coal miners launch a national strike, trying to create a socialist society, 1920.

17 Closure of the popular Liberal daily newspaper the News Chronicle is announced, 1960; it is consumed by the Daily Mail.

19 The four-acre, 1930s Ealing film studios are taken over by the BBC to become its film base, 1955.

20 Opening of the Lady Chatterley's Lover trial where the Old Bailey judge famously asks the jury if it was the sort of book they would let their wife or servants read, 1960.

22 Lord Nelson killed at the Battle of Trafalgar, 1805. First radio broadcast by the BBC Symphony Orchestra, 1930.

24 United Nations formally created, 1945. Britain's biggest co-operative-owned magazine City Limits is taken over by a private owner, 1990.

26 First radio and TV broadcast from the House of Commons, by BBC, 1950. The Beatles are awarded MBEs at Buckingham Palace, 1965.

27 The licence for the new Channel 5 television service is awarded by ITC to Channel 5 Broadcasting, 1995; Virgin Television challenges the decision in court in January 1996, but fails.

29 BBC Radio Oxford goes on-air, 1970.

30 Aspirin goes on sale in Britain for first time, 1905.

31 Lord Beaverbrook, the Candian born owner of the Express newspapers, becomes an independent MP by winning the South Paddington by-election on a free trade platform, 1930.

NOVEMBER

1 Royal assent given to the Broadcasting Act that affects much of the industry, 1990. Sir Geoffrey Howe, deputy Tory prime minister, resigns, starting the campaign that forces Thatcher to quit on the 22nd, 1990.

2 An Old Bailey jury decides DH Lawrence's long-banned novel Lady Chatterley's Lover is not breaking last year's Obscene Publications Act, 1960; this gives British culture a new liberated feel; 200,000 copies sell on its first day of publication, 10 November. Vietnam War: An anti-war Quaker commits suicide by fire in front of the Pentagon, 1965. Rupert Murdoch is controller of the new British Sky Broadcasting (BSkyB), the result of Sky TV and British Satellite Broadcasting (BSB) merging today, 1990.

3 Televising by BBC of the landmark real-life drama Up the Junction, 1965. The Queen graciously inaugurates the first pipeline to bring oil ashore from the new North Sea oil fields, 1975.

4 The Israeli prime minister Yitzhak Rabin is shot dead by a right-wing radical shortly after leaving a peace rally in Tel Aviv, 1995.

5 A conspiracy to blow up the Houses of Parliament is thwarted just hours before King James carries out the opening ceremony, 1605; five Catholics, including Guy Fawkes, are executed.

8 Workers co-operative newspaper Scottish Daily News closes down six months after starting, 1975; this happens at a time of considerable trade union action against newspapers.

9 John F Kennedy is elected USA president, 1960. The death penalty in UK is abolished for most crimes, 1965 (the current law is the same). BBC Radio Birmingham goes on-air, 1970. A terrorist bomb in the road next to Edward Heath's home in Belgravia is defused, 1975; this year has seen many IRA bombs in England.

10 In a bitter contest Michael Foot beats Dennis Healey and Tony Benn to the Labour Party leadership following James Callaghan's resignation, 1980.

11 The body of the First World War's Unknown Warrior is buried in Westminster Abbey, 1920. BBC broadcasts its first play on radio, Reginald Berkley's The White Chateau, 1925. Ian Smith, prime minister of Britain's last colony in Africa, Rhodesia, declares pro-white independence, 1965 BBC Radio Lincolnshire goes on-air, 1980. Environmental campaigning author Ken Saro-Wiwa is executed by the oil-dependent Nigerian government, 1995.

13 The Broadcasting Act is given Royal Assent, 1980; it permits the setting up of Channel 4 and SC4, plus the independent Broadcasting Complaints Commission.

15 Christopher Pile, known as the Black Baron, becomes the first UK person to be gaoled for creating and planting a computer virus, 1995.

17 The Sun publishes its first Page Three sexy photo of a nude female, 1970, a daily feature that permanently boosted sales ("A daring experiment" - Rupert Murdoch). Twenty five years laters, Murdoch closes the up-market tabloid Today, 1995; it was launched on 4 March 1986.

19 The new Labour government sticks to manifesto promises and announces it is going to nationalise electricity, gas, coal, railways, civil aviation, telecommun-ications, canals, docks and harbours, 1945.

20 Death of the right-wing Spanish dictator General Franco, 1975. An experimental scheme for televising of House of Commons proceedings is defeated 275-263 in a free vote of MPs, 1985.

23 UK government imposes ban on radio broadcasting following transmissions by the Marconi company, 1920; this stops US-style commercial radio moving into Britain and gives Whitehall time to create a state-controlled system (the BBC).

22 Magazine UK Press Gazette is first published, 1965. Tory MP Margaret Thatcher resigns as prime minister after opposition from her senior colleagues, 1990; "It's a funny old world," she says; replaced by John Major on 27th.

24 An experimental 70mph speed limit is imposed on motorways, 1965.

27 The Gay Liberation Front holds its first march in London, 1970. Ross McWhirter, the joint publisher of the Guinness Book of Records with his twin brother, is shot dead by gunmen at his Enfield home, 1975. The closure of the new liberal newspaper Sunday Correspondent, 1990, following a short life which began just over a year before on 17 September, 1989.

28 The publication of the first register listing MPs' commercial and business interests, 1975.

29 Mary Whitehouse launches the National Viewers and Listeners Association to clean up the BBC, 1965; she retires from the NVLA in 1994. UN gives Iraq a mid-January deadline to pull out of Kuwait, or face armed action, 1990.

DECEMBER

1 A Church of England report condemning the government's policies for Inner City areas is condemned by a Conservative Cabinet minister as "pure Marxist theology", 1985. Britain becomes physically connected to the European mainland when the Channel Tunnel diggers meet, 1990.

3 BBC creates a working party to explore ways of setting up a world TV service on the lines of its radio overseas service, 1985.

8 Beatle John Lennon shot dead in New York by a fake fan, 1980. The Sky TV/BSB merger is not being referred to the Monopolies and Mergers Commission, says the government, 1990.

9 Launch of Britain's longest running soap Coronation Street, set in the fictional Manchester suburb of Weatherfield, 1960; it becomes the most popular TV programme within a year.

10 Britain's first motoring organisation, the Self-Propelled Traffic Association, formed, 1895.

11 The Icelandic navy fires the first shots of the Cod War, against British fishing boats, 1975. Canadian businessman Conrad Black takes control of the Daily Telegraph, 1985; the paper which was soon to turn around under the editorship of Max Hastings had been making heavy losses.

12 Start of the Spanish revolution, 1930. Four IRA men surrender to armed police after heavily publicised six-day siege in Balcombe Street, London, 1975.

14 Birth of King George VI, 1895.

18 BBC Radio Medway goes on-air, 1970. The Evening Standard in London is taken over by Associated Newspapers, 1985.

19 Tory MP David Ashby loses his libel action against the Sunday Times, which had called him gay and a hypocrite, 1995.

22 Labour government brings in the 70 mph speed limit on all roads, 1965.

25 Scots remove the Coronation stone from Westminster Abbey, 1950; Edward I stole it from Scotland in 1296. Televising on BBC of the first pre-recorded TV Christmas message by the Queen, 1960.

26 Three Daily Telegraph journalists are revealed as being ready to leave the troubled paper to start a new quality daily to rival that recently purchased by Conrad Black, 1985; their Independent appears in 1986.

27 The International Monetary Fund is set up in Washington, 1945.

28 Lumiére brothers give the world's first public cinema show, using their new Cinématographe projector in the Grand café, Paris, 1895.

29 Sioux indians are massacred at the Battle of Wounded Knee, South Dakota, 1890. British businessman Cecil Rhodes launches unsuccessful armed attempt to seize goldfields centre Transvaal in southern Africa, 1895; beaten by Boers. First broadcasting of Radio Luxembourg, 1930. The BBC cancels all its main TV and radio news programmes as 700 journalists go on a one-day strike, 1975.

31 National Service, launched in 1939, comes to an end tonight, 1960; it forced military service onto 5.3 million civilians. The new BBC radio stations Solent and Teeside go on-air, 1970. Today is the last day of the three main broadcasting bodies, the IBA, Broadcasting Complaints Commission and Cable Authority, 1990; tomorrow sees a new dawn for independent television with the birth of the Independent Television Commission, the Radio Authority and the Broadcasting Standards Council.

UK facts and figures

The main source of basic UK data is the Government Statistical Service (GSS), run by the Office for National Statistics (ONS). The ONS collects, compiles and makes public all Whitehall's statistical information. It was created in 1996 by merging the Central Statistical Office and the Office of Population Censuses and Surveys.

ONS makes data available in print and on line. The starting points in print are the detailed annual catalogue *The Source* (free) and the *Guide to Official Statistics* (£35.95), explaining where to find all official sources of information. The most comprehensive listing is the *Annual Abstract of Statistics* (£39.50), containing tables on most aspects of UK life. A condensed version is *Key Data* (£10.95), covering all essential material. Handiest of all is the detailed leaflet *UK in Figures* (free), crammed full of the main statistics. None of these publications are analytical; for this, look at *Family Spending, General Household Survey* and *Social Trends*, all three providing graphic pictures of UK life. Most readable is the annual hardback *Britain: An Official Handbook* (£35). All are published by the Stationery Office (formerly HMSO).

ONS launched this data on Internet in July 1998. Its website *StatBase* aims to give access to most official statistics. StatBase has two components: StatSearch, an electronic catalogue of all GSS products and services , and StatStore, a database of the statistics, many (but not all of them) free of charge.

ONS is based in London's Pimlico, near Vauxhall Bridge. It has its own shop, and a library, where all the above official titles - and many more - can be consulted; phone first. There is a second library in Newport.

All statistics below are for 1997 and the UK, and come from ONS sources, except where otherwise stated.

ONS/GSS, 1 Drummond Gate, London SW1V 2QQ.
Fax 020-7533 6261   020-7533 6363
Websites: ONS   www.ons.gov.uk
   Statbase   www.statistics.gov.uk
   Stationery Office   www.national-publishing.co.uk

ENVIRONMENT

Land areas (square kilometres)

United Kingdom	242,910
England	130,423
Wales	20,779
Scotland	78,133
N Ireland	13,576

Climate: Rainfall (mm)

England & Wales	864
Scotland	1,423
N Ireland	1,051

Features

Longest river: Severn, 220 miles.
Highest mountain: Ben Nevis, 4,406 feet.
Total agricultural land: 18.4 million hectares.
Nobody in Britain lives more than about 75 miles from the sea.

POPULATIONS

World

The population reached six billion in mid-1999, doubling from three billion in 1960, and will reach at least nine billion by 2050. (Source: UN)

United Kingdom

Total	59.01 m (38.2 m in 1901)
England	49.28 m
Wales	2.93 m
Scotland	5.12 m
N Ireland	1.68 m

The UK population is expected to peak at 63 m around 2030, falling to 54.0 m in 2060.

Cities (thousands)

London	7,122
Birmingham	1,014
Leeds	727
Glasgow	612
Sheffield	530
Liverpool	464
Edinburgh	450
Manchester	428
Bristol	397
Belfast	300
Cardiff	294

Males (thousands)

United Kingdom	28,990
England & Wales	25,684
Scotland	2,484
N Ireland	821

Females (thousands)

United Kingdom	30,019
England & Wales	26,527
Scotland	2,638
N Ireland	854

Ages (thousands)

Under 20	14,960
20-64	34,770
65-74	5,006
75 plus	4,263
Percentage under 16	20.5
Percentage from 16 to retirement	61.4
Percentage over retirement (60/65+)	18.1

The UK has an ageing population: the number aged 65 and over increased by a quarter between 1971 and 1997.

In 2021 the UK population should rise 3.3 m to 62.2 m, but there will be one million fewer children under 16 and 1.3 m more pensioners. The average (mean) age is expected to rise from 38.4 years to 41.9.

The number of centenarians should rise from 6,000 in 1996 to 39,000 in 2036.

Ethnic minorities (1996, GB, thousands)

Total	3,623
Black (Caribbean)	1,186
Black (other)	655
Indian	929
Pakistani	580
Bangladeshi	208

HOUSING

Ownership

Nearly seven out of every ten households in England are owner-occupiers.

Just over 20 per cent are rented from local authorities or a registered social landlord, and one in ten are rented privately.

Moving

About 2.4 m households (12 per cent) moved in 12 months during 1997/8.

Most moves were fairly local - three out of five were of less than five miles, while about one in ten were over 50 miles.

Sizes

British households are getting smaller: the average size has almost halved since the beginning of century, to 2.4 people per household in 1998.

Just over one in ten people live alone, while nearly seven in ten live in a household headed by a couple.

DOMESTICITY

Money in

The average gross weekly income of UK householders was £420 in 1997/8, compared with £400 in 1996/7.

Money out

The average weekly expenditure of UK households was £328.80 in 1997/8, up £20 in a year.

Food and non-alcoholic drinks	55.90
Leisure goods and services	55.20
Housing	51.50
Motoring	46.60
Household goods and services	44.80
Clothing and footwear	20.00
Alcoholic drink	13.30
Fuel and power	12.70
Personal goods and services	12.50
Fares and other travel costs	8.10
Tobacco	6.10
Miscellaneous	2.00
Total family spending	£328.80

Since 1960 the biggest change in spending has been the fall in the proportion spent on food and non-alcoholic drinks, from 31 per cent in 1960 to 17 per cent in 1997/8.

The largest rise in spending has been for housing, up from nine per cent to 16 per cent.

Drink up

In 1998, fifty six per cent of all alcohol consumed was beer.

Seventy seven per cent of men and 61 per cent of women drink alcohol at least once a week, with 18 per cent of men, 12 per cent of women, drinking on at least five days a week.

Smoking

Six in ten women and more than half of men

who not smoke say they mind if other people smoke near them.

Over four-fifths of people agree with smoking restrictions at work and in public places, and three-fifths believe that tobacco advertising not should be allowed at all.

Nearly half (49 per cent) of 11-15 year old smokers would find it difficult to go without smoking for a day.

MARRIED LIFE

Marriage

The number of marriages in England and Wales fell by 20 per cent between 1986 and 1997: down from 347,924 to 278,975.

The largest fall in marriages has been among those in which both partners were marrying for the first time: 220,372 in 1986 compared with 160,680 in 1996.

The proportion of adults who are married will fall from 55 per cent to 45 per cent by 2021.

The average age of marriage continues to rise. In 1996, it was 29.3 years for bachelors (27.2 for spinsters), against 26.3 years in 1986 (spinsters 24.1). The average age in 1996 for all bride-grooms was 33.6, brides 31.1.

In 1998 four-fifths of dependent children in Great Britain lived in a family with two parents, compared with nine-tenths in 1972.

The proportion of never-married women who were cohabiting in Great Britain has increased from 9 per cent in 1981 to 27 per cent in 1996/7.

Divorce

The recent peak in divorces in England and Wales was in 1993, with 165,018. By 1995 the number had fallen to 155,499, then rising to 157,107 in 1996. Seventy per cent of those in 1996 were to couples where the marriage had been the first for both parties.

In Scotland the peak was in 1994, with 13,133 divorces, dropping to 12,222 in 1997.

Almost one in four children born in 1979 is estimated to have been affected by divorce before reaching the age of 16.

Births (thousands)

United Kingdom	726
Male	372
Female	354
England and Wales	642
Scotland	59
N Ireland	24

An average of 1.73 children per woman is born. Mothers giving birth are now, on average, nearly three years older than in the early 1970s. In 1998 the mean age was 28.9 years.

Women are having fewer children in their twenties - by the age of 30, women born in 1937 had had an average of 1.9 children, compared with only 1.3 children for women who were born in 1967.

The proportion of births outside marriage continues to rise, to 38 per cent in 1998 compared with 23 per cent in 1987 and 10 per cent in 1977.

The most popular names given to babies in 1997 were Jack and Chloe.

Deaths

There were 629,746 deaths in the UK in 1997. Male life expectancy is 74.4 years, up 4.8 years in two decades. Female life expectancy is 79.6 years, an increase of 3.8 years.

The most common cause of death for women under 65 is breast cancer and for men coronary heart disease.

The death rate is 10.7 per thousand population.

LIFESTYLES

There are over 22 million cars licensed in Great Britain, one for every two adults, plus 630,000 motor bikes.

Around 13 million people do not have regular access to a car.

About half of women, but two-thirds of men, say they never, or practically never, attend services or meetings connected with religion.

Visiting the pub is the most common activity outside the home for British adults.

The most popular non-European holiday destination in 1997 was the United States.

Each household in England and Wales generates around 21 kg of waste a week.

An average person covers 5,187 miles a year by car, 345 miles by bus, 294 miles by rail, walks 195 miles, travels 75 miles by air, goes 43 miles in cabs and cycles 39 miles.

Search engines can send you round the houses.

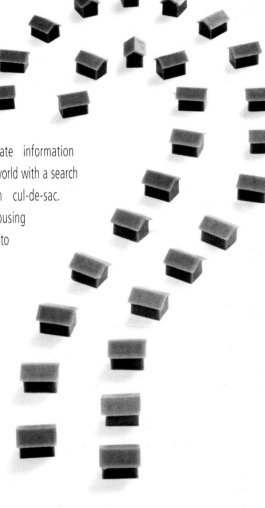

There is an easier way of finding accurate information about the UK than trawling web sites around the world with a search engine and ending up in an information cul-de-sac. After all, if you need details of the Housing Department in Birmingham why go to Alabama to find it? *KnowUK* is a unique service on the World Wide Web that provides key information on the people, places and institutions of the United Kingdom. It doesn't just point you in the right direction. It provides high quality information from respected sources such as *Who's Who, Debrett's People of Today, Hansard, The Municipal Year Book* and *Which?* If you would like to try *KnowUK* for youself, call our hotline on **0800 389 KNOW** (0800 389 5669) or visit the website and we can arrange a free trial. Alternatively, e-mail us at: **marketing@chadwyck.co.uk**

Know UK

will bring you home.

CHADWYCK-HEALEY

www.knowuk.co.uk

Parliaments and politics

NEW SCOTLAND

A Scottish referendum in September 1997 produced a clear majority in favour of establishing a Scottish Parliament. The Scotland Act received royal assent in November 1998, the first election was held on 6 May 1999 (as in Wales) and the four-year Parliament was officially opened by the Queen on 1 July. The summer recess began next day, ending on 30 August, by which time the new Edinburgh-based Scottish Parliament of 129 MSPs and its mini-government were scheduled to start. It has legislative control over roughly the same functions as those formerly run by the Scottish Office. Westminster retains power over the key issues of fiscal policy, foreign affairs, Europe, defence, energy, employment and social security. The May 1999 elections in Scotland and Wales were the first in Britain to be fought under a system of proportional representation. Scotland's equivalent of the Cabinet is the Scottish Executive, with the UK Prime Minister mirrored in Scotland's First Minister, Donald Dewar.

1999 Scottish Parliament election

Labour	56
SNP	35
Conservative	18
Liberal Democrat	17
Green Party	1
Socialist Party	1
Individual	1

Scottish contacts

Scottish Parliament	0131-348 5000
Website	www.scottish.parliament.uk
General Enquiries	0845-278 1999
Media Relations	0131-348 5389
UK Scottish Office	0131-556 8400
MSP parties: Conservative	0131-555 2900
Green	0131-478 7896
Labour	0141-572 6900
Liberal Democrat	0131-337 2314
SNP (Scottish National Party)	0131-226 3661
Socialist	0141-221 7714
Dennis Canavan	01324-825922

NEW WALES

The new political forum in Wales, the Welsh Assembly, has far less power than the Scottish Parliament. The vote in favour of devolution in September 1997 was also much smaller than in Scotland - the majority was only 6,721, just 0.6 per cent. Despite this lack of enthusiasm, the first Assembly election in May 1999 produced the shock result of nationalist Plaid Cymru doing unexpectedly well, and Labour failing to win a majority. The Cardiff-based 60 Welsh members have much less influence than their Scotland counterparts, being Westminster advisers rather than power-wielders. The First Secretary is Alun Michael.

1999 Welsh Assembly election

Labour	29
Plaid Cymru	17
Conservative	9
Liberal Democrat	6

Welsh contacts

National Assembly of Wales	029-2089 8200
Website	www.wales.gov.uk
Press	029-2082 5642
UK Welsh Office	029-2082 5111
Parties	see Parliamentary Parties, p68

NEW IRELAND

The new Northern Ireland Assembly was established as part of the Belfast Agreement reached at the multi-party negotiations on Friday 10 April 1998 - the Good Friday Agreement. The referendum six weeks later voted overwhelmingly for the Assembly, with 108 members, plus a North-South Ministerial Council. Proportional representation elections took place in the 18 Westminster constituencies on 25 June, and the Assembly met for the first time on 1 July 1998. This was followed by a schedule of many changes, but at the time of writing no progress had been made because of failure to agree about weapons decommissioning by the IRA. The Assembly PM is First Minister David Trimble

1998 Northern Ireland Assembly election

Ulster Unionist Party	28
SDLP	24
Democratic Unionist Party	20
Sinn Fein	18
Six other parties	18

Northern Ireland contacts

Northern Ireland Assembly	028-9076 3210
Website	www.ni-assembly.gov.uk
Press	028-9052 1840
First Minister	028-9052 0395
Parliament Buildings	028-9052 1333
Parties	see Parliamentary Parties, p68

OLD ENGLAND

In England, the Wales/Scotland devolution elections raised the prospect of revived Anglo-Saxon nationalism, both anti-Europe and pro-Tory. This became reality in the June 1999 Euro elections, when the Tories gave Labour a hammering in southern England. Labour hopes to defuse and divert this new nativism by creating nine English regions, but there has been little public enthusiasm for these new bureaucracies and artificial territories.

1997 GENERAL ELECTION

The last UK general election was on 1 May 1997. The turnout was 31.3 million voters, 71.6 per cent of the 43.7 million registered electors. This was the lowest turnout since 1945. There was a 10.5 per cent national swing to Labour, which won 419 seats with 43.2 per cent of the turnout. But 77 per cent of the total UK population of 58.8m did not vote Labour. The Liberal Democrats had 12.1 per cent of the turnout, but only won 46 seats. The Labour majority was 177. Labour spent £13.7 million on the election. In all by-elections to mid-1999 no seats changed hands, although

two were being held on 23 September, after going to press. Labour's 418-seat win in 1997 was its highest-ever number; 1945 was next, with 393. A record number of woman MPs was elected: 120. The Tories had the lowest share of the vote since 1832 and the lowest number of MPs since 1906.

The results for the three main parties are shown below. Seats won by other parties:

England: *Independent* (Martin Bell)	1
Wales: *Plaid Cymru*	4
Scotland: *Scottish National Party*	6
Northern Ireland: *Ulster Unionist*	10
SDLP	3
Democratic Unionist	2
Sinn Fein	2
UK Unionist	1

England had 529 seats; Labour won 329 of them, Tories 165 (all bar 17 of them in the South and Midlands), Liberal Democrats 34, Independent one. **Wales** had 40 seats; Labour won 34, Lib Dems 2, Plaid Cymru 4 (with 161,000 votes, 10 per cent of the total turnout in Wales), Tories none. **Scotland** had 72 seats; Labour won 56, Liberal Democrats 10, Scottish Nationalists 6, Tories none. **Northern Ireland** had 18 seats, all won by indigenous parties (see above). The Ulster Unionists took 56 per cent of the seats with only 33 per cent of the votes.

AND NEXT?

General elections can be held at any time, but by law the House of Commons has to be dissolved not later than five years after its first meeting following an election. This usually takes place about two weeks after polling day. In addition, the election campaigns must last for at least 23 days. So the next election deadline is June 2002. The Conservatives will need a swing of 11.6 per cent to win.

1997 General election results

	seats won	% of all seats	votes	% of turnout	% of electorate
Labour	419	63.6%	13.52m	43.2%	30.1%
Conservatives	165	25.0%	9.60m	30.7%	22.0%
Liberal Democrats	46	7.0%	5.24m	16.7%	12.1%
Total + other parties	659	100%	31.29m	100%	71.6%

COMMONS CONTACTS

Main number (all MPs)	020-7219 3000
Website	www.parliament.uk
Information/press office	020-7219 4272
Night line	020-7219 3000
Business Line	020-7219 5532
Committees office	020-7219 4300
Library	020-7219 4272
Official report (Hansard)	020-7219 3764
Parliamentary Bookshop	020-7219 3890
Parliamentary Archives	020-7219 3074
Press Gallery/Lobby: Secretary	020-7219 4395
Superintendent	020-7219 5371
Publications	020-7219 4272
Serjeant at Arms	020-7219 3030
Whips offices: Government	020-7219 4400
Opposition (Conservative)	020-7219 3237
Liberal Democrat	020-7219 5654

HOUSE OF LORDS

In mid-1999 the House of Lords had 1,289 active members, including 504 life peers, 759 hereditary and 26 spiritual. The parties were:

471	Conservatives
176	Labour
66	Liberal Democrat
339	Cross-benchers

Main number	020-7219 3000
Website	www.parliament.uk
Information/press office	020-7219 3107
Private bill office	020-7219 3231
Public bill office	020-7219 3153
Committees office	020-7219 3218
Judicial business	020-7219 3111
Library	020-7219 5242
Official report (Hansard)	020-7219 3031
Serjeant at Arms (Black Rod)	020-7219 3100
Whips offices: Government	020-7219 3131
Opposition (Conservative)	020-7219 4770
Liberal Democrat	020-7219 3114

PARLIAMENTARY PARTIES

Labour Party	020-7802 1000
Website	www.labour.org.uk
Press	020-7802 1428
Conservative Party	020-7222 9000
Website	www.conservative-party.org.uk
Press	020-7896 4140
MEPs, London	020-7222 1720
Scottish Conservative Party	0131-555 2900
Primrose League	020-7976 7158
Liberal Democrats	020-7222 7999
Website	www.libdems.org.uk

Lib Dems Wales	029-2031 3400
Scottish Lib Dems	0131-337 2314
Alliance Party of N Ireland	028-9032 4274
Plaid Cymru	029-2064 6000
Website	www.plaidcymru.org.uk
Scottish National Party	0131-226 3661
Website	www.snp.org.uk
Sinn Fein	028-9032 3214
Website	www.irlnet.com/sinnfein
Social Democratic & Labour Party	028-9024 7700
Website	www.indigo.ie/sdlp
Ulster Democratic Unionist Party	028-9047 1155
Website	www.dup.org.uk
Ulster Unionist Party	028-9032 4601
Website	www.uup.org
UK Unionist Party	028-9127 2994

OTHER ORGANISATIONS

There are many political websites, but just two are included here, because of the wide overviews they give: UK Politics from the centre, Urban75 from the underground.

Anti-Nazi League	020-7924 0333
British National Party	020-8316 4721
Campaign for a Scottish Parliament	0131-225 7814
Campaign for an Independent Britain	020-8340 0314
Charter 88	020-7684 3888
Communist League Party	020-7401 2293
Communist Party of Britain	020-7275 8162
Communist Party of Gt Britain	020-8459 7146
Co-operative Party	020-7439 0123
Democracy Movement (anti-Euro)	020-7233 7351
Democratic Left	020-7278 4443
Electoral Reform Society	020-7928 1622
English National Party	020-7278 5221
Fabian Society	020-7222 8877
Freedom Association	020-7928 9925
Freemasons	020-7831 9811
Green Left	01422-844022
Green Party	020-7272 4474
Hansard Society	020-7955 7478
Islamic Party of Britain	01908-671756
Liberal Party (not Lib-Dems)	01704-500115
Monday Club	020-72495368
Monster Raving Loony Party	01364-652205
Movement Against Monarchy (MA'M)	01523-160145
National Front (aka National Democrats)	07071-226074
Red Pepper Magazine	020-7281 7024
Referendum Movement	0990-110440
Socialist Party (ex-Militant Labour)	020-8533 3311
Socialist Party of Gt Britain	020-7622 3811
Socialist Workers Party	020-7538 5821
Solidarity Federation	0161-232 7889
UK Independence Party	020-7434 4559
UK Politics	www.ukpol.co.uk
Urban75	www.urban75.com
Western Goals Institute	020-7824 8634
Workers Revolutionary Party	020-7928 3218

Departments of state

This is the government following the reshuffle of 29 July 1999 Cabinet. Another reshuffle was due in September (after going to press) as a result of Defence Secretary George Robertson being appointed secretary-general of Nato. Below, PUSS = Parliamentary Under-Secretary of State.

PRIME MINISTER'S OFFICE

10 Downing Street, London SW1A 2AA
Main number	020-7270 3000
Website	www.cabinet-office.gov.uk
Press (24 hour)	020-7930 4433
Press Secretary	020-7930 7919
Prime Minister	Tony Blair
Deputy Prime Minister	John Prescott
Press Secretary	Alastair Campbell

AG., FISHERIES & FOOD

Nobel House, 17 Smith Square, London SW1P 3JR
MAFF: main number	020-7238 6000
Website	www.maff.gov.uk
Information Division	020-7238 5603
Press Branch	020-7238 5599
Eves	020-7270 8080
Food safety, animal/plant health	020-7238 6044
Fisheries, countryside, floods	020-7238 6001
Agricultural/food industries, CAP	020-7238 6043
Helpline	0645-335577
Minister	Nick Brown
Ministers of State	Baroness Hayman, Joyce Quin
Parliamentary Secretary	Elliot Morley

CABINET OFFICE

70 Whitehall, London SW1A 2AS
CO: main number	020-7270 1234
Website	www.cabinet-office.gov.uk
Head of Information	020-7270 0516
Press	020-7270 0635
Minister for the Cabinet Office	Jack Cunningham
Ministers of State	Ian McCartney, Lord Falconer
Lord Privy Seal	Baroness Jay

CULTURE, MEDIA & SPORT

2-4 Cockspur Street, London SW1Y 5DH
DCMS: main number	020-7211 6000
Website	www.culture.gov.uk
Public enquiries	020-7211 6200

Information Division	020-7211 6263
Press	020-7211 6273
Heritage, tourism, lottery	020-7211 6267
Media, press regulation, arts	020-7211 6266
Sport	020-7211 6275
Broadcasting & Media Group	020-7211 6410
Broadcasting Policy Division	020-7211 6469
Media Division	020-7211 6425
Secretary of State	Chris Smith
Ministers for: Art	Alan Howarth
Film, Tourism, Broadcasting	Janet Anderson
Sport	Kate Hoey

MINISTRY OF DEFENCE

Horseguards Avenue, London SW1A 2HB
MOD: main number	020-7218 9000
Website	www.mod.uk
Director of Information & News	020-7218 5317
Press	020-7218 2906
Eves	020-7218 7907
Army	020-7218 3255
Navy	020-7218 3257
RAF	020-7218 3253
Policy	020-7218 7931
Procurement	020-7218 7714
Tri-Service Joint HQ	01923-846029
Army HQ, Wilton	01722-433345
Navy HQ, Northwood	01923-837336
RAF HQ, High Wycombe	01494-496131
Chief of Defence Staff	020-7218 2116
D-Notice Committee	020-7218 2206
Secretary of State (temporary)	George Robertson
Ministers of State: Armed Forces	John Spellar
Defence Procurement	Baroness Symons
Under-Secretary of State	Peter Kilfoyle

EDUCATION & EMPLOYMENT

Great Smith Street, London SW1P 3BT
DfEE: main number	020-7925 5000
Website	www.dfee.gov.uk
Information office	020-7925 5555
Press	020-7925 5615
Employment, disability, learning	020-7925 6487
Schools, regions, campaigns	020-7925 5105
Secretary of State	David Blunkett
Ministers of State:	
Employment, disability rights	Andrew Smith
School standards	Estelle Morris
Education, employment	Baroness Blackstone
PUSS	Margaret Hodge, Malcom Wicks
	Jacqui Smith, Michael Wills

ENVIRONMENT, TRANSPORT, REGIONS

Eland House, Bressenden Place,London SW1E 5DU
DETR: main number   020-7890 3000
Website   www.detr.gov.uk
Communications Directorate   020-7890 3333
  Eves   020-7873 1985
Press: Environment   020-7890 4626
  Housing, local government   020-7890 4617
  Planning, London, construction   020-7890 4606
  Regions   020-7890 4614
  Transport   020-7890 3231
Secretary of State   John Prescott
Ministers of State   Michael Meacher
  Nick Raynsford, Hilary Armstrong
Minister of Transport   Lord Macdonald
PUSS   Lord Whitty, Keith Hill
  Chris Mullin, Beverley Hughes

FOREIGN & COMMONWEALTH

Downing Street, London SW1A 2AL
FCO: main number   020-7270 3000
Website   www.fco.gov.uk
Press   020-7270 3100
  Europe/UN/human rights   020-7270 3119
  Asia/Pacific/Americas/North Africa/
    Middle East/travel   020-7270 2861
  Consular/drugs/crime/media   020-7270 3095
Information Dept   020-7270 6052
Public enquiries   020-7270 1500
Secretary of State   Robin Cook
Ministers of State   John Battle, Peter Hain, Geoff Hoon
PUSS   Baroness Scotland

DEPARTMENT OF HEALTH

Richmond House, 79 Whitehall, London SW1A 2NS
DOH: main number   020-7210 3000
Website   www.open.gov.uk/doh
Eves   020-7210 5368
Press   020-7210 5225
  Central desk   020-7210 5227
  NHS: doctors/funds/licensing   020-7210 5226
  NHS: hospitals/ambulances   020-7210 5230
  Social care/mental illness/drugs   020-7210 5231
  Public health/food safety/Aids   020-7210 5228
Media Initiatives   020-7210 5436
NHS Executive   0113-254 5000
Public enquiries   020-7210 4850
Health Information Service   0800-665544
Secretary of State   Frank Dobson
Minister for Public Health   Tessa Jowell
Minister of State   Jack Denham
Under-Secretaries of State   John Hutton
  Lord Hunt, Gisela Stuart

HOME OFFICE

50 Queen Anne's Gate, London SW1H 9AT
HO: main number   020-7273 4000
Website   homeoffice.gov.uk
Eves   020-7273 4595
Director, Communication   020-7273 3757
Press:
  Police/emergencies/terrorism   020-7273 4610
  Criminal justice/crime   020-7273 4600
  Community relations/family   020-7273 4650
  Immigration/asylum/ID cards   020-7273 4620
  Constitution/data/drugs/fire   020-7273 4640
  Prison Service   020-7217 6633
Secretary of State   Jack Straw
Ministers of State: Paul Boateng
  Barbara Roche, Charles Clarke
PUSS   Lord Bassam, Mike O'Brien

INTERNATIONAL DEV'MENT

94 Victoria Street, London SW1E 5JL
DFID: main number   020-7917 7000
Website   www.open.gov.uk
Information Dept   020-7917 0618
Press   020-7917 0435
Secretary of State   Clare Short
PUSS   George Foulkes

LAW OFFICERS' DEPT

Attorney General's Chambers, 9 Buckingham Gate, London SW1E 6JP
Main number   020-7271 2400
Press   020-7271 2405
Attorney General   Lord Williams QC
Solicitor General   Ross Cranston QC

LORD ADVOCATE'S DEPT

2 Carlton Gardens, London SW1Y 5AA
25 Chambers Street, Edinburgh EH1 1LA
Main numbers: London   020-7210 1010
  Edinburgh   0131-226 2626
Lord-Advocate   Lord Hardie

LORD CHANCELLOR'S DEPT

54/60 Victoria Street, London SW1E 6QW
LCD: main number   020-7210 8500
Website   www.open.gov.uk/lcd
Eves   020-7210 8512
Press   020-7210 8512/3
Lord Chancellor   Lord Irvine of Lairg
Parliamentary Secretaries   David Lock, Keith Vaz

NORTHERN IRELAND OFFICE

11 Millbank, London SW1P 4QE
Stormont Castle, Belfast BT4 3ST

NIO: main numbers: Belfast	028-9052 0700
London (24 hr)	020-7210 3000
Website	www.nio.gov.uk
NI Information Service, Belfast	028-9052 8211
Press	028-9052 8233
London press office	020-7210 6473
Public enquiries	020-7210 6454
Agriculture Dept	028-9052 0100
Economic Development Dept	028-9052 9900
Education Dept	028-9127 9279
Environment Dept	028-9054 0540
Finance Dept	028-9052 0400
Health & Social Services Dept	028-9052 0500
Police Authority	028-9023 0111

Secretary of State Marjorie Mowlam
Ministers of State: Adam Ingram
Under-Secs George Howarth, Lord Dubs, John McFall

PRIVY COUNCIL OFFICE

68 Whitehall, London SW1A 2AT

Office	020-7270 0472
Judicial Committee	020-7270 0485

President of the Council and Leader of the House of Commons Margaret Beckett
Lord Privy Seal, Leader of the House of Lords and Minister for Women Baroness Jay
Parliamentary Secretary Paddy Tipping

SCOTLAND OFFICE

Dover House, Whitehall, London SW1A 2AU
St Andrew's House, Regent Rd, Edinburgh EH1 3DG

Main numbers: Edinburgh	0131-556 8400
London	020-7270 3000
Website	www.scotland.gov.uk
Information Directorate	0131-244 1111
Eves	0131-556 8400
Press	0131-244 2718/2661
Press: London	020-7270 6745
Enquiry Point	0345-741741

Secretary of State John Reid
Minister of State Brian Wilson
Advocate General for Scotland Lynda Clark QC
See also page 366

DEPT OF SOCIAL SECURITY

79 Whitehall, London SW1A 2NS

DSS: main number	020-7238 3000
Website	www.dss.gov.uk
Press	020-7238 0800
Eves	020-7238 0761
Chief press officer	020-7238 0748
Welfare reform	020-7238 0750
Child support/disability	0191-238 0749
Benefit/support/poverty	020-7238 0752
Fraud/pensions/insurance	020-7238 0754
Contributions Agency	0191-225 3502
Benefits Agency	0113-232 4499
Child Support Agency	01384-488000
Freeline help	0800-882200

Secretary of State Alistair Darling
Minister of State Jeff Rooker
PUSS Hugh Bayley, Baroness Hollis, Angela Eagle

TRADE AND INDUSTRY

1 Victoria Street, London SW1H 0ET

DTI: main number	020-7215 5000
Website	www.dti.gov.uk
Information Director	020-7215 5951
News Director	020-7215 5954
Press: Energy/industry/regions	020-7215 6424
Consumer/corporate/trade	020-7215 5970

Secretary of State Stephen Byers
Ministers of State Patricia Hewitt
Helen Liddell, Richard Caborn
PUSS Alan Johnson

TREASURY

Parliament Street, London SW1P 3AG

HMT: main number	020-7270 3000
Website	www.hm-treasury.gov.uk
Public enquiries	020-7270 4860
Press	020-7270 5238
Public finances	020-7270 5245
Private finance	020-7270 5192
Taxation	020-7270 5187

Chancellor of the Exchequer Gordon Brown
Chief Secretary Alan Milburn
Paymaster General Dawn Primarolo
Financial Secretary Stephen Timms
Economic Secretary Melonie Johnson

WELSH OFFICE

Gwydyr House, Whitehall, London SW1A 2ER
New Crown Building, Cathays Park, Cardiff CF1 3NQ

WO: main numbers: Cardiff	029-2082 5111
London	020-7270 3000
Website	www.cymru.gov.uk
Information Division: Enquiries	029-2082 5724
Press: Cardiff	029-2082 5648
London	020-7270 0558

Secretary of State Paul Murphy
PUSS David Hanson
See also page 366

GENERAL WEBSITES

CCTA Govt Info Service (official)	www.open.gov.uk
UK Politics (unofficial)	www.ukpol.co.uk

Public contacts

The corridors of Whitehall have always been shrouded in secrecy, but since 1994 some glimpses along them have been possible using the *Code of Practice on Access to Government Information*. The code - also called *Open Government* - says that almost all government departments and bodies must respond to requests for information. But there are exemptions: policing, defence and the security services. Departmental contact points are listed below, under Openness Contacts. Enquirers may be told they have to write to the appropriate office; detailed replies should come within 20 days. There may be a charge, although usually there is not. Code copies are available from Citizen's Charter, or can be read/downloaded online.

The Labour Party in opposition promised a **Freedom of Information Act** to replace the Code. The act would create the first statutory right for people to obtain internal documents held by public authorities. But the New Labour government went into retreat. Although a promising White Paper was published in December 1997, Home Secretary Jack Straw ensured it was left out of the 1998 Queens Speech. When the draft bill finally appeared in May 1999 it was widely condemned as impotent and deeply flawed. The Daily Telegraph called it "a step backwards", the Guardian "a shockingly bad bill".

The Freedom of Information Bill is fettered by 21 separate exemptions where the public will not be allowed information that could "prejudice" government, unless the public authorities agree to release it under discretionary powers. The bill is poor in comparison with the Code: its exemptions are far more wide-ranging, reply time is doubled to 40 days, and a standard charge of £10 will be levied. The Guardian launched a campaign against the bill on 21 June, seeking key changes in it. Public support came from many prominent individuals and organisations, prompting some minor concessions by Straw. Critics believe the main aim of the bill is to impose strict management on official information, not to grant it freedom. They suspect the bill may be quietly ditched in the run-up to the next general election.

The main Whitehall information-manager is the **Central Office of Information**. The COI has a wide remit, handling the flow of all information in and out of the government. Whitehall's specialist in processing raw facts and figures is the **Office for National Statistics**. This is one of the most accessible of all the official knowledge processing plants. It has its own library, open to the public, and runs a data-packed website, Statbase, on behalf of the Government Statistical Service. Another official website is the **Direct Access Government** service, created in late 1997 to provide in-depth info about regulations.

OPENNESS CONTACTS

Code copies: Citizens Charter	0345-223242
Website	www.civil-service.co.uk/opnfr.htm
Agriculture, Fisheries & Food	
Paul Fildes	0645-335577
Central Office of Information	
Mike Wheeler	020-7261 8488
Charity Commissioners	
Frances Grey	0870-333 0123
Culture, Media & Sport, Dept of	
Enquiry Unit	020-7211 6200
Customs & Excise	
David Rennie	020-7865 5777
Data Protection Registrar	
Ruth Robinson	01625-545700
Defence, Ministry of	
Secretary of State's office	020-7218 6432
Education & Employment, Dept for	
Enquiry unit: John Quinn	020-7925 5555
Electricity Regulation, Office of (OFFER)	
Ian Bickley	0121-456 6208
Employment Service	
Dean Weston	020-7389 1529
Environment, Transport & Regions, Dept of	
Public Enquiry Point	020-7890 3000
Fair Trading, Office of	
Public Liaison Unit	020-7211 8000
Foreign & Commonwealth Office	
Enquiry Unit: Kate Crowe	020-7210 3865
Gas Supply, Office of (OFGSA)	
Public Affairs	020-7828 0898
Health, Dept of	

Sarah Armstrong	020-7210 5787
Health & Safety Executive	
Infoline	0541-545500
Home Office	
Info Services: Jane Humphreys	020-7273 3072
Inland Revenue	
Jen Morgan	020-7438 6879
HM Land Registry	
Denise Reynolds	020-7917 8888
Legal Aid Board	
Jackie Collins	020-7813 1000
Lord Chancellor's Dept	
Kevin Fraser	020-7210 8533
National Lottery, Office of	
John Park	020-7227 2030
National Savings	
A Johnson	0191-374 5656
Northern Ireland Office	
Denis Carson	028-9052 7015
Ordnance Survey	
Mr A Warmington	023-8079 2605
Rail Regulator, Office of	
Ian Cooke	020-7282 2002
Royal Mint	
Linda Viner	01443-222111
Scottish Office	
Craig Russell	0131-244 0102
Social Security, Dept of	
Disclosure of Info Unit	020-7962 8142
Benefits Agency	0113-232 7932
Contributions Agency	0191-225 5492
Child Support Agency	0191-225 3154
Trade & Industry, Dept of	
Open Govt Enquiry Point	020-7215 6668
Transport, Dept of	
DVLA: Barbara Windsor	01792-782965
Highways Agency: David Buxton	020-7921 4031
Water Services, Office of (OFWAT)	
Jane Fisher	0121-625 1361
Welsh Office	
Kate Cassidy	029-2082 5275

COI + ONS

Central Office of Information
Hercules Road, London SE1 7DU

Main number	020-7928 2345
Enquiries	020-7261 8241
Press	020-7261 8815
Eves	020-7261 8820
Website	www.coi.gov.uk

Office for National Statistics
1 Drummond Gate, London SW1V 2QQ

Main number	020-7233 9233
Enquiries	020-7533 6363
Press	020-7533 5697
Social statistics, labour	020-7533 5712
Business	020-7533 5725
Websites: ONS offices	www.ons.gov.uk
StatBase, via	www.statistics.gov.uk

INFO WEBSITES

The CCTA is the huge official Whitehall directory. The DETR is a guide to regional and local government. The starting point for finding all official publications is SO Publishing. UK Politics is a top-quality unofficial directory. See the Civil Service Yearbook, COI and ONS (listed separately) for useful official data. All Whitehall departments have their own websites; see previous section, especially the Cabinet Office.

CCTA Govt Information Service	www.open.gov.uk
DETR	www.local-regions.detr.gov.uk
Direct Access Govt	http://tap.ccta.gov.uk
Europe	www.europa.eu.int
Stationery Office	www.the-stationery-office.co.uk
SO Publishing	www.national-publishing.co.uk
UK Politics (unofficial)	www.ukpol.co.uk

HANDBOOKS

Britain: An Official Handbook
ONS/Stationery Office   Tel 020-7439 2831
The official annual picture of life in Britain.
Civil Service Yearbook
Stationery Office   Tel 020-7439 2831
Website   www.civil-service.co.uk
The twice-yearly Whitehall directory, with addresses, numbers and top personnel. With CD-ROM.
IPO Directory
Central Office of Information   Tel 020-7928 2345
Twice-yearly directory of information and press officers in and around Whitehall. Only available to journalists.
Parliamentary Companions
Vachers Publications   Tel 020-7828 7526
PMS Publications   Tel 020-7233 8283
Quarterly guides to Westminster and Whitehall. PMS and Vachers also publish European Companions.

GOVERNMENT HELPLINES

Citizen's Charter	0345-223242
Crown Prosecution Service	020-7334 8505
Customs & Excise	020-7202 4227
VAT helpline	020-7202 4087
Education, OFSTED	020-7421 6664
Employment, Industrial tribunals	0345-959775
Fisheries & food (MAFF)	0645-335577
Foreign & Commonwealth Office	020-7270 1500
Health & Safety Exec	0114-289 2345
Health Info Service	0800-665544
Inland Revenue Taxback	0800-660800
National Rivers Authority: emergency	0800-807060
Royal Mail Customer Service	0345-740740
Scottish Office enquiries	0345-741741
Social Security	0800-666555
Trade & Industry	020-7215 5000
Transport, DVLA driver	01792-772151
DVLA vehicle	01792-772134
Highways Agency	0345-504030

Quangos

Quangos are public service bodies run as private businesses. The word "quango" is an abbreviation of "**QU**asi-**A**utonomous **N**on-**G**overnmental **O**rganisation". The Tory government began the privatisation process in 1988, aiming to convert three-quarters of the Civil Service into quangos within about ten years. This was widely condemned, with some people alleging that it would turn public services into undemocratic profit generators for the friends of whichever government was in power. Labour opposed quangos in opposition, but the New Labour government of 1997 adopted a mellower attitude, similar to that of the Tories.

The government officially calls most quangos either **Non-Departmental Public Bodies** (NDPBs) or **Next Steps Executive Agencies** (NSEAs). The NDPBs are almost separate from the government, while NSEAs are semi-detached subsidiaries of departments.

Whitehall defines an **NDPB** as: "A body which has a role in the process of national government, but is not a government department or part of one, and which accordingly operates to a greater or lesser extent at arms length from ministers". In 1998 there were 108,000 staff in almost 1,100 NDPBs, with a turnover of £24.1 billion. Only a third of their 36,000 governors were women.

NSEAs are commonly known as *Executive Agencies*, or just *agencies*. They are the Next Steps Programme which was launched in 1988. NSEAs are less autonomous than the NDPBs. They are partially-independent organisations performing executive functions of government, while staying part of the civil service. Examples are the Prison Service, Land Registry, Meteorological Office and Ordnance Survey. There were 142 NSEAs, or near-NSEAs, in late 1998, employing 377,000 civil servants, with 19 agencies in the pipeline.

At a local level, NDPBs, NSEAs and other types of quangos have taken over many services previously run by local authorities or by elected regional/national bodies, such as NHS hospitals, education and housing.

A major problem in understanding quangos is the similarity between semi-privatised and fully privatised bodies such as former gas, water and electricity boards, now the property of shareholders. It is often difficult to discover what formal status a quango has: is it an NSEA, private company, government department, trust, NDPB, public company or a mixture of some of these ingredients? In addition, public accountability is hard to define, often being only personal, with just the chief exec responsible to the minister of the sponsoring government department. In Whitehall, the quangos and Civil Service come under the Office of Public Service (OPS), part of the Cabinet Office. The Cabinet Office has two basic roles: providing ministers with the bureaucracy services they need; and ensuring the Cabinet has managerial power over all public services, via the OPS, headed by the Chancellor of the Duchy of Lancaster.

WEBSITES

CCTA Government Information Service
www.open.gov.uk
The starting point for finding any quango or government department.

Cabinet Office
www.cabinet-office.gov.uk
The Cabinet Office has close contacts with quangoland, and these can be pursued from here.

Commissioner for Public Appointments
www.open.gov.uk/ocpa/ocpahome.htm
Lots of background information from, and about, the official responsible for monitoring quango operators.

Stationery Office
www.national-publishing.co.uk
www.official-documents.co.uk
Combined, these sites form the compendious official bookshop online, for quango tomes or anything .

Technology Applications Group Information Superhighway
www.tagish.co.uk
Comprehensive online lists of public sector links, especially outside Whitehall.

OFFICIAL BODIES

Organisations which are still part of the civil service, and therefore not quangos.

British Standards Institution	020-8996 9000
Charity Commission	020-7210 4477
Commonwealth Secretariat	020-7839 3411
Crown Estate	020-7210 4210
Export Credit Guarantee Dept	020-7512 7000
Law Commission: England	020-7453 1220
Scotland	0131-668 2131
National Audit Office	020-7798 7000
National Savings Department	020-7605 9300
International Development	020-7917 7000
Press	020-7917 0950
Post Office	020-7490 2888
Press 24 hrs	020-7250 2468
Queens Awards Office	020-7222 2277
Registry of Friendly Societies	020-7676 1000
Royal Commission on Environmental	
Pollution	020-7276 2080
Royal Mail	020-7250 2888
Royalty - press offices:	
Buckingham Palace	020-7930 4832
Clarence House	020-7930 3141
Duchy of Cornwall	020-7834 7346
Duchy of Lancaster	020-7836 8277
Trade Unions & Employers Associations	
Certification Office	020-7210 3734
Welsh Development Agency	0345-775577

UK AND ENGLISH QUANGOS

Below are NDPBs, NSEAs and other bodies run by the quangocracy in some form. Many national quangos cannot be asked questions over the phone because they come under the wings of a government department, and are only in the phone books under the department's name, not their own. Where no phone number is given here, inquiries should be made to the sponsoring department. The initials after each name are of these departments. The asterisked entries (*) are NSEAs.

ACAS - Advisory, Conciliation & Arbitration	
Service (DfEE)	020-7396 0022
ADAS* (MAFF)	01865-842742
Advisory Committees on:	
NHS Drugs	020-7210 5221
Novel Foods	020-7210 5221
Telecommunications	020-7215 0319
Advisory Councils on:	
Public Records (LCD)	020-8876 3444
Science & Technology	via CO
The Misuse of Drugs	via HO
Agricultural Land Tribunals	via MAFF
Agricultural Wages Board	via MAFF
Arts Council (DCMS)	020-7333 0100
Audit Commission for Local Authorities and	
the NHS (DETR)	020-7828 1212
Bank of England (HMT)	020-7601 4444
BBC (Press)	020-8576 1865
Biotechnology and Biological Research	
Council (CO)	01793-413200
Boards of Visitors to Prisons	020-7217 8388
Boundary Commissions - Local Government:	
England	020-7430 8400
Wales	029-2039 5031
Scotland	0131-538 7510
Boundary Commissions - Parliamentary:	
England & Wales	020-7533 5177
Scotland	0131-538 7513
Northern Ireland	020-7210 6569
British Antarctic Survey	01223-361188
British Coal (DTI)	01782-662052
British Council (FCO)	020-7930 8466
Press	020-7389 4878
British Energy	020-7389 3406
British Film Institute (DCMS)	020-7255 1444
Press	020-7957 8920
British Library (DCMS)	020-7412 7000
Press	020-7412 7116
British Museum (DCMS)	020-7636 1555
Press	020-7323 8779
British National Space Centre	020-7215 0806
British Nuclear Fuels (DTI)	01925-832000
Sellafield (press)	01946-785838
British Overseas Trade Board (DTI)	020-7215 4936
British Tourist Authority (DCMS)	020-8846 9000
Press	020-8563 3034
British Waterways (DETR)	01923-226422
Broadcasting Complaints/Standards Commission	
(DCMS)	020-7233 0544
Building Regulations Advisory Cttee	020-7890 5742
Building Research Establishment*	
(DETR)	01923-664000
Building Societies Commission	020-7676 1000
CCTA*: Central Computer & Telecommunications	
Agency (OPS)	01603-704874
Central Fire Brigades Advisory Council	via HO
Central Office of Information* (OPS)	020-7928 2345
Press	020-7261 8815
Emergency Planning	020-7261 8221
Films & Radio	020-7261 8598
New Media	020-7261 8406
News Distribution Service	020-7261 8445
Press & Pictures	020-7261 8650
Central Rail Users Consultative Committee	
(DETR)	020-7505 9090
Central Science Laboratory* (MAFF)	01904-462000
Centre for Environment, Fisheries & Aquaculture	
Science* (MAFF)	01502-562244
Chemical & Biological Defence Establishment	
(MOD)	01980-613000
Citizens Charter Unit (CO)	020-7270 1234
Civil Aviation Authority (DETR)	020-7379 7311
Press	020-7832 5335

Civil Service College* (CO)	01344-634000
Coastguard & Marine Safety Agency*	
(DETR)	023-8032 9100
Commission for Racial Equality (HO)	020-7828 7022
Press	020-7932 5354
Commissioner for the Rights of Trade Union	
Members (DfEE)	01925-415771
Press	0161-952 4508
Committee for Monitoring Agreements on Tobacco	
Advertising/Sponsorship	020-7210 5221
Committees on:	
Carcinogenicity Food Chemicals	020-7210 5221
Medical Aspects of Food Policy	020-7210 5221
Safety of Medicines (DOH)	020-7273 0451
Standards in Public Life	020-7270 6345
Toxicity of Chemicals in Food	020-7210 5221
Commonwealth Institute (FCO)	020-7603 4535
Community Development Foundation	
(HO)	020-7226 5375
Companies House* (DTI)	029-2038 8588
Press	029-2038 0526
Consultative Panel on Badgers and	
Tuberculosis	via MAFF
Copyright Tribunal	020-7438 4776
Council on Tribunals (LCD)	020-7936 7045
Countryside Commission	01242-521381
Court Service* (LCD)	020-7210 2092
Customer service	020-7210 1793
Press	020-7210 8512
Crafts Council (DCMS)	020-7278 7700
Criminal Injuries Compensation Board	
(HO)	020-7842 6800
Crown Agents (FCO)	020-7834 3644
Crown Prosecution Service*	020-7273 8000
Customs & Excise (HMT)	020-7620 1313
Press	020-7865 5665
Investigations: press	020-7665 7829
Data Protection Registrar (HO)	01625-545700
Defence Agencies (MOD):	
Armed Forces Personnel Admin*	01452-712612
Army Base Storage*	01264-382424
Army Personnel*	0141-224 3010
Army Technical Support	01264-383753
Defence Analytical Services	020-7218 7950
Defence Animal Centre*	020-7218 7950
Joint Air Reconnaissance Intelligence	
Centre*	01480-52151x7230
Logistic Information*	01264-382424
Military Survey*	020-8890 3622
MOD Police*	01371-854000
Naval Recruiting & Training *	023-9272 7600
RAF Maintenance Group*	01480-52151
RAF Training Group*	01452-712612
Specialist Procurement*	0117-913 2724
Design Council (DTI)	020-7420 5200
Doctors/Dentists Review Body	020-7467 7229
Driver & Vehicle Licensing Agency*	
(DOT)	01792-782318
Driving Standards Agency* (DETR)	0115-901 2500
Economic and Social Research Council	
(CO)	01793-413000
Press	01793-413122

Education Assets Board	0113-234 8888
Employment Appeal Tribunal (DfEE)	020-7273 1041
Employment Service* (DfEE)	020-7273 6060
Engineering & Physical Science Research	
Council (CO)	01793-444000
English Heritage (DCMS)	020-7973 3000
Press	020-7973 3250
English Nature (DETR)	01733-455000
Press	01733-455193
English Tourist Board (DCMS)	020-8846 9000
Press	020-8563 3038
Environment Agency (DETR)	01454-624400
Press	020-7863 8600
Equal Opportunities Commission (DfEE)	0161-833 9244
Press	020-7222 1110
Farm Animal Welfare Council (MAFF)	020-8330 8077
Farming/Rural Conservation* (MAFF)	020-7238 5432
Fire Service College* (HO)	01608-650831
Fisheries Research* (SO)	01224-876544
Food Advisory Committee (MAFF)	020-7238 6267
Food From Britain (MAFF)	020-7233 5111
Football Licensing Authority (DCMS)	020-7491 7191
Forensic Science Service* (HO)	020-7230 6654
Forest Enterprise* (SO)	0131-334 0303
Forestry Commission Research*	0131-334 0303
Further Education Development Agency	
(DfEE)	020-7840 5400
Further Education Funding Council	
(DfEE)	024-7686 3000
Gaming Board (HO)	020-7306 6200
Government Car & Despatch* (OPS)	020-7217 3838
Govt Property Lawyers* (HMT)	01823-345200
Health & Safety Commission & Executive	
(DfEE)	020-7717 6000
Press	020-7717 6700
Health Education Authority (DOH)	020-7222 5300
Healthcare Advisory Service	0118-972 2696
Highways Agency* (DETR)	020-7921 4443
Historic Royal Palaces* (DCMS)	020-8781 9750
HMSO*	01603-723014
Press	020-7270 0375
Copyright section	01603 723001
Housing Corporation (DETR)	020-7393 2000
Hydrographic Office* (MOD)	01823-337900
Immigration Appellate Auth (LCD)	020-7862 4200
Independent Television Commission	
(DCMS)	020-7255 3000
Industrial Development Advisory Board	via DTI
Industrial Injuries Advisory Council	
(DSS)	020-7962 8065
Industrial Tribunals:	
National Enquiry Line (DfEE)	0345-959775
Press	020-7215 5964
Inland Revenue (HMT)	020-7438 6622
Press	020-7438 6692
Innovation Unit (DTI)	020-7215 1705
Insolvency Service* (DTI)	020-7637 1110
Intelligence Services Tribunal	020-7273 4383
Interception of Communications Tribunal	
(HO)	020-7273 4096
Intervention Board* (MAFF)	0118-958 3626
Joint Nature Conservation Committee	

(DETR)	01733-562626
Laboratory of the Government Chemist*	
(DTI)	020-8943 7000
HM Land Registry* (LCD)	020-7917 8888
Lands Tribunal (LCD)	020-7936 7200
Law Commission (LCD)	020-7453 1220
Legal Aid Board (LCD)	020-7813 1000
Library & Information Commission	via DCMS
London Docklands Urban Development	
Corporation (DETR)	abolished 1998
London Transport (DETR)	020-7222 5600
Maritime & Coastguard* (DETR)	023-8032 9467
Meat Hygiene Service* (MAFF)	01904-455501
Meat/Livestock Commission (MAFF)	01908-677577
Medical Devices Agency* (DOH)	020-7972 8000
Medical Practices Committee (DOH)	020-7972 2930
Medical Research Council (CO)	020-7636 5422
Medicines Commission/Control Agency*	
(DOH)	020-7273 0392
Mental Health Act Commission	0115-943 7100
Mental Health Review Tribunal	0115-929 4222
Meteorological Office* (MOD)	01344-420242
Press	01344-856655
Monopolies and Mergers Commission	
(DTI)	020-7324 1467
Museums & Galleries Commission	
(DCMS)	020-7233 4200
National Consumer Council (DTI)	020-7730 3469
National Council for Vocational Qualifications	
(DfEE)	020-7229 1234
National Food Survey Committee	
(MAFF)	020-7270 8563
National Health Service Tribunal	via DOH
National Heritage Memorial Fund	
(DCMS)	020-7591 6000
National Physical Laboratory (DTI)	020-8977 3222
National Radiological Protection Board	
(DOH)	01235-831600
National Weights & Measures Laboratory*	
(DTI)	020-8943 7272
National Youth Agency	0116-285 6789
Natural Environment Research Council	
(CO)	01793-411500
Natural Resources Institute* (FCO)	01634-880088
NHS Estates* (DOH)	0113-254 7000
Nuclear Electric plc (DTI)	020-7389 3406
Nuclear Powered Warships Safety Cttee	via MOD
Nuclear Weapons Safety Committee	via MOD
Occupational Health & Safety* (CO)	0131-220 9700
Office for National Statistics* (HMT)	020-7533 6207
Ordnance Survey* (DETR)	023-8079 2000
Parliamentary Boundary Commission	020-7533 5177
Parole Board (HO)	020-7217 3000
Particle Physics & Astronomy Research	
Council	01793-444000
Passport Agency* (HO)	0990-210410
Patent Office* (DTI)	01633-814000
Paymaster General*	01293-560999
Pesticides Safety Directorate* (MAFF)	01904 640500
Planning Inspectorate* (DETR)	020-7890 3043
Poisons Board	via HO
Police Advisory Board	via HO
Police Complaints Authority (HO)	020-7273 6450
Political Honours Scrutiny Committee	
(CO)	020-7219 4272
Post Office (DTI)	020-7490 2888
Post Office Users National Council (DTI)	020-7928 9458
Prescription Pricing Authority	0191-232 5371
HM Prison Service* (HO)	020-7217 6633
Property Advisers to Civil Estate (CO)	020-7271 2610
Public Health Laboratory (DOH)	020-8200 1295
Public Lending Right	01642-604699
Public Record Office* (LCD)	020-8876 3444
Public Trust Office* (LCD)	020-7664 7000
QEII Conference Centre*	020-7798 4000
Radio Authority (DCMS)	020-7430 2724
Radiocommunications Agency* (DTI)	020-7211 0211
Railway Inspectorate	0113-483 4200
Recruitment & Assessment Services*	01256-869555
Renewable Energy Advisory Committee	via DTI
Royal Commission on Environmental	
Pollution (DETR)	020-7276 2109
Royal Commission on Historical Monuments	
(DCMS)	020-7208 8200
Royal Fine Art Commission (DCMS)	020-7839 6537
Royal Mint* (HMT)	01443-222111
Royal Parks Agency*(DCMS)	020-7298 2000
Rural Development Commission	
(DETR)	020-7340 2906
School Curriculum & Assessment Authority	
(DfEE)	020-7925 5001
Sea Fish Industry Authority (MAFF)	0131-558 3331
Securities & Investments Board	020-7676 1000
Security Committee	via CO
Security Facilities Executive* (DETR)	020-7921 4813
Security Services Tribunal	020-7273 4095
Serious Fraud Office*	020-7239 7272
Social Security (DSS):	
Advisory Committee	020-7412 1506
Benefits Agency*	0113-232 4000
Child Support Agency*	0345-133133
Contributions Agency	0191-225 7665
War Pensions Agency*	01253-858858
Sports Council (DCMS)	020-7273 1500
Standing Advisory Committee on Trunk	
Road Assessment	020-7271 5766
Street Works Advisory Committee	via DETR
Top Salaries Review Body	020-7467 7217
Traffic Director for London (DETR)	020-7222 4545
Transport Research Lab* (DETR)	01344-773131
Treasury Solicitor's Dept (HMT)	020-7210 3079
Trinity House (DETR)	020-7481 6900
UK Atomic Energy Authority (DTI)	01235-821111
UK Nirex	01235-825500
Valuation Office (HMT)	020-7324 1033
Value Added Tax Tribunals (LCD)	020-7631 4242
Vehicle Certification Agency* (DETR)	0117-951 5151
Vehicle Inspectorate* (DETR)	0117-954 3200
Veterinary Laboratories Agency*	
(MAFF)	01932-341111
Veterinary Medicines Directorate	
(MAFF)	01932-336911
Wilton Park Conference Centre (FCO)	01903-815020
Womens National Commission (DfEE)	020-7712 2443

WELSH QUANGOS

Arts Council of Wales	029-2037 6500
Boundary Commission	020-7533 5177
Cadw: Historic Monuments*	029-2050 0200
Countryside Council for Wales	01248-370444
Development Board for Rural Wales	01686-626965
Fourth Channel Authority	029-2074 7444
Health Promotion Authority	029-2075 2222
Hill Farming Advisory Cttee	029-2082 5735
Housing for Wales	029-2082 5111
Land Authority for Wales	029-2022 3444
Local Government Boundary	029-2039 5031
National Library of Wales	01970-632800
National Museums of Wales	029-2039 7951
Patent Office*	01633-814000
Sports Council for Wales	029-2030 0500
Tai Cymru Housing for Wales	029-2082 5111
Wales Tourist Board	029-2049 9909
Welsh Development Agency	0345-775577
Welsh Funding Councils	029-2076 1861
Welsh Language Board	029-2022 4744
Youth Agency	029-2088 0088

SCOTTISH QUANGOS

Community Education Council	0131-313 2488
Council on the Curriculum	01382-455053
Crofters Commission	01463-663450
Deer Commission	01463-231751
Fisheries Research Services*	01244-876544
Forest Enterprise*	0131-334 0303
Forestry Commission Research*	0131-334 0303
Health Board	0131-556 8400
Health Service Committee	0131-556 8400
Highlands & Islands Enterprise	01463-234171
Hill Farming Advisory Cttee	0131-244 6417
Historic Buildings Council	0131-244 4999
Historic Scotland*	0131-668 8600
Lands Tribunal	0131-225 7996
Law Commission	0131-668 2131
Legal Aid Board	0131-226 7061
Mental Welfare Commission	0131-222 6111
National Galleries	0131-556 8921
NHS Tribunal	0131-244 4999
National Library	0131-226 4531
National Museums	0131-225 7534
Parliamentary Boundary Commission	0131-244 2196
Parole Unit	0131-244 8528
Pensions Appeal Tribunal	0131-220 1404
Police Advisory Board	0131-556 8400
Registers of Scotland*	0131-659 6111
Royal Fine Art Commission	0131-556 6699
Scottish Agricultural Science *	0131-244 8890
Scottish Arts Council	0131-226 6051
Scottish Court Service*	0131-229 9200
Scottish Enterprise	0141-248 2700
Scottish Environment Protection	01786-457700
Scottish Fisheries Protection*	0131-244 6059
Scottish Homes	0131-313 0044

Scottish Nuclear	01355-262000
Scottish Natural Heritage	0131-447 4784
Scottish Prison Service*	0131-244 8745
Scottish Qualifications Authority	0141-248 7900
Scottish Record Office*	0131-535 1314
Scottish Screen	0141-334 4445
Sports Council	0131-317 7200
Tourist Board	0131-332 2433

NORTHERN IRISH QUANGOS

Arts Council	028-9038 5200
NI Child Support Agency*	028-9089 6666
Citizen's Charter Unit	028-9052 1722
Commission for Police Complaints	028-9024 4821
Compensation Agency*	028-9024 9944
Construction Service*	028-9025 0284
Court Service*	028-9032 8594
Curriculum Council	028-9026 1200
Driver & Vehicle Testing*	028-9068 1831
Economic Council	028-9023 2125
Environment & Heritage Service*	028-9054 6569
Fishery Harbour Authority	01396-61 3844
Forensic Science Agency of NI*	028-9036 1888
Government Purchasing Service*	028-9052 6538
Health Estates*	028-9052 0025
Historic Monuments Council	028-9023 5000
Housing Executive	028-9024 0588
Human Rights	028-9024 3987
Industrial Court	028-9032 7666
Industrial Development Board	028-9023 3233
Industrial Research & Tech*	028-9052 9533
Land Registers of NI*	028-9025 1515
Law Reform Advisory Committee	028-9054 2900
NI Prison Service	028-9052 0700
Ordnance Survey of NI*	028-9025 5755
Parliamentary Boundary Commission	028-9031 1210
Police Complaints	028-9024 4821
Planning Service*	028-9054 0677
Police Authority	028-9023 0111
Probation Board	028-9026 2400
Public Record Office of NI*	028-9025 1318
Rate Collection Agency*	028-9025 2252
NI Council for the Curriculum	028-9026 1200
Social Security Agency NI*	028-9052 0520
Sports Council	028-9038 1222
Statistics and Research Agency	028-9052 0700
Tourist Board	028-9023 1221
Training/Employment Agency *	028-9025 7777
Transport Holding Company	028-9024 3456
Valuation & Lands Agency*	028-9025 0700
Water Service*	028-9024 4711

Local and regional government

Local government was transformed by the creation of unitary authorities from 1995 to 1998. These single-tier authorities, responsible for all local government services, replaced much of the two-tier structure set up in 1974/5. In Wales, 22 unitaries took over from all eight county councils and 37 district councils. In Scotland, the 12 regional and 56 district councils were replaced by 32 unitaries. These 32 included Scotland's three islands councils (Orkney, Shetland and Western Isles), which were already unitary. In England a confusing mixture of authorities with differing structures and powers were created in some places, in marked contrast to Wales and Scotland. Three of 1974's new county councils - Avon, Cleveland and Humberside - were abolished, along with the traditional county of Berkshire. Herefordshire and Worcestershire were split, becoming separate counties again. By mid-1998 England had 388 authorities: 34 county councils, 239 district councils, 36 metropolitan districts, 32 London boroughs (plus the City of London), 46 new unitary councils and 4 existing island unitaries. Northern Ireland has remained unchanged during the mainland's unitary upheavals. Since 1973 it has had 26 single-tier district councils, but these have fewer functions than the new mainland unitaries.

FUTURES

Radical changes in the way local government is run are in the pipline. The draft bill *Local Leadership, Local Choice* of March 1999 took forward proposals in the white paper *Modern Local Government: In Touch with the People*, which appeared in mid-1998. Whitehall says its aim is to make councils more open and accountable to the public by changing the political management structures. Three options are proposed: either have a directly elected mayor, a cabinet with a leader or a directly elected mayor with a council manager. The traditional committee system will be scrapped. Instead, there will be scrutiny panels running an eye over the decisions and poli-

cies of the cabinet or elected mayor. Media critics of the methods believe they will create a Downing Street-style secret elite, beyond the control of both non-cabinet councillors and the public, all barred from the main meetings. Under strong pressure from Whitehall, many councils are drawing up plans for a new style of management, whether local people want it or not. The first elected mayor will be in London. The mayor and the new 25-member Greater London Authority will be elected on 4 May 2000 and begin work on 3 July.

ELECTIONS

There were 44,692,299 local government electors in the UK in 1999. Most UK councillors are elected for four years. In England county council seats are all polled at the same time, once every four years (next: 2001). In that year there are no district council elections. In district councils each authority can choose whether to elect all seats together once every four years, or ballot a third of seats every year, except in the year of county council elections. All London boroughs and the Corporation of London are held together every four years (next: 2002). Metropolitan authority elections are in thirds (next: 2000, not 2001). Unitary authority elections are held four years after their founding elections; in England these are in different years.

Elections are also four-yearly in Wales (next: 2003) and Northern Ireland (next: 2001), but in Scotland they are three-yearly (next: 2002). Most elections are on the first Thursday in May. In the Isle of Man, the House of Keys vote is held every five years, on the third Thursday in November (next: 2001).

The annual directory is the *Municipal Year Book*. The Local Government Information Unit produces useful publications. Local finances can be examined using legal rights, spelled out in the Audit Commission's free booklet *Local Authority Accounts: The Rights of the Public*. Once an authority's accounts for the financial year are completed, it must advertise they are open to inspection for 15 days.

WEBSITES

DETR
www.local.detr.gov.uk
www.local-regions.detr.gov.uk
The Whitehall basecamp for everything official about local and regional government.

Local Government Association
www.lga.gov.uk
Data from the representative body of local authorities.

Local Government Information Unit
www.lgiu.gov.uk
The independent research and info organisation.

Scottish New Councils
www.trp.dundee.ac.uk/data/councils

Tagish
www.tagish.co.uk
The Technology Applications Group Information SuperHighway's comprehensive, wideranging details of local authorities, plus much on central government.

REGIONALISM

An experiment with regional government began in England in April 1999, with the launch of eight Regional Development Agencies. The granting of new forms of independence to Wales, Scotland and Northern Ireland during 1997/8 had produced fears in Whitehall of the Tories winning the next general election riding a warhorse of revived English nationalism.. Labour hoped to trip the horse by subdividing England into eight regions, excluding London, each home to an RDA with the role of regenerating local economies, clearing derelict land and creating jobs. The RDAs are run by small boards of local notables, appointed by the Minister for the Regions, with a third of them councillors. But by mid-1999 Whitehall seemed to have abandoned the idea of adding elected assembly status to the regions and RDAs.

Ten Government Offices (GOs) for the Regions were set up in England in 1994. The GOs run the regional programmes of the DTI, DfEE, DETR and Home Office. Each regional director reports to the relevant Secretary of State for each department. The GOs Central Unit acts as the main coordinating point. The DETR is the leader.

GOs Central Unit	020-7890 5005
East Midlands (GOEM, Nottingham)	0115-971 2753
Eastern Region (GOER, Cambridge)	01223-346766
London (GOL, Millbank)	020-7217 3456
Merseyside (GOM, Liverpool)	0151-224 6300
North East (GONE, Newcastle)	0191-201 3300
North West (GONW, Manchester)	0161-952 4000
South East (GOSE, Guildford)	01483-882255
South West (GOSW, Bristol)	0117-900 1700
West Midlands (GOWM, Birmingham)	0121-212 5050
Yorks & Humber (GOYH, Leeds)	0113-280 0600

LOCAL GOVT. CONTACTS

Assoc Electoral Administrators	0116-267 2015
Assoc of London Government	020-7222 7799
Audit Commission for Local Auths	020-7828 1212
Publications	0800-502030
Commission (Ombudman) for Local Admin in:	
England	020-7915 3210
Scotland	0131-225 5300
Wales	01656-661325
Convention of Scottish Local Auths	0131-474 9200
DETR	020-7890 3000
Public enquiries	020-7890 3333
Press (regions)	020-7890 3045
Institute of Revenues Rating and Valuation	020-7831 3505
Local Government Association	020-7834 2222
Press office	020-7664 3331
Local Government Commission for England	020-7430 8400
Local Government Boundary Commissions:	
Scotland	0131-538 7510
Wales	029-2039 5031
Local Govt Information Unit	020-7608 1051
Local Govt International Bureau	020-7664 3100
Local Govt Management Board	020-7296 6600
Municipal Yearbook	020-7973 6400
National Assoc of Local Councils	020-7637 1865
New Local Government Network	020-7357 0051
Ombudsmen: England	020-7915 3210
Wales	01656-661325
Scotland	0131-556 5574
Northern Ireland	028-90233821

ENGLISH TWO-TIER

County and district authorities, in shire areas.

Bedfordshire	**01234-363222**
Bedford	01234-267422
Mid Bedfordshire	01525-402051
South Bedfordshire	01582-472222

Berkshire
Abolished 1998. The former district councils are now unitary; see under Other English Unitary Councils.

Buckinghamshire	
	01296-395000
Aylesbury Vale	01296-585858
Chiltern	01494-729000
South Bucks	01753-533333
Wycombe	01494-461000

Cambridgeshire	
	01223-717111
Cambridge	01223-457000
East Cambs	01353-665555
Fenland	01354-654321
Huntingdonshire	01480-388388
South Cambs	01223-443000

Cheshire	**01244-602424**
Chester	01244-324324
Congleton	01270-763231
Crewe/Nantwich	01270-537777
Ellesmere Port &	
Neston	0151-356 6789
Macclesfield	01625-500500
Vale Royal	01606-862862

Cornwall & Scilly Isles	
	01872-322000
Caradon	01579-341000
Carrick	01872-224400
Isles of Scilly	01720-422537
Kerrier	01209-614000
North Cornwall	01208-893333
Penwith	01736-362341
Restormel	01726-74466

Cumbria	**01228-606060**
Allerdale	01900-326333
Barrow-in-Furness	01229-894900
Carlisle City	01228-817000
Copeland	01946-852585
Eden	01768-864671
South Lakeland	01539-733333

Derbyshire	**01629-580000**
Amber Valley	01773-570222
Bolsover	01246-240000
Chesterfield	01246-345345
Derbyshire Dales	01629-580580
Erewash	0115-944 0440
High Peak	01663-751751
NE Derbyshire	01246-231111
S Derbyshire	01283-221000

Devon	**01392-382000**
East Devon	01395-516551
Exeter	01392-277888
Mid Devon	01884-255255
North Devon	01271-327711
South Hams	01803-861234
Teignbridge	01626-361101
Torridge	01237-476711
West Devon	01822-615911

Dorset	**01305-251000**
Christchurch	01202-495000
East Dorset	01202-886201
Purbeck	01929-556561
West Dorset	01305-251010
Weymouth & Portland	
	01305-761222

Durham	**0191-386 4411**
Chester-le-Street	0191-387 1919
Derwentside	01207-218000
Durham City	0191-386 6111
Easington	0191-527 0501
Sedgefield	01388-816166
Teesdale	01833-690000
Wear Valley	01388-765555

East Sussex	**01273-481000**
Eastbourne	01323-410000
Hastings	01424-781066
Lewes	01273-471600
Rother	01424-787878
Wealden	01892-653311

Essex	**01245-492211**
Basildon	01268-533333
Braintree	01376-552525
Brentwood	01277-261111
Castle Point	01268-792711
Chelmsford	01245-606606
Colchester	01206-282222
Epping Forest	01992-564000
Harlow	01279-446611
Maldon	01621-854477
Rochford	01702-546366
Tendring	01255-425501
Uttlesford	01799-510510

Gloucestershire	
	01452-425000
Cheltenham	01242-262626
Cotswold	01285-643643
Forest of Dean	01594-810000
Gloucester City	01452-522232
Stroud	01453-766321
Tewkesbury	01684-295010

Hampshire	**01962-841841**
Basingstoke & Deane	
	01256-844844
East Hampshire	01730-266551
Eastleigh	023-8061 4646
Fareham	01329-236100
Gosport	023-9258 4242
Hart	01252-622122
Havant	023-9247 4174
New Forest	023-8028 5000
Rushmoor	01252-516222
Test Valley	01264-364144
Winchester	01962-840222

Herefordshire	
Not a county council. See under
Other English Unitary Councils.

Hertfordshire	**01992-555555**
Broxbourne	01992-631921
Dacorum	01442-260161
East Herts	01279-655261
Hertsmere	020-8207 2277
North Herts	01462-474000
St Albans	01727-866100
Stevenage	01438-356177
Three Rivers	01923-776611
Watford	01923-226400
Welwyn Hatfield	01707-357000

Kent	**01622-671411**
Ashford	01233-637311
Canterbury	01227-763763
Dartford	01322-343434
Dover	01304-821199
Gravesham	01474-564422
Maidstone	01622-602000
Sevenoaks	01732-741222
Shepway	01303-850388
Swale	01795-424341
Thanet	01843-225511
Tonbridge/Malling	01732-844522
Tunbridge Wells	01892 526121

Lancashire	**01772-254868**
Burnley	01282-425011
Chorley	01257-515151
Fylde	01253-721222
Hyndburn	01254-388111
Lancaster	01524-582000
Pendle	01282-661661
Preston	01772-906000
Ribble Valley	01200-425111
Rossendale	01706-217777
South Ribble	01772-421491
West Lancashire	01695-577177
Wyre	01253-891000

Leicestershire	
	0116-232 3232
Blaby	0116-275 0555
Charnwood	01509-263151
Harborough	01858-410000
Hinckley & Bosworth	
	01455-238141
Melton	01664-567771
NW Leicestershire	01530-833333
Oadby & Wigston	0116-288 8961

Lincolnshire	**01522-552222**
Boston	01205-314200
East Lindsey	01507-601111
Lincoln	01522-881188
North Kesteven	01529-414155
South Holland	01775-761161

South Kesteven	01476-406080
West Lindsey	01427-615411

Norfolk **01603-222222**
Breckland	01362 695333
Broadland	01603-431133
Gt Yarmouth	01493-856100
Kings Lynn & West Norfolk	
	01553-692722
North Norfolk	01263-513811
Norwich	01603-622233
South Norfolk	01508-533633

Northamptonshire **01604-236236**
Corby	01536-402551
Daventry	01327-871100
East Northants	01832-742000
Kettering	01536-410333
Northampton	01604-233500
South Northants	01327-350211
Wellingborough	01933-229777

Northumberland **01670-533000**
Alnwick	01665-510505
Berwick-upon-Tweed	
	01289-330044
Blyth Valley	01670-542000
Castle Morpeth	01670-514351
Tynedale	01434-652200
Wansbeck	01670-814444

North Yorkshire **01609-780780**
Craven	01756-700600
Hambleton	01609-779977
Harrogate	01423-568954
Richmondshire	01748-850222
Ryedale	01653-600666
Scarborough	01723-232323
Selby	01757-705101
York	01904-613161

Nottinghamshire **0115-982 3823**
Ashfield	01623-450000
Bassetlaw	01909-533533
Broxtowe	0115-917 7777
Gedling	0115-901 3901
Mansfield	01623-463463
Newark & Sherwood	
	01636-605111
Rushcliffe	0115-981 9911

Oxfordshire **01865-792422**
Cherwell	01295-252535
Oxford	01865-249811
South Oxfordshire	01491-835351
Vale of White Horse	
	01235-520202

West Oxfordshire	01993-702941

Shropshire **01743-251000**
Bridgnorth	01746-713100
North Shropshire	01939-232771
Oswestry	01691-671111
Shrewsbury & Atcham	
	01743-232255
South Shropshire	01584-874941

Somerset **01823-355455**
Mendip	01749-343399
Sedgemoor	01278-435435
South Somerset	01935-462462
Taunton Deane	01823-356356
West Somerset	01984-632291

Staffordshire **01785-223121**
Cannock Chase	01543-462621
East Staffs	01283-508000
Lichfield	01543-414000
Newcastle-under-Lyme	
	01782-717717
South Staffs	01902-696000
Stafford	01785-619000
Staffordshire Moorlands	
	01538-483409
Tamworth	01827-709709

Suffolk **01473-583000**
Babergh	01473-822801
Forest Heath	01638-719000
Ipswich	01473-262626
Mid Suffolk	01449-720711
St Edmundsbury	01284-763233
Suffolk Coastal	01394-383789
Waveney	01502-562111

Surrey **020-8541 8800**
Elmbridge	01372-474474
Epsom & Ewell	01372-732000
Guildford	01483-505050
Mole Valley	01306-885001
Reigate/Banstead	01737-276000
Runnymede	01932-838383
Spelthorne	01784-451499
Surrey Heath	01276-686252
Tandridge	01883-722000
Waverley	01483-861111
Woking	01483-755855

Warwickshire **01926-410410**
North Warwicks	01827-715341
Nuneaton & Bedworth	
	024-7637 6376
Rugby	01788-533533
Stratford-on-Avon	01789-267575
Warwick	01926-450000

West Sussex **01243-777100**
Adur	01273-455566
Arun	01903-716133

Chichester	01243-785166
Crawley	01293-438000
Horsham	01403-215100
Mid Sussex	01444-458166
Worthing	01903-239999

Wiltshire **01225-713000**
Kennet	01380-724911
North Wiltshire	01249-706111
Salisbury	01722-336272
West Wiltshire	01225-776655

Worcestershire **01905-763763**
Bromsgrove	01527-873232
Malvern Hills	01684-892700
Redditch	01527-64252
Worcester City	01905-723471
Wychavon	01386-565000
Wyre Forest	01562-820505

ENGLISH UNITARY COUNCILS

London boroughs

The Greater London Council (GLC) was abolished in 1986, leaving the 32 boroughs on their own. The Corporation of London (aka City of London) has always been unitary.

Barking & Dagenham	
	020-8592 4500
Barnet	020-8359 2000
Bexley	020-8303 7777
Brent	020-8904 1244
Bromley	020-8464 3333
Camden	020-7278 4444
Croydon	020-8686 4433
Ealing	020-8579 2424
Enfield	020-8366 6565
Greenwich	020-8854 8888
Hackney	020-8356 5000
Hammersmith & Fulham	
	020-8748 3020
Haringey	020-8975 9700
Harrow	020-8863 5611
Havering	01708-772222
Hillingdon	01895-250111
Hounslow	020-8570 7728
Islington	020-7226 1234
Kensington & Chelsea	020-
	7937 5464
Kingston-upon-Thames	
	020-8546 2121
Lambeth	020-7926 1000
Lewisham	020-8695 6000

Merton	020-8543 2222
Newham	020-8472 1430
Redbridge	020-8478 3020
Richmond-upon-Thames	
	020-8891 1411
Southwark	020-7237 6677
Sutton	020-8770 5000
Tower Hamlets	020-7364 5000
Waltham Forest	020-8527 5544
Wandsworth	020-8871 6000
Westminster	020-7641 6000
Corporation of London	020-7606 3030

Metropolitan district councils

The six metropolitan counties (Greater Manchester, Merseyside, South Yorkshire, Tyne & Wear, West Midlands and West Yorkshire) were also scrapped in 1986 with the GLC, turning the 36 district councils into unitaries.

Barnsley	01226-770770
Birmingham	0121-303 9944
Bolton	01204-522311
Bradford	01274-752111
Bury	0161-253 5000
Calderdale	01422-357257
Coventry	024-7683 3333
Doncaster	01302-734444
Dudley	01384-818181
Gateshead	0191-477 1011
Kirklees	01484-221000
Knowsley	0151-489 6000
Leeds	0113-234 8080
Liverpool	0151-227 3911
Manchester	0161-234 5000
Newcastle/North Tyneside	
	0191-200 5151
Oldham	0161-911 3000
Rochdale	01706-647474
Rotherham	01709-382121
Salford	0161-794 4711
Sandwell	0121-569 2200
Sefton	01704-533133
Sheffield	0114-272 6444
Solihull	0121-704 6000
South Tyneside	0191-427 1717
St Helens	01744-456000
Stockport	0161-480 4949
Sunderland	0191-553 1000
Tameside	0161-342 8355
Trafford	0161-912 1212
Wakefield	01924-306090
Walsall	01922-650000
Wigan	01942-244991
Wirral	0151-638 7070
Wolverhampton	01902-556556

Other English unitary councils

All were created by the local government reorganisation of 1995-98, except Guernsey, Jersey and the Isle of Man, which already existed.

Bath & North East Somerset	
	01225-477000
Blackburn with Darwen	
	01254-585585
Blackpool	01253-477477
Bournemouth	01202-451451
Bracknell Forest	01344-424642
Brighton & Hove	01273-290000
Bristol, City of	0117-922 2000
Darlington	01325-380651
Derby	01332-293111
East Riding of Yorkshire	
	01482-887700
Guernsey	01481-717000
Halton	0151-424 2061
Hartlepool	01429-266522
Herefordshire, County of	
	01432-260000
Isle of Man	01624-685685
Isle of Wight	01983-821000
Jersey	01534-603000
Kingston upon Hull, County of	
	01482-610610
Leicester	0116-254 9922
Luton	01582-746000
Medway	01634-306000
Middlesbrough	01642-245432
Milton Keynes	01908-691691
North East Lincolnshire	
	01472-313131
North Lincolnshire	01724-296296
North Somerset	01934-888888
Nottingham	0115-915 5555
Peterborough	01733-563141
Plymouth	01752-668000
Poole	01202-633633
Portsmouth	023-9282 2251
Reading	0118-939 0900
Redcar & Cleveland	
	01642-444000
Rutland	01572-722577
Slough	01753-552288
South Gloucestershire	
	01454-868686
Southampton	023-8022 3855
Southend-on-Sea	01702-215000
Stockton on Tees	01642-393939
Stoke-on-Trent	01782-234567
Swindon	01793-463000
Telford & Wrekin	01962-202100
Thurrock	01375-390000
Torbay	01803-201201
Warrington	01925-444400

West Berkshire	01635-42400
Windsor & Maidenhead	
	01628-798888
Wokingham	0118- 974 6000
York	01904-613161

WELSH UNITARY COUNCILS

Blaenau Gwent	01495-350555
Bridgend	01656-643643
Caerphilly	01443-815588
Cardiff	029-2087 2000
Carmarthenshire	01267-234567
Ceredigion	01545-570881
Conwy	01492-574000
Denbighshire	01824-706000
Flintshire	01352-704476
Gwynedd	01286-672255
Isle of Anglesey	01248-750057
Merthyr Tydfil	01685-725000
Monmouthshire	01633-644644
Neath Port Talbot	01639-763333
Newport	01633-244491
Pembrokeshire	01437-764551
Powys	01597-826000
Rhondda Cynon Taff	
	01443-424000
Swansea	01792-636000
Torfaen	01495-762200
Vale of Glamorgan	01446-700111
Wrexham	01978-292000

SCOTTISH UNITARY

Aberdeen City	01224-522000
Aberdeenshire	01467-620981
Angus	01307-461460
Argyll & Bute	01546-602127
Clackmannanshire	01259-450000
Dumfries & Galloway	
	01387-261234
Dundee City	01382-434000
East Ayrshire	01563-576000
East Dunbartonshire	
	0141-578 8000
East Lothian	01620-827827
East Renfrewshire	0141-577 3000
Edinburgh, City of	0131-200 2000
Falkirk	01324-506070
Fife	01592-414141
Glasgow City	0141-287 2000
Highland	01463-702000
Inverclyde	01475-717171
Midlothian	0131-270 7500
Moray	01343-543451
North Ayrshire	01294-324100
North Lanarkshire	01698-

	302222
Orkney Islands	01856-873535
Perth & Kinross	01738-475000
Renfrewshire	0141-842 5000
Scottish Borders	01835-824000
Shetland Islands	01595-693535
South Ayrshire	01292-612000
South Lanarkshire	01698-454444
Stirling	01786-443322
West Dunbartonshire	01389-737000
West Lothian	01506-777000
Western Isles (Eilean Siar)	01851-703773

NI DISTRICT COUNCILS

Antrim	028-9446 3113
Ards	028-9182 4000
Armagh	028-3752 9600
Ballymena	028-2566 0300
Ballymoney	028-7066 2280

Banbridge	028-4066 2991
Belfast	028-9032 0202
Carrickfergus	028-9335 1604
Castlereagh	028-9079 9021
Coleraine	028-7035 2181
Cookstown	028-7976 2205
Craigavon	028-3834 1199
Derry	028-7136 5151
Down	028-4461 0800
Dungannon	028-8772 5311
Fermanagh	028-6632 5050
Larne	028-2827 2313
Limavady	028-7172 2226
Lisburn	028-9268 2477
Magherafelt	028-7963 2151
Moyle	028-7076 2225
Newry & Mourne	028-3026 5411
Newtownabbey	028-9335 2681
North Down	028-9127 0371
Omagh	028-8224 5321
Strabane	028-7138 2204

European Union

The European Union grew out of trading organisations created by Belgium, France, Germany, Italy, Luxembourg and the Netherlands in the 1950s. These USA-backed groupings created the **European Economic Community** (EEC) in 1957. The EEC was also known as the Common Market. During the 1970s members often dropped the word "Economic" from the title, but it did not officially become the **European Community** (EC) until 1980. The title **European Union** (EU) was adopted in 1993 when the Maastricht Treaty was ratified. The UK, Denmark and Ireland joined in 1973, Greece in 1981, Spain and Portugal in 1986, and Austria, Finland and Sweden in 1995. This brought membership to 15 states, with a population of 371 million. The 1998 budget was £64 billion.

The aims of the EU are essentially economic, but broader social and political powers were given by the 1986 Single European Act and the 1992 Maastricht Treaty, aimed at eventually creating a single European state. The Euro currency was launched in January 1999 by 11 countries, excluding Britain, where a referendum should be held before joining. The Euro coins and notes do not go into circulation until January 2002.

The Maastricht Treaty gave the EU three "pillars". The first is made up of the then-established institutions and decision-making processes, described below: the Council of Ministers, European Council, Parliament, Commission, Court of Justice and Court of Auditors. The second pillar consists of defence and foreign policy, while the third encompasses policing, immigration, terrorism and legal co-operation. The second and third pillars are intergovernmental and therefore outside EU parliamentary control.

The **Council of Ministers** (CoM) is the most powerful decision-making body in the EU. Also known as the *Council of the European Union*, the CoM, consists of ministers from each state, whose meetings take place behind closed doors. The presidency rotates every six months. Germany and Finland presided in 1999, with Portugal and France in 2000.

Separate from the CoM is the **European Council**, comprising heads of state of each member country meeting two or three times a year. It sets political guidelines for the

Council of Ministers. The European Council and CoM should not be confused with the similarly-named *Council of Europe* (CoE). This is a political institution outside the EU, set up by ten states in 1949, and today having 39 members. Alongside the CoE is the European Court of Human Rights, based in the Parliament building in Strasbourg.

The **European Parliament** draws up new law, rather than initiating it. Its main role is to scrutinise the activities of the CoM and the staff-run Commission. An Ombudsman, appointed by Parliament, investigates maladministration. Parliament has 626 members (MEPs), 87 of them in the UK. Elections have been held every five years since 1979, with the most recent in June 1999. This used a proportional voting system for the first time, with the 87 former constituencies replaced by 12 regions, each with between three and 11 MEPs. The electorate voted for parties, not individuals. The election was a major victory for the anti-Euro Tories, doubling their seats while Labour lost more than half theirs. The result of the election was:

Conservatives	36
Labour	29
Liberal-Democrats	10
UK Independence Party	3
Plaid Cymru	2
Scottish Nationalist Party	2
Green Party	2
Northern Ireland: SDLP	1
Democratic Unionist Party	1
Ulster Unionist Party	1

Parliament meets 17 times each year. MEPs sit in political rather than national groupings. The largest is the centre-right European Peoples' Party with 224 members, including the UK Tories. Labour's Party of European Socialists has 179.

The main driving force of the EU is the **European Commission**, being both the EU's executive civil service and its legislature. The Commission drafts proposals, which are looked at by Parliament and decided by the CoM. In charge are 20 commissioners, non-MEPs recommended by member states for five-year renewable terms. All 20 were forced to resign in March 1999 when they were held responsible for massive fraud, corruption and cronyism being carried out at all levels of the EU bureaucracy. The EC's work is conducted by 30 Directorates-General and similar departments, employing 15,000 officials.

The **Court of Justice** is the legal administrator. Its 15 judges sit in Luxembourg. Their judgements are binding on member states and have primacy over national law. The **Court of Auditors** controls the EU's financial activities. Other influential EU bodies are the Economic and Social Committee, giving advice to the Commission; the Committee of the Regions, which must be consulted about regional interests; and the European Investment Bank, the EU's financing institution.

The EU's institutions are spread between Brussels; Luxembourg, where Commission and Parliament have offices and the Court of Justice is based; and Strasbourg, where Parliament meets a week a month. The CoM has meetings in Luxembourg two months a year. The committees meet in Brussels.

RESEARCH AND WEBSITES

EU information can be hard to find. Starting points are the London offices of the Commission and Parliament. Both have websites. Some public libraries have EU "information points". The official EU guidebook is the *Interinstitutional Directory of the European Union*, the Brussels equivalent to the UK's *Civil Service Yearbook*. More detail is in the quarterly *Vacher's European Companion*, the standard handook. EU press officers are elusive; try their main switchboards, especially the Commission in Brussels. There is no single EU press office. The Brussels bureaucrats have taken a long time to come to terms with publicly-accessible Internet, but now have some official websites. The main one is "Europa - the European Union's server", aiming to provide all types of general information about EU. The only independent body in Europe monitoring the EU's secret activities and their effects on civil liberties Europe-wide is Statewatch, based in London. It publishes a bulletin and has a website.

WEBSITES

Official websites
Europa	http://europa.eu.int
European Commission	www.cec.org.uk
European Parliament	www.europarl.eu.int
Information Societies Technology	www.cordis.lu/ist
Statistics/data	http://europa.eu.int/eurostat.html
UK Foreign Office	www.fco.gov.uk/europe

Unofficial websites
EmuNet	www.euro-emu.co.uk
Euroguide	www.euroguide.org
Rough Guides	www.hotwired.com/rough/europe
Statewatch	www.statewatch.org

COUNCIL OF MINISTERS

Secretariat, Brussels	00-322 2856111
UK Representation, Brussels	00-322 2878211

EUROPEAN PARLIAMENT

UK Information Office	020-7227 4300
Secretariat, Luxembourg	00-352 43001
Parliament, Strasbourg	00-333 88174001
Parliament, Brussels	00-322 2842111
Ombudsman	00-333 88174427

EUROPEAN PARTIES

Party of European Socialists (217 members):	
Brussels	00-322 2842111
Strasbourg	00-33 388174188
Labour MEPs, London	020-7222 1719
European People's Party (173):	
Brussels	00-322 2842111
Luxembourg	00-352 43001
Tory MEPs, London	020-7222 1994
Union for Europe (54)	00-322 2843920
European Liberal, Democratic and Reformist	
Party (52)	00-322 2842111
European United Left (33)	00-322 2842683
Greens (27)	00-322 2843045
European Radical Alliance (20)	00-322 2843324
Europe of Nations (19)	00-322 2842111
Non-attached (31)	00-322 2842579

EUROPEAN COMMISSION

HQ general	00-322 2991111
Luxembourg	00-352 43011
UK offices: London	020-7973 1992
Cardiff	029-20371631
Edinburgh	0131-225 2058
Belfast	028-90240708

OTHER EU OFFICIAL BODIES

Committee of the Regions	00-322 2822211
Economic/Social Committee	00-322 5469011
European Court of Auditors	
Secretariat, Luxembourg	00-352 43981
European Court of Justice	
Secretariat, Luxembourg	00-352 43031
European Investment Bank	020-7343 1200
European Monitoring Centre for Drugs and	
Drug Addiction	00-3511 8113000
Office for Official Publications	00-352 29291

OTHER ORGANISATIONS

Business in Europe - DTI Info Service	0117-944 4888
Consumers in Europe Group	020-7881 3021
Council of Europe	00-333 88412000
European Aid Intelligence Unit	020-7588 7070
European Disability Forum	00-322 2824600
European Broadcasting Union	
(Geneva)	00-4122 7172111
European Cultural Foundation	00-3120 6760222
European Free Trade Association	
EFTA (Geneva)	00-4122 7491111
European Institute. for the Media	00-49211 90104
European Movement	020-7233 1422
European Patent Office (Munich)	00-4989 23990
European Policy Forum	020-7839 7565
European Round Table	00-322-5343100
European Space Agency (Paris)	00-331 5697654
European Trade Union Confederation	
(Brussels)	00-322 240121
GATT (Geneva)	00-4122 7395111
House of Commons Select Committee on	
European Legislation	020-7219 5465
International Federation of Newspaper	
Publishers (Paris)	00-331 47428500
International Press Centre	00-322 2850800
Local Govt International Bureau	020-7764 3104
London Europe Society	01438-712999
NATO (Brussels)	00-322 7074111
Nordic Council (Stockholm)	00-468 111142
OECD (Paris)	00-331 45248200
Solidar	00-322 5001020
Statewatch	020-8802 1882
TUC European Information Service	020-7636 4030
United Nations (London)	020-7630 1981
Western European Union	00-322 5004411

EURO-SCEPTICS

Bruges Group	020-7287 4414
Campaign Against Euro Federalism	0151-638 2780
Campaign for an Independent Britain	020-8340 0314
Democracy Movement (anti-Euro)	020-7233 7351
Euro Facts	020-8746 1206
European Foundation	020-7930 7319
Freedom Association	020-7928 9925
Labour Euro Safeguards Campaign	020-7928 9925
Referendum Movement	020-8647 3831
Save Britain's Fish	01472-317686
UK Independence Party	020-7434 4559
Youth Against the EU	01795-539227

The legal system

There are separate legal systems in Scotland, England/Wales, and Northern Ireland, with significant differences in judicial procedures, the law and court structures. But the three systems share the common distinction between *criminal law* (dealing with offenses against state laws) and *civil law* (settling disputes between individuals or organisations).

In **England and Wales** every *criminal* case starts in juryless magistrates courts, where most are also settled. Serious crimes move on to the 93 crown courts, where they are heard in front of a judge and jury. The leading crown court is the Central Criminal Court, best-known as the Old Bailey. *Civil* actions start in: the many local county courts; the magistrates courts in certain limited actions; or the Queens Bench, Chancery or Family Divisions of the High Court in more complicated cases. The High Court is based in the Royal Court of Justice in London's Strand. The biggest reform of the civil justice system for a century took place in April 1999.

Appeals are heard by the Criminal or Civil Divisions of the Court of Appeal, housed in the Royal Court of Justice. From the Court of Appeal, cases involving important points of law can ask to be heard by the House of Lords. The Criminal Cases Review Commission investigates suspected miscarriages of justice in England, Wales and Northern Ireland.

In **Scotland**, district courts are the equivalent of the magistrates courts. Above the districts are the sheriff courts, arranged in six sheriffdoms. They hear both criminal and civil cases, combining the roles of the crown and county courts south of the border. The Procurator Fiscal Service conducts public prosecutions. The final criminal court is the High Court of Justiciary, which is both a trial and appeal court; there is no appeal to the House of Lords. The supreme civil court is the Court of Session, but subject to the Lords.

The **Northern Ireland** legal system is similar to England and Wales, with magistrates, crown and county courts. The big difference is that terrorism cases are usually heard before judges without juries. Crown court appeals go to the Northern Ireland Court of Appeal, and then the House of Lords.

The primary source of law is Parliament, which has no legal limits on what it can do, although it must comply with European Union law. The Lord Chancellor's Department oversees the courts system. The Attorney General, aided by the Solicitor General, is the government's chief legal adviser

LAW OFFICERS

Lord Chancellor's Dept	020-7210 8500
Press	020-7210 8512
Website	www.open.gov.uk/lcd
Attorney General & Solicitor General	020-7271 2400
Press	020-7271 2405
Scotland: Lord Advocate/Sol. Gen.	020-7276 3000
Northern Ireland: Law Barristers	028-9024 1523

APPEAL COURTS

Judicial Committee of Privy Council	020-7270 0483
House of Lords Appellate Committee	020-7219 3000
Lord Chancellor's secretary	020-7219 3232
Scotland: High Court	0131-225 2595
Court of Appeal, Royal Courts of:	
Justice, Strand	020-7936 6000
Civil Division	020-7936 6409
Criminal Division	020-7936 6011

SUPREME COURTS

England/Wales

Royal Courts of Justice, Strand	020-7936 6000
Crown Office	020-7936 6205
Lord Chief Justices clerk	020-7936 6001
Master of the Rolls clerk	020-7936 6371
Chancery Division	020-7936 6167
Family Division	020-7936 6540
Queens Bench Division	020-7936 6000
Court Service	020-7210 2092

Scotland

Court of Session and High Court of Justiciary	0131-225 2595
Crown Office (HQ, Procurator Fiscal)	0131-226 2626
Scottish Courts Administration	0131-229 9200

Northern Ireland

Supreme Court of Judicature	028-9023 511
Court Service	028-9032 859

CROWN COURTS

Crown Courts handle the most serious criminal cases. There are six circuits, each under an administrator responsible to the Lord Chancellor. The main court is the Central Criminal Court (Old Bailey) in the South East Circuit.

Midland and Oxford Circuit

Circuit Administrator (Bham)	0121-681 3200
Birmingham	0121-681 3300
Coventry	01203-536166
Derby	01332-622600
Grimsby	01472-311811
Hereford	01432-276118
Leicester	0116-222 2323
Lincoln	01522-883000
Northampton	01604-470400
Nottingham	0115-910 3500
Oxford	01865-264200
Peterborough	01733-349161
Shrewsbury	01743-355775
Stafford	01785-255217
Stoke-on-Trent	01782-854000
Warwick	01926-495428
Wolverhampton	01902-481000
Worcester	01905-730800

North Eastern Circuit

Circuit Administrator (Leeds)	0113-2511200
Bradford	01274-840274
Doncaster	01302-322211
Durham	0191-386 6714
Hull	01482-586161
Leeds	0113-283 0040
Newcastle-upon-Tyne	0191-383 5800
Sheffield	0114-281 2400
Teeside	01642-340000
York	01904-645121

Northern Circuit

Circuit Administrator	0161-833 1005
Barrow-in-Furness	01772-832300
Bolton	01204-392881
Burnley	01282-416899
Carlisle	01228-520619
Lancaster	01524-32454
Liverpool	0151-473 7373
Manchester	0161-954 1800
Preston	01772-832300

South Eastern Circuit

Circuit Administrator (London)	020-7936 7232
Aylesbury	01296-434401
Bury St Edmunds	01284-762676
Cambridge	01223-364436
Canterbury	01227-819200
Chelmsford	01245-603000
Chichester	01243-520700
Guildford	01483-506808

Ipswich	01473-213841
Kings Lynn	01553-760847
Lewes	01273-480400
London: Old Bailey	020-7248 3277
Croydon	020-8410 4700
Harrow	020-8424 2294
Inner London Sessions, SE1	020-7234 3100
Isleworth	020-8568 8811
Kingston-upon-Thames	020-8240 2500
Knightsbridge, SE1	020-7922 5800
Middlesex Guildhall, SW1	020-7799 2131
Snaresbrook, E11	020-8982 5500
Southwark, SE1	020-7522 7200
Wood Green, N22	020-8881 1400
Woolwich, SE28	020-8312 7000
Luton	01582-522000
Maidstone	01622-202000
Norwich	01603-761776
Reading	0118-9674400
St Albans	01727-834481
Southend	01268-458000

Wales and Chester Circuit

Circuit Administrator (Cardiff)	029-2041 5500
Caernarfon	01286-675200
Cardiff	029-2034 5931
Carmarthen	01267-236071
Chester	01244-317606
Dolgellau	01286-675200
Haverfordwest	01437-764782
Knutsford	01565-755486
Merthyr Tydfil	01685-388307
Mold	01352-754343
Newport	01633-266211
Swansea	01792-510200
Warrington	01925-572192
Welshpool	01938-553144

Western Circuit

Circuit Administrator (Bristol)	0117-974 3763
Barnstaple	01271-373286
Bournemouth	01202-502800
Bristol	0117-976 3030
Dorchester	01305-778684
Exeter	01392-210655
Gloucester	01452-529351
Newport	01983-526821
Plymouth	01752-208284
Portsmouth	023-9282 2281
Salisbury	01722-325444
Southampton	023-8021 3200
Swindon	01793-614848
Taunton	01823-335972
Truro	01872-222340
Winchester	01962-841212

N IRELAND CROWN COURTS

Court Service	028-9032 8594
Armagh	028-3752 2816

Ballymena	028-2564 9416
Belfast	028-90242099
Craigavon	028-3834 1324
Derry	028-7136 3448
Downpatrick	028-4461 4621
Enniskillen	028-6632 2356
Newtownards	028-9181 4343
Omagh	028-8224 2056

COUNTY COURTS

Midlands/Oxford
Birmingham	0121-681 4441
Nottingham	0115-910 3500
Stafford	01785-255217

North Eastern
Leeds	0113-245 9611
Newcastle-upon-Tyne	0191-201 2000
Sheffield	0114-281 2400

Northern
Liverpool	0151-473 7373
Manchester	0161-954 1800
Preston	01772-832300

South Eastern
Chelmsford	01245-264670
Kingston-upon-Thames	020-8546 8843
London	020-7917 5000
Maidstone	01622-202000

Wales & Chester
Cardiff	029-2037 6400
Chesterfield	01246-501200

Western
Bristol	0117-929 4414
Exeter	01392-210655
Winchester	01962-841212

SCOTTISH SHERIFF COURTS

Glasgow & Strathkelvin
Regional office	0141-429 5566
Sheriff courts	0141-429 8888

Grampian, Highlands & Islands
Regional office	01463 230782
Aberdeen	01224-648316
Banff	01261-812140
Dingwall	01349-863153
Dornoch	01862-810224
Elgin	01343-542505
Fort William	01397-702087
Inverness	01463-230782
Kirkwall	01856-872110
Lerwick	01595-693914
Lochmaddy	01876-500340
Peterhead	01779-476676
Portree	01478-612191
Stonehaven	01569-762758
Stornoway	01851-702231

Tain	01862-892518
Wick	01955-602846

Lothian & Borders
Regional office	0131-225 2525
Duns	01835-863231
Edinburgh	0131-225 2525
Haddington	01620-822936
Jedburgh	01835-863231
Linlithgow	01506-842922
Peebles	01721-720204
Selkirk	01750-21269

North Strathclyde
Regional office	0141-887 5225
Campbeltown	01586-552503
Dumbarton	01389-763266
Dunoon	01369-704166
Greenock	01475-787073
Kilmarnock	01563-520211
Oban	01631-562414
Paisley	0141-887 5291
Rothesay	01700-502982

South Strathclyde, Dumfries & Galloway
Regional office	01698-284000
Airdrie	01236-751121
Ayr	01292-268474
Dumfries	01387-262334
Hamilton	01698-282957
Kirkcudbright	01557-330574
Lanark	01555-661531
Stranraer	01776-702138

Tayside, Central & Fife
Regional office	01382-229961
Alloa	01259-722734
Arbroath	01241-876600
Cupar	01334-652121
Dundee	01382-229961
Dunfermline	01383-724666
Falkirk	01324-620822
Forfar	01307-462186
Kirkcaldy	01592-260171
Perth	01738-620546
Stirling	01786-462191

PROSECUTIONS

The Serious Fraud Office carries out the prosecution of the most important criminal cases. Others are handled by the Crown Prosecution Service, which takes over many of the criminal investigations started by the police in England and Wales. It has 6,000 staff in over 100 offices, handling 1.5 million cases a year.

Serious Fraud Office	020-7239 7272
Enquiries	020-7239 7004
Out-of-hours	020-7273 8341
CPS headquarters	020-7273 8000

Enquiries	020-7334 8505
Press	020-7273 8106
Website	www.cps.gov.uk
Central casework	020-7273 1217
CPS areas: Anglia	01727-818100
East Midlands	0115-852 3300
Humber	0114-291 2000
London	020-7802 3800
Mersey/Lancashire	0151-236 7575
Midlands	0121-629 7202
North	0191-260 4200
North West	0161-908 2600
Severn/Thames	01905-795477
South East	01483-882600
South West	01392-422555
Wales	029-2064 4474
Yorkshire	01904-610726

LEGAL BODIES

The Law Society is the professional organisation for lawyers. The Legal Action Group works to improve legal services for disadvantaged people and deprived areas. Liberty is a campaigning body (formerly the NCCL). Statewatch monitors the legal activities of the state, focusing especially on Europe.

Advice Services Alliance	020-7236 6022
Bar Council	020-7242 0082
Website	www.barcouncil.org.uk
Childrens Legal Centre	01206 873820
Citizens Advice Bureaux (HQ)	020-7833 2181
Website	www.adviceguide.org.uk
Criminal Cases Review Commission	0121-633 1800
Website	www.homeoffice.gov.uk/ccrc
Disability Law Service	020-7831 8031
Earthrights	07071-225011
Environmental Law Foundation	020-7404 1030
Free Representation Unit	020-7831 0692
Inquest	020-8802 7430
Justice	020-7329 5100
Law Commission	020-7430 1008
Website	www.gtnet.gov.uk/lawcomm
Law Society	020-7242 1222
Website	www.lawsociety.org.uk
Legal Action Group	020-7833 2931
Legal Aid Board	020-7813 1000
Website	www.open.gov.uk/lab
Liberty	020-7403 3888
National Civil Rights Movement	020-8843 2333
Release	020-7729 9904
Rights of Women	020-7251 6577
Statewatch	020-8802 1882
Website	www.statewatch.org

LAW CENTRES

Law centres provide free legal advice and representation. They are run by voluntary committees of local people, and are usually financed by local authorities. The centres are members of the Law Centres Federation:

Law Centres Federation
18-19 Warren St, London W1P 5DB

Fax 020-7387 8368	Tel 020-7387 8570
Sheffield office	0114-278 7008

Local law centres

Avon & Bristol	0117-924 8662
Birmingham (Saltley)	0121-328 2307
Bradford	01274-306617
Cardiff	029-2049 8117
Carlisle	01228-515129
Chesterfield	01246-550674
Coventry	024-7622 3051
Derby	01332-344557
Gateshead	0191-477 1109
Glasgow (SCastlemilk)	0141-634 0313
Gloucester	01452-423492
Humberside	01482-211180
Huddersfield (Kirklees)	01484-518525
Ireland: North (Belfast)	028-9032 1307
South (Dublin)	00-353-1820 0455
Leeds (Harehills)	0113-249 1100
Leicester	0116-255 3781
Liverpool Eight	0151-709 7222
London: Brent	020-8451 1122
Brixton	020-7737 0440
Camberwell	020-7701 9499
Camden	020-7485 6672
Central London	020-7839 2998
Greenwich	020-8853 2550
Hackney	020-8985 8364
Hammersmith & Fulham	020-8741 4021
Hillingdon	020-8561 9400
Hounslow	020-8570 9505
Newham	020-8555 3331
North Islington	020-7607 2461
North Kensington	020-8969 7473
North Lambeth	020-7582 4373
North Lewisham	020-8692 5355
Paddington	020-8960 3155
Plumstead	020-8855 9817
Southwark	020-7732 2008
Springfield	020-8767 6884
Stockwell & Clapham	020-7720 6231
Tottenham	020-8347 9792
Tower Hamlets	020-7247 8998
Wandsworth & Merton	020-7228 9462
Luton	01582-481000
Manchester: North	0161-205 5040
South	0161-225 5111
Wythenshawe	0161-498 0905
Middlesbrough	01642-223813
Newcastle	0191-230 4777
Nottingham	0115-978 7813
Oldham	0161-627 0925
Rochdale	01706-657766
Salford	0161-736 3116
Scottish Association	0141-445 6451
Sheffield	0114-273 1888
Warrington	01925-651104
Wiltshire	01793-486926

Prisons

There are 138 prisons in England and Wales (including seven run by private contractors), plus 23 in Scotland (one private) and four in Northern Ireland. Since the passing of the 1991 Criminal Justice Act, the prison services have been managed by the three agencies - government quangos - listed below. The Home Office has main responsibility.

There are 64,500 prisoners, 61,300 of them male. Britain has one of the highest imprisonment rates in western Europe, 116 per 100,000. All prisons are full to overflowing, costing over £24,000 per prisoner. In January 1999 the government began releasing prisoners early, on condition they wore electronic tags and obeyed a night-time curfew. There are 24,900 governors and officers.

Prisoners are housed in establishments ranging from open prisons to high security buildings. Nearly 96 per cent of prisoners are male. Women are held in separate prisons or in separate accommodation in mixed prisons. Over 70% of prisoners in England and Wales were found to have more than one of the main types of mental disorder in 1997, according to a survey carried out by the Department of Health.

The conditions of prisoners are monitored and reported to Parliament by independent Prisons Inspectorates. There is also a Prisons Ombudsman covering England and Wales.

PRISON AGENCIES

HM Prison Service	020-7273 4000
Press	020-7217 6633
Outside office hours	020-8840 6633
Security Group	020-7217 5574
Operations - North	020-7217 6677
Operations - South	020-7217 6447
Scottish Prison Service	0131-244 8475
Press	0131-244 8476
Prisons - South & West	0131-244 8546
Prisons - North & East	0131-244 8741
N Ireland Prison Service	028-9052 0700

GOVT DEPARTMENTS

Home Office: Main number	020-7273 4000
Press	020-7217 4600
Website	www.homeoffice.gov.uk
HM Prison Service	020-7217 6000
Website	www.hmprisonservice.gov.uk
Parole Board, Eng & Wales	0171-217 5314
Prison Inspectorate	020-7273 3702
Prisons Ombudsman	020-7273 6060
Scottish Office: Main number	0131-556 8400
Press	0131-244 1111
Website	www.scotland.gov.uk/structure
Parole Board	0131-244 8755
Prison Inspectorate	0131-244 8481
Northern Ireland Office: Press	028-9052 8233

PRISON SUPPORT BODIES

Apex Trust	020-7638 5931
Howard League for Penal Reform	020-7281 7722
Inquest	020-8802 7430
Justice	020-7329 5100
NACRO	020-7582 6500
National Assoc of Prison Visitors	01234-359763
National Assoc of Probation Officers	020-7223 4887
National Council for Prisoners Abroad	020-78333467
National Prisoners Movement	020-8542 3744
Prison Charity Shop Trust	020-7437 4334
Prison Governors Association	020-7217 8591
Prison Officers Association	020-8803 0255
Prison Reform Trust	020-7251 5070
Prison Watch	01332-756158
Prisoners Advice Service	020-7405 8090
Prisoners Families and Friends	020-7403 4091
Prisoners' Wives & Families Society	020-7278 3981
Prisons Ombudsman	020-7273 6060
Website	www.homeoffice.gov.uk/prisomb.htm
Women in Prison	020-7226 5879
Women Prisoners' Centre	020-8968 3121

MALE PRISONS (E & W)

O = open prison

Acklington, Northumberland	01670-760411
Albany, Isle of Wight	01983-524055
Aldington, Kent	01233-720436
Ashwell, Leics	01572-774100
Bedford	01234-358671
Belmarsh, London SE28	020-8317 2436
Birmingham, Winson Green	0121-554 3838
Blakenhurst, Worcs	01527-543348
Blantyre House, Kent	01580-211367
Blundeston, Suffolk	01502-730591
Brinsford, Wolverhampton	01902-791118
Bristol	0117-980 8100
Brixton, London SW2	020-8674 9811
Brockhill, Worcs	01527-550314
Buckley Hall, Lancs	01706-861610
Bullingdon, Oxon	01869-32211
Camp Hill, Isle of Wight	01983-52766
Canterbury, Kent	01227-762224
Cardiff	029-2043 3100

Channings Wood, Devon	01803-812361
Chelmsford, Essex	01245-268651
Coldingley, Surrey	01483-476721
Dartmoor, Devon	01822-890261
Doncaster	01302-760870
Dorchester, Dorset	01305-266021
Downview, Surrey	020-8770 7500
Durham	0191-386 2621
Elmley, Kent	01795-880808
Erlestoke, Wilts	01380-813475
Everthorpe, Humberside	01430-422471
Exeter, Devon	01392-278321
Featherstone, Wolverhampton	01902-790991
Feltham, Middlesex	020-8890 0061
Ford (O), West Sussex	01903-717261
Frankland, Co Durham	0191-384 5544
Full Sutton, York	01759-375100
Garth, Lancs	01772-622722
Gartree, Leics	01858-410234
Glen Parva, Leics	0116-264 3100
Gloucester	01452-529551
Grendon & Spring Hill, Bucks	01296-770301
Guernsey, Channel Islands	01481-48376
Haslar, Hants	023-9258 0381
Haverigg, Cumbria	01229-772131
Hewell Grange (O), Worcs	01527-550843
High Down, Surrey	020-8643 0063
Highpoint (O), Suffolk	01440-823100
Hindley, Lancs	01942-866255
Holme House, Cleveland	01642-673759
Hull, N Humberside	01482-320673
Isle of Man	01624-621306
Jersey, Channel Islands	01534-44181
Kingston, Hants	023-9289 1100
Kirkham (O), Lancs	01772-684343
Kirklevington Grange, Cleveland	01642-781391
Lancaster	01524-385100
Latchmere House, Surrey	020-8948 0215
Leeds, West Yorks	0113-263 6411
Leicester	0116-254 6911
Lewes, East Sussex	01273-405100
Leyhill (O), Glos	01454-260681
Lincoln	01522-533633
Lindholme, South Yorks	01302-848700
Littlehey, Cambs	01480-812202
Liverpool	0151-525 5971
Long Lartin, Worcs	01386-830101
Low Newton, Co Durham	0191-386 1141
Maidstone, Kent	01622-755611
Manchester	0161-834 8626
Moorland, South Yorks	01302-351500
Morton Hall (O), Lincs	01522-866700
The Mount, Herts	01442-834363
North Sea Camp (O), Lincs	01205-760481
Norwich	01603-437531
Nottingham	0115-962 5022
Parkhurst, Isle of Wight	01983-523855
Pentonville, London N7	020-7607 5353
Preston, Lancs	01772-257734
Ranby, Notts	01777-706721
Reading, Berks	0118-958 7031
Risley, Cheshire	01925-763871
Rochester, Kent	01634-838100
Send, Surrey	01483-223048
Shepton Mallet, Somerset	01749-343377

Shrewsbury, Salop	01743-352511
Stafford	01785-254421
Standford Hill (O), Kent	01795-880441
Stocken, Leics	01642-673759
Sudbury (O), Derbys	01283-585511
Swaleside, Kent	01795-884100
Swansea	01792-464030
Usk, Gwent	01291-672411
Verne, Dorset	01305-820124
Wakefield, West Yorks	01924-378282
Wandsworth, London SW18	020-8874 7292
Wayland, Norfolk	01953-858100
Wealston (O), West Yorks	01937-844844
Wellingborough, Northants	01933-224151
Whatton, Notts	01949-850511
Whitemoor, Cambs	01354-660653
Winchester, Hants	01962-854494
Wolds, Humberside	01430-421588
Woodhill, Bucks	01908-501999
Wormwood Scrubs, W12	020-8743 0311
Wymott, Lancs	01772-421461

FEMALE PRISONS (E & W)

Askham Grange (O), York	01904-704236
Bullwood Hall, Essex	01702-202515
Cookham Wood, Kent	01634-814981
Drake Hall (O), Staffs	01785-858100
Durham	0191-386 2621
East Sutton Park (O), Kent	01622-842711
Eastwood Park	01454-262100
Exeter, Devon	01392-278321
Holloway, London N7	020-7607 6747
Low Newton, Co Durham	0191-386 1141
New Hall, West Yorks	01924-848307
Risley, Cheshire	01925-763871
Styal, Cheshire	01625-532141

SCOTTISH PRISONS

Aberdeen	01224-876868
Barlinnie, Glasgow	0141-770 2000
Cornton Vale, Stirling	01786-832591
Dungavel, Lanarkshire	01357-440371
Edinburgh	0131-444 3000
Friarton, Perth	01738-625885
Glenochil, Clackmannanshire	01259-760471
Inverness	01463-233320
Longriggend, Lanarkshire	01236-830392
Low Moss, Glasgow	0141-762 4848
Noranside, Angus	01356-650217
Penninghame, Wigtownshire	01671-402886
Perth	01738-622293
Peterhead, Aberdeenshire	01779-479101
Shotts, Lanarkshire	01501-824000

N IRELAND PRISONS

Belfast: Crumlin Road	028-9074 1100
Maghaberry, Co Antrim	01846-611888
Magilligan, Co Londonderry	01504-763311
Maze, Co Antrim	01846-683111

International

EMBASSIES

Em = Embassy, HCom = High Commission,
Con = Consulate

Afghanistan: London Em	020-7589 8891
Albania: London Em	020-7730 5709
Algeria: London Em	020-7221 7800
UK Em, Algiers	00-2132 320068
Angola: London Em	020-7495 1752
UK Em, Luanda	00-2442 392991
Antigua: London HCom	020-7486 7073
UK HCom, St Johns	00-1268 4620008
Argentina: London Em	020-7318 1300
UK Em, Buenos Aires	00-541 8037070
Australia: London HCom	020-7379 4334
UK HCom, Canberra	00-612 62706666
UK Con, Melbourne	00-613 96504155
UK Con, Perth	00-618 92215400
UK Con, Sydney	00-612 92477521
Austria: London Em	020-7235 3731
UK Em, Vienna	00-431 716130
Azerbaijan: London Em	020-7938 3412
Bahamas: London HCom	020-7408 4488
UK HCom, Nassau	00-1242 3257471
Bahrain: London Em	020-7370 5132
UK Em, Bahrain	00-973 534404
Bangladesh: London Em	020-7584 0081
UK HCom, Dhaka	00-8802 882705
Barbados: London HCom	020-7631 4975
UK HCom, Bridgetown	00-1246 4366694
Belarus: London Em	020-7937 3288
Belgium: London Em	020-7470 3700
UK Em, Brussels	00-322 2876211
Belize: London HCom	020-7499 9728
UK HCom, Belmopan	00-5018 22146
Bolivia: London Em	020-7235 4248
UK Em, La Paz	00-5912 433424
Bosnia: London Em	020-7255 3758
UK Em, Sarejevo	00-38771 444429
Botswana: London HCom	020-7499 0031
UK HCom, Gaborone	00-267 352841
Brazil: London Em	020-7499 0877
UK Con, Rio	00-5521 5533223
Brunei: London HCom	020-7581 0521
UK HCom, Begawan	00-6732 222231
Bulgaria: London Em	020-7584 9400
UK Em, Sofia	00-3592 4923335
Burma: London Em	020-7499 8841
UK Em, Rangoon	00-951 295300
Burundi: UK Con, Bujumbura	00-2564 1257054
Cameroon: London HCom	020-7727 0771
UK Em, Yaounde	00-237 220545
Canada: London HCom	020-7258 6600
UK HCom, Ottawa	00-1613 2371530
UK Con,Vancouver	00-1604 6834421
Chad: UK Em, Ndjamena	00-235 513064
Chile: London Em	020-7580 6392
UK Em, Santiago	00-562 2313737
China: London Em	020-7636 9375
UK Em, Beijing	00-8610 65321961
UK Con, Hong Kong	00-852 29013000
Colombia: London Em	020-7589 9177
UK Em, Bogota	00-571 2185111
Costa Rica: London Em	020-7706 8844
UK Em, San Jose	00-506 2215566
Cote d'Ivoire: London Em	020-7235 6991
UK Em, Abidjan (via operator)	225-22685C
Croatia: London Em	020-7387 2022
UK Em, Zagreb	00-3851 4555310
Cuba: London Em	020-7240 2488
UK Em, Havana	00-537 241771
Cyprus: London HCom	020-7499 8272
UK HCom, Nicosia	00-3572 86110C
Czech Republic: London Em	020-7243 1115
UK Em, Prague	00-4202 57320355
Denmark: London Em	020-7333 0200
UK Em, Copenhagen	00-45 35264600
Dominican Republic:UK HCom	020-7370 5194
UK Em, Santo Domingo	00-1809 4727111
Eastern Caribbean: London HCom	020-7937 9522
UK HCom, Castries	00-1758 4522484
Ecuador: London Em	020-7584 1367
UK Em, Quito	00-5932 560669
Egypt: London Em	020-7499 2401
UK Em, Cairo	00-202 3540850
El Salvador: London Em	020-7436 8282
UK Em, San Salvador	00-503 2239047
Estonia: London Em	020-7589 3428
UK Em, Tallinn	00-372 6313353
Ethiopia: London Em	020-7589 7212
UK Em, Addis Ababa	00-2511 612354
Fiji: London Em	020-7584 3661
UK Em, Suva	00-679 311033
Finland: London Em	020-7838 6200
UK Em, Helsinki	00-3589 22865100
France: London Em	020-7201 1000
UK Em, Paris	00-331 44513100
UK Con, Marseille	00-334 91157210
Gabon: London Em	020-7823 9986
UK Em, Libreville	00-241 762200
Gambia: London HCom	020-7937 6316
UK HCom, Banjul	00-220 495133
Georgia: London Em	020-7937 8233
UK Em, Tbilisi	00-99532 955497
Germany: London Em	020-7824 1300
UK Em, Bonn	00-49228 9167C
UK Em, Berlin	00-4930 201840
UK Con, Frankfurt	00-4969 1700020
Ghana: London HCom	020-7235 4142

UK Em, Accra	00-23321 221665
Greece: London Em	020-7229 3850
UK Em, Athens	00-301 7236211
Grenada: London HCom	020-7373 7809
UK HCom, St Georges	00-1473 4403222
Guatemala: London Em	020-7351 3042
UK Em, Guatemala City	00-5022 321601
Guinea: UK Em, Conakry	00-224 442959
Guyana: London HCom	020-7229 7684
UK Em, Georgetown	00-5922 65881
Haiti: UK Em, Port au Prince	00-509 573969
Honduras: London Em	020-7486 4880
UK Em, Tegucigalpa	00-504 325429
Hungary : London Em	020-7235 5218
UK Em, Budapest	00-361 2662888
Iceland: London Em	020-7590 1100
UK Em, Reykjavik	00-354 5515883
India: London HCom	020-7836 8484
UK HCom, Bombay	00-9122 2830517
UK HCom, Calcutta	00-9133 2425171
Indonesia: London Em	020-7499 7661
UK Em, Jakarta	00-6221 330904
Iran: London Em	020-7225 3000
UK Em, Tehran	00-9821 675011
Iraq: London via Jordan Em	020-7937 3685
UK Em, Baghdad	00-9641 5372121
Irish Republic: London Em	020-7235 2171
UK Em, Dublin	00-3531 2053700
Israel: London Em	020-7957 9500
UK Em, Tel Aviv	00-9723 5249171
Italy: London Em	020-7312 2200
UK Em, Rome	00-396 4825441
UK Con, Milan	00-3902 723001
UK Con, Naples	00-3981 663511
Ivory Coast: London Em	020-7235 6991
UK Em, Abidjan	00-225 226850
Jamaica: London HCom	020-7823 9911
UK HCom, Kingston	00-1876 9269050
Japan: London Em	020-7465 6500
UK Em, Tokyo	00-813 52111100
Jerusalem: UK Con	00-9722 5828281
Jordan: London Em	020-7937 3685
UK Em, Amman	00-9626 823100
Kazakhstan: London Em	020-7581 4646
UK Em, Almaty	00-73272 506192
Kenya: London HCom	020-7636 2371
UK HCom, Nairobi	00-2542 335944
Korea: London Em	020-7227 5500
UK Em, Seoul	00-822 7357341
Kuwait: London Em	020-7590 3400
UK Em, Kuwait	00-965 24320461
Latvia: London Em	020-7312 0040
UK Em, Riga	00-371 7338126
Lebanon: London Em	020-7229 7265
UK Em, Beirut	00-9614 417007
Lesotho: London HCom	020-7235 5686
UK HCom	00-266 313961
Liberia: London Em	020-7221 1036
Libya: London via Saudia Arabian Em,	

Libyan Interests Section	020-7486 8387
Lithuania: London Em	020-7486 6401
UK Em, Vilnius	00-3702 222070
Luxembourg: London Em	020-7235 6961
UK Em, Luxembourg	00-352 229864
Malawi: London HCom	020-7491 4172
UK HCom, Lilongwe	00-265 782400
Malaysia: London HCom	020-7235 8033
UK HCom, Kuala Lumpur	00-603 2482122
Malta: London HCom	020-7292 4800
UK HCom, Valletta	00-356 233134
Mauritius: London HCom	020-7581 0294
UK HCom, Port Louis	00-230 2111361
Mexico: London Em	020-7499 8586
UK Em, Mexico City	00-525 2072089
Mongolia: London Em	020-7937 0150
UK Em, Ulaan Bataar	00-9761 458133
Morocco: London Em	020-7581 5001
UK Em, Rabat	00-2127 720905
Mozambique: London Em	020-7383 3800
UK Em, Maputo	00-2581 420111
Namibia: London HCom	020-7636 6244
UK HCom, Windhoek	00-26461 223022
Nepal: London Em	020-7229 1594
UK Em, Kathmandu	00-9771 416460
Netherlands: London Em	020-7590 3200
UK Em, The Hague	00-3170 4270427
UK Con, Amsterdam	00-3120 6764343
New Zealand: London HCom	020-7930 8422
UK HCom, Wellington	00-644 4726049
Nicaragua: UK Em, Managua	00-5052 780014
Niger: UK Em, Niamey	00-227 732015
Nigeria: London HCom	020-7839 1244
UK HCom, Lagos	00-2341 2632903
Norway: London Em	020-7591 5500
UK Em, Oslo	00-4722 552400
UK Con, Bergen	00-4755 944705
Oman: London Em	020-7225 0001
UK Em, Muscat	00-968 693077
Pakistan: London HCom	020-7664 9200
UK HCom, Islamabad	00-9251 822131
UK HCom, Karachi	00-9221 5872436
Panama: London Em	020-7493 4646
UK Em, Panama City	00-507 2690866
Papua New Guinea: London HCom	020-7930 0922
UK HCom, Port Moresby	00-675 3251643
Paraguay: London Em	020-7937 1253
UK Em, Asuncion	00-59521 444472
Peru: London Em	020-7235 1917
UK Em, Lima	00-5114 334735
Philippines: London Em	020-7937 1600
UK Em, Manila	00-632 8167116
Poland: London Em	020-7580 4324
UK Em, Warsaw	00-4822 6253030
Portugal: London Em	020-7235 5331
UK Em, Lisbon	00-3511 3924000
Qatar: London Em	020-7493 2200
UK Em, Doha	00-974 421991
Romania: London Em	020-7937 9666

UK Em, Bucharest	00-401 3120305
Russian Fed. London Em	020-7229 3628
UK Em, Moscow	00-7503 9567200
Saudi Arabia: London Em	020-7917 3000
UK Em, Riyadh	00-9661 4880077
Senegal: London Em	020-7937 7237
UK Em, Dakar	00-221 8237392
Seychelles: London HCom	020-7224 1660
UK HCom, Victoria	00-248 225225
Sierra Leone: London HCom	020-7636 6483
UK HCom, Freetown	00-23222 223961
Singapore: London HCom	020-7233 9189
UK HCom, Singapore	00-65 4739333
Slovak Republic: London Em	020-7243 0803
UK Em, Bratislava	00-4217 54419632
Slovenia: London Em	020-7495 7775
UK Em, Ljubljona	00-38661 1257191
Somalia: UK HCom	00-2521 20288
South Africa: London Em	020-7451 7299
UK Em, Cape Town	00-2721 4617220
UK Em, Pretoria	00-2712 433121
UK Con, Jo'burg	00-2711 3378940
Spain: London Em	020-7235 5555
UK Em, Madrid	00-3491 3190200
UK Con, Barcelona	00-3493 4199044
UK Con, Malaga	00-3495 2217571
Sri Lanka: London HCom	020-7262 1841
UK HCom, Colombo	00-941 437336
Sudan: London Em	020-7839 8080
UK Em, Khartoum	00-24911 777105
Swaziland: London HCom	020-7630 6611
UK HCom, Mbabane	00-268 4042581
Sweden: London Em	020-7917 6400
UK Em, Stockholm	00-468 6719000
Switzerland: London Em	020-7616 6000
UK Em, Berne	00-4131 3525021
UK Con, Geneva	00-4122 9182400
UK Con, Zurich	00-411 2611520
Syria: London Em	020-7245 9012
UK Em, Damascus	00-96311 3712561
Tanzania: London HCom	020-7499 8951
UK HCom, Dar es Salaam	00-25551 29601
Thailand: London Em	020-7589 2944
UK Em, Bangkok	00-662 2530191
Trinidad: London HCom	020-7245 9351
UK HCom, Port of Spain	00-1868 6229087
Tunisia: London Em	020-7584 8117
UK Em, Tunis	00-2161 341444
Turkey: London Em	020-7393 0202
UK Em, Ankara	00-90312 4686230
Uganda: London HCom	020-7839 5783
UK HCom, Kampala	00-25641 257054
Ukraine: London Em	020-7727 6312
UK Em, Kiev	00-38044 4620011
UAE London Em	020-7581 1281
UK Em, Abu Dhabi	00-9712 326600
United States: London Em	020-7499 9000
UK Em, Washington	00-1202 4621340
UK Con, Chicago	00-1312 3461810
UK Con, Dallas	00-1214 5214090
UK Con, Los Angeles	00-1310 4773322
UK Con, Miami	00-1305 3741522
UK Con, New York	00-1212 7450200
Uruguay: London Em	020-7584 8192
UK Em, Montevideo	00-5982 623630
Uzbekistan: London Em	020-7229 7679
UK Em, Tashkent	00-998 716338416
Vanuatu: UK HCom, Vila	00-678 23100
Venezuela: London Em	020-7584 4206
UK Em, Caracas	00-582 9934111
Vietnam: London Em	020-7937 1912
UK Em, Hanoi	00-844 8252510
Yemen: London Em	020-7584 6607
UK Em, Sanaa	00-9671 264081
Yugoslavia: London Em	020-7370 6105
UK Em, Belgrade	00-38111 645055
Zaire: London Em	020-7235 6137
UK Em, Kinshasa	00-24312 34775
Zambia: London HCom	020-7589 6655
UK HCom Lusaka	00-2601 251133
Zimbabwe: London HCom	020-7836 7755
UK HCom, Harare	00-2634 793781

OVERSEAS TERRITORIES

The UK's Overseas Territories (OTs) are the last remnants of the British Empire. A century ago, Britain ruled 400 million people on a third of the planet. Today there are 190,000 people living in the 13 remaining colonies, fragments of land whose governors are still appointed by the Queen, and whose government is the responsibility of the Foreign and Commonwealth Office (FCO). Much of the old empire now forms the Commonwealth, an association bound by affinity rather than treaty. It comprises 54 states with 1.6 billion people, a quarter of the world's population.

Several of the OTs play military, telecomms or strategy roles for the UK. The OTs were called the Dependent Territories until early 1999, when the UK government aimed to reflect the independent spirit and character of the territories by giving them a clearer identity and a stronger partnership with Britain. A White Paper began the process of granting full UK citizenship to the 125,000 residents who had lost it under the 1983 British Nationality Act. A new Overseas Territories Department is being created inside the FCO. The FCO's West Indian and Atlantic Department is responsible for Caribbean and neighbouring territories, marked with an asterisk (*).

Foreign & Commonwealth Office

Main number	020-7270 3000
West Indian & Atlantic Dept	020-7270 2643
Press	020-7270 3100
Information dept	020-7270 6052
Website	www.fco.gov.uk

Dept for International Development

Main number	020-7917 7000
Eves	020-7917 0950
Press	020-7917 0435
Information Dept	020-7917 0618
Website	www.dfid.gov.uk

Anguilla*
Small eastern Caribbean island. 35 sq miles, 8,960 population.

Governor, Anguilla   00-1264 4972621

Bermuda*
West Atlantic group of 100 small islands, 20 inhabited, 600 miles off North Carolina. 60,100 population. 21 sq miles in total.

Governor, Hamilton   00-1441 2955151

British Antarctic Territory
Uninhabited section of Antarctica, including South Orkney and South Shetland islands. Run from London.

FCO Antarctic Dept   020-7270 2742

British Indian Ocean Territory
Large group of the small Chagos Archipelago islands in central Indian Ocean, south of India. Uninhabited, except for joint UK/USA military base on Diego Garcia.

Port Louis   00-230 2111361

British Virgin Islands*
Eastern Caribbean group of 46 islands, 11 inhabited, near Anguilla. 16,100 population.

Governor, Tortola   00-1284 4942345

Cayman Islands*
Three tax-free, wealthy Caribbean islands south of Cuba. Home of 33,600 people and nearly as many companies, dodging everything. 100 sq miles.

Governor, George Town   00-1345 9497900

Falkland Islands
Largest islands in South Atlantic, off southern Argentina. 2,200 population, plus military.

FCO	020-7270 2749
Governor, Stanley	00-500 27433

Gibraltar
2.5 sq mile promontory of southernmost Spain, captured 1704. 28,000 population.

FCO	020-7270 2975
Governor	00-350 70071

Hong Kong
Ceased being a dependent territory from 1 July 1997.

Montserrat*
Eastern Caribbean volcanic island, 38 sq miles. 9,000 population.

Governor   00-1664 4912688

Pitcairn Islands
Eastern group in Pacific, midway between north New Zealand and Peru. 1.9 sq miles, 54 population, all Seventh Day Adventists.

FCO	020-7270 2955
Governor	00-644 726049

St Helena
Island in the middle of the South Atlantic, 1,100 miles off Angola. Former prison of Napoleon. 5,650 population, with dependencies.

FCO	020-7270 2749
Governor	00-290 3510

St Helena dependent: Ascension Island
700 miles north-west of St Helena.

Administrator   00-247 6311

St Helena dependent: Tristan da Cunha
Island group 1,850 miles west of Cape Town.

Administrator   00-8741 4545435

South Georgia and South Sandwich Islands
Scattered islands east and south-east of Cape Horn. South Georgia is military, South Sandwich uninhabited volcanic.

Commissioner, Stanley   00-500 27433

Turks and Caicos Islands*
Caribbean group of 30 islands, north of Haiti. 19,000 population.

Governor, Grand Turk   00-1649 9462308

INTERNATIONAL BODIES

The Commonwealth Institute has a comprehensive list of commonwealth organisations on its website. Many other overseas bodies can be found on the One World.net website.

British Council	020-7930 8466
Website	www.britcoun.org
Commonwealth Institute	020-7603 4535
Website	www.commonwealth.org.uk
Commonwealth Journalists Assoc	020-7486 3844
Commonwealth Press Union	020-7583 7733
Commonwealth Secretariat	020-7839 3411
Federal Trust	020-7799 2818
International Coffee Organisation	020-7580 8591
Int. Fed. for Info & Documentation	00-3170 3140671
Int. Fed. of Newspaper Publishers	00-331 47428500
International Grains Council	020-7513 1122
International Labour Organisation	020-7828 6401
International Maritime Organisation	020-7735 7611
International Mobile Satellite Org	020-7728 1000
International Sugar Organisation	020-7513 1144
International Whaling Commission	01223-233971
NATO	00-322 7074111
Website	www.nato.int
One World.net	01494-481629
Website	www.oneworld.org
United Nations UK Info Centre	020-7630 1981
HQ, New York	00-1212 9634475
Website	www.un.org
World Bank Group	020-7930 8511

Disasters and emergencies

At national level, there is an **emergency government** system kept in readiness for the most serious disasters. It can be activated either as a whole or in part, and is most likely to be used during a foreign attack or mass civil unrest. The top layer consists of the prime minister, key ministers and civil servants, plus chief military and police officers. In the most extreme emergency this would become the UK government, operating from a hardened communications base, especially the Crisis Management Centre, an expensive, high-tech nuclear-proofed bunker 20 metres below the main MoD building in Whitehall. The Emergency Powers Act 1920 gives the government extra authority when needed; it has been invoked so far on 12 occasions, all resulting from industrial disputes.

The Cabinet Office is responsible for creating disaster policies, the Home Office for administering them. The Cabinet Office is the home of the **Civil Contingencies Committee** (CCC), known as the Civil Contingencies Unit until disaster plans were rethought in 1997. The CCC has the main responsibility for co-ordinating the state's response to emergencies. The committee comprises civil servants and some ministers, chaired by the Home Secretary. It decides the state's approach to serious threats, appointing a government department (the "lead" department) to put plans into effect.

The Home Office **Emergency Planning Division** (EPD) runs the disaster system day-to-day on behalf of the CCC. The Division sets and maintains standards, represents the UK in an international context and initiates central government arrangements. At the core of the EPD is the **Central Government and International Section** (CGIS), playing policy and operational roles. It operates the unique **Emergency Operations Suite** in the Home Office main building. The suite is maintained in a constant state of preparedness for any major disaster. It was placed on standby from September 1999 for the Millennium bug. The

Suite has specially trained staff, supported by the latest high-tech equipment, supervised by another EPD unit, the **Telecommunications Group** (TG).

The TG runs the **Emergency Communications Network** (ECN), a resilient, heavily-protected network, linking key elements of central government with regional and local emergency services, via its own telephone system. It is designed to ensure that Whitehall will maintain contact with, and therefore control of, all UK civil and military forces in the worst possible disasters. The creation of the ECN in the 1980s and '90s rendered redundant the post-war regional underground bunkers that were designed to set up a devolved form of government in emergencies, especially the Cold War, which itself ended c1990.

Home Office	020-7273 4000
Press	020-7273 4610
Website	www.homeoffice.gov.uk
Emergency Planning Division	020-7273 3212
Website	www.homeoffice.gov.uk/epd
CGIS	020-7273 3310
Telecommunications Group	020-7273 3195
Emergency Planning College	01347-821406
Cabinet Office	020-7270 1234
Press	020-7270 0635
Website	www.open.gov.uk/co/cohome.htm

REGIONS AND LEADERS

Below national level, Whitehall maintains regional control through the ten Government Offices in England. These have to replicate at regional and local level the work being done on the national infrastructure by the CCC.

Also spreading emergency planning out of Whitehall are the **lead government departments**. In an emergency, a specific department is the leader in co-ordinating affected departments in their handling of regional and local issues. The lead department acts as the focal point for communications between central government and any local Strategic Co-ordinating Group. Individual departments responsible for handling certain disasters are

Flooding - MAFF or equivalents in Scottish, Welsh and Northern Ireland Offices.

Gas clouds - (DETR).
Marine and coastal pollution - DETR.
Marine: offshore installations - DETR.
Military - MoD.
Miscellaneous (building collapse, dam failures, earthquakes) - DETR or Scottish/Welsh/N Ireland Office.
Overseas disasters - FCO.
Radiation inside UK - Civil installations: DTI & Scottish Offices. Civil in transit: DETR. Military: MoD.
Radiation from outside UK - DETR.
Rivers, water services - DETR or Scottish/Welsh/N Ireland Offices.
Satellites - Home Office.
Search and rescue - Civil shipping: DETR (Coastguard Agency). Military shipping and aircraft, and civil aircraft at sea: MoD. Civil aircraft on land: DETR.
Sports accidents - DCMS, Scottish/Welsh Offices.
Transport accidents - DETR.
Weather - DETR (high winds: Home Office) or Scottish/Welsh/N Ireland Offices.

LOCAL PLANS

Local authorities have emergency planning duties. Each county-type authority has its own **emergency planning officer** (EPO), drawing up management plans. The EPOs are grant-aided local limbs of the Home Office EPD. The EPO is the starting point for inquiring about proposals for dealing with local disasters. Contact via the county councils, listed in this book under Local Government.

In the front line handling any disaster are the four emergency services, with the military in special reserve. All operate emergency procedures day-to-day, and have press offices for handling queries. They also have their own schemes for dealing with major incidents.

These services and the EPOs operate within a three-level, Home Office-agreed management framework. In 1999 the Home Office reviewed this system, with the aim of creating joint 999 call centres and shared buildings for the three emergency services. Three local pilot projects were set up.

Many volunteer agencies help the official services, including the WRVS, RNLI, Red Cross, St John Ambulance, Raynet (a network of radio amateurs) and mountain rescue.

MILLENNIUM BUG

Widespread fears of the effect of the millennium bug on computers and embedded microprocessors led the government to make detailed emergency plans. A special Cabinet committee, MISC 4, was set up to co-ordinate all action. It created a nationwide campaigning and PRO team called Action 2000, with its own website (www.bug2000.co.uk). This is turn formed the National Infrastructure Forum, bringing together all affected organisations, to help inform contingency planning at central and local government level. All emergency services were put on alert.

INFORMATION

As the police normally take initial charge at a disaster, the Home Office says they should set up as soon as possible a **media liaison point** run by an experienced press officer. Media access to the disaster site would be controlled. If media relations are difficult, the regional office of the Central Office of Information can send a press officer. A media centre could also be set up, supplying working accommodation for the media, plus a news conference area and telecoms equipment.

There is no single guidebook covering all contingency planning. The nearest is the official handbook *Dealing with Disaster* (Brodie Publishing 0151-707 2323, 3rd ed 1997). The Home Office publishes the quarterly magazine *Civil Protection*. Its website is useful.

EMERGENCY BODIES

Air Accidents Investigation, DTI	01252-510300
BASICS	01473-218407
British Airways Crisis Team, Gatwick	020-8513 0917
British Divers Marine Life Rescue	01634-281680
British Red Cross	020-7235 5454
British Safety Council	020-8741 1231
Casualties Union	020-7278 6264
Disasters Emergency Committee	020-7580 6550
Emergency Planning Society	020-8937 4984
International Rescue Corps	01324-665011
London Emergency Planning	020-7587 4048
Marine Accident Investigation, DTI	023-80395500
National Chemical Emergency Centre	01235-463060
National Voluntary Civil Aid Service	020-8977 2806
Royal Life Saving Society	01789-773994
Royal Society for the Prevention of Accidents	0121-248 2000
Search & Rescue Dog Assoc: Wales	01492-622195
England	0702-0960970
Lake District	01768-772463
Southern Scotland	01835-822211
Highlands	01721-721998
Underwater Search Unit	020-7275 4488
WRVS	020-7793 9917

The military

The UK armed forces are run by the Defence Council, comprising Ministry of Defence (MoD) ministers and leading officers, including the Chief of the Defence Staff, the top militarist. Whitehall's basic policy is to maintain the "freedom and territorial integrity" of the UK and its Overseas Territories, and the "ability to pursue its legitimate interests at home and abroad".

At the heart of this policy is **NATO**, to which most British forces are committed. NATO was set up in 1949 to unite Western Europe and North America in the anti-Soviet Cold War. This came to an end around 1990. In 1994 NATO adopted a more global perspective because of problems of instability, extremism and nationalism. A Combined Joint Task Force was set up to carry out a wider range of missions around the world. In mid-1997 military ties between NATO, all Europe, Russia and central Asia were created. The multinational Allied Command Europe Rapid Reaction Corps (ARRC) has 55,000 UK troops and is commanded by a UK general.

Britain's pre-Cold War NATO policies were transformed by the **Strategic Defence Review** of 1998. It firmly committed the UK to a worldwide role with the ability to send large expeditionary forces to any kind of trouble spot, as it anticipated significant changes in the methods of warfare by 2015.

The strength of the UK armed forces is: Army 109,800, RAF 55,800, Navy 44,500; plus 121,300 civilians. Total 331,400. The budget for 1999/2000 was £22.8 billion, with £9 billion going on military equipment, including £1.6 billion on aircraft .

The MoD's administrative HQ is the **Main Building** (known by staff as "The Building") in Whitehall. At its core is a newly-renovated underground nuclear-proof bunker. This is called the Joint Operations Centre by militarists and the Crisis Management Centre by civilians. In the most severe crisis it would act as government HQ, and it has secure communications links with all departments.

Day-to-day military action is run from the new **Permanent Joint Headquarters** (PJHQ) in another bunker, next to the Navy's headquarters at Northwood, north-west London. PJHQ is the overall control centre for national military operations, superseding many former single-service bodies. It is also the control point of another new organisation, the 15,000 strong **Joint Rapid Development Force** (JRDF). This military fire brigade is designed to "strengthen the UK's ability to project military Forces quickly worldwide in support of our interests". Specially trained National Contingency forces are assigned to the JRDF.

The Army's own operations centre is the Land Command, sited in (and under) the village of Wilton, just west of Salisbury. This is the hatching ground for any Army direct action inside the UK. The Royal Navy is run from Northwood and the Portsmouth Naval Base. The RAF is controlled by its HQ Strike Command at High Wycombe and the HQ Logistic Command at Huntingdon.

The UK also now has little-publicised (by the MoD) **Special Forces**, which the MoD says have "four primary roles: reconnaissance, offensive action, the provision of support to indigenous forces and counter-terrorism". Journalists are warned that operations are so sensitive that the MoD "will pursue all appropriate legal options to prevent the publication of information about the Special Forces which it considers to be potentially damaging".

Inside the UK troops have three roles, jointly called **Military Aid to the Civil Authorities**. Military Aid to the Civil Power (**MaC-P**) is providing armed forces to help the police during violent civil challenges to state authority, as in Northern Ireland. Military Assistance to Civil Ministries (**MaC-M**) involves using troops to carry out specialised services for government departments, especially during strikes, such as Liverpool firefighters in 1995. Military Aid to the Civil Community (**MaC-C**) is arranging for service personnel to help the public during emergencies like the Millennium Bug scare.

MINISTRY OF DEFENCE

MoD main number	020-7218 9000
Website	www.mod.uk
Press office: Policy	020-7218 7931
Procurement	020-7218 7714
Army	020-7218 3255
Navy	020-7218 3257
RAF	020-7218 3253
Outside office hours	020-7218 7907
Chief of Defence Staff	020-7218 6313
Air Force: Chief of Staff	020-7218 6313
Army Department: Chief of Staff	020-7218 7873
Navy Department: First Sea Lord	020-7218 6193
UK-CICC (Wilton)	01722-433208

Permanent Joint HQ

At Northwood, Mdx	01923 826161
Press	01923-846029
24-hr duty officer	01923-846260

Army

Website	www.army.mod.uk
HQ Land Command (Wilton)	01722-336222
HQ Northern Ireland (Lisburn)	01846-609261
HQ Scotland (Edinburgh)	0131-310 2092
London District	020-7414 2396
Second Division (York)	01904-662433
Third Division (Wilts)	01980-672946
Fourth Division (Aldershot)	01252-347011
Fifth Division (Shrewsbury)	01743-262252
Infantry HQ (Warminster)	01985-214000

Royal Navy

Website	www.royal-navy.mod.uk
Commander-in-Chief Fleet (Northwood)	01923-837635

Naval Home Command (Portsmouth)	023-9272 3737
Surface Flotilla HQ (Portsmouth)	023-9272 2351
Aviation Command (Yeovilton)	01935-455548
Royal Marines (Plymouth)	01752-554558
Website	www.royal-marines.mod.uk
Naval Bases: Devonport	01752-554344
Faslane	01436-674321

RAF

Website	www.raf.mod.uk
Strike Command (High Wycombe)	01494-461461
Logistics Command (Huntingdon)	01480-52151
Air Warfare Centre (Lincs)	01522-720271
No 1 Group	01494-461461
No 11/18 Group	020-8838 7000
No 38 Group	01494-461461
USAF HQ (Mildenhall)	01638-543000
Military Air Traffic Operations (Uxbridge)	01895-276009

Other MoD sections

D Notice Committee	020-7218 3820
Defence Intelligence Staff	020-7218 2407
Magazines: Navy News	023-9282 6040
RAF News	01452-712612
Soldier Magazine	01252-347355
Ministry of Defence Police	01371-854000
Overseas forces: Cyprus	00357-2802505
Falkland Islands	00500-74204
Germany	004921-61472392
Gibraltar	003505-4231
NATO HQs: Supreme, Europe	003265-447111
Allied Forces NW Europe	01494-461461
Allied Forces Central Europe	003145-261111
Allied Forces South Europe	003981-5709053
Supreme Commander Atlantic	001757-4453258

Intelligence

Britain's three main intelligence agencies are MI5, MI6 and GCHQ. Parliamentary supervision of them comes from the all-party **Intelligence and Security Committee**, which has to "examine the expenditure, administration and policy" of the trio. It meets in secret and publishes an uninformative annual report. Chairman is Tory MP Tom King.

Management of the three agencies is supervised by the Cabinet Office's **Joint Intelligence Organisation** (JIO). It administers the **Joint Intelligence Committee** (JIC) which oversees MI6 and GCHQ, but not MI5. The JIC sets the UK's national intelligence priorities and produces regular assessments of raw material gathered by MI6 and GCHQ. The committee

is made up of officers from many departments and meets weekly. MI5 is monitored by another part of the JIO, the **Sub-Committee on Security Service Priorities and Performance** (SO-SSPP), set up in 1996 following a review of the role of the intelligence agencies after the demise of the Cold War. MI5 also comes under the **Intelligence and Security Liaison Unit** (ISLU) of the Home Office.

Working alongside MI5, MI6 and GCHQ, but separately, is the military's **Defence Intelligence Staff** (DIS), part of the MoD. It analyses information from a "wide variety of sources", and passes it on as necessary. The DIS is buried deep within the MoD, and virtually impossible to contact.

MI5

Britain's internal counter-subversion organisation is MI5, officially called the **Security Service** Set up in 1909, it currently holds 290,000 files on individuals. Only 17,500 of these are "open for inquiries" (ie, in active use; the rest are dormant). MI5's main role is: "The protection of national security and, in particular, its protection against threats from espionage, terrorism and sabotage, from the activities of agents of foreign powers and from actions intended to overthrow or undermine parliamentary democracy by political, industrial or violent means" and to "safeguard the economic well-being of the UK" (1989 Security Service Act). In 1996 MI5 was given a wider remit, allowing it to intervene in areas unrelated to "national security".

Since then MI5 has joined the police in fighting "serious crime". Its definition takes in "conduct by a large number of persons in pursuit of a common purpose", a catch-all description. The activities of some environmentalists are one of its areas of operation. In this and similar cases MI5 co-ordinates with the police via the new National Public Order Intelligence Unit, set up in 1999 in New Scotland Yard. MI5's main police contact point is the Special Branch (SB). All 55 police forces have their own SB, but in practice they are subsidiaries of the Metropolitan Police.

Stephen Lander is Director-General of MI5, with about 1,900 staff, 54 per cent aged under 40. It is run on an official budget of "less than £140 million". Two-fifths is spent on terrorism, 12 per cent on espionage and 7.5 per cent on "protective security". This is MI5's most sensitive work, defending the core structure of the State from any form of disruption. MI5 is based in Thames House, the former ICI headquarters on Millbank, refurbished for about £265 million in 1993/4. In 1998, MI5 for the first time ever made public one of its phone numbers (but only for informants) and opened a website. It also publishes regularly a descriptive guide called *MI5: The Security Service* (3rd edition July 1998).

MI5 (for informants only)	020-7930 9000
Website	www.mi5.gov.uk
Home Office press contacts	020-7273 4610

MI6

The **Secret Intelligence Service** (SIS, or MI6) is Britain's overseas spying agency. The 1994 Intelligence Services Act put MI6 and GCHQ on a statutory footing for the first time and widened MI6's role. It operates "in the interests of national security or of the economic well-being of the UK, or in support of the prevention or detection of serious crime", where "persons outside the British Islands" are suspects. The MI6 Chief is Richard Dearlove, appointed in September 1999. He has 2,000 staff. The annual budget is £140 million. MI6 in 1994 moved into its brand new £240 million headquarters next to Vauxhall Bridge, and almost facing MI5 across the Thames.

Foreign Office press contacts	020-7270 3100
FCO website	www.fco.gov.uk

GCHQ

The **Government Communications Headquarters** (GCHQ) is Britain's most powerful intelligence gathering agency. This secret eavesdropping centre, with 4,500 staff, is based in Cheltenham. Its role, like MI6's, is defined by the 1994 Intelligence Services Act. Its primary work is providing government departments and the military with signal intelligence (Sigint) and eavesdropping on all types of communication, including Internet. This is in support of Whitehall's security, military, foreign and economic policies, and "the prevention or detection of serious crime" (1994 Act). GCHQ works with its US equivalent, the **National Security Agency** (NSA), which together with Britain runs UKUSA, a worldwide intelligence operation. The NSA is the largest intelligence agency in the world. Its main listening post is on 560 acres of Menwith Hill, near Harrogate. With nearly as many staff as all of MI5, Menwith intercepts all European phone, fax and e-mail communications. GCHQ, responsible to the Foreign Office, has an annual budget of £440 million. Its director since 1998 is Kevin Tebbit. A glamourous new HQ at Cheltenham costing over £300 million, was commissioned in mid-1999, with completion due by mid-2002.

GCHQ, Cheltenham	01242-221491
Website	www.gchq.gov.uk

Police

The UK has 52 **police forces**: 39 in England, four in Wales, eight in Scotland and one in Northern Ireland (the Royal Ulster Constabulary - RUC). Two of England's forces are in London: the *Metropolitan* (the "Met"), based at New Scotland Yard on Victoria Street; and the *City of London*, responsible only for the City, with its headquarters close to the Guildhall. There are about 127,000 police officers in England and Wales, 14,800 in Scotland and 8,500 in the RUC. The Met is the biggest force, with 26,000 officers.

In England and Wales, all forces except the Met are maintained by local **police authorities.** By law, these must have 17 members: nine local councillors, three magistrates and five "independents" (chosen by the other members from a short-list supplied by the Home Office). The Home Secretary directly controls the Met, acting as its authority. In Scotland, the police authorities are the new unitary councils. The RUC is controlled by an authority appointed by the government.

Each police force is run by a chief constable, who is only nominally responsible to the police authority. The Home Office provides just over half the finance for the forces, giving it more power than the authorities. This means Britain has a national police force in many respects, but one that is not acknowledged or controllable as such.

The **Home Office** oversees policing through its Police Policy Directorate. Much of the Home Office was reorganised in the mid-1990s to give it a more business-like structure, to tune it in more closely with new technology and to make policing more capable of responding to unpredictable internal security problems, such as the environment movement. The Home Office has also played a prominent role in setting up and running Europol, the European police service which is outside the authority of the EU parliament.

The key police organisation is the Association of Chief Police Officers (**ACPO**), the professional body for ranks above chief superintendent. In practice, ACPO is the unofficial equivalent of the government's Cabinet, making strategy and policy decisions. The Police Federation represents the interests of the other officers.

Several police **national services** are provided by either the government or through co-operation between forces. A central organisation is the **Police Information Technology Organisation** (PITO), a Home Office section created in 1996. This oversees many operations, including the **Police National Computer** (PNC). The PNC provides all forces with 24-hour on-screen essential material, especially the **Criminal Justice Record Service** (Phoenix) of all criminal records. Another PITO unit is the **Police National Network** which gives a full range of telecommunications to all forces.

The **National Criminal Intelligence Service** (NCIS) plays a central role in collecting and analysing criminal intelligence. It was set up in 1992 and placed on an independent statutory basis in 1998. NCIS supplies the PNC with much of its information. The NCIS's London headquarters and regional offices gather, store and analyze a wide range of material. It also liaises with the International Criminal Police Organisation (Interpol). Also in 1998, the regional crime squads were replaced by the new independent **National Crime Squad** (NCS). The 1,450-strong NCS tries to solve the crimes the NCIS detects.

Both also work on the Euro front, where a key body is the **Schengen Information System**, a Europe-wide computerised database available to all police, immigration and border officials.

There was much public concern over the passing of the 1997 Police Act. It increased the strength of the police by authorising chief constables to carry out covert "intrusive surveillance" of the public in cases of "serious crime". This power to bug homes and offices was seen by some as a major infringement of civil liberties. Criminal records are now made available to employers.

Official **statistics** show the number of "notifiable offenses" recorded by the police in England and Wales rose steadily from the half million of the early 1950s to 5.6 million in 1992. It then dropped to 4.6 million in 1997, although critics say many members of the public have just given up reporting crime. Of these, 350,700 were violent, an increase of 1.7 per cent on 1996. The Met had the most offenses - 790,302 - and Dyfed-Powys the least - 18,098. The Met was also the most expensive police force, costing £215 per head of population, with the national average being £109. In late 1998 the Association of British Insurers estimated that the UK had a £35 billion annual crime bill, being £31 per week per household. The average police officer solved 9.4 crimes pa, with the top rate in Gwent, 15.5, and the lowest in Surrey, 5.8.

A Guardian investigation in early 1999 showed police forces across the country were taking part in a "huge fiddle" in which they pretended to have detected tens of thousands of crimes, while wiping from the records a mass of other petty crimes. The public inquiry into the death of Stephen Lawrence, published in February 1999, concluded that there was "professional incompetence, institutional racism and a failure of leadership" in the Metropolitan Police. The leading annual directory of the police is the *Police and Constabulary Almanac* (R Hazell & Co, 01491-641018), only available from the publisher.

GOVT. DEPARTMENTS

Home Office	020-7273 4000
Press offices: Main	020-7273 4600
Prisons	020-7217 6633
Directorates: Criminal Policy	020-7273 3183
Immigration & Nationality	0870-606766
Organised & International Crime	020-7273 2830
Police Policy	020-7273 3601
Website	www.homeoffice.gov.uk
Northern Ireland Office	01232-520700
Police Division	01232-527547
NI Police Authority	01232-230111
Scottish Office: Home Dept	0131-556 8400
Press	0131-244 2661
Crime Squad	0141-302 1000
Criminal Record Office	0141-532 2777
Inspector of Constabulary	0131-244 5614

NATIONAL POLICE ORGS

Action Against Drugs Unit	020-7273 2185
Crime Prevention Agency	020-7273 2548
Crown Prosecution Service	020-7273 8000
Outside office hours	020-7273 8341
Press office	020-7273 8106
Public enquiries	020-7334 8505
Customs & Excise Investigation	020-7283 5353
Forensic Science Service	0121-607 6800
HM Inspector of Constabulary	020-7273 2116
HM Inspector of Probation	020-7273 3906
Intelligence & Security Liaison Unit	020-7273 2991
Interpol	020-7238 8600
Missing Persons Helpline	020-8392 4545
National/Regional Crime Squads: HQ	020-7238 2500
Midland	0121-626 4052
North East	01924-293665
North West	0161-848 5050
South East	020-7238 8499
South & West Wales	029-2022 2111
South West	01454-628301
National Criminal Intelligence Service	020-7238 8000
Press office	020-7238 8431
Enquiries	020-7238 8610
National Identification Service	020-7230 2780
National Police Training, Bramshill	01256-602200
Operational Policing Policy Unit	020-7273 2593
Parole Board (E&W)	020-7217 5314
Police Complaints Authority	020-7273 6450
Police Information Technology Org	020-7217 8179
Police National Computer	020-8200 3200
Police Science & Technology	020-7217 8609
Police Scientific Development Branch	01727-865051
Police Staff College, Bramshill	01256-602100
Policing & Organised Crime Unit	020-7273 3244
Serious Fraud Office	020-7239 7272

POLICE FORCES: ENGLAND

Metropolitan Police, London	020-7230 1212
24-hour press bureau	020-7230 2171/2/3/4
Voicebank	0891-900099
Fax	020-7230 2818
Race/violent crimes	020-7230 3382
Facility requests	020-7230 4094
Director, Public Affairs	020-7230 2691
Area headquarters:	
1 Central (at Cannon Row)	020-7925 1212
Press	020-8321 9056
2 North West (at Colindale)	020-8205 1012
Press	020-8733 4086
3 North East (at Edmonton)	020-8807 9332
Press	020-8345 4377
4 South East (at Sidcup)	020-8853 1212
Press	020-7230 1751
5 South West (at Kingston)	020-8541 1212
Press	020-8230 1751
Met Police Committee	020-7271 8350
Website	www.met.police.uk

Avon/Somerset	01275-818181
Voicebanks:	
Bristol	01426-957011
Taunton	01426-950441
Bedfordshire	01234-841212
Voicebank	01426-925682
Berks/Bucks	see Thames Valley
Cambridgeshire	01480-456111
Voicebank	01426-950160
Cheshire	01244-350000
Voicebank	01426-955487
Cleveland	01642-326326
Voicebank	01426 979651
Cumbria	01768-891999
Voicebank	01426-972830
Derbyshire	01773-570100
Voicebank	01426-955020
Devon & Cornwall	0990-777444
Voicebank	01392-452198
Dorset	01929-462727
Voicebank	01426-932345
Durham	0191-386 4929
Voicebank	01426-984458
Essex	01245-491491
Voicebank	01426-925680
Gloucestershire	01242-521321
Voicebank	01426-955884
Guernsey	01481-725111
Hampshire	01962-841500
Voicebank	01426-932024
Herefordshire	see West Mercia
Hertfordshire	01707-354200
Voicebank	01426-934068
Humberside	01482-326111
Voicebank	01426-978223
Isle of Man	01624-631212
Jersey	01534-612612
Kent	01622-650100
Voicebank	01622-683932
Lancashire	01772-614444
Voicebank	01772-618194
Leicestershire	0116-222 2222
Lincolnshire	01522-532222
Voicebank	01426-957180
London, City of	020-7601-2222
Manchester, Gr	0161-872 5050
Voicebank	0891-335559
Merseyside	0151-709 6010
Voicebank	0891-557725
Norfolk	01603-768769
Voicebank	01426-952342
Northamptonshire	01604-700700
Voicebank	01426-952401
Northumbria	01661-872555
Voicebank	01426-979793
Nottinghamshire	0115-967 0999
Voicebank	01426-957125
Oxfordshire	see Thames Valley
Shropshire	see West Mercia
Staffordshire	01785-257717
Voicebank	01785-232525
Suffolk	01473-613500

Voicebank	01426-932403
Surrey	01483-571212
Voicebank	01426-953808
Sussex (E & W)	01273-475432
Voicebank	01273-479221
Thames Valley (Berks, Bucks,	
Oxon)	01865-846000
Voicebank	01426-932012
Warwickshire	01926-415000
Voicebank	01426-952404
West Mercia (Hereford, Salop,	
Worcs)	01905-723000
Voicebank	01426-913005
West Midlands	0121-626 5000
Voicebank	01426-952009
Wiltshire	01380-722341
Voicebank	01426-961045
Worcestershire	see West Mercia
Yorkshire - North	01609-783131
Voicebank	01426-979568
Yorkshire - South	0114-220 2020
Voicebank	01426-952018
Yorkshire - West	01924-375222
Voicebank	01426-979656

POLICE: SCOTLAND

Central Scotland	01786-456000
Clackman'shire	01259-723255
Falkirk	01324-634212
Stirling	01786-456000
Dumfries/Galloway	01387-252112
Fife	01592-418888
Grampian	01224-386000
Lothian & Borders	0131-311 3131
Borders	01450-375051
Edinburgh	0131-311 3131
Midlothian	0131-663 2855
West Lothian	01506-31200
Northern	01463-715555
Command areas:	
Badenoch	01479-810222
Caithness and	
Sutherland	01955-603551
Inverness/Nairn	01463-715555
Lochaber	01397-702361
Orkney	01856-872241
Ross, Cromarty and	
Skye	01349-862444
Shetland	01595-692110
Western Isles	01851-702222
Strathclyde	0141-532 2000
Dunbartonshire	01389-822000
East Ayrshire	1563-505000
Glasgow	0141-532 2000
Inverclyde	01475-492500
N Lanarkshire	01698-483000
S Lanarkshire	01698-483300
Paisley	0141-532 5900
S Ayrshire	01292-664000
Tayside	01382-223200

Divisions:	
Eastern (Angus)	01307-302200
Western (Perth and	
Kinross)	01738-621141
Central (Dundee)	01382-223200

POLICE: WALES

Dyfed-Powys	01267-222020
Divisions:	
Aberystwyth	01970-612791
Carmarthen	01267-222020
Eastern	01554-772222
Pembrokeshire	01437-763355
Powys, north	01686-625704
Powys, south	01874-622331
Gwent	01633-838111
Voicebank	01633-642219
Divisions:	
Blaenau Gwent	01495-350999
Caerphilly	029-2085 2999
Newport	01633-244999
Torfaen	01495-764711
North Wales	01492-517171
Voicebank	01426-950443
Web	www.north-wales.police.uk
Divisions:	
Anglesey	01286-684950
Conwy	01492-511314
Denbighshire	01492-511336
Flintshire	01978-294710
Gwynedd	01286-673333
Wrexham	01978-294600
South Wales	01656-655555
Voicebank	01656-869292
Divisions:	
Bridgend	01656-655555
Cardiff	029-2022 2111
Merthyr Tydfil	01685-722541
Neath/Pt Talbot	01639-635321
Rhondda Cynon	
Taff	01443-485351
Swansea	01792-456999
Vale Glamorgan	01446-734451

POLICE: N IRELAND

Royal Ulster Constabulary	
(RUC)	028-9065 0222
Website	www.rucpolice.uk
Belfast Region	028-9065 0222
North Region:	
Ballymena	028-2565 3355
Coleraine	028-7034 4122
Londonderry	028-7136 7337
Enniskillen	028-6632 2823
South Region:	
Armagh	028-3752 3311
Dungannon	028-8775 2525
Newtownards	028-9181 8080
Portadown	028-3833 4411

SPECIALIST POLICE FORCES

British Transport Police
Headquarters	020-7388 7541
PR officer	020-7830 8854
London Tube	020-7380 1400

Military
MoD Police	01371-854000
RAF Police	01452-712612
Royal Marines	01752-836372
Royal Military Police (Army)	01980-615653
Royal Naval Regulating Branch (RN police)	023-9272 7243
Ports: Belfast	028-9055 3000
Dover	01304-216084
Falmouth	01326-212100
Felixstowe	01394-604747
Liverpool	0151-949 1212
London (Tilbury)	01375-846781
Tees	01642-277215
Royal Botanic Gardens Constabulary (Kew)	020-8332 5121
Royal Parks Constabulary	020-7298 2000
Scotland	0131-668 8735
UK Atomic Energy Authority Police	01235-463760

OTHER ORGANISATIONS

Assoc of British Investigators	020-8546 3368
Assoc of Police Authorities	020-7664 3051
Assoc of Police Suppliers	01428-602627
British Security Industry Assoc	01905-21464
BT Security & Investigation	0800-321999
Common Agricultural Policy Anti-Fraud Unit	0118-958 3626
Customs & Excise Investigation Service	020-7283 5353
Data Protection Registrar	01625-545745
Dept of Social Security Benefits Agency: Organised Fraud Units	0113-232 4419
Federation Against Copyright Theft	020-8568 6646
Federation Against Software Theft	01753-527999
Gaming Board	020-7306 6200
ICC Counterfeiting Intelligence Bureau	020-8591 3000
Immigration Service Intelligence and Investigation Unit	020-8745 2400
Inland Revenue Special Compliance Office	020-7234 3702
Institute of Professional Investigators	01254-680072
Jockey Club Security Dept	020-7343 3261
MAFF Food Investigation Branch	020-7270 8364
Medicines Control Agency	020-7273 0607
Personal Investment Authority	020-7676 1000
Post Office Investigation Dept	020-8681 9876
Radio Investigation Service (DTI)	020-7215 5961
Road Haulage Assoc Security	01932-841515
Sea Fisheries Inspectorate (MAFF)	020-7238 5798
Security Industry Inspectorate	01905-773131

STAFF BODIES

ACPO (Association of Chief Police Officers):	
England, Wales, N Ireland	020-7230 7184
Scotland	0131-311 3051
Assoc of Chief Officers of Probation	020-7823 2551
British Assoc of Women Police	01543-276165
Fingerprint Society	0121-236 5000
International Police Association	0115-981 3638
International Professional Security	01803-554849
Police Federation: England & Wales	020-8399 2224
N Ireland	028-9076 0831
Scotland	0141-332 5234
Police Superintendents Association:	
England & Wales	0118-984 4005
Scotland	0141-221 5796
Charities: National Police Fund	020-7273 3684
Police Dependents Trust	020-7273 2921
Police Foundation	020-7582 3744

MONITORING GROUPS

Monitoring the police from a civil liberties perspective are Statewatch and Liberty. Inquest provides personal help following deaths in police or secure custody. The Police Complaints Authority has close links with the police and is therefore not believed by critics to be objective.

Inquest	020-8802 7430
Justice	020-7329 5100
Lesbian & Gay Police Assoc	01426-943011
Liberty (NCCL)	020-7403 3888
Missing Persons Bureau	020-8392 4545
Police Complaints Authority	020-7273 6450
Police Review (magazine)	020-7440 4700
Statewatch	020-8802 1882
Website	www.statewatch.org

Fire services

Fire services in England are run by Fire and Civil Defence Authorities (FCDAs) in London and the six metropolitan areas, and elsewhere by county councils, reorganised with new unitary authorities if necessary. In Wales, all eight county brigades merged into three combined fire authorities in 1996. Fire services in Scotland and Northern Ireland remained unchanged during the unitary shake-up. Overseeing services in England and Wales is the Central Fire Brigades Advisory Council, part of the Home Office's Fire Services Unit, with a same-named council in Scotland under the Scottish Office Home Department. There are 34,000 full-time fire officers in the UK. The annual cost is around £1,400 million.

ENGLAND

Avon	0117-926 2061
Bedfordshire	01234-351081
Berkshire	0118-945 2888
Buckinghamshire	01494-786943
Cambridgeshire	01480-444500
Channel Islands - Guernsey	01481-724491
Jersey	01534-37444
Cheshire	01606-868700
Cleveland	01429-872311
Cornwall	01872-273117
Cumbria	01900-822503
Derbyshire	01332-771221
Devon	01392-872200
Dorset	01305-251133
Durham	0191-384 3381
Essex	01277-222531
Gloucestershire	01242-512041
Hampshire	023-80620000
Hereford & Worcester	01905-24454
Hertfordshire	01992-507507
Humberside	01482-565333
Isle of Man	01624-673333
Isle of Wight	01983-823194
Isles of Scilly	01872-273117
Kent	01622-692121
Lancashire	01772-862545
Leicestershire	0116-287 2241
Lincolnshire	01522-582222
London	020-7582 3811
Greater Manchester	0161-736 5866
Merseyside	0151-227 4466
Norfolk	01603-810351
Northamptonshire	01604-797000
Northumberland	01670-513161

Nottinghamshire	0115-967 0880
Oxfordshire	01865-842999
Shropshire	01743-260200
Somerset	01823-337222
Staffordshire	01785-813234
Suffolk	01473-588888
Surrey	01737-242444
Sussex - East	01273-406000
Sussex - West	01243-786211
Tyne and Wear	0191-232 1224
Warwickshire	01926-423231
West Midlands	0121-359 5161
Wiltshire	01380-731100
Yorkshire - North	01609-780150
Yorkshire - South	0114-272 7202
Yorkshire - West	01274-682311

WALES

Mid & West Wales	01267-221444
North Wales	01745-343431
South West Wales	01443-232000

SCOTLAND

Central Scotland	01324-716996
Dumfries & Galloway	01387-252222
Fife	01592-774451
Grampian	01224-696666
Highland & Islands	01463-222722
Lothian & Borders	0131-228 2401
Strathclyde	01698-284200
Tayside	01382-322222

NORTHERN IRELAND

NI Fire Brigade HQ (Lisburn)	028-9266 4221
A Division (Belfast)	028-9031 0360
B Division (Bangor)	028-9127 1906
C Division (Portadown)	028-3833 2222
D Division (Derry)	028-7131 1162
E Division (Ballymena)	028-2564 3370
F Division (Omagh)	028-8224 1190

ORGANISATIONS

Home Office:	020-7273 4000
Press Office	020-7273 4640
Fire Services Unit	020-7217 8749
Fire Services Inspectorate	020-7217 8728
Website	www.homeoffice.gov.uk/fepd
Fire Brigades Union	020-8541 1765
Northern Ireland: Environment Dept	028-9054 0540
Fire Division	028-9054 0845
Scottish Office Home Dept	0131-556 8400
Press Office	0131-244 2718
Fire Service	0131-244 2184

Ambulances

Most ambulances in England and Wales are managed by NHS trusts, whose names are in brackets below if responsible for more than one county. Overseeing the services is the Department of Health's NHS Executive, based in Leeds. All Scottish ambulances are run by the Scottish Ambulance Service, with its headquarters in Edinburgh. There are about 16,000 ambulance staff. Ambulance services cost £470 million in 1998, responding to 4.4 million calls. Demands for the service rose 40% between 1990 and 1998.

ENGLAND

Avon	0117-927 7046
Bedfordshire	01234-408999
Berkshire	0118-977 1200
Bucks (Two Shires)	01908-262422
Cambridgeshire (East Anglian)	01603-424255
Channel Islands: Guernsey	01481-725211
Jersey	01534-622343
Cheshire (Mersey Trust)	0151-260 5220
Cleveland	01642-850888
Cornwall (Westcountry)	01884-259563
Cumbria	01228-596909
Derbyshire	01332-372441
Devon (Westcountry)	01752-767839
Dorset	01202-896111
Durham	0191-386 4488
Essex	01245-443344
Gloucestershire	01452-395050
Hampshire	01962-863511
Hereford & Worcester	01886-834200
Hertfordshire	01234-408999
Humberside	01482-561191
Isle of Man	01624-642642
Isle of Wight	01983-821655
Kent	01622-747010
Lancashire	01772-862666
Leicestershire	0116-275 0700
Lincolnshire	01522-545171
London	020-7928 0333
Greater Manchester	0161-231 7921
Merseyside (Mersey Trust)	0151-260 5220
Norfolk (East Anglian)	01603-424255
Northants (Two Shires)	01908-262422
Northumbria	0191-273 1212
Nottinghamshire	0115-929 6151
Oxfordshire	01865-740100
Scilly Isles	01884-254565
Shropshire	01743-364061
Somerset (Westcountry)	01823-278114
Staffordshire	01785-253521

Suffolk (East Anglian)	01603-424255
Surrey	01737-353333
Sussex	01273-489444
Warwickshire	01926-881331
West Midlands	01384-215555
Wiltshire	01249-443939
Yorkshire: North	01904-666000
South	01709-820520
West	01274-707070

WALES

Mid-Glamorgan	01443-217005
North Wales	01745-585106
South & East Wales	029-2055 2011
West Wales	01792-562900

SCOTLAND

Scottish Ambulance Service HQ	0131-447 7711
North Region:	
HQ: Aberdeen	01224-662244
Inverness	01463-236611
Dundee	01382-817171
South East Region:	
HQ: Edinburgh	0131-447 8746
Motherwell	01698-276441
West Region:	
HQ: Glasgow	0141-353 6001
Ayr	01292-284101
Paisley	0141-848 1434

NORTHERN IRELAND

Dept of Health	028-9052 4309
Eastern (Belfast)	028-9024 6113
Northern (Antrim)	028-9442 8911
Western (Derry)	028-7134 8063

OFFICIAL ORGANISATIONS

Department of Health Press:	020-7210 5221
NHS Executive	0113-254 5000
Website	www.open.gov.uk/doh
Welsh Office Health Dept Press	029-2082 5647
Scottish Office Press	0131-244 2656
DoH Northern Ireland	028-9052 0500

SUPPORT ORGANISATIONS

Assoc of Ambulance Personnel	01749-344044
British Red Cross	020-7235 5454
Patients Association	020-8423 9111
Royal Life Saving Society	01789-295222
St Andrews Ambulance Assoc	0141-332 4031
St John Ambulance	020-7235 5231

Hospitals

The National Health Service (NHS) employs 950,000 staff, occupies 46,000 acres of land and oversees 1,600 hospitals with 270,000 beds. It spent £36.44 billion in 1997/8. Since 1991 self-governing trusts (quangos) have taken over most services, including hospitals, on a contractual basis. The trusts in England are monitored by the NHS Executive and its eight regional offices. These replaced the 14 regional health authorities (RHAs) in 1996. At the same time the district health authorities and family health services authorities below the RHAs were superseded by 100 all-purpose health authorities in England and five in Wales. About 81 per cent of the cost of the health service is met through general taxation, with National Insurance providing 13%. About 500 million prescriptions, worth £4.4 billion, are dispensed annually

Below are the hospitals with an accident and emergency department and some acute hospitals in larger towns without an emergency hospital.

ENGLISH HOSPITALS

Avon

Bath (Royal United)	01225-428331
Bristol (Frenchay)	0117-970 1212
Bristol (Royal Infirmary)	0117-923 0000
Bristol (Southmead)	0117-950 5050
Weston-super-Mare	01934-636363

Bedfordshire

Bedford	01234-355122
Luton & Dunstable	01582-491122

Berkshire

Ascot (Heatherwood)	01344-623333
Slough (Wexham Park)	01753-633000

Buckinghamshire

Aylesbury (Stoke Mandeville)	01296-315000
High Wycombe (Wycombe)	01494-526161

Cambridgeshire

Cambridge (Addenbrookes)	01223-245151
Huntingdon (Hinchingbrooke)	01480-416416
Peterborough	01733-874000

Channel Islands

Guernsey (Princess Elizabeth)	01481-725241
Jersey General	01534-59000

Cheshire

Chester (Countess)	01244-365000
Crewe (Leighton)	01270-255141
Macclesfield	01625-421000
Northwich (Victoria)	01606-564000
Warrington	01925-635911

Cleveland

Hartlepool	01429-266654
Middlesborough	01642-850850
North Tees	01642-617617

Cornwall

Penzance (West Cornwall)	01736-362382
Truro (Treviske)	01872-274242

Cumbria

Carlisle (Cumberland)	01228-523444
Furness, Cumbria	01229-870870

Derbyshire

Chesterfield	01246-277271
Derby (Derbyshire Royal)	01332-347141

Devon

Barnstaple (North Devon)	01271-322577
Exeter (Royal Devon)	01392-411611
Plymouth (Derriford)	01752-777111
Torbay	01803-614567

Dorset

Poole	01202-665511
Weymouth	01305-760022

Durham

Bishop Auckland, Co Durham	01388-454000
Darlington, Co Durham	01325-380100
Durham (Dryburn)	0191-333 2333
Shotley Bridge	01207-214444

Essex

Basildon, Essex	01268-533911
Chelmsford (Broomfield)	01245-440761
Epping (St Margarets)	01992-561666
Essex	01206-853535
Harlow (Princess Alexandra)	01279-444455
Harold Wood, Essex	01708-345533
Rochford/Southend	01702-435555

Gloucestershire

Cheltenham	01242-222222
Gloucester (Glos Royal)	01452-528555

Hampshire

Basingstoke	01256-473202
Portsmouth (Queen Alexandra)	023-9228 6000
Southampton	023-8077 7222
Winchester (Royal Hampshire)	01962-863535

Hereford & Worcester

Hereford	01432-355444
Kidderminster	01562-823424
Redditch (Alexandra)	01527-503030
Worcester Royal Infirmary	01905-763333

Hertfordshire

Hemel Hempstead	01442-213141
Stevenage (Lister)	01438-314333
Welwyn (Queen Elizabeth II)	01707-328111
Watford	01923-244366

Humberside

Bridlington	01262-606666
Grimsby	01472-874111
Hull (Royal Infirmary)	01482-328541
Scunthorpe	01724-282282

Isle of Man

Douglas (Nobles)	01624-642642

Isle of Wight

Newport (St Marys)	01983-524081

Kent

Ashford (William Harvey)	01233-633331
Canterbury (Kent & Canterbury)	01227-766877
Dartford (West Hill)	01322-223223
Gillingham (Medway)	01634-830000
Maidstone	01622-729000
Margate (Thanet)	01843-225544
Tunbridge Wells (Kent/Sussex)	01892-526111

Lancashire

Blackburn (Royal)	01254-263555
Blackpool (Victoria)	01253-300000
Burnley	01282-425071
Bury	0161-764 6081
Lancaster	01524-65944
Leigh	01942-672333
Ormskirk	01695-577111
Preston (Royal)	01772-716565
Southport	01704-547471

Leicestershire

Leicester	0116-254 1414

Lincolnshire

Boston (Pilgrim)	01205-364801
Grantham	01476-565232
Lincoln (County)	01522-512512
Louth (County)	01507-600100
Stamford	01780-764151

London - Emergency

Acton (Central Middlesex)	020-8965 5733
Ashford	01784-884488
Barnet	020-8216 4000
Bromley	020-8289 7000
Camberwell (Kings College)	020-7737 4000
Carshalton (St Helier)	020-8644 4343
City (St Bartholomews)	020-7601 8888
Ealing	020-8574 2444
Edgware	020-8952 2381
Edmonton (North Middlesex)	020-8887 2000
Enfield (Chase Farm)	020-8366 6600
Euston (University College)	020-7387 9300
Fulham (Charing Cross)	020-8846 1234
Greenwich	020-8858 8141
Hammersmith	020-8743 2030
Hampstead (Royal Free)	020-7794 0500
Harrow (Northwick)	020-8864 3232

Highgate (Whittington)	020-7272 3070
Hillingdon	01895-238282
Homerton	020-8510 5555
Ilford (King George)	020-8983 8000
Isleworth (West Middlesex)	020-8560 2121
Kingston	020-8546 7711
Lambeth (St Thomass)	020-7928 9292
Lewisham	020-8333 3000
Leytonstone (Whipps Cross)	020-8539 5522
Newham	020-7476 4000
North Kensington (St Charles)	020-8969 2488
Paddington (St Marys)	020-7886 6666
Roehampton (Queen Marys)	020-8789 6611
Romford (Oldchurch)	01708-746090
Sidcup (Queen Marys)	020-8302 2678
Southwark (Guys)	020-7955 5000
Thornton Heath (Mayday)	020-8401 3000
Tooting (St Georges)	020-8672 1255
Wembley	020-8903 1323
Westminster, SW1	020-8746 8000
Whitechapel (Royal London)	020-7377 7000
Woolwich (Queen Elizabeth)	020-8858 8141

London - Non-emergency

Brompton Heart, SW3	020-7352 8121
Eastman Dental, WC1	020-7915 1000
Eliz. Garrett Anderson, NW1	020-7387 2501
Gt Ormond St Childrens, WC1	020-7405 9200
London Homeopathic, WC1	020-7837 8833
Maudsley, SE5	020-7703 6333
Middlesex, W1	020-7636 8333
Moorfields Eye, EC1	020-7253 3411
National Orthopaedic	020-8954 2300
Neurology, WC1	020-7837 3611
Royal Marsden, SW3	020-7352 8171
Throat, Nose & Ear, WC1	020-7837 8855
Tropical Diseases, NW1	020-7387 4411

Greater Manchester

Ashton-under-Lyne (Tameside)	0161-331 6000
Bolton	01204-390390
Bury	0161-764 6081
Manchester Royal Infirmary	0161-276 1234
North Manchester	0161-795 4567
Royal Oldham	0161-624 0420
Rochdale Infirmary	01706-377777
Salford (Hope)	0161-789 7373
South Manchester (Withington)	0161-445 8111
Stockport	0161-483 1010
Wigan (Royal Albert Edward)	01942-244000
Wythenshawe	0161-998 7070

Merseyside

Liverpool (Alder Hay Childrens)	0151-228 4811
Liverpool (Broadgreen)	0151-282 6000
Liverpool (Royal)	0151-709 0141
Liverpool (Walton)	0151-525 3611
Whiston	0151-426 1600
Wirral	0151-678 5111

Norfolk

Gt Yarmouth (James Paget)	01493-452452
Kings Lynn (Queen Elizabeth)	01553-766266
Norfolk & Norwich	01603-286286

Northamptonshire
Kettering	01536-492000
Northampton	01604-634700

Northumberland
Ashington, Northumberland	01670-812541
Hexham, Northumberland	01434-606161

Nottinghamshire
Mansfield	01623-622515
Newark	01636-681681
Nottingham (City)	0115-969 1169
Nottingham (University)	0115-924 9924
Worksop	01909-500990

Oxfordshire
Banbury (Horton)	01295-275500
Headington (John Radcliffe)	01865-741166

Shropshire
Shrewsbury	01743-261000

Somerset
Bridgwater	01278-451501
Minehead	01643-707251
Taunton (Musgrove)	01823-333444
Yeovil	01935-475122

Staffordshire
Burton-upon-Trent (Queens)	01283-566333
Stafford	01785-257731
Stoke-on-Trent(North Staffs)	01782-715444

Suffolk
Ipswich	01473-712233
West Suffolk	01284-713000

Surrey
Ashford	01784-884488
Chertsey (St Petrs)	.01932-872000
Camberley (Frimley Park)	01276-604604
Epsom	01372-735735
Guildford (Royal Surrey)	01483-571122
Redhill & Dorking (E Surrey)	01737-768511

Sussex - East
Brighton (Royal Sussex)	01273-696955
Eastbourne	01323-417400
Hastings (Conquest)	01424-755255

Sussex - West
Chichester (St Richards)	01243-788122
Haywards Heath (Princess Royal)	01444-441881
Worthing	01903-205111

Tyne & Wear
Gateshead (Queen Elizabeth)	0191-482 0000
Newcastle	0191-273 8811
Newcastle (Royal Victoria)	0191-232 5131
North Tyneside	0191-259 6660
South Tyneside (South Shields)	0191-454 8888
Sunderland	0191-565 6256

Warwickshire
Nuneaton (George Eliot)	024-76351351
Rugby (St Cross)	01788-572831
Warwick(South Warwickshire)	01926-495321

West Midlands
Birmingham (Dudley Road)	0121-554 3801
Birmingham (Heartlands)	0121-766 6611
Coventry & Warwick	024-7622 4055
Dudley (Russells Hall)	01384-456111
Solihull	0121-711 4455
Sutton Coldfield (Good Hope)	0121-378 2211
University Hospital	0121-627 1627
West Bromwich (Sandwell)	0121-553 1831
Wolverhampton (Royal)	01902-307999

Wiltshire
Salisbury	01722-336262
Swindon (Princess Margaret)	01793-536231

Yorkshire -North
Harrogate	01423-885959
Northallerton (Friarage)	01609-779911
Scarborough	01723-368111
York	01904-631313

Yorkshire -South
Barnsley	01226-730000
Doncaster (Royal Infirmary)	01302-366666
Rotherham Hospital	01709-820000
Sheffield (Childrens)	0114-276 1111
Sheffield (Northern General)	0114-243 4343
Sheffield (Royal Hallamshire)	0114-271 1900

Yorkshire - West
Bradford (Royal)	01274-542200
Dewsbury	01924-465105
Halifax	01422-357222
Huddersfield (Royal Infirmary)	01484-422191
Keighley (Airedale)	01535-652511
Leeds (General Infirmary)	0113-243 2799
Leeds (St Jamess University)	0113-243 3144
Pontefract	01977-600600
Wakefield(Pinderfields)	01924-201688

SCOTTISH HOSPITALS

Borders
Melrose (Borders General)	01896-754333

Central
Falkirk (Royal)	01324-624000
Stirling (Royal)	01786-434000

Dumfries & Galloway
Dumfries (Royal Infirmary)	01387-246246

Fife
Dunfermline (Queen Margarets)	01383-623623

Grampian
Aberdeen (Royal)	01224-681818

Highland
Inverness (Raigmore)	01463-704000

Lothian
Edinburgh (Eastern General)	0131-536 7000
Edinburgh (Royal Infirmary)	0131-536 1000
Edinburgh (Western General)	0131-537 1000
Livingston (St Johns)	01506-419666

Orkney
Kirkwall (Balfour)   01856-885400

Shetland
Lerwick (Gilbert Bain)   01595-695678

Strathclyde
Airdrie (Monklands)   01236-748748
Ayr   01292-610555
Carluke (Law)   01698-361100
East Kilbride (Hairmyres)   01355-220292
Glasgow (Royal Infirmary)   0141-211 4000
Glasgow (Sick Children)   0141-201 0000
Glasgow (Southern)   0141-201 1100
Glasgow (Stobhill)   0141-201 3000
Glasgow (Victoria Infirmary)   0141-201 6000
Glasgow (Western Infirmary)   0141-211 2000
Greenock (Inverclyde)   01475-633777
Kilmarnock (Crosshouse)   01563-521133
Paisley (Royal Alexandra)   0141-887 9111

Tayside
Brechin (Stracathro)   01356-647291
Dundee (Royal Infirmary)   01382-660111
Perth (Royal)   01738-623311

Western Isles
Stornoway (Western Isles)   01851-704704

WELSH HOSPITALS

Clwyd
Rhyl (Clwyd)   01745-583910

Dyfed
Aberystwyth (Bronglais)   01970-623131
Carmarthen (West Wales)   01267-235151
Haverfordwest (Withybush)   01437-764545
Llanelli (Prince Phillip)   01554-756567

Glamorgan - Mid
Bridgend (Princess of Wales)   01656-752752
Merthyr Tydfil (Prince Charles)   01685-721721
Pontypridd (East Glamorgan)   01443-218218

Glamorgan - West
Swansea (Singleton)   01792-205666

Gwent
Abergavenny (Neill Hall)   01873-852091
Newport (Royal Gwent)   01633-234234

Gwynedd
Bangor (Gwynedd)   01248-384384
Llandudno   01492-860066

N IRELAND HOSPITALS

Antrim
Ballymena (Wavney)   028-9442 4000
Belfast City   028-9032 9241
Belfast (Musgrave Park)   028-9066 9501
Belfast (Royal Victoria)   028-9024 0503
Belfast (Ulster)   028-9048 4511
Larne (Moyle)   028-2827 5431
Lisburn (Lagan Valley)   028-9266 5141
Newtownabbey (Whiteabbey)   028-9086 5181
Newtownards (Ards)   028-9181 2661

Armagh
Craigavon   028-3833 4444

Down
Newry (Daisy Hill)   028-3026 5511

Fermanagh
Enniskillen (Erne)   028-6632 4711

Londonderry
Coleraine   028-7034 4177
Derry (Altnagelvin)   028-7186 0261
Magheragelt (Mid-Ulster)   028-7963 1031

Tyrone
Dungannon (South Tyrone)   028-8772 2821
Omagh (Tyrone County)   028-8224 5211

MILITARY HOSPITALS

Army
MoD Hospital Unit (Frimley Park)   01276-604320
Duchess of Kent, Catterick   01748-832521

Navy
Haslar, Gosport   023-9258 4255
Derford, Plymouth   01752-777111

SPECIAL HOSPITALS

Ashworth, Merseyside   0151-473 0303
Carstairs, Lanark   01555-840293
Broadmoor, Berkshire   01344-773111
Rampton, Notts   01777-248321

OFFICIAL ORGANISATIONS

Department of Health (Press office   020-7210 5221
NHS Executive: HQ (Leeds)   0113-254 5000
  Anglia & Oxford   01908-844400
  Northern & Yorkshire   0191-301 1300
  North Thames   020-7725 5300
  North West   01925-704000
  South Thames   020-7725 2500
  South & West   0117-984 1750
  Trent   0114-263 0300
  West Midlands   0121-224 4600
Welsh Office   029-2082 5111
Scottish Office DoH   0131-244 2410
DoH Northern Ireland   028-9052 0500
Health & Safety Commission   020-7717 6000

The sea

HM Coastguard is responsible for **Search and Rescue** (SAR) operations in the 1.25 million square miles of UK seas and on the 10,500 miles of coastline. When accidents occur, the Coastguard can call on RNLI lifeboats, plus military and civilian aircraft, helicopters and ships, to provide assistance. There are about 500 professional Coastguard officers managing the service. In addition, 3,100 volunteer Auxiliary Coastguards carry out rescues on cliffs and beaches.

Seafarers **in distress** make radio calls on Channel 16, the distress and safety channel monitored by Coastguard control centres. In 1998 the Coastguard handled 11,553 incidents, assisting 6,328 people; 249 lives were lost. Coastguard officers need to have an international view of life; in 1997 they rescued off the Shetlands ten members of the crew of a ship which was registered in the Bahamas, managed from Norway, run by Croation officers and crewed by Filipinos.

The UK is divided into five **Search and Rescue Regions**, each of which is overseen by a large Maritime Rescue Co-ordination Centre (MRCC). Every region has subsidiary Maritime Rescue Sub-Centres (MRSCs). There are currently 21 of these MRCCs and MRSCs (listed below) around the UK coast, staffed 24-hours a day. Each has a Publicity Liaison Officer who can talk to the press. The five regions have their coastlines divided into a total of 64 sectors, each run by one Sector Manager, who co-ordinates the work of the Auxiliaries in the area.

Since 1997 the Coastguard has been undergoing major controversial changes, many of them opposed by large sectors of the public. Despite widespread opposition, three of the 21 co-ordination centres will close: Oban and Pentland in 2000; and Tyne Tees in 2001. Plans to shut Liverpool and merge two south coast MRSCs - Portland and Lee-on-Solent - were scrapped in 1999.

Auxiliary Coastguards are volunteers who are officially part of HM Coastguard. Some other volunteers in the mid-1990s formed the unofficial National Coastwatch Institution. Usually known as Coastwatch, the charity in certain places provides a coastal surveillance service to the Coastguard.

HM Coastguard operates the **Channel Navigation Information Service** (CNIS), a traffic separation scheme operating in the eastern English Channel. The Channel is the busiest shipping lane in the world, and CNIS is the world's most sophisticated radar surveillance and monitoring system. HM Coastguard hopes to revolutionise all ship rescue operations with the new satellite Global Maritime Distress and Safety System, due to be completed in 1999.

The work of HM Coastguard is administered on behalf of the Department of Transport by the **Maritime and Coastguard Agency** (MCA), a quango based in Southampton. The MCA was created in April 1998 by the merger of the Coastguard Agency and the Marine Safety Agency, quangos which both started in 1994. The annual budget is £90 million. The select committee of MPs condemned the high level of bureaucracy in the MCA, and said it should be dismantled.

The MCA has several other marine safety roles alongside the SAR carried out by HM Coastguard. Its **Port State Control Section** surveys merchant ships in UK waters to ensure they meet international standards. The **Registry of Shipping and Seamen** in Cardiff registers and keeps records on all UK merchant and fishing vessels. The **Marine Pollution Control Unit** (MPCU) deals with major spillages of oil and other hazardous substances, and maintains the National Contingency Plan which sets out the responsibilities of government departments and other organisations. In major events the Unit works in the Marine Operations Emergency Room in the Coastguard HQ at Southampton. The MCA also runs the **marine safety** services of the former Marine Safety Agency. The **Receiver of Wreck**, investigating the ownership of items found in the sea, is also based in the Coastguard building.

MCA

Maritime & Coastguard Agency, Spring Place,
105 Commercial Road, Southampton, SO15 1EG.
Main number   023-8032 9100
Press   023-8032 9401
Website   www.mcagency.org.uk
HM Coastguard   023-8032 9100
Marine Emergency Operations Room 023-8032 9445
Marine Pollution Control Unit   023-8032 9415
Port State Control Section   023-8032 9218
Receiver of Wreck   023-8032 9474
Registry of Shipping & Seamen   029-2074 7333
Dept of Environment, Transport and
   Regions   020-7890 3000
   Press: Transport   020-7890 3060
   Duty Officer   020-7276 5999
   Website   www.detr.gov.uk

HM COASTGUARD CENTRES

North & East Scotland Region
MRCC, Aberdeen   01224-592334
MRSCs: Shetland   01595-692976
   Pentland   01856-873268
   Forth   01333-450666
Northern North Sea, from Scottish border to Shetlands
and then west to Cape Wrath, including oil and gas
installations.

Eastern Region
MRCC, Yarmouth   01493-851338
MRSCs: Tyne Tees   0191-257 2691
   Humber   01262-672317
Southern North Sea, from Scottish border to Aldeburgh,
including oil and gas installations.

Southern Region (east)
MRCC, Dover   01304-210008
MRSCs: Thames (Walton)   01255-675518
   Lee-on-Solent   023-9255 2100
South East coast from Aldeburgh to Bournemouth, includ-
ing eastern English Channel. The CNIS system is run from
Dover.

Southern Region (west)
MRCC, Falmouth   01326-317575
MRSCs: Portland   01305-760439
   Brixham   01803-882704
Southern Region Controller   01425-271700
From Bournemouth to Bude Bay, South West Atlantic
approaches. The controller for the whole region
(Aldeburgh to Bude Bay) is based in Christchurch.

Western Region
MRCC, Swansea   01792-366534
MRSCs: Milford Haven   01646-690909

Holyhead   01407-762051
Liverpool   0151-931 3341
Bristol Channel from Bude Bay, Irish Sea to North Channel
(excluding Northern Ireland coastal waters) and West
Atlantic approaches.

West of Scotland & Northern Ireland Region
MRCC, Clyde   01475-729988
MRSCs: Belfast   01247-463933
   Oban   01631-563720
   Stornoway   01851-702013
Northern Ireland, west of Scotland coast, North West
Atlantic approaches.

LIFEBOATS

The Royal National Lifeboat Institution
(RNLI) is a voluntary body supported entirely
by public donations. It has saved over 131,000
lives since it was set up in 1824. There were
6,727 launches in 1998, saving 1,386 lives
and assisting 5,181 other people. The RNLI
runs 222 lifeboat stations around the British
Isles. It has a total of 300 operational boats,
128 of them all-weather vessels. The largest
class is the 17-metre long Severn. In addition
there are 130 relief boats. Each lifeboat station
is run by a voluntary committee, whose honorary secretary authorises the launch of the
boat, usually on the request of the local
Coastguard. Larger lifeboats may have a paid
officer; otherwise nearly all the crews are volunteers. During rescue operations the lifeboat
is controlled by the coxswain, in liaison with
the local Coastguard MRCC. The RNLI likes
all press enquiries to go to the press office at
its headquarters in Poole, Dorset. Out of
hours, contact the central operations room.

RNLI headquarters, Poole   01202-663000
Central operations room   01202-668222
Website   www.rnli.org.uk

RNLI BOATHOUSES

Listed below are all the UK and Irish Republic
stations with a large lifeboat (which is defined
as being over 10 metres, and capable of offshore work). The numbers are mainly for the
boathouses themselves, rather than officers:

Aberdeen 01224-591658
Aith, Shetland 01595-810276
Aldeburgh, Suffolk 01728-452552
Alderney, Channel Islands
01481-823456
Amble, Northumberland
01665-712460
Angle, Dyfed 01646-641204
Anstruther, Fife 01333-310526
Appledore, Devon 01237-473969
Arbroath, Tayside 01241-873235
Arklow, Wicklow
00-353402 32850
Arranmore, Donegal
00-35375 21580
Ballycotton, Cork
00-35321 646903
Ballyglass, Mayo 00-35397 82072
Baltimore, Cork 00-35328 20174
Barmouth, Gwynedd
01341-280274
Barra Island, Western Isles
01871-810307
Barrow, Cumberland
01229-820941
Barry Dock, South Glamorgan
01446-735678
Beaumaris, Gwynedd
01248-810260
Bembridge, IoW 01983-872201
Berwick-upon-Tweed
01289-306217
Blyth, Northumberland
01670-352201
Bridlington, Humberside
01262-672450
Broughty Ferry, Tayside
01382-779956
Buckie, Grampian 01542-831289
Calshot, Hants 023-80893509
Campbeltown, Strathclyde
01586-552414
Clogher Head, Louth
00-35341 22600
Courtmacsherry, Cork
00-35323 46111
Cromer, Norfolk 01263-512237
Donaghadee, Down
028-9188 8556
Douglas, IoM 01624-621367
Dover, Kent 01304-204280
Dun Laoghaire, Dublin
00-3531 280 2667
Dunbar, Lothian 01368-863966
Dungeness, Kent 01797-321300
Dunmore East, Waterford
00-35351 383808
Eastbourne, East Sussex
01323-722648
Exmouth, Devon 01395-263579

Eyemouth, Borders 01890-750293
Falmouth, Cornwall 01326-374177
Fishguard, Dyfed 01348-873231
Flamborough, Humberside
01262-850947
Fleetwood, Lancs 01253-874000
Fowey, Cornwall 01726-832156
Fraserburgh, Grampian
01346-515162
Galway Bay, Galway
00-35399 61166
Girvan, Strathclyde 01465-714454
Gt Yarmouth, Norfolk
01493-662508
Hartlepool, Cleveland
01429-266103
Harwich, Essex 01255-502258
Hastings, East Sussex
01424-425502
Holyhead, Gwynedd
01407-762583
Howth, Dublin 00-3531 8393311
Hoylake, Merseyside
0151-632 2103
Humber 01964-650228
Ilfracombe, Devon 01271-863771
Invergordon, Highland
01349-853915
Islay, Strathclyde 01496-840242
Kilmore Quay, Wexford
00-35353 29690
Kirkwall, Orkney 01856-875201
Lerwick, Shetland 01595-693827
Lizard, Cornwall 01326-290451
Llandudno, Gwynedd
01492-875777
Lochinver, Highland
01571-844513
Longhope, Orkney 01856-701460
Lowestoft, Suffolk 01502-573757
Lytham St Annes, Lancs
01253-736316
Mallaig, Highland 01687-462579
Margate, Kent 01843-221613
Moelfre, Clwyd 01248-410367
Montrose, Tayside 01674-674341
Mumbles, West Glamorgan
01792-390424
Newcastle, Down 01396-725138
Newhaven, East Sussex
01273-514143
North Sunderland, Northmblnd
01665-720370
Oban, Strathclyde 01631-563733
Padstow, Cornwall 01841-520667
Penlee, Cornwall 01736-369246
Peterhead, Grampian
01779-473331
Plymouth, Devon 01752-662623
Poole, Dorset 01202-665607

Port Erin, IoM 01624-832154
Port St Mary, IoM 01624-835015
Porthdinllaen, Gwynedd
01758-720241
Portpatrick, Dumfries
01776-810251
Portree, Highland 01478-613610
Portrush, Antrim 028-7082 3216
Pwllheli, Gwynedd 01758-612200
Ramsey, IoM 01624-812169
Ramsgate, Kent 01843-227324
Rhyl, Clwyd 01745-344040
Rosslare, Wexford
00-35353 33249
St Davids, Dyfed 01437-720215
St Helier, Jersey 01534-24173
St Ives, Cornwall 01736-796422
St Marys, Scilly Isles
01720-422347
Salcombe, Devon 01548-842158
Scarborough, North Yorks
01723-360520
Selsey, West Sussex
01243-602833
Sennen Cove, Cornwall
01736-871222
Sheerness, Kent 01795-664624
Sheringham, Norfolk
01263-823212
Shoreham, West Sussex
01273-462670
Skegness, Lincs 01754-763011
Stornoway, Western Isles
01851-703987
Stromness, Orkney 01856-850204
Sunderland, Tyne & Wear
0191-567 3536
Swanage, Dorset 01929-423237
Teesmouth, Cleveland
01642-486636
Tenby, Dyfed 01834-842197
Thurso, Highland 01847-893433
Tobermory, Strathclyde
01688-302250
Torbay, Devon 01803-853136
Troon, Strathclyde 01292-314414
Tynemouth, Tyne & Wear
0191-257 0913
Valentia, Kerry 00-35366 76126
Walton, Essex 01255-675650
Wells, Norfolk 01328-710230
Weymouth, Dorset 01305-785817
Whitby, North Yorkshire
01947-602216
Wick, Highland 01955-603723
Wicklow 00-353404 67163
Workington, Cumberland
01900-604124
Yarmouth, IoW 01983-872201

Businesses

Britain has about 3.7 million businesses, including 2.5 million sole traders. Roughly 97% of businesses employ less than 20 people, while at the other extreme 250 industrial companies have an annual turnover of more than £500 million. In 1998 the UK's most valuable companies, in terms of the market value of their share prices, were: Glaxo Wellcome £51.4 billion, BP £47.1 billion, Shell £43.7 billion and HSBC £41.0 billion. BP merged with Amoco in early 1999 to become BP Amoco, and then took over the American firm Arco to become Britain's biggest company and the world's second largest oil producer, after Exxon-Mobil (Esso in Britain). The UK has 12 million shareholders, up a third following the demutualisation of several building societies in 1997.

COMPANIES HOUSE

The main source of raw material when carrying out company research is Companies House. This is the official title given to the Department of Trade's company registry (and, confusingly, to its offices). Its three statutory functions are: incorporating and dissolving companies; examining and holding company documents required under legislation; and making this information available to the public. All the 1.25 million registered companies must submit annual returns and other data to the registrars in the Companies House head offices in Cardiff (for England and Wales), Edinburgh (for Scotland) and Belfast (for N Ireland). Also on record are 250,000 recently dissolved companies.

The public can carry out personal research into this information in these registries, and in the London office in Bloomsbury St (junction Bedford Avenue). This new London Companies House replaced 55 City Road early in 1999. Search facilities are also available in the satellite offices in Birmingham, Manchester, Leeds and Glasgow. All offices are open 9.00-4.00 (London 5.00) Monday-Friday.

Certain basic information about companies can be viewed free of charge on computer screens in the Search Rooms at these offices, or via the Companies House website. More detailed data is available in many ways - fax, phone, post, Internet, on-line, CD-ROM - but all at a charge. The key is the company registration number which identifies which of the businesses is being examined.

The starting point in company research is often the "standard search", a microfiche of the documents received by Companies House from the company secretary over the last three years. The standard search costs £5.00 when bought in person, or £8 by post. Much company data is also available on-line via the Companies House Direct service, via which orders can be made. The one-off registration fee for Direct is £50, the monthly sub £7.50. Basic data is also on the Companies House Directory CD-ROM, updated monthly. Single copies are £30, an annual sub for 12 is £300. A new European Business Register was created in 1998, giving access to 14 national registers. Details from Cardiff.

Companies House: main offices

Cardiff Registry	029-2038 8588
Crown Way, Cardiff, CF14 3UZ	
All enquiries (8.30am-6pm	029-2038 0801
Search room	029-2038 0124
Edinburgh Registry	0131-535 5800
37 Castle Terrace, EH1 2EB	
Belfast Registry	028-9023 4488
64 Chichester Street, BT1 4JX	
London Search Rooms	029-2038 0801
21 Bloomsbury Street, WC1B 3XD.	
Website	www.companieshouse.gov.uk
Companies House Direct help desk	0345-573991

Satellite offices

Birmingham	0121-233 9047
Glasgow	0141-221 5513
Leeds	0113-233 8338
Manchester	0161-236 7500

Other company registries

Alderney	01481-822817
Guernsey/Sark	01481-725277
Isle of Man	01624-685233
Jersey	01534-603000

OTHER COMPANY INFO

Quoted companies usually produce glossy annual reports. These can be obtained from the company itself, or consulted in London's City Business Library, the best public library of its type in Britain. It has many reference sources, including all directories, plus PC workstations displaying the Extel Financial UK Quoted Companies Service (up-to-date financial data), and FT-McCarthy (newspaper stories about many companies). Most other public libraries only stock some annual directories with details of the bigger companies. Company data is also available on a variety of on-line computer and CD-ROM services, for a charge. Dunn & Bradstreet and Financial Times Electronic Publishing are the leading suppliers in these and other formats. The Office for National Statistics runs a Business Statistics Data Analysis Service drawing on its huge supplies of material. UK electronic specialists are:

Bloomberg	020-7330 7500
Business Statistics (ONS)	0800-731 5761
Dash	01494-422299
Dun & Bradstreet	01494-422299
Economist Intelligence Unit	020-7830 1007
Euromonitor	020-7251 1105
FT Electronic Publishing	0800-007777
ICC Information	020-8783 1122
Knight-Ridder Information	020-7930 7646
Lexis-Nexis	020-7464 1300
Reed Business Info (Kompass)	01342-335649
Reuters Business Briefing	020-7250 1122
RM Online	020-7729 1234

Other company views

All the national media covers the ups and downs of corporate life, but there is only one UK publication focusing on global capitalism from an openly critical perspective. This is *Corporate Watch*, the non-profit occasional magazine which "aims to provide information to grass roots campaigners about the environmental, social and ethical behaviour of big business". It hopes to "reform corporations and ultimately to end corporate dominance".

Corporate Watch	01865-791391
Box E, 111 Magdalen Road, Oxford OX4 1RQ.	
Website	www.oneworld.org/cw

BUSINESS LIBRARIES

British Library Business Information Service
96 Euston Road, London NW1 2DB.
BL-Lloyds TSB City Business Line   020-7412 7454
Part of the British Library's St Pancras HQ. Free, but a Library pass is needed. Was off Chancery Lane till 1999.
Business Archives Council
4 Maguire Street, London SE12NQ.   020-7407 6110
Charity giving advice and information on managing business archives and modern records.
City Business Library (Corporation of London)
1 Brewers Hall Garden, London EC2V 5BX
    Enquiries   020-7638 8215
    Recorded details   020-7480 7638
    Fee-paying research service   020-7600 1461
The most comprehensive of the business libraries.
Open weekdays 9.30-5.00.
Export Market Information Centre (DTI)
66-74 Victoria Street, London SW1E 6SW
DTI   020-7215 5444

DIRECTORIES

Directory of Directors
Annual. Reed Information
Details of 50,000 directors and the 14,000 companies they control.
Financial Times 500
Annual. FT Republishing.
Wide-ranging data on the top 500 companies.
Hemscott Company Guide
Quarterly. Hemmington Scott.
Latest details on stockmarket companies.
Kelly's Directory
Annual. Kompass (Reed Information)
Trade directory, detailing over 110,000 companies.
Key British Enterprises
Annual. Dun & Bradstreet
Six volumes covering the top 50,000 companies, with trade name sections. The best of its kind.
Macmillan's Unquoted Companies
Annual. Waterlow.
20,000 unquoted companies, turnovers above £15m.
Major UK Companies
Twice pa. Extel
Specialise in financial information. One of the best.
Stock Exchange Yearbook
Annual. Macmillan
A profile of 4,100 companies and securities listed on the London and Dublin Stock Exchanges.
UK Kompass Register
Annual. Kompass (Reed Information)
CBI-backed, four volumes, giving a wide range of data.
Who Owns Whom
Annual. Dun and Bradstreet
Detailing the corporate structures of over 1 million companies.

KEY CONTACTS

Whitehall is replacing many of the regulatory bodies listed below with the new Financial Services Authority, due to take over in 1999.

ACAS	020-7210 3613
Bank of England	020-7601 4444
Press	020-7601 4411(-5)
Bankruptcy Association	01524-64305
British Bankers Association	020-7216 8800
British Chambers of Commerce	020-7565 2000
British Institute of Management	01536-204222
British Standards Institution	01908-220022
Building Societies Association	020-7437 0655
CBI	020-7379 7400
Chamber of Shipping	020-7417 8400
Corporation of London	020-7606 3030
Dept of Trade & Industry	020-7215 5000
Press	020-7215 5970
Company Law Directorate	020-7215 0403
Ethical Investors Group	01242-604550
Export Credits Guarantee Dept	020-7512 7000
Federation of Small Businesses	020-7233 7900
ICOF (Industrial Common Ownership Fund)	0121-523 6886
ICOM (Industrial Common Ownership Movement)	0113-246 1737
Industrial Society	020-7262 2401
Inland Revenue - main number	020-7438 6622
Press office	020-7438 7356
Insolvency Service	020-7637 1110
Inst of Chartered Accountants	020-7920 8100
Institute of Taxation	020-7235 9381
Lloyds of London	020-7327 1000
London Chamber of Commerce	020-7248 4444
London Metal Exchange	020-7264 5555
Low Pay Unit	020-7713 7616
Monopolies and Mergers Comm.	020-7324 1467
National Assoc of Pension Funds	020-7730 0585
Office of Fair Trading	020-7211 8000
Patent Office	01633-814000
Personal Investment Authority	020-7676 1000
Rural Development	020-7340 2900
Securities & Investments Board	020-7676 1000
Serious Fraud Office	020-7239 7272
Eves	020-7239 7050
Stock Exchange	020-7588 2355
Takeovers & Mergers Panel	020-7382 9026
HM Treasury - press	020-7270 5238
TUC (Trades Union Congress)	020-7636 4030

TOP COMPANIES

Most of these companies have websites.

Abbey National (banking)	0870-607 6000
Aegis Group (communications)	020-7838 9393
Alfred McAlpine (construction)	01565-756200
Alliance & Leicester (BS)	020-7629 6661
Alliance Trust (Investments)	01382-201700
Allied Domecq (alcohol)	020-7323 9000
Allied Irish Bank	020-7629 8881
AMEC (construction)	01606-883885
Amerada Hess (fuel)	020-7823 2626
Amersham International	01494-544000
Amstrad (electronics)	01277-228888
Anglia Television	01603-615151
Anglian Water	01480-323000
Argos (retailing)	01908-690333
Arjo Wiggins Appleton (paper)	01256-723000
Asda (supermarkets)	0113-243 5435
Associated British Foods	020-7589 6363
Associated British Ports	020-7430 1177
B&Q (DIY)	023-8025 6256
BAA (airports)	020-7834 9449
Balfour Beatty (construction)	020-7216 6800
Bank of China	020-7282 8888
Bank of England	020-7601 4444
Bank of India	020-7628 3165
Bank of Ireland	020-7236 2000
Bank of Japan	020-7606 2454
Bank of Scotland	0131-442 7777
Barclays Bank	020-7699 5000
Barratt Development (building)	0191-286 6811
Bass (alcohol)	020-7409 1919
BAT Industries (tobacco)	020-7845 1000
Benetton UK (clothing)	020-7495 5482
Bernard Matthews (food)	01603-872611
BFI (waste disposal)	01753-662700
BG (ex-British Gas)	0118-935 3222
BICC (electrical)	020-7629 6622
Birmingham Midshires BS	01902-302000
Blue Circle (building)	020-7828 3456
BOC (chemicals)	01276-477222
Body Shop (retailing)	01903-731500
Booker (agriculture/health)	020-7411 5500
Boots (retailing)	0115-950611
BP Mobil (oil)	01908-853000
BPB	01753-898800
Bradford & Bingley BS	01274-555555
Brent Walker (leisure)	020-7465 011
Britannia BS	01538-399391
Britannic Assurance	01564-288888
British Aerospace	01252-373232
British Airways	020-8759 5511
British Bakeries	01753-857121
British Energy	020-7957 9703
British Land (property)	020-7486 4466
British Nuclear Fuels	020-7222 9711
British Petroleum (oil/gas)	020-7496 4000
British Railways Board	020-7928 5151
British Shoe Corporation	0116-280 6001
British Steel	020-7314 5501
British Telecommunications	020-7356 5000
BSkyB (media)	020-7705 3000
BTR (conglomerate)	020-7834 3848
Budgens (supermarkets)	020-8422 9511
Burmah Castrol (oil/gas)	01793-511521
Burton (retailing)	020-7636 8040
Cable & Wireless (telecomms)	020-7363 2000
Cadbury Schweppes (food)	020-7409 1313

Calor (oil/gas)	0118-933 2363
Camellia (agriculture)	020-7629 5728
Camelot (lottery)	01923-425000
Carlton Communications (TV)	020-7663 6363
Central Broadcasting (TV)	0121-643 9898
Centrica (gas)	01753-758000
Channel 4 (TV)	020-7396 4444
Channel 5 (TV)	020-7497 5225
Chase Manhatten Bank	020-7777 2000
Cheltenham & Gloucester BS	01452-372372
Chevron (fuel)	020-7487 8100
Christian Salvesen (food)	01604-662600
Christie's (auctioneers)	020-7839 9060
Ciba-Speciality Chemicals)	01625-421933
Clydesdale Bank	020-7699 6400
Coats Viyella (textiles)	0161-252 2600
Comet (retailing)	01482-320681
Commercial Union (insurance)	020-7283 7500
Conoco (fuel)	01926-404000
Cookson (industry)	020-7766 4500
The Co-operative (retailing)	01244-520900
Co-operative Bank	0345-212212
Co-operative Retail Services	01706-713000
Co-operative Wholesale Society	0161-834 1212
Cordiant Communications (adverts)	020-7262 5077
Costain (construction)	020-7705 8444
Courtaulds (chemicals)	020-7612 1000
Coutts & Co (banking)	020-7623 3434
Dalgety (food)	020-7486 0200
De La Rue (printing)	01256-329122
Debenhams (retailing)	020-7408 4444
Deutsche Morgan Grenfell (banking)	020-7545 8000
Diageo (ex-Grand Met, food)	020-7518 5200
Dixons (retailing)	020-7499 3494
Do-It-All (DIY)	01384-456456
Dow Chemical (oil)	020-8848 8688
Dowty (engineering)	01235-559999
Dunhill Holdings (consumer)	020-7838 8000
East Midlands Electricity	0115-926 9711
Eastern Group (electricity)	01473-221331
Elementis	020-7711 1400
Engelhard (metals)	020-7456 7300
English China Clays (building)	0118-930 4010
Enterprise Oil	020-7925 4000
Esso (oil/gas)	020-7834 6677
European Bank	020-7338 6000
Eurotunnel (transport)	020-7872 5496
Ferranti (air systems)	0161-946 3600
First National Bank of Chicago	020-7388 3456
Firstgroup (bus operators)	01934-750111
Ford (vehicles)	01277-253000
Forte (leisure)	020-7301 2000
Gallaher (tobacco)	01932-859777
GEC (electronics)	020-7493 8484
General Accident (insurance)	020-7626 8711
George Wimpey (building)	020-8748 2000
Girobank	020-7843 3000
GKN (engineering)	01527-517715
Glaxo Wellcome (household)	020-7493 4060
GMTV (TV)	020-7827 7000
Granada (media/leisure)	020-7451 3000
Grand Metropolitan (Diadgeo, food)	020-7518 5200
Great Portland Estates	020-7580 3040
Greenalls (leisure)	01925-651234
Greycoat (property)	020-7379 1000
Gt Universal Stores (retailing)	0161-273 8282
Guardian Insurance	020-7283 7101
Guinness (aka Diadgeo, alcohol)	020-7486 0288
Halfords (retailing)	01527-517601
Halifax BS	01422-333333
Hambros (banking)	020-7480 5000
Hammerson (property)	020-7887 1000
Hanson (conglomerate)	020-7245 1245
Hawtin (fabrics)	029-2048 8961
Hill Samuel Bank	020-7661 4861
Hillsdown (food)	020-7794 0677
Homebase (DIY)	01933-679679
House of Fraser (retailing)	020-7963 2000
HSBC Holdings (banking)	020-7260 8000
Hyder (water)	029-2050 0600
IBM (computers)	023-9256 1000
ICI (chemicals)	020-7834 4444
Imperial Tobacco	0117-963 6636
Inchcape (transport)	020-7546 0022
John Laing (construction)	020-8959 3636
John Lewis (retailing)	020-7828 1000
John Menzies (retailing)	0131-225 8555
John Mowlem (construction)	020-8568 9111
John Swire & Sons (transport)	020-7834 7717
Kingfisher (retailing)	020-7724 7749
Kleinwort Benson (banking)	020-7623 8000
Kvaerner (mixture)	020-7766 2000
Kwik Save (supermarkets)	01745-887111
Ladbroke (leisure)	020-8459 8031
Land Securities (property)	020-7413 9000
Lasmo (oil & gas)	020-7892 9000
Lawrie (agriculture)	01732-884488
Legal & General (insurance)	020-7528 6200
Liberty Int (property/finance)	020-7222 5496
Littlewoods (retailing)	0151-235 2222
Lloyds TSB Group	020-7626 1500
London Electricity	020-7242 9050
London Regional Transport	020-7222 5600
London Weekend Television	020-7620 1620
Lonrho (conglomerate)	020-7201 6000
Lucasvarity (engineering)	0121-627 3939
Magnox Electric (electricity)	01453-810451
Marks & Spencer (retailing)	020-7935 4422
Marley (building materials)	01732-455255
McCarthy & Stone (building)	01202-292480
McDonalds (fast food)	020-8700 7000
MEPC (property)	020-7911 5300
MFI (furnishings)	020-8200 8000
Midland Bank - aka HSBC	020-7260 8000
Milk Marque	01905-858500
Mirror Group (media)	020-7510 3000
Morgan Crucible (industrial)	01753-837000
Morgan Grenfell (banking)	020-7588 4545
Mothercare (parenting)	01923-241000
National Bank of Canada	020-7726 6581
National Grid (electricity)	024-7653 7777
National Power (electricity)	020-7454 9494

National Westminster Bank	020-7726 1000
Nationwide (BS)	01793-513513
Nestle (food)	020-8686 3333
News International (media)	020-7782 6000
Next (retailing)	0116-286 6411
NFC (transport)	01234-272222
NFU Mutual Insurance Society	01789-204211
Nortel (communications)	01628-812000
North West Water	01925-234000
Northern Foods	01482-325432
Northern Rock (BS)	0191-286 7191
Northern Telecom	020-7291 3000
Northern Trust (banking)	020-7628 2233
Northumbrian Water	0191-284 3151
Nuclear Electric	01452 652222
P&O (transport)	020-7930 4343
Paragon (loans)	0121-711 3333
Pearson (media)	020-7411 2000
Pentos (retailing)	020-7281 6236
Peugeot (vehicles)	024-7688 4000
Pilkington (glass)	01744-28882
Post Office (communications)	020-7490 2888
Powell Duffryn (transport)	01344-666800
Powergen (electricity)	024-7642 4000
Press Association (media)	020-7963 7000
Prudential (insurance)	020-7334 9000
Racal Electronics	01344-481222
Railtrack (transport)	020-7344 7100
Rank Organisation (leisure)	020-7706 1111
Rank Xerox (electronics)	01895-251133
Rechem (waste treatment)	01628-810011
Reckitt & Colman (household)	020-8994 6464
Redland (building materials)	01306-872000
Reed Elsevier (media)	020-7222 8420
Rentokil (chemicals)	01342-833022
Reuters (media)	020-7250 1122
Rexam (paper)	020-7584 7070
Rhone Poulenc Rorer	01477-537112
RMC (building materials)	01932-568833
Rolls-Royce (engineering)	020-7222 9020
Rosehaugh (property)	01463-811205
Rothmans (tobacco)	020-7491 4366
NM Rothschild (banking)	020-7280 5000
Rover (vehicles)	0121-475 2101
Royal Bank of Scotland	0131-556 8555
Royal Sun Alliance (insurance)	0151-802 8000
RTZ Corporation (mining)	020-7930 2399
Rugby Group (building)	01788-542666
Saatchi & Saatchi (advertising)	020-7636 5060
Safeway (supermarkets)	020-8848 8744
J Sainsbury (supermarkets)	020-7695 6000
Salomon Brothers (financial)	020-7721 2000
SBC Warburg (banking)	020-7606 1066
Schroders (banking)	020-7658 6000
Scottish & Newcastle (beer)	0131-528 2000
Scottish Hydro-Electric	01738-455040
Scottish Investment Trust	0131-225 7781
Scottish Mortgage	0131-222 4000
Scottish Nuclear	01355-262000
Scottish Power (electricity)	0141-568 2000
Sears (retailing)	020-7200 5999
Securicor (miscellaneous)	020-8770 7000
Sentrica	0118-935 8222
Severn Trent (water)	0121-722 4000
Shell UK (oil/gas)	020-7257 3000
Siebe (engineering)	01753-855411
Signet Group	0121-554 3871
Sketchley (miscellaneous)	01455-238133
Slough Estates (property)	01753-537171
Smithkline Beecham (health)	020-8975 2000
Smiths Industries (engineers)	020-8458 3232
Somerfield (supermarkets)	0117-935 9359
South West Water	01392-446688
Southern Electric	01628-822166
Southern Water	01273-606766
St Ivel (food)	01793-848444
Standard Chartered (banking)	020-7280 7500
Storehouse (retailing)	020-7262 3456
Sunblest Bakeries (food)	01784-451366
Superdrug (household/health)	020-8684 7000
Swiss Bank Corporation	020-7329 0329
Syseca	0161-946 1001
T&N (engineering)	0161-955 5200
Tarmac (construction)	01902-307407
Tate & Lyle (food)	020-7626 6525
Taylor Woodrow (building)	020-7629 1201
Telewest (media)	01483-750900
Tesco (supermarkets)	01992-632222
Texaco (oil/gas)	020-7719 3000
Thames Water	020-7636 8686
Thomson Corporation (media)	020-7437 9787
Thorn EMI (leisure)	020-7355 4848
3i Group (investments)	020-7928 3131
TI Group (engineering)	01235-555570
Tomkins (engineering)	020-8871 4544
Total Oil	020-7629 1111
TSB (banking)	0121-600 6000
Unigate (food)	01892-534424
Unilever (food/household)	020-7822 5252
United Biscuits (food)	01895-432100
United Utilities (water)	01925-285000
Vauxhall (vehicles)	01582-721122
Vickers (engineering)	020-7828 7777
Vodafone (telecomms)	01635-3325
Waitrose (supermarkets)	01344-424680
Waste Management	020-8563 7000
Welsh Water	01874-62318
Wessex Water	0117-929 061
WH Smith (retailing)	020-7404 4242
Whitbread (alcohol)	020-7606 4455
Witan Investment	020-7638 575
Wolseley (building materials)	01905-79444
Woolwich (building society)	020-8298 500
Woolworths (retailing)	020-7262 122
WPP Group (advertising)	020-7408 220
Yorkshire Electricity	0113-289 212
Yorkshire Water	0113-234 323
Zeneca (health)	020-7304 500

Charities

ngland and Wales have 188,400 registered harities. Of these, 161,200 are "main" charies and the other 27,200 are their subdiaries. Their total annual income in 1998 was £19,747 million. Seventy per cent have an annual income below £10,000, with 91% below £100,000, while 5 per cent receive over 5 per cent of the total income, with the argest 271 attracting two-fifths of it (£8,045 million). The RNLI, Oxfam, National Trust alvation Army and cancer funds are usually he largest receivers. The biggest corporate onors in 1997/8 were: Glaxo Wellcome 24.0 million, Diageo £21.7 million, Lloyds SB £21.5 million and BP £19.5 million.

Charities come under the umbrella of the harity Commission, which gives administrave advice to trustees and ensures they comly with legal rules. The Commissioners' owers were tightened up in the mid-1990s o try and stop malpractice and make charities nore accountable. The Commission, established in 1853, is based in central London; it noved from the Haymarket to just off Fleet treet in 1999. There are regional offices in iverpool and Taunton. These three centres ogether form the **Central Register of harities**. They hold the public records of all harities, which can be inspected free of harge. Much archive material is held by the Greater London Record Office, Clerkenwell.

In Scotland, charities are supervised by the cottish Charities Office on behalf of the Lord Advocate. The Scottish Council for Voluntary Organisations is the charity acting as an mbrella body for voluntary organisations in cotland. In Northern Ireland charities do not eed to register, and are monitored by the OHSS Charities Branch.

The **Charities Aid Foundation** (CAF), an ndependent body, is one of the main organisations that help the flow of funds to charities rom companies, individuals and trusts. It ublishes the annual *Directory of Grant-Making Trusts*, the best-known handbook on now to raise money for a charity. CAF's reco

mmended website is called Charitynet. The **National Council for Voluntary Organisations** (NCVO) is the leading co-ordinating body for charities and other public-spirited bodies. Its wide-ranging annual is the *Voluntary Agencies Directory*. Another reference annual is the *Charities Digest*, launched in 1882, published by Waterlow.

When major global disasters occur, Britain's 15 leading overseas aid charities launch appeals together as the Disasters Emergency Committee. Formed in 1966, the DEC is kept on low-key permanent standby.

The **National Lottery** Charities Board dis tributes the portion of the proceeds of the National Lottery allocated to charities. The Lottery is the largest in the world, with about 70 per cent of adults regularly buying tickets from the 35,500 retail outlets. Camelot Group plc, a private sector consortium, has the franchise to run the Lottery until 2001. It is regulated by the Office of the National Lottery.

CO-ORDINATORS

Charity Commission	0870-333 0123
13-15 Bouverie Street, London EC4Y 8DP	
Press office	020-7674 2333
Annual return helpline	0151-703 1515
Liverpool	0151-703 1500
Taunton	01823-345000
Website	www.charity-commission.gov.uk
Charities Aid Foundation	01732-520000
Website	www.charitynet.org
Card Aid	020-7794 9835
Community Matters	020-7226 0189
Directory of Social Change	020-7209 5151
Disasters Emergency Committee	020-7580 6550
Inst of Charity Fundraising Managers	020-7627 3436
London Metropolitan Archives	020-7606 3030
National Council for Voluntary Orgs	020-7713 6161
Website	www.ncvo-vol.org.uk
National Lotteries Charity Board	020-7747 5300
N Ireland Charities Branch DHSS	028-9052 2780
Scottish Charities Office	0131-226 2626
Scottish Council for Voluntary Orgs	0131-556 3882
Website	www.sol.co.uk/s/scvo
Waterlow Information	020-7490 0049

MAIN CHARITIES

Actionaid	020-7281 4101
Action research	01403-210406
Afasic	020-7236 6487
Age Concern England	020-8679 8000
Alzheimer's Disease Society	020-7306 0606
Arthritis Research Campaign	01246-558033
Arts Council	020-7333 0100
Baring Foundation	020-7767 1348
Barnardo's	020-8550 8822
BBC Children in Need Appeal	020-8735 5057
Blue Cross	01993-822651
Bridge House Estate Fund	020-7332 3710
British Council	020-7930 8466
British Diabetic Association	020-7323 1531
British Film Institute	020-7255 1444
British Heart Foundation	020-7935 0185
British Library	020-7412 7000
British Museum	020-7636 1555
British Red Cross Society	020-7235 5454
CAFOD	020-7733 7900
Cancer Relief Macmillan Fund	020-7351 7811
Cancer Research Campaign	020-7224 1333
Cats Protection League	01403-221900
Charity Projects	020-7436 1122
Christ's Hospital	01403-211293
Christian Aid	020-7620 4444
Church Commissioners	020-7898 1000
City & Guilds of London	020-7294 2468
City Parochial Foundation	020-7606 6145
Consumers Association	020-7830 6000
Construction Industry.Training Board	01485-577577
Distressed Gentlefolk's Aid Assoc	020-7396 6700
Dogs' Home Battersea	020-7622 3626
Donkey Sanctuary	01395-578222
English Churches Housing	020-8203 9233
Foundation for Sport and Arts	0151-259 5505
Garfield Weston Foundation	020-7589 6363
Gatsby Charitable Foundation	020-7410 0330
Great Ormond St Children's Hospital	020-7405 9200
Guide Dogs for the Blind	0118-983 5555
Help the Aged	020-7253 0253
Henry Smith's (Kensington Estate)	020-7242 1212
Imperial Cancer Research Fund	020-7242 0200
Independent Living Alternative	020-8906 9265
Institute of Cancer Research	020-7352 8133
Institute of Child Health	020-7242 9789
Institute of Psychiatry	020-7703 5411
International Planned Parenthood	020-7487 7900
Jewish Care (UJIA)	020-8922 2000
Jewish Philanthropic Assoc.	020-8446 1477
JNF Charitable Trust	020-8421 7600
John Ellerman Foundation	020-7930 8566
Joint Israel Appeal	020-8446 1477
Joseph Rowntree Foundation	01904-629241
JW Laing Trust	01225-310893
Leonard Cheshire Foundation	020-7802 8200
Leverhulme Trust	020-7822 6938
Ludwig Institute of Cancer Research	020-7878 4000
Marie Curie Foundation	020-7235 3325

Medecins sans Frontieres	020-7713 560(
MENCAP	020-7454 045
Methodist Homes for the Aged	01332-29620(
Monument Trust	020-7410 033(
MS Society	020-7610 717
National Association for the Care and Resettlement of Offenders (NACRO)	020-7582 650(
National Canine Defence League	020-7837 000(
National Trust	020-7222 925
Natural History Museum	020-7938 912:
NCH Action for Children	020-7226 203:
Norwood Ravenswood	020-8954 455!
NSPCC	020-7825 250(
Nuffield Foundation	020-7631 056(
Order of St John	020-7253 664
Oxfam	01865-31131
Parkinson's Disease Society	020-7233 537:
Peabody Trust	020-7928 781
Prince's Trust	0800-84284:
Quantum Fund	020-7925 255!
RAF Benevolent Fund	020-7580 834:
Rank Foundation	020-7834 773
RNLI	01202-66300(
Robertson Trust	0141-352 662(
Royal British Legion	020-7973 720(
Royal College of Surgeons	020-7405 347
Royal Horticultural Society	020-7834 433:
Royal National Institute for the Blind	020-7388 126(
Royal National Institute Deaf People	020-7296 800(
Royal Opera House	020-7240 120(
RSPB	01767-68055
RSPCA	01403-26418
Salvation Army Trust	020-7367 450(
Save the Children Fund	020-7703 540(
Scope	020-7619 710(
Sense	020-7272 777
Soros Global Research	020-7451 200(
Stonham Housing Association	020-7401 202(
Stroke Association	020-7490 799!
Tear Fund	020-8977 914
UNICEF-UK	020-7405 559:
Variety Club Children's Foundation	020-7428 810(
Wellcome Trust	020-7611 888!
Wolfson Foundation	020-7930 105
WWF UK	01483-42644
YMCA	020-8520 559!

Communications

The UK has 28 million phone lines and over 15 million mobile phones in use. Both methods of communicating are mushrooming, and both are dominated by BT. In the financial year 1998/9 BT's profits reached the dizzying height of £4.3 billion - £136 per second, on a turnover of £18.2 billion, up 13 per cent. The boom in the late '90s was caused by the explosions in the usage of Internet (18 per cent of local residential calls in March 1999, compared with 8 per cent just 12 months before) and the mobile phone. Tweny eight per cent of Britons had 17 million mobiles by June 1999. A third of these had been sold since autumn 1998, when the launch of the prepay system sparked a mammoth boom in the market. More than half the UK population is expected to have a mobile by 2001.

BT is Britain's biggest telecoms company, employing 125,000 people. It runs 20.1 million residential lines and 7.8 million business lines. All 17 million listed phone numbers are available either in 170 local phone books, or on the website directory launched in May 1999 (free, except for the cost of the phone call). But the percentage of numbers which are ex-directory has risen to nearly 40%.

Mobile phones were made lawful in January 1985, but did not become both useful and fashionable for almost a decade. Until now the government has only issued four licences to mobile phone operators: Vodafone (the biggest and oldest), Orange, One2One and Cellnet But in February 1999 Whitehall said that by mid-2000 it hoped to hold an auction for five licences to operate new "third generation" mobile phone networks. These will be based on a technological standard called UMTS (Universal Mobile Telecommunications Standard), capable of running multimedia services, including surfing Internet and downloading e-mails, music and high-quality pictures. If legal opposition from the four operators is overcome, UMTS should start in 2002, igniting another communications explosion.

New phone codes

In June 1999 the government began a major revamp of all codes to try to simplify the system and meet the ever-increasing demand for new phone numbers. The biggest change until then had been in April 1995, when the initial "0" had "1" added to it for nearly all area codes. But that did not go far enough, so in 1999 Whitehall began what it called "the biggest and most important change ever undertaken". Overseeing the operation was Oftel, the regulator of the telecomms industry. The new codes are:

01	Existing area codes
02	New area codes
03	Reserved for area codes
04/5/6	Reserved for future use
07	Mobiles/personal/paging, incl:
070	Personal
076	Paging
077/8/9	Mobiles
08	Free + special rate services, incl:
0800	Freephone
0808	Freephone
0820	Schools' use of Internet
0845	Local rate
0870	National rate
09	Premium rate services

Area codes

The new area codes - 02 - cover six parts of the UK, and run in parallel with the pre-June 1999 codes until 22 April 2000. Confusing is the way a new "local number" is being added to the new code. BT does not call this ingredient the code, so anyone asking BT about the new "code" may not be told about the hitherto unknown "local number". But without the local number the new code will not work. Also changing is the layout of the whole number. BT wants the new area codes to be three digits, followed by two blocks of four each. In the list below, the new area codes are the first three digits, followed by a dash; the new local numbers are the next digits and must be used as well. But until changeover day 22 April

2000 diallers within the six areas making local calls must only use the old number. Outsiders dialling into the six zones can use the old or new codes until then.

Cardiff	01222-xxxxxx
now	029-20xx xxxx
Coventry	01203-xxxxxx
now	024-76xx xxxx
London	0171-xxx xxxx
now	020-7xxx xxxx
London	0181-xxx xxxx
now	020-8xxx xxxx
Portsmouth	01705-xxxxxx
now	023-92xx xxxx
Southampton	01703-xxxxxx
now	023-80xx xxxx

In Northern Ireland, every number is changing. There used to be 38 different area codes; now there is just one: 028. In addition, 38 different local numbers are added, to replace the old area codes, eg:

Belfast 01232-xxxxxx is now 028-90xx xxxx

Mobiles, pagers, personals

All mobiles, pagers and personal numbering services will have the exclusive use of the prefix 07. The changeover began in September 1999 and will finish in April 2000. The old and the new can be used together until then. The first two digits of all mobiles (except those already beginning 07) will be replaced by either 077, 078 or 079. Pagers will have the first three digits replaced by 076 (except 09, which will only lose those two). The new personal numbers will keep the prefix 070.

Specials: 3, 4, 5, 6, 8, 9

The prefixes 03, 04, 05 and 06 are being taken out of current use, and will be held in reserve for future demand. So all numbers using those prefixes at present should change. The 08 range of numbers has been reserved for special rate services, including freephone, local and national rate numbers normally used when business or contacts over the phone. All freephones will come under 08. The 09 prefix has been set aside for premium rate services: those with the highest charges. Any number starting 09 will be expensive.

BT DIRECTORY

* = free of charge

British Telecommunications	020-7356 5000
Administrative enquiries	0800-382011
Website	www.bt.com
Adviceline (re unwanted calls)	0800-666700
Advisory Committee on Telecoms	020-7634 8774
Billing queries: Home/work	0800-800192
Public payphone	0800-115511
Chargecards	0800-345144
BT Internet	0800-800001
Business Connections	0800-800800
Call prices	0800-150555
Fax preference service	0541-554555
General enquiries	0800-309409
ICSTIS	020-7240 551
ISDN	0800-181514
Malicious calls adviceline	0800-666700
Mobile communications	0113-272 2000
Oftel	020-7634 8700
Website	www.oftel.gov.uk
Phone books: Home	150
Business	0800-833400
International	0800-7312437
Phone Disc	0800-919199
Press office	020-7356 5369
Telephone preference service	0800-398893
Yellow Pages	0118-959 211

BT services

100*	Operator (UK calls
123*	Time (talking clock
141*	Withholds number dialled from
150*	Customer services (residential
151*	Fault reporting (residential
152*	Customer services (business
153	Directory enquiries (international
154*	Fault reporting (business
155*	Operator (international calls
190*	Message service
192	Directory enquiries (UK/Eire
1471*	Calling Line Identification

Mobile operators

Cellnet	0800-21400
One 2 One	0500-50012
Orange	0800-80108
Vodafone	0800-10111

New phone code helpers

Freephone helplines	0808-224200
	0800-7310202 or 783526
Websites	www.bt.com
	www.numberchange.or

Phone directories

BT	www.bt.com/phonenet
Non-BT global	www.teledir.com
Non-BT UK	www.192.com
Yellow pages	www.yell.co.u

Consumer watchdogs

There are four breeds of consumer watchdog in business to snap at many corporate heels:

1) Regulatory bodies
2) Ombudsmen
3) Advisory committees
4) Pressure groups

REGULATORY BODIES

These are official or semi-official organisations ensuring that legal regulations are complied with by suppliers. The Office of Fair Trading (OFT) is the non-ministerial government department which safeguards shopping consumers by administering these regulations and monitoring competition. The OFT ensures all laws are enforced, especially the two most important ones, the 1979 Sale of Goods Act and 1968 Trades Description Act. Individual consumer problems are taken up by Trading Standards Departments in county councils, which handled 900,000 complaints in 1998, with secondhand car sales biggest.

Problems for finance consumers have been handled until now by a wide range of individual agencies. The main ones have been the Building Societies Commission, IMRO, OPRA, PIA, SFA and SIB. These were replaced in 1999 by a new statutory body, the Financial Services Authority (FSA), with 2,000 staff and major new powers.

All Whitehall's consumer policies are supervised by the Consumer Affairs Directorate of the Department of Trade and Industry. Also listed below are the two government auditing departments: the National Audit Office, which audits accounts of government departments and public bodies; and the Audit Commission, which examines the accounts of both the local authorities and the NHS. The Adjudicator's Office investigates complaints about the way the Inland Revenue, Customs and Excise and National Insurance Contributions Agency handle their affairs.

In April 1999 the government said it would be setting up new consumer watchdog bodies to cover the gas, electricity, water and telecoms industries. The changes, planned for 2000, would also merge OFGAS and OFFER.

Adjudicator's Office	020-7930 2292
Advertising Standards Authority	020-7580 5555
Audit Commission:Press	020-7930 6077
British Standards Institution	020-8996 9000
Broadcasting Standards Commission	020-7233 0544
Broadcasting Standards Council	020-7233 0544
Building Societies Commission	020-7676 1000
Copyright Tribunal	020-7438 4776
Data Protection Registrar	01625-545700
Dept of Trade & Industry	020-7215 5000
Trade	020-7215 5960
Corporate & Consumer Affairs	020-7215 5971
Science & Technology	020-7215 5962
Industry & Employment	020-7215 5965
Financial Services Authority	020-7676 1000
Gaming Board	020-7306 6200
Investors Compensation Scheme	020-7367 6000
Lands Tribunal	020-7936 7200
Monopolies & Mergers Commission	020-7324 1467
National Audit Office	020-7798 7000
Occupational Pensions Regulatory Authority (OPRA)	01273-627600
Parliament Standards Commissioner	020-7219 0320
Personal Investment Authority (PIA)	020-7676 1000
Police Complaints Authority	020-7273 6450
Press Complaints Commission	020-7353 1248
Security and Futures Authority (SFA)	020-7676 1000
Office for the Supervision of Solicitors	01926-820082
Press	01926-822043

Office of:

Electricity Regulation (OFFER)	0845-601 3131
Scotland	0141-331 2678
Northern Ireland	028-9031 1575
Fair Trading (OFT)	020-7211 8000
Consumer Line	0345-224499
Website	www.oft.gov.uk
Gas Supply (OFGAS)	020-7828 0898
Website	www.ofgas.gov.uk
Health Economics	020-7930 9203
National Lottery (OFLOT)	020-7227 2000
Passenger Rail Franchising (OFPRAF)	020-7478 4470
Public Service & Science	020-7270 1234
Rail Regulator (ORR)	020-7282 2000
Website	www.rail-reg.gov.uk
Social Security Commissioners	020-7353 5145
Standards in Education (OFSTED)	020-7421 6800
Website	www.ofsted.gov.uk
Telecomms (OFTEL)	020-7634 8700
Website	www.oftel.gov.uk
Water Services (OFWAT)	0121-625 1300
Website	www.open.gov.uk/ofwat

OMBUDSMEN

Ombudsmen answer complaints about specific areas of consumerism. Most ombudsmen are government officers, appointed to help enforce legal regulations. But some are not Whitehallers; they are PR specialists privately employed by industry sectors to give the impression that their businesses are well-behaved and publicly accountable, when in reality they do little to help customers. One example: Over 6,000 people complaining to the Building Societies Ombudsman in 1997/8 were told he was powerless to help them. Eight different ombudsman schemes were due to be merged in 1999 by the Financial Services Authority. All entries below are ombudsmen, eg Banking Ombudsman.

Banking	020-7404 9944
Building Societies	020-7931 0044
Estate Agents	01722-333306
European Union	003388-172313
Funerals	020-7430 1112
Health Service: England	020-7217 4051
Wales	029-2039 4621
Scotland	0131-225 7465
Independent Housing	020-7836 3630
Insurance	020-7902 8100
Investment Management (IMRO)	020-7796 3065
Legal Services	0161-236 9532
Scotland	0131-556 5574
Local Government: SE England	020-7915 3210
North of England	01904-663200
Rest of England	024-7669 5999
Wales	01656-661325
Scotland	0131-225 5300
Northern Ireland	028-9023 3821
Parliamentary	020-7276 2130
Press	020-7276 2082
N Ireland	028-9023 3821
Pensions	020-7834 9144
Prisons	020-7276 2876

ADVISORY COMMITTEES

These are the officially sponsored bodies giving consumers' views of industries and services to government ministers before decisions are made. The National Consumer Council (NCC) conducts research, lobbies policy makers and publishes reports. The NCC also helps run the Consumer Congress, the forum for consumer bodies, and publishes the annual *Consumer Congress Directory* with details of 150 organisations.

Advisory Committees on Telecomms	020-7634 8700
Air Transport Users Council	020-7240 6061
Assoc of Community Health Councils	020-7609 8405
British Standards Institution Consumer Policy Committee	020-8996 7390
Central Rail Users Consultative Cttee	020-7505 9090
Electricity Regional Consumers Cttees	0121-456 6359
Food Advisory Cttee	020-7238 6289
Gas Consumers Council	020-7931 0977
General Consumer Council for NI	028-9067 2488
London Regional Passengers Cttee	020-7505 9000
Meat & Livestock Commission Consumers' Committee	01908-677577
National Consumer Council	020-7730 3469
Scottish CC	0131-556 5574
Welsh CC	029-2025 5454
Post Office Users National Council	020-7928 9458
Rail Users Consultative Cttees	020-7222 0391
Telecomms Advisory Cttees	020-7634 8774
Water Customer Service Cttees	0345-023953

ADVICE/PRESSURE GROUPS

The largest of the independent pressure groups is the Consumers Association, which has 700,00 members. It publishes the advertisement-free magazine (one of the few in existence) *Which?*, and in mid-1999 launched its own scheme for vetting companies advertising on Internet. The 700 local Citizens Advice Bureaux give help to consumers suffering problems; see local phone books.

Buswatch	023-9286 3080
CAMRA (Campaign for Real Ale)	01727-867201
Consumer Credit Trade Assoc	020-7636 7564
Consumers' Association	020-7830 6000
Website	www.which.net/webtrader
Consumers in Europe Group	020-7881 3021
Consumers International	020-7226 6663
Enough	0161-226 6668
Ethical Consumer (magazine)	0161-226 2929
Fed of Independent Advice Centres	020-7489 1800
Food Commission	020-7837 2250
Institute of Trading Standards Admin	01702-559922
Local Authorities Co-ordinating Body on Trading Standards	020-8688 1996
Money Advice Association	01822-855118
National Association of Citizens Advice Bureaux	020-7833 2181
National Debtline	0121-359 8501
National Federation of Consumer Groups	0113-264 834
National Food Alliance	020-7837 1228
Research Institute for Consumer Affairs	020-7704 5200

Education

Britain has 29,300 state schools, 1,500 specials and 2,500 independents. They have over half a million teachers and 9.9 million pupils. About 93 per cent of pupils attend publicly-funded **state schools**. These are primary schools for 5-11 year olds and secondary schools for 11-16. Most are controlled by Local Education Authorities (LEAs). Exceptions are: grant-maintained schools which have opted out of LEA control and are overseen by the DfEE; and schools receiving public funds but run by voluntary bodies. **Independent schools** are not publicly-funded, charging fees to pupils. They have 610,000 pupils and are called: boarding, private, preparatory and public schools (in Scotland and most of the world "public" schools are actually publicly-funded schools); details from Independent Schools Information Service. Seventy per cent of pupils continue studying beyond the age of 16. About 859,000 become full-time students in further education colleges. These are mainly vocational, with exams to GCE Advanced level. Other exams here are GCSE and NVQ. Beyond "further" education is "higher" education, the shorthand for the 90 universities and 34 colleges examining above GCE A level. They have 1.2 million full-time students.

WEBSITES

BBC
A wealth of educational material, for all levels, including adult. www.bbc.co.uk/education
Higher Education Statistics Agency
Handy raw data. www.hesa.ac.uk
NISS Information Gateway
Giving access to information for the UK academic community. www.niss.ac.uk
Social Science Information Gateway
One of the best of Internet's information directories, covering wideranging sources. http://sosig.ac.uk.
UCAS
The Universities and Colleges Admission Service's invaluable service, available online. www.ucas.ac.uk.

CENTRAL BODIES

Convention of Scottish Local Auths	0131-474 9200
Dept for Education & Employment	020-7925 5000
Press	020-7925 5615
Independent Schools Info Service	020-7798 1500
Local Government Assoc	020-7834 2222
National Curriculum Council	020-7229 1234
N Ireland Dept of Education	01247-279279
Office for Standards in Education (OFSTED)	020-7421 6800
Qualification & Curriculum Auth	020-7509 5555
School Curriculum and Assessment Authority	020-7229 1234
Scottish Office Education	0131-556 8400
Society of Education Officers	0161-236 5766
Welsh Joint Education Committee	029-2026 5000
Welsh Office Education Dept	029-2082 3207

TEACHING UNIONS

Assoc of Teachers & Lecturers	020-7930 6441
Assoc of University Teachers	020-7670 9700
Headmasters Conference	0116-285 4810
National Assoc of Head Teachers	01444-472472
NAS/UWT	0121-453 6150
NATFHE	020-7837 3636
National Union of Teachers	020-7388 6191
Prof Assoc of Teachers	01332-372337
Secondary Heads Assoc	0116-299 1122

UNIVERSITIES

Aberdeen	01224-272000
Abertay Dundee	01382-308000
Anglia Polytechnic	01245-493131
Aston (Birmingham)	0121-359 3611
Bath	01225-826826
Birmingham	0121-414 3344
Bournemouth	01202-524111
Bradford	01274-232323
Brighton	01273-600900
Bristol	0117-928 9000
Brunel (Uxbridge)	01895-274000
Buckingham	01280-814080
Cambridge	01223-337733
Central England in Birmingham	0121-331 5000
Central Lancashire (Preston)	01772-201201
City (London EC1)	020-7477 8000
Coventry	024-7663 1313
Cranfield (Bedfordshire)	01234-750111
De Montfort (Leicester)	0116-255 1551
Derby	01332-622222
Dundee	01382-223181
Durham	0191-374 2000
East Anglia (Norwich)	01603-456161
East London (Dagenham)	020-8590 7722
Edinburgh	0131-650 1000
Essex (Colchester)	01206-873333
Exeter	01392-263263
Glamorgan	01443-480480
Glasgow	0141-339 8855
Glasgow Caledonian	0141-331 3000

Greenwich	020-8331 8590	Nottingham	0115-951 5151
Heriot-Watt (Edinburgh)	0131-449 5111	Open University	01908-274066
Hertfordshire (Hatfield)	01707-284000	Oxford	01865-270000
Huddersfield	01484-422288	Oxford Union	01865-241353
Hull	01482-346311	Oxford Brookes	01865-741111
Humberside (Hull)	01482-440550	Paisley	0141-848 3000
Keele (Staffs)	01782-621111	Plymouth	01752-600600
Kent (Canterbury)	01227-764000	Portsmouth	023-9287 6543
Kingston (W London)	020-8547 2000	Queens (Belfast)	028-9024 5133
Lancaster	01524-65201	Reading	0118-987 5123
Leeds	0113-233 2332	Royal Agricultural College	01285-652531
Leeds Metropolitan	0113-283 2600	Royal College of Music	020-7589 3643
Leicester	0116-252 2522	Salford	0161-745 5000
Liverpool	0151-794 2000	Sheffield	0114-222 2000
Liverpool John Moores	0151-231 2121	Sheffield Hallam	0114-272 0911
London Guildhall (Whitechapel)	020-7320 1000	South Bank (London SE1)	020-7928 8989
University of London	020-7636 8000	Southampton	023-8059 5000
Birkbeck College	020-7631 6000	St Andrews (Fife)	01334-47616
Courtauld Institute	020-7872 0220	Staffordshire	01782-294000
Goldsmiths College	020-7919 7171	Stirling	01786-47317
Imperial College	020-7589 5111	Strathclyde (Glasgow)	0141-552 4400
Kings College	020-7836 5454	Sunderland	0191-515 2000
London School of Economics	020-7405 7686	Surrey (Guildford)	01483-300800
Queen Mary College	020-7975 5555	Sussex (Brighton)	01273-606755
Royal Holloway	01784-434455	Teeside	01642-21812
Royal Veterinary College	020-7468 5000	Thames Valley (Ealing)	020-8579 5000
School of Oriental Studies	020-7637 2388	Ulster (Coleraine)	01265-44114
Senate House	020-7636 8000	UMIST (Manchester)	0161-236 331
University College	020-7387 7050	University of Wales	029-2038 2656
Wye	01233-812401	Aberystwyth	01970-62311
Loughborough	01509-263171	Bangor	01248-35115
Luton	01582-734111	Cardiff	029-2087 4000
Manchester	0161-275 2000	Lampeter	01570-42235
Manchester Metropolitan	0161-247 2000	Swansea	01792-205678
Middlesex (London N17)	020-8362 5000	Warwick	024-7652 3523
Napier (Edinburgh)	0131-444 2266	West of England (Bristol)	0117-965 626
Newcastle-upon-Tyne	0191-222 6000	Westminster (Central London)	020-7911 5000
North London (N7)	020-7607 2789	Wolverhampton	01902-32100
Northumbria (Newcastle)	0191-232 6002	York	01904-430000

Religion

The UK's largest religion is Christianity, primarily the Anglicans, Presbyterians (including the Church of Scotland), Roman Catholics and Free Churches. The second biggest is the Muslim religion, followed by the Sikhs, Jews, Buddhists and Hindus.

In the **Anglican** Communion group, the Church of England is the leading body. It has been the established church since the mid-16th century. The country is divided into the provinces of Canterbury and York, each run by an archbishop: George Carey (Canterbury)

and David Hope (York). There are 44 diocese within the provinces, with 13,000 parishes The Church of England is governed by it General Synod, which itself is run Cabinet style by the new Archbishop Council, set u in 1999. There are 16,100 churches an about 10,000 CoE staff.

The other main Anglican churches in th UK are the Church in Wales, the Episcopa Church in Scotland and the Church c Ireland. They are independent, but hav strong links with the Church of England along with the other Anglican churches around the world. In Scotland, the leading religious body is the non-Anglican Church of Scotland, the national church also set up in the 16th century. It has a Presbyterian structure, with 47 districts and about 750,000 members. It is governed by its General Assembly. Every ten years all Anglican bishops meet for the international Lambeth Conference to discuss common issues, although without any policy-making formal power. The next conference is in 2008.

Roman Catholics form by far the world's largest Christian movement, with nearly a billion members. The Roman Catholic Church is the global organisation run from the autonomous Vatican City State in Rome. The leading figure is the Pope, currently John Paul II. In England and Wales the governing body is the Bishops Conference, headed by the President, Cardinal Basil Hume, Archbishop of Westminster. In Scotland there is a similar Bishops Conference. The UK has about 12,800 staff and 8,600 churches.

The **Free Churches** are Protestant churches which, unlike the Church of England and Church of Scotland, are not established, ie, officially recognised by the State. The largest of the Free is the Methodist Church. Others include the Salvation Army, Baptists and United Reformed Church.

Muslims are followers of the Islam. Many Muslims have come to Britain since the late nineteenth century, and there are now over 600 mosques. There is no central organisation, but the most influential bodies are the Islamic Cultural Centre (the London Central Mosque) and the Imams and Mosque Council. **Sikhism** grew up in the Punjab four centuries ago, coming to Britain in the 1950s. It has no central body, but the Sikh Missionary Society has an information service.

Christianity has been overshadowed by many new religious movements, often called cults. These include the Church of Scientology and the Unification Church (the Moonies). Paganism has revived in England, especially in the form of Druidism. Many new pagans are members of the environmental movement that has shaped the more radical political undercurrents since the late 1980s. The UK government helped set up the Information Network Focus on Religious Movements (Inform) to provide objective information to the public.

The main religious directory is: *Religions in the UK*, published by the University of Derby and the Inter Faith Network 01332-622222.

ANGLICAN

Church of England	
General Synod (main CoE contacts)	020-7898 1000
Archbishop of Canterbury	020-7928 8282
Archbishop of York	01904-707021
Church Commissioners	020-7898 1000
Record Centre	020-7231 1251
Church in Wales	029-2023 1638
Episcopal Church in Scotland	0131-225 6357

ROMAN CATHOLIC

Bishops Conferences: E&W	020-7630 8220
Scotland	0141-221 1168
Archbishops: Westminster	020-7798 9033
Liverpool	0151-724 6398
Glasgow	0141-226 5898
Media offices: London	020-7828 8709
Glasgow	0141-221 1168
Dublin	00-35312885043
Catholic Enquiry Centre	020-8458 3316

OTHER CHRISTIAN

Baptist Union	01235-517700
Church of Jesus Christ of Latter-day Saints (Mormons)	0121-712 1200
Church of Scotland	0131-225 5722
Churches of Christ	01842 810357
Congregational Federation	0115-911 1460
Council of Churches for Britain	020-7620 4444
Eastern Orthodox Churches: Greek	020-7723 4787
Russian	020-8995 9503
Serbian	020-7727 8367
Other nationalities	01986-896708
Free Church Federal Council	020-7387 8413
Free Church of England	0151-638 2564
Free Presbyterian Church of Scotland	0131-229 0649
Independent Methodist Churches	01942-223526
International Churches of Christ	020-7713 6028
Jehovah's Witnesses	020-8906 2211
Lutheran Council	020-7383 3081
Methodist Church	020-7222 8010
Moravian Church	020-8883 3409
Pentecostal Church bodies:	
Apostolic	01792-473992
Assemblies of God	0115-9811188
New Testament	01604-643311

Presbyterian Church in Ireland	028-9032 2284
Presbyterian Church of Wales	029-2049 4913
Religious Society of Friends (Quakers)	020-7387 3601
Salvation Army: E&W	020-7367 4500
Scotland	0131-443 4740
Seventh Day Adventist Church	01923-672251
Unification Church	020-7723 0721
Union of Welsh Independents	01792-467040
Unitarian Churches	020-7240 2384
United Reformed Church	020-7916 2020
World Council of Churches	00-4122 7916111

OTHER RELIGIONS

Aetherius Society	020-7736 4187
Baha'i Community of UK	020-7584 2566
Buddhist:	
Buddhist Society	020-7834 5858
Friends of Western Buddhist Order	0121-449 8272
London Buddhist Vihara	020-8995 9493
Network of Buddhist Orgs	020-7582 5797
Church of Christ, Scientist	020-7371 0600
Church of Scientology	020-7580 3601
Hindu:	
Int Soc for Krishna Consciousness	01923-856269
National Council of Hindu Temples	01923-856269
Swaminarayan Hindu Mission	020-8965 2651
Vishwa Hindu Parishad	020-8552 0143
Jain Centre	0116-254 3091
Jesus Army	020-8992 0100
Jewish:	
Board of Deputies of British Jews	020-7543 5400
United Synagogue	020-8343 6301
Jewish Care	020-8922 2000
Jewish Policy Research Institute	020-7935 8266
Reform Synagogues	020-8349 4731

Muslim:	
Al-Muhajiroun	020-8803 4541
Imama & Mosques Council	020-8993 7168
Islamic Brotherhood	01203 222169
Islamic Cultural Centre & London Central	
Mosque	020-7724 3363
Muslim Information Centre	020-7272 5170
UK Action Cttee Islamic Affairs	020-8974 2780
World Ahl Ul-Bayt, Islamic League	020-8954 9881
Pagan Federation	01787 238257
Sikh Missionary Society	020-8574 1902
Sikh Temple	020-8854 1786
Theosophical Society	020-7935 9261
Transcendental Meditation	0990 143733

OTHER RELIGIOUS BODIES

British Humanist Assoc	020-7430 0908
Christian Research Assoc.	020-8294 1989
Church Army	020-8318 1226
Church Commissioners	020-7898 1000
Church House Bookshop	020-7898 1000
Church Missionary Society	020-7928 8681
Council of Christians & Jews	020-7388 3322
Cult Information Centre	01689-833800
Evangelical Alliance UK	020-7582 0228
Fellowship of Reconciliation	01832-720257
Inform (Information Network Focus on	
Religious Movements)	020-7955 7654
Inter Faith Network for the UK	020-7388 0008
Lesbian and Gay Christians	020-7739 1249
Pagan Anti-Defamation Network	01704-573283
Spiritualist Assoc of Gt Britain	020-7235 3351
Spiritualists National Union	01279-816363
Three Faiths Forum	020-7485 2358

Shopping

Britain in 1996 had 321,000 shops, employing 2.4 million people. 156 businesses had 100 or more of these outlets, totalling 49,200, with a turnover of £105 billion, being over half the total value of retail trade (£193 billion). The £60 billion supermarket industry is dominated by five groups, which control half the grocery market. Tesco is the biggest, with a 1998 turnover of £16.2 billion and a profit of £882 million, followed by Sainsbury (£15.5b, £801m), Asda (£7.6b, £414m), Argyll-cum-Safeway (£7.0b, £427m) and Somerfield (£6.1b, £187m). The USA's cheap-goods giant Wal-mart bought Asda in mid-1999, raising the hope (or fear) of a major war in UK supermarket prices. Online shopping is mushrooming, and most businesses now have websites. The Consumers Association runs an Internet traders vetting service, via Which?.

ONLINE UK MALLS

Barclay Square	www.barclaysquare.com
Enterprise City	www.enterprisecity.co.uk
Excite	www.excite.co.uk
Money Extra	www.moneyextra.com
Quixell Auctions	www.qxl.com
Sell It Auctions	www.sellituk.com
Shop Guide	www.shopguide.com
Shoppers Universe	www.shoppersuniverse.com
Shops on the Net	www.shopsonthenet.com

Shops UK www.shops-uk.com
UK Shopping City www.ukshops.co.uk
Which? Web Traders www.which.net/webtrader

LARGE RETAILERS

Allders	020-89295500
Allied Bakeries	01784-451366
Argos	01908-690333
Argyll (Safeway)	020-8848 8744
Asda	0113-243 5435
Associated British Foods	020-7589 6363
B & Q	023-8025 6256
BhS	020-7262 3288
Boots	0115-950 6111
Burton Group	020-7636 8040
Co-op (CRS - retail)	01706-713000
Co-op (CWS - wholesale)	0161-834 1212
Comet	01482-320681
Debenhams	020-7408 4444
Diadgeo (ex-Grand Metropolitan)	020-7518 5200
Dixons	01442-353000
Forte	0345-404040
Freemans	020-7735 7644
Gateway	0117-935 9359
Great Universal Stores	0161-273 8282
Habitat	020-7255 2545
Halfords	01527-517601
Harrods	020-7730 1234
House of Fraser (Harrods, Army & Navy,	
Rackhams)	020-7963 2000
Iceland	01244-830100
John Lewis	020-7828 1000
John Menzies	0131-467 8070
Kingfisher (Comet, Woolworth, B&Q)	020-7724 7749
Kwik Save	01745-887111
Littlewoods (mail order)	0151-235 2222
Marks & Spencer	020-7935 4422
McDonalds Restaurants	020-8700 7000
MFI	020-8200 8000
Next	0116-286 6411
Owen Owen	0151-707 4000
Sainsbury	020-7695 6000
Sears (Freemans, Selfridges, Olympus)	020-7200 5999
WH Smith	020-7404 4242
Somerfield	0117-935 9359
Storehouse (Bhs, Habitat, Mothercare)	020-7262 3456
Superdrug	020-8684 7000
Tesco	01992-632222
Texas Homecare (Homebase)	01933-679679
EMI Group (HMV, Radio Rentals)	020-7355 4848
Toys R Us	01628-414141
Waitrose	01344-424680
FW Woolworth	020-7262 1222

LARGE SHOPPING CENTRES

Britain has nine regional mega shop malls:
Bluewater, near Dartford, Kent, M25/A2 junc.
320 shops, 1.5 m sq ft. Opened March 1999.

MetroCentre, edge of Gateshead, Tyneside.
320 shops, 1.4m sq ft.
Merry Hill, Dudley, West Midlands.
260 shops, 1.8m sq ft.
Lakeside, West Thurrock, south Essex, M25.
309 shops, 1.3m sq ft.
Trafford Centre, outskirts of Manchester.
280 shops, 1.3m sq ft.
Meadowhall, on outskirts of Sheffield.
285 shops, 1.2m sq ft.
Cribbs Causeway, near Bristol.
140 shops, 725,000 sq ft.
Braehead, Renfrew, near Glasgow.
100 shops, 600,000 sq ft.

Biggest centres (space for 1,500+ cars):

Basildon (Eastgate)	01268-533631
Belfast (Castle Court)	028-9023 4591
Birmingham (One Stop)	0121-344 3697
Birmingham (The Fort)	0121-386 4442
Bournemouth (Hampshire)	01202-516131
Brent Cross	020-8202 8095
Brighton (Churchill Square)	01273-327428
Bromley (Glades)	020-8313 9292
Crawley (County Mall)	01293-611975
Croydon (Whitgift)	020-8688 8522
Dartford (Bluewater Park)	01322-388989
Dudley (Merry Hill)	01384-481141
Edinburgh (Gyle)	0131-539 9000
Ellesmere Port	0151-357 2118
Gateshead (Metro)	0191-493 2040
Gillingham (Hempstead Valley)	01634-387076
Glasgow (Clyde)	0141-952 4594
Glasgow (Forge)	0141-556 6661
Hartlepool (Middleton Grange)	01429-861220
Hatfield (Galleria)	01707-278301
Leeds (White Rose)	01132-291234
Leicester (Fosse Park)	0116-263 0603
Livingston (Almondvale)	01506-432961
Luton (Arndale)	01582-412636
Milton Keynes (Central)	01908-678641
Nottingham (Broad Marsh)	0115-950 7133
Nottingham (Victoria)	0115-912 1111
Peterborough (Queensgate)	01733-311666
Redditch (Kingfisher)	01527-61355
Runcorn (Halton Lea)	01928-716363
Sheffield (Meadowhall)	0114-256 8800
Stockport (Mersey Way)	0161-480 2839
Swindon (Brunel)	01793-525857
Telford	01952-230032
Tunbridge Wells (Royal Victoria)	01892-514141
Warrington (Golden Square)	01925-655053
Washington (Galleries)	0191-416 7177
Watford (Harlequin)	01923-250292
Welwyn Garden (Howard)	01707-320026
West Thurrock (Lakeside)	01708-869933

Sport

About 71% of British men and 58% of women take part in sport or physical recreation at least once a month. The Department for Culture, Media and Sport (DCMS) oversees sport and recreation from Whitehall. Immediately below it is the UK Sports Council (UKSC), authorised to set up its own Sports Cabinet in mid-1998. The UKSC oversees the four national **Sports Councils**, which in turn support the governing bodies of individual sports, manage the 13 National Sports Centres and distribute National Lottery Sports Funds. Working with the Sports Councils are advisory and co-ordinating bodies. The **Central Council of Physical Recreation** (CCPR), the largest sports federation in the world, represents the views of 300 English sporting bodies. Equivalent federations are the Scottish and Welsh Sports Associations and the Northern Ireland Council of Physical Recreation. The **British Olympic Association** organises British participation in the four-yearly Olympics Games (next: Sydney, Australia, 2000). The next football World Cup is in Japan and Korea in 2002, the Commonwealth Games in Manchester also in 2002. On Internet, the only official search engine for British sport is Sports On Line.

ONLINE SPORTS

Sports On Line	www.sportsonline.co.uk
News: Eurosport	www.eurosport.com
PA	www.pa.press.net/sport
Reuters	www.sportsweb.com
Future fixtures	www.sportcal.co.uk
Athletics	www.iaaf.org
Baseball	www.bbf.org
Canoeing	www.bcu.org.uk
Cricket	www-ukcricket.org
Cycling	www.cycling.uk.com
Horses	www.bhs.org.uk
Fencing	www.britishfencing.com
Football	www.soccernet.com
Golf	www.golfweb.com
Gymnastics	www.baga.co.uk
Judo	www.britishjudo.org.uk
Motor cycling	www.acu.org.uk
Motor sports	www.ukmotorsport.com
Mountaineering	www.thebmc.co.uk
Rugby league	www.rfl.uk.com
Rugby union	www.scrum.com
Show jumping	www.bsja.co.uk
Skiing	www.complete-skier.com
Squash	www.squash.co.uk
Tennis	www.lta.org.uk
Tennis: Wimbledon	www.wimbledon.org
Yachting/sailing	www.rya.org.uk

SPORTS COUNCILS

UK Sports Council	020-7273 1500
English Sports Council	020-7273 1500
Website	www.english.sports.gov.uk
East Midlands	0115-982 1887
Eastern	01234-345222
London	020-8778 8600
North West	0161-834 0338
Northern	0191-384 9595
South East	020-8778 8600
South Western	01460-73491
Southern	0118-9483311
West Midlands	0121-456 3444
Yorkshire	0113-243 6443
Sports Council for Wales	01244-822600
Scottish Sports Council	0131-317 7200
Sports Council for N Ireland	028-9038 1222

NATIONAL BODIES

British Blind Sport	01926-424247
British Deaf Sports Council	01943-850214
British Olympic Association	020-8871 2677
British Paralympic Association	020-8681 9655
British Universities Sports Fed	020-7357 8555
British Wheelchair Sports Foundation	01296-395995
Central Council of Physical Recreation	020-7828 3163
Commonwealth Games Fed	020-7383 5596
Dept of Culture, Media & Sport	020-7211 6000
Disability Sport England	020-7490 4919
Institute of Sport and Recreation	01664-565531
Institute of Sports Sponsorship	020-7233 7747
National Coaching Foundation	0113-274 4802
National Council for Schools Sports	01287-631013
National Lottery Charities Board	0345-919191
National Playing Fields Assoc	020-7584 6445
Physical Education Assoc	0118-931 6240
Sports Aid Foundation	020-7387 9380
Ulster Sports Trust	028-9038 1222
Womens Sports Foundation	020-8697 5370
Youth Clubs UK	020-7242 4045

NATIONAL SPORTS CENTRES

Bisham Abbey, Bucks	01628-476911
Crystal Palace, South London	020-8778 0131
Cumbrae & Inverclyde, Ayrshire	01475-674666

Glenmore Lodge, Aviemore	01479-861256
Holme Pierrepont, Notts	0115-982 1212
Lilleshall, Shropshire	01952-603003
Plas Menai. Gwynedd	01248-670964
Plas y Brenin, Gwynedd	01690-720214
Welsh Institute, Cardiff	029-2030 0500
Tollymore, County Down	01396-722158

SPORTS BODIES

Royal Aero Club	0116-253 1051
Aircraft Owners & Pilots Association	020-7834 5631
British Microlight Aircraft Assoc	01869-338888
British American Football Assoc	01205-363522
National Federation of Anglers	01283-734735
Scottish Anglers National Assoc	0131-339 8808
National Fed of Sea Anglers	01626-331330
Wales	01646-600313
Scotland	0131-317 7192
Grand National Archery Society	024-7669 6631
Scottish Archery Centre	01620 850401
Amateur Athletic Assoc	0121-456 5098
Scotland	0131-317 7320
N Ireland Sports Council	028-9038 1222
British Athletic Federation	0121-456 5098
Gaelic Athletic Assoc	020-8841 2468
Athletics Assoc of Wales	01792-456237
Badminton Assoc	01908-268400
British Balloon & Airship Club	01604-870025
British Baseball Federation	01482-643551
English Basketball Assoc	0113-236 1166
Scottish Basketball Assoc	0131-317 7260
World Professional Billiards & Snooker Assoc	0117-974 4491
British Bobsleigh Assoc	01722-340014
British Crown Green Bowling	0151-648 5740
English Bowling Assoc	01903-820222
Wales	01446-733747
Scotland	0141-221 8999
Northern Ireland	01247-469374
English Bowling Federation	0114-247 7763
English Indoor Bowling Assoc	01664-481900
Wales	01656-841361
Scotland	01294-468372
Ireland	028-9079 4869
English Womens Indoor Bowling	01604-494163
English Bowls Council	01603-427551
Amateur Boxing Assoc	020-8778 0251
Wales	029-2062 3566
Scotland	01382-508261
Ireland	00353-4540777
British Boxing Board	020-7403 5879
British Canoe Union	0115-982 1100
Veteran Car Club (pre-1919)	01462-742818
Vintage Sports Car Club	01608-644777
Caravan Club	01342-326944
National Caving Assoc	01225-311364
British Chess Federation	01424-442500
Clay Pigeon Shooting Assoc	01536-443566
England & Wales Cricket Board	020-7432 1200
Marylebone Cricket Club (MCC)	020-7289 1611
Scottish Cricket Union	0131-317 7247
Croquet Assoc	020-7736 3148
National Crossbow Federation	01902-758870
English Curling Assoc	01923-825004
Royal Caledonian Curling Club	0131-333 3003
British Cycling Federation	0161-230 2301
Northern Ireland	028-9181 7396
Welsh Cycling Union	01222 577052
Cyclists Touring Club	01483-417217
Scottish Cyclists Union	0131-652 0187
British Equestrian Federation	01926-707700
British Fencing Assoc	020-8742 3032
English Folk Dance & Song Society	020-7485 2206
Football Assoc	020-7262 4542
Wales	029-2037 2325
Scotland	0141-332 6372
Northern Ireland	028-9066 9458
Football League	01772-325800
Scotland	0141-248 3844
Football Supporters Assoc	0151-737 2385
Football Trust	020-7388 4504
Womens Football Assoc	01707-651840
Scotland	0141-353 1162
British Gliding Assoc	0116-253 1051
English Golf Union	01526-354500
Wales	01633-430830
English Ladies Golf Assoc	0121-456 2088
Ladies Golf Union	01334-475811
Royal & Ancient Golf Club	01334-472112
Professional Golfers Assoc	01675-470333
British Amateur Gymnastics	01952-820330
Scotland	0131-458 5657
Irish	028-9038 3813
British Hang-Gliding Assoc	0116-261 1322
Hockey Association	01908-544644
English Hockey	01908-689290
Scottish Hockey Union	0131-312 8870
British Horse Society	01926-707700
British Horseracing Board	020-7396 0011
Jockey Club (horse racing)	020-7486 4921
Racecourse Assoc (horse racing)	01344-625912
British Ice Hockey Assoc	0115-915 9204
Scotland	01292-266203
National Ice Skating Assoc	020-7613 1188
British Judo Assoc	0116-255 9669
British Ju-Jitsu Assoc	0114-266 6733
English Karate Governing Body	01225-834008
Welsh Karate Federation	01834-813776
Keep Fit Assoc	020-7233 8898
English Lacrosse Assoc	0121-773 4422
British Microlight Aircraft Assoc	01869-338888
British Automobile Racing Club	01264-772607
British Racing & Sports Car	01732-848884
RAC Motor Sports Assoc	01753-681736
Auto-Cycle Union (motorcycling)	01788-540519
British Motorcyclists Federation	020-8942 7914
British Mountain Bike Federation	0161-230 2301
British Mountaineering Council	0161-445 4747
Scotland	01738-638227
Central Council for Naturism	01604-620361
All England Netball Assoc	01462-442344

Wales	029-2023 7048	British Softball Federation	01886-884204
Scotland	0141-570 4016	Squash Rackets Assoc	020-8746 1616
British Orienteering Federation	01629-734042	British Surfing Assoc	01736-360250
British Parachute Assoc	0116-278 5271	Amateur Swimming Assoc	01509-618700
Hurlingham Polo Assoc	01869-350044	Wales	029-2048 8820
English Pool Assoc	01922-635587	Scotland	0141-641 8818
National Quoits Assoc	01947-841100	English Table Tennis Assoc	01424-722525
Ramblers Assoc	020-7339 8500	Wales	01495-756112
British Federation of Roller Skating	01473-401430	Scotland	0131-317 8077
National Rounders Assoc	0115-938 5478	Tennis & Rackets Assoc	020-7386 3448
Amateur Rowing Assoc	020-8748 3632	Lawn Tennis Assoc	020-7381 7000
Wales	01600-714244	All England Club	020-8944 1066
Scotland	01387-264233	Wales	029-2045 2000
Henley Royal Regatta (rowing)	01491-572153	Scotland	0131-444 1984
British Amateur Rugby League	01484-544131	British Ten-Pin Bowling Assoc	020-8478 1745
Rugby Football League	0113-232 9111	British Trampoline Federation	020-8863 7278
Rugby Football Union	020-8892 2000	Tug-of-War Assoc	01494-783057
Wales	029-2039 0111	English Volleyball Assoc	0115-981 6324
Scotland	0131-346 5000	Northern Ireland	028-9066 7011
Camanachd Assoc (shinty)	01397-772772	Long Distance Walkers Assoc	0113-264 2205
Br Assoc for Shooting/Conservation	01244-573000	British Water Ski Federation	020-7833 2855
National Rifle Assoc (shooting)	01483-797777	British Weightlifters Assoc	01865-200339
British Show Jumping Assoc	024-7669 8800	Scotland	0131-556 4116
Showmens' Guild	01784-461805	British Amateur Wrestling Assoc	0161-832 9209
British Ski Federation	01506-884343	British Federation of Sand & Land Yacht	
English Ski Council	0121-501 2314	Clubs	01509-842292
Wales	029-2061 9637	Royal Ocean Racing Club (yachting)	020-7493 2248
Scotland	0131-317 7280	Royal Yachting Assoc	023-8062 7400
World Professional Billiards & Snooker	0117-974 4491	British Wheel of Yoga	01529-306851

Think tanks

Adam Smith Institute
23 Great Smith Street, London SW1P 9PL
Fax 020-7222 7544   020-7222 4995
The Bow Group
92 Bishopsbridge Rd, London WC2   020-7431 6400
Centre for Policy Studies
52 Rochester Row, London SW1P 1JU
Fax 020-7222 4388   020-7222 4488
Director: Tessa Keswick
Chatham House
10 St James Square, London SW1   020-7957 5700
Formerly called Royal Institute for International Affairs.
Conservative 2000 Foundation
2 Wilfred Street, London SW1E 6PH   020-7630 6400
Demos
Paton House, 25 Haymarket, London SW1Y 4EN
Fax 020-7321 2342   020-7321 2200
E-mail martin@demos.demon.co.uk
Director: Geoff Mulgan
Employment Policy Institute
Southbank House, Black Prince Rd, London SE1 7SJ
Fax 020-7793 8192   020-7735 0777
Director: John Philpott

Fabian Society
11 Dartmouth Street, London SW1H 9BN
Fax 020-7976 7153   020-7222 8877
General Secretary: Michael Jacobs
Henley Centre for Forecasting
9 Bridewell Place, London EC4V 6AY
Fax 020-7955 1805   020-7955 1800
Chairman: Paul Edwards
Institute of Economic Affairs
2 Lord North Street, London SW1P 3LB
Fax 020-7799 2137   020-7799 3745
General Director: John Blundell
Institute for Employment Studies
University of Sussex, Falmer, Brighton BN1 9RF
Fax 01273-690430   01273-686751
Institute for Jewish Policy Research
79 Wimpole Street, London W1M 7DD
Fax 020-7935 3252   020-7935 8266
Director: Antony Lerman
Institute for Fiscal Studies
7 Ridgmount Street, London WC1E 7AE
Fax 020-7323 4780   020-7636 3784
E-mail mailbox@ifs.org.uk
Director: Andrew Dilnot

Institute for Public Policy Research
30-32 Southampton Street, London WC2E 7RA
Fax 020-7470 6111   020-7470 6100
E-mail ippr@easynet.co.uk
Director: Gerald Holtham
Established in 1988 IPPR provides the main centre-left
alternative to the free market think tanks of the Right.
International Institute for Strategic Studies
23 Tavistock Street, London WC2
Fax 020-7836 3108   020-7379 7676
Nexus
Fax 020-7353 7171   020-7353 4141
Director: Neil Lawson
Established 1996 to develop centre-left thought. It is
formally independent though in close contact with
Labour and the Lib Dems.

Policy Studies Institute
100 Park Village East, London NW1 3SR
Fax 020-7388 0914   020-7468 0468
Director: Pamela Meadows
Politeia
22 Charing Cross Road, London WC2H 0HR
Fax 020-7240 5095   020-7240 5070
Director: Sheila Lawlor
Social Affairs Unit
314 Regent Street, London W1
Fax 020-7436 8530   020-7637 4356
Social Market Foundation
11 Tufton Street, London SW1P 3QB
Fax 020-7222 0310   020-7222 7060
Chairman: Professor Lord Skidelsky
A non-libertarian free market think tank.

Travel

TOURING WEBLAND

Tourists planning to explore the new global
village of Webland can make most arrangements online. But don't get caught in the web:
do not assume everything is true or up to date,
prices are not always the lowest, and it's best
to use the web when Americans are dozing
(mornings). Check with the Foreign Office
that the destination is trouble-free.

Destination info
Lonely Planet   www.lonelyplanet.com
Rough Guides   www.travel.roughguides.com
Bookings
Bargain Holidays   www.bargainholidays.com
Cheapflights   www.cheapflights.com
Deckchair   www.deckchair.com
Last Minute Holidays   www.lastminute.com
Microsoft Expedia   www.expedia.co.uk
Boats
Canals   www.british-waterways.org
Coastguards, marine safety   www.mcagency.org.uk
Buses/coaches
Coach info   www.coach-hire.uk.com
National Express   www.nationalexpress.co.uk
Planes
Airports guide   www.a2bairports.com
Airways   www.airways.uk.com
Aviation industry data   www.inter-plane.com
British Airports Authority news   www.baa.co.uk
Trains
Railtrack's timetable service   www.railtrack.co.uk
Wide-ranging rail news   www.rail.co.uk
Rail industry contacts   www.railway-technology.com

Weather
UK Met Office   www.meto.gov.uk
BBC   www.bbc.co.uk/weather
Three-day   www.weather.com
Five-day   www.rainorshine.com
And ...
Currency conversions   www.oanda.com/converter
Foreign Office   www.fco.gov.uk/travel
Passport Office   www.open.gov.uk/ukpass
Public Transport Information   www.pti.org.uk
Maps: UK towns   www.multimap.com
Maps: world cities   www.mapquest.com
Walking Britain   www.visitbritain.com/walking

TRAINS

Britain has 32,000 kilometres of rail track,
2,500 stations and 40,000 bridges, tunnels
and viaducts. The number of passenger journeys in 1997/8 was 695 million, travelling
34,200 million kilometres. Britain's busiest
station is Victoria, with over 300,000 passengers daily. London's Underground in 1997/8
had 832 million passenger journeys, using
165,000 seats along 392 kilometres of track
(171 subterranean), stopping at 245 stations.

The railway was nationalised in 1948 and
then denationalised following the 1993
Railways Act, splitting British Rail into more
than 90 separate businesses. The passenger
services were divided into 25 regional units,
which were franchised to private companies

in 1996/7. BR's operational infrastructure was sold to Railtrack plc (1998 turnover: £2.5 billion, profit £428 million). Railtrack manages all track, signals, stations, bridges, tunnels and depots. Three companies franchised all British Rail's 11,000-strong rolling stock of passenger trains and carriages, which in turn were leased to the 25 passenger service operators. Freight services were split into seven components, which are now run by four companies, the largest being EWSR.

RAIL TRAVEL ENQUIRIES

All national rail enquiries, 24-hour	0345-484950
Rail Europe	0990-848848
Channel Tunnel: Le Shuttle passengers	0990-353535
Eurostar passengers	0990-186186
London Transport/tube, 24-hour	020-7222 1234
Travel Check (recorded)	020-7222 1200
TBC (Train, Bus, Coach) Hotline	0891-910910
Timetables: Printed, on sale	0906-550000
Internet	www.rail.co.uk

RAIL ORGANISATIONS

Assoc of Train Operating Companies	020-7928 5151
Press	020-7214 9941
British Railways Board	020-7928 5151
British Transport Police	020-7388 7541
Central Rail Users Consultative Cttee	020-7505 9090
Scotland	0141-221 7760
Wales	029-2022 7247
DETR	020-7890 3000
Railways Directorate	020-7271 5238
Office of Passenger Rail Franchising	020-7940 4200
Office of Rail Regulator	020-7282 2000

RAIL OPERATORS

Passenger train companies

Anglia	01473-693333
Cardiff	029-2043 0000
Central	020-7930 6655
Chiltern	01296-332100
Connex South Central	020-8667 2780
Connex South Eastern	020-7928 5151
Cross-Country (Virgin)	0121-654 7400
Eurostar	0345-303030
Gatwick Express	020-7973 5005
Great Eastern	020-7928 5151
Great North Eastern	01904-653022
Great Western	01793-499400
Heathrow Express	020-8745 0578
InterCity West Coast	0121-643 4444
Island Line (IoW)	01983-812591
LTS (London, Tilbury, Southend)	01702-357889
Merseyrail Electrics	0151-709 8292

Midland MainLine	01332-221125
North Spirit	01904-653022
North Western	0161-228 2141
ScotRail	0141-332 9811
Silverlink (North London)	01923-207258
South West	020-7928 5151
Thames	0118-908 3678
Thameslink	020-7620 5760
Wales & West	029-2043 0400
West Anglia Great Northern	0345-818919

Freight companies

Freightliner	020-7214 9491
English, Welsh & Scottish Railway	020-7713 2422
Railfreight Distribution	020-7922 9311

Railtrack plc

Company HQ	020-7344 7100
East Anglia	020-7295 2524
Great Western	01793-499500
London North Eastern	01904-522825
Midlands	0121-643 4444
North West	0161-228 8500
Scotland	0141-335 2424
Southern	020-7344 7292

BOATS

Britain's Merchant Navy was once the biggest commercial fleet in the world, but is now one of the smallest. From 1987 to 1997 the number of UK-owned merchant trading ships over 500 gross tons fell from 657 to 486. Total gross tonnage in 1997 was 7.8 million (11.3 million in 1987), deadweight tonnage 10.5 million. The biggest single type was the tanker, with 123 vessels of 2.7 million tons.

In 1997 there were 559 million tons of traffic through **British ports** (457 million in 1987). There are about 80 ports of commercial significance, plus several hundred smaller ones handling local cargo, fishing vessels, ferries and recreation. The largest in tonnage handling are (in descending order): London, Tees/Hartlepool, Grimsby/Immingham and Forth. Dover is Britain's main port for roll-on roll-off traffic. The 1991 Ports Act allowed the privatisation of ports that were then owned by trusts, a fate which befell seven. Britain's largest port owner and operator is Associated British Ports, with 23 under its control, handling nearly a quarter of traffic. The **Port of London Authority** (PLA) is organising "the biggest maritime festival ever!" on the Isle of Dogs 26 May - 4 June 2000 to celebrate the millennium. The PLA is responsible for 96 miles of the tidal Thames downriver from Teddington, and incorporating 82 operational wharves and terminals. It handles 55 million tonnes of cargo a year.

Britain has 3,200 kilometres of inland waterways, including canals with 22,000 canal boats, used by 10 million people a year.

WATER ORGANISATIONS

Associated British Ports	020-7430 1177
British Ports Association	020-7242 1200
British Waterways	01923-226422
Inland Waterways Assoc	01923-711114
Register of Shipping, Seamen & Fishing Boats	029-2074 7333
Westminster Passenger Services Fed	020-8977 5702

PORTS AND HARBOURS

Aberdeen, Grampian	01224-597000
Ardrossan, Strathclyde	01294-463972
Belfast	028-9055 4422
Bristol, Avon	0117-982 0000
Brixham, Devon	01803-853321
Cardiff	029-2040 0500
Clyde Ports	0141-221 8733
Cowes, Isle of Wight	01983-293952
Dover, Kent	01304-240400
Dundee, Tayside	01382-224121
Falmouth, Cornwall	01326-211376
Felixstowe, Suffolk	01394-604500
Fishguard, Dyfed	01348-404453
Fleetwood, Lancs	01253-872323
Folkestone, Kent	0990-755785
Forth Ports	0131-555 8750
Gt Yarmouth, Norfolk	01493-335500
Harwich, Essex	01255-243030
Heysham, Lancs	01524-852373
Holyhead, Anglesey	01407-762304
Grimsby, Humberside	01472-359181
Hull, Humberside	01482-327171
Immingham, Humberside	01469-571555
Ipswich, Suffolk	01473-231010
Isle of Man	01624-686628
Larne, Antrim	01574-872100
Lerwick, Shetland	01595-692991
Liverpool	0151-949 6000
London:	
Port of London Authority	020-7265 2656
Chief Harbour Master (Gravesend)	01474-562200
Duty Officer (Woolwich)	020-8855 0315
Port Controller (Gravesend)	01474-560311
Website	www.portoflondon.co.uk
London: Tilbury	01375-852200
Londonderry	028-7186 0555
Lowestoft, Suffolk	01502-572286
Manchester	0161-872 2411

Medway Ports, Kent	01795-561234
Milford Haven, Dyfed	01646-693091
Newhaven, East Sussex	01273-514131
Peterhead, Grampian	01779-474281
Poole, Dorset	01202-440200
Portsmouth, Hants	023-9229 7395
Ramsgate, Kent	01843-592277
Rye, East Sussex	01797-225225
Scarborough, North Yorks	01723-373530
Shoreham, West Sussex	01273-598100
Southampton, Hants	023-8033 0022
Stornoway, Western Isles	01851-702688
Sunderland, Tyne & Wear	0191-553 2100
Swansea, West Glamorgan	01792-633000
Tees & Hartlepool	01642-877000
Tyne	0191-455 2671
Weymouth, Dorset	01305-206421
Whitby, North Yorks	01947-602354
Workington, Cumbria	01900-602301

FERRY COMPANIES

Brittany Ferries:	
Portsmouth	023-9289 2207
Plymouth	01752-227941
Caledonian MacBrayne Ferries	01475-650100
Condor Ferries	01305-761555
Hoverspeed:	
Belfast/Stranraer	0990-523523
Dover/Folkestone	01304-865000
Irish Ferries:	
Dublin	00-3531 855 2222
Holyhead	01407-760223
Liverpool	0345-171717
Isle of Man Steam Packet Co	0990-523523
Isles of Scilly Steamship Co	01736-362009
Mersey Ferries	0151-630 1030
North Sea Ferries (Hull)	01642-431400
Orkney Ferries	01856-872044
P&O:	
All European ferries	0990-980980
Head office	020-7930 4343
Aberdeen	01224-572615
Cairnryan	01581-200276
Dover	0990-980980
Felixstowe	01394-604040
Fishguard	01348-404404
Larne	0990-980777
Portsmouth	0990-980555
Scrabster	01847-892052
Red Funnel Ferries (Southampton)	023-8033 3042
Holyman Sally Ferries	020-7401 7470
Scandinavian Seaways (Harwich)	01255-240240
Stena:	
All reservations	0990-707070
Harwich	01255-243333
Holyhead	01407-606666
Stranraer	01776-702531
Swansea Cork Ferries	01792-456116
Wightlink (Portsmouth)	01983-882432

PLANES

The UK has 142 licensed civil aerodromes. Nearly a quarter of them have over 100,000 passengers a year each, with 11 handling more than 2.5 million. There were 132 million passengers in 1997. The busiest airports were: Heathrow with 57.8 million passengers, Gatwick 26.8m, Manchester 15.7m and Glasgow 6.0m. Heathrow is the busiest airport in the world for international passengers. Seven British airports, including Heathrow and Gatwick, are owned by BAA plc, and together handle 70 per cent of all passengers and 80 per cent of air cargo traffic in Britain. British Airways is the world's largest international airline. It has 291 aircraft, a turnover of £8.6 billion and 55,000 staff. Britannia Airways is the world's largest charter airline.

The **Civil Aviation Authority** (CAA) oversees all non-military flying and enforces all regulations, on behalf of the Civil Aviation Division of the DETR. The CAA subsidiary **National Air Traffic Services** (NATS) controls day-to-day all air traffic and safety over Britain and its surrounding seas, in collaboration with the Ministry of Defence. At the heart of NATS is its **air traffic control centre** at West Drayton near Heathrow. The replacement of this with a new technology operation based at Swanwick, near Fareham in Hampshire has been severely delayed because of major computer problems. The cost has risen from £375m to £623m, with completion unlikely before 2002, raising fears about public safety.

FLIGHT ENQUIRIES

Aberdeen (Dyce)	01224-722331
Barra, Hebrides	01871-890283
Belfast (Aldergrove)	01849-422888
Belfast (City)	028-9045 7745
Benbecula, Outer Hebrides	01870-602051
Biggin Hill, Kent	01959-571111
Birmingham International	0121-767 5511
Blackpool, Lancs	01253-343434
Bournemouth (Hurn), Dorset	01202-364000
Bristol (Lulsgate), Avon	01275-474444
Brize Norton, Oxon (RAF)	01993-842551
Cambridge	01223-361133
Campbeltown (Strathclyde)	01586-553797
Cardiff	01446-711111
Carlisle	01228-573641
Channel Islands: Alderney	01481-822888
Guernsey	01481-37766
Jersey	01534-492000
Coventry, West Midlands	024-7630 1717
Culdrose, Cornwall (RAF)	01326-574121
Dundee, Tayside	01382-643242
East Midlands	01332-852852
Edinburgh (Turnhouse)	0131-333 1000
Exeter, Devon	01392-367433
Gatwick	01293-535353
Glasgow	0141-887 1111
Gloucester-Cheltenham	01452-857700
Heathrow	020-8759 4321
Inverness (Dalcross), Highland	01463-232471
Ipswich	0956-701015
Isle of Man (Ronaldsway)	01624-824313
Kent International (Manston)	01843-823333
Lands End	01736-788771
Leeds/Bradford (Yeadon)	0113-250 9696
Liverpool (Speke)	0151-288 4000
London: Battersea Heliport	020-7228 0181
City, Docklands	020-7646 0000
Gatwick, West Sussex	01293-535353
Heathrow, Middx	020-8759 4321
Stansted, Essex	01279-680500
Luton, Beds	01582-405100
Lydd, Kent	01797-320401
Manchester (Ringway)	0161-489 3000
Newcastle (Woolsington)	0191-286 0966
Northolt, Middx (RAF)	020-8845 2300
Norwich, Norfolk	01603-411923
Orkney: Kirkwall	01856-872421
Penzance Heliport, Cornwall	01736-363871
Plymouth, Devon	01752-772752
Prestwick, Strathclyde	01292-479822
St Mawgan, Cornwall	01637-860551
Scilly Isles: St Marys	01720-422646
Tresco Heliport	01720-422970
Shetland: Lerwick	01595-840246
Shoreham, West Sussex	01273-296900
Southampton (Eastleigh)	023-8062 9600
Southend, Essex	01702-340201
Stornoway, Western Isles	01851-702256
Teeside	01325-332811
Tiree, Argyll	01879-220456
Wick, Caithness	01955-602215

AIRLINES: BOOKINGS

Aer Lingus	020-8899 4747
Air Canada	0990-247226
Air France	020-8742 6600
Air New Zealand	020-8741 2299
Air UK	0990-074074
Alitalia	020-7602 7111
American Airlines	020-8572 5555
Britannia Airways	0990-502555
British Airways	0345-222111
British Midland	0345-554554

British World Airlines	01702-354435
Cathay Pacific	020-7747 8888
Easyjet	0870-6000000
El Al	020-7957 4100
Gulf Air	020-7408 1717
Icelandair	020-7388 5599
Japan Airlines	0345-747777
KLM	0990-750900
Lufthansa	0345-737747
Northwest Airlines	0990-561000
Qantas	0345-747767
Sabena	020-8780 1444
SAS	020-7734 4020
Singapore Airlines	020-8747 0007
South African Airways	020-7312 5000
Swissair	020-7434 7300
TWA	020-8814 0707
United	0845-8444777
Virgin Atlantic	01293-747747

AIR ORGANISATIONS

Airport Operators Assoc	020-7222 2249
Air Transport Users Council	020-7240 6061
Assoc of British Travel Agents (ABTA)	020-7637 2444
British Air Line Pilots Assoc	020-8476 4000
British Air Transport Assoc	020-7930 5746
Civil Aviation Authority	020-7379 7311
DETR	020-7890 3000
Civil Aviation Division	020-7271 4890
International Air Transport Association	
(IATA) (Geneva)	00-4122 7992525
London	020-7240 9036
Passport enquiries	0990-210410

ROADS

Britain has 229,800 miles of roads. The 2,019 miles of motorways and 7,620 miles of other trunk roads carry a third of all traffic and over half all goods vehicles. Motor traffic rose by 28 per cent from 1987-97, with motorways increasing 57 per cent. There are 27 million licensed vehicles, 21.7 million of which are cars and 414,000 heavy goods vehicles. There are 76,200 buses and coaches, almost all owned by private companies. The 1979-97 Conservative government deregulated and privatised the bus service, and between 1987/8 and 1997/8 the number of local bus passenger journeys fell from 5.29 billion to 4.33 billion. A handful of big companies now dominate the industry. The top five are Arriva, Stagecoach, National Express, Go-Ahead and FirstBus. Most dynamic of all is Stagecoach, almost monopolising large areas of the country. The largest coach operator is National Express, with 14 million passengers.

Below are the main bus and coach groups, plus London Transport (LT), which is not an owner but a statutory corporation, responsible for providing public transport in London. Its day-to-day operations on all 700 bus routes are provided under contract by over 30 private companies, contactable via LT itself.

MOTORING ORGANISATIONS

AA: HQ	0990-448866
24-hr breakdown	0800-887766
AA Roadwatch	0990-500600
British Motorcyclists Fed	020-8942 7914
British Parking Assoc	01444-476300
British Roads Federation	020-7703 9769
Department of Transport	020-7890 3000
DVLA Vehicles	01792-772134
DVLA Drivers	01792-772151
Greenflag: HQ	0113-239 3666
Breakdown service	0800-400600
RAC: HQ	020-8917 2500
24-hr breakdown	0800-828282
Live road news: Website	www.rac.co.uk
Retail Motor Industry	020-7580 9122
Road Haulage Association	01932-841515
Road Operators Safety Council	01865-775552
Soc of Motor Manufacturers	020-7235 7000

COACH/BUS COMPANIES

Arriva	020-8800 8010
Blazefield Holdings	01535-611606
EYMS Group	01482-327142
FirstBus	01224-650100
Go-Ahead Group	0191-232 3123
London Transport	020-7222 5600
National Express Group	0121-625 1122
Southern Vectis	01983-522456
Stagecoach Holdings	01738-442111
Yorkshire Traction	01226-202555

Women

There are more women than men in the UK, and they live longer - but they are paid less and are more likely to be unemployed. Official figures show there are 30.02 million females and 28.99 million males. A baby girl can now expect to reach the age of 79.4, while a male toddler can only manage 74.1. Over 80 per cent of all crimes are committed by men. The average age of women giving birth is 28.9. The most popular name for a newborn girl in 1998 was Chloe, followed by Emily. Men aged 15-44 are almost four times more likely to commit suicide than women. 61 per cent of men are overweight or obese, against 52 per cent of women. In eight out of ten couples, women do the washing up and ironing.

WOMEN'S ORGANISATIONS

Abortion Law Reform Assoc	020-7637 7264
Action for Sick Children	020-8542 4848
African & Caribbean Women Assoc	0141-341 0030
Amnesty International - Women's Action Network	020-7814 6200
Army Families Federation	01980-615525
Ash Women & Smoking Group	020-7314 1360
Asian Women's Advice Assoc	020-8533 5796
Associated Country Women of the World	020-7834 8635
Assoc of Catholic Women	020-8399 1459
Assoc of Greater London Older Women	020-7281 3485
Assoc for Improvements in the Maternity Service	020-8960 5585
Assoc of Radical Midwives	01695-572776
Assoc for Teachers' Widows	01322-663833
Assoc of Women Solicitors	020-7320 5793
Baha'i National Womens Committee	020-7584 2566
Baby Milk Action	01223-464420
Baby Products Assoc	01296-662789
Breast Cancer Care	020-7384 2984
British Assoc of Women Entrepreneurs	020-7935 9455
British Assoc of Women Police	01543-276165
British Fed of Women Graduates	020-7498 8037
British Pregnancy Advisory Service	01564-793225
Brook Advisory Centres	020-7713 9000
Catholic Women's League	020-7738 4894
Change	020-7430 0692
Co-operative Women's Guild	020-8804 5905
Conservative Women's National Cttee	020-7222 9000
Crossroads Womens Centre	020-7482 2496
English Collective of Prostitutes	020-7482 2496
Family Planning Assoc	020-7837 5432

Farm Women's Club	020-8652 492
Fawcett Library	020-7320 118
Fawcett Society	020-7628 444
Feminist Library & Information Centre	020-7928 778
Gingerbread	020-7336 818
Girls Friendly Society	020-7589 962
Guide Assoc	020-7834 624
Justice for Women	020-8374 294
League of Jewish Women	020-7387 768
Lesbian & Gay Police Assoc	01426-94301
London Lesbian Line	020-7251 691
Marriage Counselling Scotland	0131-225 500
Maternity Alliance	020-7588 858
Medical Women's Federation	020-7387 776
Merched Y Wawr	01970-61166
Mothers' Union	020-7222 553
Muslim Women's Helpline	020-8908 320
National Abortion Campaign	020-7923 497
National Alliance of Women's Organisations	020-8788 105
National Assoc for Maternal & Child Welfare	020-7383 4117
National Assoc of Widows	0121-643 8348
National Assoc of Women's Clubs	020-7837 1434
National Childbirth Trust	020-8992 8637
National Childminding Assoc	020-8464 6164
National Council for One-Parent Families	020-7267 1361
National Council of Women of GB	020-7354 2395
National Federation of Women's Institutes	020-7371 9300
National Free Church Womens Council	020-7387 8413
National Group on Homeworking	0113-245 4273
National Women's Network for International Solidarity	020-8809 2388
One Parent Families Scotland	0131-556 3899
Positively Women	020-7713 0444
Pro-Choice Alliance	020-7636 4619
Rape Crisis Centre	020-7837 1600
Refuge	0990-995 4430
Relate	01788-573241
Rights of Women	020-7251 6577
Royal College of Midwives	020-7872 5100
Royal College of Nursing	020-7409 3333
Scottish Women's Aid	0131-475 2372
Scottish Women's Rural Institutes	0131-225 1724
Sexwise	0800-282930
Society of Women Writers and Journalists	020-8529 0886
Soroptimist International	0161-480 7686
Suffragette Fellowship	020-7222 2597
The 300 Group	01403-733797
Townswomen's Guilds	0121-456 3435
UK Asian Women's Conference	020-8946 2858
Victim Support	020-7735 9166
Wales Assembly of Women	01267-267428
Watch? (What About the Children?)	01386-561635

WATCH (Women & the Church)	01763-848822	Women's Advisory Council (UNA)	01395-263688
Welsh Women's Aid	029-2039 0874	Women's Aid Federation	0117-944 4411
West Indian Women's Assoc	020-8521 4456	Women's Environmental Network	020-7247 3327
Womankind Worldwide	020-8563 8608	Women's Farm & Garden Assoc	01285-658339
Women Against Rape	020-7482 2496	Women's Health	020-7251 6580
WomenAid International	020-7925 1331	Women's Health Concern	020-8780 3916
Women & Practical Conservation	020-7278 4294	Women's Inter-Church Council	020-7387 8413
Women in Film and TV	020-7379 0344	Women's Liberation (Lesbian Line)	020-7837 8602
Women in Journalism	020-7274 2413	Women's National Commission	020-7238 0386
Women in Management	020-8891 1740	Women's Resource Centre	020-7729 4010
Women in Music	01449-736287	Women's Royal Voluntary Service	020-7793 9917
Women in Prison	020-7226 5879	Women's Sports Foundation	020-8697 5370
Women Through the Millennium	020-7730 0533	Women's Therapy Centre	020-7263 6200
Women Working Worldwide	0161-247 1760		

The workers

Trade unions and staff associations had 7.9 million members in 1997, a fall of 5.4 million since 1979. The number of unions dropped from 453 to 226, with many merging to cope with the effects of fewer members. Only about 30 per cent of employees are now union members. 1998 saw just 166 stoppages, the lowest number since records began in 1891.

The UK workforce is 29.2 million adults, but the number actually working is unclear because of the ways in which Whitehall has frequently changed its method of measuring the figures. The current method began in April 1998 and is based on the internationally recognised Labour Force Survey, using its definition of unemployment as being people out of work who have looked for a job in the last four weeks and are available to start within two weeks. In April 1999 there were 1,814,000 "unemployed", a rate of 6.2 per cent. But there were another 2,269,00 who were "economically inactive", while "wanting a job". Seventy four per cent of the UK population - 27,358,000 - were in employment or a training scheme, or doing unpaid family work. The average weekly hours worked were 32.9, totalling 899 million in a week. A national minimum wage of £3.60, for certain types of people, began in April 1999.

Seventy six unions, with 6.75 million members, are affiliated to the TUC (Trades Union Congress). The largest unions are:

Unison	1.30 million members
TGWU	881,400
AEEU	720,300
GMB	709,700
MSF	429,600
USDAW	293,500

Founded in 1886, the TUC belongs to the International Confederation of Free Trade Unions, based in Brussels, with members from 124 countries.

One of the reasons for the decline in trade unionism in the 1980s and 90s has been the reshaping of their legal environment. The Certification Office for Trade Unions and Employers Associations is the statutory body overseeing many of the legal criteria and rules applying to unions. The Commissioner for the Rights of Trade Union Members helps trade unionists take legal action against their own union, a rare event.

There are three main employers organisations. The CBI (Confederation of British Industry) has 250,000 companies as members. It is based in Centrepoint, very near the TUC in Great Russell Street. The BCC (British Chambers of Commerce) represents 196 chambers, with their 200,000 local businesses. The IoD (Institute of Directors) looks after 35,000 company directors

EMPLOYERS AND OFFICIALS

ACAS	020-7210 3613
British Chamber of Commerce (BCC)	020-7565 2000
CBI	020-7379 7400
Central Arbitration Committee	020-7210 3737
Certification Office for Trade Unions & Employers Assocs	020-7210 3734
Commissioners for the Rights of Trade Union Members /Protection Against Unlawful Industrial Action	01925-415771
Dept for Education & Employment	020-7925 5000
Press	020-7925 5132
Dept of Trade & Industry	020-7215 5000
Press	020-7215 6424
Employment Appeal Tribunal	020-7273 1041
Engineering Employers Federation	020-7222 7777
Federation of Small Businesses	020-7233 7900
Industrial Injuries Advisory Council	020-7962 8065
Industrial Society	020-7262 2401
Industrial Tribunals HQ	020-7273 8666
Help desk	0345-959775
Institute of Directors	020-7839 1233
Monopolies & Mergers Commission	020-7324 1467

UNIONS AND ASSOCIATIONS

Amalgamated Engineering & Electrical Union (AEEU)	020-8462 7755
Associated Metalworkers Union (AMU)	020-7317 8600
Associated Society of Locomotive Engineers & Firemen (ASLEF)	020-7317 8600
Assoc of First Division Civil Servants	020-7343 1111
Assoc of Teachers & Lecturers	020-7930 6441
Assoc of University Teachers (AUT)	020-7670 9700
Bakers, Food & Allied Workers Union	01707-259450
Banking, Insurance & Finance Union	020-8946 9151
British Airline Pilots Assoc (BALPA)	020-8476 4000
British Assoc of Journalists	020-7353 3003
British Assoc of Social Workers	0121-622 3911
British Medical Assoc (BMA)	020-7387 4499
Broadcasting, Entertainment, Cinematograph & Theatre Union (BECTU)	020-7437 8506
Ceramic and Allied Trades Union	01782-272755
Civil & Public Services Assoc (CPSA) - now part of PCS (see below)	020-7924 2727
Communication Managers Assoc	0118-934 2300
Communication Workers Union	020-8971 7200
Community & Youth Workers Union	0121-244 3344
Engineers & Managers Assoc	01932-577007
Equity (British Actors Equity Assoc)	020-7379 6000
Fire Brigades Union	020-8541 1765
GMB	020-8947 3131
Graphical, Paper & Media Union (GPMU)	01234-351521
Institute of Journalists (IOJ)	020-7252 1187
Institution of Professionals, Managers & Specialists (IPMS, ex-IPCS)	020-7902 6600
International Transport Workers Fed	020-7403 2733
Iron & Steel Trades Confederation	020-7837 6691
Managerial & Professional Officers	01279-434444
Manufacturing Science Finance (MSF)	020-7505 3000
Musicians Union	020-7582 5566
NATFHE - Lecturers' Union	020-7837 3636
NAS/UWT	0121-453 6150
National Farmers Union (NFU)	020-7331 7200
National Union of Insurance Workers	020-7405 6798
National Union of Journalists (NUJ)	020-7278 7916
National Union of Marine, Aviation & Shipping Transport Officers (NUMAST)	020-8989 6677
National Union of Mineworkers (NUM)	01226-215555
National Union of Rail, Maritime & Transport Workers (RMT)	020-7387 4771
National Union of Students (NUS)	020-7272 8900
National Union of Teachers (NUT)	020-7388 6191
Police Federation	020-8399 2224
Prison Officers Assoc (POA)	020-8803 0255
Professional Footballers Assoc	0161-236 0575
Public & Commercial Services Union (merger in 1998 of CPSA & PTC)	020-7924 2727
Royal College of Nursing	020-7409 3333
Royal College of Midwives	020-7872 5100
Society of Authors	020-7373 6642
Society of Radiographers	020-7391 4500
Society of Telecom Executives	020-8971 6000
Transport & General Workers Union	020-7828 7788
Transport Salaried Staffs Assoc	020-7387 2101
Union of Construction, Allied Trades & Technicians (UCATT)	020-7622 2442
Union of Shop, Distributive & Allied Workers (USDAW)	0161-224 2804
Unison (ex-NALGO/NUPE/COHSE)	020-7388 2366
United Road Transport Union	0161-881 6245
Writers Guild	020-7723 8074

WORKERS' FEDERATIONS

Centre for Alternative Industrial Technological Systems	0114-266 5063
Confederation of Shipbuilding & Engineering Unions	020-7703 2215
Council of Civil Service Unions	020-7834 8393
European TU Confederation	00-322 224 0411
European TU Institute	00-322 224 0470
Federation of Entertainment Unions	01962-713134
General Federation of Trade Unions	020-7387 2578
Groundswell	01865-723750
Institute of Employment Rights	020-7498 6919
International Confederation of Free Trade Unions (ICFTU)	00-322 224 0211
International Federation of Chemical, Energy, Mine & General Workers Unions (ICEM)	00-322 626 2020
International Fed. of Journalists	00-322 223 2265
International Labour Org	020-7828 6401
Labour Research Dept	020-7928 3649
Media & Entertainment International	00-322 223 5537
Public Concern at Work	020-7404 6609
Tolpuddle Martyrs Museum	01305-848237
Trades Union Congress (TUC)	020-7636 4030
Brussels	00-322 224 0478
Website	www.tuc.org.uk
Unions 21	020-7278 9944

Action

ANIMALS, FARMING & FOOD

.nimal Aid Society	01732-364546
.nimal Concern	0141-445 3570
.nimal Health Trust	01638-751000
.nimal Rights Coalition	01902-711935
.nimal Welfare Trust	020-8950 8215
.rboricultural Association	01794-368717
3at Conservation Trust	020-7627 2629
3eauty Without Cruelty	020-7254 2929
3reach-Whale Wars	01405-769375
3ritish Association for Shooting & Conservation	01244-573000
3ritish Beekeepers Association	024-7669 6679
3ritish Dietic Association	0121-616 4900
3ritish Trust for Ornithology	01842-750050
3ritish Union for Abolition of Vivisection	020-7700 4888
3utterfly Conservation	01206-322342
:ats Protection League	01403-221900
:hickens Lib	01732-364546
:ompassion in World Farming	01730-264208
:ountry Landowners Association	020-7235 0511
)onkey Sanctuary	01395-578222
:ast Kent Animal Welfare	01304-363071
:arthkind	020-8889 1595
:nough	0161-226 6668
:arm Animal Welfare Council	020-8330 8022
:arm Animal Welfare Network	01484-688650
:armers Union of Wales	01970-820820
:arming & Wildlife Advisory Gp	024-7669 6699
:ood & Drink Federation	020-7836 2460
:ame Conservancy	01425-652381
:lutamate Information Service	020-7631 3434
⁻enry Doubleday Research	024-7630 3517
⁻unt Saboteurs Association	01273-622827
nternational Dolphin Watch	01482-643403
nternational Fund for Animal Welfare	01892-601900
nternational Whaling Commission	01223-233971
<ennel Club	020-7493 6651

League Against Cruel Sports	020-7403 6155
London Animal Action	020-7278 3068
London Wildlife Trust	020-7261 0447
Mammal Society	020-7498 4358
National Anti-Vivisection Soc	020-8846 9777
National Canine Defence	020-7837 0006
National Farmers Union	020-7331 7200
National Fed of Badger Groups	020-7498 3220
National Organisation Working Against Live Exports	01869-345243
National Society of Allotment & Leisure Gardeners	01536-266576
Orkney Seal Rescue	01856-831463
Otter Trust	01986-893470
Passports for Pets	020-8870 5960
Peoples Dispensary for Sick Animals	01952-290999
Pesticides Trust	020-7274 8895
PETA (People for the Ethical Treatment of Animals)	020-8785 3113
Rare Breeds Survival Trust	024-7669 6551
Royal Agricultural Society	024-7669 6969
Royal Horticultural Society	020-7834 4333
RSPB (Birds)	01767 680551
RSPCA (Animals)	01403-264181
Scottish Landowners Federation	0131-653 5400
Scottish Wildlife & Countryside Link	01738-630804
Scottish Wildlife Trust	0131-312 7765
Soil Association	0117-929 0661
Sportsman's Association	01743-356868
Sustainable Agriculture (SAFE)	020-7837 1228
Ulster Wildlife Trust	01396-830282
Uncaged	0114-253 0020
Urban Wildlife Trust	0121-666 7474
Vegan Society	01424-427393
Vegetarian Society	0161-928 0793
Veggies Catering Campaign	0115-958 5666
Whale & Dolphin Conservation	01225-334511
Wildfowl & Wetlands Trust	01453-890333
Wildlife Trusts (ex RSNC)	01522-544400
Womens Farming Union	024-7669 3171
Wood Green Animal Shelters	01763-838329
Working for Organic Growers	01273-476286
World Society Protection of Animals	020-7793 0540
World Wide Fund for Nature	01483-426444
Zoo Federation	020-7586 0230
Zoological Society of London	020-7722 3333

CLAIMANTS

Bootstrap Enterprises	020-7254 0775
Industrial Common Ownership Movement (ICOM)	0113-246 1737
Low Pay Unit	020-7713 7616
New Ways to Work	020-7226 4026
Public Concern at Work	020-7404 6609
Rural Development Comm.	020-7340 2900
Unemployed Workers Charter	020-8459 7146
Unemployment Unit	020-7833 1222

COMMUNITY ACTION & WORK

Advice Services Alliance	020-7236 6022
Association of British Credit Unions	0161-832 3694
Centre for Alternative Industrial & Technological	
Systems	0114-266 5063
Charities Aid Foundation	020-7400 2300
Child Poverty Action Group	020-7837 7979
Childline-info	020-7239 1000
Citizen Organising Foundation	020-8981 6200
Citizens Advice Bureaux (HQ)	020-7833 2181
Communities That Care	020-7837 5900
Community Development Foundation	020-7226 5375
Community Organisations Forum	020-7426 9970
Community Service Volunteers	020-7278 6601
Construction Safety Campaign	020-7537 7220
Direct Action Network	020-8889 1361
Directory of Social Change	020-7209 4949
Everyman Centre	020-7737 6747
Gamblers Anonymous	020-7384 3040
Inter-Action Trust	020-7583 2652
Law Centres Federation	020-7387 8570
Letslink UK	023-9273 0639
London Advice Services Alliance	020-7377 2748
London Hazards Centre	020-7267 3387
Low Pay Unit	020-7713 7616
Missing Persons Helpline	0500-700700
National Council for Voluntary Orgs	020-7713 6161
National Fed. of Community Orgs	020-7226 0189
National Group on Homeworking	0113-245 4273
Rotary International	01789-765411
Samaritans	020-7734 2800
Saneline	0345-678000
Scottish Council for Voluntary Orgs	0131-556 3882
Scottish Crofters' Union	01471-822529
Small World	020-7272 1394
Undercurrents Productions	01865-203661
Unions 21	020-7278 9944
Victim Support	020-7735 9166

DIY CULTURE

Activists Networking	020-8341 3794
Association of Festival Organisers	01296-394411
Cannabis Hemp Information Club	020-8888 9277
Conscious Cinema	01273-679544
Festival Eye (annual festival guide)	01568-760492
Freedom Trail	01935-863349
Frontline Magazine	09762-36216
Glastonbury Festival (late June)	0870-607 7380
Green Events	020-7267 2552
Justice	020-7329 5100
Notting Hill Carnival	020-8964 0544
Reclaim the Streets	020-7281 4621
Red Pepper Magazine	020-7281 7024
SchNews Magazine	01273-685913
The Land is Ours	01865-722016
Undercurrents Videos	01865-203661

DRUGS AND ADDICTION

Addaction	020-7251 58(
Alcohol Concern	020-7928 73′
Alcoholics Anonymous	01904-6440₂
ASH (Action on Smoking and Health)	020-7224 07₄
Association for Nonsmokers Rights	01344-4262₅
Cannabis Hemp Info Club	01458-8357₆
Cannabis In Avalon	01458-8332₃
Gamblers Anonymous	020-7384 30₄
Institute for the Study of Drug	
Dependence	020-7928 12′
National Drugs Helpline	0800-7766(
Libra Trust	01273-4800′
Mainliners	020-7582 54₃
Medical Council on Alcoholism	020-7487 444
Narcotics Anonymous	020-7251 40(
Promis Helpline	0800-37431
Release	020-7729 99(
Helpline	020-7603 86₅
Drugs in Schools Helpline	0808-80008(
Resolve	0808-80023₄
Scottish Council on Alcohol	0141-333 967
Standing Conf on Drug Abuse	020-7928 95(
Transform	0117-939 80₅

EDUCATION AND FAMILY

Abortion Law Reform Association	020-7637 72₆
Active Birth Centre	020-7482 55₅
Advisory Centre for Education	020-7354 832
Age Concern	020-8679 80(
Association of Radical Midwives	01695-57277
Baby Life Support Systems	020-7831 93₉
Baby Milk Action	01223-46442
Baby Products Association	01296-66278
Barnardos	020-8550 88₂
Birth Control Campaign	020-7278 724
British Pregnancy Advisory Service	01564-79322
Brook Advisory Centres	020-7833 848
Campaign Against the Child Support	
Act	020-7482 249
Campaign for State Education	020-8944 82C
Carers National Association	020-7490 881
Child Poverty Action Group	020-7837 797
Child Rescue	01273-69294
Childline	020-7239 100(
Childrens Legal Centre	01206-87246
Childrens Society	020-7837 429(
Divorce, Mediation & Counselling	
Service	020-7730 242(
EPOCH (End Physical Punishment of	
Children)	020-7700 062(
Exploring Parenthood	020-7221 447
Families Need Fathers	020-7613 506(
Family Caring Trust	01693-6417
Family Planning Association	020-7837 543(
Family Rights Group	020-7923 262
Family Welfare Association	020-7254 625
Gingerbread	020-7336 818(
Guides Association	020-7834 624

SIS 020-7798 1530
Inter-Action 020-7583 2652
International Planned Parenthood
  Federation 020-7487 7900
Marie Stopes International 020-7574 7400
Mary Ward Centre 020-7831 7711
Message Home 0500-700740
Mothers Union 020-7222 5533
National Abortion Campaign 020-7923 4976
National Childbirth Trust 020-8992 8637
National Childcare 020-7739 2866
National Childrens Bureau 020-7843 6000
National Council for One Parent
  Families 020-7267 1361
National Infertility Support Network 01424-732361
NCH Action for Children 020-7226 2033
NSPCC 020-7825 2500
National Youth Agency 0116-285 3700
One Parent Families in Scotland 0131-556 3899
Parent Network 020-7735 1214
Pensioners Voice 01254-52606
Pre-School Learning Alliance 020-7833 0991
Relate (Marriage Guidance) 01788-573241
Save the Children Fund 020-7703 5400
Socialist Teachers Alliance 024-7633 2320
Watch? (What About the Children?) 01386-561635
Woodcraft Folk 020-8672 6031
Workers Educational Association 020-8983 1515

ENVIRONMENT & ECOLOGY

Action with Communities in Rural
  England 01285-653477
Advisory Committee on Protection of the
  Sea 020-7799 3033
Agenda 21 Network (London) 020-7296 6599
Association for the Protection of Rural
  Scotland 0131-225 7012
Black Environment Network 01286-870715
British Assoc of Nature Conservationists 01604-405285
British Earth Sheltering Association 01993 703619
British Ecological Society 020-8871 9797
British Mountaineering Council 0161-445 4747
British Society of Dowsers 01233-750253
British Trust for Conservation Volunteers
  England 01491-839766
British Unidentified Flying Object Research
  Association 020-8449 5908
Campaign for Environmentally Responsible
  Tourism 01268-795772
Campaign for the Protection of Rural
  Wales 01938-552525
Centre for Alternative Technology 01654-702400
Civic Trust 020-7930 9730
  Wales 029-2048 4606
  Scotland 0141-221 1466
Clean Rivers Trust 01636-892627
Climate Action Network 020-7836 1110
Communities Against Toxics 0151-339 5473
Community Recycling Network 0117-942 0142
Conservation Foundation 020-7591 3111

Council for Environmental Education 0118-950 2550
Council for National Parks 020-7924 4077
Council for the Protection of Rural England
  (CPRE) 020-7976 6433
Docklands Forum (London) 020-7377 1822
Earth First! 0161-224 4846
EarthAction Network 020-7865 4009
Earthwatch Europe 01865-311600
Environment Centre 0131-557 2135
Environment Council 020-7836 2626
Environmental Information Service 01603-871048
Environmental Investigation Agency 020-7490 7040
Environmental Law Foundation 020-7404 1030
Ethical Property Company 020-7263 9759
Farming & Wildlife Advisory Group 024-7669 6699
Fauna & Flora International 01223-571000
Freedom Trail 01935-863349
Friends of the Earth 020-7490 1555
  FoE Scotland 0131-554 9977
  FoE Cymru 029-2022 9577
Frontline Magazine 09762-36216
GenetiX Snowball 0161-834 0295
Georgian Group 020-7387 1720
Global Witness 020-7272 6731
Green Alliance 020-7836 0341
Green Events Magazine 020-7267 2552
Green Party 020-7272 4474
Green World Magazine 01252-330506
GreenNet 020-7713 1941
Greenpeace (London) 020-7713 1269
Greenpeace UK 020-7865 8100
Groundwork Foundation 0121-236 8565
Gypsy Council 01708-868986
Historic Churches Preservation Trust 020-7736 3054
Institute of Public Rights of Way 01535 637957
League Against Cruel Sports 020-7403 6155
Local Agenda 21 Steering Group 020-7296 6600
London Ecology Unit 020-7267 7944
London Green Party 020-7272 4474
London Greenpeace 020-7713 1269
Marine Conservation Society 01989-566017
Marine Society 020-7261 9535
Media Natura 020-7928 9556
Mountaineering Council of Scotland 01738-638227
National Council for the Conservation of
  Plants & Gardens 01483-211465
National Energy Action 0191-261 5677
National Federation of City Farms 0117-923 1800
National Pure Water Association. 01924-254433
National Recycling Forum 020-7253 6266
National Small Woods Association 01743-792644
National Society for Clean Air 01273-326313
National Trust 020-7222 9251
National Trust for Scotland 0131-226 5922
Noise Abatement Society 01322-862789
Noise Network 020-8312 9997
N Ireland Environment Link 028-9031 4944
Nukewatch UK 023-8055 4434
Oilwatch 020-7435 5000
Open Spaces Society 01491-573535
Oxleas Wood Hotline 01426-921900

Pedestrians Association	020-7820 1010
Permaculture Association	01654-712188
Pesticides Trust	020-7274 8895
Planning Exchange	0141-248 8541
Plantlife	020-7938 9111
Rainbow Centre	0115-958 5666
Ramblers Association	020-7339 8500
Reclaim the Streets	020-7281 4621
Reforest the Earth	01603-611953
Reforesting Scotland	0131-226 2496
Royal Entomological Society	020-7584 8361
Royal Forestry Society	01442-822028
Royal Scottish Forestry Society	0131-660 9480
Royal Society for Nature Conservation: Wildlife	
Trusts Partnership	01522-544400
Royal Town Planning Institute	020-7636 9107
Save Britains Heritage	020-7253 3500
Scottish Conservation Projects Trust	01786-479697
Scottish Crofters Union	01471-822529
Scottish Green Party	020-7571 0086
Scottish Native Woods	01887-820392
Scottish Wildlife & Countryside Link	01738-630804
Sea Action	01273-620125
SERA (Socialist Environment & Resources	
Association)	020-7263 7389
Society for the Protection of Ancient	
Buildings	020-7377 1644
Surfers Against Sewage	01872-553001
The Land is Ours	01865-722016
Tourism Concern	020-7753 3330
Town & Country Planning Association	020-7930 8903
Tree Council	020-7828 9928
Trust for Urban Ecology	020-7237 9175
UK Environmental Law Association	01491-671631
Undercurrents Productions	01865-203661
Urban Pollution Research	020-8362 6374
Wales Green Party	01970-611226
Waste Watch	0870-243 0136
Waterwatch Network	01904-421588
Waterway Recovery Group	01923-711114
Wild Flower Society	01509-215598
Wildfowl & Wetlands Trust	01453-890333
Womens Environmental Network	020-7247 3327
Woodland Trust	01476-581111
World Conservation Monitoring	01223-277314

ETHNIC GROUPS

Black Environment Network	01286-870715
Civic Trust (Community Action)	020-7930 9730
Commission for Racial Equality	020-7828 7022
Gandhi Foundation	020-8981 7628
Gypsy Council	01708-868986
Immigration Advisory Service	020-7357 6917
India Association (UK)	020-8559 2922
Indian Workers Association	020-8574 6019
Institute of Race Relations	020-7837 0041
Irish Campaigns Network	0961-361518
Joint Council for the Welfare of	
Immigrants (JCWI)	020-7251 8706
Kurdish Cultural Centre	020-7735 0918

Legal Advice for Travellers	029-2087 458
Migrant Resource Centre	020-7233 986
Minority Rights Group	020-7978 949
National Assembly Against Racism	020-7247 990
National Group on Homeworking	0113-245 427
National Gypsy Council	01928-72313
Newham Monitoring Project	020-8555 818
Pakistan Welfare Association	020-8679 092
Refugee Council	020-7820 300
Refugee Legal Centre	020-7827 909
Runnymede Trust	020-7600 966
Scottish Asian Action Committee	0141-341 002
Scottish Crofters Union	01471-82252
Searchlight Magazine	020-7284 404
Standing Conference of West Indian	
Organisations	020-7928 786
Survival	020-7242 144
Youth Against Racism in Europe	020-8533 453

HEALTH

Age Concern	020-8679 800
Alzheimers Disease Society	020-7306 060
Arthritis Research Campaign	01246-55803
ASH (Action on Smoking & Health)	020-7224 074
Body Positive	020-7287 801
Breast Cancer Campaign	020-7404 395
British Council of Disabled People	01332-29555
British Deaf Association	020-7588 352
British Dental Health	01788-54636
British Heart Foundation	020-7935 018
British Holistic Medicine Association	01743-26115
British Homeopathic Association	020-7935 216
British Kidney Patient Association	01420-47202
British Lung Foundation	020-7831 583
British Medical Association	020-7387 449
British Organ Donor Society	01223-89363
British Psychological Society	0116-254 956
British Wheel of Yoga	01529-30685
Cancer Relief Macmillan Fund	020-7351 781
Cancer Research Campaign	020-7224 133
Casualties Union	020-7278 626
Clic (Cancer and Leukaemia in	
Childhood)	0117 924 884
Crusaid	020-7833 393
Dial UK (Disability Information and Advice	
Lines)	01302-31012
Direct Action Network	020-8889 136
Disability Alliance	020-7247 877
Disability Wales	029-2088 732
Downs Syndrome Association	020-8682 400
Festival for Mind, Body, Spirit	020-7938 378
Food Commission	020-7837 225
Foundation for the Study of Infant	
Death	020-7235 096
GLAD (Greater London Association of Disabled	
People)	020-7346 580
Haemophilia Society	020-7380 060
Health Rights	020-7501 985
Health Unlimited	020-7582 599
Hearing Dogs for the Deaf	01844-35389

Help the Aged	020-7253 0253
Herpes Association	020-7609 9061
Hospice Information Service	020-8778 9252
Imperial Cancer Research Fund	020-7242 0200
Inquest	020-8802 7430
Institute for Complementary Medicine	020-7237 5165
Leonard Cheshire Foundation	020-7802 8200
Leukaemia Research Fund	020-7405 0101
London Lighthouse	020-7792 1200
Migraine Action Association	01932-352468
ME Association	01375-642466
Medic Alert	0800-581420
Mediical Foundation	020-7813 9999
MENCAP	020-7454 0454
Mental After Care Association	020-7436 6194
Mental Health Foundation	020-7535 7400
Mental Health Media	020-7700 8173
Migraine Trust	020-7831 4818
MIND (National Association for Mental Health)	020-8884 5000
Multiple Sclerosis Society	020-7610 7171
National Aids Trust	020-7814 6767
National Asthma Campaign	020-7226 2260
National Autistic Society	020-8813 8222
National Schizophrenia Fellowship	020-8547 3937
Natural Medicines Society	020-8941 6600
NDT (learning disabilities)	0161-228 7055
No Panic	01952-590005
Outset	020-8692 7141
Overeaters Anonymous	01745-888127
Parkinsons Disease Society	020-7931 8080
Patients Association	020-8423 8999
Pregnancy Advisory Service	020-7637 8962
RADAR (Royal Association for Disability & Rehabilitation)	020-7250 3222
Re-Solv (Society for the Prevention of Solvent Abuse)	01785-817885
Repetitive Strain Injury Association	01895-431134
Royal National Institute for the Blind	020-7388 1266
Royal National Institute for the Deaf	020-7296 8000
Royal Society for the Prevention of Accidents (RSPCA)	029-2025 0600
Samaritans	01753-532713
Sane	020-7375 1002
SCODA (Standing Conference on Drug Abuse)	020-7928 9500
Scope	020-7619 7100
Scottish Council on Alcohol	0141-333 9677
Socialist Health Association	020-7490 0057
St John Ambulance Association	020-7235 5231
Tenovus Cancer Helpline	0800-526527
Terence Higgins Trust	020-7831 0330
Voluntary Euthanasia Society	020-7937 7770

HISTORY

Ancient Monuments Society	020-7236 3934
Architectural Heritage Fund	020-7925 0199
British Assoc of Friends of Museums	01276-66617
British Records Association	020-7833 0428
British Society for History of Science	01367-718963
Council for British Archaeology	01904-671417
English Civil War Society	01430-430695
Folklore Society	020-7387 5894
Historical Association	020-7735 3901
Rescue (British Archaeological Trust)	01992-553377
Society for Folk Life Studies	0113-275 6537
Subterranea Britannica	01737-823456
Victorian Society	020-8994 1019

HOUSING

Advisory Service for Squatters	020-7359 8814
Alone in London Service	020-7278 4486
Big Issue Magazine	020-7526 3200
Building Industry Link Up	020-8534 5352
Centrepoint (Youth Homelessness)	020-7544 5000
Communities & Homes in Central London	020-7378 8300
Crisis (ex Crisis at Christmas)	020-7377 0489
Girls Alone Project	020-7383 4103
Homeless Information Project	020-7277 7639
Homes for Homeless People	01582-481426
Housing Centre Trust	020-7251 2363
Housing Law Practitioners Assoc	020-7233 8322
Institute of Housing	024-7685 1700
The Land is Ours	01865-724360
London Connection	020-7766 5544
London Housing Unit	020-7428 4910
National Homeless Alliance	020-7833 2071
National Housing Federation	020-7278 6571
National Housing & Town Planning Council	020-7251 2363
National Missing Persons Helpline	0500-700 700
New Horizon	020-7388 5560
Piccadilly Advice Centre	020-7437 1579
Rural Housing Trust	020-7793 8114
Save Our Building Societies (SOBS)	01727-847370
Scottish Crofters Union	01471-822529
SHAC (Housing Advice Line)	020-7404 6929
SHAC: Edinburgh	0131-466 8031
Shelter	020-7505 2000
Shelter Nightline	0800-446441
Simon Community	020-7485 6639

HUMAN RIGHTS

Action for Southern Africa	020-7833 3133
Amnesty International	020-7814 6200
Anti-Racist Alliance	020-8422 4849
Anti-Nazi League	020-7924 0333
Anti-Slavery International	020-7924 9555
Article 19	020-7278 9292
British Humanist Association	020-7430 0908
British Irish Rights Watch	020-7405 6415
British Red Cross Society	020-7235 5454
Burman Action Group	020-7281 7377
Call for Peace (NI)	020-8372 6789
Campaign Against Asylum Bill	020-7247 9907
Campaign Against Racism & Fascism (CARF)	020-7837 1450
Campaign Against Racist Laws	020-8571 1437

Campaign for Freedom of Info	020-7831 7477
Campaign for Press and Broadcasting Freedom (CPBF)	020-7278 4430
Canon Colins Educational Trust for Southern Africa	020-7354 1462
Central America Human Rights	020-7631 4200
Charter 88	020-7684 3888
China Solidarity Campaign	020-8205 5781
Christian Aid	020-7620 4444
CIIR (Catholic Institute for International Relations	020-7354 0883
Cuba Solidarity Campaign	020-7263 6452
Cymdeithas yr Iaith Gymraeg	01970-624501
European Dialogue	020-7713 5723
Fourth World	020-7286 4366
Freedom Press	020-7247 9249
Howard League for Penal Reform	020-7281 7722
Human Rights Watch	020-7713 1995
Inquest	020-8802 7430
Intermediate Technology Development Group	020-7436 9761
Interights	020-7278 3230
International Alert	020-7793 8383
International Association for Religious Freedom	01865-202744
Iraqi National Congress	020-7629 2960
Irish Peace Initiative	020-8372 6789
Justice	020-7329 5100
Kashmir Freedom Movement	020-8810 0104
Kurdistan Solidarity Campaign	020-7586 5892
Labour Campaign for Travellers Rights	0113-248 6746
Latin America Bureau	020-7278 2829
Law Centres Federation	020-7387 8570
Legal Action Group	020-7833 2931
Liberty (NCCL)	020-7403 3888
Minority Rights Group	020-7978 9498
National Assembly Against Racism	020-7247 9907
National Civil Rights Movement	020-8843 2333
New Internationalist Magazine	01865-728181
Nicaragua Solidarity Campaign	020-7272 9619
Oxfam	01865-311311
Palestine Solidarity Campaign	020-7700 6192
Peru Support Group	020-7620 1103
Philippine Resource Centre	020-7281 4561
Prisoners Abroad	020-7833 3467
Public Law Project	020-7467 9800
Redress	020-7278 9502
Release	020-7729 9904
Returned Volunteer Action	020-7278 0804
Scottish Council for Civil Liberties	0141-332 5960
Statewatch	020-8802 1882
Survival International	020-7242 1441
Third World First	01865-245678
Tibet Information Network	020-7814 9011
Tibet Society of the UK	020-7383 7533
Tools for Self Reliance	023-8086 9697
Travellers Support Group	01273-234777
Troops Out	0961-361518
War on Want	020-7620 1111
WaterAid	020-7793 4500
World Development Movement	020-7737 6215

ROADS AND TRANSPORT

Capital Transport Campaign	020-7388 2489
Cyclists Public Affairs Group	01483-414320
Environmental Transport Association	01932-828882
Freedom of the Skies	01570-493576
Freedom Trail	01935-863349
Friends, Families and Travellers Group	01273-234777
Heritage Railway Association	01233-712130
London Cycling Campaign	020-7928 7220
London Lorry Control Scheme	020-7582 0852
Motorcycle Action Group	0121-605 3553
No M11 Link Road Campaign	020-8530 7577
PACTS	020-7922 8112
Pedestrians Association	020-7820 1010
Public Transport Campaign	0161-839 9040
Reclaim the Streets	020-7281 4621
Road Alert	01635 521770
Save Our Railways	020-7582 6060
South Coast Against Road Building	01273-324455
Streetlife	020-7833 2071
Sustrans: Paths for People	0117-926 8893
Transport 2000	020-7388 8386
Travellers Advice Team	0468-316755
Travellers Support Group	01458-832371

SCIENCE

Association for Science Education	01707-283000
Assoc for Advancement of Science	020-7973 3500
British Astrological & Psychic Society	01634-827259
British Society for History of Science	01367-718963
Centre for Alternative Technological	01142-665063
Centre for Alternative Technology	01654-702400
Centre for Exploitation of Science	020-7354 9942
Institute for Social Inventions	020-82082853
Royal Society	020-7839 5561
Science Policy Research Unit	01273-686758
Scientists for Global Responsibility	020-8871 5175

SEX

Albany Trust	020-8767 1827
Campaign Against Pornography	020-7263 1833
Campaign for Homosexual Equality	0402-326151
English Collective of Prostitutes	020-7482 2496
Gay Employment Rights	020-7704 8066
Gay Legal Advice	020-7837 5212
Gay & Lesbian Switchboard	020-7837 7324
Gay London Policing	020-7704 2040
Lesbian & Gay Christian Movement	020-7739 1249
Lesbian Employment Rights	020-7704 8066
Lesbian & Gay Switchboard	0121-622 6589
Lesbian Information Service	01706-817235
London Bisexual Group	020-8569 7500
London Lesbian Line	020-7251 6911
London Rape Crisis Centre	020-7916 5466
Outrage	020-8240 0222
Sexual Compulsives Anon	020-8914 7599
Stonewall	020-7336 8860
Terence Higgins Trust	020-7831 0330

WAR AND PEACE

Amnesty International	020-7814 6200
International Secretariat	020-7413 5500
At Ease	020-7247 5164
Bertrand Russell Foundation	0115-978 4504
Call for Peace (N Ireland)	020-8372 6789
Campaign Against Arms Trade	020-7281 0297
Campaign Against Militarism	020-7269 9220
CND	020-7700 2393
Children and War	020-7424 9444
Clergy Against Nuclear Arms	01243-372428
Council for Arms Control	020-7848 2065
Faslane Peace Camp	01436-820901
Housmans Peace Resource Project	020-7278 4474
Institute for Law and Peace	020-7267 2153
International Institute for Strategic Studies	020-7379 7676
Labour Action for Peace	020-8467 5367
Landmines Working Group	020-7281 6073
Medical Action for Global Security	020-7272 2020
Moral Re-Armament - Initiatives for Change	020-7828 6591
National Peace Council	020-7354 5200
Non-Violent Resistance Network	020-7607 2302
Nukewatch UK	023-8055 4434
Pax Christi	020-8203 4884
Peace Brigades International	020-7713 0392
Peace Education Project	020-7424 9444
Peace News	020-7278 3344
Peace Pledge Union	020-7424 9444
Quaker Peace & Service	020-7663 1000
Royal British Legion	020-7973 7200
Scientists for Global Responsibility	020-8871 5175
Scottish CND	0141-423 1222
Statewatch	020-8802 1882
Troops Out Campaign (out of Northern Ireland)	020-7609 1743
War Child	020-7916 9276
War Resisters International	020-7278 4040
Working Party on Chemical & Biological Weapons	01579-384492
World Court Project	01323-844269
World Disarmament Campaign	020-7729 2523
World Peace Movement	01276-24353
Youth Action for Peace	01903-528619

HELPLINES

Organisations providing help and general info.

Accident Legal Line	0500-192939
Advice Services Alliance	020-7236 6022
Advisory Service for Squatters	020-7359 8814
Age Concern	020-8679 8000
Aids Helpline	0800-567123
Alcoholics Anonymous Helpline	020-7352 3001
Child Death Helpline	0800-282986
ChildLine	0800-1111
Citizens Advice Bureaux (HQ)	020-7833 2181
Cot Death Helpline	020-7235 1721
Crimestoppers	0800-555111
Cruse Bereavement Line	020-8332 7227
Dept of Social Security Helpline	0800-882200
Dial Disability Helpline	01302-310123
Drinkline National Alcohol Helpline	0345-320202
Eating Disorders Association	01603-765050
Environment Agency Emergencies	0800-807060
Federation of Independent Advice Centres	020-7489 1800
Gamblers Anonymous	020-7384 3040
Gingerbread (lone parents)	020-7336 8183
Health Information Service	0800-665544
Hearing Concern Helpline	01245-344600
Immigration Advisory Service	020-7378 9191
Legal Advice for Travellers	029-2087 4580
Lesbian & Gay Switchboard	0207837 7324
London Lesbian Line	020-7251 6911
London Marriage Guidance	020-7580 1087
Medic Alert	0800-581420
Mencap	020-7454 0454
Message Home (from missing person)	0800-700740
MIND	0345-660163
Missing Persons Helpline	0500-700700
Money Advice Association	01822-855118
Narcotics Anonymous Helpline	020-7730 0009
National Aids Helpline	0800-567123
National Debtline	0645-500511
National Drugs Helpline	0800-776600
NHS Helpline	0800-665544
NSPCC Helpline	0800-800500
Parent Network	020-7735 1214
Parentline	0808-8002222
Pregnancy Advisory Service	0345-304030
Promis Helpline (drugs/alcohol)	0800-374318
Rape Crisis Centre	020-7837 1600
Rape & Sexual Abuse Helpline	020-8239 1122
Refuge (domestic violence)	0990-995443
Release Emergency (drugs)	020-7603 8654
Rights of Women Advice	020-7251 6577
RNIB	020-7388 1266
RSPCA	0990-555999
Samaritans	0345-909090
SaneLine	0345-678000
Seniorline (info for elderly)	0800-650065
Sexwise	0800-282930
Shelter Nightline	0800-446441
Smokers Quitline	020-7487 3000
Stillbirth & Neonatal Death Society	020-7436 5881
Travellers Advice Team	0468-316755
Turning Point (drugs)	020-7702 2300
Victim Support (crime)	020-7735 9166
Womens Aid Helpline (violence)	0345-023468
Womens Health	020-7251 6580
Young Minds	0345-626376

Media Guide index